PRINCIPIA MATHEMATICA

PRINCIPIA MATHEMATICA

BY

ALFRED NORTH WHITEHEAD, Sc.D., F.R.S.

FELLOW OF TRINITY COLLEGE, CAMBRIDGE, PROFESSOR OF PHILOSOPHY IN HARVARD UNIVERSITY, AND SOMETIME PROFESSOR OF APPLIED MATHEMATICS IN THE IMPERIAL COLLEGE OF SCIENCE AND TECHNOLOGY

AND

BERTRAND RUSSELL, M.A., F.R.S.

LATE LECTURER AND LATE FELLOW OF TRINITY COLLEGE, CAMBRIDGE

VOLUME III

SECOND EDITION

CAMBRIDGE
AT THE UNIVERSITY PRESS
1950

PUBLISHED BY
THE SYNDICS OF THE CAMBRIDGE UNIVERSITY PRESS
London Office: Bentley House, N.W. 1
American Branch: New York
Agents for Canada, India, and Pakistan: Macmillan

First printed in Great Britain at the University Press, Cambridge
Reprinted by offset-litho
by Messrs Lowe & Brydone Printers Ltd., London, N.W.10

First Edition 1913
Second Edition 1927
Reprinted 1950

PREFACE TO VOLUME III

THE present volume continues the theory of series begun in Volume II, and then proceeds to the theory of measurement. Geometry we have found it necessary to reserve for a separate final volume.

In the theory of well-ordered series and compact series, we have followed Cantor closely, except in dealing with Zermelo's theorem (∗257—8), and in cases where Cantor's work tacitly assumes the multiplicative axiom. Thus what novelty there is, is in the main negative. In particular, the multiplicative axiom is required in all known proofs of the fundamental proposition that the limit of a progression of ordinals of the second class (*i.e.* applicable to series whose fields have $\aleph_0$ terms) is an ordinal of the second class (cf. ∗265). In consequence of this fact, a very large part of the recognized theory of transfinite ordinals must be considered doubtful.

Part VI, on the theory of ratio and measurement, on the other hand, is new, though it is a development of the method initiated in Euclid Book V and continued by Burali-Forti* Among other points in our treatment of quantity to which we wish to draw attention we may mention the following. (1) We regard our quantities as in a generalized sense "vectors," and therefore we regard ratios as holding between *relations*. (2) The hypothesis that the vectors concerned in any context form a *group*, which has generally been made prominent in such investigations, sinks with us into a very subordinate position, being sometimes not verified at all, and at other times a consequence of other more fruitful hypotheses. (3) We have developed a theory of ratios and real numbers which is prior to our theory of measurement, and yet is not purely arithmetical, *i.e.* does not treat ratios as mere couples of integers, but as relations between actual quantities such as two distances or two periods of time. (4) In our theory of "vector families," which are families of the kind to which some form of measurement is

* Cf. Peano's *Formulaire*, I. (1895), pp. 28—57.

applicable, we have been able to develop a very large part of their properties before introducing numbers; thus the theory of measurement results from the combination of two other theories, one a pure arithmetic of ratios and real numbers without reference to vectors, the other a pure theory of vectors without reference to ratios or real numbers. (5) With a view to geometrical applications, we have devoted a special Section to cyclic families, such as the angles about a given point in a given plane.

The theory of measurement developed in Part VI will be required in the next volume for the introduction of coordinates in Geometry.

We have to thank various friends for their kindness in bringing to our notice mistakes and misprints noted in the Errata, both in this and in previous volumes.

A. N. W.

B. R.

15 *February* 1913

CONTENTS OF VOLUME III

SECTION D.

WELL-ORDERED SERIES.

Summary of Section D.

A "well-ordered" series is one which is such that every existent class contained in it has a first term, or, what comes to the same thing, one which is such that every class which has successors has a sequent. We will call a relation in general well-ordered if every existent class contained in its field has one or more minima. Then a well-ordered series is a series which is a well-ordered relation.

Well-ordered series have many important properties not possessed by series in general. A well-ordered series is Dedekindian, except for the fact that it may have no last term; *i.e.* every section having a last term is Dedekindian. A well-ordered series which is not null has a first term, and every term of the series (except the last, if there is one) has an immediate successor. A very important property of well-ordered series is that they obey an extended form of mathematical induction, which we shall call "transfinite induction," namely the following: If σ is a class such that the sequent (if any) of any class contained in σ and in the series is a member of σ, then the whole series is contained in σ. (It will be observed that Λ is contained in σ, and therefore, by ∗206·14, $B'P$ is a member of σ.) This differs from ordinary mathematical induction by the fact that, instead of dealing with the successors of single terms, it deals with the successors of classes. A closely analogous property, which holds for all well-ordered relations, whether serial or not, is the following. If σ is a class such that, whenever $\overrightarrow{P}'x \subset \sigma$, where x is any member of $C'P$, x itself belongs to σ, then $C'P \subset \sigma$. If P is well-ordered, this property holds for all σ's; and conversely, if this property holds for all σ's, P is well-ordered. Hence this property is equivalent to well-orderedness.

If P is a well-ordered series, min_P selects one term out of each member of $\text{Cl ex}'C'P$. Hence $C'P$, which is $\text{min}_P``\text{Cl ex}'C'P$, is a member of the multiplicative class of $\text{Cl ex}'C'P$; hence the multiplicative class of $\text{Cl ex}'C'P$ exists, and therefore the multiplicative class of any class contained in $\text{Cl ex}'C'P$ exists (by ∗88·22). It follows that if $s'\kappa$ can be well-ordered, and $\Lambda \sim \epsilon\, \kappa$, the multiplicative class of κ exists; and that, if every class can be well-ordered, the multiplicative axiom holds. The converse of this latter proposition also holds, as has been proved by Zermelo (cf. ∗258).

Another important set of properties of well-ordered series results from ∗208·41 ff. Two ordinally similar well-ordered series can only be correlated in one way; and no proper section of a well-ordered series is ordinally similar to the whole series. (A "proper" section is a section not the whole.)

From the uniqueness of the correlator of two similar well-ordered series, it follows that all the uses of the multiplicative axiom in ∗164 can be avoided if the fields of the relations concerned consist of well-ordered series. *I.e.* taking ∗164·45, which is the fundamental proposition in this subject, we have, without assuming the multiplicative axiom,

$$P, Q \in \mathrm{Rel}^2\,\mathrm{excl} \,.\supset: \exists !\, P\,\overline{\mathrm{smor}}\,Q \cap \mathrm{Rl}\text{‘}\mathrm{smor} \,.\equiv.\, P\,\mathrm{smor}\,\mathrm{smor}\,Q,$$

whenever $C\text{‘}P$ and $C\text{‘}Q$ consist of well-ordered series. Hence, under this hypothesis, the multiplicative axiom disappears from the hypotheses of all the consequences of ∗164·45.

Ordinal numbers (∗251) are defined as the relation-numbers of well-ordered series. (This definition is in accordance with usage: otherwise, there would be no special reason against defining "ordinal numbers" as the relation-numbers of series in general. The relation-numbers of series will be called *serial numbers.*) Sums of an ordinal number of ordinal numbers are ordinal numbers, but products of an ordinal number of ordinal numbers are not in general ordinal numbers. The product of an ordinal number of serial numbers is a serial number, and the product of an ordinal number (not zero) of ordinal numbers other than zero is not zero, *i.e.* a product of ordinal numbers, in which the number of factors is an ordinal number, does not vanish unless one of the factors vanishes. (For relations in general, the corresponding proposition requires the multiplicative axiom.) If ν is an ordinal number, and μ is any serial number, $\mu \exp_r \nu$ (*i.e.* μ^ν as it would naturally be called) is a serial number; but if $\mu > 1$, $\mu \exp_r \nu$ is not an *ordinal* number unless ν is finite.

The theory of sections and segments (∗252, ∗253) is much simplified for well-ordered series, owing to the fact that every proper section has a sequent. Proper sections are identical with proper segments, and both are identical with $\overrightarrow{P}\text{“}C\text{‘}P$. The series of sections, $\mathfrak{s}\text{‘}P_*$, is $\overrightarrow{P};P \nrightarrow C\text{‘}P$. The series of segments, $\mathfrak{s}\text{‘}P$, is $\overrightarrow{P};P$ or $\overrightarrow{P};P \nrightarrow C\text{‘}P$ according as there is or is not a last term of $C\text{‘}P$. The series of sectional relations, $P_\mathfrak{s}$, is $P \upharpoonright ;\overrightarrow{P};P \upharpoonright \text{Ꮷ}\text{‘}P \nrightarrow P$; its domain is $P \upharpoonright \text{“}\overrightarrow{P}\text{“}C\text{‘}P$, and its field is $P \upharpoonright \text{“}\overrightarrow{P}\text{“}C\text{‘}P \cup \iota\text{‘}P$. If $x \in C\text{‘}P$, $P \upharpoonright \overrightarrow{P}\text{‘}x$ is never similar to P.

The theory of greater and less among well-ordered series and ordinal numbers is dealt with in *254 and *255. Cantor has proved, by means of segments, that of any two different ordinal numbers one must be the greater. This is proved by showing that of any two well-ordered series which are not similar, one must be similar to a segment of the other. We define an ordinal number α as *less than* another β if series P and Q can be found such that P is an α and Q is a β and P is similar to some relation contained in Q, but not to Q. It can be proved that all the ordinals less than Nr‘Q belong, one each, to the proper segments of Q. Hence to say that the ordinal number of P is less than that of Q is equivalent to saying that there is a proper segment of Q to which P is similar.

When two series have the same ordinal, they also have the same cardinal, in virtue of *151·18, but the converse does not hold. When the cardinal number of one series is greater than that of the other, so is the ordinal number. When two classes can be well-ordered, any well-ordering will make the one class similar to a part of the other, or the other similar to a part of the one, in virtue of the properties of segments of well-ordered series. Hence of two different cardinals each of which is applicable to classes which can be well-ordered, one must be the greater—a property which cannot be proved concerning cardinals in general.

In *256 we deal with the series of ordinals in order of magnitude. We show that this is a well-ordered series. and that the series of all ordinals of a given type has an ordinal number which is greater than any of the ordinals of the given type. This constitutes the solution of Burali-Forti's paradox concerning the greatest ordinal: there is no greatest ordinal in any one type, and all the ordinals of a given type are surpassed by ordinals of higher types.

*257, *258 and *259 deal with "transfinite induction" and its applications, of which the most important is Zermelo's theorem, namely,

*258·34. $\vdash :. \mu \sim\epsilon 1 . \supset : S \epsilon \epsilon_\Delta‘\mathrm{Cl\,ex}‘\mu . \equiv .$
$$(\exists P) . P \epsilon \Omega . C‘P = \mu . S = \min_P \upharpoonright \mathrm{Cl\,ex}‘\mu$$

where Ω is the class of well-ordered series. This proposition leads to the following:

*258·36. $\vdash : \mu \epsilon C“\Omega \cup 1 . \equiv . \exists ! \epsilon_\Delta‘\mathrm{Cl\,ex}‘\mu$

I.e. a class can be well-ordered or is a unit class when, and only when, a selection can be made from its existent sub-classes. Hence we arrive at

*258·37. $\vdash : \mathrm{Mult\,ax} . \equiv . C“\Omega \cup 1 = \mathrm{Cls}$

I.e. the multiplicative axiom is equivalent to the assumption that every class can be well-ordered or consists of a single member.

The proof of Zermelo's theorem uses an extension to transfinite induction of the ideas of *90 and *91, which is explained in *257.

$*250$. ELEMENTARY PROPERTIES OF WELL-ORDERED SERIES.

Summary of $*250$.

A relation is called "well-ordered" when every existent sub-class of its field has one or more minima. A well-ordered series is defined as a well-ordered relation which is a series. We shall denote the class of well-ordered relations by "Bord," which is an abbreviation for "bene ordinata" or "bien ordonnée." The class of well-ordered series will be denoted by Ω. Thus our definitions are

$$\text{Bord} = \hat{P}\,(\text{Cl ex}`C`P \subset \text{Ɑ}`\text{min}_P) \quad \text{Df},$$

$$\Omega = \text{Ser} \cap \text{Bord} \quad \text{Df}.$$

Well-ordered relations other than series will be seldom referred to after the present number.

By applying the definition of "Bord" to unit classes, it appears that a well-ordered relation must be contained in diversity ($*250\cdot104$). A well-ordered relation is one whose existent upper sections all have minima ($*250\cdot102$). Hence by $*211\cdot17$,

$*250\cdot103$. $\vdash : P \in \text{Bord} . \equiv . P_{po} \in \text{Bord}$

Hence by $*250\cdot104$,

$*250\cdot105$. $\vdash : P \in \text{Bord} . \supset . P_{po} \mathrel{\dot{\subset}} J$

By considering couples, it can be shown ($*250\cdot111$) that a well-ordered relation in which no class has more than one minimum is connected; hence by $*204\cdot16$ and $*250\cdot105$, it is a series. Thus we have

$*250\cdot125$. $\vdash : P \in \Omega . \equiv . \text{E}\,!!\, \text{min}_P``\text{Cl ex}`C`P$,

I.e. a well-ordered series is a relation such that every existent sub-class of the field has a unique minimum. This might have been taken as the definition of Ω.

By the definition of Ω we have

$*250\cdot121$. $\vdash :. P \in \Omega . \equiv : P \in \text{Ser} : \alpha \subset C`P . \exists ! \alpha . \supset_\alpha . \text{E}\,!\, \text{min}_P`\alpha :$

$\equiv : P \in \text{Ser} : \exists ! \alpha \cap C`P . \supset_\alpha . \text{E}\,!\, \text{min}_P`\alpha$

Applying this to $C`P$ we have

$*250\cdot13$. $\vdash : P \in \Omega - \iota`\dot{\Lambda} . \supset . \text{E}\,!\, B`P$

We have also

***250·141.** $\vdash : P \epsilon \Omega . \supset . P \upharpoonright \alpha \epsilon \Omega$

***250·17.** $\vdash :. P, Q \epsilon \Omega - \iota`\dot\Lambda . \supset : P \text{ smor } Q . \equiv . P \upharpoonright \text{Q}`P \text{ smor } Q \upharpoonright \text{Q}`Q$

This proposition justifies the subtraction of $\dot 1$ from the beginning, and is useful in the theory of segments of well-ordered series.

We have next (*250·2—·243) an important set of propositions on P_1 when $P \epsilon \Omega$. The most useful of these is

***250·21.** $\vdash : P \epsilon \Omega . \supset . \text{D}`P = \text{D}`P_1$

I.e. in a well-ordered series every term except the last (if any) has an immediate successor. (It is not in general the case that every term except the first has an immediate predecessor.) Another useful proposition is

***250·242.** $\vdash : P \epsilon \Omega . \supset . P = P_1 \cup P_1 | P$

The next set of propositions (*250·3—·362) is concerned with "transfinite induction." We have

***250·33.** $\vdash . \Omega = \text{connex} \cap \hat P \{\alpha \subset C`P \cap \sigma . \supset_\alpha . \overrightarrow{\text{seq}}_P`\alpha \subset \sigma : \supset_\sigma . C`P \subset \sigma\}$

I.e. a well-ordered series is a connected relation P such that the whole field of P is contained in every class σ which is such that the sequent (if any) of every sub-class of $C`P \cap \sigma$ is a member of σ.

***250·35.** $\vdash . \text{Bord} = \hat P \{x \epsilon C`P . \overrightarrow{P}`x \subset \sigma . \supset_x . x \epsilon \sigma : \supset_\sigma . C`P \subset \sigma\}$

I.e. a well-ordered relation is a relation P whose field is contained in every class σ which contains every member of $C`P$ whose predecessors are all contained in $\sigma$. We may say that a property is "transfinitely hereditary" in $P$ if it belongs to the sequents of all classes composed of members of $C`P$ which possess the property. In virtue of *250·33, if P is well-ordered, every transfinitely hereditary property belongs to every member of $C`P$, and conversely.

Our next set of propositions (*250·4—·44) is concerned with $\dot\Lambda$ and couples. We prove that $\dot\Lambda \epsilon \Omega$ (*250·4) and that $x \neq y . \supset . x \downarrow y \epsilon \Omega$ (*250·41).

*250·5—·54 are concerned with selections. We have

***250·5.** $\vdash : P \epsilon \Omega . \supset .$

$$\min_P \upharpoonright \text{Cl ex}`C`P \epsilon \epsilon_\Delta`\text{Cl ex}`C`P . \iota`C`P = \text{Prod}`\text{Cl ex}`C`P$$

whence

***250·51.** $\vdash : \alpha \epsilon C``\Omega . \supset . \exists ! \epsilon_\Delta`\text{Cl ex}`\alpha$

Observe that $C``\Omega$ is the class of those classes that can be well-ordered. From *250·51 we deduce

***250·54.** $\vdash : C``\Omega \cup 1 = \text{Cls} . \supset . \text{Mult ax}$

The converse, which is Zermelo's theorem, is proved in *258.

$*250{\cdot}6$—$\cdot67$ are concerned with consequences of $*208$. We show that two well-ordered series cannot have more than one correlator ($*250{\cdot}6$); that if P is a well-ordered series, and β is contained in a proper section of P, $P \upharpoonright \beta$ is not similar to P ($*250{\cdot}65$); and that if P is any well-ordered relation, and α is any class such that there are terms in $C\text{‘}P$ which are later than any member of $\alpha \cap C\text{‘}P$, then P is not similar to $P \upharpoonright \alpha$ ($*250{\cdot}67$).

$*250{\cdot}01$. $\text{Bord} = \hat{P}\,(\text{Cl ex‘}C\text{‘}P \subset \text{ᗡ‘min}_P)$ Df

$*250{\cdot}02$. $\Omega = \text{Ser} \cap \text{Bord}$ Df

$*250{\cdot}1$. $\vdash : P \in \text{Bord} . \equiv . \text{Cl ex‘}C\text{‘}P \subset \text{ᗡ‘min}_P$ [($*250{\cdot}01$)]

$*250{\cdot}101$. $\vdash :. P \in \text{Bord} . \equiv : \exists ! \, \alpha \cap C\text{‘}P . \supset_\alpha . \exists ! \, \overrightarrow{\text{min}}_P\text{‘}\alpha$ [$*250{\cdot}1 . *205{\cdot}15$]

$*250{\cdot}102$. $\vdash : P \in \text{Bord} . \equiv . \text{sect‘}\breve{P} - \iota\text{‘}\Lambda \subset \text{ᗡ‘min}_P$

Dem.

$\vdash . *250{\cdot}1 . \supset \vdash : P \in \text{Bord} . \supset . \text{sect‘}\breve{P} - \iota\text{‘}\Lambda \subset \text{ᗡ‘min}_P$ (1)

$\vdash . *205{\cdot}19 . \supset \vdash . \overrightarrow{\text{min}}\,(P_{\text{po}})\text{‘}\alpha = \overrightarrow{\text{min}}\,(P_{\text{po}})\text{‘}\breve{P}_*\text{“}\alpha$

[$*205{\cdot}68$] $= \overrightarrow{\text{min}}_P\text{‘}\breve{P}_*\text{“}\alpha$ (2)

$\vdash . *90{\cdot}331 . *211{\cdot}13 . \supset \vdash : \exists ! \, \alpha \cap C\text{‘}P . \supset . \breve{P}_*\text{“}\alpha \in \text{sect‘}\breve{P} - \iota\text{‘}\Lambda$ (3)

$\vdash . (3) . \supset \vdash :. \text{sect‘}\breve{P} - \iota\text{‘}\Lambda \subset \text{ᗡ‘min}_P . \supset : \exists ! \, \alpha \cap C\text{‘}P . \supset_\alpha . \exists ! \, \overrightarrow{\text{min}}_P\text{‘}(\breve{P}_*\text{“}\alpha) .$

[(2)] $\supset_\alpha . \exists ! \, \overrightarrow{\text{min}}\,(P_{\text{po}})\text{‘}\alpha .$

[$*205{\cdot}26$] $\supset_\alpha . \exists ! \, \overrightarrow{\text{min}}_P\text{‘}\alpha :$

[$*250{\cdot}101$] $\supset : P \in \text{Bord}$ (4)

$\vdash . (1) . (4) . \supset \vdash . \text{Prop}$

$*250{\cdot}103$. $\vdash : P \in \text{Bord} . \equiv . P_{\text{po}} \in \text{Bord}$ [$*250{\cdot}102 . *211{\cdot}17$]

$*250{\cdot}104$. $\vdash . \text{Bord} \subset \text{Rl‘}J$

Dem.

$\vdash . *250{\cdot}1 . \supset \vdash : P \in \text{Bord} . x \in C\text{‘}P . \supset . x \in \overrightarrow{\text{min}}_P\text{‘}\iota\text{‘}x .$

[$*205{\cdot}194$] $\supset . \sim(xPx) : \supset \vdash . \text{Prop}$

$*250{\cdot}105$. $\vdash : P \in \text{Bord} . \supset . P_{\text{po}} \mathrel{G} J$ [$*250{\cdot}103{\cdot}104$]

$*250{\cdot}11$. $\vdash :: P \in \text{connex} . \supset :. P \in \text{Bord} . \equiv : \exists ! \, \alpha \cap C\text{‘}P . \supset_\alpha . E ! \, \text{min}_P\text{‘}\alpha :$

$\equiv : \alpha \subset C\text{‘}P . \exists ! \, \alpha . \supset_\alpha . E ! \, \text{min}_P\text{‘}\alpha$

[$*250{\cdot}1{\cdot}101 . *205{\cdot}32$]

$*250{\cdot}111$. $\vdash :. P \in \text{Bord} . \supset : P \in \text{connex} . \equiv . \text{min}_P \in 1 \rightarrow \text{Cls}$

Dem.

$\vdash . *250{\cdot}1 . *71{\cdot}1 . \supset$

$\vdash :: P \in \text{Bord} . \text{min}_P \in 1 \rightarrow \text{Cls} . \supset :. x, y \in C\text{‘}P . \supset : (\iota\text{‘}x \cup \iota\text{‘}y) - \breve{P}\text{“}(\iota\text{‘}x \cup \iota\text{‘}y) \in 1 :$

[$*54{\cdot}4$] $\supset : \iota\text{‘}x \cup \iota\text{‘}y - \breve{P}\text{“}(\iota\text{‘}x \cup \iota\text{‘}y) = \iota\text{‘}x . \vee .$

$\iota\text{‘}x \cup \iota\text{‘}y - \breve{P}\text{“}(\iota\text{‘}x \cup \iota\text{‘}y) = \iota\text{‘}y$ (1)

$\vdash . (1) . \supset \vdash :. P \in \text{Bord} . \text{min}_P \in 1 \rightarrow \text{Cls} . x, y \in C{}^{\text{‘}}P . x \neq y . \supset :$

$y \in \breve{P}{}^{\text{‘‘}}(\iota{}^{\text{‘}}x \cup \iota{}^{\text{‘}}y) . \vee . x \in \breve{P}{}^{\text{‘‘}}(\iota{}^{\text{‘}}x \cup \iota{}^{\text{‘}}y) :$

[∗250·104] $\supset : xPy . \vee . yPx$ (2)

$\vdash . (2) . *202{\cdot}103 . \supset \vdash : P \in \text{Bord} . \text{min}_P \in 1 \rightarrow \text{Cls} . \supset . P \in \text{connex}$ (3)

$\vdash . (3) . *205{\cdot}31 . \supset \vdash . \text{Prop}$

∗250·112. $\vdash : P \in \text{connex} \cap \text{Bord} . \equiv . \text{E} !! \, \text{min}_P{}^{\text{‘‘}}\text{Cl ex}{}^{\text{‘}}C{}^{\text{‘}}P$

Dem.

$\vdash . *250{\cdot}1{\cdot}111 . \supset$

$\vdash : P \in \text{connex} \cap \text{Bord} . \equiv . \text{min}_P \in 1 \rightarrow \text{Cls} . \text{Cl ex}{}^{\text{‘}}C{}^{\text{‘}}P \subset \text{Cl}{}^{\text{‘}}\text{min}_P .$

[∗71·16] $\equiv . \text{E} !! \, \text{min}_P{}^{\text{‘‘}}\text{Cl}{}^{\text{‘}}\text{min}_P . \text{Cl ex}{}^{\text{‘}}C{}^{\text{‘}}P \subset \text{Cl}{}^{\text{‘}}\text{min}_P .$

[∗205·15·16] $\equiv . \text{E} !! \, \text{min}_P{}^{\text{‘‘}}\text{Cl ex}{}^{\text{‘}}C{}^{\text{‘}}P : \supset \vdash . \text{Prop}$

∗250·113. $\vdash . \text{connex} \cap \text{Bord} = \Omega$

Dem.

$\vdash . *204{\cdot}1 . (*250{\cdot}02) . \supset \vdash . \Omega \subset \text{connex} \cap \text{Bord}$ (1)

$\vdash . *250{\cdot}105 . \supset \vdash : P \in \text{connex} \cap \text{Bord} . \supset . P \in \text{connex} . P_{\text{po}} \subseteq J .$

[∗204·16] $\supset . P \in \text{Ser}$ (2)

$\vdash . (2) . (*250{\cdot}02) . \supset \vdash : P \in \text{connex} \cap \text{Bord} . \supset . P \in \Omega$ (3)

$\vdash . (1) . (3) . \supset \vdash . \text{Prop}$

∗250·12. $\vdash : P \in \Omega . \equiv . P \in \text{Ser} \cap \text{Bord}$ [(∗250·02)]

∗250·121. $\vdash :. P \in \Omega . \equiv : P \in \text{Ser} : \alpha \subset C{}^{\text{‘}}P . \exists ! \alpha . \supset_\alpha . \text{E} ! \, \text{min}_P{}^{\text{‘}}\alpha :$

$\equiv : P \in \text{Ser} : \exists ! \alpha \cap C{}^{\text{‘}}P . \supset_\alpha . \text{E} ! \, \text{min}_P{}^{\text{‘}}\alpha$ [∗250·12·11]

∗250·122. $\vdash :. P \in \Omega . \equiv : P \in \text{Ser} : \exists ! C{}^{\text{‘}}P \cap p{}^{\text{‘}}\overleftarrow{P}{}^{\text{‘‘}}(\alpha \cap C{}^{\text{‘}}P) . \supset_\alpha . \text{E} ! \, \text{seq}_P{}^{\text{‘}}\alpha$

Dem.

$\vdash . *206{\cdot}13 . *250{\cdot}121 . \supset$

$\vdash :. P \in \Omega . \supset : P \in \text{Ser} : \exists ! C{}^{\text{‘}}P \cap p{}^{\text{‘}}\overleftarrow{P}{}^{\text{‘‘}}(\alpha \cap C{}^{\text{‘}}P) . \supset_\alpha . \text{E} ! \, \text{seq}_P{}^{\text{‘}}\alpha$ (1)

$\vdash . *204{\cdot}62 . \supset$

$\vdash : P \in \text{Ser} . \exists ! \alpha \cap C{}^{\text{‘}}P . \supset . \exists ! C{}^{\text{‘}}P \cap p{}^{\text{‘}}\overleftarrow{P}{}^{\text{‘‘}}p{}^{\text{‘}}\overrightarrow{P}{}^{\text{‘‘}}(\alpha \cap C{}^{\text{‘}}P) .$

[∗40·62] $\supset . \exists ! C{}^{\text{‘}}P \cap p{}^{\text{‘}}\overleftarrow{P}{}^{\text{‘‘}}\{C{}^{\text{‘}}P \cap p{}^{\text{‘}}\overrightarrow{P}{}^{\text{‘‘}}(\alpha \cap C{}^{\text{‘}}P)\}$ (2)

$\vdash . (2) . *10{\cdot}1 . \supset$

$\vdash :. P \in \text{Ser} : \exists ! C{}^{\text{‘}}P \cap p{}^{\text{‘}}\overleftarrow{P}{}^{\text{‘‘}}(\alpha \cap C{}^{\text{‘}}P) . \supset_\alpha . \text{E} ! \, \text{seq}_P{}^{\text{‘}}\alpha : \supset :$

$\exists ! \alpha \cap C{}^{\text{‘}}P . \supset_\alpha . \text{E} ! \, \text{seq}_P{}^{\text{‘}}\{C{}^{\text{‘}}P \cap p{}^{\text{‘}}\overrightarrow{P}{}^{\text{‘‘}}(\alpha \cap C{}^{\text{‘}}P)\} .$

[∗206·131·54] $\supset_\alpha . \text{E} ! \, \text{min}_P{}^{\text{‘}}\alpha :$

[∗250·121] $\supset : P \in \Omega$ (3)

$\vdash . (1) . (3) . \supset \vdash . \text{Prop}$

***250·123.** $\vdash :. P \in \Omega - \iota`\dot{\Lambda} . \equiv : P \in \mathrm{Ser} : \exists ! p`\overleftarrow{P}``(\alpha \cap C`P) . \supset_\alpha . E ! \mathrm{seq}_P`\alpha$

Dem.

$\vdash . *250·122 . \supset$

$\vdash :. P \in \mathrm{Ser} : \exists ! p`\overleftarrow{P}``(\alpha \cap C`P) . \supset_\alpha . E ! \mathrm{seq}_P`\alpha : \supset . P \in \Omega$ (1)

$\vdash . *40·6 . *24·52 . \supset$

$\vdash :. \exists ! p`\overleftarrow{P}``(\alpha \cap C`P) . \supset_\alpha . E ! \mathrm{seq}_P`\alpha : \supset . E ! \mathrm{seq}_P`\Lambda .$

[*206·18] $\supset . \dot{\exists} ! P$ (2)

$\vdash . *250·122 . *40·62 . \supset$

$\vdash :. P \in \Omega . \supset : P \in \mathrm{Ser} : \exists ! \alpha \cap C`P . \exists ! p`\overleftarrow{P}``(\alpha \cap C`P) . \supset_\alpha . E ! \mathrm{seq}_P`\alpha$ (3)

$\vdash . *206·14 . \supset \vdash : \alpha \cap C`P = \Lambda . \supset . \overrightarrow{\mathrm{seq}_P}`\alpha = \overrightarrow{B}`P$

[*205·12] $= \overrightarrow{\min_P}`C`P$ (4)

$\vdash . *33·24 . *250·121 . \supset \vdash : P \in \Omega - \iota`\dot{\Lambda} . \supset . E ! \min_P`C`P$ (5)

$\vdash . (4) . (5) . \supset \vdash : P \in \Omega - \iota`\dot{\Lambda} . \alpha \cap C`P = \Lambda . \supset . E ! \mathrm{seq}_P`\alpha$ (6)

$\vdash . (3) . (6) . \supset$

$\vdash :. P \in \Omega - \iota`\dot{\Lambda} . \supset : P \in \mathrm{Ser} : \exists ! p`\overleftarrow{P}``(\alpha \cap C`P) . \supset_\alpha . E ! \mathrm{seq}_P`\alpha$ (7)

$\vdash . (1) . (2) . (7) . \supset \vdash . \mathrm{Prop}$

***250·124.** $\vdash : P \in \Omega . \equiv . P \in \mathrm{Ser} . \mathrm{sect}`P - \iota`C`P \subset \mathrm{G}`\mathrm{seq}_P$

Dem.

$\vdash . *250·122 . *211·703 . \supset \vdash : P \in \Omega . \supset . P \in \mathrm{Ser} . \mathrm{sect}`P - \iota`C`P \subset \mathrm{G}`\mathrm{seq}_P$ (1)

$\vdash . *211·7 . \quad \supset \vdash :. P \in \mathrm{Ser} . \mathrm{sect}`P - \iota`C`P \subset \mathrm{G}`\mathrm{seq}_P . \supset :$

$\beta \in \mathrm{sect}`\breve{P} - \iota`\Lambda . \supset_\beta . E ! \mathrm{seq}_P`(C`P - \beta) .$

[*211·723] $\supset_\beta . E ! \min_P`\beta :$

[*250·102·12] $\supset : P \in \Omega$ (2)

$\vdash . (1) . (2) . \supset \vdash . \mathrm{Prop}$

***250·125.** $\vdash : P \in \Omega . \equiv . E !! \min_P``\mathrm{Cl\,ex}`C`P$ [*250·112·113]

The above proposition might be demonstrated, independently of *250·112·113, as follows:

(*a*) If $E !! \min_P``\mathrm{Cl\,ex}`C`P$, it follows that $x \in C`P . \supset . E ! \min_P`\iota`x$, whence $x \in C`P . \supset . \sim(xPx)$, whence $P \Subset J$.

(*b*) If $E !! \min_P``\mathrm{Cl\,ex}`C`P$, it follows that

$$x, y \in C`P . x \neq y . \supset . E ! \min_P`(\iota`x \cup \iota`y),$$

whence it follows that

$$xPy . \sim(yPx) . \vee . yPx . \sim(xPy).$$

Hence $$P \in \mathrm{connex} . P^2 \Subset J.$$

(*c*) If $E !! \min_P``\mathrm{Cl\,ex}`C`P$, it follows that

$$xPy . yPz . \supset . E ! \min_P`(\iota`x \cup \iota`y \cup \iota`z),$$

whence $$xPy \,.\, yPz \,.\, \supset \,.\, \sim(zPx),$$
and by $P^2 \Subset J$ (which has just been proved)
$$xPy \,.\, yPz \,.\, \supset \,.\, x \neq z.$$
Hence, since, by (*b*), $P \in \text{connex}$, we must have
$$xPy \,.\, yPz \,.\, \supset \,.\, xPz, \text{ i.e. } P \in \text{trans}.$$
Hence $$\text{E}\,!!\, \text{min}_P\text{“}\text{Cl ex}\text{‘}C\text{‘}P \,.\, \supset \,.\, P \in \text{Ser}.$$
Hence the above proposition is obvious.

***250·126.** $\vdash : P \in \Omega \,.\, \text{E}\,!\, \text{max}_P\text{‘}\alpha \,.\, \sim \text{E}\,!\, \text{seq}_P\text{‘}\alpha \,.\, \supset \,.\, B\text{‘}\breve{P} \in \alpha \,.\, B\text{‘}\breve{P} = \text{max}_P\text{‘}\alpha$

Dem.

$\vdash \,.\, *250·123 \,.\, \text{Transp} \,.\, \supset \vdash : \text{Hp} \,.\, \supset \,.\, \sim \exists\,!\, p\text{‘}\overleftarrow{P}\text{“}(\alpha \cap C\text{‘}P) \,.$

$[*205·65] \qquad \supset \,.\, \sim \exists\,!\, \overleftarrow{P}\text{‘}\text{max}_P\text{‘}\alpha \,.$

$[*33·4] \qquad \supset \,.\, \text{max}_P\text{‘}\alpha \sim \in \text{D}\text{‘}P \,.$

$[*93·103] \qquad \supset \,.\, \text{max}_P\text{‘}\alpha \in \overrightarrow{B}\text{‘}\breve{P} \,.$

$[*202·52] \qquad \supset \,.\, \text{max}_P\text{‘}\alpha = B\text{‘}\breve{P} : \supset \vdash \,.\, \text{Prop}$

***250·13.** $\vdash : P \in \Omega - \iota\text{‘}\dot{\Lambda} \,.\, \supset \,.\, \text{E}\,!\, B\text{‘}P$

Dem.

$\vdash \,.\, *33·24 \,.\, \supset \vdash : \text{Hp} \,.\, \supset \,.\, \exists\,!\, C\text{‘}P \,.$

$[*250·121] \qquad \supset \,.\, \text{E}\,!\, \text{min}_P\text{‘}C\text{‘}P \,.$

$[*205·12] \qquad \supset \,.\, \text{E}\,!\, B\text{‘}P : \supset \vdash \,.\, \text{Prop}$

***250·131.** $\vdash :. P \in \Omega \,.\, \supset : \dot{\exists}\,!\, P \,.\, \equiv \,.\, \text{E}\,!\, B\text{‘}P$

Dem.

$\vdash \,.\, *93·102 \,.\, *33·24 \,.\, \supset \vdash : \text{E}\,!\, B\text{‘}P \,.\, \supset \,.\, \dot{\exists}\,!\, P$ (1)

$\vdash \,.\, (1) \,.\, *250·13 \,.\, \supset \vdash \,.\, \text{Prop}$

***250·14.** $\vdash : P \in \text{Bord} \,.\, \supset \,.\, \text{Rl}\text{‘}P \subset \text{Bord}$

Dem.

$\vdash \,.\, *250·1 \,.\, *205·26 \,.\, \supset$

$\vdash : P \in \text{Bord} \,.\, Q \Subset P \,.\, \supset \,.\, \text{Cl ex}\text{‘}C\text{‘}P \subset \text{G}\text{‘}\text{min}_P \,.\, \text{min}_P \upharpoonright \text{Cl ex}\text{‘}C\text{‘}Q \Subset \text{min}_Q \,.$ (1)

$[*60·42 \,.\, *35·64] \supset \,.\, \text{Cl ex}\text{‘}C\text{‘}Q \subset \text{Cl ex}\text{‘}C\text{‘}P \,.\, \text{G}\text{‘}\text{min}_P \cap \text{Cl ex}\text{‘}C\text{‘}Q \subset \text{G}\text{‘}\text{min}_Q$ (2)

$\vdash \,.\, (1) \,.\, (2) \,.\, *22·44·621 \,.\, \supset \vdash : P \in \text{Bord} \,.\, Q \Subset P \,.\, \supset \,.\, \text{Cl ex}\text{‘}C\text{‘}Q \subset \text{G}\text{‘}\text{min}_Q \,.$

$[*250·1] \qquad \supset \,.\, Q \in \text{Bord} : \supset \vdash \,.\, \text{Prop}$

***250·141.** $\vdash : P \in \Omega \,.\, \supset \,.\, P \upharpoonleft \alpha \in \Omega \quad [*250·14 \,.\, *204·4]$

***250·142.** $\vdash : P \in \text{Bord} \,.\, \supset \,.\, \text{Rl}\text{‘}P \cap \text{connex} \subset \Omega$

Dem.

$\vdash \,.\, *250·14 \,.\, \supset \vdash : \text{Hp} \,.\, \supset \,.\, \text{Rl}\text{‘}P \cap \text{connex} \subset \text{Bord} \cap \text{connex}$

$[*250·113] \qquad \subset \Omega : \supset \vdash \,.\, \text{Prop}$

***250·15.** $\vdash : P \in \Omega . \mathrm{E} ! B\text{‘}\breve{P} . \supset . P \in \mathrm{Ded}$

Dem.

$\vdash . *250\cdot101 . \supset \vdash :. \mathrm{Hp} . \supset : \exists ! \alpha \cap C\text{‘}P . \supset_\alpha . \exists ! \overrightarrow{\mathrm{min}}_P\text{‘}\alpha$ (1)

$\vdash . *206\cdot14 . \supset \vdash :. \mathrm{Hp} . \supset : \alpha \cap C\text{‘}P = \Lambda . \supset_\alpha . \exists ! \overrightarrow{\mathrm{prec}}_P\text{‘}\alpha$ (2)

$\vdash . (1) . (2) . \supset \vdash : \mathrm{Hp} . \supset . (\alpha) . \exists ! (\overrightarrow{\mathrm{min}}_P\text{‘}\alpha \cup \overrightarrow{\mathrm{prec}}_P\text{‘}\alpha) .$

[*214·1] $\supset . \breve{P} \in \mathrm{Ded} .$

[*214·14] $\supset . P \in \mathrm{Ded} : \supset \vdash . \mathrm{Prop}$

***250·151.** $\vdash : P \in \Omega . x \in \text{Ɑ}\text{‘}P . \supset . P \upharpoonright \overrightarrow{P_*}\text{‘}x \in \mathrm{Ded}$

Dem.

$\vdash . *250\cdot141 . \supset \vdash : \mathrm{Hp} . \supset . P \upharpoonright \overrightarrow{P_*}\text{‘}x \in \Omega$ (1)

$\vdash . *205\cdot41 . \supset \vdash : \mathrm{Hp} . \supset . \overrightarrow{B}\text{‘}\mathrm{Cnv}\text{‘}(P \upharpoonright \overrightarrow{P_*}\text{‘}x) = \overrightarrow{\mathrm{max}}_P\text{‘}\overrightarrow{P_*}\text{‘}x$

[*205·197] $= \iota\text{‘}x .$

[*53·3] $\supset . \mathrm{E} ! B\text{‘}\mathrm{Cnv}\text{‘}(P \upharpoonright \overrightarrow{P_*}\text{‘}x)$ (2)

$\vdash . (1) . (2) . *250\cdot15 . \supset \vdash . \mathrm{Prop}$

***250·152.** $\vdash . \Omega \subset \mathrm{semi\ Ded}$ [*214·7 . *250·124]

***250·16.** $\vdash : P \in \Omega . \exists ! \alpha \cap C\text{‘}P . \supset . \overrightarrow{P}\text{‘}\mathrm{min}_P\text{‘}\alpha = p\text{‘}\overrightarrow{P}\text{‘‘}(\alpha \cap C\text{‘}P)$

[*205·65 . *250·121]

***250·17.** $\vdash :. P, Q \in \Omega - \iota\text{‘}\dot{\Lambda} . \supset : P \,\mathrm{smor}\, Q . \equiv . P \upharpoonright \text{Ɑ}\text{‘}P \,\mathrm{smor}\, Q \upharpoonright \text{Ɑ}\text{‘}Q$

[*204·47 . *250·13]

This proposition is useful in connection with the series of segmental relations in a well-ordered series, for the series of proper segmental relations in a well-ordered series is (as will be proved later)

$$P \upharpoonright ; \overrightarrow{P} ; P \upharpoonright \text{Ɑ}\text{‘}P,$$

and this is ordinally similar to $P \upharpoonright \text{Ɑ}\text{‘}P$. Hence, by the above proposition, two well-ordered series which are not null are ordinally similar when, and only when, the series of their segmental relations are ordinally similar.

***250·2.** $\vdash : P \in \mathrm{Bord} . \supset . \mathrm{D}\text{‘}P = \mathrm{D}\text{‘}(P \dot{-} P^2)$

Dem.

$\vdash . *33\cdot4 . \supset \vdash : x \in \mathrm{D}\text{‘}P . \equiv . \exists ! \overleftarrow{P}\text{‘}x$ (1)

$\vdash . *250\cdot1 . *205\cdot16 . \supset \vdash :. P \in \mathrm{Bord} . \supset : \exists ! \overleftarrow{P}\text{‘}x . \equiv . \exists ! \overrightarrow{\mathrm{min}}_P\text{‘}\overleftarrow{P}\text{‘}x .$

[*205·251] $\equiv . x \in \mathrm{D}\text{‘}(P \dot{-} P^2)$ (2)

$\vdash . (1) . (2) . \supset \vdash . \mathrm{Prop}$

***250·21.** $\vdash : P \in \Omega . \supset . \text{D}‘P = \text{D}‘P_1$ [*201·63 . *250·2]

In virtue of this proposition, every term of a well-ordered series (except the last, if any) has an immediate successor.

***250·22.** $\vdash : P \in \text{Ser} \cap \text{Ded} . \text{D}‘P = \text{D}‘P_1 . \supset . P \in \Omega - \iota‘\dot{\Lambda}$

Dem.

$\vdash . *214·101 . \supset \vdash : \text{Hp} . \sim E ! \, \max_P‘\alpha . \supset . E ! \, \text{seq}_P‘\alpha$ (1)

$\vdash . *206·45 . \supset \vdash : \text{Hp} . \max_P‘\alpha \in \text{D}‘P . \supset . E ! \, \overrightarrow{\text{seq}_P}‘\max_P‘\alpha .$

[*206·46] $\supset . E ! \, \text{seq}_P‘\alpha$ (2)

$\vdash . (1) . (2) . \supset \vdash :. \text{Hp} . \supset : \sim (\max_P‘\alpha = B‘\breve{P}) . \supset_\alpha . E ! \, \text{seq}_P‘\alpha :$

[*93·118] $\supset : \sim (B‘\breve{P} \in \alpha) . \supset_\alpha . E ! \, \text{seq}_P‘\alpha :$

[*202·511.*214·5] $\supset : \exists ! \, p‘\overleftarrow{P}“(\alpha \cap C‘P) . \supset_\alpha . E ! \, \text{seq}_P‘\alpha :$

[*250·123] $\supset : P \in \Omega - \iota‘\dot{\Lambda} :. \supset \vdash . \text{Prop}$

***250·23.** $\vdash : P \in \Omega . E ! \, B‘\breve{P} . \equiv . P \in \text{Ser} \cap \text{Ded} . \text{D}‘P = \text{D}‘P_1$

Dem.

$\vdash . *250·22 . *214·5 . \supset \vdash : P \in \text{Ser} \cap \text{Ded} . \text{D}‘P = \text{D}‘P_1 . \supset . P \in \Omega . E ! \, B‘\breve{P}$ (1)

$\vdash . *250·15·21 . \supset \vdash : P \in \Omega . E ! \, B‘\breve{P} . \supset . P \in \text{Ser} \cap \text{Ded} . \text{D}‘P = \text{D}‘P_1$ (2)

$\vdash . (1) . (2) . \supset \vdash . \text{Prop}$

***250·24.** $\vdash : P \in \Omega . \supset . P^2 \,|\, \breve{P}_1 = P \upharpoonright \text{D}‘P$

Dem.

$\vdash . *201·1 . *13·12 . \supset \vdash :. \text{Hp} . xP^2z . \supset : yPx . \supset . yP^2z : y = x . \supset . yP^2z :$

[Transp] $\supset : \sim (yP^2z) . \supset . \sim (yPx) . y \neq x :$

[*201·63.*202·103] $\supset : yP_1z . \supset . xPy$ (1)

$\vdash . (1) . *201·63 . \supset \vdash : \text{Hp} . xP^2z . z\breve{P}_1y . \supset . xPy . x, y \in \text{D}‘P$ (2)

$\vdash . *250·21 . \supset \vdash : \text{Hp} . x, y \in \text{D}‘P . xPy . \supset . (\exists z) . yP_1z .$

[*201·63] $\supset . (\exists z) . yPz . z\breve{P}_1y .$

[*34·1] $\supset . x(P^2 \,|\, \breve{P}_1)y$ (3)

$\vdash . (2) . (3) . \supset \vdash . \text{Prop}$

***250·241.** $\vdash : P \in \Omega . \supset . \breve{P}_1 \,|\, P^2 = (\text{Ɑ}‘P_1) \upharpoonleft P$ [Proof as in *250·24]

***250·242.** $\vdash : P \in \Omega . \supset . P = P_1 \cup P_1 \,|\, P$

Dem.

$\vdash . *201·63 . \supset \vdash :: \text{Hp} . \supset :. xPy . \equiv : xP_1y . \vee . xP^2y :$

[*250·21] $\equiv : xP_1y . \vee . (\exists z) . xP_1z . xP^2y :$

[*250·241] $\equiv : xP_1y . \vee . (\exists z) . xP_1z . zPy :: \supset \vdash . \text{Prop}$

***250·243.** $\vdash : P \epsilon \Omega \,.\supset .\, P \upharpoonright \text{D}'P_1 = (\text{D}'P_1) \upharpoonleft (P_1 \cup P \mid P_1)$

[Proof as in *250·242]

The following propositions deal with the extended form of mathematical induction which is characteristic of well-ordered series.

***250·3.** $\vdash :. P \epsilon \text{Bord} : \alpha \subset C'P \cap \sigma \,.\supset_\alpha .\, \overrightarrow{\text{seq}}_P{}'\alpha \subset \sigma : \supset .\, C'P \subset \sigma$

Dem.

$\vdash .\, *250\cdot101 \,.\supset \vdash : P \epsilon \text{Bord} \,.\, \exists \,!\, C'P - \sigma \,.\supset .\, \exists \,!\, \overrightarrow{\min}_P{}'(C'P - \sigma) \,.$

$[*205\cdot14] \qquad \supset .\, (\exists x) \,.\, x \epsilon C'P - \sigma \,.\, \overleftarrow{P}'x \subset \sigma \,.$

$[*206\cdot4 . *250\cdot104] \supset .\, (\exists x) \,.\, x \epsilon C'P - \sigma \,.\, \overrightarrow{P}'x \subset \sigma \,.\, x \,\text{seq}_P\, (\overrightarrow{P}'x) \,.$

$[*13\cdot195] \qquad \supset .\, (\exists x, \alpha) \,.\, \alpha = \overrightarrow{P}'x \,.\, \alpha \subset C'P \cap \sigma \,.\, x \epsilon \overrightarrow{\text{seq}}_P{}'\alpha - \sigma \,.$

$[*10\cdot24] \qquad \supset .\, (\exists \alpha) \,.\, \alpha \subset C'P \cap \sigma \,.\, \exists \,!\, \overrightarrow{\text{seq}}_P{}'\alpha - \sigma \qquad (1)$

$\vdash .\, (1) \,.\, \text{Transp} \,.\supset \vdash .\, \text{Prop}$

***250·301.** $\vdash : P \epsilon \text{connex} \,.\, \sim \exists \,!\, \overrightarrow{\min}_P{}'\tau \,.\, \sigma = C'P - \breve{P}``\tau \,.\, \alpha \subset \sigma \,.\supset .\, \overrightarrow{\text{seq}}_P{}'\alpha \subset \sigma$

Dem.

$\vdash .\, *205\cdot122 \,.\, *202\cdot501 \,.\supset \vdash : \text{Hp} \,.\supset .\, \sigma \subset p'\overrightarrow{P}``\tau \,.$

$[*40\cdot67] \qquad \supset .\, \tau \subset p'\overleftarrow{P}``\sigma \qquad (1)$

$\vdash .\, *206\cdot134 \,.\supset \vdash : \text{Hp} \,.\, x \,\text{seq}_P\, \alpha \,.\supset .\, \overrightarrow{P}'x \subset - p'\overleftarrow{P}``\alpha$

$[*40\cdot16] \qquad \subset - p'\overleftarrow{P}``\sigma$

$[(1)] \qquad \subset - \tau \,.$

$[*37\cdot462] \qquad \supset .\, x \sim\epsilon \breve{P}``\tau \,.$

$[*206\cdot18 . \text{Hp}] \qquad \supset .\, x \epsilon \sigma : \supset \vdash .\, \text{Prop}$

***250·31.** $\vdash :: P \epsilon \text{connex} :. \alpha \subset C'P \cap \sigma \,.\supset_\alpha .\, \overrightarrow{\text{seq}}_P{}'\alpha \subset \sigma : \supset_\sigma .\, C'P \subset \sigma :. \supset .\, P \epsilon \Omega$

Dem.

$\vdash .\, *250\cdot301 \,.\supset$

$\vdash :. P \epsilon \text{connex} \,.\, \exists \,!\, C'P \cap \tau \,.\, \sim \exists \,!\, \overrightarrow{\min}_P{}'\tau \,.\, \sigma = C'P - \breve{P}``\tau \,.\supset :$

$\qquad \alpha \subset \sigma \,.\supset_\alpha .\, \overrightarrow{\text{seq}}_P{}'\alpha \subset \sigma : \exists \,!\, C'P - \sigma \qquad (1)$

$\vdash .\, (1) \,.\, *10\cdot28 \,.\supset$

$\vdash :. P \epsilon \text{connex} : (\exists \tau) \,.\, \exists \,!\, C'P \cap \tau \,.\, \sim \exists \,!\, \overrightarrow{\min}_P{}'\tau : \supset :$

$\qquad (\exists \sigma) : \alpha \subset \sigma \,.\supset_\alpha .\, \overrightarrow{\text{seq}}_P{}'\alpha \subset \sigma : \exists \,!\, C'P - \sigma \qquad (2)$

$\vdash .\, (2) \,.\, \text{Transp} \,.\supset$

$\vdash :: P \epsilon \text{connex} :. \alpha \subset \sigma \,.\supset_\alpha .\, \overrightarrow{\text{seq}}_P{}'\alpha \subset \sigma : \supset_\sigma .\, C'P \subset \sigma :. \supset :$

$\qquad \exists \,!\, C'P \cap \tau \,.\supset_\tau .\, \exists \,!\, \overrightarrow{\min}_P{}'\tau :$

$[*250\cdot101] \quad \supset : P \epsilon \text{Bord} \qquad (3)$

$\vdash .\, (3) \,.\, *250\cdot113 \,.\supset \vdash .\, \text{Prop}$

$*250{\cdot}32$. $\vdash :: . P \epsilon \text{connex} . \supset :: P \epsilon \text{Bord} . \equiv :.$

$$\alpha \subset C‘P \cap \sigma . \supset_\alpha . \overrightarrow{\text{seq}}_P‘\alpha \subset \sigma : \supset_\sigma . C‘P \subset \sigma \quad [*250{\cdot}3{\cdot}31]$$

$*250{\cdot}33$. $\vdash . \Omega = \text{connex} \cap \hat{P} \{\alpha \subset C‘P \cap \sigma . \supset_\alpha . \overrightarrow{\text{seq}}_P‘\alpha \subset \sigma : \supset_\sigma . C‘P \subset \sigma\}$

$[*250{\cdot}32{\cdot}113]$

$*250{\cdot}34$. $\vdash :. P \epsilon \text{Bord} : x \epsilon C‘P . \overrightarrow{P}‘x \subset \sigma . \supset_x . x \epsilon \sigma : \supset . C‘P \subset \sigma$

Dem.

$\vdash . *250{\cdot}11 . \supset \vdash : P \epsilon \text{Bord} . \exists ! C‘P - \sigma . \supset . \exists ! \overrightarrow{\text{min}}_P‘(C‘P - \sigma) .$

$[*205{\cdot}14] \qquad \supset . (\exists x) . x \epsilon C‘P - \sigma . \overrightarrow{P}‘x \subset \sigma \quad (1)$

$\vdash . (1) . \text{Transp} . \supset \vdash . \text{Prop}$

$*250{\cdot}341$. $\vdash :: x \epsilon C‘P . \overrightarrow{P}‘x \subset \sigma . \supset_x . x \epsilon \sigma : \supset_\sigma . C‘P \subset \sigma :. \supset . P \epsilon \text{Bord}$

Dem.

$\vdash . *205{\cdot}122 . *37{\cdot}462 . \supset$

$\vdash : \exists ! C‘P \cap \tau . \sim \exists ! \overrightarrow{\text{min}}_P‘\tau . \sigma = C‘P - \breve{P}“\tau . x \epsilon C‘P . \overrightarrow{P}‘x \subset \sigma . \supset .$

$\qquad x \sim \epsilon \breve{P}“\tau . \exists ! C‘P - \sigma .$

$[\text{Hp}] \qquad \supset . x \epsilon \sigma . \exists ! C‘P - \sigma \quad (1)$

$\vdash . (1) . *10{\cdot}28 . \supset \vdash :. (\exists \tau) . \exists ! C‘P \cap \tau . \sim \exists ! \overrightarrow{\text{min}}_P‘\tau . \supset :$

$\qquad (\exists \sigma) : x \epsilon C‘P . \overrightarrow{P}‘x \subset \sigma . \supset_x . x \epsilon \sigma : \exists ! C‘P - \sigma \quad (2)$

$\vdash . (2) . \text{Transp} . \supset \vdash :. \text{Hp} . \supset : \exists ! C‘P \cap \tau . \supset_\tau . \exists ! \overrightarrow{\text{min}}_P‘\tau :$

$[*250{\cdot}101] \qquad \supset : P \epsilon \text{Bord} :. \supset \vdash . \text{Prop}$

$*250{\cdot}35$. $\vdash . \text{Bord} = \hat{P} \{x \epsilon C‘P . \overrightarrow{P}‘x \subset \sigma . \supset_x . x \epsilon \sigma : \supset_\sigma . C‘P \subset \sigma\}$

$[*250{\cdot}34{\cdot}341]$

$*250{\cdot}36$. $\vdash :. P \epsilon \Omega : \lambda \subset \sigma . \exists ! \lambda \cap C‘P . \supset_\lambda . \overrightarrow{\text{seq}}_P‘\lambda \subset \sigma : \supset . \breve{P}“\sigma \subset \sigma$

Dem.

$\vdash . *250{\cdot}121 . \supset \vdash : P \epsilon \Omega . \exists ! \breve{P}“\sigma - \sigma . \supset . E ! \text{min}_P‘(\breve{P}“\sigma - \sigma) \quad (1)$

$\vdash . *205{\cdot}14 . *37{\cdot}46 . \supset$

$\vdash : x = \text{min}_P‘(\breve{P}“\sigma - \sigma) . \supset . \exists ! \sigma \cap \overrightarrow{P}‘x . \overrightarrow{P}‘x \cap (\breve{P}“\sigma - \sigma) = \Lambda .$

$[*24{\cdot}311] \qquad \supset . \exists ! \sigma \cap \overrightarrow{P}‘x . \overrightarrow{P}‘x - \sigma \subset - \breve{P}“\sigma \quad (2)$

$\vdash . (2) . *202{\cdot}501 . \supset$

$\vdash : P \epsilon \text{Ser} . x = \text{min}_P‘(\breve{P}“\sigma - \sigma) . \supset . \exists ! \sigma \cap \overrightarrow{P}‘x . \overrightarrow{P}‘x - \sigma \subset p‘\overrightarrow{P}“(\sigma \cap C‘P) .$

$[*40{\cdot}16] \qquad \supset . \exists ! \sigma \cap \overrightarrow{P}‘x . \overrightarrow{P}‘x - \sigma \subset p‘\overrightarrow{P}“(\sigma \cap \overrightarrow{P}‘x) .$

$[*40{\cdot}61] \qquad \supset . \overrightarrow{P}‘x - \sigma \subset P“(\sigma \cap \overrightarrow{P}‘x) \quad (3)$

$\vdash . (3) . \supset \vdash : \text{Hp} (3) . \supset . \overrightarrow{P}‘x \subset (\sigma \cap \overrightarrow{P}‘x) \cup P“(\sigma \cap \overrightarrow{P}‘x) .$

[*206·171] $\supset . x = \text{seq}_P‘(\sigma \cap \overrightarrow{P}‘x)$.

[(2)] $\supset . \exists ! \sigma \cap \overrightarrow{P}‘x . \sigma \cap \overrightarrow{P}‘x \subset \sigma . \sim \{\overrightarrow{\text{seq}_P}‘(\sigma \cap \overrightarrow{P}‘x) \subset \sigma\}$.

[*10·24] $\supset . (\exists \lambda) . \lambda \subset \sigma . \exists ! \lambda \cap C‘P . \sim (\overrightarrow{\text{seq}_P}‘\lambda \subset \sigma)$ (4)

$\vdash . (4) . \text{Transp} . \supset \vdash : \text{Hp} . \supset . \sim E ! \min_P‘(\breve{P}“\sigma - \sigma)$.

[(1).Transp] $\supset . \breve{P}“\sigma - \sigma = \Lambda : \supset \vdash . \text{Prop}$

***250·361.** $\vdash :. P \epsilon \Omega . \breve{P}_1“\sigma \subset \sigma : \lambda \subset \sigma . \exists ! (\lambda \cap C‘P) . \supset_\lambda . \overrightarrow{\text{limax}_P}‘\lambda \subset \sigma : \supset .$

$\breve{P}“\sigma \subset \sigma$

Dem.

$\vdash . *206·46·43 . \supset \vdash : \text{Hp} . \lambda \subset \sigma . E ! \max_P‘\lambda . \supset . \overrightarrow{\text{seq}_P}‘\lambda = \overleftarrow{P_1}‘\max_P‘\lambda$.

[Hp] $\supset . \overrightarrow{\text{seq}_P}‘\lambda \subset \sigma$ (1)

$\vdash . *207·4 . \supset \vdash : \text{Hp} . \lambda \subset \sigma . \exists ! (\lambda \cap C‘P) . \sim E ! \max_P‘\lambda . \supset . \overrightarrow{\text{seq}_P}‘\lambda = \overrightarrow{\text{limax}_P}‘\lambda$.

[Hp] $\supset . \overrightarrow{\text{seq}_P}‘\lambda \subset \sigma$ (2)

$\vdash . (1) . (2) . \supset \vdash :. \text{Hp} . \supset : \lambda \subset \sigma . \exists ! (\lambda \cap C‘P) . \supset_\lambda . \overrightarrow{\text{seq}_P}‘\lambda \subset \sigma :$

[*250·36] $\supset : \breve{P}“\sigma \subset \sigma :. \supset \vdash . \text{Prop}$

***250·362.** $\vdash :. \breve{P} \epsilon \Omega . P_1“\sigma \subset \sigma : \lambda \subset \sigma . \exists ! \lambda \cap C‘P . \supset_\lambda . \overrightarrow{\text{limin}_P}‘\lambda \subset \sigma : \supset .$

$P“\sigma \subset \sigma$

$\left[*250·361 \frac{\breve{P}}{P} . *121·26 \right]$

***250·4.** $\vdash . \dot{\Lambda} \epsilon \Omega$

Dem.

$\vdash . *60·33 . \supset \vdash . \text{Cl ex}‘C‘\dot{\Lambda} \subset \text{C}\!\!\text{I}‘\min(\dot{\Lambda})$ (1)

$\vdash . (1) . *250·1 . \supset \vdash . \dot{\Lambda} \epsilon \text{Bord}$ (2)

$\vdash . (2) . *204·24 . \supset \vdash . \text{Prop}$

***250·41.** $\vdash : x \neq y . \supset . x \downarrow y \epsilon \Omega$

Dem.

$\vdash . *60·39 . \supset \vdash . \text{Cl ex}‘C“(x \downarrow y) = \iota‘\iota‘x \cup \iota‘\iota‘y \cup \iota‘(\iota‘x \cup \iota‘y)$ (1)

$\vdash . *205·18 . \supset \vdash : \text{Hp} . P = x \downarrow y . \supset . \min_P‘\iota‘x = x . \min_P‘\iota‘y = y$ (2)

$\vdash . *205·181 . \supset \vdash : \text{Hp}(2) . \supset . \min_P‘(\iota‘x \cup \iota‘y) = x$ (3)

$\vdash . (1) . (2) . (3) . \supset \vdash : \text{Hp}(2) . \supset . \text{Cl ex}‘C‘(x \downarrow y) \subset \text{C}\!\!\text{I}‘\min_P$.

[*250·1] $\supset . x \downarrow y \epsilon \text{Bord}$ (4)

$\vdash . (4) . *204·25 . \supset \vdash . \text{Prop}$

***250·42.** $\vdash : P \epsilon \Omega - \iota`\dot{\Lambda} . \supset . E ! 2_P . 2_P = \breve{P}_1`B`P . \overrightarrow{P}`2_P = \iota`B`P . P \upharpoonright \overrightarrow{P}`2_P = \dot{\Lambda}$

Dem.

$\vdash . *121·13 . \supset \vdash : x = 2_P . \equiv . x = \breve{P}_1`B`P$ (1)

$\vdash . *250·13 . \supset \vdash : \text{Hp} . \supset . E ! B`P .$

[*250·21.*204·7] $\supset . E ! \breve{P}_1`B`P$ (2)

$\vdash . (1) . (2) . \supset \vdash : \text{Hp} . \supset . E ! 2_P . 2_P = \breve{P}_1`B`P$ (3)

[*204·71] $\supset . \overrightarrow{P}`2_P = \iota`B`P$ (4)

[*200·35] $\supset . P \upharpoonright \overrightarrow{P}`2_P = \dot{\Lambda}$ (5)

$\vdash . (3) . (4) . (5) . \supset \vdash . \text{Prop}$

***250·43.** $\vdash . 0_r = \Omega \cap \breve{C}``0$

Dem.

$\vdash . *56·104 . \supset \vdash : P \epsilon 0_r . \equiv . P = \dot{\Lambda} .$

[*250·4.*33·241] $\equiv . P \epsilon \Omega . C`P = \Lambda .$

[*71·37.*54·1] $\equiv . P \epsilon \Omega \cap \breve{C}``0 : \supset \vdash . \text{Prop}$

***250·44.** $\vdash . 2_r = \Omega \cap \breve{C}``2$

Dem.

$\vdash . *56·11 . \supset \vdash :. P \epsilon 2_r . \equiv : (\exists x, y) . x \neq y . P = x \downarrow y :$

[*250·41] $\equiv : P \epsilon \Omega : (\exists x, y) . x \neq y . P = x \downarrow y :$

[*56·11·38] $\equiv : P \epsilon \Omega \cap \breve{C}``2 . P \dot{\cap} \breve{P} = \dot{\Lambda} :$

[*204·14] $\equiv : P \epsilon \Omega \cap \breve{C}``2 :. \supset \vdash . \text{Prop}$

***250·5.** $\vdash : P \epsilon \Omega . \supset . \text{min}_P \upharpoonright \text{Cl ex}`C`P \epsilon \epsilon_\Delta`\text{Cl ex}`C`P .$
$\iota`C`P = \text{Prod}`\text{Cl ex}`C`P$ [*205·33 . *250·1 . *115·17]

This proposition is of great importance, since it gives the existence-theorem for selections from any class of existent classes whose sum can be well-ordered (cf. *250·53, below). Observe that "$\alpha \epsilon C``\Omega$" means "$\alpha$ is a class which can be well-ordered."

***250·51.** $\vdash : \alpha \epsilon C``\Omega . \supset . \exists ! \epsilon_\Delta`\text{Cl ex}`\alpha$ [*250·5]

***250·52.** $\vdash : \alpha \epsilon C``\Omega . \beta \subset \alpha . \supset . \exists ! \epsilon_\Delta`\text{Cl ex}`\beta$ [*88·22·2 . *250·51]

***250·53.** $\vdash : s`\kappa \epsilon C``\Omega . \Lambda \sim \epsilon \kappa . \supset . \exists ! \epsilon_\Delta`\kappa$

Dem.

$\vdash . *60·23·57 . \supset \vdash : \text{Hp} . \supset . \kappa \subset \text{Cl ex}`s`\kappa .$

[*88·22.*250·51] $\supset \exists ! \epsilon_\Delta`\kappa : \supset \vdash . \text{Prop}$

***250·54.** $\vdash : C``\Omega \cup 1 = \text{Cls} . \supset . \text{Mult ax}$

Dem.

$\vdash . *250·53 . *83·4 . \supset \vdash :. \text{Hp} . \supset : \Lambda \sim \epsilon \kappa . \supset_\kappa . \exists ! \epsilon_\Delta`\kappa :$

[*88·37] $\supset : \text{Mult ax} :. \supset \vdash . \text{Prop}$

The above proposition states that if every class which is not a unit class is the field of some well-ordered series, then the multiplicative axiom holds. The converse of this proposition has been proved by Zermelo (cf. *258·47).

***250·6.** $\vdash : P, Q \epsilon \Omega . P \text{ smor } Q . \supset . P \overline{\text{smor}} Q \epsilon 1$ [*208·41 . *250·12·1]

This proposition is very useful, since it enables us, when two similar series of similar well-ordered series are given, to pick out the correlators of all the pairs without assuming the multiplicative axiom. *I.e.* given $P, Q \epsilon \text{Rel}^2 \text{excl} . S \epsilon P \overline{\text{smor}} Q . S \subset \text{smor}$, if $N \epsilon C`Q$, the correlator of $S`N$ and N will be $\breve{\iota}`(S`N) \overline{\text{smor}} N$ if $S`N, N \epsilon \Omega$. This enables us to dispense with the multiplicative axiom in the hypotheses of *164·44 and its consequences, whenever the relations concerned have fields whose members are well-ordered series.

***250·61.** $\vdash : P \epsilon \Omega . \supset . P \overline{\text{smor}} P = \iota`(I \upharpoonright C`P)$ [*208·42]

***250·62.** $\vdash : P \epsilon \text{Bord} . S \epsilon \text{cror}`P . \supset . \sim (\exists x) . (S`x) P x$ [*208·43]

***250·63.** $\vdash : P \epsilon \Omega \cap \text{Cnv}``\Omega . \supset . \text{Rl}`P \cap \text{Nr}`P = \iota`P$ [*208·45]

This proposition will be useful in showing that a *finite* series is not similar to any proper part of itself, and is a series which is well-ordered and has a converse which is also well-ordered.

***250·64.** $\vdash : P \epsilon \text{Bord} . S \epsilon \text{cror}`P . \supset . C`P \cap p`\overleftarrow{P}``\text{D}`S = \Lambda$ [*208·46]

In virtue of this proposition, a part of a well-ordered series can only be similar to the whole if the part extends to the end of the series. Thus *e.g.* no proper section of a well-ordered series can be similar to the whole.

***250·65.** $\vdash : P \epsilon \Omega . \alpha \epsilon \text{sect}`P - \iota`C`P . \beta \subset \alpha . \supset . \sim \{P \text{ smor } P \upharpoonright \beta\}$

Dem.

$\vdash . *40 \cdot 16 . \quad \supset \vdash : \text{Hp} . \supset . p`\overleftarrow{P}``C`(P \upharpoonright \alpha) \subset p`\overleftarrow{P}``C`(P \upharpoonright \beta)$ (1)

$\vdash . *211 \cdot 133 . \supset \vdash : \text{Hp} . \alpha \sim \epsilon 1 . \supset . \alpha = C`(P \upharpoonright \alpha) .$

[*211·703] $\supset . \exists ! p`\overleftarrow{P}``C`(P \upharpoonright \alpha) .$

[(1)] $\supset . \exists ! p`\overleftarrow{P}``C`(P \upharpoonright \beta)$ (2)

$\vdash . (2) . *40 \cdot 6 \cdot 62 . \supset \vdash : \text{Hp} . \alpha \sim \epsilon 1 . \dot{\exists} ! P . \supset . \exists ! C`P \cap p`\overleftarrow{P}``C`(P \upharpoonright \beta) .$

[*208·47] $\supset . \sim \{P \text{ smor } (P \upharpoonright \beta)\}$ (3)

$\vdash . *211 \cdot 1 . *24 \cdot 13 . \supset \vdash : P = \dot{\Lambda} . \supset . \text{sect}`P - \iota`C`P = \Lambda$ (4)

$\vdash . (4) . \text{Transp} . \quad \supset \vdash : \text{Hp} . \supset . \dot{\exists} ! P$ (5)

$\vdash . *200 \cdot 35 . *250 \cdot 104 . \supset \vdash : \text{Hp} . \dot{\exists} ! P . \alpha \epsilon 1 . \supset . \sim \{P \text{ smor } (P \upharpoonright \beta)\}$ (6)

$\vdash . (3) . (5) . (6) . \supset \vdash . \text{Prop}$

***250·651.** $\vdash : P \epsilon \Omega . \supset . \text{Nr}`P \cap P \upharpoonright ``(\text{sect}`P - \iota`C`P) = \Lambda$ [*250·65]

***250·652.** $\vdash : P \in \text{Bord} . Q \Subset P . \exists ! C\text{‘}P \cap p\text{‘}\overleftarrow{P}\text{“}C\text{‘}Q . \supset . \sim (P \text{ smor } Q)$
[*208·47]

***250·653.** $\vdash : P \in \text{Bord} . \exists ! C\text{‘}P \cap p\text{‘}\overleftarrow{P}\text{“}(\alpha \cap C\text{‘}P) . \supset . \sim (P \text{ smor } P \upharpoonright \alpha)$

Dem.

$\vdash . *37\cdot41 . \supset \vdash . C\text{‘}(P \upharpoonright \alpha) \subset \alpha \cap C\text{‘}P .$
[*40·16] $\supset \vdash . p\text{‘}\overleftarrow{P}\text{“}(\alpha \cap C\text{‘}P) \subset p\text{‘}\overleftarrow{P}\text{“}C\text{‘}(P \upharpoonright \alpha)$ (1)
$\vdash . (1) . \supset \vdash : \text{Hp} . \supset . \exists ! C\text{‘}P \cap p\text{‘}\overleftarrow{P}\text{“}C\text{‘}(P \upharpoonright \alpha) .$
[*250·652] $\supset . \sim \{P \text{ smor } (P \upharpoonright \alpha)\} : \supset \vdash . \text{Prop}$

***250·66.** $\vdash : P \in \Omega . \alpha \in \text{sect}\text{‘}P . P \text{ smor } (P \upharpoonright \alpha) . \supset . \alpha = C\text{‘}P$ [*250·65 . Transp]

***250·67.** $\vdash : P \in \Omega . x \in C\text{‘}P . \supset . \sim \{P \text{ smor } (P \upharpoonright \overrightarrow{P}\text{‘}x)\}$

Dem.

$\vdash . *211\cdot302 . \supset \vdash : \text{Hp} . \supset . \overrightarrow{P}\text{‘}x \in \text{sect}\text{‘}P$ (1)
$\vdash . *200\cdot52 . \supset \vdash : \text{Hp} . \supset . \overrightarrow{P}\text{‘}x \neq C\text{‘}P$ (2)
$\vdash . (1) . (2) . *250\cdot65 . \supset \vdash . \text{Prop}$

***250·7.** $\vdash :. P \in \Omega . \equiv : x \in C\text{‘}P . \supset_x . P \upharpoonright \overrightarrow{P_*}\text{‘}x \in \Omega : P \in \text{Ser}$

Dem.

$\vdash . *250\cdot141 . \supset \vdash :. P \in \Omega . \supset : x \in C\text{‘}P . \supset_x . P \upharpoonright \overrightarrow{P_*}\text{‘}x \in \Omega$ (1)
$\vdash . *250\cdot121 . \supset$
$\vdash :. x \in C\text{‘}P . \supset_x . P \upharpoonright \overrightarrow{P_*}\text{‘}x \in \Omega : \equiv : x \in C\text{‘}P . \exists ! \alpha \cap C\text{‘}(P \upharpoonright \overrightarrow{P_*}\text{‘}x) . \supset_{x,\alpha} .$
$E ! \min (P \upharpoonright \overrightarrow{P_*}\text{‘}x)\text{‘}\alpha :$
[*202·55] $\supset : x \in \text{D}\text{‘}P \cap \alpha . \supset_{x,\alpha} . E ! \min (P \upharpoonright \overrightarrow{P_*}\text{‘}x)\text{‘}\alpha :$
[*205·27] $\supset_{x,\alpha} . E ! \min_P\text{‘}\alpha :$
[*10·23] $\supset : \exists ! \text{D}\text{‘}P \cap \alpha . \supset_\alpha . E ! \min_P\text{‘}\alpha$ (2)
$\vdash . *205\cdot18 . *202\cdot52 . \supset \vdash : P \in \text{Ser} . \alpha = \overrightarrow{B}\text{‘}P . \supset . E ! \min_P\text{‘}\alpha$ (3)
$\vdash . (2) . (3) . \supset \vdash :. x \in C\text{‘}P . \supset_x . P \upharpoonright \overrightarrow{P_*}\text{‘}x \in \Omega : P \in \text{Ser} : \supset :$
$\exists ! \alpha \cap C\text{‘}P . \supset_\alpha . E ! \min_P\text{‘}\alpha :$
[*250·121] $\supset : P \in \Omega$ (4)
$\vdash . (1) . (4) . \supset \vdash . \text{Prop}$

This proposition is used in proving that the series of ordinals in order of magnitude is well-ordered (*256·3). We prove first that if $P \in \Omega$, the ordinals up to and including $\text{Nr}\text{‘}P$ are well-ordered; thence, by the above proposition, it follows that the whole series of ordinals is well-ordered.

$*251$. ORDINAL NUMBERS.

Summary of $*251$.

The name "ordinal numbers" is commonly confined to the relation-numbers of well-ordered series, and will be so confined in what follows. The relation-numbers of series in general are commonly called "order-types*." Thus α is an order-type if $\alpha \in \text{Nr}``\text{Ser}$, and $\alpha$ is an ordinal number if $\alpha \in \text{Nr}``\Omega$. In the present number we shall be concerned with a few of the simpler properties of ordinal numbers and of the sums, products, and powers of well-ordered series.

We put $$\text{NO} = \text{Nr}``\Omega \quad \text{Df},$$
where "NO" stands for "ordinal number."

We prove in this number that any relation similar to a well-ordered relation is well-ordered ($*251\cdot11$), and therefore any relation similar to a well-ordered series is a well-ordered series ($*251\cdot111$). We prove

$*251\cdot132\cdot142$. $\vdash : \alpha \in \text{NO} . \equiv . \alpha \dot{+} \dot{1} \in \text{NO} . \equiv . \dot{1} \dot{+} \alpha \in \text{NO}$

$*251\cdot15\cdot16$. $\vdash . 0_r, 2_r \in \text{NO}$

$*251\cdot24$. $\vdash : \alpha, \beta \in \text{NO} . \supset . \alpha \dot{+} \beta \in \text{NO}$

We prove that if P is a well-ordered series of mutually exclusive well-ordered series, $\Sigma`P$ is a well-ordered series ($*251\cdot21$); that if $P$ is a well-ordered series of series, $\Pi`P$ is a series ($*251\cdot3$); that if P is a series and Q is a well-ordered series, P^Q and $P \exp Q$ are series ($*251\cdot42$); that if P, Q are well-ordered series, so is $P \times Q$ ($*251\cdot55$), and therefore the product of two ordinal numbers is an ordinal number ($*251\cdot56$).

In virtue of the uniqueness of the correlator of two well-ordered series, we have

$*251\cdot61$. $\vdash :. P, Q \in \text{Rel}^2 \text{excl} . C`P \subset \Omega . \supset :$
$$\exists ! (P \,\overline{\text{smor}}\, Q) \cap \text{Rl}`\text{smor} . \equiv . P \,\text{smor smor}\, Q$$
whence, without assuming the multiplicative axiom,

* We shall also speak of them as "serial numbers."

***251·621.** $\vdash : C`P \subset \Omega \, . \, \exists ! (P \,\overline{\text{smor}}\, Q) \cap \text{Rl}`\text{smor} \, . \supset .$
$$\Sigma \text{Nr}`P = \Sigma \text{Nr}`Q \, . \, \Pi \text{Nr}`P = \Pi \text{Nr}`Q$$

***251·65.** $\vdash : \alpha \in \text{NO} - \iota`\Lambda \, . \, \beta \in \text{NR} \, . \, P \in \beta \, . \, C`P \subset \alpha \, . \supset .$
$$\Sigma \text{Nr}`P = \beta \dot{\times} \alpha \, . \, \Pi \text{Nr}`P = \alpha \exp_r \beta$$

Finally, we have propositions (*251·7·71) showing that the existence of an existent Ω in any type is equivalent to the existence of 2_r in that type, and therefore holds for every type of homogeneous relations, except (possibly, so far as our primitive propositions can show) in the type of relations of individuals to individuals.

***251·01.** $\text{NO} = \text{Nr}``\Omega$ Df

***251·1.** $\vdash : \alpha \in \text{NO} \, . \equiv . \, (\exists P) \, . \, P \in \Omega \, . \, \alpha = \text{Nr}`P$ [(*251·01)]

***251·11.** $\vdash : P \in \text{Bord} \, . \, P \text{ smor } Q \, . \supset . \, Q \in \text{Bord}$

Dem.

$\vdash . *205·8 . *250·1 . *37·431 . \supset$

$\vdash :. P \in \text{Bord} \, . \, S \in P \,\overline{\text{smor}}\, Q \, . \supset : \alpha \subset C`P \, . \, \exists ! \alpha \, . \supset_\alpha . \, \exists ! \overrightarrow{\text{min}}_Q`\breve{S}``\alpha :$

[*37·63·431] $\supset : \beta \in \breve{S}```\text{Cl ex}`C`P \, . \, \exists ! \beta \, . \supset_\beta . \, \exists ! \overrightarrow{\text{min}}_Q`\beta :$

[*71·491] $\supset : \beta \in \text{Cl ex}`\breve{S}``C`P \, . \supset_\beta . \, \exists ! \overrightarrow{\text{min}}_Q`\beta :$

[*151·11·131.*37·25] $\supset : \beta \in \text{Cl ex}`C`Q \, . \supset_\beta . \, \exists ! \overrightarrow{\text{min}}_Q`\beta :$

[*250·1] $\supset : Q \in \text{Bord} :. \supset \vdash . \text{Prop}$

***251·111.** $\vdash : P \in \Omega \, . \, P \text{ smor } Q \, . \supset . \, Q \in \Omega$ [*251·11 . *204·21]

***251·12.** $\vdash : P \in \text{Bord} \, . \supset . \, \text{Nr}`P \subset \text{Bord}$ [*251·11]

***251·121.** $\vdash : P \in \Omega \, . \supset . \, \text{Nr}`P \subset \Omega$ [*251·111]

***251·122.** $\vdash : \alpha \in \text{NO} \, . \supset . \, \alpha \subset \Omega$ [*251·121·1]

***251·13.** $\vdash : P \in \text{Bord} \, . \, z \sim \in C`P \, . \equiv . \, P \mathbin{\rightarrow\!\!\!+} z \in \text{Bord}$

Dem.

$\vdash . *205·83 . *250·1 . \supset \vdash : \text{Hp} \, . \, \exists ! C`P \cap \alpha \, . \supset . \, \exists ! \overrightarrow{\text{min}} (P \mathbin{\rightarrow\!\!\!+} z)`\alpha$ (1)

$\vdash . *205·831 . \supset \vdash : \text{Hp} \, . \, C`(P \mathbin{\rightarrow\!\!\!+} z) \cap \alpha = \iota`z \, . \supset . \, \exists ! \overrightarrow{\text{min}} (P \mathbin{\rightarrow\!\!\!+} z)`\alpha$ (2)

$\vdash . *161·14 . \supset \vdash :. \text{Hp} \, . \, \exists ! C`(P \mathbin{\rightarrow\!\!\!+} z) \cap \alpha \, . \supset :$

$\exists ! C`P \cap \alpha \, . \vee . \, C`P \cap \alpha = \Lambda \, . \, \exists ! \iota`z \cap \alpha :$

[*161·14] $\supset : \exists ! C`P \cap \alpha \, . \vee . \, C`(P \mathbin{\rightarrow\!\!\!+} z) \cap \alpha = \iota`z$ (3)

$\vdash . (1) . (2) . (3) . \supset$

$\vdash :. \text{Hp} \, . \supset : \exists ! C`(P \mathbin{\rightarrow\!\!\!+} z) \cap \alpha \, . \supset_\alpha . \, \exists ! \overrightarrow{\text{min}} (P \mathbin{\rightarrow\!\!\!+} z)`\alpha$ (4)

$\vdash . (4) . *250·101 . \supset \vdash : P \in \text{Bord} \, . \, z \sim \in C`P \, . \supset . \, P \mathbin{\rightarrow\!\!\!+} z \in \text{Bord}$ (5)

$\vdash . *250·14·104 . *200·41 . \supset \vdash : P \mathbin{\rightarrow\!\!\!+} z \in \text{Bord} \, . \supset . \, P \in \text{Bord} \, . \, z \sim \in C`P$ (6)

$\vdash . (5) . (6) . \supset \vdash . \text{Prop}$

***251·131**. $\vdash : P \in \Omega \,.\, z \sim\in C`P \,.\, \equiv \,.\, P \dot{\rightarrow} z \in \Omega$ [*204·51 . *251·13]

***251·132**. $\vdash : \alpha \in \mathrm{NO} \,.\, \equiv \,.\, \alpha \dotplus \dot{1} \in \mathrm{NO}$

Dem.

$\vdash \,.\, *251\cdot111 \,.\, *181\cdot12 \,.\, \supset \vdash : P \in \Omega \,.\, \equiv \,.\, \downarrow \Lambda_x \,;\iota\,; P \in \Omega \,.$

$[*181\cdot11.(*181\cdot01).*251\cdot131] \qquad \equiv \,.\, P \dot{\rightarrow} x \in \Omega \,.$

$[*181\cdot3.*251\cdot1] \qquad \equiv \,.\, \mathrm{Nr}`P \dotplus \dot{1} \in \mathrm{NO} \quad (1)$

$\vdash \,.\, (1) \,.\, *251\cdot1 \,.\, \supset \vdash \,.\, \mathrm{Prop}$

***251·14**. $\vdash : P \in \mathrm{Bord} \,.\, z \sim\in C`P \,.\, \equiv \,.\, z \leftarrow\!\!\!+ P \in \mathrm{Bord}$

Dem.

$\vdash \,.\, *205\cdot832 \,.\, *161\cdot12 \,.\, \supset$

$\vdash :. \mathrm{Hp} \,.\, \supset : z \sim\in \alpha \,.\, \supset \,.\, \overrightarrow{\min}\,(z \leftarrow\!\!\!+ P)`\alpha = \overrightarrow{\min}_P`\alpha :$

$[*250\cdot101] \supset : \exists ! (\alpha \cap C`P) \,.\, z \sim\in \alpha \,.\, \supset \,.\, \exists ! \overrightarrow{\min}\,(z \leftarrow\!\!\!+ P)`\alpha \quad (1)$

$\vdash \,.\, *205\cdot833 \,.\, *161\cdot12 \,.\, \supset$

$\vdash : \mathrm{Hp} \,.\, z \in \alpha \,.\, \dot{\exists} ! P \,.\, \supset \,.\, \exists ! \overrightarrow{\min}\,(z \leftarrow\!\!\!+ P)`\alpha \quad (2)$

$\vdash \,.\, (1) \,.\, (2) \,.\, \supset$

$\vdash :. \mathrm{Hp} \,.\, \dot{\exists} ! P \,.\, \supset : \exists ! \alpha \cap C`(z \leftarrow\!\!\!+ P) \,.\, \supset_\alpha \,.\, \exists ! \overrightarrow{\min}\,(z \leftarrow\!\!\!+ P)`\alpha :$

$[*250\cdot101] \qquad \supset : z \leftarrow\!\!\!+ P \in \mathrm{Bord} \quad (3)$

$\vdash \,.\, *161\cdot201 \,.\, *250\cdot4 \,.\, \qquad \supset \vdash : P = \dot{\Lambda} \,.\, \supset \,.\, z \leftarrow\!\!\!+ P \in \mathrm{Bord} \quad (4)$

$\vdash \,.\, (3) \,.\, (4) \,.\, \qquad \supset \vdash : P \in \mathrm{Bord} \,.\, z \sim\in C`P \,.\, \supset \,.\, z \leftarrow\!\!\!+ P \in \mathrm{Bord} \quad (5)$

$\vdash \,.\, *250\cdot14\cdot104 \,.\, *200\cdot41 \,.\, \supset \vdash : z \leftarrow\!\!\!+ P \in \mathrm{Bord} \,.\, \supset \,.\, P \in \mathrm{Bord} \,.\, z \sim\in C`P \quad (6)$

$\vdash \,.\, (5) \,.\, (6) \,.\, \supset \vdash \,.\, \mathrm{Prop}$

***251·141**. $\vdash : P \in \Omega \,.\, z \sim\in C`P \,.\, \equiv \,.\, z \leftarrow\!\!\!+ P \in \Omega$ [*204·51 . *251·14]

***251·142**. $\vdash : \alpha \in \mathrm{NO} \,.\, \equiv \,.\, \dot{1} \dotplus \alpha \in \mathrm{NO}$ [Proof as in *251·132]

***251·15**. $\vdash \,.\, 0_r \in \mathrm{NO}$ [*250·4 . *153·11]

***251·16**. $\vdash \,.\, 2_r \in \mathrm{NO}$ [*250·41 . *153·211]

***251·17**. $\vdash : x \neq y \,.\, x \neq z \,.\, y \neq z \,.\, \supset \,.\, x \downarrow y \dot{\rightarrow} z \in \Omega$ [*251·131 . *250·41]

***251·171**. $\vdash \,.\, 2_r \dotplus \dot{1} \in \mathrm{NO}$ [*251·16·132]

***251·2**. $\vdash : P \in \mathrm{Rel}^2\,\mathrm{excl} \cap \mathrm{Bord} \,.\, C`P \subset \mathrm{Bord} \,.\, \supset \,.\, \Sigma`P \in \mathrm{Bord}$

Dem.

$\vdash \,.\, *162\cdot23 \,.\, \qquad \supset \vdash : \exists ! \alpha \cap C`\Sigma`P \,.\, \supset \,.\, \exists ! \alpha \cap F``C`P \,.$

$[*37\cdot264] \qquad \supset \,.\, \exists ! C`P \cap \breve{F}``\alpha \quad (1)$

$\vdash \,.\, *37\cdot46 \,.\, *33\cdot5 \,.\, \supset \vdash : Q \in \breve{F}``\alpha \,.\, \supset \,.\, \exists ! \alpha \cap C`Q \quad (2)$

$\vdash \,.\, (1) \,.\, (2) \,.\, *250\cdot101 \,.\, \supset$

$\vdash :. \mathrm{Hp} \,.\, \supset : \exists ! \alpha \cap C`\Sigma`P \,.\, \supset \,.\, (\exists Q) \,.\, Q \min_P \breve{F}``\alpha \,.\, \exists ! \overrightarrow{\min}_Q`\alpha \,.$

$[*205\cdot85] \qquad \supset \,.\, \exists ! \overrightarrow{\min}\,(\Sigma`P)`\alpha \quad (3)$

$\vdash \,.\, (3) \,.\, *250\cdot101 \,.\, \supset \vdash \,.\, \mathrm{Prop}$

∗251·21. $\vdash : P \epsilon \mathrm{Rel}^2 \mathrm{excl} \cap \Omega \,.\, C{}^{\backprime}P \subset \Omega \,.\supset .\, \Sigma{}^{\backprime}P \epsilon \Omega$ [∗204·52 . ∗251·2]

∗251·211. $\vdash : \mathrm{Nr}{}^{\backprime}P \epsilon \mathrm{NO} \,.\, \mathrm{Nr}{}^{\backprime\backprime}C{}^{\backprime}P \subset \mathrm{NO} \,.\supset .\, \Sigma\, \mathrm{Nr}{}^{\backprime}P \epsilon \mathrm{NO}$

Dem.

$\vdash . *182{\cdot}16{\cdot}162 \,.\qquad \supset \vdash : \mathrm{Hp} \,.\supset .\, \mathrm{Nr}{}^{\backprime}\, \underset{;}{\hat{\downarrow}}\,{}^{;}P \epsilon \mathrm{NO} \,.\, \underset{;}{\hat{\downarrow}}\,{}^{;}P \epsilon \mathrm{Rel}^2 \mathrm{excl}$ (1)

$\vdash . *182{\cdot}05{\cdot}11 \,.\, *151{\cdot}65 \,.\supset \vdash : \mathrm{Hp} \,.\supset .\, \mathrm{Nr}{}^{\backprime\backprime}C{}^{\backprime}\, \underset{;}{\hat{\downarrow}}\,{}^{;}P \subset \mathrm{NO}$ (2)

$\vdash . (1) . (2) . *251{\cdot}122 \,.\supset \vdash : \mathrm{Hp} \,.\supset .\, \underset{;}{\hat{\downarrow}}\,{}^{;}P \epsilon \mathrm{Rel}^2 \mathrm{excl} \cap \Omega \,.\, C{}^{\backprime}\, \underset{;}{\hat{\downarrow}}\,{}^{;}P \subset \Omega \,.$

[∗251·21] $\qquad \supset .\, \Sigma{}^{\backprime}\, \underset{;}{\hat{\downarrow}}\,{}^{;}P \epsilon \Omega \,.$

[∗251·1.(∗183·01)] $\qquad \supset .\, \Sigma\, \mathrm{Nr}{}^{\backprime}P \epsilon \mathrm{NO} : \supset \vdash . \mathrm{Prop}$

∗251·22. $\vdash : P, Q \epsilon \mathrm{Bord} \,.\, C{}^{\backprime}P \cap C{}^{\backprime}Q = \Lambda \,.\supset .\, P \ddagger Q \epsilon \mathrm{Bord}$

Dem.

$\vdash . *162{\cdot}3 \,.\, *163{\cdot}42 \,.\supset \vdash : \mathrm{Hp} \,.\, \sim(P = \dot{\Lambda} \,.\, Q = \dot{\Lambda}) \,.\supset .$

$\qquad P \downarrow Q \epsilon \mathrm{Bord} \,.\, C{}^{\backprime}(P \downarrow Q) \subset \mathrm{Bord} \,.\, P \downarrow Q \epsilon \mathrm{Rel}^2 \mathrm{excl} \,.$

$\qquad \Sigma{}^{\backprime}(P \downarrow Q) = P \ddagger Q \,.$

[∗251·2] $\qquad \supset .\, P \ddagger Q \epsilon \mathrm{Bord}$ (1)

$\vdash . *160{\cdot}21 \,.\, *250{\cdot}4 \,.\supset \vdash : P = \dot{\Lambda} \,.\, Q = \dot{\Lambda} \,.\supset .\, P \ddagger Q \epsilon \mathrm{Bord}$ (2)

$\vdash . (1) . (2) \,.\supset \vdash . \mathrm{Prop}$

∗251·23. $\vdash : P, Q \epsilon \Omega \,.\, C{}^{\backprime}P \cap C{}^{\backprime}Q = \Lambda \,.\supset .\, P \ddagger Q \epsilon \Omega$ [∗204·5 . ∗251·22]

∗251·24. $\vdash : \alpha, \beta \epsilon \mathrm{NO} \,.\supset .\, \alpha \dotplus \beta \epsilon \mathrm{NO}$

Dem.

$\vdash . *251{\cdot}111 \,.\, *180{\cdot}12{\cdot}11 \,.\supset$

$\vdash : P, Q \epsilon \Omega \,.\supset .\, \downarrow (\Lambda \cap C{}^{\backprime}Q){}^{;}\iota{}^{;}P \epsilon \Omega \,.\, (\Lambda \cap C{}^{\backprime}P) \downarrow {}^{;}\iota{}^{;}Q \epsilon \Omega \,.$

$\qquad C{}^{\backprime} \downarrow (\Lambda \cap C{}^{\backprime}Q){}^{;}\iota{}^{;}P \cap C{}^{\backprime}(\Lambda \cap C{}^{\backprime}P) \downarrow {}^{;}\iota{}^{;}Q = \Lambda \,.$

[∗251·23.(∗181·01)] $\supset .\, P + Q \epsilon \Omega \,.$

[∗180·3.∗251·1] $\qquad \supset .\, \mathrm{Nr}{}^{\backprime}P \dotplus \mathrm{Nr}{}^{\backprime}Q \epsilon \mathrm{NO}$ (1)

$\vdash . (1) \,.\, *251{\cdot}1 \,.\supset \vdash . \mathrm{Prop}$

∗251·25. $\vdash : P \ddagger Q \epsilon \Omega \,.\equiv .\, P, Q \epsilon \Omega \,.\, C{}^{\backprime}P \cap C{}^{\backprime}Q = \Lambda$

Dem.

$\vdash . *204{\cdot}5 \,.\qquad \supset \vdash : P \ddagger Q \epsilon \Omega \,.\supset .\, P, Q \epsilon \mathrm{Ser} \,.\, C{}^{\backprime}P \cap C{}^{\backprime}Q = \Lambda$ (1)

$\vdash . (1) \,.\, *205{\cdot}84 \,.\quad \supset \vdash :. P \ddagger Q \epsilon \Omega \,.\supset : \exists ! C{}^{\backprime}P \cap \alpha \,.\supset_\alpha .\, \exists ! \overrightarrow{\min}_P{}^{\backprime}\alpha :$

[∗250·11] $\qquad \supset : P \epsilon \mathrm{Bord}$ (2)

$\vdash . (1) \,.\, *205{\cdot}841 \,.\supset \vdash :. P \ddagger Q \epsilon \Omega \,.\supset :$

$\qquad \exists ! \alpha - C{}^{\backprime}P \cap C{}^{\backprime}(P \ddagger Q) \,.\supset_\alpha .\, \exists ! \overrightarrow{\min}_Q{}^{\backprime}(\alpha - C{}^{\backprime}P) :$

[*160·14.(1)] $\supset : \exists ! \alpha \cap C'Q . \supset_\alpha . \exists ! \overrightarrow{\min_Q}'(\alpha - C'P)$.

[*205·15.(1)] $\supset_\alpha . \exists ! \overrightarrow{\min_Q}'\alpha :$

[*250·101] $\supset : Q \in \text{Bord}$ (3)

$\vdash . (1) . (2) . (3) . \supset \vdash : P \ddagger Q \in \Omega . \supset . P, Q \in \Omega . C'P \cap C'Q = \Lambda$ (4)

$\vdash . (4) . *251·23 . \supset \vdash . \text{Prop}$

***251·26.** $\vdash : \alpha, \beta \in \text{NO} - \iota'\Lambda . \equiv . \alpha \dotplus \beta \in \text{NO} - \iota'\Lambda$ [*251·25]

***251·3.** $\vdash : P \in \Omega . C'P \subset \text{Ser} . \supset . \Pi'P \in \text{Ser}$ [*204·57 . *250·1]

***251·31.** $\vdash : \text{E}!! B``C'P . \supset . B \upharpoonright C'P \in F_\Delta`C'P$

Dem.

$\vdash . *71·571 . \supset \vdash : \text{Hp} . \supset . B \upharpoonright C'P \in 1 \to \text{Cls} . \text{Cl}'(B \upharpoonright C'P) = C'P$ (1)

$\vdash . *93·103 . \supset \vdash . B \Subset F$ (2)

$\vdash . (1) . (2) . *80·14 . \supset \vdash . \text{Prop}$

***251·32.** $\vdash : \text{E}!! B``C'P . \dot{\exists} ! P . \supset . B \upharpoonright C'P = B'\Pi'P$

Dem.

$\vdash . *172·162 . \supset \vdash : \text{Hp} . \supset . \overrightarrow{B}'\Pi'P = B_\Delta`C'P$

[*82·21] $= \iota'(B \upharpoonright C'P) : \supset \vdash . \text{Prop}$

***251·33.** $\vdash : C'P \subset \Omega - \iota'\dot{\Lambda} . \dot{\exists} ! P . \supset . \dot{\exists} ! \Pi'P . B \upharpoonright C'P = B'\Pi'P$ [*250·13 . *251·32]

***251·34.** $\vdash : P \in \text{Rel}^2 \text{excl} . C'P \subset \Omega - \iota'\dot{\Lambda} . \supset . \exists ! \epsilon_\Delta`C``C'P$

Dem.

$\vdash . *251·33 . *173·16 . \supset \vdash : \text{Hp} . \dot{\exists} ! P . \supset . \dot{\exists} ! \text{Prod}'P$.

[*173·161] $\supset . \exists ! \text{Prod}'C``C'P$

[*115·1] $\supset . \exists ! \epsilon_\Delta`C``C'P$ (1)

$\vdash . *83·15 . \supset \vdash : P = \dot{\Lambda} . \supset . \exists ! \epsilon_\Delta`C``C'P$ (2)

$\vdash . (1) . (2) . \supset \vdash . \text{Prop}$

***251·35.** $\vdash :: P \in \Omega . \supset :.$

$$\alpha P_{\text{cl}} \beta . \equiv : \alpha, \beta \in \text{Cl}'C'P : (\exists z) . z \in \alpha - \beta . \alpha \cap \overrightarrow{P}'z = \beta \cap \overrightarrow{P}'z$$

Dem.

$\vdash . *170·2 . \supset$

$\vdash :. \alpha, \beta \in \text{Cl}'C'P : (\exists z) . z \in \alpha - \beta . \alpha \cap \overrightarrow{P}'z = \beta \cap \overrightarrow{P}'z : \supset . \alpha P_{\text{cl}} \beta$ (1)

$\vdash . *170·23·1 . *250·121 . \supset$

$\vdash :: \text{Hp} . \supset :. \alpha P_{\text{cl}} \beta . \supset : \alpha, \beta \in \text{Cl}'C'P : (\exists z) . z \in \alpha - \beta . \alpha \cap \overrightarrow{P}'z = \beta \cap \overrightarrow{P}'z$ (2)

$\vdash . (1) . (2) . \supset \vdash . \text{Prop}$

*251·351. $\vdash :: \breve{P} \in \Omega . \supset :. \alpha P_{\mathrm{lc}} \beta . \equiv :$

$\alpha, \beta \in \mathrm{Cl}`C`P : (\exists z) . z \in \beta - \alpha . \alpha \cap \overleftarrow{P}`z = \beta \cap \overleftarrow{P}`z$ [*251·35 . *170·101]

*251·36. $\vdash : P \in \Omega . \supset . P_{\mathrm{cl}} \in \mathrm{Ser}$

Dem.

$\vdash . *170·17 . \supset \vdash . P_{\mathrm{cl}} \Subset J$ (1)

$\vdash . *251·35 . \supset \vdash :: \mathrm{Hp} . \supset :. \alpha P_{\mathrm{cl}} \beta . \beta P_{\mathrm{cl}} \gamma . \supset :$

$(\exists z, w) . z \in \alpha - \beta . w \in \beta - \gamma . \alpha \cap \overrightarrow{P}`z = \beta \cap \overrightarrow{P}`z . \beta \cap \overrightarrow{P}`w = \gamma \cap \overrightarrow{P}`w$ (2)

$\vdash . *201·14 . \supset$

$\vdash :. \mathrm{Hp} . z \in \alpha - \beta . w \in \beta - \gamma . \alpha \cap \overrightarrow{P}`z = \beta \cap \overrightarrow{P}`z . \beta \cap \overrightarrow{P}`w = \gamma \cap \overrightarrow{P}`w . \supset :$

$zPw . \supset . z \in \alpha - \gamma . \alpha \cap \overrightarrow{P}`z = \gamma \cap \overrightarrow{P}`z$ (3)

$\vdash . *201·14 . \supset \vdash :. \mathrm{Hp}(3) . \supset : wPz . \supset . w \in \alpha - \gamma . \alpha \cap \overrightarrow{P}`w = \gamma \cap \overrightarrow{P}`w$ (4)

$\vdash . (2) . (3) . (4) . *202·104 . *251·35 . \supset \vdash :. \mathrm{Hp} . \supset : \alpha P_{\mathrm{cl}} \beta . \beta P_{\mathrm{cl}} \gamma . \supset . \alpha P_{\mathrm{cl}} \gamma$ (5)

$\vdash . *250·121 . \supset$

$\vdash : \mathrm{Hp} . \alpha, \beta \in \mathrm{Cl}`C`P . \alpha \neq \beta . \supset . (\exists z) . z = \min_P`\{(\alpha - \beta) \cup (\beta - \alpha)\} .$

[*205·14] $\supset . (\exists z) . z \in \{(\alpha - \beta) \cup (\beta - \alpha)\} . \alpha \cap \overrightarrow{P}`z = \beta \cap \overrightarrow{P}`z .$

[*251·35] $\supset . \alpha (P_{\mathrm{cl}} \cup \breve{P}_{\mathrm{cl}}) \beta$ (6)

$\vdash . (1) . (5) . (6) . \supset \vdash . \mathrm{Prop}$

*251·361. $\vdash : \breve{P} \in \Omega . \supset . P_{\mathrm{lc}} \in \mathrm{Ser}$ [*251·36 . *170·101]

*251·37. $\vdash : P \in \Omega . \supset . P_{\mathrm{cl}} = P_{\mathrm{df}}$ [*251·35 . *171·2]

*251·371. $\vdash : \breve{P} \in \Omega . \supset . P_{\mathrm{lc}} = P_{\mathrm{fd}}$ [*251·37 . *170·101 . *171·101]

*251·4. $\vdash : P \in \mathrm{Rel}^3 \mathrm{arithm} \cap \mathrm{Bord} . C`P \subset \mathrm{Bord} . C`\Sigma`P \subset \mathrm{Bord} . \supset .$

$\Sigma`\Sigma`P \in \mathrm{Bord}$

Dem.

$\vdash . *251·2 . \supset : \mathrm{Hp} . \supset . \Sigma`P \in \mathrm{Rel}^2 \mathrm{excl} \cap \mathrm{Bord} . C`\Sigma`P \subset \mathrm{Bord} .$

[*251·2] $\supset . \Sigma`\Sigma`P \in \mathrm{Bord} : \supset \vdash . \mathrm{Prop}$

*251·41. $\vdash : P \in \mathrm{Rel}^3 \mathrm{arithm} \cap \Omega . C`P \subset \Omega . C`\Sigma`P \subset \Omega . \supset . \Sigma`\Sigma`P \in \Omega$

[*204·54 . *251·4]

*251·42. $\vdash : P \in \mathrm{Ser} . Q \in \Omega . \supset . P^Q, (P \exp Q) \in \mathrm{Ser}$ [*204·59 . *250·1]

*251·43. $\vdash : \alpha \in \mathrm{NR} . \alpha \subset \mathrm{Ser} . \beta \in \mathrm{NO} . \supset . (\alpha \exp_r \beta) \in \mathrm{NR} . (\alpha \exp_r \beta) \subset \mathrm{Ser}$

[*186·13 . *251·42]

*251·44. $\vdash : \alpha \in \mathrm{NO} - \iota`0_r . \beta \in \mathrm{NO} - \iota`0_r . \supset . \alpha \exp_r \beta \neq 0_r$

Dem.

$\vdash . *165·27 . \supset$

$\vdash : \mathrm{Hp} . P \in \alpha . Q \in \beta . \supset . P \downarrow ; Q \in \Omega - \iota`\dot{\Lambda} . C`P \downarrow ; Q \subset \Omega - \iota`\dot{\Lambda} .$

[*251·33 . *176·1] $\supset . \dot{\exists} ! (P \exp Q)$ (1)

$\vdash . (1) . *186·13 . \supset \vdash . \mathrm{Prop}$

***251·5.** $\vdash : \dot{\exists} ! P . Q \in \text{Bord} . \supset . P \underset{\cdot,}{\downarrow} ; Q \in \text{Bord}$ [*165·25 . *251·11]

***251·51.** $\vdash : \dot{\exists} ! P . Q \in \Omega . \supset . P \underset{\cdot,}{\downarrow} ; Q \in \Omega$ [*165·25 . *204·21 . *251·5]

***251·52.** $\vdash : P \in \text{Bord} . \supset . C'P \underset{\cdot,}{\downarrow} ; Q \subset \text{Bord}$ [*165·26 . *251·12]

***251·53.** $\vdash : P \in \Omega . \supset . C'P \underset{\cdot,}{\downarrow} ; Q \in \Omega$ [*165·26 . *204·22 . *251·52]

***251·54.** $\vdash : P, Q \in \text{Bord} . \supset . P \times Q \in \text{Bord}$

Dem.

$\vdash . *165{\cdot}21 . *251{\cdot}5{\cdot}52 . \supset$

$\vdash : \text{Hp} . \dot{\exists} ! Q . \supset . Q \underset{\cdot,}{\downarrow} ; P \in \text{Rel}^2 \text{excl} \cap \text{Bord} . C'Q \underset{\cdot,}{\downarrow} ; P \subset \text{Bord} .$

$[*251{\cdot}2 . *166{\cdot}1] \supset . P \times Q \in \text{Bord}$ (1)

$\vdash . *166{\cdot}13 . *250{\cdot}4 . \supset \vdash : Q = \dot{\Lambda} . \supset . P \times Q \in \text{Bord}$ (2)

$\vdash . (1) . (2) . \supset \vdash . \text{Prop}$

***251·55.** $\vdash : P, Q \in \Omega . \supset . P \times Q \in \Omega$ [*251·54 . *204·55]

***251·56.** $\vdash : \alpha, \beta \in \text{NO} . \supset . \alpha \dot{\times} \beta \in \text{NO}$ [*184·13 . *251·55·1]

***251·6.** $\vdash : P, Q \in \text{Rel}^2 \text{excl} . C'P \subset \Omega . S \in P \,\overline{\text{smor}}\, Q \cap \text{Rl}'\text{smor} .$

$\breve{\mu} = \hat{\lambda} \{ (\exists N) . N \in C'Q . \lambda = (S'N) \,\overline{\text{smor}}\, N \} . \supset .$

$\iota \upharpoonright \breve{\mu} \in \epsilon_\Delta{}'\mu . \dot{s}'\iota``\mu \in P \,\overline{\text{smor}}\, \overline{\text{smor}}\, Q$

Dem.

$\vdash . *250{\cdot}6 . *251{\cdot}111 . \supset \vdash : \text{Hp} . \supset . \mu \subset 1 .$

$[*83{\cdot}43] \qquad \supset . \iota \upharpoonright \breve{\mu} \in \epsilon_\Delta{}'\mu .$ (1)

$[*164{\cdot}43] \qquad \supset . \dot{s}'\iota``\mu \in P \,\overline{\text{smor}}\, \overline{\text{smor}}\, Q$ (2)

$\vdash . (1) . (2) . \supset \vdash . \text{Prop}$

***251·61.** $\vdash :. P, Q \in \text{Rel}^2 \text{excl} . C'P \subset \Omega . \supset :$

$\exists ! (P \,\overline{\text{smor}}\, Q) \cap \text{Rl}'\text{smor} . \equiv . P \text{ smor smor } Q$

Dem.

$\vdash . *251{\cdot}6 . \supset \vdash : \text{Hp} . \exists ! (P \,\overline{\text{smor}}\, Q) \cap \text{Rl}'\text{smor} . \supset . P \text{ smor smor } Q$ (1)

$\vdash . (1) . *164{\cdot}17 . \supset \vdash . \text{Prop}$

***251·62.** $\vdash : \text{Hp } *251{\cdot}61 . \exists ! P \,\overline{\text{smor}}\, Q \cap \text{Rl}'\text{smor} . \supset .$

$\Sigma'P \text{ smor } \Sigma'Q . \Pi'P \text{ smor } \Pi'Q .$

$\Sigma \text{Nr}'P = \Sigma \text{Nr}'Q . \Pi \text{Nr}'P = \Pi \text{Nr}'Q$

Dem.

$\vdash . *164{\cdot}151 . *251{\cdot}61 . \supset \vdash : \text{Hp} . \supset . \Sigma'P \text{ smor } \Sigma'Q$ (1)

$\vdash . *172{\cdot}44 . *251{\cdot}61 . \supset \vdash : \text{Hp} . \supset . \Pi'P \text{ smor } \Pi'Q$ (2)

$\vdash . (1) . *183{\cdot}13 . \supset \vdash : \text{Hp} . \supset . \Sigma \text{Nr}'P = \Sigma \text{Nr}'Q$ (3)

$\vdash . (2) . *185{\cdot}1 . \supset \vdash : \text{Hp} . \supset . \Pi \text{Nr}'P = \Pi \text{Nr}'Q$ (4)

$\vdash . (1) . (2) . (3) . (4) . \supset \vdash . \text{Prop}$

In the above proposition, the hypothesis "$P, Q \epsilon \text{Rel}^2 \text{excl}$" is unnecessary for $\Sigma \text{Nr}`P = \Sigma \text{Nr}`Q$ and $\Pi \text{Nr}`P = \Pi \text{Nr}`Q$, as appears from *183·14 and *185·12. Thus we have

***251·621.** $\vdash : C`P \subset \Omega \,.\, \exists ! (P \,\overline{\text{smor}}\, Q) \cap \text{Rl}`\text{smor} \,.\, \supset .$

$$\Sigma \text{Nr}`P = \Sigma \text{Nr}`Q \,.\, \Pi \text{Nr}`P = \Pi \text{Nr}`Q$$

Dem.

$\vdash . *151·65 . *182·05·162 . \supset \vdash . \overset{\frown}{\downarrow} \upharpoonright C`P \,\epsilon\, (\overset{\frown}{\downarrow} ; P) \,\overline{\text{smor}}\, P \cap \text{Rl}`\text{smor}$ (1)

$\vdash . (1) . *151·162 . \supset \vdash : \text{Hp} . \supset . \exists ! \{(\overset{\frown}{\downarrow} ; P) \,\overline{\text{smor}}\, (\overset{\frown}{\downarrow} ; Q)\} \cap \text{Rl}`\text{smor}$ (2)

$\vdash . (1) . *251·111 . *182·16 . \supset \vdash : \text{Hp} . \supset . C`\overset{\frown}{\downarrow} ; P \subset \Omega \,.\, \overset{\frown}{\downarrow} ; P, \overset{\frown}{\downarrow} ; Q \,\epsilon\, \text{Rel}^2 \text{excl}$ (3)

$\vdash . (2) . (3) . *251·62 . *183·14 . *185·12 . \supset \vdash .$ Prop

***251·63.** $\vdash : \alpha \,\epsilon\, \text{NO} - \iota`\Lambda \,.\, \beta \,\epsilon\, \text{NR} \,.\, P \,\epsilon\, \text{Rel}^2 \text{excl} \,.\, P \,\epsilon\, \beta \,.\, C`P \subset \alpha \,.\, \supset .$

$$\Sigma`P \,\epsilon\, \beta \dot{\times} \alpha \,.\, \Sigma \text{Nr}`P = \beta \dot{\times} \alpha$$

Dem.

$\vdash . *164·47 . *165·27·21 . \supset$

$\vdash : \text{Hp} . Q \,\epsilon\, \alpha \,.\, \alpha \neq 0_r \,.\, \supset . Q \downarrow ; P \,\epsilon\, \beta \,.\, C`Q \downarrow ; P \subset \alpha \,.\, P, Q \downarrow ; P \,\epsilon\, \text{Rel}^2 \text{excl} .$

[*164·47] $\supset . \exists ! (Q \downarrow ; P) \,\overline{\text{smor}}\, P \cap \text{Rl}`\text{smor} \,.\, P, Q \downarrow ; P \,\epsilon\, \text{Rel}^2 \text{excl} .$

[*251·61] $\supset . (Q \downarrow ; P) \text{ smor smor } P .$

[*164·151.*166·1] $\supset . (P \times Q) \text{ smor } \Sigma`P .$

[*184·13] $\supset . \Sigma`P \,\epsilon\, \beta \dot{\times} \alpha$ (1)

$\vdash . (1) . \supset \vdash : \text{Hp} . \alpha \neq 0_r \,.\, \supset . \Sigma`P \,\epsilon\, \beta \dot{\times} \alpha$ (2)

$\vdash . *162·42 . \text{Transp} . \supset \vdash : \text{Hp} . \alpha = 0_r \,.\, \supset . \Sigma`P = \dot{\Lambda} .$

[*184·16] $\supset . \Sigma`P \,\epsilon\, \beta \dot{\times} \alpha$ (3)

$\vdash . (2) . (3) . \supset \vdash : \text{Hp} . \supset . \Sigma`P \,\epsilon\, \beta \dot{\times} \alpha$ (4)

[*183·13] $\supset . \Sigma \text{Nr}`P = \beta \dot{\times} \alpha$ (5)

$\vdash . (4) . (5) . \supset \vdash .$ Prop

***251·64.** $\vdash : \text{Hp } *251·63 . \supset . \Pi`P \,\epsilon\, (\alpha \exp_r \beta) \,.\, \Pi \text{Nr}`P = \alpha \exp_r \beta$

[Proof as in *251·63]

***251·65.** $\vdash : \alpha \,\epsilon\, \text{NO} - \iota`\Lambda \,.\, \beta \,\epsilon\, \text{NR} \,.\, P \,\epsilon\, \beta \,.\, C`P \subset \alpha \,.\, \supset .$

$$\Sigma \text{Nr}`P = \beta \dot{\times} \alpha \,.\, \Pi \text{Nr}`P = \alpha \exp_r \beta$$

Dem.

$\vdash . *182·16 . *183·231 . \supset$

$\vdash : \text{Hp} . Q \,\epsilon\, \alpha \,.\, \supset . \overset{\frown}{\downarrow} ; P \,\epsilon\, \text{Rel}^2 \text{excl} \,.\, \overset{\frown}{\downarrow} ; P \,\epsilon\, \text{Nr}`P \,.\, C`\overset{\frown}{\downarrow} ; P \subset \text{Nr}`Q .$ (1)

[*251·63] $\supset . \Sigma \mathrm{Nr}`\overset{\frown}{\downarrow}\!\!\!\!_{,}\,;P = \mathrm{Nr}`P \dot{\times} \mathrm{Nr}`Q .$

[*183·14] $\supset . \Sigma \mathrm{Nr}`P = \mathrm{Nr}`P \dot{\times} \mathrm{Nr}`Q$

[*152·45] $= \beta \dot{\times} \alpha$ (2)

$\vdash . (2) . *10{\cdot}23 . \supset \vdash : \mathrm{Hp} . \supset . \Sigma \mathrm{Nr}`P = \beta \dot{\times} \alpha$ (3)

$\vdash . (1) . *251{\cdot}64 . \supset \vdash : \mathrm{Hp} . Q \in \alpha . \supset . \Pi \mathrm{Nr}`\overset{\frown}{\downarrow}\!\!\!\!_{,}\,;P = (\mathrm{Nr}`Q) \exp_r (\mathrm{Nr}`P) .$

[*185·1·12] $\supset . \Pi \mathrm{Nr}`P = (\mathrm{Nr}`Q) \exp_r (\mathrm{Nr}`P)$

[*152·45] $= \alpha \exp_r \beta$ (4)

$\vdash . (4) . *10{\cdot}23 . \supset \vdash : \mathrm{Hp} . \supset . \Pi \mathrm{Nr}`P = \alpha \exp_r \beta$ (5)

$\vdash . (3) . (5) . \supset \vdash . \mathrm{Prop}$

In virtue of the above proposition, the usual relations of addition to multiplication, and of multiplication to exponentiation, when the summands or the factors are all equal, can be established without the multiplicative axiom, provided the summands, or the factors, are *ordinal* numbers.

***251·7.** $\vdash : \exists ! \Omega - \iota`\dot{\Lambda} \cap t_{00}`\alpha . \equiv . \exists ! 2_r \cap t_{00}`\alpha . \equiv . \exists ! 2 \cap t`\alpha . \equiv . \exists ! 2_\alpha$

Dem.

$\vdash . *64{\cdot}55 . \supset \vdash : \exists ! \Omega - \iota`\dot{\Lambda} \cap t_{00}`\alpha . \equiv . (\exists P) . P \in \Omega - \iota`\dot{\Lambda} . C`P \subset t_0`\alpha$ (1)

$\vdash . *200{\cdot}12 . \supset \vdash : P \in \Omega - \iota`\dot{\Lambda} . \supset . (\exists x, y) . x, y \in C`P . x \neq y .$

[*153·201.*55·3] $\supset . \exists ! 2_r \cap \mathrm{Rl}`P$ (2)

$\vdash . (1) . (2) . \supset \vdash : \exists ! \Omega - \iota`\dot{\Lambda} \cap t_{00}`\alpha . \supset . (\exists P) . C`P \subset t_0`\alpha . \exists ! 2_r \cap \mathrm{Rl}`P .$

[*33·265] $\supset . (\exists Q) . Q \in 2_r . C`Q \subset t_0`\alpha .$

[*64·55] $\supset . \exists ! 2_r \cap t_{00}`\alpha$ (3)

$\vdash . *251{\cdot}16{\cdot}122 . \supset \vdash : \exists ! 2_r \cap t_{00}`\alpha . \supset . \exists ! \Omega - \iota`\dot{\Lambda} \cap t_{00}`\alpha$ (4)

$\vdash . (3) . (4) . \quad \supset \vdash : \exists ! \Omega - \iota`\dot{\Lambda} \cap t_{00}`\alpha . \equiv . \exists ! 2_r \cap t_{00}`\alpha$ (5)

$\vdash . *64{\cdot}55 . \quad \supset \vdash : \exists ! 2_r \cap t_{00}`\alpha . \equiv . (\exists x, y) . x \neq y . x, y \in t_0`\alpha .$

[*63·62] $\equiv . (\exists x, y) . x \neq y . \iota`x \cup \iota`y \in t`\alpha .$

[*54·26] $\equiv . \exists ! 2 \cap t`\alpha$ (6)

$\vdash . (5) . (6) . (*65{\cdot}01) . \supset \vdash . \mathrm{Prop}$

***251·71.** $\vdash . \exists ! \Omega - \iota`\dot{\Lambda} \cap t_{00}`\mathrm{Cls} . \exists ! \Omega - \iota`\dot{\Lambda} \cap t_{00}`\mathrm{Rel}$
[*251·7 . *101·42·43]

*252. SEGMENTS OF WELL-ORDERED SERIES.

Summary of *252.

The properties of sections and segments are greatly simplified in the case of series which are well-ordered, owing to the fact that every proper section has a sequent, whence it follows that the class of proper sections is $\overrightarrow{P}\text{“}C\text{‘}P$; and this is also the class of proper segments. Hence also the series of proper sections or of proper segments is the series $\overrightarrow{P} ; P$ (*252·37). The series of all sections is $\overrightarrow{P} ; P \dotplus C\text{‘}P$ (*252·38); hence (*252·381)

$$\mathrm{Nr}\text{‘}\varsigma\text{‘}P_* = \mathrm{Nr}\text{‘}P \dotplus \dot{1}.$$

The most useful propositions in this number are (apart from the above)

***252·12.** $\vdash : P \in \Omega \,.\supset.$

$$\mathrm{sect}\text{‘}P - \iota\text{‘}C\text{‘}P = \mathrm{D}\text{‘}P_\epsilon - \iota\text{‘}C\text{‘}P = \overrightarrow{P}\text{“}C\text{‘}P \,.\, \mathrm{sect}\text{‘}P = \overrightarrow{P}\text{“}C\text{‘}P \cup \iota\text{‘}C\text{‘}P$$

***252·17.** $\vdash : P \in \Omega - \iota\text{‘}\dot{\Lambda} \,.\supset.\, \mathrm{sect}\text{‘}P - \iota\text{‘}\Lambda = \overrightarrow{P}\text{“}\text{C}\!\!\!\text{I}\text{‘}P \cup \iota\text{‘}C\text{‘}P$

***252·171.** $\vdash : P \in \Omega \,.\supset.\, \mathrm{sect}\text{‘}P - \iota\text{‘}\Lambda - \iota\text{‘}C\text{‘}P = \overrightarrow{P}\text{“}\text{C}\!\!\!\text{I}\text{‘}P$

***252·372.** $\vdash :. P \in \Omega \,.\supset: \varsigma\text{‘}P \in \Omega : \mathrm{E}\,!\, B\text{‘}\breve{P} \,.\supset.\, \mathrm{Nr}\text{‘}\varsigma\text{‘}P = \mathrm{Nr}\text{‘}P :$

$$\sim \mathrm{E}\,!\, B\text{‘}\breve{P} \,.\supset.\, \mathrm{Nr}\text{‘}\varsigma\text{‘}P = \mathrm{Nr}\text{‘}P \dotplus \dot{1}$$

***252·4.** $\vdash : P \in \Omega \,.\, \lambda \subset \mathrm{sect}\text{‘}P \,.\, \exists\,!\,\lambda \,.\supset.\, p\text{‘}\lambda \in \lambda$

***252·1.** $\vdash : P \in \Omega \,.\, \alpha \in \mathrm{sect}\text{‘}P - \iota\text{‘}C\text{‘}P \,.\supset.\, \mathrm{E}\,!\, \mathrm{seq}_P\text{‘}\alpha$ [*250·124]

***252·11.** $\vdash : P \in \Omega \,.\supset.\, \mathrm{sect}\text{‘}P - \iota\text{‘}C\text{‘}P = \mathrm{sect}\text{‘}P \cap \text{C}\!\!\!\text{I}\text{‘}\mathrm{seq}_P$

Dem.

$\vdash . *206{\cdot}18{\cdot}2 \,.\supset \vdash .\, C\text{‘}P \sim\in \text{C}\!\!\!\text{I}\text{‘}\mathrm{seq}_P$ (1)

$\vdash . (1) . *252{\cdot}1 \,.\supset \vdash .$ Prop

***252·12.** $\vdash : P \in \Omega . \supset .$

$$\text{sect}‘P - \iota‘C‘P = \text{D}‘P_\epsilon - \iota‘C‘P = \overrightarrow{P}‘‘C‘P \,.\, \text{sect}‘P = \overrightarrow{P}‘‘C‘P \cup \iota‘C‘P$$

Dem.

$\vdash . *211·24 . *252·11 . \supset \vdash : \text{Hp} . \alpha \in \text{sect}‘P - \iota‘C‘P . \supset . \alpha \in \text{D}‘P_\epsilon$ (1)

$\vdash . *211·15 . \qquad \supset \vdash : \text{Hp} . \alpha \in \text{D}‘P_\epsilon - \iota‘C‘P . \supset . \alpha \in \text{sect}‘P - \iota‘C‘P$ (2)

$\vdash . (1) . (2) . \qquad \supset \vdash : \text{Hp} . \supset . \text{sect}‘P - \iota‘C‘P = \text{D}‘P_\epsilon - \iota‘C‘P$ (3)

$\vdash . *211·302 . *252·11 . \supset \vdash : \text{Hp} . \supset . \text{sect}‘P - \iota‘C‘P = \overrightarrow{P}‘‘C‘P$ (4)

$\vdash . (3) . (4) . *211·26 . \supset \vdash . \text{Prop}$

In dealing with sections and segments of well-ordered series, it is necessary to distinguish series with a last term from such as have no last term. If a series has no last term, $C‘P = P‘‘C‘P$, so that $C‘P \in \text{D}‘P_\epsilon$. But if a series has a last term, $C‘P \sim\in \text{D}‘P_\epsilon$; in this case, $\text{D}‘P_\epsilon = \overrightarrow{P}‘‘C‘P$. Thus $\text{D}‘P_\epsilon$ is either $\overrightarrow{P}‘‘C‘P$ or sect‘P, according as there is or is not a last term. In either case,

$$\text{sect}‘P = \overrightarrow{P}‘‘C‘P \cup \iota‘C‘P,$$

as has been already proved in *252·12.

***252·13.** $\vdash : P \in \Omega . \text{E} ! B‘\breve{P} . \supset . \text{sect}‘P - \iota‘C‘P = \text{D}‘P_\epsilon = \overrightarrow{P}‘‘C‘P .$

$$\text{sect}‘P = \text{D}‘P_\epsilon \cup \iota‘C‘P = \overrightarrow{P}‘‘C‘P \cup \iota‘C‘P$$

Dem.

$\vdash . *250·21 . *211·36 . \supset \vdash : \text{Hp} . \supset . \text{sect}‘P - \text{D}‘P_\epsilon = \iota‘C‘P .$

$[*24·492 . *211·15] \qquad \supset . \text{sect}‘P - \iota‘C‘P = \text{D}‘P_\epsilon$ (1)

$[*252·12] \qquad = \overrightarrow{P}‘‘C‘P$ (2)

$\vdash . (1) . (2) . *211·26 . \supset \vdash . \text{Prop}$

***252·14.** $\vdash : P \in \Omega . \sim\text{E} ! B‘\breve{P} . \supset . \text{sect}‘P = \text{D}‘P_\epsilon = \overrightarrow{P}‘‘C‘P \cup \iota‘C‘P$
[*250·21 . *211·361 . *252·12]

***252·15.** $\vdash : P \in \Omega . \supset . \text{D}‘P_\epsilon = \overrightarrow{P}‘‘\text{D}‘P \cup \iota‘\text{D}‘P$

Dem.

$\vdash . *252·13 . \supset \vdash : \text{Hp} . \text{E} ! B‘\breve{P} . \supset . \text{D}‘P_\epsilon = \overrightarrow{P}‘‘\text{D}‘P \cup \iota‘\overrightarrow{P}‘B‘\breve{P}$

$[*202·524] \qquad = \overrightarrow{P}‘‘\text{D}‘P \cup \iota‘\text{D}‘P$ (1)

$\vdash . *252·14 . \supset \vdash : \text{Hp} . \sim\text{E} ! B‘\breve{P} . \supset . \text{D}‘P_\epsilon = \overrightarrow{P}‘‘\text{D}‘P \cup \iota‘\text{D}‘P$ (2)

$\vdash . (1) . (2) . \supset \vdash . \text{Prop}$

***252·16.** $\vdash : P \in \Omega - 2_r . \supset . \text{D}‘P_\epsilon = \text{sect}‘(P \upharpoonright \text{D}‘P)$

Dem.

$\vdash . *204·271 . \supset \vdash : \text{Hp} . \supset . \text{D}‘P \sim\in 1 .$

$[*202·55] \qquad \supset . C‘(P \upharpoonright \text{D}‘P) = \text{D}‘P .$

$[*250·141 . *252·12] \qquad \supset . \text{sect}‘(P \upharpoonright \text{D}‘P) = \overrightarrow{P \upharpoonright \text{D}‘P}‘‘\text{D}‘P \cup \iota‘\text{D}‘P$

$[*37·42·421] \qquad = \overrightarrow{P}‘‘\text{D}‘P \cup \iota‘\text{D}‘P$

$[*252·15] \qquad = \text{D}‘P_\epsilon : \supset \vdash . \text{Prop}$

***252·17.** $\vdash : P \in \Omega - \iota`\dot{\Lambda} . \supset . \text{sect}`P - \iota`\Lambda = \overrightarrow{P}``\text{G}`P \cup \iota`C`P$

Dem.

$\vdash . *252·12 . \supset \vdash : \text{Hp} . \supset . \text{sect}`P - \iota`\Lambda = (\overrightarrow{P}``C`P - \iota`\Lambda) \cup \iota`C`P$

$[*33·41] \quad = \overrightarrow{P}``\text{G}`P \cup \iota`C`P : \supset \vdash . \text{Prop}$

***252·171.** $\vdash : P \in \Omega . \supset . \text{sect}`P - \iota`\Lambda - \iota`C`P = \overrightarrow{P}``\text{G}`P$

Dem.

$\vdash . *252·12 . \supset \vdash : \text{Hp} . \supset . (\text{sect}`P - \iota`C`P) - \iota`\Lambda = \overrightarrow{P}``C`P - \iota`\Lambda$

$[*33·41] \quad = \overrightarrow{P}``\text{G}`P : \supset \vdash . \text{Prop}$

***252·3.** $\vdash : P \in \Omega . \supset . \text{D}`\varsigma`P_* = \overrightarrow{P}``C`P$ [*212·171 . *252·12]

***252·31.** $\vdash : P \in \Omega . \dot{\exists} ! P . \supset . C`\varsigma`P_* = \overrightarrow{P}``C`P \cup \iota`C`P$
[*212·172 . *252·12]

***252·311.** $\vdash : P \in \Omega . \dot{\exists} ! P . \supset . \text{G}`\varsigma`P_* = \overrightarrow{P}``\text{G}`P \cup \iota`C`P$
[*212·171 . *252·17]

***252·32.** $\vdash : P \in \Omega . \supset . \text{D}`\varsigma`P = \overrightarrow{P}``\text{D}`P$ [*212·132 . *252·15]

***252·33.** $\vdash : P \in \Omega - \iota`\dot{\Lambda} . \supset . C`\varsigma`P = \overrightarrow{P}``\text{D}`P \cup \iota`\text{D}`P$
[*212·133 . *252·15]

***252·34.** $\vdash : P \in \Omega . \text{E} ! B`\breve{P} . \supset . C`\varsigma`P = \overrightarrow{P}``C`P$

Dem.

$\vdash . *202·524 . \supset \vdash : \text{Hp} . \supset . \overrightarrow{P}`B`\breve{P} = \text{D}`P .$

$[*252·33] \quad \supset . C`\varsigma`P = \overrightarrow{P}``C`P : \supset \vdash . \text{Prop}$

***252·35.** $\vdash : P \in \Omega - \iota`\dot{\Lambda} . \sim \text{E} ! B`\breve{P} . \supset . C`\varsigma`P = \overrightarrow{P}``C`P \cup \iota`C`P$
[*212·133 . *252·14]

***252·36.** $\vdash : P \in \Omega . \text{E} ! B`\breve{P} . \supset . \varsigma`P = \overrightarrow{P} ; P$

Dem.

$\vdash . *212·25 . *252·34 . \supset \vdash : \text{Hp} . \supset . \overrightarrow{P} ; P = (\varsigma`P) \upharpoonright (C`\varsigma`P)$

$[*36·33] \quad = \varsigma`P : \supset \vdash . \text{Prop}$

***252·37.** $\vdash : P \in \Omega . \supset . (\varsigma`P) \upharpoonright (-\iota`C`P) = \overrightarrow{P} ; P$

Dem.

$\vdash . *36·3 . \quad \supset \vdash . (\varsigma`P) \upharpoonright (-\iota`C`P) = (\varsigma`P) \upharpoonright (C`\varsigma`P - \iota`C`P)$

$[*212·133·134] \quad = (\varsigma`P) \upharpoonright (\text{D}`P_\epsilon - \iota`C`P) \quad (1)$

$\vdash . (1) . *252·12 . \supset \vdash : \text{Hp} . \supset . (\varsigma`P) \upharpoonright (-\iota`C`P) = (\varsigma`P) \upharpoonright (\overrightarrow{P}``C`P)$

$[*212·25] \quad = \overrightarrow{P} ; P : \supset \vdash . \text{Prop}$

***252·371**. $\vdash : P \epsilon \Omega . \sim E ! B`\breve{P} . \supset . s`P = \overrightarrow{P} ; P \nrightarrow C`P$

Dem.

$\vdash . *212\cdot25 . *252\cdot32 . \quad \supset \vdash : \text{Hp} . \supset . \overrightarrow{P} ; P = (s`P) \upharpoonright (D`s`P)$ (1)

$\vdash . *212\cdot133 . \quad \supset \vdash : \text{Hp} . \dot{\exists} ! P . \supset . C`P = B`\text{Cnv}`s`P$ (2)

$\vdash . *252\cdot32 . \quad \supset \vdash : \text{Hp} . \supset . D`s`P = \overrightarrow{P}``C`P .$

$[*200\cdot12 . *204\cdot34] \quad \supset . D`s`P \sim \epsilon 1$ (3)

$\vdash . (1) . (2) . (3) . *204\cdot461 . \supset \vdash : \text{Hp} . \dot{\exists} ! P . \supset . \overrightarrow{P} ; P \nrightarrow C`P = s`P$ (4)

$\vdash . *212\cdot134 . *161\cdot2 . \quad \supset \vdash : \text{Hp} . P = \dot{\Lambda} . \supset . s`P = \dot{\Lambda} . \overrightarrow{P} ; P \nrightarrow C`P = \dot{\Lambda}$ (5)

$\vdash . (4) . (5) . \supset \vdash . \text{Prop}$

***252·372**. $\vdash :. P \epsilon \Omega . \supset : s`P \epsilon \Omega : E ! B`\breve{P} . \supset . \text{Nr}`s`P = \text{Nr}`P :$

$\sim E ! B`\breve{P} . \supset . \text{Nr}`s`P = \text{Nr}`P \dot{+} \dot{1}$

Dem.

$\vdash . *252\cdot36 . *204\cdot35 . \supset \vdash : \text{Hp} . E ! B`\breve{P} . \supset . s`P \text{ smor } P .$

$[*251\cdot111 . *152\cdot321] \quad \supset . s`P \epsilon \Omega . \text{Nr}`s`P = \text{Nr}`P$ (1)

$\vdash . *252\cdot371 . *204\cdot35 . *200\cdot52 . \supset$

$\vdash : \text{Hp} . \sim E ! B`\breve{P} . \supset . \text{Nr}`s`P = \text{Nr}`P \dot{+} \dot{1} .$ (2)

$[*251\cdot132] \quad \supset . s`P \epsilon \Omega$ (3)

$\vdash . (1) . (2) . (3) . \supset \vdash . \text{Prop}$

***252·38**. $\vdash : P \epsilon \Omega . \supset . s`P_{*} = \overrightarrow{P} ; P \nrightarrow C`P$

Dem.

$\vdash . *252\cdot12 . *212\cdot24 . \supset$

$\vdash :: \text{Hp} . \supset :. \alpha (s`P_{*}) \beta . \equiv : \alpha, \beta \epsilon \overrightarrow{P}``C`P \cup \iota`C`P . \alpha \subset \beta . \alpha \neq \beta :$

$[*37\cdot6 . *200\cdot52]$

$\equiv : (\exists x, y) . x, y \epsilon C`P . \alpha = \overrightarrow{P}`x . \beta = \overrightarrow{P}`y . \overrightarrow{P}`x \subset \overrightarrow{P}`y . \overrightarrow{P}`x \neq \overrightarrow{P}`y . \vee .$

$(\exists x) . x \epsilon C`P . \alpha = \overrightarrow{P}`x . \beta = C`P :$

$[*204\cdot33\cdot34] \equiv : (\exists x, y) . x P y . \alpha = \overrightarrow{P}`x . \beta = \overrightarrow{P}`y . \vee .$

$(\exists x) . x \epsilon C`P . \alpha = \overrightarrow{P}`x . \beta = C`P :$

$[*150\cdot5\cdot22] \quad \equiv : \alpha (\overrightarrow{P} ; P) \beta . \vee . \alpha \epsilon C`\overrightarrow{P} ; P . \beta = C`P :$

$[*161\cdot11] \quad \equiv : \alpha (\overrightarrow{P} ; P \nrightarrow C`P) \beta :: \supset \vdash . \text{Prop}$

***252·381**. $\vdash : P \epsilon \Omega . \supset . s`P_{*} \epsilon \Omega . \text{Nr}`s`P_{*} = \text{Nr}`P \dot{+} \dot{1}$

$[*252\cdot38 . *200\cdot52 . *204\cdot35 . *251\cdot131]$

***252·4.** $\vdash : P \in \Omega \,.\, \lambda \subset \text{sect}`P \,.\, \exists ! \lambda \,.\, \supset \,.\, p`\lambda \in \lambda$

Dem.

$\vdash \,.\, *211{\cdot}44{\cdot}1 \,.\, \supset \vdash : \text{Hp} \,.\, P = \dot{\Lambda} \,.\, \supset \,.\, \lambda = \iota`\dot{\Lambda} \,.$

[*53·01] $\supset \,.\, p`\lambda \in \lambda$ (1)

$\vdash \,.\, *212{\cdot}172 \,.\, \supset \vdash : \text{Hp} \,.\, \dot{\exists} ! P \,.\, \supset \,.\, \lambda \subset C`\varsigma`P_* \,.\, \exists ! \lambda \,.$

[*252·381.*250·121] $\supset \,.\, E ! \min(\varsigma`P_*)`\lambda \,.$

[*210·222.*211·67·66] $\supset \,.\, p`\lambda \in \lambda$ (2)

$\vdash \,.\, (1) \,.\, (2) \,.\, \supset \vdash \,.\, \text{Prop}$

***252·41.** $\vdash : \breve{P} \in \Omega \,.\, \lambda \subset \text{sect}`P \,.\, \exists ! \lambda \,.\, \supset \,.\, s`\lambda \in \lambda$ [Proof as in *252·4]

***252·42.** $\vdash :. P \in \Omega \,.\, (\text{Cnv}`\varsigma`P_*)_1``\sigma \subset \sigma :$

$\lambda \subset \sigma \,.\, \exists ! \lambda \cap C`\varsigma`P_* \,.\, \supset_\lambda \,.\, s`(\lambda \cap C`\varsigma`P_*) \in \sigma : \supset \,.$

$(\text{Cnv}`\varsigma`P_*)``\sigma \subset \sigma$

[*250·361 . *252·381 . *212·322]

***252·43.** $\vdash :. \breve{P} \in \Omega \,.\, (\varsigma`P_*)_1``\sigma \subset \sigma :$

$\lambda \subset \sigma \,.\, \exists ! \lambda \cap C`\varsigma`P_* \,.\, \supset_\lambda \,.\, p`(\lambda \cap C`\varsigma`P_*) \in \sigma : \supset \,.\, (\varsigma`P_*)``\sigma \subset \sigma$

Dem.

$\vdash \,.\, *212{\cdot}181 \,.\, \supset \vdash \,.\, (\text{Cnv}`\varsigma`P_*) \text{ smor } (\varsigma`\breve{P}_*)$ (1)

$\vdash \,.\, (1) \,.\, *252{\cdot}381 \,.\, \supset \vdash : \text{Hp} \,.\, \supset \,.\, \text{Cnv}`\varsigma`P_* \in \Omega$ (2)

$\vdash \,.\, (2) \,.\, *212{\cdot}34 \,.\, *250{\cdot}362 \,.\, \supset \vdash \,.\, \text{Prop}$

$*253$. SECTIONAL RELATIONS OF WELL-ORDERED SERIES.

Summary of $*253$.

In the present number we shall consider the properties of the relation P_s (defined in $*213$) when $P \epsilon \Omega$. The relation P_s has great importance in this case, owing to the fact (to be proved later) that $\mathrm{Nr}``\mathrm{D}`P_s$ is the class of all ordinals less than $\mathrm{Nr}`P$, and that, if P, Q are any two well-ordered series, either P is similar to a member of $C`Q_s$, or $Q$ is similar to a member of $C`P_s$, whence it follows that of any two unequal ordinals one must be the greater.

The present number consists merely of the more elementary properties of P_s when $P \epsilon \Omega$. The interesting properties connected with greater and less will be treated in the following number.

The most useful propositions of the present number are the following:

$*253{\cdot}13.\ \ \vdash : P \epsilon \Omega . \supset . \mathrm{D}`P_s = P \upharpoonright ``\overrightarrow{P}``\text{Ɑ}`P = P \upharpoonright ``\overrightarrow{P}``C`P$

$*253{\cdot}18.\ \ \vdash : P \epsilon \Omega . \supset . C`P_s \subset P \upharpoonright ``\overrightarrow{P}``\text{Ɑ}`P \cup \iota`P . C`P_s \subset \Omega$

Instead of $C`P_s \subset P \upharpoonright ``\overrightarrow{P}``\text{Ɑ}`P \cup \iota`P$ we shall have equality, unless $P = \dot{\Lambda}$ ($*253{\cdot}15$).

$*253{\cdot}2.\ \ \vdash : P \epsilon \Omega - 2_r . \supset . \mathrm{Nr}`P_s = \mathrm{Nr}`(P \upharpoonright \text{Ɑ}`P) \dot{+} \dot{1}$

The case when $P \epsilon 2_r$ has to be excluded, because then $P \upharpoonright \text{Ɑ}`P = \dot{\Lambda}$.

$*253{\cdot}21.\ \ \vdash : P \epsilon \Omega . \supset . \dot{1} \dot{+} \mathrm{Nr}`P_s = \mathrm{Nr}`P \dot{+} \dot{1}$

This proposition involves $\mathrm{Nr}`P_s = \mathrm{Nr}`P$ when P is finite, but when P is infinite it involves $\mathrm{Nr}`P_s = \mathrm{Nr}`P \dot{+} \dot{1}$ (cf. $*261{\cdot}38$).

$*253{\cdot}22.\ \ \vdash : P \epsilon \Omega . \supset . P_s \upharpoonright \mathrm{D}`P_s \ \mathrm{smor}\ P \upharpoonright \text{Ɑ}`P$

$*253{\cdot}24.\ \ \vdash : P \epsilon \Omega . \supset . P_s \epsilon \Omega$

$*253{\cdot}4.\ \ \vdash : P \epsilon \Omega - \iota`\dot{\Lambda} . \supset .$

$$C`P_s = \hat{Q}\{(\exists R) . P = Q \nleftrightarrow R . \mathtt{v} . (\exists x) . P = Q \rightarrow x\}$$

$*253{\cdot}421.\ \ \vdash : P \epsilon \Omega . Q \epsilon \mathrm{D}`P_s . \supset . \sim(Q \ \mathrm{smor}\ P)$

$*253{\cdot}44.\ \ \vdash : \alpha, \beta \epsilon \mathrm{NO} - \iota`\Lambda . \beta \neq 0_r . \supset . \alpha \dot{+} \beta \neq \alpha$

This proposition marks a difference between ordinals and cardinals. An ordinal is always increased by the addition of anything at the end, whereas this is (often if not always) not the case with a cardinal if it is reflexive and greater than the addendum. The above proposition ceases to be true if we add β at the beginning instead of the end: $\beta \dot{+} \alpha = \alpha$ will be true if α is infinite and $\omega \dot{\times} \beta$ is not greater than α. (For the definition of ω, cf. $*263$.)

$*253{\cdot}45$. $\vdash : \alpha \,\epsilon\, \text{NO} - \iota`\Lambda - \iota`0_r \,.\supset .\, \alpha \dot{+} \dot{1} \,\dot{\neq}\, \alpha$

Similar remarks apply to this proposition as to $*253{\cdot}44$.

$*253{\cdot}46$. $\vdash : P \,\epsilon\, \Omega \,.\, Q, R \,\epsilon\, C`P_s \,.\, Q \,\text{smor}\, R \,.\supset .\, Q = R$

I.e. no two different sections of a well-ordered series are similar.

It follows from $*253{\cdot}46$ that the series of the ordinals of proper sections of a well-ordered series P is similar to the series of proper sections, and therefore, by $*253{\cdot}22$, to the series P with its first term omitted ($*253{\cdot}463$).

We have next a set of propositions ($*253{\cdot}5$—$\cdot574$) on the circumstances under which $\text{Nr}`P_s = \text{Nr}`P$ and those under which $\text{Nr}`P_s = \text{Nr}`P \dot{+} \dot{1}$. As a matter of fact, the former holds when P is finite, the latter when P is infinite. But the distinction of finite and infinite will not be introduced till the next section. In the present number, we prove that (assuming $P \,\epsilon\, \Omega$) $\text{Nr}`P_s = \text{Nr}`P$ if $\text{ᗡ}`P_1 = \text{ᗡ}`P \,.\, \text{E!}\, B`\breve{P}$, and if not, then $\text{Nr}`P_s = \text{Nr}`P \dot{+} \dot{1}$ ($*253{\cdot}56$). This is proved by using $P_1$ as a correlator. ($P_1$ as a correlator moves every term one place down, except the first, which disappears.) For, if $P \,\epsilon\, \Omega$, we have $P_1 ; P = P \upharpoonright \text{D}`P$ ($*253{\cdot}5$); hence we prove $P \upharpoonright \text{ᗡ}`P_1 \,\text{smor}\, P \upharpoonright \text{D}`P$ ($*253{\cdot}502$), and hence, if $\text{ᗡ}`P_1 = \text{ᗡ}`P$, we obtain $P \upharpoonright \text{ᗡ}`P \,\text{smor}\, P \upharpoonright \text{D}`P$ ($*253{\cdot}503$). Hence by $*253{\cdot}2$ (with special consideration of the case when $P \,\epsilon\, 2_r$) we have the two propositions

$*253{\cdot}51$. $\vdash : P \,\epsilon\, \Omega \,.\, \text{ᗡ}`P_1 = \text{ᗡ}`P \,.\, \text{E!}\, B`\breve{P} \,.\supset .\, \text{Nr}`P_s = \text{Nr}`P$

$*253{\cdot}511$. $\vdash : P \,\epsilon\, \Omega \,.\, \text{ᗡ}`P_1 = \text{ᗡ}`P \,.\, \sim \text{E!}\, B`\breve{P} \,.\supset .$

$$\text{Nr}`P_s = \text{Nr}`P \dot{+} \dot{1} \,.\, \text{Nr}`P \upharpoonright \text{ᗡ}`P = \text{Nr}`P$$

But if there is a term, say x, belonging to $\text{ᗡ}`P - \text{ᗡ}`P_1$, use P_1 as a correlator for the predecessors of x; we thus find that, in this case, $P \,\text{smor}\, P \upharpoonright \text{ᗡ}`P$. Hence, by $*253{\cdot}2$, $\text{Nr}`P_s = \text{Nr}`P \dot{+} \dot{1}$.

The hypothesis $\text{ᗡ}`P_1 = \text{ᗡ}`P \,.\, \text{E!}\, B`\breve{P}$ means that there is a last term, and every other term has an immediate successor. This, as we shall prove later, and as is indeed obvious, is equivalent to the assumption that P is finite but not null.

From the above propositions it results immediately that

$*253{\cdot}573$. $\vdash :. P \,\epsilon\, \Omega \,.\supset : \text{ᗡ}`P_1 = \text{ᗡ}`P \,.\, \text{E!}\, B`\breve{P} \,. \equiv .\, \dot{1} \dot{+} \text{Nr}`P \,\dot{\neq}\, \text{Nr}`P$

Hence it will follow that finite ordinals other than 0_r are those which are increased by the addition of $\dot{1}$ at the beginning. We have also

$*253{\cdot}574.\ \vdash :.\ P \in \Omega - \iota`\Lambda \,.\supset :\ D`P_1 = D`P \,.\, E\,!\,B`\breve{P} \,.\equiv.\ \dot{1} \dotplus \mathrm{Nr}`P = \mathrm{Nr}`P \dotplus \dot{1}$

Whence it will follow that finite ordinals are those for which the addition of $\dot{1}$ is commutative.

$*253{\cdot}1.\quad \vdash :.\ P \in \Omega \,.\supset :\ QP_sR \,.\equiv.$

$$(\exists \alpha, \beta) \,.\, \alpha, \beta \in \overrightarrow{P}``D`P \cup \iota`C`P \,.\, \exists\,!\,\beta - \alpha \,.\, Q = P \upharpoonright \alpha \,.\, R = P \upharpoonright \beta$$

Dem.

$\vdash .\, *213{\cdot}1 \,.\, *252{\cdot}17 \,.\supset \vdash :.\ \mathrm{Hp} \,.\, \exists\,!\,P \,.\supset :\ QP_sR \,.\equiv.$

$$(\exists \alpha, \beta) \,.\, \alpha, \beta \in \overrightarrow{P}``D`P \cup \iota`C`P \,.\, \exists\,!\,\beta - \alpha \,.\, Q = P \upharpoonright \alpha \,.\, R = P \upharpoonright \beta \quad (1)$$

$\vdash .\, *33{\cdot}241 \,.\supset \vdash :.\ P = \dot{\Lambda} \,.\supset :\ \overrightarrow{P}``D`P \cup \iota`C`P = \iota`\Lambda :$

$[*24{\cdot}53] \qquad \supset :\ \sim(\exists \alpha, \beta) \,.\, \alpha, \beta \in \overrightarrow{P}``D`P \cup \iota`C`P \,.\, \exists\,!\,\beta - \alpha :$

$[*213{\cdot}3] \supset :\ QP_sR \,.\equiv.$

$$(\exists \alpha, \beta) \,.\, \alpha, \beta \in \overrightarrow{P}``D`P \cup \iota`C`P \,.\, \exists\,!\,\beta - \alpha \,.\, Q = P \upharpoonright \alpha \,.\, R = P \upharpoonright \beta \quad (2)$$

$\vdash .\, (1) \,.\, (2) \,.\supset \vdash .$ Prop

$*253{\cdot}11.\quad \vdash ::\ P \in \Omega \,.\supset :.\ QP_sR \,.\equiv :$

$$(\exists x, y) \,.\, x \in D`P \,.\, xPy \,.\, Q = P \upharpoonright \overrightarrow{P}`x \,.\, R = P \upharpoonright \overrightarrow{P}`y \,.\vee.$$

$$(\exists x) \,.\, x \in D`P \,.\, Q = P \upharpoonright \overrightarrow{P}`x \,.\, R = P$$

Dem.

$\vdash .\, *33{\cdot}152 \,. \qquad \supset \vdash :\ \alpha = C`P \,.\, \beta \in \overrightarrow{P}``D`P \,\dot{\cup}\, \iota`C`P \,.\supset.\, \sim \exists\,!\,\beta - \alpha \quad (1)$

$\vdash .\, *200{\cdot}52 \,.\, (1) \,. \qquad \supset \vdash :\ \mathrm{Hp} \,.\, \alpha \in \overrightarrow{P}``D`P \,.\, \beta = C`P \,.\supset.\, \exists\,!\,\beta - \alpha \quad (2)$

$\vdash .\, (1) \,.\, (2) \,.\, *253{\cdot}1 \,.\supset \vdash ::\ \mathrm{Hp} \,.\supset :.\ QP_sR \,.\equiv :$

$$(\exists \alpha, \beta) \,.\, \alpha, \beta \in \overrightarrow{P}``D`P \,.\, \exists\,!\,\beta - \alpha \,.\, Q = P \upharpoonright \alpha \,.\, R = P \upharpoonright \beta \,.\vee.$$

$$(\exists \alpha, \beta) \,.\, \alpha \in \overrightarrow{P}``D`P \,.\, \beta = C`P \,.\, Q = P \upharpoonright \alpha \,.\, R = P \upharpoonright \beta :$$

$[*37{\cdot}6 \,.\, *36{\cdot}33]$

$$\equiv :\ (\exists x, y) \,.\, x, y \in D`P \,.\, \exists\,!\,\overrightarrow{P}`y - \overrightarrow{P}`x \,.\, Q = P \upharpoonright \overrightarrow{P}`x \,.\, R = P \upharpoonright \overrightarrow{P}`y \,.\vee.$$

$$(\exists x) \,.\, x \in D`P \,.\, Q = P \upharpoonright \overrightarrow{P}`x \,.\, R = P :$$

$[*211{\cdot}61 \,.\, *210{\cdot}1]$

$$\equiv :\ (\exists x, y) \,.\, x, y \in D`P \,.\, \overrightarrow{P}`x \subset \overrightarrow{P}`y \,.\, \overrightarrow{P}`x \neq \overrightarrow{P}`y \,.\, Q = P \upharpoonright \overrightarrow{P}`x \,.\, R = P \upharpoonright \overrightarrow{P}`y \,.\vee.$$

$$(\exists x) \,.\, x \in D`P \,.\, Q = P \upharpoonright \overrightarrow{P}`x \,.\, R = P :$$

$[*204{\cdot}33{\cdot}34] \equiv :\ (\exists x, y) \,.\, x, y \in D`P \,.\, xPy \,.\, Q = P \upharpoonright \overrightarrow{P}`x \,.\, R = P \upharpoonright \overrightarrow{P}`y \,.\vee.$

$$(\exists x) \,.\, x \in D`P \,.\, Q = P \upharpoonright \overrightarrow{P}`x \,.\, R = P \quad (3)$$

$\vdash .\, (3) \,.\, *33{\cdot}14 \,.\supset \vdash .$ Prop

$*253{\cdot}12.\quad \vdash :\ P \in \Omega \,.\, P \sim\in 2_r \,.\supset.\, P_s = (P \upharpoonright ;\, \overrightarrow{P} ;\, P \upharpoonright D`P) \nrightarrow P$

Dem.

$\vdash .\, *204{\cdot}272 \,.\supset \vdash :\ \mathrm{Hp} \,.\supset.\, D`P \sim\in 1 \,.$

$[*202{\cdot}55 \,.\, *213{\cdot}151] \qquad \supset.\, P \upharpoonright`` \overrightarrow{P}``D`P = C`P \upharpoonright ;\, \overrightarrow{P} ;\, P \upharpoonright D`P \quad (1)$

$\vdash . (1) . *253{\cdot}11 . \supset \vdash :: \mathrm{Hp} . \supset :. QP_sR . \equiv :$

$Q(P \upharpoonright ; \overrightarrow{P} ; P \upharpoonright \text{Ɑ}‘P) R . \vee . Q \in C‘(P \upharpoonright ; \overrightarrow{P} ; P \upharpoonright \text{Ɑ}‘P) . R = P :$

$[*161{\cdot}11] \quad \equiv : Q \{(P \upharpoonright ; \overrightarrow{P} ; P \upharpoonright \text{Ɑ}‘P) \mathbin{+\!\!\!\rightarrow} P\} R :: \supset \vdash . \mathrm{Prop}$

$*253{\cdot}121$. $\vdash : P \in \Omega . \supset . P \sim\in C‘P \upharpoonright ; \overrightarrow{P} ; P \upharpoonright \text{Ɑ}‘P$

Dem.

$\vdash . *200{\cdot}52 . \supset \vdash : \mathrm{Hp} . \supset . C‘P \sim\in \overrightarrow{P}‘‘\text{Ɑ}‘P .$

$[*36{\cdot}25] \qquad \supset . P \sim\in C‘P \upharpoonright ; \overrightarrow{P} ; P \upharpoonright \text{Ɑ}‘P : \supset \vdash . \mathrm{Prop}$

$*253{\cdot}13$. $\vdash : P \in \Omega . \supset . \mathrm{D}‘P_s = P \upharpoonright ‘‘\overrightarrow{P}‘‘\text{Ɑ}‘P = P \upharpoonright ‘‘\overrightarrow{P}‘‘C‘P$

Dem.

$\vdash . *213{\cdot}141 . *252{\cdot}171 . \supset \vdash : \mathrm{Hp} . \supset . \mathrm{D}‘P_s = P \upharpoonright ‘‘\overrightarrow{P}‘‘\text{Ɑ}‘P \qquad (1)$

$\vdash . *37{\cdot}22 . *250{\cdot}13 . \supset$

$\vdash : \mathrm{Hp} . \dot{\exists} ! P . \supset . P \upharpoonright ‘‘\overrightarrow{P}‘‘C‘P = P \upharpoonright ‘‘\overrightarrow{P}‘‘\text{Ɑ}‘P \cup \iota‘P \upharpoonright \overrightarrow{P}‘B‘P$

$[*33{\cdot}41 . \mathrm{Transp}] \qquad = P \upharpoonright ‘‘\overrightarrow{P}‘‘\text{Ɑ}‘P \cup \iota‘\dot{\Lambda} \qquad (2)$

$\vdash . *250{\cdot}42 . \supset \vdash : \mathrm{Hp} . \dot{\exists} ! P . \supset . \dot{\Lambda} \in P \upharpoonright ‘‘\overrightarrow{P}‘‘\text{Ɑ}‘P \qquad (3)$

$\vdash . (2) . (3) . \supset \vdash : \mathrm{Hp} . \dot{\exists} ! P . \supset . P \upharpoonright ‘‘\overrightarrow{P}‘‘C‘P = P \upharpoonright ‘‘\overrightarrow{P}‘‘\text{Ɑ}‘P \qquad (4)$

$\vdash . *33{\cdot}241 . \supset \vdash : P = \dot{\Lambda} . \supset . P \upharpoonright ‘‘\overrightarrow{P}‘‘C‘P = \Lambda . P \upharpoonright ‘‘\overrightarrow{P}‘‘\text{Ɑ}‘P = \Lambda \qquad (5)$

$\vdash . (4) . (5) . \supset \vdash : \mathrm{Hp} . \supset . P \upharpoonright ‘‘\overrightarrow{P}‘‘C‘P = P \upharpoonright ‘‘\overrightarrow{P}‘‘\text{Ɑ}‘P \qquad (6)$

$\vdash . (1) . (6) . \supset \vdash . \mathrm{Prop}$

$*253{\cdot}14$. $\vdash : P \in \Omega . \supset .$

$\text{Ɑ}‘P_s = (P \upharpoonright ‘‘\overrightarrow{P}‘‘\text{Ɑ}‘P \cup \iota‘P) - \iota‘\dot{\Lambda} = (P \upharpoonright ‘‘\overrightarrow{P}‘‘C‘P \cup \iota‘P) - \iota‘\dot{\Lambda}$

Dem.

$\vdash . *213{\cdot}162 . \supset \vdash : \mathrm{Hp} . \supset . \text{Ɑ}‘P_s = P \upharpoonright ‘‘\mathrm{sect}‘P - \iota‘\dot{\Lambda}$

$[*252{\cdot}12 . *36{\cdot}33] \qquad = (P \upharpoonright ‘‘\overrightarrow{P}‘‘C‘P \cup \iota‘P) - \iota‘\dot{\Lambda} \qquad (1)$

$[*253{\cdot}13] \qquad = (P \upharpoonright ‘‘\overrightarrow{P}‘‘\text{Ɑ}‘P \cup \iota‘P) - \iota‘\dot{\Lambda} \qquad (2)$

$\vdash . (1) . (2) . \supset \vdash . \mathrm{Prop}$

$*253{\cdot}15$. $\vdash : P \in \Omega - \iota‘\dot{\Lambda} . \supset . C‘P_s = P \upharpoonright ‘‘\overrightarrow{P}‘‘\text{Ɑ}‘P \cup \iota‘P = P \upharpoonright ‘‘\overrightarrow{P}‘‘C‘P \cup \iota‘P$

$[*253{\cdot}13{\cdot}14]$

$*253{\cdot}16$. $\vdash : P \in \Omega - \iota‘\dot{\Lambda} . \supset . B‘P_s = \dot{\Lambda} . B‘\breve{P}_s = P \quad [*213{\cdot}155{\cdot}158 . *250{\cdot}13]$

$*253{\cdot}17$. $\vdash : P \in \Omega . \supset . P_s \upharpoonright \mathrm{D}‘P_s = P \upharpoonright ; \overrightarrow{P} ; P \upharpoonright \text{Ɑ}‘P$

Dem.

$\vdash . *253{\cdot}11 . \supset$

$\vdash :: \mathrm{Hp} . \supset :. QP_sR . \equiv : Q(P \upharpoonright ; \overrightarrow{P} ; P \upharpoonright \text{Ɑ}‘P) R . \vee . Q \in P \upharpoonright ‘‘\overrightarrow{P}‘‘\text{Ɑ}‘P . R = P :.$

$[*253{\cdot}121] \supset :. Q(P_s \upharpoonright \mathrm{D}‘P_s) R . \equiv . Q(P \upharpoonright ; \overrightarrow{P} ; P \upharpoonright \text{Ɑ}‘P) R :: \supset \vdash . \mathrm{Prop}$

***253·18.** $\vdash : P \in \Omega . \supset . C`P_s \subset P \upharpoonright ``\overrightarrow{P}``\text{G}`P \cup \iota`P . C`P_s \subset \Omega$

Dem.

$\vdash . *253·11 . \supset$

$\vdash :: \text{Hp} . \supset :. Q \in C`P_s . \supset : (\exists x) . x \in \text{G}`P . Q = P \upharpoonright \overrightarrow{P}`x . \vee . Q = P :$

[*37·6] $\supset : Q \in P \upharpoonright ``\overrightarrow{P}``\text{G}`P \cup \iota`P$ (1)

$\vdash . (1) . *250·141 . \supset \vdash : \text{Hp} . \supset . C`P_s \subset \Omega$ (2)

$\vdash . (1) . (2) . \supset \vdash . \text{Prop}$

***253·181.** $\vdash : P \in \Omega . \supset . C`P_s \subset \text{D}`P_s \cup \iota`P$ [*253·18·13]

***253·2.** $\vdash : P \in \Omega - 2_r . \supset . \text{Nr}`P_s = \text{Nr}`(P \upharpoonright \text{G}`P) \dot{+} \dot{1}$

Dem.

$\vdash . *253·12·121 . \supset \vdash : \text{Hp} . \supset . \text{Nr}`P_s = \text{Nr}`P \upharpoonright ; \overrightarrow{P} ; P \upharpoonright \text{G}`P \dot{+} \dot{1}$

[*213·151.*252·171] $= \text{Nr}`\overrightarrow{P} ; P \upharpoonright \text{G}`P \dot{+} \dot{1}$

[*204·34] $= \text{Nr}`(P \upharpoonright \text{G}`P) \dot{+} \dot{1} : \supset \vdash . \text{Prop}$

***253·21.** $\vdash : P \in \Omega . \supset . \dot{1} \dot{+} \text{Nr}`P_s = \text{Nr}`P \dot{+} \dot{1}$

Dem.

$\vdash . *253·2 . \supset \vdash : \text{Hp} . P \sim \in 2_r . \supset . \dot{1} \dot{+} \text{Nr}`P_s = \dot{1} \dot{+} \text{Nr}`(P \upharpoonright \text{G}`P) \dot{+} \dot{1}$

[*204·46·272] $= \text{Nr}`P \dot{+} \dot{1}$ (1)

$\vdash . *213·32 . \supset \vdash : P \in 2_r . \supset . \dot{1} \dot{+} \text{Nr}`P_s = \dot{1} \dot{+} 2_r$

[*161·211] $= 2_r \dot{+} \dot{1}$

[Hp] $= \text{Nr}`P \dot{+} \dot{1}$ (2)

$\vdash . (1) . (2) . \supset \vdash . \text{Prop}$

It would be an error to infer from the above proposition that $\text{Nr}`P_s = \text{Nr}`P$, since addition of ordinals is not in general commutative. When $P \in \Omega$, $\text{Nr}`P_s = \text{Nr}`P$ holds when $C`P$ is finite, but not otherwise. When $C`P$ is not finite, $\dot{1} \dot{+} \text{Nr}`P_s = \text{Nr}`P_s$, so that $\text{Nr}`P_s = \text{Nr}`P \dot{+} \dot{1}$; but $\text{Nr}`P \neq \text{Nr}`P \dot{+} \dot{1}$.

***253·22.** $\vdash : P \in \Omega . \supset . P_s \upharpoonright \text{D}`P_s \text{ smor } P \upharpoonright \text{G}`P$
[*253·17 . *213·151 . *252·171 . *204·34]

***253·23.** $\vdash :. P \in \Omega . \supset : \text{Nr}`P = \text{Nr}`Q . \equiv . \text{Nr}`P_s = \text{Nr}`Q_s :$
$P \text{ smor } Q . \equiv . P_s \text{ smor } Q_s$

Dem.

$\vdash . *181·33 . \supset \vdash : \text{Nr}`P = \text{Nr}`Q . \equiv . \text{Nr}`P \dot{+} \dot{1} = \text{Nr}`Q \dot{+} \dot{1}$ (1)

$\vdash . (1) . *253·21 . \supset$

$\vdash :. \text{Hp} . \supset : \text{Nr}`P = \text{Nr}`Q . \equiv . \dot{1} \dot{+} \text{Nr}`P_s = \dot{1} \dot{+} \text{Nr}`Q_s .$

[*181·33] $\equiv . \text{Nr}`P_s = \text{Nr}`Q_s :. \supset \vdash . \text{Prop}$

***253·24.** $\vdash : P \in \Omega . \supset . P_s \in \Omega$

Dem.

$\vdash . *253·2 . *250·141 . *251·132 . \supset \vdash : \text{Hp} . P \sim\in 2_r . \supset . \text{Nr}‘P_s \in \text{NO}$ (1)

$\vdash . *213·32 . *251·16 . \supset \vdash : P \in 2_r . \supset . \text{Nr}‘P_s \in \text{NO}$ (2)

$\vdash . (1) . (2) . \quad \supset \vdash : \text{Hp} . \supset . \text{Nr}‘P_s \in \text{NO} .$

$[*251·122] \quad \supset . P_s \in \Omega : \supset \vdash . \text{Prop}$

***253·25.** $\vdash :. P, Q \in \Omega - \iota‘\dot{\Lambda} . \supset : P_s \upharpoonright D‘P_s \text{ smor } Q_s \upharpoonright D‘Q_s . \equiv . P \text{ smor } Q$
[*253·22 . *250·17]

***253·3.** $\vdash : P \in \Omega . \supset . \overrightarrow{P_s}‘P = P \upharpoonright“\overrightarrow{P}“\text{Cl}‘P = P \upharpoonright“\overrightarrow{P}“C‘P = D‘P_s$
[*213·243 . *253·13]

***253·31.** $\vdash :. P \in \Omega . \supset : Q P_s R . \equiv . R \in P \upharpoonright“\overrightarrow{P}“C‘P \cup \iota‘P . Q \in R \upharpoonright“\overrightarrow{R}“C‘R$

Dem.

$\vdash . *213·245 . *253·13 . \supset$

$\vdash :. \text{Hp} . \supset : Q P_s R . \equiv . R \in C‘P_s . Q \in R \upharpoonright“\overrightarrow{R}“C‘R .$

$[*33·24 . *213·3] \quad \equiv . R \in C‘P_s . \dot{\exists} ! P . Q \in R \upharpoonright“\overrightarrow{R}“C‘R .$

$[*253·15] \quad \equiv . R \in P \upharpoonright“\overrightarrow{P}“C‘P \cup \iota‘P . \dot{\exists} ! P . Q \in R \upharpoonright“\overrightarrow{R}“C‘R$ (1)

$\vdash . *37·29 . *33·24 . \supset \vdash : Q \in R \upharpoonright“\overrightarrow{R}“C‘R . \supset . \dot{\exists} ! R :$ (2)

$[*13·12] \quad \supset \vdash : Q \in R \upharpoonright“\overrightarrow{R}“C‘R . R = P . \supset . \dot{\exists} ! P$ (3)

$\vdash . (2) \dfrac{R, P}{Q, R} . \quad \supset \vdash : R \in P \upharpoonright“\overrightarrow{P}“C‘P . \supset . \dot{\exists} ! P$ (4)

$\vdash . (3) . (4) . \quad \supset \vdash : R \in P \upharpoonright“\overrightarrow{P}“C‘P \cup \iota‘P . Q \in R \upharpoonright“\overrightarrow{R}“C‘R . \supset . \dot{\exists} ! P$ (5)

$\vdash . (1) . (5) . \supset \vdash . \text{Prop}$

***253·32.** $\vdash : P \in \Omega . R \in C‘P_s . \supset . \overrightarrow{P_s}‘R = R \upharpoonright“\overrightarrow{R}“C‘R = D‘R_s$
[*213·246 . *253·13]

***253·33.** $\vdash :. P \in \Omega . \supset : Q (P_s \upharpoonright D‘P_s) R . \equiv . R \in P \upharpoonright“\overrightarrow{P}“C‘P . Q \in R \upharpoonright“\overrightarrow{R}“C‘R$
[*213·247 . *253·13]

If α is any ordinal number, and $P \in \alpha$, the ordinal numbers of the sectional relations of P are all those ordinals which can be made equal to α by being added to, *i.e.* all ordinals β such that, for a suitable γ, $\alpha = \beta \dot{+} \gamma$. (Here γ must be an ordinal or $\dot{1}$.) Further, in virtue of *250·67, no member of $D‘P_s$ is similar to P; hence, if α is an ordinal, and $\alpha = \beta \dot{+} \gamma$, where $\gamma \neq 0_r$, it follows that $\alpha \neq \beta$. (Observe that $\alpha \neq \gamma$ does not follow from $\beta \neq 0_r . \alpha = \beta \dot{+} \gamma$.) These and kindred propositions, which are important in the theory of ordinals, are now to be proved.

***253·4.** $\vdash : P \in \Omega - \iota‘\dot{\Lambda} . \supset . C‘P_s = \hat{Q} \{(\exists R) . P = Q \dagger R . \vee . (\exists x) . P = Q \rightarrow x\}$
[*213·41 . *250·13]

***253·401.** $\vdash : P \in \Omega . \supset .$

$$P \upharpoonright {}^{\prime\prime}\overrightarrow{P}{}^{\prime\prime}C^{\prime}P \cup \iota^{\prime}P = \hat{Q}\{(\exists R) . P = Q \nrightarrow R . \text{v} . (\exists x) . P = Q \leftrightarrow x\}$$

Dem.

$\vdash . *253·4·15 . \supset \vdash : \text{Hp} . \dot{\exists} ! P . \supset .$

$$P \upharpoonright {}^{\prime\prime}\overrightarrow{P}{}^{\prime\prime}C^{\prime}P \cup \iota^{\prime}P = \hat{Q}\{(\exists R) . P = Q \nrightarrow R . \text{v} . (\exists x) . P = Q \leftrightarrow x\} \quad (1)$$

$\vdash . *37·29 . \quad \supset \vdash : P = \dot{\Lambda} . \supset . P \upharpoonright {}^{\prime\prime}\overrightarrow{P}{}^{\prime\prime}C^{\prime}P \cup \iota^{\prime}P = \iota^{\prime}\dot{\Lambda}$ (2)

$\vdash . *160·14 . *33·241 . \supset \vdash :. P = \dot{\Lambda} . \supset : P = Q \nrightarrow R . \equiv . Q = \dot{\Lambda} . R = \dot{\Lambda} :$

[*10·281] $\supset : (\exists R) . P = Q \nrightarrow R . \equiv . Q = \dot{\Lambda}$ (3)

$\vdash . *161·13 . *33·241 . \supset \vdash :. P = \dot{\Lambda} . \supset : P = Q \leftrightarrow x . \equiv . Q = \dot{\Lambda} :$

[*10·24·23] $\supset : (\exists x) . P = Q \leftrightarrow x . \equiv . Q = \dot{\Lambda}$ (4)

$\vdash . (3) . (4) . \supset \vdash :: P = \dot{\Lambda} . \supset :. (\exists R) . P = Q \nrightarrow R . \text{v} . (\exists x) . P = Q \leftrightarrow x : \equiv . Q = \dot{\Lambda} .$

[(2)] $\equiv . Q \in P \upharpoonright {}^{\prime\prime}\overrightarrow{P}{}^{\prime\prime}C^{\prime}P \cup \iota^{\prime}P$ (5)

$\vdash . (1) . (5) . \supset \vdash . \text{Prop}$

***253·402.** $\vdash : P \in \Omega - \iota^{\prime}\dot{\Lambda} . \supset .$

$$D^{\prime}P_s = \hat{Q}\{(\exists R) . R \neq \dot{\Lambda} . P = Q \nrightarrow R . \text{v} . (\exists x) . P = Q \leftrightarrow x\}$$

Dem.

$\vdash . *253·16·4 . \supset$

$\vdash :: \text{Hp} . \supset :. Q \in D^{\prime}P_s . \equiv : Q \neq P : (\exists R) . P = Q \nrightarrow R . \text{v} . (\exists x) . P = Q \leftrightarrow x$ (1)

$\vdash . *161·14 . *200·41 . \supset \vdash : \text{Hp} . P = Q \leftrightarrow x . \supset . x \in C^{\prime}P . x \sim \in C^{\prime}Q .$

[*13·14] $\supset . Q \neq P$ (2)

$\vdash . *160·21 . \supset \vdash : Q \neq P . P = Q \nrightarrow R . \supset . \dot{\exists} ! R$ (3)

$\vdash . *160·14 . *200·4 . \supset$

$\vdash : \text{Hp} . P = Q \nrightarrow R . \dot{\exists} ! R . \supset . \exists ! C^{\prime}P \cap C^{\prime}R . \sim \exists ! C^{\prime}Q \cap C^{\prime}R .$

[*13·14] $\supset . P \neq Q$ (4)

$\vdash . (3) . (4) . \supset$

$\vdash :: \text{Hp} . \supset :. Q \neq P : (\exists R) . P = Q \nrightarrow R : \equiv . (\exists R) . R \neq \dot{\Lambda} . P = Q \nrightarrow R$ (5)

$\vdash . (1) . (2) . (5) . \supset \vdash :: \text{Hp} . \supset :. Q \in D^{\prime}P_s . \equiv :$

$$(\exists R) . R \neq \dot{\Lambda} . P = Q \nrightarrow R . \text{v} . (\exists x) . P = Q \leftrightarrow x :: \supset \vdash . \text{Prop}$$

***253·41.** $\vdash :. P \in \Omega . Q \in C^{\prime}P_s . \supset :$

$$(\exists \alpha) . \alpha \in \text{NO} . \text{Nr}^{\prime}P = \text{Nr}^{\prime}Q \dotplus \alpha . \text{v} . \text{Nr}^{\prime}P = \text{Nr}^{\prime}Q \dotplus \dot{1}$$

Dem.

$\vdash . *213·3 . \supset \vdash :. \text{Hp} . \supset : P \neq \dot{\Lambda} :$

[*253·4] $\supset : (\exists R) . P = Q \nrightarrow R . \text{v} . (\exists x) . P = Q \leftrightarrow x :$

[*211·283.*200·41]

$$\supset : (\exists R) . P = Q \nrightarrow R . C^{\prime}Q \cap C^{\prime}R = \Lambda . \text{v} . (\exists x) . P = Q \leftrightarrow x . x \sim \in C^{\prime}Q :$$

[*180·32.*181·32] $\supset : (\exists R) . \text{Nr}^{\prime}P = \text{Nr}^{\prime}Q \dotplus \text{Nr}^{\prime}R . \text{v} . \text{Nr}^{\prime}P = \text{Nr}^{\prime}Q \dotplus \dot{1} :$

[*251·26] $\supset : (\exists \alpha) . \alpha \in \text{NO} . \text{Nr}^{\prime}P = \text{Nr}^{\prime}Q \dotplus \alpha . \text{v} . \text{Nr}^{\prime}P = \text{Nr}^{\prime}Q \dotplus \dot{1} :. \supset \vdash . \text{Prop}$

***253·42.** $\vdash : P \in \Omega . \supset . \text{Nr}`P \cap \text{D}`P_s = \Lambda$ [*250·651 . *213·141]

***253·421.** $\vdash : P \in \Omega . Q \in \text{D}`P_s . \supset . \sim (Q \text{ smor } P)$ [*253·42]

***253·43.** $\vdash :. P \in \Omega . x, y \in C`P . \supset : P \upharpoonright \overrightarrow{P}`x \text{ smor } P \upharpoonright \overrightarrow{P}`y . \equiv . x = y$

Dem.

$\vdash . *253\cdot11 . \supset \vdash : \text{Hp} . xPy . \supset . (P \upharpoonright \overrightarrow{P}`x) P_s (P \upharpoonright \overrightarrow{P}`y) .$

[*213·245] $\supset . P \upharpoonright \overrightarrow{P}`x \in \text{D}`(P \upharpoonright \overrightarrow{P}`y)_s .$

[*253·421] $\supset . \sim \{(P \upharpoonright \overrightarrow{P}`x) \text{ smor } (P \upharpoonright \overrightarrow{P}`y)\}$ (1)

Similarly $\vdash : \text{Hp} . yPx . \supset . \sim \{(P \upharpoonright \overrightarrow{P}`x) \text{ smor } (P \upharpoonright \overrightarrow{P}`y)\}$ (2)

$\vdash . (1) . (2) . \supset \vdash :. \text{Hp} . \supset : (P \upharpoonright \overrightarrow{P}`x) \text{ smor } (P \upharpoonright \overrightarrow{P}`y) . \supset . \sim (xPy) . \sim (yPx) .$

[*202·103] $\supset . x = y$ (3)

$\vdash . (3) . *151\cdot13 . \supset \vdash . \text{Prop}$

***253·431.** $\vdash : P \dagger Q \in \Omega . \dot{\exists} ! Q . \supset . \text{Nr}`P \neq \text{Nr}`(P \dagger Q)$

Dem.

$\vdash . *253\cdot402 . \supset \vdash : \text{Hp} . \supset . P \in \text{D}`(P \dagger Q)_s$ (1)

$\vdash . (1) . *253\cdot421 . \supset \vdash . \text{Prop}$

***253·432.** $\vdash : P \leftrightarrow x \in \Omega . \dot{\exists} ! P . \supset . \text{Nr}`P \neq \text{Nr}`(P \leftrightarrow x)$ [*253·402·421]

***253·44.** $\vdash : \alpha, \beta \in \text{NO} - \iota`\Lambda . \beta \neq 0_r . \supset . \alpha \dot{+} \beta \neq \alpha$

Dem.

$\vdash . *251\cdot1 . *155\cdot34 . \supset$

$\vdash : \text{Hp} . \supset . (\exists P, Q) . P, Q \in \Omega . \alpha = \text{N}_0\text{r}`P . \beta = \text{N}_0\text{r}`Q . \dot{\exists} ! Q .$

[*180·3]

$\supset . (\exists P, Q) . P, Q \in \Omega . \alpha = \text{N}_0\text{r}`P . \beta = \text{N}_0\text{r}`Q . \dot{\exists} ! Q . \alpha \dot{+} \beta = \text{Nr}`(P + Q)$ (1)

$\vdash . *180\cdot12 . *253\cdot431 . (*180\cdot01) . \supset$

$\vdash : P, Q \in \Omega . \dot{\exists} ! Q . \supset . \text{Nr}`(P + Q) \neq \text{Nr}`P .$

[*155·16] $\supset . \text{Nr}`(P + Q) \neq \text{N}_0\text{r}`P$ (2)

$\vdash . (1) . (2) . \supset$

$\vdash : \text{Hp} . \supset . (\exists P, Q) . P, Q \in \Omega . \alpha = \text{N}_0\text{r}`P . \beta = \text{N}_0\text{r}`Q . \alpha \dot{+} \beta \neq \text{N}_0\text{r}`P .$

[*13·195] $\supset . \alpha \dot{+} \beta \neq \alpha : \supset \vdash . \text{Prop}$

***253·45.** $\vdash : \alpha \in \text{NO} - \iota`\Lambda - \iota`0_r . \supset . \alpha \dot{+} \dot{1} \neq \alpha$

[Proof as in *253·44, using *253·432 instead of *253·431]

***253·46.** $\vdash : P \in \Omega . Q, R \in C`P_s . Q \text{ smor } R . \supset . Q = R$

Dem.

$\vdash . *253\cdot421\cdot16 . \supset \vdash : \text{Hp} . Q = P . \supset . R = Q$ (1)

$\vdash . *253\cdot16 . \supset \vdash : \text{Hp} . Q \neq P . R \neq P . \supset . Q, R \in \text{D}`P_s .$

[*253·13] $\supset . (\exists x, y) . x, y \in C`P . Q = P \upharpoonright \overrightarrow{P}`x . R = P \upharpoonright \overrightarrow{P}`y .$

[*253·43.Hp] $\supset . Q = R$ (2)

$\vdash . (1) . (2) . \supset \vdash . \text{Prop}$

***253·461.** $\vdash : P \in \Omega . \supset . \mathrm{Nr} \upharpoonright C`P_s \in 1 \to 1$

Dem.

$\vdash . *253 \cdot 46 . \supset \vdash : \mathrm{Hp} . Q, R \in C`P_s . \mathrm{Nr}`Q = \mathrm{Nr}`R . \supset . Q = R : \supset \vdash . \mathrm{Prop}$

***253·462.** $\vdash : P \in \Omega . \supset .$

$\mathrm{Nr} \; (P \sqsubset) \; \overrightarrow{P} \upharpoonright \text{Ɑ}`P \in 1 \to 1 . \mathrm{Nr} ; P \sqsubset ; \overrightarrow{P} ; P \sqsubset \text{Ɑ}`P \; \mathrm{smor} \; P \sqsubset \text{Ɑ}`P$

[*253·43]

***253·463.** $\vdash : P \in \Omega . \supset .$

$\mathrm{Nr} ; (P_s \sqsubset \mathrm{D}`P_s) \; \mathrm{smor} \; P_s \sqsubset \mathrm{D}`P_s . \mathrm{Nr} ; (P_s \sqsubset \mathrm{D}`P) \; \mathrm{smor} \; P \sqsubset \text{Ɑ}`P$

[*253·462·17·22]

***253·47.** $\vdash : P \in \Omega - \iota`\dot{\Lambda} . \supset .$

$\mathrm{Nr}``C`P_s = \hat{\alpha} \{(\exists \beta) . \alpha \dot{+} \beta = \mathrm{Nr}`P . \mathbf{v} . \alpha \dot{+} \dot{1} = \mathrm{Nr}`P\}$ [*253·4]

***253·471.** $\vdash : P \in \Omega . \supset .$

$\mathrm{Nr}``(\mathrm{D}`P_s \cup \iota`P) = \hat{\alpha} \{(\exists \beta) . \alpha \dot{+} \beta = \mathrm{Nr}`P . \mathbf{v} . \alpha \dot{+} \dot{1} = \mathrm{Nr}`P\}$

[*253·401·13]

The following propositions are concerned in proving that $\mathrm{Nr}`P_s$ is either $\mathrm{Nr}`P$ or $\mathrm{Nr}`P \dot{+} \dot{1}$. This is proved by using $P_1$ as a correlator. The methods employed anticipate the discussion of finite and infinite series; in fact, when $P$ is finite, $\mathrm{Nr}`P_s = \mathrm{Nr}`P$, and when $P$ is infinite, $\mathrm{Nr}`P_s = \mathrm{Nr}`P \dot{+} \dot{1}$. But it is important at this stage to know that $\mathrm{Nr}`P_s$ is either equal to or greater than $\mathrm{Nr}`P$, and the propositions are therefore inserted here.

***253·5.** $\vdash : P \in \Omega . \supset . P_1 ; P = P \sqsubset \mathrm{D}`P$

Dem.

$\vdash . *201 \cdot 63 . *25 \cdot 411 . \supset \vdash :: \mathrm{Hp} . \supset :. P = P_1 \cup P^2 :.$

$[*150 \cdot 11] \supset :. x (P_1 ; P) w . \equiv : (\exists y, z) : x P_1 y : y P_1 z . \mathbf{v} . y P^2 z : w P_1 z :$

$[*204 \cdot 7] \quad \equiv : (\exists z) . x P_1 w . w P_1 z . \mathbf{v} . (\exists y, z) . x P_1 y . y P^2 z . w P_1 z :$

$[*250 \cdot 21 \cdot 24] \quad \equiv : x P_1 w . w \in \mathrm{D}`P . \mathbf{v} . (\exists y) . x P_1 y . y, w \in \mathrm{D}`P . y P w :$

$[*33 \cdot 14 . *34 \cdot 1] \quad \equiv : x (P_1 \cup P_1 | P) w . w \in \mathrm{D}`P :$

$[*33 \cdot 14 . *250 \cdot 242] \equiv : x . w \in \mathrm{D}`P . x P w :: \supset \vdash . \mathrm{Prop}$

***253·501.** $\vdash : P \in \Omega . \supset . \breve{P}_1 ; P = P \sqsubset \text{Ɑ}`P_1$

Dem.

$\vdash . *250 \cdot 242 . \supset \vdash : \mathrm{Hp} . \supset . \breve{P}_1 | P = \breve{P}_1 | P_1 \cup \breve{P}_1 | P_1 | P$

$[*71 \cdot 191 . *204 \cdot 7] \quad = I \upharpoonright \text{Ɑ}`P_1 \cup (\text{Ɑ}`P_1) \upharpoonright P .$

$[*150 \cdot 1 . *50 \cdot 65] \quad \supset . \breve{P}_1 ; P = (\text{Ɑ}`P_1) \upharpoonright P_1 \cup (\text{Ɑ}`P_1) \upharpoonright P | P_1$

$[*250 \cdot 243] \quad = P \sqsubset \text{Ɑ}`P_1 : \supset \vdash . \mathrm{Prop}$

$*253{\cdot}502$. $\vdash : P \epsilon \Omega . \supset . P \upharpoonright \mathrm{C}'P_1 \ \mathrm{smor}\ P \upharpoonright \mathrm{D}'P$

Dem.

$\vdash . *253{\cdot}5 . *150{\cdot}36 . \supset \vdash : \mathrm{Hp} . \supset . P \upharpoonright \mathrm{D}'P = P_1 ; (P \upharpoonright \mathrm{C}'P_1)$ (1)

$\vdash . *151{\cdot}21 . *204{\cdot}7 . \supset \vdash : \mathrm{Hp} . \supset . P_1 ; (P \upharpoonright \mathrm{C}'P_1) \ \mathrm{smor}\ P \upharpoonright \mathrm{C}'P_1$ (2)

$\vdash . (1) . (2) . \supset \vdash . \mathrm{Prop}$

$*253{\cdot}503$. $\vdash : P \epsilon \Omega . \mathrm{C}'P_1 = \mathrm{C}'P . \supset . P \upharpoonright \mathrm{C}'P \ \mathrm{smor}\ P \upharpoonright \mathrm{D}'P$ [$*253{\cdot}502$]

This proposition shows that if P is a well-ordered series in which every term except the first has an immediate predecessor, the series obtained by omitting the last term (if any) is similar to that obtained by omitting the first term. The converse also holds, as will be shown later. The hypothesis $P \epsilon \Omega . \mathrm{C}'P_1 = \mathrm{C}'P$ is equivalent to the hypothesis that P is finite or a progression. (Here a *progression* is not what was defined as "Prog" in $*121$, but what Cantor calls ω; *i.e.* if $R \epsilon \mathrm{Prog}$, R_{po} is a progression in our present sense.)

$*253{\cdot}51$. $\vdash : P \epsilon \Omega . \mathrm{C}'P_1 = \mathrm{C}'P . \mathrm{E} ! B'\breve{P} . \supset . \mathrm{Nr}'P_s = \mathrm{Nr}'P$

Dem.

$\vdash . *253{\cdot}2 . \supset \vdash : \mathrm{Hp} . P \sim \epsilon 2_r . \supset . \mathrm{Nr}'P_s = \mathrm{Nr}'(P \upharpoonright \mathrm{C}'P) \dot{+} \dot{1}$

[$*253{\cdot}503$] $= \mathrm{Nr}'(P \upharpoonright \mathrm{D}'P) \dot{+} \dot{1}$

[$*204{\cdot}461{\cdot}272$] $= \mathrm{Nr}'P$ (1)

$\vdash . *213{\cdot}32 . \supset \vdash : P \epsilon 2_r . \supset . \mathrm{Nr}'P_s = \mathrm{Nr}'P$ (2)

$\vdash . (1) . (2) . \supset \vdash . \mathrm{Prop}$

$*253{\cdot}511$. $\vdash : P \epsilon \Omega . \mathrm{C}'P_1 = \mathrm{C}'P . \sim \mathrm{E} ! B'\breve{P} . \supset .$
$\mathrm{Nr}'P_s = \mathrm{Nr}'P \dot{+} \dot{1} . \mathrm{Nr}'P \upharpoonright \mathrm{C}'P = \mathrm{Nr}'P$

Dem.

$\vdash . *93{\cdot}103 . *202{\cdot}52 . \supset \vdash : \mathrm{Hp} . \supset . P \upharpoonright \mathrm{D}'P = P .$

[$*253{\cdot}503$] $\supset . \mathrm{Nr}'P \upharpoonright \mathrm{C}'P = \mathrm{Nr}'P .$ (1)

[$*253{\cdot}2$] $\supset . \mathrm{Nr}'P_s = \mathrm{Nr}'P \dot{+} \dot{1}$ (2)

$\vdash . (1) . (2) . \supset \vdash . \mathrm{Prop}$

$*253{\cdot}52$. $\vdash : P \epsilon \Omega . x = \min_P{}'(\mathrm{C}'P - \mathrm{C}'P_1) . \supset .$
$\mathrm{C}'P \cap \overrightarrow{P}'x \subset \mathrm{C}'P_1 . P_1{}''\overrightarrow{P}'x = \overrightarrow{P}'x . \breve{P}_1{}''\overrightarrow{P}'x = \overrightarrow{P}'x - \iota'B'P$

Dem.

$\vdash . *205{\cdot}14 . \supset \vdash : \mathrm{Hp} . \supset . \mathrm{C}'P \cap \overrightarrow{P}'x \subset \mathrm{C}'P_1$ (1)

$\vdash . *250{\cdot}242 . \supset \vdash : \mathrm{Hp} . \supset . \overrightarrow{P}'x = \overrightarrow{P_1}'x \cup P_1{}''\overrightarrow{P}'x$

[$*33{\cdot}41 . \mathrm{Hp}$] $= P_1{}''\overrightarrow{P}'x .$ (2)

[$*72{\cdot}501 . *204{\cdot}7$] $\supset . \breve{P}_1{}''\overrightarrow{P}'x = \overrightarrow{P}'x \cap \mathrm{C}'P_1$ (3)

$\vdash . (1) . \supset \vdash : \mathrm{Hp} . \supset . \mathrm{C}'P \cap \overrightarrow{P}'x = \mathrm{C}'P \cap \overrightarrow{P}'x \cap \mathrm{C}'P_1$

[$*121{\cdot}305$] $= \mathrm{C}'P_1 \cap \overrightarrow{P}'x$ (4)

$\vdash . (3) . (4) . \supset \vdash : \mathrm{Hp} . \supset . \breve{P}_1{}''\overrightarrow{P}'x = \overrightarrow{P}'x \cap \mathrm{C}'P$

[$*33{\cdot}15 . *202{\cdot}52$] $= \overrightarrow{P}'x - \iota'B'P$ (5)

$\vdash . (1) . (2) . (5) . \supset \vdash . \mathrm{Prop}$

***253·521.** $\vdash : P \in \Omega \,.\, x \in \text{Ɑ}\text{‘}P - \text{Ɑ}\text{‘}P_1 \,.\supset .\, \overrightarrow{P}\text{‘}x, \text{Ɑ}\text{‘}P \sim \in 1$.

Dem.

$\vdash .\, {*}201{\cdot}66 \,.\quad \supset \vdash : P \in \Omega \,.\, \overrightarrow{P}\text{‘}x \in 1 \,.\supset .\, x \in \text{Ɑ}\text{‘}P_1$ (1)

$\vdash .\, (1) \,.\, \text{Transp} \,.\supset \vdash : \text{Hp} \,.\supset .\, \overrightarrow{P}\text{‘}x \sim \in 1$ (2)

$\vdash .\, {*}201{\cdot}662 \,.\quad \supset \vdash : \text{Hp} \,.\supset .\, \text{Ɑ}\text{‘}P \sim \in 1$ (3)

$\vdash .\, (2) \,.\, (3) \,.\supset \vdash .\, \text{Prop}$

***253·522.** $\vdash : P \in \Omega \,.\, x = \min_P\text{‘}(\text{Ɑ}\text{‘}P - \text{Ɑ}\text{‘}P_1) \,.\, S = P_1 \upharpoonright \overrightarrow{P}\text{‘}x \cup I \upharpoonright \overleftarrow{P_*}\text{‘}x \,.\supset .$
$S ; (P \pounds \text{Ɑ}\text{‘}P) = P$

Dem.

$\vdash .\, {*}34{\cdot}25{\cdot}26 \,.\, {*}50{\cdot}5{\cdot}51 \,.\supset$

$\vdash : \text{Hp} \,.\supset .\, S ; (P \pounds \text{Ɑ}\text{‘}P) = (P_1 \upharpoonright \overrightarrow{P}\text{‘}x) ; P \pounds \text{Ɑ}\text{‘}P \cup (I \upharpoonright \overleftarrow{P_*}\text{‘}x) ; P \cup$
$(P_1 \upharpoonright \overrightarrow{P}\text{‘}x) \,|\, P \,|\, I \upharpoonright \overleftarrow{P_*}\text{‘}x \cup I \upharpoonright \overleftarrow{P_*}\text{‘}x \,|\, P \,|\, \overrightarrow{P}\text{‘}x \upharpoonleft \breve{P}_1$

$[{*}50{\cdot}6{\cdot}61 . {*}150{\cdot}36 . {*}35{\cdot}452] = (P_1 \upharpoonright \overrightarrow{P}\text{‘}x) ; P \cup P \pounds \overleftarrow{P_*}\text{‘}x \cup P_1 \upharpoonright \overrightarrow{P}\text{‘}x \,|\, P \upharpoonright \overleftarrow{P_*}\text{‘}x \cup$
$\overleftarrow{P_*}\text{‘}x \upharpoonleft P \upharpoonright \overrightarrow{P}\text{‘}x \,|\, P_1$

$[{*}74{\cdot}141 . {*}253{\cdot}52 . {*}200{\cdot}381] = (P_1 \upharpoonright \overrightarrow{P}\text{‘}x) ; P \cup P \pounds \overleftarrow{P_*}\text{‘}x \cup \overrightarrow{P}\text{‘}x \upharpoonleft P_1 \,|\, P \upharpoonright \overleftarrow{P_*}\text{‘}x$

$[{*}250{\cdot}242 . \text{Hp}] \quad = (P_1 \upharpoonright \overrightarrow{P}\text{‘}x) ; P \cup P \pounds \overleftarrow{P_*}\text{‘}x \cup \overrightarrow{P}\text{‘}x \upharpoonleft P \upharpoonright \overleftarrow{P_*}\text{‘}x$

$[{*}150{\cdot}36] \quad = (P_1 ; P) \pounds P_1\text{“}\overrightarrow{P}\text{‘}x \cup P \pounds \overleftarrow{P_*}\text{‘}x \cup \overrightarrow{P}\text{‘}x \upharpoonleft P \upharpoonright \overleftarrow{P_*}\text{‘}x$

$[{*}253{\cdot}5{\cdot}52] \quad = P \pounds \overrightarrow{P}\text{‘}x \cup P \pounds \overleftarrow{P_*}\text{‘}x \cup \overrightarrow{P}\text{‘}x \upharpoonleft P \upharpoonright \overleftarrow{P_*}\text{‘}x$

$[{*}35{\cdot}413 . {*}200{\cdot}381] \quad = P \pounds (\overrightarrow{P}\text{‘}x \cup \overleftarrow{P_*}\text{‘}x)$

$[{*}202{\cdot}101] \quad = P : \supset \vdash .\, \text{Prop}$

***253·53.** $\vdash : P \in \Omega \,.\, x = \min_P\text{‘}(\text{Ɑ}\text{‘}P - \text{Ɑ}\text{‘}P_1) \,.\supset .$
$P_1 \upharpoonright \overrightarrow{P}\text{‘}x \cup I \upharpoonright \overleftarrow{P_*}\text{‘}x \in \{P \,\overline{\text{smor}}\, (P \pounds \text{Ɑ}\text{‘}P)\}$

Dem.

$\vdash .\, {*}204{\cdot}7 \,.\, {*}200{\cdot}381 \,.\supset \vdash : \text{Hp} \,.\supset .\, P_1 \upharpoonright \overrightarrow{P}\text{‘}x \cup I \upharpoonright \overleftarrow{P_*}\text{‘}x \in 1 \rightarrow 1$ (1)

$\vdash .\, {*}253{\cdot}52 \,.\, {*}50{\cdot}5{\cdot}52 \,.\supset$

$\vdash : \text{Hp} \,.\supset .\, \text{Ɑ}\text{‘}(P_1 \upharpoonright \overrightarrow{P}\text{‘}x \cup I \upharpoonright \overleftarrow{P_*}\text{‘}x) = (\overrightarrow{P}\text{‘}x - \iota\text{‘}B\text{‘}P) \cup \overleftarrow{P_*}\text{‘}x$

$[{*}202{\cdot}101] \quad = C\text{‘}P - \iota\text{‘}B\text{‘}P$

$[{*}93{\cdot}103] \quad = \text{Ɑ}\text{‘}P$

$[{*}202{\cdot}55 . {*}253{\cdot}521] \quad = C\text{‘}(P \pounds \text{Ɑ}\text{‘}P)$ (2)

$\vdash .\, {*}253{\cdot}522 \,.\supset \vdash : \text{Hp} \,.\supset .\, (P_1 \upharpoonright \overrightarrow{P}\text{‘}x \cup I \upharpoonright \overleftarrow{P_*}\text{‘}x) ; (P \pounds \text{Ɑ}\text{‘}P) = P$ (3)

$\vdash .\, (1) \,.\, (2) \,.\, (3) \,.\, {*}151{\cdot}11 \,.\supset \vdash .\, \text{Prop}$

***253·54.** $\vdash : P \in \Omega \,.\, \exists ! \,\text{Ɑ}\text{‘}P - \text{Ɑ}\text{‘}P_1 \,.\supset .\, P \,\text{smor}\, P \pounds \text{Ɑ}\text{‘}P$

Dem.

$\vdash .\, {*}250{\cdot}121 \,.\supset \vdash : \text{Hp} \,.\supset .\, \text{E} ! \min_P\text{‘}(\text{Ɑ}\text{‘}P - \text{Ɑ}\text{‘}P_1)$ (1)

$\vdash .\, (1) \,.\, {*}253{\cdot}53 \,.\supset \vdash .\, \text{Prop}$

***253·55.** $\vdash : P \in \Omega . \exists ! \text{C}'P - \text{C}'P_1 . \supset . \text{Nr}'P_s = \text{Nr}'P \dot{+} \dot{1}$

Dem.

$\vdash . *253{\cdot}521 . *204{\cdot}272 . \supset \vdash : \text{Hp} . \supset . P \sim \in 2_r$ (1)

$\vdash . (1) . *253{\cdot}54{\cdot}2 . \supset \vdash . \text{Prop}$

***253·56.** $\vdash :. P \in \Omega . \supset : \text{C}'P_1 = \text{C}'P . \text{E} ! B'\breve{P} . \supset . \text{Nr}'P_s = \text{Nr}'P :$

$\sim (\text{C}'P_1 = \text{C}'P . \text{E} ! B'\breve{P}) . \supset . \text{Nr}'P_s = \text{Nr}'P \dot{+} \dot{1}$

[*253·51·511·55]

***253·57.** $\vdash : P \in \Omega . \text{C}'P_1 = \text{C}'P . \text{E} ! B'\breve{P} . \supset .$

$\dot{1} \dot{+} \text{Nr}'P = \text{Nr}'P \dot{+} \dot{1} . \dot{1} \dot{+} \text{Nr}'P \neq \text{Nr}'P$

Dem.

$\vdash . *253{\cdot}51 . \supset \vdash : \text{Hp} . \supset . \text{Nr}'P_s = \text{Nr}'P .$

[*253·21] $\supset . \dot{1} \dot{+} \text{Nr}'P = \text{Nr}'P \dot{+} \dot{1} .$ (1)

[*253·45] $\supset . \dot{1} \dot{+} \text{Nr}'P \neq \text{Nr}'P$ (2)

$\vdash . (1) . (2) . \supset \vdash . \text{Prop}$

***253·571.** $\vdash : P \in \Omega . \sim (\text{C}'P_1 = \text{C}'P . \text{E} ! B'\breve{P}) . \supset . \dot{1} \dot{+} \text{Nr}'P = \text{Nr}'P$

Dem.

$\vdash . *253{\cdot}56 . \supset \vdash : \text{Hp} . \supset . \text{Nr}'P_s = \text{Nr}'P \dot{+} \dot{1} .$

[*253·21] $\supset . \dot{1} \dot{+} \text{Nr}'P \dot{+} \dot{1} = \text{Nr}'P \dot{+} \dot{1} .$

[*181·33] $\supset . \dot{1} \dot{+} \text{Nr}'P = \text{Nr}'P : \supset \vdash . \text{Prop}$

***253·572.** $\vdash : P \in \Omega - \iota'\dot{\Lambda} . \sim (\text{C}'P_1 = \text{C}'P . \text{E} ! B'\breve{P}) . \supset . \dot{1} \dot{+} \text{Nr}'P \neq \text{Nr}'P \dot{+} \dot{1}$

[*253·571·45]

***253·573.** $\vdash :. P \in \Omega . \supset : \text{C}'P_1 = \text{C}'P . \text{E} ! B'\breve{P} . \equiv . \dot{1} \dot{+} \text{Nr}'P \neq \text{Nr}'P$

[*253·57·571]

***253·574.** $\vdash :. P \in \Omega - \iota'\dot{\Lambda} . \supset : \text{C}'P_1 = \text{C}'P . \text{E} ! B'\breve{P} . \equiv . \dot{1} \dot{+} \text{Nr}'P = \text{Nr}'P \dot{+} \dot{1}$

[*253·57·572]

$*254$. GREATER AND LESS AMONG WELL-ORDERED SERIES.

Summary of $*254$.

In the present number we have to prove that of any two well-ordered series one must be similar to a sectional relation of the other. From this it will follow that of any two unequal ordinals one must be the greater. The propositions of the present number are due to Cantor*.

Our procedure is as follows. We define a relation "$RP_{sm}Q$," meaning "R is a proper section of P, and is similar to Q," *i.e.*

$$RP_{sm}Q \,.\equiv.\, R \in \mathrm{D}‘P_s \,.\, R \operatorname{smor} Q.$$

In virtue of $*253{\cdot}46$, if $P, Q \in \Omega$, $P_{sm} \in 1 \to \mathrm{Cls}$ ($*254{\cdot}22$) and $P_{sm} \upharpoonright D‘Q_s \in 1 \to 1$ ($*254{\cdot}222$). Thus if S is any proper section of Q which is similar to some proper section of P_s, the proper section of P to which it is similar is $P_{sm}‘S$. It is easy to prove that $P_{sm} \mathbin{;} Q_s \upharpoonright \mathrm{D}‘Q_s$ is a section of P; and if $\mathrm{D}‘P_s \subset \text{Ɑ}‘Q_{sm}$, *i.e.* if every proper section of P is similar to some proper section of Q, we shall have ($*254{\cdot}261$)

$$P_s \upharpoonright \mathrm{D}‘P_s = P_{sm} \mathbin{;} Q_s \upharpoonright \mathrm{D}‘Q_s.$$

Hence it follows ($*254{\cdot}27$) that if, further, $\mathrm{D}‘Q_s \subset \text{Ɑ}‘P_{sm}$, we shall have

$$P_s \upharpoonright \mathrm{D}‘P_s \operatorname{smor} Q_s \upharpoonright \mathrm{D}‘Q_s,$$

i.e. by $*253{\cdot}25$, $\quad P \operatorname{smor} Q \quad (*254{\cdot}31)$.

Thus (A) if every proper section of P is similar to some proper section of Q, and vice versa, then P is similar to Q.

Consider next the case in which every proper section of P is similar to a proper section of Q (*i.e.* $\mathrm{D}‘P_s \subset \text{Ɑ}‘Q_{sm}$), but not vice versa, so that $\exists ! \, \mathrm{D}‘Q_s - \text{Ɑ}‘P_{sm}$. It is easy to prove that, under this hypothesis, if $S \in \mathrm{D}‘Q_s - \text{Ɑ}‘P_{sm}$, then $\mathrm{D}‘P_s \subset \text{Ɑ}‘S_{sm}$ ($*254{\cdot}32$). But if S is the minimum (in the order Q_s) of the class $\mathrm{D}‘Q_s - \text{Ɑ}‘P_{sm}$, then $\mathrm{D}‘S_s \subset \text{Ɑ}‘P_{sm}$. Hence, by (A),

$$S \operatorname{smor} P \quad (*254{\cdot}321).$$

Thus (B) if every proper section of P is similar to a proper section of Q, but not vice versa, then P is similar to a proper section of Q ($*254{\cdot}33$).

* *Math. Annalen*, Vol. 49.

From (B), by transposition, we find that if every proper section of P is similar to a proper section of Q, but P itself is not similar to any proper section of Q, then every proper section of Q is similar to a proper section of P, whence, by (A), P is similar to Q (*254·34). Hence, if there are proper sections of P which are not similar to any proper section of Q, the smallest of such sections (say P') must be similar to Q, since it is not itself similar to any proper section of Q, but all its proper sections are similar to proper sections of Q. Hence (C) if there are proper sections of P which are not similar to any proper section of Q, then there is a proper section of P which is similar to Q, *i.e.*

$$\vdash : P, Q \in \Omega \,.\, \exists \,!\, \mathrm{D}`P_s - \mathrm{Cl}`Q_{\mathrm{sm}} \,.\, \supset \,.\, Q \in \mathrm{Cl}`P_{\mathrm{sm}} \quad (*254{\cdot}35).$$

Thus, either (1) $\exists \,!\, \mathrm{D}`P_s - \mathrm{Cl}`Q_{\mathrm{sm}}$, in which case $Q \in \mathrm{Cl}`P_{\mathrm{sm}}$, or (2) $\exists \,!\, \mathrm{D}`Q_s - \mathrm{Cl}`P_{\mathrm{sm}}$, in which case $P \in \mathrm{Cl}`Q_{\mathrm{sm}}$, or (3) $\mathrm{D}`P_s \subset \mathrm{Cl}`Q_{\mathrm{sm}}$ and $\mathrm{D}`Q_s \subset \mathrm{Cl}`P_{\mathrm{sm}}$, in which case, by (A), $P \,\mathrm{smor}\, Q$. Thus (D) if P and Q are any two well-ordered series, either they are similar or one is similar to a proper section of the other (*254·37).

We now proceed to define one well-ordered series P as *less than* another well-ordered series Q if P is similar to a part of Q, but not to Q, *i.e.* we put

$$\mathrm{less} = \hat{P}\hat{Q}\{P, Q \in \Omega \,.\, \exists \,!\, \mathrm{Rl}`Q \cap \mathrm{Nr}`P \,.\, \sim(P \,\mathrm{smor}\, Q)\} \quad \mathrm{Df.}$$

(Observe that we have $\mathrm{Rl}`Q$ in this definition, not $\mathrm{D}`Q_s$.)

It follows from (D) that, P and Q being well-ordered series, if P and Q are not similar, one must be less than the other (*254·4). It follows also from *250·65 that if P is similar to a proper section of Q Q cannot be less than P (*254·181). Hence P is less than Q when, and only when, P is similar to a proper section of Q, *i.e.*

$$P \,\mathrm{less}\, Q \,.\, \equiv \,.\, P, Q \in \Omega \,.\, P \in \mathrm{Cl}`Q_{\mathrm{sm}} \quad (*254{\cdot}41).$$

Hence if each of two well-ordered series is similar to a part of the other, the two series are similar (*254·45); and in any other case, one of them is similar to a proper section of the other.

From the above results we easily obtain the following propositions, which are useful in the ordinal theory of finite and infinite.

***254·51.** $\vdash : P \,\mathrm{less}\, Q \,.\, \equiv \,.\, P, Q \in \Omega \,.\, \mathrm{Rl}`P \cap \mathrm{Nr}`Q = \Lambda$

I.e. one well-ordered series is less than another when, and only when, no part of it is similar to the other.

***254·52.** $\vdash : P \in \Omega \,.\, \alpha \subset C`P \,.\, \exists \,!\, C`P \cap p`\overleftarrow{P}``\alpha \,.\, \supset \,.\, P \upharpoonright \alpha \,\mathrm{less}\, P$

I.e. any part of a well-ordered series which stops short of the end is less than the whole series.

***254·55.** $\vdash :. Q \text{ less } P . \equiv : P, Q \in \Omega : (\exists R) . R \text{ smor } Q . R \Subset P . \exists ! C`P \cap p`\overleftarrow{P}``C`R$

I.e. one well-ordered series is less than another when, and only when, it is similar to a part of the other which stops short of the end.

***254·01.** $\text{less} = \hat{P}\hat{Q} \{P, Q \in \Omega . \exists ! \text{Rl}`Q \cap \text{Nr}`P . \sim (P \text{ smor } Q)\}$ Df

***254·02.** $P_{sm} = (\text{D}`P_s) \upharpoonright \text{smor}$ Df

***254·1.** $\vdash : P \text{ less } Q . \equiv . P, Q \in \Omega . \exists ! \text{Rl}`Q \cap \text{Nr}`P . \sim (P \text{ smor } Q)$ [(*254·01)]

***254·101.** $\vdash : P, Q \in \Omega . P \Subset Q . \sim (P \text{ smor } Q) . \supset . P \text{ less } Q$ [*254·1]

***254·11.** $\vdash : R P_{sm} Q . \equiv . R \in \text{D}`P_s . R \text{ smor } Q$ [(*254·02)]

***254·111.** $\vdash . \overrightarrow{P_{sm}}`Q = \text{D}`P_s \cap \text{Nr}`Q$ [*254·11]

***254·12.** $\vdash : Q \in \text{Cl}`P_{sm} . \equiv . \exists ! \text{D}`P_s \cap \text{Nr}`Q$ [*254·111]

***254·121.** $\vdash . \text{D}`P_s \subset \text{Cl}`P_{sm}$ [*254·12 . *152·3]

***254·13.** $\vdash :. P \text{ smor } P' . Q \text{ smor } Q' . \supset : P \text{ less } Q . \equiv . P' \text{ less } Q'$
[*151·15 . *152·321 . *254·1]

***254·14.** $\vdash : S \in \text{D}`Q_s . T \in P \,\overline{\text{smor}}\, Q . \supset . T ; S \in \text{D}`P_s \cap \text{Nr}`S$

Dem.

$\vdash . *213·141 . \supset \vdash : \text{Hp} . \supset . (\exists \beta) . \beta \in \text{sect}`Q - \iota`\Lambda - \iota`C`Q . S = Q \upharpoonright \beta$ (1)

$\vdash . *150·37 . \supset \vdash : \text{Hp} . S = Q \upharpoonright \beta . \supset . T ; S = (T ; Q) \upharpoonright T``\beta$

[*151·11] $= P \upharpoonright T``\beta$ (2)

$\vdash . *212·7 . \supset \vdash : \text{Hp} . \beta \in \text{sect}`Q . \supset . T``\beta \in \text{sect}`P$ (3)

$\vdash . *37·43 . \supset \vdash : \text{Hp} . \beta \in \text{sect}`Q - \iota`\Lambda . \supset . \exists ! T``\beta$ (4)

$\vdash . *150·22 . \supset \vdash : \text{Hp} . T``\beta = C`P . \supset . T``\beta = T``C`Q :$

[*72·481] $\supset \vdash : \text{Hp} . T``\beta = C`P . \beta \in \text{sect}`Q . \supset . \beta = C`Q :$

[Transp] $\supset \vdash : \text{Hp} . \beta \in \text{sect}`Q - \iota`C`Q . \supset . T``\beta \neq C`P$ (5)

$\vdash . (3) . (4) . (5) . \supset$

$\vdash : \text{Hp} . \beta \in \text{sect}`Q - \iota`\Lambda - \iota`C`Q . \supset . T``\beta \in \text{sect}`P - \iota`\Lambda - \iota`C`P$ (6)

$\vdash . (1) . (2) . (6) . \supset \vdash : \text{Hp} . \supset . (\exists \alpha) . \alpha \in \text{sect}`P - \iota`\Lambda - \iota`C`P . T ; S = P \upharpoonright \alpha .$

[*213·141] $\supset . T ; S \in \text{D}`P_s$ (7)

$\vdash . *151·21 . \supset \vdash : \text{Hp} . \supset . (T ; S) \text{ smor } S$ (8)

$\vdash . (7) . (8) . \supset \vdash . \text{Prop}$

***254·141.** $\vdash : P \text{ smor } Q . \supset . \text{D}`Q_s \subset \text{Cl}`P_{sm} . \text{D}`P_s \subset \text{Cl}`Q_{sm}$

Dem.

$\vdash . *254·12·14 . \supset \vdash :. \text{Hp} . \supset : S \in \text{D}`Q_s . \supset . S \in \text{Cl}`P_{sm}$ (1)

$\vdash . (1) . *151·14 . \supset \vdash . \text{Prop}$

***254·142.** $\vdash : R \in C`P_s . \supset . R_{sm} \Subset P_{sm}$

Dem.

$\vdash . *213·241 . \supset \vdash : \text{Hp} . \supset . \text{D}`R_s \subset \text{D}`P_s$ (1)

$\vdash . (1) . *254·11 . \supset \vdash . \text{Prop}$

***254·143.** $\vdash : Q \in \text{Ɑ}`P_{sm} . \supset . C`Q_s \subset \text{Ɑ}`P_{sm}$

Dem.

$\vdash . *254\cdot12 . \supset \vdash : \mathrm{Hp} . \supset . (\exists R) . R \in \mathrm{D}`P_s . R \text{ smor } Q .$

$[*254\cdot141] \qquad \supset . (\exists R) . R \in \mathrm{D}`P_s . \mathrm{D}`Q_s \subset \text{Ɑ}`R_{sm} .$

$[*254\cdot142] \qquad \supset . \mathrm{D}`Q_s \subset \text{Ɑ}`P_{sm} .$

$[*213\cdot16.\mathrm{Hp}] \qquad \supset . Q \upharpoonright``(\mathrm{sect}`Q - \iota`\Lambda) \subset \text{Ɑ}`P_{sm} .$

$[*213\cdot1] \qquad \supset . C`Q_s \subset \text{Ɑ}`P_{sm} : \supset \vdash . \mathrm{Prop}$

***254·144.** $\vdash : P = \dot{\Lambda} . \supset . P_{sm} = \dot{\Lambda}$ $\quad [*213\cdot3 . *254\cdot11]$

***254·15.** $\vdash :. Q_{po} \Subset J . \exists ! \overrightarrow{B}`P . P_{po} \Subset J . \supset : Q \in \text{Ɑ}`P_{sm} . \equiv . C`Q_s \subset \text{Ɑ}`P_{sm}$

Dem.

$\vdash . *254\cdot143 . \qquad \supset \vdash : Q \in \text{Ɑ}`P_{sm} . \supset . C`Q_s \subset \text{Ɑ}`P_{sm}$ (1)

$\vdash . *213\cdot142 . *211\cdot26 . \supset \vdash :. \mathrm{Hp} . \dot{\exists} ! Q . \supset : Q \in C`Q_s :$

$[*22\cdot441] \qquad \supset : C`Q_s \subset \text{Ɑ}`P_{sm} . \supset . Q \in \text{Ɑ}`P_{sm}$ (2)

$\vdash . *211\cdot18 . \qquad \supset \vdash : \mathrm{Hp} . \supset . \exists ! \mathrm{sect}`P \cap 1 .$

$[*200\cdot35] \qquad \supset . \dot{\Lambda} \in P \upharpoonright``(\mathrm{sect}`P - \iota`\Lambda) .$

$[*213\cdot16] \qquad \supset . \dot{\Lambda} \in \mathrm{D}`P_s .$

$[*254\cdot121] \qquad \supset . \dot{\Lambda} \in \text{Ɑ}`P_{sm}$ (3)

$\vdash . (2) . (3) . \qquad \supset \vdash :. \mathrm{Hp} . \supset : C`Q_s \subset \text{Ɑ}`P_{sm} . \supset . Q \in \text{Ɑ}`P_{sm}$ (4)

$\vdash . (1) . (4) . \supset \vdash . \mathrm{Prop}$

***254·16.** $\vdash :. Q \text{ smor } Q' . \supset : \overrightarrow{P_{sm}}`Q = \overrightarrow{P_{sm}}`Q' : Q \in \text{Ɑ}`P_{sm} . \equiv . Q' \in \text{Ɑ}`P_{sm}$

Dem.

$\vdash . *254\cdot111 . *152\cdot321 . \supset \vdash :. \mathrm{Hp} . \supset : \overrightarrow{P_{sm}}`Q = \overrightarrow{P_{sm}}`Q' :$ (1)

$[*13\cdot12] \qquad \supset : \exists ! \overrightarrow{P_{sm}}`Q . \equiv . \exists ! \overrightarrow{P_{sm}}`Q' :$

$[*33\cdot41] \qquad \supset : Q \in \text{Ɑ}`P_{sm} . \equiv . Q' \in \text{Ɑ}`P_{sm}$ (2)

$\vdash . (1) . (2) . \supset \vdash . \mathrm{Prop}$

***254·161.** $\vdash : P \text{ smor } P' . \supset . \text{Ɑ}`P_{sm} = \text{Ɑ}`P'_{sm}$

Dem.

$\vdash . *254\cdot14 . \qquad \supset \vdash : T \in P \,\overline{\mathrm{smor}}\, P' . S \in \mathrm{D}`P'_s \cap \mathrm{Nr}`Q . \supset . T ; S \in \mathrm{D}`P_s \cap \mathrm{Nr}`Q :$

$[*254\cdot12] \qquad \supset \vdash : T \in P \,\overline{\mathrm{smor}}\, P' . Q \in \text{Ɑ}`P'_{sm} . \supset . Q \in \text{Ɑ}`P_{sm} :$

$[*151\cdot12] \qquad \supset \vdash : P \text{ smor } P' . \supset . \text{Ɑ}`P'_{sm} \subset \text{Ɑ}`P_{sm}$ (1)

$\vdash . (1) . *151\cdot14 . \supset \vdash : P \text{ smor } P' . \supset . \text{Ɑ}`P_{sm} \subset \text{Ɑ}`P'_{sm}$ (2)

$\vdash . (1) . (2) . \supset \vdash . \mathrm{Prop}$

***254·162.** $\vdash :. P \text{ smor } P' . Q \text{ smor } Q' . \supset : Q \in \text{Ɑ}`P_{sm} . \equiv . Q' \in \text{Ɑ}`P'_{sm}$
$[*254\cdot16\cdot161]$

***254·163.** $\vdash : R \in \text{Ɑ}`Q_{sm} . \supset . \text{Ɑ}`R_{sm} \subset \text{Ɑ}`Q_{sm}$

Dem.

$\vdash . *254\cdot12 . \supset \vdash : \mathrm{Hp} . \supset . (\exists S) . R \text{ smor } S . S \in \mathrm{D}`Q_s .$

$[*254\cdot161\cdot142] \qquad \supset . (\exists S) . \text{Ɑ}`R_{sm} = \text{Ɑ}`S_{sm} . \text{Ɑ}`S_{sm} \subset \text{Ɑ}`Q_{sm} .$

$[*13\cdot195] \qquad \supset . \text{Ɑ}`R_{sm} \subset \text{Ɑ}`Q_{sm} : \supset \vdash . \mathrm{Prop}$

$*254{\cdot}164$. $\vdash : \text{D}`P_s \subset \text{Ɑ}`Q_{sm} . \supset . \text{D}`P_s = P_{sm}``(\text{D}`Q_s \cap \text{Ɑ}`P_{sm}) = P_{sm}``\text{D}`Q_s$

Dem.

$\vdash . *254{\cdot}11 . \supset \vdash : \text{Hp} . R \in \text{D}`P_s . \supset . (\exists S) . S \in \text{D}`Q_s . R \text{ smor } S .$

$[*254{\cdot}11] \qquad \supset . (\exists S) . S \in \text{D}`Q_s . R P_{sm} S$

$[*37{\cdot}1] \qquad \supset . R \in P_{sm}``\text{D}`Q_s \qquad (1)$

$\vdash . *254{\cdot}11 . \supset \vdash . P_{sm}``\text{D}`Q_s \subset \text{D}`P_s \qquad (2)$

$\vdash . (1) . (2) . \supset \vdash : \text{Hp} . \supset . \text{D}`P_s = P_{sm}``\text{D}`Q_s$

$[*37{\cdot}26] \qquad = P_{sm}``(\text{D}`Q_s \cap \text{Ɑ}`P_{sm}) : \supset \vdash . \text{Prop}$

$*254{\cdot}17$. $\vdash : P \in \Omega . Q \in \text{D}`P_s . R \Subset Q . \supset . \sim(R \text{ smor } P)$

Dem.

$\vdash . *204{\cdot}21 . \supset \vdash : P \in \Omega . R \Subset P . R \text{ smor } P . \supset . R \in \text{Ser} .$

$[*204{\cdot}41] \qquad \supset . R = P \upharpoonright C`R \qquad (1)$

$\vdash . *250{\cdot}65 . \text{Transp} . \supset$

$\vdash : P \in \Omega . R \text{ smor } P . R = P \upharpoonright C`R . \supset . \sim(\exists \alpha) . \alpha \in \text{sect}`P - \iota`C`P . C`R \subset \alpha .$

$[*211{\cdot}133{\cdot}44] \supset . \sim(\exists Q) . Q \in P \upharpoonright ``(\text{sect}`P - \iota`C`P) . R \Subset Q .$

$[*213{\cdot}141] \qquad \supset . \sim(\exists Q) . Q \in \text{D}`P_s . R \Subset Q \qquad (2)$

$\vdash . (1) . (2) . \supset \vdash : P \in \Omega . R \text{ smor } P . R \Subset P . \supset . \sim(\exists Q) . Q \in \text{D}`P_s . R \Subset Q \qquad (3)$

$\vdash . (3) . \text{Transp} . \supset \vdash . \text{Prop}$

$*254{\cdot}18$. $\vdash : Q \in \text{D}`P_s . \supset . \sim(P \text{ less } Q) \quad [*254{\cdot}17{\cdot}1]$

$*254{\cdot}181$. $\vdash : Q \in \text{Ɑ}`P_{sm} . \supset . \sim(P \text{ less } Q)$

Dem.

$\vdash . *254{\cdot}18{\cdot}12 . \supset \vdash : \text{Hp} . \supset . (\exists R) . R \text{ smor } Q . \sim(P \text{ less } R) .$

$[*254{\cdot}13] \qquad \supset . \sim(P \text{ less } Q) : \supset \vdash . \text{Prop}$

$*254{\cdot}182$. $\vdash : P \in \Omega . Q \in \text{D}`P_s . \supset . Q \text{ less } P \quad [*254{\cdot}101 . *253{\cdot}421{\cdot}18]$

$*254{\cdot}2$. $\vdash : P \in \Omega . Q \in \text{Ɑ}`P_{sm} . \supset . Q \text{ less } P$

Dem.

$\vdash . *254{\cdot}11 . \supset \vdash : \text{Hp} . \supset . (\exists R) . R \in \text{D}`P_s . R \text{ smor } Q .$

$[*254{\cdot}182] \qquad \supset . (\exists R) . R \text{ less } P . R \text{ smor } Q .$

$[*254{\cdot}13] \qquad \supset . Q \text{ less } P : \supset \vdash . \text{Prop}$

$*254{\cdot}21$. $\vdash : P \in \Omega . Q \in \text{Ɑ}`P_{sm} . R \Subset Q . R \in \Omega . \supset . R \text{ less } P$

Dem.

$\vdash . *254{\cdot}12 . \supset \vdash : \text{Hp} . \supset . (\exists S, T) . S \in \text{D}`P_s . T \in S \,\overline{\text{smor}}\, Q .$

$[*151{\cdot}21 . *150{\cdot}31] \qquad \supset . (\exists S, T) . S \in \text{D}`P_s . T \in S \,\overline{\text{smor}}\, Q . T \dot{;} R \text{ smor } R . T \dot{;} R \Subset S .$

$[*254{\cdot}17] \qquad \supset . (\exists T) . T \dot{;} R \text{ smor } R . T \dot{;} R \Subset P . \sim(T \dot{;} R \text{ smor } P) .$

$[*151{\cdot}17] \qquad \supset . (\exists T) . T \dot{;} R \text{ smor } R . T \dot{;} R \Subset P . \sim(R \text{ smor } P) .$

$[*254{\cdot}1] \qquad \supset . R \text{ less } P : \supset \vdash . \text{Prop}$

***254·22.** $\vdash : P \epsilon \Omega . \supset . P_{sm} \epsilon 1 \rightarrow \text{Cls}$

Dem.

$\vdash . *254·11 . \supset \vdash :. R P_{sm} Q . S P_{sm} Q . \supset : R, S \epsilon \text{D}`P_s . R \text{ smor } S :$

[*253·46] $\supset : P \epsilon \Omega . \supset . R = S$ (1)

$\vdash . (1) . \text{Comm} . \supset \vdash . \text{Prop}$

***254·221.** $\vdash : P \epsilon \Omega . \supset . \text{G}`P_{sm} \subset \Omega$

Dem.

$\vdash . *254·12 . *253·13 . \supset$

$\vdash : \text{Hp} . Q \epsilon \text{G}`P_{sm} . \supset . (\exists R, \alpha) . R = P \upharpoonright \alpha . R \text{ smor } Q .$

[*250·141.*251·111] $\supset . Q \epsilon \Omega : \supset \vdash . \text{Prop}$

***254·222.** $\vdash : P, Q \epsilon \Omega . \supset . P_{sm} \upharpoonright \text{D}`Q_s \epsilon 1 \rightarrow 1$

Dem.

$\vdash . *254·11 . \supset \vdash :. R (P_{sm} \upharpoonright \text{D}`Q_s) S . R (P_{sm} \upharpoonright \text{D}`Q_s) S' . \supset :$

$S, S' \epsilon \text{D}`Q_s . R \text{ smor } S . R \text{ smor } S' :$

[*253·46] $\supset : Q \epsilon \Omega . \supset . S = S'$ (1)

$\vdash . (1) . \text{Comm} . \supset \vdash : \text{Hp} . \supset . P_{sm} \upharpoonright \text{D}`Q_s \epsilon \text{Cls} \rightarrow 1$ (2)

$\vdash . (2) . *254·22 . \supset \vdash . \text{Prop}$

***254·223.** $\vdash . \text{Cnv}`(P_{sm} \upharpoonright \text{D}`Q_s) = Q_{sm} \upharpoonright \text{D}`P_s$

Dem.

$\vdash . *254·11 . \supset \vdash : R (P_{sm} \upharpoonright \text{D}`Q_s) S . \equiv . R \epsilon \text{D}`P_s . S \epsilon \text{D}`Q_s . R \text{ smor } S .$

[*151·14] $\equiv . S \epsilon \text{D}`Q_s . R \epsilon \text{D}`P_s . S \text{ smor } R .$

[*254·11] $\equiv . S (Q_{sm} \upharpoonright \text{D}`P_s) R : \supset \vdash . \text{Prop}$

***254·224.** $\vdash : Q \epsilon \Omega . \text{E} ! P_{sm}`S . S \epsilon \text{D}`Q_s . \supset . S = Q_{sm}`P_{sm}`S$

Dem.

$\vdash . *254·223 . \supset \vdash :. \text{Hp} . \supset : S Q_{sm} (P_{sm}`S) . \equiv . (P_{sm}`S) P_{sm} S$ (1)

$\vdash . (1) . *30·32 . *254·22 . \supset \vdash . \text{Prop}$

***254·23.** $\vdash : P \epsilon \Omega . Q \epsilon \text{G}`P_{sm} . \supset . P_{sm}`Q = \breve{\iota}`(\text{D}`P_s \cap \text{Nr}`Q)$ [*254·22·111]

***254·24.** $\vdash : P, Q \epsilon \Omega . R \epsilon \text{D}`P_s \cap \text{G}`Q_{sm} . S \epsilon \text{Rl}`R \cap \text{D}`P_s . \supset . S \epsilon \text{G}`Q_{sm}$

Dem.

$\vdash . *213·24 . \supset \vdash : \text{Hp} . \supset . S \epsilon \text{D}`R_s .$

[*254·143.Hp] $\supset . S \epsilon \text{G}`Q_{sm} : \supset \vdash . \text{Prop}$

***254·241.** $\vdash :. P \in \Omega . Q, R \in C`P_s . \supset : R \in \text{Cl}`Q_{sm} . \equiv . R \in D`Q_s$

Dem.

$\vdash . *254\cdot121 . \supset \vdash : R \in D`Q_s . \supset . R \in \text{Cl}`Q_{sm}$ (1)

$\vdash . *254\cdot142 . \supset \vdash : \text{Hp} . Q \in C`R_s . \supset . Q_{sm} \subseteq R_{sm}$ (2)

$\vdash . *253\cdot42 . \supset \vdash : R \in \Omega . \supset . R \sim\in \text{Cl}`R_{sm}$ (3)

$\vdash . (2) . (3) . \supset \vdash : \text{Hp} . Q \in C`R_s . \supset . R \sim\in \text{Cl}`Q_{sm}$ (4)

$\vdash . (4) . \text{Transp} . (3) . \supset \vdash : \text{Hp} . R \in \text{Cl}`Q_{sm} . \supset . Q \sim\in C`R_s . Q \neq R .$

$[*213\cdot245] \quad \supset . \sim (Q P_s R) . Q \neq R .$

$[*213\cdot153 . \text{Hp}] \quad \supset . R P_s Q .$

$[*213\cdot245] \quad \supset . R \in D`Q_s$ (5)

$\vdash . (1) . (5) . \supset \vdash . \text{Prop}$

***254·242.** $\vdash : Q \in \Omega . T \in P \,\overline{\text{smor}}\, Q . S \in D`Q_s . \supset . T;S = P_{sm}`S$

Dem.

$\vdash . *254\cdot14 . \supset \vdash : \text{Hp} . \supset . T;S \in D`P_s \cap \text{Nr}`S .$

$[*254\cdot11] \quad \supset . (T;S) P_{sm} S .$

$[*254\cdot22 . *251\cdot111] \quad \supset . T;S = P_{sm}`S : \supset \vdash . \text{Prop}$

***254·243.** $\vdash : Q \in \Omega . S \in D`Q_s . T \in P \,\text{smor}\, S . S' Q_s S . \supset . T;S' = P_{sm}`S'$

Dem.

$\vdash . *213\cdot245 . *253\cdot18 . \supset \vdash : \text{Hp} . \supset . S \in \Omega . S' \in D`S_s .$

$[*254\cdot242] \quad \supset . T;S' = P_{sm}`S' : \supset \vdash . \text{Prop}$

***254·244.** $\vdash : P, Q \in \Omega . S \in D`Q_s \cap \text{Cl}`P_{sm} . T \in (P_{sm}`S) \,\overline{\text{smor}}\, S . S' Q_s S . \supset .$
$T;S = P_{sm}`S . T;S' = P_{sm}`S' . (T;S') P_s (T;S)$

Dem.

$\vdash . *254\cdot243 . \supset \vdash : \text{Hp} . R = P_{sm}`S . \supset . T;S' = R_{sm}`S'$ (1)

$\vdash . *254\cdot11 . \supset \vdash : \text{Hp}(1) . \supset . R \in D`P_s .$ (2)

$[*254\cdot142] \quad \supset . R_{sm} \subseteq P_{sm}$ (3)

$\vdash . (1) . (3) . *254\cdot22 . \supset \vdash : \text{Hp}(1) . \supset . T;S' = P_{sm}`S'$ (4)

$\vdash . *151\cdot11 . \supset \vdash : \text{Hp}(1) . \supset . R = T;S .$ (5)

$[(2)] \quad \supset . T;S \in D`P_s$ (6)

$\vdash . (1) . (5) . *254\cdot11 . \supset \vdash : \text{Hp}(1) . \supset . T;S' \in D`(T;S)$ (7)

$\vdash . (6) . (7) . *213\cdot244 . \supset \vdash : \text{Hp}(1) . \supset . (T;S') P_s (T;S)$ (8)

$\vdash . (5) . \supset \vdash : \text{Hp} . \supset . T;S = P_{sm}`S$ (9)

$\vdash . (9) . (4) . (8) . \supset \vdash . \text{Prop}$

***254·245.** $\vdash : P, Q \in \Omega . S \in D`Q_s \cap \text{Cl}`P_{sm} . S' Q_s S . \supset . (P_{sm}`S') P_s (P_{sm}`S)$

Dem.

$\vdash . *254\cdot22\cdot11 . \supset \vdash : \text{Hp} . \supset . (P_{sm}`S) \,\text{smor}\, S$ (1)

$\vdash . (1) . *254\cdot244 . \supset \vdash . \text{Prop}$

$*254\cdot25$. $\vdash :. P, Q \,\epsilon\, \Omega . S, S' \,\epsilon\, D'Q_s \,\cap\, \Box'P_{sm} . \supset : S'Q_s S . \equiv . (P_{sm}`S') P_s (P_{sm}`S)$

Dem.

$\vdash . *254\cdot245 . \supset \vdash :. \text{Hp} . \supset : S'Q_s S . \supset . (P_{sm}`S') P_s (P_{sm}`S)$ (1)

$\vdash . (1) \dfrac{P_{sm}`S,\ P_{sm}`S',\ P,\ Q}{S,\quad S',\quad Q, P} . \supset$

$\vdash :. \text{Hp} . \supset : (P_{sm}`S') P_s (P_{sm}`S) . \supset . (Q_{sm}`P_{sm}`S') Q_s (Q_{sm}`P_{sm}`S) .$
$[*254\cdot224] \qquad\qquad\qquad\qquad \supset . S'Q_s S$ (2)

$\vdash . (1) . (2) . \supset \vdash . \text{Prop}$

$*254\cdot26$. $\vdash : P, Q \,\epsilon\, \Omega . \supset . Q_s \,\llcorner\, (D'Q_s \,\cap\, \Box'P_{sm}) = Q_{sm}\,;(P_s \,\llcorner\, D'P_s)$

Dem.

$\vdash . *254\cdot25 . \supset \vdash :: \text{Hp} . \supset :. S' \{Q_s \,\llcorner\, (D'Q_s \,\cap\, \Box'P_{sm})\} S . \equiv :$
$\qquad\qquad\qquad\qquad S, S' \,\epsilon\, D'Q_s \,\cap\, \Box'P_{sm} . (P_{sm}`S') P_s (P_{sm}`S) :$
$[*254\cdot22] \quad \equiv : S, S' \,\epsilon\, D'Q_s : (\exists R, R') . RP_{sm}S . R'P_{sm}S' . R'P_s R :$
$[*254\cdot223] \equiv : (\exists R, R') . SQ_{sm}R . S'Q_{sm}R' . R, R' \,\epsilon\, D'P_s . R'P_s R :$
$[*150\cdot11] \quad \equiv : S' \{Q_{sm}\,;(P_s \,\llcorner\, D'P_s)\} S :: \supset \vdash . \text{Prop}$

$*254\cdot261$. $\vdash : P, Q \,\epsilon\, \Omega . D'Q_s \,\subset\, \Box'P_{sm} . \supset . Q_s \,\llcorner\, D'Q_s = Q_{sm}\,;(P_s \,\llcorner\, D'P_s)$
$\qquad\qquad [*254\cdot26]$

$*254\cdot27$. $\vdash : P, Q \,\epsilon\, \Omega . D'P_s \,\subset\, \Box'Q_{sm} . D'Q_s \,\subset\, \Box'P_{sm} . \supset .$
$\qquad\qquad\qquad Q_{sm} \,\lceil\, C`(P_s \,\llcorner\, D'P_s) \,\epsilon\, (Q_s \,\llcorner\, D'Q_s) \,\overline{\text{smor}}\, (P_s \,\llcorner\, D'P_s)$

Dem.

$\vdash . *254\cdot222 . \supset \vdash : \text{Hp} . \supset . Q_{sm} \,\lceil\, C`(P_s \,\llcorner\, D'P_s) \,\epsilon\, 1 \to 1$ (1)
$\vdash . *37\cdot41 . \quad \supset \vdash : \text{Hp} . \supset . C`(P_s \,\llcorner\, D'P_s) \,\subset\, \Box'Q_{sm}$ (2)
$\vdash . (1) . (2) . *254\cdot261 . *151\cdot22 . \supset \vdash . \text{Prop}$

In virtue of the above proposition, we have, when its hypothesis is
realized,

$$(Q_s \,\llcorner\, D'Q_s) \text{ smor } (P_s \,\llcorner\, D'P_s),$$

whence, by $*253\cdot25$, $Q \text{ smor } P$.

This proposition is the converse of $*254\cdot141$.

In the above proposition we take $Q_{sm} \,\lceil\, C`(P_s \,\llcorner\, D'P_s)$ as the correlator,
rather than $Q_{sm} \,\lceil\, D'P_s$, so as not to have to make an exception for the case
when $P \,\epsilon\, 2_r$. For if $P \,\epsilon\, 2_r$, $D'P_s \,\epsilon\, 1$, but $P_s \,\llcorner\, D'P_s = \dot{\Lambda}$. Thus $Q_{sm} \,\lceil\, D'P_s$ is
not a correlator in this case.

The following propositions, down to the end of the present number, are
important, and give the foundations of the theory of inequality between well-
ordered series and between ordinals.

***254·31.** $\vdash : P, Q \in \Omega . \text{D}`P_s \subset \text{ᗡ}`Q_{sm} . \text{D}`Q_s \subset \text{ᗡ}`P_{sm} . \supset . P \text{ smor } Q$

Dem.

$\vdash . *254{\cdot}27 . \supset \vdash :. \text{Hp} . \supset : (P_s \upharpoonright \text{D}`P_s) \text{ smor } (Q_s \upharpoonright \text{D}`Q_s) :$

$[*253{\cdot}25] \qquad \supset : \dot{\exists} ! P . \dot{\exists} ! Q . \supset . P \text{ smor } Q \qquad (1)$

$\vdash . *254{\cdot}144 . \supset \vdash : \text{Hp} . P = \dot{\Lambda} . \supset . \text{D}`Q_s = \Lambda .$

$[*213{\cdot}302] \qquad \supset . Q = \dot{\Lambda} .$

$[*153{\cdot}101] \qquad \supset . P \text{ smor } Q \qquad (2)$

Similarly $\vdash : \text{Hp} . Q = \dot{\Lambda} . \supset . P \text{ smor } Q \qquad (3)$

$\vdash . (1) . (2) . (3) . \supset \vdash . \text{Prop}$

***254·311.** $\vdash :. P, Q \in \Omega . \supset : \text{D}`P_s \subset \text{ᗡ}`Q_{sm} . \text{D}`Q_s \subset \text{ᗡ}`P_{sm} . \equiv . P \text{ smor } Q$ $[*254{\cdot}31{\cdot}141]$

***254·32.** $\vdash : P, Q \in \Omega . \text{D}`P_s \subset \text{ᗡ}`Q_{sm} . S \in \text{D}`Q_s - \text{ᗡ}`P_{sm} . \supset . \text{D}`P_s \subset \text{ᗡ}`S_{sm}$

Dem.

$\vdash . *254{\cdot}24 . \supset \vdash : \text{Hp} . R, S' \in \text{D}`Q_s . S' \in R . R \in \text{ᗡ}`P_{sm} . \supset . S' \in \text{ᗡ}`P_{sm} \qquad (1)$

$\vdash . (1) . \text{Transp} . \supset \vdash : \text{Hp} . R \in \text{D}`Q_s \cap \text{ᗡ}`P_{sm} . \supset . \sim (S \in R) .$

$[*213{\cdot}21] \qquad \supset . R Q_s S .$

$[*254{\cdot}22{\cdot}11 . *213{\cdot}245] \supset . (P_{sm}`R) \text{ smor } R . R \in \text{D}`S_s .$

$[*254{\cdot}12] \qquad \supset . (P_{sm}`R) \in \text{ᗡ}`S_{sm} \qquad (2)$

$\vdash . (2) . *37{\cdot}61 . \supset \vdash : \text{Hp} . \supset . P_{sm}``(\text{D}`Q_s \cap \text{ᗡ}`P_{sm}) \subset \text{ᗡ}`S_{sm} .$

$[*254{\cdot}164] \qquad \supset . \text{D}`P_s \subset \text{ᗡ}`S_{sm} : \supset \vdash . \text{Prop}$

***254·321.** $\vdash : P, Q \in \Omega . \text{D}`P_s \subset \text{ᗡ}`Q_{sm} . S = \min(Q_s)`(\text{D}`Q_s - \text{ᗡ}`P_{sm}) . \supset . S \text{ smor } P$

Dem.

$\vdash . *205{\cdot}14 . \supset \vdash : \text{Hp} . \supset . \overrightarrow{Q_s}`S \subset \text{ᗡ}`P_{sm} .$

$[*213{\cdot}246] \qquad \supset . \text{D}`S_s \subset \text{ᗡ}`P_{sm} \qquad (1)$

$\vdash . *254{\cdot}32 . \supset \vdash : \text{Hp} . \supset . \text{D}`P_s \subset \text{ᗡ}`S_{sm} \qquad (2)$

$\vdash . (1) . (2) . *254{\cdot}31 . \supset \vdash . \text{Prop}$

***254·33.** $\vdash : P, Q \in \Omega . \text{D}`P_s \subset \text{ᗡ}`Q_{sm} . \exists ! \text{D}`Q_s - \text{ᗡ}`P_{sm} . \supset . P \in \text{ᗡ}`Q_{sm}$

Dem.

$\vdash . *253{\cdot}24 . \supset \vdash : \text{Hp} . \supset . \text{E} ! \min(Q_s)`(\text{D}`Q_s - \text{ᗡ}`P_{sm}) .$

$[*254{\cdot}321] \qquad \supset . (\exists S) . S \in \text{D}`Q_s . S \text{ smor } P .$

$[*254{\cdot}11] \qquad \supset . P \in \text{ᗡ}`Q_{sm} : \supset \vdash . \text{Prop}$

***254·34.** $\vdash : P, Q \in \Omega . P \sim \in \text{ᗡ}`Q_{sm} . \text{D}`P_s \subset \text{ᗡ}`Q_{sm} . \supset . P \text{ smor } Q$

Dem.

$\vdash . *254{\cdot}33 . \text{Transp} . \supset \vdash : \text{Hp} . \supset . \text{D}`Q_s \subset \text{ᗡ}`P_{sm} . \text{D}`P_s \subset \text{ᗡ}`Q_{sm} .$

$[*254{\cdot}31] \qquad \supset . P \text{ smor } Q : \supset \vdash . \text{Prop}$

***254·35.** $\vdash : P, Q \in \Omega \,.\, \exists ! \, D`Q_s - \text{Ɑ}`P_{sm} \,.\supset.\, P \in \text{Ɑ}`Q_{sm}$

Dem.

$\vdash .\, *253{\cdot}24 \,.\supset\vdash : \mathrm{Hp} \,.\supset.\, E ! \min (Q_s)`(D`Q_s - \text{Ɑ}`P_{sm}) \,.$

$[*205{\cdot}14] \qquad \supset .\, (\exists S) \,.\, S \in D`Q_s - \text{Ɑ}`P_{sm} \,.\, \overrightarrow{Q_s}`S \subset \text{Ɑ}`P_{sm} \,.$

$[*213{\cdot}246] \qquad \supset .\, (\exists S) \,.\, S \in D`Q_s - \text{Ɑ}`P_{sm} \,.\, D`S_s \subset \text{Ɑ}`P_{sm} \,.$

$[*254{\cdot}34] \qquad \supset .\, (\exists S) \,.\, S \in D`Q_s \,.\, S \text{ smor } P \,.$

$[*254{\cdot}11] \qquad \supset .\, P \in \text{Ɑ}`Q_{sm} : \supset \vdash .\, \mathrm{Prop}$

***254·36.** $\vdash : P, Q \in \Omega \,.\, \exists ! \, D`Q_s - \text{Ɑ}`P_{sm} \,.\supset.\, C`P_s \subset \text{Ɑ}`Q_{sm}$ $[*254{\cdot}35{\cdot}143]$

***254·37.** $\vdash :.\, P, Q \in \Omega \,.\supset : P \text{ smor } Q \,.\vee.\, P \in \text{Ɑ}`Q_{sm} \,.\vee.\, Q \in \text{Ɑ}`P_{sm}$

Dem.

$\vdash .\, *254{\cdot}31 \,.\supset\vdash : \mathrm{Hp} \,.\, D`P_s \subset \text{Ɑ}`Q_{sm} \,.\, D`Q_s \subset \text{Ɑ}`P_{sm} \,.\supset.\, P \text{ smor } Q$ (1)

$\vdash .\, *254{\cdot}35 \,.\supset\vdash : \mathrm{Hp} \,.\, \exists ! \, D`Q_s - \text{Ɑ}`P_{sm} \,.\supset.\, P \in \text{Ɑ}`Q_{sm}$ (2)

$\vdash .\, *254{\cdot}35 \,.\supset\vdash : \mathrm{Hp} \,.\, \exists ! \, D`P_s - \text{Ɑ}`Q_{sm} \,.\supset.\, Q \in \text{Ɑ}`P_{sm}$ (3)

$\vdash .\, (1) \,.\, (2) \,.\, (3) \,.\supset\vdash .\, \mathrm{Prop}$

This proposition is the most important on the relations of two well-ordered series to each other's segments. It shows that of every two well-ordered series which are not similar, one must be similar to a segment of the other.

***254·4.** $\vdash :.\, P, Q \in \Omega \,.\supset : P \text{ less } Q \,.\vee.\, P \text{ smor } Q \,.\vee.\, Q \text{ less } P$

Dem.

$\vdash .\, *254{\cdot}2 \,.\supset\vdash : \mathrm{Hp} \,.\, P \in \text{Ɑ}`Q_{sm} \,.\supset.\, P \text{ less } Q$ (1)

$\vdash .\, *254{\cdot}2 \,.\supset\vdash : \mathrm{Hp} \,.\, Q \in \text{Ɑ}`P_{sm} \,.\supset.\, Q \text{ less } P$ (2)

$\vdash .\, *254{\cdot}37 \,.\supset\vdash : \mathrm{Hp} \,.\, P \sim\in \text{Ɑ}`Q_{sm} \,.\, Q \sim\in \text{Ɑ}`P_{sm} \,.\supset.\, P \text{ smor } Q$ (3)

$\vdash .\, (1) \,.\, (2) \,.\, (3) \,.\supset\vdash .\, \mathrm{Prop}$

***254·401.** $\vdash :.\, P, Q \in \Omega \,.\supset : \overrightarrow{\text{less}}`P = \overrightarrow{\text{less}}`Q \,.\equiv.\, P \text{ smor } Q$

Dem.

$\vdash .\, *254{\cdot}1 \,.\supset\vdash : \mathrm{Hp} \,.\, \overrightarrow{\text{less}}`P = \overrightarrow{\text{less}}`Q \,.\supset.\, \sim(P \text{ less } Q) \,.\, \sim(Q \text{ less } P) \,.$

$[*254{\cdot}4] \qquad \supset .\, P \text{ smor } Q$ (1)

$\vdash .\, *254{\cdot}13 \,.\supset\vdash : \mathrm{Hp} \,.\, P \text{ smor } Q \,.\supset.\, \overrightarrow{\text{less}}`P = \overrightarrow{\text{less}}`Q$ (2)

$\vdash .\, (1) \,.\, (2) \,.\supset\vdash .\, \mathrm{Prop}$

***254·41.** $\vdash : P \text{ less } Q \,.\equiv.\, P, Q \in \Omega \,.\, P \in \text{Ɑ}`Q_{sm} \,.\equiv.\, Q \in \Omega \,.\, P \in \text{Ɑ}`Q_{sm}$

Dem.

$\vdash .\, *254{\cdot}2 \,. \qquad \supset\vdash : Q \in \Omega \,.\, P \in \text{Ɑ}`Q_{sm} \,.\supset.\, P \text{ less } Q$ (1)

$\vdash .\, *254{\cdot}181 \,. \qquad \supset\vdash : Q \in \text{Ɑ}`P_{sm} \,.\supset.\, \sim(P \text{ less } Q)$ (2)

$\vdash .\, *253{\cdot}421 \,. \qquad \supset\vdash : Q \in \Omega \,.\, R \in D`Q_s \,.\, P \text{ smor } R \,.\supset.\, \sim(P \text{ smor } Q) :$

$[*254{\cdot}11] \qquad \supset\vdash : Q \in \Omega \,.\, P \in \text{Ɑ}`P_{sm} \,.\supset.\, \sim(P \text{ smor } Q)$ (3)

$\vdash .\, (2) \,.\, (3) \,.\, *254{\cdot}4 \,.\supset\vdash : Q \in \Omega \,.\, P \in \text{Ɑ}`P_{sm} \,.\supset.\, P \text{ less } Q$ (4)

$\vdash .\, (1) \,.\, (4) \,. \qquad \supset\vdash : P \text{ less } Q \,.\equiv.\, Q \in \Omega \,.\, P \in \text{Ɑ}`Q_{sm} \,.$

$[*254{\cdot}1] \qquad \equiv .\, P, Q \in \Omega \,.\, P \in \text{Ɑ}`Q_{sm} : \supset \vdash .\, \mathrm{Prop}$

***254·42.** $\vdash . \text{less} \Subset J . \text{less}^2 \Subset \text{less}$

Dem.

$\vdash . *254\cdot1 . \quad \supset \vdash : P \,\text{less}\, Q . \supset . \sim (P \,\text{smor}\, Q) .$

$[*151\cdot13] \qquad \supset . P \mp Q \qquad (1)$

$\vdash . *254\cdot163 . \supset \vdash : R \in \text{Ɑ}\text{‘}Q_{\text{sm}} . S \in \text{Ɑ}\text{‘}R_{\text{sm}} . \supset . S \in \text{Ɑ}\text{‘}Q_{\text{sm}} :$

$[*254\cdot41] \qquad \supset \vdash : R \,\text{less}\, Q . S \,\text{less}\, R . \supset . S \,\text{less}\, Q \qquad (2)$

$\vdash . (1) . (2) . \supset \vdash . \text{Prop}$

The relation "less" fails to generate a series, because it is not connected, two similar well-ordered series being neither greater nor less than each other. On the other hand, the relation Nr⁏less is serial, since two similar well-ordered series both contribute the same term to the field of Nr⁏less, and therefore connection does not fail. The relation Nr⁏less will be dealt with in the next number.

***254·43.** $\vdash : Q \in \Omega - \iota\text{‘}\dot{\Lambda} . \supset . \dot{\Lambda} \,\text{less}\, Q \quad [*254\cdot1 . *250\cdot4 . *152\cdot11]$

***254·431.** $\vdash . \text{Ɑ}\text{‘}\text{less} = \Omega - \iota\text{‘}\dot{\Lambda} . C\text{‘}\text{less} \subset \Omega$

Dem.

$\vdash . *254\cdot43 . \qquad \supset \vdash : Q \in \Omega - \iota\text{‘}\dot{\Lambda} . \supset . \dot{\Lambda} \,\text{less}\, Q \qquad (1)$

$\vdash . *254\cdot1 . *25\cdot13 . \quad \supset \vdash : Q = \dot{\Lambda} . \supset . Q \sim\in \text{Ɑ}\text{‘}\text{less} \qquad (2)$

$\vdash . *254\cdot1 . \qquad \supset \vdash . C\text{‘}\text{less} \subset \Omega \qquad (3)$

$\vdash . (3) . (2) . \text{Transp} . \supset \vdash . \text{Ɑ}\text{‘}\text{less} \subset \Omega - \iota\text{‘}\dot{\Lambda} \qquad (4)$

$\vdash . (1) . (4) . \qquad \supset \vdash . \text{Ɑ}\text{‘}\text{less} = \Omega - \iota\text{‘}\dot{\Lambda} \qquad (5)$

$\vdash . (3) . (5) . \supset \vdash . \text{Prop}$

In order to obtain $C\text{‘}\text{less} = \Omega$, we need, as appears from (1) in the above proof, $\exists ! \Omega - \iota\text{‘}\dot{\Lambda}$. In virtue of *251·7, this requires $\exists ! 2$. By *101·42·43, this holds if "less" has its field defined as belonging to a class-type or a relation-type. If, however, "less" has its field defined as composed of individuals, the primitive propositions assumed in the present work do not enable us to prove $\exists ! 2$, nor therefore to prove $\dot{\exists} ! \text{less}$.

It should be observed that "less," like "sm" and "smor," is significant when it is not homogeneous; but "$C\text{‘}$less" is only significant for homogeneous typical determinations of "less," because only homogeneous relations have fields.

***254·432.** $\vdash : \exists ! 2_a . \equiv . \dot{\exists} ! \text{less} \mathbin{\dot{\cap}} t_{00}\text{‘}\alpha \uparrow t_{00}\text{‘}\alpha . \equiv . \exists ! \Omega - \iota\text{‘}\dot{\Lambda} \cap t_{00}\text{‘}\alpha$

Dem.

$\vdash . *251\cdot7 . \supset \vdash : \exists ! 2_a . \equiv . \exists ! \Omega - \iota\text{‘}\dot{\Lambda} \cap t_{00}\text{‘}\alpha . \qquad (1)$

$[*254\cdot43] \qquad \equiv . (\exists Q) . Q \in \Omega - \iota\text{‘}\dot{\Lambda} \cap t_{00}\text{‘}\alpha . \dot{\Lambda} \,\text{less}\, Q .$

$[*55\cdot37] \qquad \supset . (\exists Q) . \dot{\Lambda} \,\text{less}\, Q . \dot{\Lambda} \downarrow Q \Subset t_{00}\text{‘}\alpha \uparrow t_{00}\text{‘}\alpha .$

$[*55\cdot3] \qquad \supset . \dot{\exists} ! \text{less} \mathbin{\dot{\cap}} t_{00}\text{‘}\alpha \uparrow t_{00}\text{‘}\alpha \qquad (2)$

$\vdash . *35\cdot103 . \supset \vdash : \dot{\exists} ! \,\text{less} \mathbin{\dot{\cap}} t_{00}`\alpha \upharpoonright t_{00}`\alpha . \supset . (\exists P, Q) . P \,\text{less}\, Q . P, Q \,\epsilon\, t_{00}`\alpha .$

$[*254\cdot431] \quad \supset . \exists ! \Omega - \iota`\dot{\Lambda} \cap t_{00}`\alpha .$

$[(1)] \quad \supset . \exists ! 2_a \qquad (3)$

$\vdash . (1) . (2) . (3) . \supset \vdash . \text{Prop}$

***254·433.** $\vdash . \dot{\exists} ! \,\text{less} \mathbin{\dot{\cap}} t_{00}`\text{Cls} \upharpoonright t_{00}`\text{Cls} . \dot{\exists} ! \,\text{less} \mathbin{\dot{\cap}} t_{00}`\text{Rel} \upharpoonright t_{00}`\text{Rel}$

$[*254\cdot432 . *101\cdot42\cdot43]$

***254·434.** $\vdash : \dot{\exists} ! \,\text{less} . \equiv . C`\text{less} = \Omega . \equiv . B`\text{less} = \dot{\Lambda}$

Dem.

$\vdash . *250\cdot4 . *33\cdot24 . \supset \vdash : C`\text{less} = \Omega . \supset . \dot{\exists} ! \,\text{less} \qquad (1)$

$\vdash . *93\cdot102 . *33\cdot24 . \supset \vdash : B`\text{less} = \dot{\Lambda} . \supset . \dot{\exists} ! \,\text{less} \qquad (2)$

$\vdash . *254\cdot43 . \quad \supset \vdash : Q \,\epsilon\, \Omega - \iota`\dot{\Lambda} . \supset . \dot{\Lambda} \,\text{less}\, Q \qquad (3)$

$\vdash . (3) . \quad \supset \vdash : \exists ! \Omega - \iota`\dot{\Lambda} . \supset . \dot{\Lambda} \,\epsilon\, \text{D}`\text{less} .$

$[*254\cdot431] \quad \supset . \dot{\Lambda} = B`\text{less} \qquad (4)$

$\vdash . (4) . *254\cdot431 . \quad \supset \vdash : \exists ! \Omega - \iota`\dot{\Lambda} . \supset . C`\text{less} = \Omega \qquad (5)$

$\vdash . (1) . (2) . (4) . (5) . \supset \vdash . \text{Prop}$

***254·44.** $\vdash : P \,\epsilon\, C`\text{less} . \supset . C`\text{less} = \overrightarrow{\text{less}}`P \cup \text{Nr}`P \cup \overleftarrow{\text{less}}`P$

Dem.

$\vdash . *254\cdot13 . \quad \supset \vdash : \text{Hp} . \supset . \text{Nr}`P \subset C`\text{less} \qquad (1)$

$\vdash . (1) . *33\cdot152 . \supset \vdash : \text{Hp} . \supset . \overrightarrow{\text{less}}`P \cup \text{Nr}`P \cup \overleftarrow{\text{less}}`P \subset C`\text{less} \qquad (2)$

$\vdash . *254\cdot1 . \quad \supset \vdash . C`\text{less} \subset \Omega .$

$[*254\cdot4] \supset \vdash :. P \,\epsilon\, C`\text{less} . \supset : Q \,\epsilon\, C`\text{less} . \supset . Q \,\epsilon\, \overrightarrow{\text{less}}`P \cup \text{Nr}`P \cup \overleftarrow{\text{less}}`P \qquad (3)$

$\vdash . (2) . (3) . \supset \vdash . \text{Prop}$

***254·45.** $\vdash : P, Q \,\epsilon\, \Omega . \exists ! \text{Rl}`P \cap \text{Nr}`Q . \exists ! \text{Rl}`Q \cap \text{Nr}`P . \supset . P \,\text{smor}\, Q$

Dem.

$\vdash . *254\cdot42 . \supset \vdash : P \,\text{less}\, Q . \supset . \sim (Q \,\text{less}\, P) \qquad (1)$

$\vdash . *254\cdot1 . \quad \supset \vdash : P, Q \,\epsilon\, \Omega . \exists ! \text{Rl}`Q \cap \text{Nr}`P . \sim (P \,\text{smor}\, Q) . \supset . P \,\text{less}\, Q .$

$[(1)] \quad \supset . \sim (Q \,\text{less}\, P) .$

$[*254\cdot1 . \text{Transp}] \quad \supset . \sim \exists ! \text{Rl}`P \cap \text{Nr}`Q \qquad (2)$

$\vdash . (2) . \text{Transp} . \supset \vdash . \text{Prop}$

This proposition is the analogue, for ordinals, of the Schröder-Bernstein theorem.

∗254·46. $\vdash : P \text{ less } Q . \equiv . P, Q \epsilon \Omega . \exists ! \text{Rl}`Q \cap \text{Nr}`P . \sim \exists ! \text{Rl}`P \cap \text{Nr}`Q$

Dem.

$\vdash . *152·11 . *61·34 . \supset$

$\vdash : P, Q \epsilon \Omega . \exists ! \text{Rl}`Q \cap \text{Nr}`P . \sim \exists ! \text{Rl}`P \cap \text{Nr}`Q . \supset .$

$P, Q \epsilon \Omega . \exists ! \text{Rl}`Q \cap \text{Nr}`P . \sim (P \text{ smor } Q) .$

$[*254·1] \quad \supset . P \text{ less } Q \quad (1)$

$\vdash . *254·1·45 . \text{Transp} . \supset$

$\vdash : P \text{ less } Q . \supset . P, Q \epsilon \Omega . \exists ! \text{Rl}`Q \cap \text{Nr}`P . \sim \exists ! \text{Rl}`P \cap \text{Nr}`Q \quad (2)$

$\vdash . (1) . (2) . \supset \vdash . \text{Prop}$

∗254·47. $\vdash : P \epsilon \Omega . \supset . P_s = \text{less} \upharpoonright C`P_s$

Dem.

$\vdash . *213·245 . \supset \vdash :. \text{Hp} . \supset : R P_s Q . \equiv . R \epsilon \text{D}`Q_s . Q \epsilon C`P_s .$

$[*254·121] \quad \supset . R \epsilon \text{Cl}`Q_{sm} .$

$[*254·41] \quad \supset . R \text{ less } Q \quad (1)$

$\vdash . *254·181 . \text{Transp} . \supset \vdash : \text{Hp} . Q, R \epsilon C`P_s . R \text{ less } Q . \supset . Q \sim \epsilon \text{Cl}`R_{sm} .$

$[*254·121] \quad \supset . Q \sim \epsilon \text{D}`R_s \quad (2)$

$\vdash . (2) . *213·25 . *254·42 . \supset \vdash : \text{Hp} . Q, R \epsilon C`P_s . R \text{ less } Q . \supset . R \epsilon \text{D}`Q_s .$

$[*213·245] \quad \supset . R P_s Q \quad (3)$

$\vdash . (1) . (3) . \supset \vdash . \text{Prop}$

∗254·5. $\vdash :. P, Q \epsilon \Omega . \supset :$

$\text{Rl}`P \cap \text{Nr}`Q = \Lambda . \equiv . \exists ! \text{Rl}`Q \cap \text{Nr}`P . \sim (P \text{ smor } Q) . \equiv . P \text{ less } Q$

Dem.

$\vdash . *254·46 . \quad \supset \vdash : \text{Hp} . \text{Rl}`P \cap \text{Nr}`Q = \Lambda . \supset . \sim (Q \text{ less } P) \quad (1)$

$\vdash . *61·34 . *152·11 . \supset \vdash : P \text{ smor } Q . \supset . P \epsilon \text{Rl}`P \cap \text{Nr}`Q \quad (2)$

$\vdash . (2) . \text{Transp} . \quad \supset \vdash : \text{Rl}`P \cap \text{Nr}`Q = \Lambda . \supset . \sim (P \text{ smor } Q) \quad (3)$

$\vdash . (1) . (3) . *254·4 . \supset \vdash : \text{Hp} . \text{Rl}`P \cap \text{Nr}`Q = \Lambda . \supset . P \text{ less } Q \quad (4)$

$\vdash . *254·46 . \quad \supset \vdash : P \text{ less } Q . \supset . \text{Rl}`P \cap \text{Nr}`Q = \Lambda \quad (5)$

$\vdash . (4) . (5) . \quad \supset \vdash :. \text{Hp} . \supset : \text{Rl}`P \cap \text{Nr}`Q = \Lambda . \equiv . P \text{ less } Q .$

$[*254·1] \quad \equiv . \exists ! \text{Rl}`Q \cap \text{Nr}`P . \sim (P \text{ smor } Q) :. \supset \vdash . \text{Prop}$

∗254·51. $\vdash : P \text{ less } Q . \equiv . P, Q \epsilon \Omega . \text{Rl}`P \cap \text{Nr}`Q = \Lambda \quad [*254·5·1]$

∗254·52. $\vdash : P \epsilon \Omega . \alpha \subset C`P . \exists ! C`P \cap p`\overleftarrow{P}``\alpha . \supset . P \upharpoonright \alpha \text{ less } P$

Dem.

$\vdash . *250·141 . \supset \vdash : \text{Hp} . \supset . P \upharpoonright \alpha \epsilon \Omega \quad (1)$

$\vdash . *250·653 . \supset \vdash : \text{Hp} . \supset . \sim (P \upharpoonright \alpha \text{ smor } P) \quad (2)$

$\vdash . (1) . (2) . *254·101 . \supset \vdash . \text{Prop}$

***254·53.** $\vdash : P, Q \in \Omega \,.\, Q \Subset P \,.\, \exists ! C\text{‘}P \cap p\text{‘}\overleftarrow{P}\text{“}C\text{‘}Q \,.\, \supset \,.\, Q \text{ less } P$

Dem.

$\vdash \,.\, *250{\cdot}652 \,.\, \supset \vdash : \text{Hp} \,.\, \supset \,.\, \sim(Q \text{ smor } P)$ (1)

$\vdash \,.\, (1) \,.\, *254{\cdot}101 \,.\, \supset \vdash \,.\, \text{Prop}$

***254·54.** $\vdash : P, Q \in \Omega \,.\, R \text{ smor } Q \,.\, R \Subset P \,.\, \exists ! C\text{‘}P \cap p\text{‘}\overleftarrow{P}\text{“}C\text{‘}R \,.\, \supset \,.\, Q \text{ less } P$

[*254·53·13]

***254·55.** $\vdash :. Q \text{ less } P \,.\, \equiv : P, Q \in \Omega : (\exists R) \,.\, R \text{ smor } Q \,.\, R \Subset P \,.\, \exists ! C\text{‘}P \cap p\text{‘}\overleftarrow{P}\text{“}C\text{‘}R$

Dem.

$\vdash \,.\, *254{\cdot}41 \,.\, \supset \vdash :. Q \text{ less } P \,.\, \supset : P, Q \in \Omega : (\exists R) \,.\, R \text{ smor } Q \,.\, R \in \text{D}\text{‘}R_s :$

$[*213{\cdot}18] \supset : P, Q \in \Omega : (\exists R) \,.\, R \text{ smor } Q \,.\, R \Subset P \,.\, \exists ! C\text{‘}P \cap p\text{‘}\overleftarrow{P}\text{“}C\text{‘}R$ (1)

$\vdash \,.\, (1) \,.\, *254{\cdot}54 \,.\, \supset \vdash \,.\, \text{Prop}$

$*255$. GREATER AND LESS AMONG ORDINAL NUMBERS.

Summary of $*255$.

If P and Q are well-ordered series, we say that $\mathrm{Nr}'P$ is less than $\mathrm{Nr}'Q$ if P is less than Q. Thus if μ and ν are ordinal numbers, we say that μ is less than ν if there are well-ordered series P, Q, such that $\mu = \mathrm{Nr}'P$ and $\nu = \mathrm{Nr}'Q$ and P is less than Q. In order to exclude the case where, in the type concerned, we have $\mathrm{Nr}'P = \Lambda$ or $\mathrm{Nr}'Q = \Lambda$, we assume $\mu = \mathrm{N_0r}'P$ and $\nu = \mathrm{N_0r}'Q$. Thus we put

$$\mu \lessdot \nu \,.\equiv.\, (\exists P, Q) \,.\, \mu = \mathrm{N_0r}'P \,.\, \nu = \mathrm{N_0r}'Q \,.\, P \;\mathrm{less}\; Q,$$

i.e. we put

$$\lessdot = \mathrm{N_0r} ; \mathrm{less} \quad \mathrm{Df.}$$

In order to be able to speak of $\mathrm{Nr}'P$ (where the type of "Nr" is left ambiguous) as greater or less than $\mathrm{Nr}'Q$, we put

$$\mu \lessdot \mathrm{Nr}'P \,.=.\, \mu \lessdot \mathrm{N_0r}'P \quad \mathrm{Df},$$

$$\mathrm{Nr}'P \lessdot \mu \,.=.\, \mathrm{N_0r}'P \lessdot \mu \quad \mathrm{Df.}$$

The treatment of types proceeds, mutatis mutandis, as in $*117$, to which, together with the prefatory statement in Vol. II, the reader is referred for explanations.

In virtue of $*254{\cdot}46$ and $*117{\cdot}1$, there is a close analogy between cardinal and ordinal inequality. That is to say, most of the properties of cardinal inequality have exact analogues for ordinal inequality, and these analogues have analogous proofs. (In the present number, when a proposition is analogous to the proposition with the same decimal part in $*117$, and has an analogous proof, we shall omit the proof.) But ordinal inequality has a good many properties which have no analogues for cardinal inequality. The chief of these, upon which most of the rest depend, is

$$*255{\cdot}112.\ \vdash :.\, \mu, \nu \in \mathrm{N_0O} \,.\supset:\, \mu \lessdot \nu \,.\vee.\, \mu = \mathrm{smor}``\nu \,.\vee.\, \nu \lessdot \mu$$

where "$\mathrm{N_0O}$" stands for "homogeneous ordinals," *i.e.* $\mathrm{NO} \cap \mathrm{N_0R}$. We have also, what is often important,

$$*255{\cdot}17.\ \vdash : \mathrm{Nr}'P \gtrdot \mathrm{Nr}'Q \,.\equiv.\, Q \;\mathrm{less}\; P \,.\equiv.\, P, Q \in \Omega \,.\, Q \in \text{ᗡ}'P_{\mathrm{sm}} \,.$$

$$\equiv.\, P, Q \in \Omega \,.\, \exists ! \,\mathrm{D}'P_s \cap \mathrm{Nr}'Q$$

so that

***255·171.** $\vdash :. P \epsilon \Omega . \supset : \mu \lessdot \text{Nr}`P . \equiv . \mu \epsilon \text{Nr}``\text{D}`P_s - \iota`\Lambda$

and more generally,

***255·172.** $\vdash :. P \epsilon \Omega . \supset :$

$$\mu \lessdot \text{Nr}`P . \equiv . (\exists \alpha) . \alpha \subset C`P . \exists ! C`P \cap p`\overleftarrow{P}``\alpha . \mu = \text{Nr}`P \upharpoonright \alpha . \exists ! \mu$$

As in cardinals, μ is greater than ν if (and only if) μ is the sum of ν and an ordinal other than zero, including $\dot{1}$ except when $\nu = 0_r$ (*255·33). But it is necessary to the truth of this proposition that the addendum should come after ν, not before it; *i.e.* $\nu \dotplus \varpi \gtrdot \nu$ unless $\varpi = 0_r$ (*255·32·321), but $\varpi \dotplus \nu$ is often equal to ν.

If α, β, γ are ordinals, and $\alpha \gtrdot \beta$, we shall have

$$\gamma \dotplus \alpha \gtrdot \gamma \dotplus \beta \quad (*255·561),$$

$$\alpha \dot{\times} \beta \gtrdot \beta \text{ if } \alpha \neq 0_r . \beta \neq 0_r \quad (*255·571),$$

$$\alpha \dot{\times} \gamma \gtrdot \beta \dot{\times} \gamma \text{ if } \gamma \neq 0_r \quad (*255·58),$$

$$\gamma \dot{\times} \beta \gtrdot \gamma \text{ if } \gamma \text{ is of the form } \delta \dotplus \dot{1} \quad (*255·573),$$

$$\gamma \dot{\times} \alpha \gtrdot \gamma \dot{\times} \beta \text{ if } \gamma \text{ is of the form } \delta \dotplus \dot{1} \quad (*255·582).$$

From the above propositions it follows that if α, β, γ are ordinals,

$$\gamma \dotplus \alpha = \gamma \dotplus \beta . \supset . \alpha = \beta$$

(*255·565, where β may be substituted for smor``β whenever significance permits; cf. note to *120·51), which gives the uniqueness of subtraction from the end (subtraction from the beginning is not unique);

$$\alpha \dot{\times} \gamma = \beta \dot{\times} \gamma . \supset . \alpha = \beta \text{ unless } \gamma = 0_r \quad (*255·59),$$

which gives the uniqueness of division by an end-factor;

$$\gamma \dot{\times} \alpha = \gamma \dot{\times} \beta . \supset . \alpha = \beta \text{ if } \gamma = \delta \dotplus \dot{1} \quad (*255·591),$$

which gives the uniqueness of division by a beginning-factor of the form $\delta \dotplus \dot{1}$.

We do not have generally

$$\alpha, \beta, \gamma \epsilon \text{N}_0\text{O} . \alpha \lessdot \beta . \supset . \alpha \exp_r \gamma \lessdot \beta \exp_r \gamma,$$

because $\alpha \exp_r \gamma$ and $\beta \exp_r \gamma$ are in general not *ordinal* numbers, since series having these numbers are in general not well-ordered. Thus the theory of ordinal inequality has only a restricted application to exponentiation. This subject cannot be adequately dealt with until we have considered finite and infinite series.

If α is an ordinal, $C``\alpha$ is the corresponding cardinal, *i.e.* the cardinal number of terms in a series whose ordinal number is α. Thus the cardinal numbers of classes which can be well-ordered are $C```\text{NO}$, *i.e.*

***255·7.** $\vdash . \text{Nc}``C``\Omega = C```\text{NO}$

It is evident that

***255·71.** $\vdash : P \text{ less } Q . \supset . \text{Nc}'C'P \leqslant \text{Nc}'C'Q$

whence, by *254·4,

***255·73.** $\vdash :. P, Q \in \Omega . \supset :$

$$\text{Nc}'C'P < \text{Nc}'C'Q . \vee . \text{Nc}'C'P = \text{Nc}'C'Q . \vee . \text{Nc}'C'P > \text{Nc}'C'Q$$

whence also

***255·74.** $\vdash :. \alpha, \beta \in C``\text{NO} - \iota'\Lambda . \supset : \alpha \leqslant \beta . \vee . \alpha > \beta$

Thus if two classes can both be well-ordered, they either have the same cardinal, or the cardinal of one is less than that of the other.

We have

***255·75.** $\vdash : P . Q \in \Omega . \text{Nc}'C'P < \text{Nc}'C'Q . \supset . P \text{ less } Q$

or, what comes to the same thing,

***255·76.** $\vdash : \alpha, \beta \in \text{NO} . C``\alpha < C``\beta . \supset . \alpha \lessdot \beta$

The converse of this proposition only holds for finite ordinals. If α is an infinite ordinal, $\alpha \dot{+} \dot{1}$ always exists and is greater than α, but $C``\alpha = C``(\alpha \dot{+} \dot{1})$. (The existence of $\alpha \dot{+} \dot{1}$ is deduced from that of α by taking a member of α, and removing its first term to the end. The result is a series whose number is $\alpha \dot{+} \dot{1}$, in virtue of *253·503·54.)

***255·01.** $\lessdot = \text{N}_0\text{r}'\text{less}$ Df

***255·02.** $\gtrdot = \text{Cnv}'\lessdot$ Df

***255·03.** $\text{N}_0\text{O} = \text{NO} \cap \text{N}_0\text{R}$ Df

Thus "N_0O" means "homogeneous ordinals." In virtue of *155·34·22, this is the same as "ordinals other than Λ." It is not, however, strictly correct to put $\text{N}_0\text{O} = \text{NO} - \iota'\Lambda$, because if the "NO" on the right is derived from an ascending Nr, it will not contain all the ordinals in the type to which it takes us, but only those which are not too big to be derived from the lower type from which "Nr" starts. Thus in this case N_0O will be a larger class than $\text{NO} - \iota'\Lambda$. If, however, the "Nr" from which the "NO" on the right is derived is homogeneous or descending, we shall have

$$\text{N}_0\text{O} = \text{NO} - \iota'\Lambda.$$

***255·04.** $\leqslant = \lessdot \cup \text{smor}_\epsilon \upharpoonright \text{N}_0\text{O}$ Df

This definition leads to the usual meaning of "less than or equal to." We want the relation "less than or equal to" to hold only between numbers of the sort in question (cardinal or ordinal), and we want "equal to" to hold between two numbers which are merely different typical determinations of a given number, provided neither of these typical determinations is Λ. That is, if μ is an ordinal which is not Λ, $\text{smor}``\mu$ is to be reckoned equal to $\mu$ in every type in which it is not $\Lambda$. Thus if $\nu = \text{smor}``\mu$, *i.e.* if $\nu = \text{smor}_\epsilon'\mu$, we shall reckon ν equal to μ if both are ordinals and neither is Λ, *i.e.* in virtue of $*155{\cdot}34{\cdot}22$, if $\mu, \nu \,\epsilon\, \mathrm{N_0O}$. This leads to the above definition.

$*255{\cdot}05$. $\geqslant = \mathrm{Cnv}{}^{\prime}\!\leqslant$ Df

$*255{\cdot}06$. $\mu < \mathrm{Nr}{}^{\prime}P \,.=.\, \mu < \mathrm{N_0r}{}^{\prime}P$ Df

On this definition, compare the remarks on $*117{\cdot}02$.

$*255{\cdot}07$. $\mathrm{Nr}{}^{\prime}P < \mu \,.=.\, \mathrm{N_0r}{}^{\prime}P < \mu$ Df

The following propositions (down to $*255{\cdot}108$) merely re-state the above definitions.

$*255{\cdot}1$. $\vdash : \mu < \nu \,.\equiv.\, (\exists P, Q) \,.\, \mu = \mathrm{N_0r}{}^{\prime}P \,.\, \nu = \mathrm{N_0r}{}^{\prime}Q \,.\, P \text{ less } Q$

$*255{\cdot}101$. $\vdash : \mu < \mathrm{Nr}{}^{\prime}Q \,.\equiv.\, \mu < \mathrm{N_0r}{}^{\prime}Q$

$*255{\cdot}102$. $\vdash : \mathrm{Nr}{}^{\prime}P < \nu \,.\equiv.\, \mathrm{N_0r}{}^{\prime}P < \nu$

$*255{\cdot}103$. $\vdash : \mu > \nu \,.\equiv.\, \nu < \mu$

$*255{\cdot}104$. $\vdash :. \mu \leqslant \nu \,.\equiv: \mu < \nu \,.\vee.\, \mu, \nu \,\epsilon\, \mathrm{N_0O} \,.\, \mu = \mathrm{smor}{}^{\prime\prime}\nu$

$*255{\cdot}105$. $\vdash :. \mu \geqslant \nu \,.\equiv: \nu \leqslant \mu :\equiv: \nu < \mu \,.\vee.\, \mu, \nu \,\epsilon\, \mathrm{N_0O} \,.\, \mu = \mathrm{smor}{}^{\prime\prime}\nu$
[$*255{\cdot}104 \,.\, (*255{\cdot}05) \,.\, *155{\cdot}44$]

$*255{\cdot}106$. $\vdash : \mathrm{Nr}{}^{\prime}P < \mathrm{Nr}{}^{\prime}Q \,.\equiv.\, \mathrm{N_0r}{}^{\prime}P < \mathrm{N_0r}{}^{\prime}Q$ [$*255{\cdot}101{\cdot}102$]

$*255{\cdot}107$. $\vdash : \mathrm{Nr}{}^{\prime}P \leqslant \mathrm{Nr}{}^{\prime}Q \,.\equiv.\, \mathrm{N_0r}{}^{\prime}P \leqslant \mathrm{N_0r}{}^{\prime}Q$

$*255{\cdot}108$. $\vdash :. \mathrm{Nr}{}^{\prime}P \leqslant \mathrm{Nr}{}^{\prime}Q \,.\equiv: \mathrm{N_0r}{}^{\prime}P < \mathrm{N_0r}{}^{\prime}Q \,.\vee.\, \mathrm{Nr}{}^{\prime}P = \mathrm{Nr}{}^{\prime}Q \,.\, P \,\epsilon\, \Omega$
[$*255{\cdot}107{\cdot}104 \,.\, *155{\cdot}16 \,.\, *152{\cdot}53$]

$*255{\cdot}11$. $\vdash : \mu < \nu \,.\equiv.\, (\exists P, Q) \,.\, P, Q \,\epsilon\, \Omega \,.\, \mu = \mathrm{N_0r}{}^{\prime}P \,.\, \nu = \mathrm{N_0r}{}^{\prime}Q \,.$
$\exists \,!\, \mathrm{Rl}{}^{\prime}Q \cap \mathrm{Nr}{}^{\prime}P \,.\, \sim\exists \,!\, \mathrm{Rl}{}^{\prime}P \cap \mathrm{Nr}{}^{\prime}Q$ [$*255{\cdot}1 \,.\, *254{\cdot}46$]

$*255{\cdot}111$. $\vdash : \mu > \nu \,.\equiv.\, (\exists P, Q) \,.\, P, Q \,\epsilon\, \Omega \,.\, \mu = \mathrm{N_0r}{}^{\prime}P \,.\, \nu = \mathrm{N_0r}{}^{\prime}Q \,.$
$\exists \,!\, \mathrm{Rl}{}^{\prime}P \cap \mathrm{Nr}{}^{\prime}Q \,.\, \sim\exists \,!\, \mathrm{Rl}{}^{\prime}Q \cap \mathrm{Nr}{}^{\prime}P$ [$*255{\cdot}11{\cdot}103$]

This proposition is exactly analogous to $*117{\cdot}1$, except for the addition $P, Q \,\epsilon\, \Omega$. Hence except where this addition is relevant, the analogues of the propositions of $*117$ follow by analogous proofs. Such analogues will be given without proof in what follows, and will have the same decimal part as the corresponding propositions in $*117$. Where proofs are given, there are no analogues in $*117$, or else the method of proof is not analogous.

$*255{\cdot}112$. $\vdash :. \mu, \nu \,\epsilon\, \mathrm{N_0O} \,.\supset: \mu < \nu \,.\vee.\, \mu = \mathrm{smor}{}^{\prime\prime}\nu \,.\vee.\, \nu < \mu$

Dem.

$\vdash \,.\, *255{\cdot}1 \,.\, *254{\cdot}4 \,.\supset\vdash :. \mathrm{Hp} \,.\supset:$

$\mu < \nu \,.\vee.\, \nu < \mu \,.\vee.\, (\exists P, Q) \,.\, P, Q \,\epsilon\, \Omega \,.\, \mu = \mathrm{N_0r}{}^{\prime}P \,.\, \nu = \mathrm{N_0r}{}^{\prime}Q \,.\, P \text{ smor } Q :$

[$*155{\cdot}4 \,.\, *152{\cdot}321$]

$\supset: \mu < \nu \,.\vee.\, \nu < \mu \,.\vee.\, (\exists P, Q) \,.\, \mu = \mathrm{N_0r}{}^{\prime}P \,.\, \mathrm{Nr}{}^{\prime}P = \mathrm{Nr}{}^{\prime}Q \,.\, \mathrm{Nr}{}^{\prime}Q = \mathrm{smor}{}^{\prime\prime}\nu :$

[$*155{\cdot}16$]

$\supset: \mu < \nu \,.\vee.\, \nu < \mu \,.\vee.\, (\exists P, Q) \,.\, \mu = \mathrm{N_0r}{}^{\prime}P \,.\, \mathrm{N_0r}{}^{\prime}P = \mathrm{Nr}{}^{\prime}Q \,.\, \mathrm{Nr}{}^{\prime}Q = \mathrm{smor}{}^{\prime\prime}\nu :$

[$*13{\cdot}17$] $\supset: \mu < \nu \,.\vee.\, \nu < \mu \,.\vee.\, \mu = \mathrm{smor}{}^{\prime\prime}\nu :. \supset\vdash \,.\, \mathrm{Prop}$

***255·113.** $\vdash :. P, Q \in \Omega . \supset : \text{Nr}‘P \lessdot \text{Nr}‘Q . \vee . \text{Nr}‘P = \text{Nr}‘Q . \vee . \text{Nr}‘Q \lessdot \text{Nr}‘P$

Dem.

$\vdash . *255·112·106 . \supset \vdash :. \text{Hp} . \supset :$

$\text{Nr}‘P \lessdot \text{Nr}‘Q . \vee . \text{N}_0\text{r}‘P = \text{smor}“\text{N}_0\text{r}‘Q . \vee . \text{Nr}‘Q \lessdot \text{Nr}‘P :$

[*155·4·16] $\supset : \text{Nr}‘P \lessdot \text{Nr}‘Q . \vee . \text{Nr}‘P = \text{Nr}‘Q . \vee . \text{Nr}‘Q \lessdot \text{Nr}‘P :. \supset \vdash . \text{Prop}$

***255·114.** $\vdash :. \mu, \nu \in \text{N}_0\text{O} . \supset : \mu \leqslant \nu . \vee . \nu \lessdot \mu : \mu \geqslant \nu . \vee . \nu \gtrdot \mu$ [*255·112·104·105·103]

***255·115.** $\vdash :. P, Q \in \Omega . \supset : \text{Nr}‘P \leqslant \text{Nr}‘Q . \vee . \text{Nr}‘Q \lessdot \text{Nr}‘P :$
$\text{Nr}‘P \geqslant \text{Nr}‘Q . \vee . \text{Nr}‘Q \gtrdot \text{Nr}‘P$ [*255·113·108]

***255·12.** $\vdash :. \mu \gtrdot \nu . \equiv : \mu, \nu \in \text{N}_0\text{O} :$
$P \in \mu . Q \in \nu . \supset_{P,Q} . \exists ! \text{Rl}‘P \cap \text{Nr}‘Q . \sim \exists ! \text{Rl}‘Q \cap \text{Nr}‘P$

***255·121.** $\vdash :. \mu \gtrdot \nu . \equiv : \mu, \nu \in \text{N}_0\text{O} :$
$P \in \mu . \supset_P . (\exists Q) . Q \in \nu . \exists ! \text{Rl}‘P \cap \text{Nr}‘Q . \sim \exists ! \text{Rl}‘Q \cap \text{Nr}‘P$

***255·13.** $\vdash : \text{Nr}‘P \gtrdot \text{Nr}‘Q . \equiv . P, Q \in \Omega . \exists ! \text{Rl}‘P \cap \text{Nr}‘Q . \sim \exists ! \text{Rl}‘Q \cap \text{Nr}‘P$

***255·131.** $\vdash : \text{Nr}‘P \gtrdot \text{Nr}‘Q . \equiv . \text{Nr}‘P \geqslant \text{Nr}‘Q . \text{Nr}‘P \neq \text{Nr}‘Q$
[*255·13 . *254·45]

***255·14.** $\vdash : \mu \gtrdot \nu . \equiv . (\exists P, Q) . P, Q \in \Omega . \mu = \text{N}_0\text{r}‘P . \nu = \text{N}_0\text{r}‘Q . \text{Nr}‘P \gtrdot \text{Nr}‘Q$

***255·141.** $\vdash : \mu \gtrdot \nu . \equiv . \mu \geqslant \nu . \mu \neq \text{smor}“\nu$ [*255·131·14]

***255·15.** $\vdash : \mu \gtrdot \nu . \equiv . \mu, \nu \in \text{N}_0\text{O} . \exists ! s‘\text{Rl}“\mu \cap \text{smor}“\nu . \sim \exists ! s‘\text{Rl}“\nu \cap \text{smor}“\mu$

***255·16.** $\vdash :. \mu, \nu \in \text{N}_0\text{O} . \supset :$
$\mu \gtrdot \nu . \equiv . \text{smor}“\mu \gtrdot \nu . \equiv . \mu \gtrdot \text{smor}“\nu . \equiv . \text{smor}“\mu \gtrdot \text{smor}“\nu$

***255·17.** $\vdash : \text{Nr}‘P \gtrdot \text{Nr}‘Q . \equiv . Q \text{ less } P . \equiv . P, Q \in \Omega . Q \in \text{d}‘P_{\text{sm}} .$
$\equiv . P, Q \in \Omega . \exists ! \text{D}‘P_s \cap \text{Nr}‘Q$

Dem.

$\vdash . *255·13 . *254·46 . \supset \vdash : \text{Nr}‘P \gtrdot \text{Nr}‘Q . \equiv . Q \text{ less } P .$ (1)

[*254·41] $\equiv . P, Q \in \Omega . Q \in \text{d}‘P_{\text{sm}} .$ (2)

[*254·12] $\equiv . P, Q \in \Omega . \exists ! \text{D}‘P_s \cap \text{Nr}‘Q$ (3)

$\vdash . (1) . (2) . (3) . \supset \vdash . \text{Prop}$

***255·171.** $\vdash :. P \in \Omega . \supset : \mu \lessdot \text{Nr}‘P . \equiv . \mu \in \text{Nr}“\text{D}‘P_s - \iota‘\Lambda$

Dem.

$\vdash . *255·14 . \supset \vdash :. \text{Hp} . \supset : \mu \lessdot \text{Nr}‘P . \equiv . (\exists Q) . \mu = \text{N}_0\text{r}‘Q . \text{Nr}‘Q \lessdot \text{Nr}‘P .$

[*255·17] $\equiv . (\exists Q) . \mu = \text{N}_0\text{r}‘Q . Q \in \Omega . \exists ! \text{D}‘P_s \cap \text{Nr}‘Q .$

[*152·1] $\equiv . (\exists Q, R) . \mu = \text{N}_0\text{r}‘Q . Q \in \Omega . Q \text{ smor } R . R \in \text{D}‘P_s .$

[*152·35.*155·16] $\equiv . (\exists R) . \mu = \text{Nr}‘R . R \in \Omega . R \in \text{D}‘P_s . \exists ! \mu .$

[*253·18.*37·6] $\equiv . \mu \in \text{Nr}“\text{D}‘P_s - \iota‘\Lambda :. \supset \vdash . \text{Prop}$

***255·172.** $\vdash :. P \in \Omega . \supset :$

$$\mu < \mathrm{Nr}`P . \equiv . (\exists \alpha) . \alpha \subset C`P . \exists ! C`P \cap p`\overleftarrow{P}``\alpha . \mu = \mathrm{Nr}`P \upharpoonright \alpha . \exists ! \mu$$

Dem.

$\vdash . *211{\cdot}703 . *213{\cdot}141 . \supset$

$\vdash : Q \in \mathrm{D}`P_s . \supset . (\exists \alpha) . \alpha \subset C`P . \exists ! C`P \cap p`\overleftarrow{P}``\alpha . Q = P \upharpoonright \alpha \quad (1)$

$\vdash . (1) . *255{\cdot}171 . \supset \vdash : \mathrm{Hp} . \mu < \mathrm{Nr}`P . \supset .$

$(\exists \alpha) . \alpha \subset C`P . \exists ! C`P \cap p`\overleftarrow{P}``\alpha . \mu = \mathrm{Nr}`P \upharpoonright \alpha . \exists ! \mu \quad (2)$

$\vdash . *250{\cdot}653 . *254{\cdot}47 . \supset$

$\vdash : \mathrm{Hp} . \alpha \subset C`P . \exists ! C`P \cap p`\overleftarrow{P}``\alpha . \supset . P \upharpoonright \alpha \text{ less } P .$

$[*255{\cdot}17] \qquad \supset . \mathrm{Nr}`P \upharpoonright \alpha < \mathrm{Nr}`P \quad (3)$

$\vdash . (2) . (3) . \supset \vdash . \mathrm{Prop}$

***255·173.** $\vdash :. P \in \Omega . \supset :$

$$\mathrm{Nr}`Q < \mathrm{Nr}`P . \equiv . (\exists \alpha) . \alpha \subset C`P . \exists ! C`P \cap p`\overleftarrow{P}``\alpha . Q \,\mathrm{smor}\, (P \upharpoonright \alpha)$$

Dem.

$\vdash . *255{\cdot}172{\cdot}102 . *155{\cdot}22 . \supset$

$\vdash :. \mathrm{Hp} . \supset : \mathrm{Nr}`Q < \mathrm{Nr}`P . \equiv . (\exists \alpha) . \alpha \subset C`P . \exists ! C`P \cap p`\overleftarrow{P}``\alpha . \mathrm{N_0r}`Q = \mathrm{Nr}`P \upharpoonright \alpha .$

$[*152{\cdot}35 . *155{\cdot}22] \equiv . (\exists \alpha) . \alpha \subset C`P . \exists ! C`P \cap p`\overleftarrow{P}``\alpha . Q \,\mathrm{smor}\, (P \upharpoonright \alpha) : \supset \vdash . \mathrm{Prop}$

***255·174.** $\vdash : \mathrm{Nr}`Q < \mathrm{Nr}`P . \equiv . P \in \Omega . \mathrm{Nr}`Q \in \mathrm{Nr}``\mathrm{D}`P_s$

Dem.

$\vdash . *255{\cdot}171{\cdot}102{\cdot}13 . \supset$

$\vdash :. \mathrm{Nr}`Q < \mathrm{Nr}`P . \equiv : P \in \Omega . \mathrm{N_0r}`Q \in \mathrm{Nr}``\mathrm{D}`P_s - \iota`\Lambda :$

$[*37{\cdot}6 . *155{\cdot}22] \qquad \equiv : P \in \Omega : (\exists R) . R \in \mathrm{D}`P_s . \mathrm{N_0r}`Q = \mathrm{Nr}`R :$

$[*155{\cdot}16] \qquad \equiv : P \in \Omega : (\exists R) . R \in \mathrm{D}`P_s . \mathrm{Nr}`Q = \mathrm{Nr}`R :$

$[*37{\cdot}6] \qquad \equiv : P \in \Omega . \mathrm{Nr}`Q \in \mathrm{Nr}``\mathrm{D}`P_s :. \supset \vdash . \mathrm{Prop}$

***255·175.** $\vdash : \mathrm{Nr}`Q \leqslant \mathrm{Nr}`P . \equiv . P \in \Omega . \mathrm{Nr}`Q \in \mathrm{Nr}``(\mathrm{D}`P_s \cup \iota`P)$ [*255·174·108]

***255·176.** $\vdash :. \dot{\exists} ! P . \supset : \mathrm{Nr}`Q \leqslant \mathrm{Nr}`P . \equiv . P \in \Omega . \mathrm{Nr}`Q \in \mathrm{Nr}`C`P_s$

[*213·158 . *255·175]

***255·21.** $\vdash : \mathrm{Nr}`P < \mathrm{Nr}`Q . \equiv . P, Q \in \Omega . \mathrm{Rl}`P \cap \mathrm{Nr}`Q = \Lambda$ [*254·51 . *255·17]

This proposition has no analogue in cardinals, because it depends upon *254·4. In cardinals, if $\mathrm{Cl}`\alpha \cap \mathrm{Nc}`\beta = \Lambda$, it does not follow that $\exists ! \mathrm{Cl}`\beta \cap \mathrm{Nc}`\alpha$, so that $\mathrm{Nc}`\alpha$ may be neither less than, nor equal to, nor greater than $\mathrm{Nc}`\beta$.

***255·211.** $\vdash :. P, Q \in \Omega . \supset : \exists ! \mathrm{Rl}`P \cap \mathrm{Nr}`Q . \exists ! \mathrm{Rl}`Q \cap \mathrm{Nr}`P . \equiv . \mathrm{Nr}`P = \mathrm{Nr}`Q$

[*254·45]

This proposition is the ordinal analogue of the Schröder-Bernstein theorem. If P and Q are series which may be not well-ordered, the proposition fails. Thus *e.g.* the series of rationals is like the series of proper fractions, which is a part of the series of rationals > 0 and $\leqslant 1$, and this latter series is part of the series of rationals, but is not similar to the series of rationals, since it has a last term, which the series of rationals has not.

***255·22.** $\vdash : P, Q \in \Omega . \exists ! \, \text{Rl}‘P \cap \text{Nr}‘Q . \equiv . \text{Nr}‘P \geqslant \text{Nr}‘Q$

***255·221.** $\vdash :. \text{Nr}‘P \geqslant \text{Nr}‘Q . \equiv : P, Q \in \Omega : (\exists R) . R \Subset P . R \,\text{smor}\, Q$

***255·222.** $\vdash : Q \Subset P . P, Q \in \Omega . \supset . \text{Nr}‘P \geqslant \text{Nr}‘Q$

***255·23.** $\vdash : \text{Nr}‘P \geqslant \text{Nr}‘Q . \text{Nr}‘Q \geqslant \text{Nr}‘P . \equiv . P, Q \in \Omega . \text{Nr}‘P = \text{Nr}‘Q$

***255·24.** $\vdash : \mu \geqslant \nu . \equiv . (\exists P, Q) . \mu = \text{N}_0\text{r}‘P . \nu = \text{N}_0\text{r}‘Q . \text{Nr}‘P \geqslant \text{Nr}‘Q$

***255·241.** $\vdash : \mu \geqslant \nu . \equiv . (\exists P, Q) . \mu = \text{N}_0\text{r}‘P . \nu = \text{N}_0\text{r}‘Q . P, Q \in \Omega . \exists ! \, \text{Rl}‘P \cap \text{Nr}‘Q$

***255·242.** $\vdash :. \mu, \nu \in \text{NO} . \supset : \mu \geqslant \nu . \equiv . (\exists P, Q) . P \in \mu . Q \in \nu . \exists ! \, \text{Rl}‘P \cap \text{Nr}‘Q$

***255·243.** $\vdash :. \mu \geqslant \nu . \equiv :$

$$(\exists P, Q) : P, Q \in \Omega . \mu = \text{N}_0\text{r}‘P . \nu = \text{N}_0\text{r}‘Q : (\exists R) . R \Subset P . R \,\text{smor}\, Q$$

***255·244.** $\vdash :. \mu, \nu \in \text{N}_0\text{O} . \supset :$

$$\mu \geqslant \nu . \equiv . \text{smor}“\mu \geqslant \nu . \equiv . \mu \geqslant \text{smor}“\nu . \equiv . \text{smor}“\mu \geqslant \text{smor}“\nu$$

***255·25.** $\vdash : \mu \geqslant \nu . \nu \geqslant \mu . \equiv . \mu, \nu \in \text{N}_0\text{O} . \text{smor}“\mu = \text{smor}“\nu$

***255·27.** $\vdash : \text{Nr}‘P < \text{Nr}‘Q . \equiv . \text{Nr}‘P \leqslant \text{Nr}‘Q . \text{Nr}‘P \neq \text{Nr}‘Q$

***255·28.** $\vdash : \text{Nr}‘P > \text{Nr}‘Q . \equiv . \text{Nr}‘P \geqslant \text{Nr}‘Q . \sim (\text{Nr}‘Q \geqslant \text{Nr}‘P) .$

$$\equiv . P, Q \in \Omega . \sim (\text{Nr}‘Q \geqslant \text{Nr}‘P) \quad [*255 \cdot 13 \cdot 22 \cdot 21]$$

***255·281.** $\vdash : \mu > \nu . \equiv . \mu \geqslant \nu . \sim (\nu \geqslant \mu) . \equiv . \mu, \nu \in \text{N}_0\text{O} . \sim (\nu \geqslant \mu)$ $[*255 \cdot 114]$

***255·29.** $\vdash : \text{Nr}‘P < \text{Nr}‘Q . \equiv . \text{Nr}‘P \leqslant \text{Nr}‘Q . \sim (\text{Nr}‘Q \leqslant \text{Nr}‘P) .$

$$\equiv . P, Q \in \Omega . \sim (\text{Nr}‘Q \leqslant \text{Nr}‘P) \quad [*255 \cdot 115]$$

***255·291.** $\vdash : \mu < \nu . \equiv . \mu \leqslant \nu . \sim (\nu \leqslant \mu) . \equiv . \mu, \nu \in \text{N}_0\text{O} . \sim (\nu \leqslant \mu)$ $[*255 \cdot 114]$

In the following proposition, we employ an abbreviation which is justified by its convenience, namely we put

$$(\exists \varpi) . \varpi \in \text{NO} \cup \iota‘\dot{1} . \text{Nr}‘P = \text{Nr}‘Q \dotplus \varpi$$

instead of

$$(\exists \varpi) . \varpi \in \text{NO} . \text{Nr}‘P = \text{Nr}‘Q \dotplus \varpi . \vee . \text{Nr}‘P = \text{Nr}‘Q \dotplus \dot{1} .$$

In virtue of $*51 \cdot 239$, these two expressions would be equivalent if $\dot{1}$ had any independent meaning; but as $\dot{1}$ is only significant as an addendum, $*51 \cdot 239$ cannot be applied. We will, however, adopt the following definitions:

***255·298.** $(\exists \varpi) . \varpi \in \kappa \cup \iota‘\dot{1} . f(\mu \dotplus \varpi) . = : (\exists \varpi) . \varpi \in \kappa . f(\mu \dotplus \varpi) . \vee . f(\mu \dotplus \dot{1})$ Df

***255·299.** $\varpi \in \kappa \cup \iota‘\dot{1} . \supset_\varpi . f(\mu \dotplus \varpi) . = : \varpi \in \kappa . \supset_\varpi . f(\mu \dotplus \varpi) : f(\mu \dotplus \dot{1})$ Df

These definitions enable us to state many propositions, in which $\dot{1}$ occurs, as though $\dot{1}$ were an ordinal number.

***255·3.** $\vdash :. \mathrm{Nr}`P \geqslant \mathrm{Nr}`Q . \equiv : P, Q \in \Omega : (\exists \varpi) . \varpi \in \mathrm{NO} \cup \iota`\dot{1} . \mathrm{Nr}`P = \mathrm{Nr}`Q \dot{+} \varpi$

Dem.

$\vdash . *255·175 . *253·471 . \supset$

$\vdash :. \mathrm{Nr}`P \geqslant \mathrm{Nr}`Q . \equiv : P \in \Omega : (\exists \varpi) . \mathrm{Nr}`Q \dot{+} \varpi = \mathrm{Nr}`P . \mathbf{v} . \mathrm{Nr}`Q \dot{+} \dot{1} = \mathrm{Nr}`P :$

$[*251·132·26] \equiv : P \in \Omega : (\exists \varpi) . \mathrm{Nr}`Q, \varpi \in \mathrm{NO} . \mathrm{Nr}`Q \dot{+} \varpi = \mathrm{Nr}`P . \mathbf{v} .$

$\mathrm{Nr}`Q \in \mathrm{NO} . \mathrm{Nr}`Q \dot{+} \dot{1} = \mathrm{Nr}`P :$

$[*251·1·111] \quad \equiv : P, Q \in \Omega : (\exists \varpi) . \varpi \in \mathrm{NO} . \mathrm{Nr}`Q \dot{+} \varpi = \mathrm{Nr}`P . \mathbf{v} .$

$\mathrm{Nr}`Q \dot{+} \dot{1} = \mathrm{Nr}`P :$

$[(*255·298)] \quad \equiv : P, Q \in \Omega : (\exists \varpi) . \varpi \in \mathrm{NO} \cup \iota`\dot{1} . \mathrm{Nr}`P = \mathrm{Nr}`Q \dot{+} \varpi :. \supset \vdash . \mathrm{Prop}$

***255·31.** $\vdash :. \mu \geqslant \nu . \equiv : \mu, \nu \in \mathrm{N_0O} : (\exists \varpi) . \varpi \in \mathrm{NO} \cup \iota`\dot{1} . \mu = \nu \dot{+} \varpi$

[*255·3·14]

***255·32.** $\vdash :. \nu, \varpi \in \mathrm{N_0O} . \supset : \nu \dot{+} \varpi > \nu . \equiv . \varpi \neq 0_r$

Dem.

$\vdash . *253·44 . \quad \supset \vdash : \mathrm{Hp} . \varpi \neq 0_r . \supset . \nu \dot{+} \dot{1} \neq \nu \quad (1)$

$\vdash . *255·31 . \quad \supset \vdash : \mathrm{Hp} . \supset . \nu \dot{+} \varpi \geqslant \nu \quad (2)$

$\vdash . (1) . (2) . *255·141 . \supset \vdash : \mathrm{Hp} . \varpi \neq 0_r . \supset . \nu \dot{+} \varpi > \nu \quad (3)$

$\vdash . *255·141 . \quad \supset \vdash : \mathrm{Hp} . \nu \dot{+} \varpi > \nu . \supset . \nu \dot{+} \varpi \neq \mathrm{smor}``\nu .$

$[*180·6] \quad \supset . \varpi \neq 0_r \quad (4)$

$\vdash . (3) . (4) . \supset \vdash . \mathrm{Prop}$

***255·321.** $\vdash :. \nu \in \mathrm{N_0O} . \supset : \nu \neq 0_r . \equiv . \nu \dot{+} \dot{1} > \nu$

Dem.

$\vdash . *253·45 . \quad \supset \vdash : \mathrm{Hp} . \nu \neq 0_r . \supset . \nu \dot{+} \dot{1} \neq \nu \quad (1)$

$\vdash . *255·31 . \quad \supset \vdash : \mathrm{Hp} . \supset . \nu \dot{+} \dot{1} \geqslant \nu \quad (2)$

$\vdash . (1) . (2) . *255·141 . \supset \vdash : \mathrm{Hp} . \nu \neq 0_r . \supset . \nu \dot{+} \dot{1} > \nu \quad (3)$

$\vdash . *255·141 . \quad \supset \vdash : \mathrm{Hp} . \nu \dot{+} \dot{1} > \nu . \supset . \nu \dot{+} \dot{1} \neq \mathrm{smor}``\nu .$

$[*161·2] \quad \supset . \nu \neq 0_r \quad (4)$

$\vdash . (3) . (4) . \supset \vdash . \mathrm{Prop}$

***255·33.** $\vdash :. \mu > \nu . \equiv :$

$\mu, \nu \in \mathrm{N_0O} : (\exists \varpi) . \varpi \in \mathrm{NO} - \iota`0_r . \mu = \nu \dot{+} \varpi . \mathbf{v} . \nu \neq 0_r . \mu = \nu \dot{+} \dot{1}$

Dem.

$\vdash . *255·31 . \supset$

$\vdash :. \mu > \nu . \equiv : \mu, \nu \in \mathrm{N_0O} : (\exists \varpi) . \varpi \in \mathrm{NO} . \mu = \nu \dot{+} \varpi . \mu > \nu . \mathbf{v} . \mu = \nu \dot{+} \dot{1} . \mu > \nu :$

$[*255·32·321]$

$\equiv : \mu, \nu \in \mathrm{N_0O} : (\exists \varpi) . \varpi \in \mathrm{NO} - \iota`0_r . \mu = \nu \dot{+} \varpi . \mathbf{v} . \nu \neq 0_r . \mu = \nu \dot{+} \dot{1} :. \supset \vdash . \mathrm{Prop}$

***255·4.** $\vdash : \mu \geqslant \nu . \nu \geqslant \varpi . \supset . \mu \geqslant \varpi$

***255·41.** $\vdash : \mu \leqslant \nu . \nu \leqslant \varpi . \supset . \mu \leqslant \varpi$

***255·42.** $\vdash . \sim (\mu > \mu) . \sim (\mu < \mu)$

***255·43.** $\vdash : \mu \geqslant \nu . \sim (\mu \geqslant \varpi) . \supset . \sim (\nu \geqslant \varpi)$

***255·431.** $\vdash : \mu \geqslant \nu . \varpi \epsilon \text{N}_0\text{O} . \sim (\mu \geqslant \varpi) . \supset . \varpi > \nu$ [*255·43·114]

***255·44.** $\vdash : \nu \geqslant \varpi . \sim (\mu \geqslant \varpi) . \supset . \sim (\mu \geqslant \nu)$

***255·441.** $\vdash : \nu \geqslant \varpi . \mu \epsilon \text{N}_0\text{O} . \sim (\mu \geqslant \varpi) . \supset . \nu > \mu$ [*255·44·114]

***255·45.** $\vdash : \mu \geqslant \nu . \nu > \varpi . \supset . \mu > \varpi$

***255·46.** $\vdash : \mu > \nu . \nu \geqslant \varpi . \supset . \mu > \varpi$

***255·47.** $\vdash : \mu > \nu . \nu > \varpi . \supset . \mu > \varpi$

***255·471.** $\vdash : \mu < \nu . \nu < \varpi . \supset . \mu < \varpi$

***255·482.** $\vdash : \mu \geqslant \nu . \equiv . \mu, \nu \epsilon \text{N}_0\text{O} . \sim (\nu > \mu)$

***255·483.** $\vdash : \mu \leqslant \nu . \equiv . \mu, \nu \epsilon \text{N}_0\text{O} . \sim (\nu < \mu)$

***255·5.** $\vdash : \mu \epsilon \text{N}_0\text{O} . \equiv . \mu \geqslant 0_r$

Dem.

$\vdash . *255·31 . \supset \vdash :. \mu \geqslant 0_r . \equiv : \mu \epsilon \text{N}_0\text{O} : (\exists \varpi) . \varpi \epsilon \text{NO} \cup \iota`\text{i} . \mu = 0_r \dotplus \varpi :$

[*180·61] $\equiv : \mu \epsilon \text{N}_0\text{O} :. \supset \vdash . \text{Prop}$

***255·51.** $\vdash : \mu \epsilon \text{N}_0\text{O} - \iota`0_r . \equiv . \mu > 0_r$ [*255·141·5 . *153·15]

***255·52.** $\vdash : P \epsilon \Omega - \iota`\dot{\Lambda} . \equiv . \text{Nr}`P \geqslant 2_r$

Dem.

$\vdash . *250·13 . \supset \vdash : P \epsilon \Omega - \iota`\dot{\Lambda} . \supset . \text{E} ! B`P .$

[*93·101] $\supset . (\exists y) . (B`P) Py . B`P \neq y .$

[*56·11.*55·3] $\supset . (\exists y) . (B`P) \downarrow y \epsilon 2_r \cap \text{Rl}`P .$

[*13·195] $\supset . \exists ! 2_r \cap \text{Rl}`P .$

[*255·22] $\supset . \text{Nr}`P \geqslant 2_r$ (1)

$\vdash . *255·22 . \supset \vdash : \text{Nr}`P \geqslant 2_r . \supset . P \epsilon \Omega . \exists ! 2_r \cap \text{Rl}`P .$

[*61·361] $\supset . P \epsilon \Omega - \iota`\dot{\Lambda}$ (2)

$\vdash . (1) . (2) . \supset \vdash . \text{Prop}$

***255·53.** $\vdash : \mu \epsilon \text{N}_0\text{O} - \iota`0_r . \equiv . \mu \geqslant 2_r$ [*255·52]

***255·54.** $\vdash :. 2_r \geqslant \mu . \equiv : \mu = 0_r . \vee . \mu = 2_r$

Dem.

$\vdash . *255·53 . \text{Transp} . *255·281 . \supset \vdash : 2_r > \mu . \equiv . \mu = 0$ (1)

$\vdash . (1) . *255·105 . \supset \vdash . \text{Prop}$

***255·55.** $\vdash : \mu > 2_r . \equiv . \mu \in N_0O - \iota`0_r - \iota`2_r$

Dem.

$\vdash . *255·54 . \text{Transp} . *255·281 . \supset$

$\vdash : \mu > 2_r . \equiv . \mu \in N_0O . \mu \neq 0_r . \mu \neq 2_r : \supset \vdash . \text{Prop}$

***255·56.** $\vdash : R \in \Omega . \text{Nr}`P > \text{Nr}`Q . \supset . \text{Nr}`R \dot{+} \text{Nr}`P > \text{Nr}`R \dot{+} \text{Nr}`Q$

Dem.

$\vdash . *255·3 . \supset \vdash :. \text{Hp} . \supset : P, Q, R \in \Omega : (\exists \varpi) . \varpi \in \text{NO} \cup \iota`\dot{1} . \text{Nr}`P = \text{Nr}`Q \dot{+} \varpi :$

[*180·56]

$\supset : P, Q, R \in \Omega : (\exists \varpi) . \varpi \in \text{NO} \cup \iota`\dot{1} . \text{Nr}`R \dot{+} \text{Nr}`P = (\text{Nr}`R \dot{+} \text{Nr}`Q) \dot{+} \varpi :$

[*255·31.*251·26] $\supset : \text{Nr}`R \dot{+} \text{Nr}`P > \text{Nr}`R \dot{+} \text{Nr}`Q :. \supset \vdash . \text{Prop}$

***255·561.** $\vdash : \gamma \in N_0O . \alpha > \beta . \supset . \gamma \dot{+} \alpha > \gamma \dot{+} \beta$ [*255·56]

***255·562.** $\vdash : R \in \Omega . \text{Nr}`P \geqslant \text{Nr}`Q . \supset . \text{Nr}`R \dot{+} \text{Nr}`P \geqslant \text{Nr}`R \dot{+} \text{Nr}`Q$

Dem.

$\vdash . *180·3 . \supset \vdash : \text{Nr}`P = \text{Nr}`Q . \supset . \text{Nr}`R \dot{+} \text{Nr}`P = \text{Nr}`R \dot{+} \text{Nr}`Q$ (1)

$\vdash . (1) . *255·108·56 . \supset$

$\vdash :. \text{Hp} . \supset : \text{Nr}`R \dot{+} \text{Nr}`P > \text{Nr}`R \dot{+} \text{Nr}`Q . \vee . \text{Nr}`R \dot{+} \text{Nr}`P = \text{Nr}`R \dot{+} \text{Nr}`Q :$

[*255·108] $\supset : \text{Nr}`R \dot{+} \text{Nr}`P \geqslant \text{Nr}`R \dot{+} \text{Nr}`Q :. \supset \vdash . \text{Prop}$

***255·563.** $\vdash : \gamma \in N_0O . \alpha \geqslant \beta . \supset . \gamma \dot{+} \alpha \geqslant \gamma \dot{+} \beta$ [*255·562]

***255·564.** $\vdash : P, Q, R \in \Omega . \text{Nr}`R \dot{+} \text{Nr}`P = \text{Nr}`R \dot{+} \text{Nr}`Q . \supset . \text{Nr}`P = \text{Nr}`Q$

Dem.

$\vdash . *255·42 . \supset \vdash : \text{Hp} . \supset . \sim(\text{Nr}`R \dot{+} \text{Nr}`P > \text{Nr}`R \dot{+} \text{Nr}`Q) .$

[*255·56.Transp] $\supset . \sim(\text{Nr}`P > \text{Nr}`Q)$ (1)

Similarly $\vdash : \text{Hp} . \supset . \sim(\text{Nr}`Q > \text{Nr}`P)$ (2)

$\vdash . (1) . (2) . *255·113 . \supset \vdash . \text{Prop}$

This proposition establishes the uniqueness of subtraction from the end. Owing to the fact that ordinal addition is not commutative, we have to distinguish "subtraction from the end" from "subtraction from the beginning." They may be called *terminal* and *initial* subtraction respectively. Thus by the above proposition, *terminal* subtraction among ordinals is unique. This does not hold in general for *initial* subtraction among ordinals.

***255·565.** $\vdash : \alpha, \beta, \gamma \in N_0O . \gamma \dot{+} \alpha = \gamma \dot{+} \beta . \supset . \alpha = \text{smor}``\beta$ [*255·564]

The above proposition is still true if we put $\alpha = \beta$ instead of $\alpha = \text{smor}``\beta$ in the conclusion, but in that case it is only significant when α and β are of the same type, whereas in the above form it is free from this limitation.

∗255·57. $\vdash : P, Q \in \Omega - \iota`\dot{\Lambda} . \supset . Q \text{ less } (P \times Q) . \text{Nr}`Q \lessdot \text{Nr}`P \dot{\times} \text{Nr}`Q$

Dem.

$\vdash . *250{\cdot}13 . \quad \supset \vdash : \text{Hp} . \supset . \text{E} ! B`P .$ (1)

$[*165{\cdot}251] \qquad \supset . Q \text{ smor } Q \downarrow_{;} (B`P)$ (2)

$\vdash . (1) . *166{\cdot}1 . \supset \vdash : \text{Hp} . \supset . Q \downarrow_{;} (B`P) \subseteq P \times Q$ (3)

$\vdash . (1) . *93{\cdot}101 . \supset \vdash : \text{Hp} . \supset . (\exists x) . (B`P) P x$ (4)

$\vdash . *166{\cdot}113 . \supset \vdash : (B`P) P x . R \in C`Q \downarrow_{;} (B`P) . y \in C`Q . \supset . R (P \times Q) (y \downarrow x)$ (5)

$\vdash . (5) . (4) . *33{\cdot}24 . *166{\cdot}12 . *113{\cdot}106 . \supset$

$\vdash :. \text{Hp} . \supset : (\exists x, y) : R \in C`Q \downarrow_{;} (B`P) . \supset_R . R (P \times Q) (y \downarrow x) : y \downarrow x \in C`(P \times Q)$ (6)

$\vdash . (2) . (3) . (6) . \supset \vdash : \text{Hp} . \supset .$

$Q \downarrow_{;} (B`P) \text{ smor } Q . Q \downarrow_{;} (B`P) \subseteq P \times Q . \exists ! C`(P \times Q) \cap p`\overleftarrow{P \times Q}``C`Q \downarrow_{;} (B`P) .$

$[*254{\cdot}54] \supset . Q \text{ less } (P \times Q)$ (7)

$\vdash . (7) . *255{\cdot}17 . \supset \vdash . \text{Prop}$

∗255·571. $\vdash : \alpha, \beta \in \text{N}_0\text{O} - \iota`0_r . \supset . \beta \lessdot \alpha \dot{\times} \beta \quad [*255{\cdot}57]$

∗255·572. $\vdash : P, Q \in \Omega - \iota`\dot{\Lambda} . \text{E} ! B`\breve{P} . \supset . P \text{ less } (P \times Q) . \text{Nr}`P \lessdot \text{Nr}`P \dot{\times} \text{Nr}`Q$

Dem.

$\vdash . *250{\cdot}13 . \quad \supset \vdash : \text{Hp} . \supset . \text{E} ! B`Q .$ (1)

$[*166{\cdot}111] \qquad \supset . (B`Q) \downarrow ; P \subseteq P \times Q$ (2)

$\vdash . *151{\cdot}64 . (1) . \supset \vdash : \text{Hp} . \supset . (B`Q) \downarrow ; P \text{ smor } P$ (3)

$\vdash . *202{\cdot}511 . \supset \vdash :. \text{Hp} . \supset : B`\breve{P} \in p`\overleftarrow{P}``\text{D}`P :$

$[*166{\cdot}111] \qquad \supset : x \in \text{D}`P . y \in \text{Cl}`Q . \supset . \{(B`Q) \downarrow x\} (P \times Q) \{y \downarrow (B`\breve{P})\}$ (4)

$\vdash . *202{\cdot}511 . \supset \vdash :. \text{Hp} . \supset : B`Q \in p`\overrightarrow{Q}``\text{Cl}`Q :$

$[*166{\cdot}111] \qquad \supset : x = B`\breve{P} . y \in \text{Cl}`Q . \supset . \{(B`Q) \downarrow x\} (P \times Q) \{y \downarrow (B`\breve{P})\}$ (5)

$\vdash . (4) . (5) . \supset \vdash :. \text{Hp} . \supset : x \in C`P . y \in \text{Cl}`Q . \supset . \{(B`Q) \downarrow x\} (P \times Q) \{y \downarrow (B`\breve{P})\} :$

$[*150{\cdot}22] \qquad \supset : M \in C`(B`Q) \downarrow ; P . y \in \text{Cl}`Q . \supset . M (P \times Q) \{y \downarrow (B`\breve{P})\} :$

$[\text{Hp} . *33{\cdot}24 . *166{\cdot}111]$

$\qquad \supset : (\exists N) : N \in C`(P \times Q) : M \in C`(B`Q) \downarrow ; P . \supset_M . M (P \times Q) N$ (6)

$\vdash . (2) . (3) . (6) . *254{\cdot}54 . \supset \vdash : \text{Hp} . \supset . P \text{ less } (P \times Q)$ (7)

$\vdash . (7) . *255{\cdot}17 . \supset \vdash . \text{Prop}$

∗255·573. $\vdash :. \alpha, \beta \in \text{N}_0\text{O} - \iota`0_r : (\exists \gamma) . \gamma \in \text{NO} - \iota`0_r \cup \iota`\dot{1} . \alpha = \gamma \dot{+} \dot{1} : \supset . \alpha \lessdot \alpha \dot{\times} \beta$

Dem.

$\vdash . *204{\cdot}483 . \supset \vdash : \text{Hp} . \supset . (\exists P, Q) . \alpha = \text{N}_0\text{r}`P . \beta = \text{N}_0\text{r}`Q . \exists ! B`\breve{P}$ (1)

$\vdash . (1) . *255{\cdot}572 . \supset \vdash . \text{Prop}$

***255·58.** $\vdash : \gamma \in N_0O - \iota`0_r . \alpha > \beta . \supset . \alpha \dot{\times} \gamma > \beta \dot{\times} \gamma$

Dem.

$\vdash . *255·31 . \supset$

$\vdash :. Hp . \supset : (\exists \varpi) . \varpi \in NO - \iota`0_r . \alpha = \beta \dot{+} \varpi . v . \beta \neq 0_r . \alpha = \beta \dot{+} \dot{1}$ (1)

$\vdash . *184·35 . \quad \supset \vdash : \alpha = \beta \dot{+} \varpi . \supset . \alpha \dot{\times} \gamma = (\beta \dot{\times} \gamma) \dot{+} (\varpi \dot{\times} \gamma)$ (2)

$\vdash . *184·16 . \quad \supset \vdash : Hp . \varpi \neq 0_r . \supset . \varpi \dot{\times} \gamma \neq 0_r$ (3)

$\vdash . (2) . (3) . *255·32 . \supset \vdash : Hp . \varpi \in NO - \iota`0_r . \alpha = \beta \dot{+} \varpi . \supset . \alpha \dot{\times} \gamma > \beta \dot{\times} \gamma$ (4)

$\vdash . *184·41 . \quad \supset \vdash : Hp . \alpha = \beta \dot{+} \dot{1} . \supset . \alpha \dot{\times} \gamma = (\beta \dot{\times} \gamma) \dot{+} \gamma .$

[*255·32] $\quad \supset . \alpha \dot{\times} \gamma > \beta \dot{\times} \gamma$ (5)

$\vdash . (1) . (4) . (5) . \supset \vdash . Prop$

***255·581.** $\vdash : P \in \Omega . E ! B`\breve{P} . Q \text{ less } R . \supset .$

$P \times Q \text{ less } P \times R . Nr`P \dot{\times} Nr`Q < Nr`P \dot{\times} Nr`R$

Dem.

$\vdash . *254·55 . \supset \vdash : Hp . \supset . (\exists S) . S \text{ smor } Q . S \subseteq R . \exists ! C`R \cap p`\overleftarrow{R}``C`S$ (1)

$\vdash . *166·11 . \supset \vdash : S \subseteq R . \supset . P \times S \subseteq P \times R$ (2)

$\vdash . *166·23 . \supset \vdash : S \text{ smor } Q . \supset . P \times S \text{ smor } P \times Q$ (3)

$\vdash . *202·524 . *40·53 . \supset \vdash :. Hp . z \in C`P . w \in C`S . y \in C`R \cap p`\overleftarrow{R}``C`S . \supset :$

$zP(B`\breve{P}) . v . z = B`\breve{P} : wRy :$

[*166·113] $\quad \supset : (w \downarrow z)(P \times R)\{y \downarrow (B`\breve{P})\}$ (4)

$\vdash . (4) . *166·111 . \supset \vdash :. Hp . y \in C`R \cap p`\overleftarrow{R}``C`S . \supset :$

$M \in C`(P \times S) . \supset_M . M(P \times R)\{y \downarrow (B`\breve{P})\}$ (5)

$\vdash . (5) . *10·28 . \supset \vdash :. Hp . \exists ! C`R \cap p`\overleftarrow{R}``C`S . \supset :$

$(\exists N) : N \in C`(P \times R) : M \in C`(P \times S) . \supset_M . M(P \times R) N$ (6)

$\vdash . (2) . (3) . (6) . \supset \vdash :. Hp . S \text{ smor } Q . S \subseteq R . \exists ! C`R \cap p`\overleftarrow{R}``C`S . \supset :$

$(P \times S) \text{ smor } (P \times Q) . P \times S \subseteq P \times R . \exists ! C`(P \times R) \cap p`\overleftarrow{P \times R}``C`(P \times S) :$

[*254·54] $\quad \supset . P \times Q \text{ less } P \times R$ (7)

$\vdash . (1) . (7) . \supset \vdash : Hp . \supset . P \times Q \text{ less } P \times R$ (8)

$\vdash . (8) . *255·17 . \supset \vdash . Prop$

***255·582.** $\vdash :. \alpha \in N_0O : (\exists \delta) . \delta \in NO - \iota`0_r \cup \iota`\dot{1} . \alpha = \delta \dot{+} \dot{1} : \beta < \gamma : \supset .$

$\alpha \dot{\times} \beta \lessdot \alpha \dot{\times} \gamma$ [*255·581 . *204·483]

***255·59.** $\vdash : \alpha, \beta, \gamma \in N_0O . \gamma \neq 0_r . \alpha \dot{\times} \gamma = \beta \dot{\times} \gamma . \supset . \alpha = \text{smor}``\beta$

Dem.

$\vdash . *255·58 . Transp . \supset \vdash : Hp . \supset . \sim(\alpha > \beta) . \sim(\alpha < \beta) .$

[*255·112] $\quad \supset . \alpha = \text{smor}``\beta : \supset \vdash . Prop$

This proposition establishes the uniqueness of *terminal* division, *i.e.* division by an end-factor. *Initial* division (*i.e.* division by a beginning-factor) is only unique if the divisor is of the form $\delta \dot{+} \dot{1}$.

***255·591.** $\vdash :. \alpha, \beta, \gamma \in N_0O : (\exists \delta) . \delta \in NO - \iota`0_r \cup \iota`\dot{1} . \alpha = \delta \dot{+} \dot{1} :$
$\alpha \dot{\times} \beta = \alpha \dot{\times} \gamma : \supset . \beta = \text{smor}``\gamma$ [*255·582·112]

***255·6.** $\vdash : Nr`P > Nr`Q . \supset . \dot{1} \dot{+} Nr`P > \dot{1} \dot{+} Nr`Q$

Dem.

$\vdash . *255·33 . \supset \vdash :. Hp . \supset : (\exists \varpi) . \varpi \in NO - \iota`0_r . Nr`P = Nr`Q \dot{+} \varpi . v .$
$Nr`P \neq 0_r . Nr`P = Nr`Q \dot{+} \dot{1} :$
[*181·55] $\supset : (\exists \varpi) . \varpi \in NO - \iota`0_r . \dot{1} \dot{+} Nr`P = (\dot{1} \dot{+} Nr`Q) \dot{+} \varpi . v .$
$Nr`P \neq 0_r . \dot{1} \dot{+} Nr`P = (\dot{1} \dot{+} Nr`Q) \dot{+} \dot{1} :$
[*255·33] $\supset : \dot{1} \dot{+} Nr`P > \dot{1} \dot{+} Nr`Q :. \supset \vdash . Prop$

***255·601.** $\vdash : Nr`P > Nr`Q . \equiv . \dot{1} \dot{+} Nr`P > \dot{1} \dot{+} Nr`Q$

Dem.

$\vdash . *255·6 \frac{Q, P}{P, Q} . *255·103 . \supset$
$\vdash : Nr`P < Nr`Q . \supset . \dot{1} \dot{+} Nr`P < \dot{1} \dot{+} Nr`Q$ (1)
$\vdash . (1) . *255·108 . \supset \vdash : Nr`P \leqslant Nr`Q . \supset . \dot{1} \dot{+} Nr`P \leqslant \dot{1} \dot{+} Nr`Q$ (2)
$\vdash . (2) . Transp . *251·142 . \supset$
$\vdash : \dot{1} \dot{+} Nr`P, \dot{1} \dot{+} Nr`Q \in NO . \sim(\dot{1} \dot{+} Nr`P \leqslant \dot{1} \dot{+} Nr`Q) . \supset .$
$Nr`P, Nr`Q \in NO . \sim(Nr`P \leqslant Nr`Q)$ (3)
$\vdash . (3) . *255·281 . \supset \vdash : \dot{1} \dot{+} Nr`P > \dot{1} \dot{+} Nr`Q . \supset . Nr`P > Nr`Q$ (4)
$\vdash . (4) . *255·6 . \supset \vdash . Prop$

***255·61.** $\vdash : Q, R \in \Omega . Nr`P = Nr`Q \dot{+} Nr`R . \text{C}`R_1 = \text{C}`R . E! B`\breve{R} . \supset .$
$Nr`P \dot{+} \dot{1} > Nr`Q \dot{+} \dot{1}$

Dem.

$\vdash . *253·57 . \supset \vdash : Hp . \supset . Nr`P \dot{+} \dot{1} = Nr`Q \dot{+} \dot{1} \dot{+} Nr`R .$
[*255·32] $\supset . Nr`P \dot{+} \dot{1} > Nr`Q \dot{+} \dot{1} : \supset \vdash . Prop$

***255·62.** $\vdash : Q, R \in \Omega . Nr`P = Nr`Q \dot{+} Nr`R . Nr`R \neq 0_r .$
$\sim(\text{C}`R_1 = \text{C}`R . E! B`\breve{R}) . \supset .$
$Nr`P > Nr`Q \dot{+} \dot{1} . Nr`P \dot{+} \dot{1} > Nr`Q \dot{+} \dot{1}$

Dem.

$\vdash . *253·571 . \supset \vdash : Hp . \supset . Nr`P = Nr`Q \dot{+} \dot{1} \dot{+} Nr`R .$
[*255·32] $\supset . Nr`P > Nr`Q \dot{+} \dot{1} .$ (1)
[*255·321] $\supset . Nr`P \dot{+} \dot{1} > Nr`Q \dot{+} \dot{1}$ (2)
$\vdash . (1) . (2) . \supset \vdash . Prop$

$*255\cdot63$. $\vdash : \mathrm{Nr}‘P > \mathrm{Nr}‘Q . \supset . \mathrm{Nr}‘P \dotplus \dot{1} > \mathrm{Nr}‘Q \dotplus \dot{1}$

Dem.

$\vdash . *255\cdot33 . \supset \vdash :. \mathrm{Hp} . \supset : (\exists R) . \mathrm{Nr}‘R \neq 0_r . \mathrm{Nr}‘P = \mathrm{Nr}‘Q \dotplus \mathrm{Nr}‘R . \vee .$
$\mathrm{Nr}‘Q \neq 0_r . \mathrm{Nr}‘P = \mathrm{Nr}‘Q \dotplus \dot{1} :$

$[*255\cdot62\cdot321]$ $\supset : \mathrm{Nr}‘P \dotplus \dot{1} > \mathrm{Nr}‘Q \dotplus \dot{1} :. \supset \vdash . \mathrm{Prop}$

$*255\cdot64$. $\vdash : \mathrm{Nr}‘P > \mathrm{Nr}‘Q . \equiv . \mathrm{Nr}‘P \dotplus \dot{1} > \mathrm{Nr}‘Q \dotplus \dot{1}$

Dem.

$\vdash . *255\cdot63\cdot103 .$ $\supset \vdash : \mathrm{Nr}‘P < \mathrm{Nr}‘Q . \supset . \mathrm{Nr}‘P \dotplus \dot{1} < \mathrm{Nr}‘Q \dotplus \dot{1}$ (1)

$\vdash . *181\cdot31 .$ $\supset \vdash : \mathrm{Nr}‘P = \mathrm{Nr}‘Q . \supset . \mathrm{Nr}‘P \dotplus \dot{1} = \mathrm{Nr}‘Q \dotplus \dot{1}$ (2)

$\vdash . (1) . (2) . *255\cdot113 . \supset \vdash : P, Q \in \Omega . \sim(\mathrm{Nr}‘P > \mathrm{Nr}‘Q) . \supset .$
$\mathrm{Nr}‘P \dotplus \dot{1} \leqslant \mathrm{Nr}‘Q \dotplus \dot{1} .$

$[*255\cdot483]$ $\supset . \sim(\mathrm{Nr}‘P \dotplus \dot{1} > \mathrm{Nr}‘Q \dotplus \dot{1})$ (3)

$\vdash . *251\cdot132 .$ $\supset \vdash : \sim(P, Q \in \Omega) . \supset . \sim(\mathrm{Nr}‘P \dotplus \dot{1}, \mathrm{Nr}‘Q \dotplus \dot{1} \in \mathrm{NR}) .$

$[*255\cdot12]$ $\supset . \sim(\mathrm{Nr}‘P \dotplus \dot{1} > \mathrm{Nr}‘Q \dotplus \dot{1})$ (4)

$\vdash . (3) . (4) .$ $\supset \vdash : \sim(\mathrm{Nr}‘P > \mathrm{Nr}‘Q) . \supset . \sim(\mathrm{Nr}‘P \dotplus \dot{1} > \mathrm{Nr}‘Q \dotplus \dot{1})$ (5)

$\vdash . (5) . *255\cdot63 . \supset \vdash . \mathrm{Prop}$

$*255\cdot65$. $\vdash :. \mu \in \mathrm{N_0O} - \iota‘0_r . \supset : \nu > \mu . \equiv . \nu \geqslant \mu \dotplus \dot{1}$

Dem.

$\vdash . *255\cdot33 . \supset \vdash :. \nu > \mu . \supset : (\exists \varpi) . \varpi \in \mathrm{NO} - \iota‘0_r . \nu = \mu \dotplus \varpi . \vee . \nu = \mu \dotplus \dot{1}$ (1)

$\vdash . *255\cdot53\cdot31 . \supset$

$\vdash :. \mathrm{Hp} . \varpi \in \mathrm{NO} - \iota‘0_r . \nu = \mu \dotplus \varpi . \supset : (\exists \rho) . \rho \in \mathrm{NO} \cup \iota‘\dot{1} . \nu = \mu \dotplus \dot{2} \dotplus \rho :$

$[*181\cdot56]$ $\supset : (\exists \rho) . \rho \in \mathrm{NO} \cup \iota‘\dot{1} . \nu = \mu \dotplus \dot{1} \dotplus \dot{1} \dotplus \rho :$

$[(*255\cdot298)]$ $\supset : \nu = \mu \dotplus \dot{1} \dotplus \dot{1} . \vee . \nu = \mu \dotplus \dot{1} \dotplus \dot{1} \dotplus \dot{1} . \vee .$
$(\exists \rho) . \rho \in \mathrm{NO} - \iota‘0_r . \nu = \mu \dotplus \dot{1} \dotplus \dot{1} \dotplus \rho :$

$[*255\cdot33]$ $\supset : \nu > \mu \dotplus \dot{1}$ (2)

$\vdash . (1) . (2) .$ $\supset \vdash : \nu > \mu . \supset . \nu \geqslant \mu \dotplus \dot{1}$ (3)

$\vdash . *255\cdot45\cdot321 . \supset \vdash : \mathrm{Hp} . \nu \geqslant \mu \dotplus \dot{1} . \supset . \nu > \mu$ (4)

$\vdash . (3) . (4) . \supset \vdash . \mathrm{Prop}$

The following propositions are concerned with the relations of ordinals to the corresponding cardinals, *i.e.* to the cardinals of the fields of well-ordered series having the given ordinals. If P is a well-ordered series whose ordinal is α, $C‘‘\alpha = \mathrm{Nc}‘C‘P$, so that $C‘‘\alpha$ is a cardinal whose members can be well-ordered. Such cardinals have the property that of any two which are not equal, one must be the greater.

If the cardinal number of one series is greater than that of another, so is the ordinal number; but the converse does not hold except for finite numbers.

$*255\cdot7$. $\vdash . \mathrm{Nc}``C``\Omega = C```\mathrm{NO}$ [$*152\cdot7 . (*251\cdot01)$]

$*255\cdot701$. $\vdash . \mathrm{Nc}``C``\Omega - \iota`\Lambda = C```(\mathrm{NO} - \iota`\Lambda) = C```\mathrm{NO} - \iota`\Lambda$ [$*255\cdot7 . *37\cdot45$]

$*255\cdot71$. $\vdash : P \text{ less } Q . \supset . \mathrm{Nc}`C`P \leqslant \mathrm{Nc}`C`Q$

Dem.

$\vdash . *254\cdot1 . \supset \vdash : \mathrm{Hp} . \supset . \exists ! \mathrm{Rl}`Q \cap \mathrm{Nr}`P .$

$[*154\cdot1] \quad \supset . \exists ! \mathrm{Cl}`C`Q \cap \mathrm{Nc}`C`P .$

$[*117\cdot22] \quad \supset . \mathrm{Nc}`C`P \leqslant \mathrm{Nc}`C`Q : \supset \vdash . \mathrm{Prop}$

$*255\cdot711$. $\vdash : \mathrm{Nr}`P \leqslant \mathrm{Nr}`Q . \supset . \mathrm{Nc}`C`P \leqslant \mathrm{Nc}`C`Q$

[Proof as in $*255\cdot71$, using $*255\cdot22$]

$*255\cdot72$. $\vdash : \alpha \leqslant \beta . \supset . C``\alpha \leqslant C``\beta$

Dem.

$\vdash . *255\cdot24 . \supset \vdash : \mathrm{Hp} . \supset . (\exists P, Q) . \alpha = \mathrm{N_0r}`P . \beta = \mathrm{N_0r}`Q . \mathrm{Nr}`P \leqslant \mathrm{Nr}`Q .$

$[*255\cdot711] \quad \supset . (\exists P, Q) . \alpha = \mathrm{N_0r}`P . \beta = \mathrm{N_0r}`Q . \mathrm{Nc}`C`P \leqslant \mathrm{Nc}`C`Q .$

$[*152\cdot7] \quad \supset . C``\alpha \leqslant C``\beta : \supset \vdash . \mathrm{Prop}$

$*255\cdot73$. $\vdash :. P, Q \in \Omega . \supset :$

$\mathrm{Nc}`C`P < \mathrm{Nc}`C`Q . \vee . \mathrm{Nc}`C`P = \mathrm{Nc}`C`Q . \vee . \mathrm{Nc}`C`P > \mathrm{Nc}`C`Q$

Dem.

$\vdash . *255\cdot711 . \supset \vdash : \mathrm{Hp} . \mathrm{Nr}`P \leqslant \mathrm{Nr}`Q . \supset . \mathrm{Nc}`C`P \leqslant \mathrm{Nc}`C`Q$ (1)

$\vdash . *255\cdot71 . \supset \vdash : \mathrm{Hp} . \mathrm{Nr}`Q < \mathrm{Nr}`P . \supset . \mathrm{Nc}`C`Q < \mathrm{Nc}`C`P$ (2)

$\vdash . (1) . (2) . *255\cdot115 . \supset \vdash . \mathrm{Prop}$

$*255\cdot74$. $\vdash :. \alpha, \beta \in C```\mathrm{NO} - \iota`\Lambda . \supset : \alpha \leqslant \beta . \vee . \alpha > \beta$

Dem.

$\vdash . *255\cdot701 . \supset \vdash : \mathrm{Hp} . \supset . \alpha, \beta \in C```(\mathrm{NO} - \iota`\Lambda) .$

$[*155\cdot34] \quad \supset . (\exists P, Q) . P, Q \in \Omega . \alpha = C``\mathrm{N_0r}`P . \beta = C``\mathrm{N_0r}`Q .$

$[*152\cdot7] \quad \supset . (\exists P, Q) . P, Q \in \Omega . \alpha = \mathrm{N_0c}`C`P . \beta = \mathrm{N_0c}`C`Q$ (1)

$\vdash . *255\cdot73 . *117\cdot106\cdot107\cdot108 . \supset$

$\vdash :. P, Q \in \Omega . \supset : \mathrm{N_0c}`C`P \leqslant \mathrm{N_0c}`C`Q . \vee . \mathrm{N_0c}`C`P > \mathrm{N_0c}`C`Q$ (2)

$\vdash . (1) . (2) . \supset \vdash . \mathrm{Prop}$

$*255\cdot75$. $\vdash : P, Q \in \Omega . \mathrm{Nc}`C`P < \mathrm{Nc}`C`Q . \supset . P \text{ less } Q$

Dem.

$\vdash . *117\cdot291 . \supset \vdash : \mathrm{Hp} . \supset . \sim(\mathrm{Nc}`C`Q \leqslant \mathrm{Nc}`C`P) .$

$[*255\cdot711 . \mathrm{Transp}] \quad \supset . \sim(\mathrm{Nr}`Q \leqslant \mathrm{Nr}`P) .$

$[*255\cdot29] \quad \supset . \mathrm{Nr}`P < \mathrm{Nr}`Q .$

$[*255\cdot17] \quad \supset . P \text{ less } Q : \supset \vdash . \mathrm{Prop}$

$*255\cdot76$. $\vdash : \alpha, \beta \in \mathrm{NO} . C``\alpha < C``\beta . \supset . \alpha < \beta$ [$*255\cdot75 . *152\cdot7$]

*256. THE SERIES OF ORDINALS.

Summary of *256.

In the present number, we have to consider the series of ordinals in order of magnitude. Propositions on this subject deserve close attention, because it is in this connection that Burali-Forti's paradox* arises. This paradox, as we shall show in the present number, is avoided by the doctrine of types. But before discussing the paradox, it will be well to explain various propositions which raise no difficulty.

For convenience of notation, we shall, in the present number, employ the letter M for the relation "$\dot{<}$". (This letter is chosen as the initial of "minor.") Thus "$\alpha M \beta$" means that α and β are ordinals of which α is less than β. $\overrightarrow{M}`\beta$ will be the class of ordinals less than $\beta$, $\breve{M}_1`\beta$ will be $\beta \dotplus \dot{1}$, and $M_1`\beta$, when it exists, will be such that either $M_1`\beta \dotplus \dot{1} = \beta$, or $\beta = 2_r . M_1`\beta = 0_r$. Thus $\mathrm{Ɑ}`M_1$ is the class of ordinals having immediate predecessors, and $\overrightarrow{B}`M_1$ is the class of ordinals not having immediate predecessors.

We have (*256·12)

$$\vdash :. \alpha M \beta . \equiv : \alpha, \beta \in \mathrm{N_0O} : (\exists \gamma) . \gamma \in \mathrm{NO} - \iota`0_r \cup \iota`\dot{1} . \beta = \alpha \dotplus \gamma,$$

that is, one ordinal is less than another when something not zero can be added to the first to make it equal to the second;

***256·11.** $\vdash : P \in \Omega . \supset . \overrightarrow{M}`\mathrm{Nr}`P = \mathrm{Nr}``\mathrm{D}`P_s$

I.e. the numbers less than that of P are the numbers of the proper segments of P. Also, if $P \in \Omega$,

$$M \sqsubset \overrightarrow{M}`\mathrm{Nr}`P = \mathrm{N_0r} \,;\, (P_s \sqsubset \mathrm{D}`P_s) . \mathrm{N_0r} \upharpoonright \mathrm{D}`P_s \in 1 \to 1 \quad (*256·2·201),$$

so that (*256·202) the series of ordinals less than that of P is similar to the series of the proper segments of P, *i.e.* to $P \sqsubset \mathrm{Ɑ}`P$ (in virtue of *253·22). It follows (*256·22) that every section of M is well-ordered, and therefore that M is well-ordered (*256·3), *i.e.* that the ordinals in order of magnitude form a well-ordered series.

* "Una questione sui numeri transfiniti," *Rendiconti del circolo matematico di Palermo*, Vol. XI. (1897).

For the purposes of the present number, it is convenient to include 1_s (cf. $*153$) in the series of ordinals; we therefore get

$$N = M \cup 0_r \downarrow 1_s \cup (\iota`1_s) \uparrow \text{C}`M \quad \text{Dft } [*256].$$

The effect of this definition is merely to insert 1_s in the series M between 0_r and 2_r. We then have ($*256{\cdot}42$)

$$\text{Nr}`N = \dot{1} \dotplus \text{Nr}`M.$$

Now if $P \epsilon \Omega$, $P \upharpoonright \text{C}`P$ (as we have just seen) is similar to a proper segment of M, so that if we omit to mention types we obtain

$$\vdash : P \epsilon \Omega \,.\supset.\, \text{Nr}`P \upharpoonright \text{C}`P \lessdot \text{Nr}`M.$$

Hence $\text{Nr}`P$, which is $\dot{1} \dotplus \text{Nr}`P \upharpoonright \text{C}`P$, is less than $\dot{1} \dotplus \text{Nr}`M$ (by $*255{\cdot}63$), *i.e.* is less than N. Hence

$$\vdash : P \epsilon \Omega \,.\supset.\, \text{Nr}`P \lessdot \text{Nr}`N.$$

Nevertheless $N \epsilon \Omega$, so that it might seem as if $\text{Nr}`N$ must be less than itself, which is impossible by $*255{\cdot}42$. Hence we are led to Burali-Forti's paradox concerning the ordinal number of all ordinals.

Burali-Forti's own statement of his paradox, which is somewhat different from the above, may be summarized as follows. Assuming

$$\alpha, \beta \epsilon \text{N}_0\text{O} \,.\supset:\, \alpha \lessdot \beta \,.\vee.\, \alpha = \beta \,.\vee.\, \alpha \gtrdot \beta \qquad \text{(A)},$$

we shall have $\qquad \alpha \epsilon \text{N}_0\text{O} \,.\supset.\, \alpha \lessdot \alpha \dotplus \dot{1}$.

But we also have $\qquad \alpha \epsilon \text{N}_0\text{O} \,.\supset.\, \alpha \leqslant \text{Nr}`N$.

Hence $\qquad \text{Nr}`N \lessdot \text{Nr}`N \dotplus \dot{1} \,.\, \text{Nr}`N \dotplus \dot{1} \leqslant \text{Nr}`N$,

which is impossible. The conclusion drawn by Burali-Forti is that the above proposition (A) is false. This, however, cannot be maintained in view of Cantor's proof, reproduced above ($*255{\cdot}112$, depending on $*254{\cdot}4$). The solution of the paradox must therefore be sought elsewhere.

With regard to Burali-Forti's statement of the paradox, it is to be observed that "$\alpha \lessdot \alpha \dotplus \dot{1}$" only holds if $\exists ! \alpha \dotplus \dot{1}$, *i.e.* if $(\exists P) \,.\, P \epsilon \alpha \,.\, C`P \neq \text{V}$. This will always hold if $\alpha$ exists and is infinite, because then, if $P \epsilon \alpha$, $P \upharpoonright \text{C}`P \nrightarrow B`P \epsilon \alpha \dotplus \dot{1}$. But if α is finite, this method fails, since

$$P \upharpoonright \text{C}`P \nrightarrow B`P \epsilon \alpha.$$

Thus if the total number of entities in the universe (of any one type) is finite, "$\alpha \lessdot \alpha \dotplus \dot{1}$" fails when $C``\alpha = \iota`\text{V}$, which is just the crucial case for Burali-Forti's proof. Hence as it stands, his proof is only applicable if we assume the axiom of infinity; it might, therefore, be regarded as a reductio ad absurdum of the axiom of infinity, *i.e.* as showing that the total number of entities of any one type is finite.

In order to make it plain that the paradox does not depend upon the axiom of infinity, we have above stated it in a form independent of this axiom. The paradox, stated simply, is as follows: The ordinal number of the series of ordinals from 0_r (including 1_s) to any ordinal α is $\alpha \dot{+} \dot{1}$; hence $\alpha \dot{+} \dot{1}$ exists, and is therefore $> \alpha$. But the ordinal α is similar to the segment of the series of ordinals consisting of the predecessors of α, and is therefore less than the ordinal number of all ordinals. Hence the ordinal number of all ordinals is greater than every ordinal, and therefore than itself, which is absurd; moreover, though the greatest of all ordinals, it can be increased by the addition of $\dot{1}$, which is again absurd.

In order to dispel the above paradox, it is only necessary to make the types explicit. In the proposition

$$P \epsilon \Omega . \supset . P \text{ less } N \quad \text{(B)},$$

upon which the paradox depends, the relation "less" is not homogeneous. N is of the same type as M, which is defined as Nr'less, where $C\text{'less} = \Omega$. Thus $\text{Nr}'P \, \epsilon \, C'N$. Thus N, as it occurs in (B), should really be $N \upharpoonright t'\text{N}_0\text{r}'P$, *i.e.* $N \upharpoonright t't'P$, *i.e.* $N(P, P)$, according to the definition *65·12. We have therefore

*256·53. $\vdash : P \epsilon \Omega . \supset . P \text{ less } N \upharpoonright t'\text{N}_0\text{r}'P$

but this does not allow the inference

$$N \upharpoonright t'\text{N}_0\text{r}'P \text{ less } N \upharpoonright t'\text{N}_0\text{r}'P,$$

which is what would be required in order to elicit a paradox. The correct inference is, substituting for $N \upharpoonright t'\text{N}_0\text{r}'P$ the equivalent form $N(P, P)$,

$N(P, P) \text{ less } N\{N(P, P), N(P, P)\}$, or, more generally,

*256·56. $\vdash . (N \upharpoonright \lambda) \text{ less } \{N \upharpoonright (t't_{00}'\lambda)\}$

Thus in higher types there are greater ordinals than any to be found in lower types. This fact is what gave rise to the paradox, as the corresponding fact in cardinals gave rise to the paradox of the greatest cardinal.

---

*256·01. $M = \lessdot$ Dft [*256]

*256·02. $N = M \cup 0_r \downarrow 1_s \cup (\iota'1_s) \uparrow \text{Œ}'M$ Dft [*256]

*256·1. $\vdash . M \epsilon \text{Ser} . C'M \subset \text{N}_0\text{O}$

Dem.

$\vdash . *255·42 . \qquad \supset \vdash . M \Subset J \qquad (1)$

$\vdash . *255·471 . \qquad \supset \vdash . M \epsilon \text{ trans} \qquad (2)$

$\vdash . *255·12 . \qquad \supset \vdash . C'M \subset \text{N}_0\text{O} \qquad (3)$

$\vdash . (3) . *255·112 . *155·43 . \supset \vdash . M \epsilon \text{ connex} \qquad (4)$

$\vdash . (1) . (2) . (3) . (4) . \supset \vdash . \text{Prop}$

The above proposition assumes that M is homogeneous, since otherwise "$C'M$" is not significant. But M is significant even when it is not homogeneous. Thus the conditions of significance in the above proposition impose a limitation upon M which is not always imposed upon M.

***256·101.** $\vdash : \dot{\exists} ! M . \supset . C'M = N_0 O . 0_r = B'M : N_0 O - \iota' 0_r = \text{ᗡ}'M$

Dem.

$\vdash . *200·12 . *256·1 . \supset \vdash . C'M \sim \epsilon 1$ (1)

$\vdash . (1) . *51·4 . \quad \supset \vdash : \dot{\exists} ! M . \supset . \exists ! C'M - \iota' 0_r .$

$[*256·1] \quad \supset . \exists ! N_0 O - \iota' 0_r$ (2)

$\vdash . *255·51 . \quad \supset \vdash : \mu \epsilon N_0 O - \iota' 0_r . \equiv . 0_r M \mu$ (3)

$\vdash . (3) . \quad \supset \vdash . N_0 O - \iota' 0_r \subset \text{ᗡ}'M . 0_r \sim \epsilon \text{ᗡ}'M$ (4)

$\vdash . (2) . (3) . \quad \supset \vdash : \dot{\exists} ! M . \supset . 0_r \epsilon D'M$ (5)

$\vdash . (4) . *256·1 . \quad \supset \vdash . \text{ᗡ}'M \subset N_0 O - \iota' 0_r$ (6)

$\vdash . (4) . (5) . (6) . \supset \vdash . \text{Prop}$

The hypothesis $\dot{\exists} ! M$ will fail in the lowest type for which M is significant, if the universe contains only one individual. Under any other circumstances, $\dot{\exists} ! M$ must hold.

***256·102.** $\vdash : \exists ! N_0 O - \iota' 0_r . \supset . \dot{\exists} ! M$

Dem.

$\vdash . *256·101 . \supset \vdash : \text{Hp} . \supset . \exists ! \text{ᗡ}'M$ (1)

$\vdash . (1) . *33·24 . \supset \vdash . \text{Prop}$

***256·11.** $\vdash : P \epsilon \Omega . \supset . \overrightarrow{M}'\text{Nr}'P = \text{Nr}''D'P_s$ [*225·174]

***256·12.** $\vdash :. \alpha M \beta . \equiv : \alpha, \beta \epsilon N_0 O :$

$(\exists \gamma) . \gamma \epsilon \text{NO} - \iota' 0_r . \beta = \alpha \dot{+} \gamma . \vee . \alpha \neq 0_r . \beta = \alpha \dot{+} \dot{1}$ [*255·33]

***256·2.** $\vdash : P \epsilon \Omega . \supset .$

$$M \upharpoonright (\overrightarrow{M_*}'\text{Nr}'P) = N_0 r ; P_s . M \upharpoonright (\overrightarrow{M}'\text{Nr}'P) = N_0 r ; (P_s \upharpoonright D'P_s)$$

Dem.

$\vdash . *256·101 . \supset \vdash : \text{Hp} . P \epsilon 0_r . \supset . M \upharpoonright \overrightarrow{M_*}'\text{Nr}'P = \dot{\Lambda} . M \upharpoonright (\overrightarrow{M}'\text{Nr}'P) = \dot{\Lambda}$ (1)

$\vdash . *213·3 . \quad \supset \vdash : \text{Hp} . P \epsilon 0_r . \supset . N_0 r ; P_s = \dot{\Lambda} . N_0 r ; (P_s \upharpoonright D'P_s) = \dot{\Lambda}$ (2)

$\vdash . *256·11 . *213·158 . \supset \vdash : \text{Hp} . P \sim \epsilon 0_r . \supset . \overrightarrow{M_*}'\text{Nr}'P = \text{Nr}''C'P_s$ (3)

$\vdash . (3) . *255·17 . \supset \vdash :. \text{Hp} . P \sim \epsilon 0_r . \supset : \alpha \{M \upharpoonright (\overrightarrow{M_*}'\text{Nr}'P)\} \beta . \equiv .$

$(\exists Q, R) . \alpha = N_0 r'Q . \beta = N_0 r'R . Q, R \epsilon C'P_s . Q \text{ less } R .$

$[*254·47] \quad \equiv . (\exists Q, R) . \alpha = N_0 r'Q . \beta = N_0 r'R . Q P_s R .$

$[*150·4] \quad \equiv . \alpha (N_0 r ; P_s) \beta$ (4)

Similarly $\vdash :. \text{Hp} . P \sim \epsilon 0_r . \supset : \alpha \{M \upharpoonright (\overrightarrow{M}'\text{Nr}'P)\} \beta . \equiv . \alpha \{N_0 r ; (P_s \upharpoonright D'P_s)\} \beta$ (5)

$\vdash . (1) . (2) . (4) . (5) . \supset \vdash . \text{Prop}$

***256·201.** $\vdash : P \epsilon \Omega . \supset . N_0 r \upharpoonright D'P_s \epsilon \{M \upharpoonright (\overrightarrow{M}'\text{Nr}'P)\} \overline{\text{smor}} (P_s \upharpoonright D'P_s) .$

$N_0 r \upharpoonright C'P_s \epsilon \{M \upharpoonright (\overrightarrow{M_*}'\text{Nr}'P)\} \overline{\text{smor}} P_s$ [*253·461 . *256·2]

***256·202.** $\vdash : P \epsilon \Omega . \supset . \mathrm{Nr}`\{M \upharpoonright (\overrightarrow{M}`\mathrm{Nr}`P)\} = \mathrm{Nr}`(P_s \upharpoonright \mathrm{D}`P_s) = \mathrm{Nr}`(P \upharpoonright \mathrm{G}`P)$
[*256·201 . *253·22]

***256·203.** $\vdash : P \epsilon \Omega . \supset . \mathrm{Nr}`\{M \upharpoonright (\overrightarrow{M_*}`\mathrm{Nr}`P)\} = \mathrm{Nr}`P_s$ [*256·201]

***256·204.** $\vdash : \alpha \epsilon \mathrm{N_0O} - \iota`2_r . \supset . \dot{1} \dotplus \mathrm{Nr}`(M \upharpoonright \overrightarrow{M}`\alpha) = \alpha$

Dem.

$\vdash . *255·101 . *256·202 . \supset$

$\vdash :. P \epsilon \Omega . \alpha = \mathrm{N_0r}`P . \supset : \mathrm{Nr}`\{M \upharpoonright \overrightarrow{M}`\alpha\} = \mathrm{Nr}`(P \upharpoonright \mathrm{G}`P) :$

[*204·46·272] $\supset : P \sim \epsilon 2_r . \supset . \dot{1} \dotplus \mathrm{Nr}`(M \upharpoonright \overrightarrow{M}`\alpha) = \mathrm{Nr}`P :. \supset \vdash . \mathrm{Prop}$

***256·21.** $\vdash : \mu \epsilon \mathrm{NO} . P \epsilon \mu . \supset . \overrightarrow{M}`\mu = \mathrm{Nr}``\mathrm{D}`P_s$ [*256·11]

***256·211.** $\vdash : \mu \epsilon \mathrm{NO} - \iota`0_r . P \epsilon \mu . \supset . \overrightarrow{M_*}`\mu = \mathrm{Nr}``C`P_s$ [*213·158 . *256·21]

***256·22.** $\vdash : \mu \epsilon \mathrm{NO} . \supset . M \upharpoonright \overrightarrow{M_*}`\mu \epsilon \Omega$

Dem.

$\vdash . *256·203 . \supset \vdash : \mathrm{Hp} . P \epsilon \mu . \supset . \mathrm{Nr}`(M \upharpoonright \overrightarrow{M_*}`\mu) = \mathrm{Nr}`P_s .$

[*253·24] $\supset . M \upharpoonright \overrightarrow{M_*}`\mu \epsilon \Omega$ (1)

$\vdash . (1) . \supset \vdash : \mu \neq \Lambda . \supset . M \upharpoonright \overrightarrow{M_*}`\mu \epsilon \Omega$ (2)

$\vdash . (2) . *250·4 . \supset \vdash . \mathrm{Prop}$

***256·221.** $\vdash : \mu \epsilon \mathrm{NO} . \supset . M \upharpoonright \overrightarrow{M}`\mu \epsilon \Omega$ [*256·202]

***256·3.** $\vdash . M \epsilon \Omega$ [*256·22·1 . *250·7]

***256·31.** $\vdash : \exists ! M . \supset . 2_r = 2_M = \breve{M}_1`0_r$

Dem.

$\vdash . *255·51·53 . \supset \vdash : \mathrm{Hp} . \supset . \overleftarrow{M}`0_r = \iota`2_r \cup \overleftarrow{M}`2_r .$

[*205·196.*256·1] $\supset . 2_r = \min_M`\overleftarrow{M}`0_r$

[*206·42.*201·63] $= \breve{M}_1`0_r$

[*250·42.*256·101] $= 2_M : \supset \vdash . \mathrm{Prop}$

We shall have, for every finite ν, $\nu_r = \nu_M$, where ν_r will be defined as the ordinal corresponding to ν, *i.e.* as

$$\Omega \cap \breve{C}``\nu.$$

(This is a single ordinal when ν is finite; otherwise, it is the sum of a class of ordinals.) This subject will be considered in the next section.

***256·32.** $\vdash :. \alpha M_1 \beta . \equiv : \alpha, \beta \in \mathrm{N_0O} : \alpha \neq 0_r . \beta = \alpha \dot{+} \dot{1} . \lor . \alpha = 0_r . \beta = 2_r$

Dem.

$\vdash . *255·65 . \supset \vdash : \alpha \in \mathrm{N_0O} - \iota`0_r . \supset . \overleftarrow{M}`\alpha = \iota`(\alpha \dot{+} \dot{1}) \cup \overleftarrow{M}`(\alpha \dot{+} \dot{1}) .$

[*205·196] $\supset . \alpha \dot{+} \dot{1} = \min_M `\overleftarrow{M}`\alpha .$

[*206·42.*201·63] $\supset . \alpha \dot{+} \dot{1} = \breve{M}_1`\alpha$ (1)

$\vdash . (1) . *256·31 . \supset \vdash . \mathrm{Prop}$

***256·4.** $\vdash . 1_s \sim \in \mathrm{NO}$

Dem.

$\vdash . *153·36 . \supset \vdash : R \in 1_s . \supset . C`R \in 1 .$

[*200·12.*250·12] $\supset . R \sim \in \Omega$ (1)

$\vdash . (1) . *251·122 . \supset \vdash : \alpha \in \mathrm{NO} . \supset . \alpha \cap 1_s = \Lambda$ (2)

$\vdash . (2) . *153·34 . \supset \vdash . \mathrm{Prop}$

***256·41.** $\vdash . N = M \cup 0_r \downarrow 1_s \cup (\iota`1_s) \uparrow \mathrm{C}`M$ [(*256·02)]

***256·411.** $\vdash :. \alpha N \beta . \equiv : \alpha = 0_r . \beta \in \iota`1_s \cup \mathrm{C}`M . \lor .$
$\alpha = 1_s . \beta \in \mathrm{C}`M . \lor . \alpha, \beta \in \mathrm{C}`M . \alpha M \beta$ [*256·41]

***256·412.** $\vdash : M = \dot{\Lambda} . \supset . N = 0_r \downarrow 1_s . N \in 2_r$ [*256·41]

***256·413.** $\vdash : M = 0_r \downarrow 2_r . \supset . N = 0_r \downarrow 1_s \cup 0_r \downarrow 2_r \cup 1_r \downarrow 2_r . N \in \dot{1} \dot{+} 2_r$
[*256·41 . *161·211]

***256·414.** $\vdash : \mathrm{C}`M \sim \in 1 . \supset . N = 0_r \downarrow 1_s \dotplus M \upharpoonright \mathrm{C}`M$

Dem.

$\vdash . *204·46 . *256·101 . \supset$

$\vdash : \mathrm{Hp} . \dot{\exists} ! M . \supset . N = 0_r \leftarrow\!\!+ M \upharpoonright \mathrm{C}`M \cup 0_r \downarrow 1_s \cup (\iota`1_s) \uparrow C`(M \upharpoonright \mathrm{C}`M)$

[*161·101] $= 0_r \downarrow 1_s \cup (\iota`0_r \cup \iota`1_s) \uparrow C`(M \upharpoonright \mathrm{C}`M) \cup M \upharpoonright \mathrm{C}`M$

[*160·1] $= 0_r \downarrow 1_s \dotplus M \upharpoonright \mathrm{C}`M$ (1)

$\vdash . (1) . *256·412 . \supset \vdash . \mathrm{Prop}$

***256·42.** $\vdash : \dot{\exists} ! M . \supset . \mathrm{Nr}`N = \dot{1} \dot{+} \mathrm{Nr}`M$

Dem.

$\vdash . *256·414 . \supset \vdash : \mathrm{Hp} . \mathrm{C}`M \sim \in 1 . \supset . \mathrm{Nr}`N = 2_r \dot{+} \mathrm{Nr}`(M \upharpoonright \mathrm{C}`M)$

[*181·57] $= \dot{1} \dot{+} \dot{1} \dot{+} \mathrm{Nr}`(M \upharpoonright \mathrm{C}`M)$

[*204·46] $= \dot{1} \dot{+} \mathrm{Nr}`M$ (1)

$\vdash . (1) . *256·413 . \supset \vdash . \mathrm{Prop}$

***256·43.** $\vdash : N \in \Omega - \iota`\dot{\Lambda}$ [*256·412·42]

***256·44.** $\vdash :. P \epsilon \Omega . \supset : P \upharpoonright \text{Ɑ}‘P \text{ less } M . \equiv . P \text{ less } N . \dot{\exists} ! M$

Dem.

$\vdash . *255·17·601 . \supset$

$\vdash :. \text{Hp} . \supset : P \upharpoonright \text{Ɑ}‘P \text{ less } M . \equiv . \dot{1} \dot{+} \text{Nr}‘P \upharpoonright \text{Ɑ}‘P < \dot{1} \dot{+} \text{Nr}‘M$ (1)

$\vdash . *256·412·42 . \supset \vdash : P = \dot{\Lambda} . \supset . P \text{ less } N$ (2)

$\vdash . *255·51 . \quad \supset \vdash :. P = \dot{\Lambda} . \supset : P \upharpoonright \text{Ɑ}‘P \text{ less } M . \equiv . \dot{\exists} ! M$ (3)

$\vdash . (2) . (3) . \quad \supset \vdash :. P = \dot{\Lambda} . \supset : P \upharpoonright \text{Ɑ}‘P \text{ less } M . \equiv . P \text{ less } N . \dot{\exists} ! M$ (4)

$\vdash . *200·35 . *255·51 . \supset \vdash :. \text{Ɑ}‘P \epsilon 1 . \supset : P \upharpoonright \text{Ɑ}‘P \text{ less } M . \equiv . \dot{\exists} ! M$ (5)

$\vdash . *256·42 . \quad \supset \vdash :. \text{Hp} . \text{Ɑ}‘P \epsilon 1 . \dot{\exists} ! M . \supset . P \text{ less } N$ (6)

$\vdash . (5) . (6) . \supset \vdash :. \text{Hp} . \text{Ɑ}‘P \epsilon 1 . \supset : P \upharpoonright \text{Ɑ}‘P \text{ less } M . \equiv . \dot{\exists} ! M . P \text{ less } N$ (7)

$\vdash . *204·46 . \supset \vdash :. \text{Hp} . \dot{\exists} ! P . \text{Ɑ}‘P \sim \epsilon 1 . \supset : \dot{1} \dot{+} \text{Nr}‘P \upharpoonright \text{Ɑ}‘P = \text{Nr}‘P :$

[(1)] $\quad \supset : P \upharpoonright \text{Ɑ}‘P \text{ less } M . \equiv . \text{Nr}‘P < \dot{1} \dot{+} \text{Nr}‘M .$

[*256·101·42] $\quad \equiv . \text{Nr}‘P < \text{Nr}‘N . \dot{\exists} ! M$ (8)

$\vdash . (4) . (7) . (8) . \supset \vdash . \text{Prop}$

We now make use of the above propositions to show that every well-ordered relation P of the type we start from is less than N, where N is to hold between ordinals of the type to which $\text{N}_0\text{r}‘P$ belongs. This proposition embodies what Burali-Forti's paradox becomes when account is taken of types.

***256·5.** $\vdash : \dot{\exists} ! M . P \epsilon \Omega . \supset . \text{N}_0\text{r};(P_s \upharpoonright \text{D}‘P_s) \epsilon \text{D}‘(M \upharpoonright t‘\text{N}_0\text{r}‘P)_s$

Dem.

$\vdash . *256·2 . *253·13 . \supset \vdash : \text{Hp} . \supset . \text{N}_0\text{r};(P_s \upharpoonright \text{D}‘P_s) \epsilon \text{D}‘M_s$ (1)

$\vdash . (1) . *150·22 . \quad \supset \vdash : \text{Hp} . \supset . \text{N}_0\text{r}‘‘\text{D}‘P_s \subset t_0‘C‘M_s .$

[*213·141] $\quad \supset . \text{N}_0\text{r}‘P \epsilon t_0‘C‘M_s .$

[*63·53] $\quad \supset . t_0‘C‘M_s = t‘\text{N}_0\text{r}‘P$ (2)

$\vdash . (1) . (2) . \supset \vdash . \text{Prop}$

***256·51.** $\vdash : P \epsilon \Omega . \supset . \text{N}_0\text{r};(P_s \upharpoonright \text{D}‘P_s) \text{ smor } P \upharpoonright \text{Ɑ}‘P$ [*253·463]

***256·52.** $\vdash : \dot{\exists} ! M . P \epsilon \Omega . \supset . P \upharpoonright \text{Ɑ}‘P \text{ less } M \upharpoonright t‘\text{N}_0\text{r}‘P$ [*256·5·51 . *254·182]

***256·53.** $\vdash : P \epsilon \Omega . \supset . P \text{ less } N \upharpoonright t‘\text{N}_0\text{r}‘P$

Dem.

$\vdash . *256·44·52 . \supset \vdash : \text{Hp} . \dot{\exists} ! M . \supset . P \text{ less } N \upharpoonright t‘\text{N}_0\text{r}‘P$ (1)

$\vdash . *256·102 . \quad \supset \vdash : \text{Hp} . M = \dot{\Lambda} . \supset . P = \dot{\Lambda} .$

[*256·43] $\quad \supset . P \text{ less } N$ (2)

$\vdash . (1) . (2) . \supset \vdash . \text{Prop}$

***256·54.** $\vdash : P \epsilon \Omega . \supset . \text{Nr}(P)‘(N \upharpoonright t‘\text{N}_0\text{r}‘P) = \Lambda$

Dem.

$\vdash . *256·53 . \supset \vdash :. \text{Hp} . \supset : Q \epsilon t‘P . \supset_Q . \sim \{Q \text{ smor } N \upharpoonright t‘\text{N}_0\text{r}‘P\} :$

[*152·11] $\quad \supset : t‘P \cap \text{Nr}‘(N \upharpoonright t‘\text{N}_0\text{r}‘P) = \Lambda :$

[(*65·04)] $\quad \supset : \text{Nr}(P)‘(N \upharpoonright t‘\text{N}_0\text{r}‘P) = \Lambda :. \supset \vdash . \text{Prop}$

***256·55.** $\vdash : P \epsilon \Omega . \supset .$

$$\text{Nr}(P)\text{‘}(N \upharpoonright t\text{‘N}_0\text{r‘}P) = \text{Nr}(P)\text{‘}(N \upharpoonright t\text{‘}t\text{‘}P) = \text{Nr}(P)\text{‘}\{N(P,P)\} = \Lambda$$

Dem.

$\vdash . *155\cdot12 . \supset \vdash . P \epsilon \text{N}_0\text{r‘}P .$

$[*63\cdot105] \quad \supset \vdash . P \epsilon t_0\text{‘N}_0\text{r‘}P .$

$[*63\cdot53] \quad \supset \vdash . t\text{‘}t\text{‘}P = t\text{‘N}_0\text{r‘}P \quad (1)$

$\vdash . (1) . \quad \supset \vdash . \text{Nr}(P)\text{‘}(N \upharpoonright t\text{‘N}_0\text{r‘}P) = \text{Nr}(P)\text{‘}(N \upharpoonright t\text{‘}t\text{‘}P) \quad (2)$

$[(*65\cdot12)] \quad = \text{Nr}(P)\text{‘}\{N(P,P)\} \quad (3)$

$\vdash . (2) . (3) . *256\cdot54 . \supset \vdash . \text{Prop}$

***256·56.** $\vdash . (N \upharpoonright \lambda) \text{ less } \{N \upharpoonright (t\text{‘}t_{00}\text{‘}\lambda)\}$

Dem.

$\vdash . *256\cdot43\cdot53 . \supset \vdash . (N \upharpoonright \lambda) \text{ less } \{N \upharpoonright (t\text{‘N}_0\text{r‘}N \upharpoonright \lambda)\} \quad (1)$

$\vdash . *155\cdot12 . \quad \supset \vdash . N \upharpoonright \lambda \epsilon \text{N}_0\text{r‘}N \upharpoonright \lambda .$

$[*63\cdot105] \quad \supset \vdash . N \upharpoonright \lambda \epsilon t_0\text{‘N}_0\text{r‘}N \upharpoonright \lambda .$

$[*63\cdot53] \quad \supset \vdash . t\text{‘}t\text{‘}N \upharpoonright \lambda = t\text{‘N}_0\text{r‘}N \upharpoonright \lambda \quad (2)$

$\vdash . *64\cdot16 . \quad \supset \vdash . N \upharpoonright \lambda \epsilon t\text{‘}(t_0\text{‘}\lambda \uparrow t_0\text{‘}\lambda) .$

$[(*64\cdot01)] \quad \supset \vdash . N \upharpoonright \lambda \epsilon t_{00}\text{‘}\lambda \quad (3)$

$\vdash . (2) . (3) . \quad \supset \vdash . t\text{‘}t_{00}\text{‘}\lambda = t\text{‘N}_0\text{r‘}N \upharpoonright \lambda \quad (4)$

$\vdash . (1) . (4) . \supset \vdash . \text{Prop}$

When types are neglected, the above proposition appears as

$$N \text{ less } N,$$

which is impossible, and embodies Burali-Forti's paradox. In the form proved above, however, the paradox has disappeared, and we have instead the proposition that in higher types longer series are possible than in lower ones.

*257. THE TRANSFINITE ANCESTRAL RELATION.

Summary of *257.

In this number, we are concerned with an extension of the notions of R_* and R_{po}. This extension requires two relations, R and Q. It is most easily explained by first defining the "transfinite posterity" of a term x with respect to R and Q; this class is an extension of $\overleftarrow{R_*}`x$. This class is generated as follows. Let us suppose, to aid the imagination, that Q is more or less serial in character, and that R is a many-one relation contained in Q. Then the transfinite posterity of x with respect to R and Q is generated as follows: Starting from x, we travel down the posterity of x with respect to R (*i.e.* $\overleftarrow{R_*}`x$) as long as we can; if the whole class $\overleftarrow{R_*}`x$ has a limit with respect to Q, we begin again with this limit, which is to be included in the transfinite posterity of x with respect to R and Q; if the limit is y, we travel down $\overleftarrow{R_*}`y$, and include the limit of this class with respect to $Q$, and so on, as long as we still have either terms belonging to $\mathrm{D}`R$ or classes belonging to $\mathrm{G}`\mathrm{lt}_Q$. The whole of the terms so obtainable constitute the transfinite posterity of $x$ with respect to $R$ and $Q$, which we will denote* by $(R * Q)`x$.

In order to obtain a symbolic definition of this class, let us call a class σ "transfinitely hereditary" when not only $\breve{R}``\sigma \subset \sigma$, as in the ordinary hereditary class, but also if we take any existent sub-class μ of $\sigma \cap C`Q$, if $\mu$ has a limit with respect to $Q$, that limit is to be a member of $\sigma$. Thus $\sigma$ is to be such that the $R$-successor of any member of $\sigma$ belongs to $\sigma$ and the $Q$-limit of any existent sub-class of $\sigma \cap C`Q$ belongs to σ (so long as these exist). That is, $\breve{R}``\sigma \subset \sigma$ and $\mu \subset \sigma \,.\, \exists ! \mu \cap C`Q \,.\, \supset_\mu \,.\, \overrightarrow{\mathrm{lt}_Q}`\mu \subset \sigma$. Using the notion of the derivative of a class with respect to Q, introduced in *216, the condition $\mu \subset \sigma \,.\, \exists ! \mu \cap C`Q \,.\, \supset_\mu \,.\, \overrightarrow{\mathrm{lt}_Q}`\mu \subset \sigma$ reduces to $\delta_Q`\sigma \subset \sigma$, in virtue of *216·1. Hence σ is transfinitely hereditary with respect to R and Q if

$$\breve{R}``\sigma \cup \delta_Q`\sigma \subset \sigma.$$

* This meaning for $R * Q$ has no connection with the meaning temporarily assigned to this symbol in *95.

We may now define the transfinite posterity of x with respect to R and Q as all members of C'Q which belong to every transfinitely hereditary class to which x belongs, *i.e.* we put

$$(R*Q)'x = C'Q \cap \hat{y}\{x \in \sigma . \breve{R}``\sigma \cup \delta_Q`\sigma \subset \sigma . \supset_\sigma . y \in \sigma\} \quad \text{Df.}$$

Then the analogue of R_* is $\hat{x}\hat{y}\{y \in (R*Q)'x\}$. This relation, however, is less important than the analogue of R_{po} limited to the posterity of x. This analogue, assuming Q to be transitive, will be $Q \upharpoonright (R*Q)'x$. For this we introduce the two notations Q_{Rx} and $Q(R, x)$, the latter being more convenient when either R or x is replaced by a more complicated expression. Thus we put

$$Q_{Rx} = Q(R, x) = Q \upharpoonright (R*Q)'x \quad \text{Df.}$$

If Q is a well-ordered series and $R = Q_1$, Q_{Rx} is merely the series Q beginning with x, and $(R*Q)'x = \overleftarrow{Q_*}'x = \overleftarrow{Q}'x \cup \iota'x$ if $x \in C'Q$. Thus in this case, if $x = B'Q$, $Q_{Rx} = Q$. But the importance of Q_{Rx} is in cases where Q is not completely serial, but becomes so when limited to $(R*Q)'x$. In these cases, Q will, in applications, almost always be logical inclusion combined with diversity, or the converse of this; *i.e.* it will be either

$$\hat{\alpha}\hat{\beta}(\alpha \subset \beta . \alpha \neq \beta)$$

or

$$\hat{M}\hat{N}(M \Subset N . M \neq N),$$

or the converse of one of these. In the case of $\hat{\alpha}\hat{\beta}(\alpha \subset \beta . \alpha \neq \beta)$, we have

$$\text{lt}_Q = s \upharpoonright (-\text{Cl}'\text{max}_Q) . \text{tl}_Q = p \upharpoonright (-\text{Cl}'\text{min}_Q),$$

as will be proved in *258.

In the present number, we are concerned in proving that, under certain circumstances, $Q_{Rx} \in \Omega$. The proof proceeds on the lines of Zermelo's second proof* of his theorem that if a selection exists from all the existent sub-classes of a given class, then the given class can be well-ordered.

Before proceeding to treat of this subject, however, it is necessary to prove some elementary properties of $(R*Q)'x$. These are given in the propositions preceding *257·2.

We have

***257·11.** $\vdash : x \in \sigma . \breve{R}``\sigma \cup \delta_Q`\sigma \subset \sigma . \supset . (R*Q)'x \subset \sigma$

Thus in order to prove that $(R*Q)'x$ is contained in a class σ, we have to prove (1) that x belongs to σ, (2) that the R-successors of members of σ are members of σ, *i.e.* that σ is hereditary with respect to R, (3) that the derivative of σ with respect to Q is contained in σ, *i.e.* that if μ is any existent sub-class of $\sigma \cap C'Q$ which has a Q-limit, this limit is a member of σ.

* "Neuer Beweis für die Möglichkeit einer Wohlordnung," *Math. Annalen*, LXV. p. 107 (1907). His first proof, which was somewhat more complicated, was published in *Math. Annalen*, LIX. p. 514 (1904).

***257·111.** $\vdash . (R * Q)`x \subset C`Q$

***257·12.** $\vdash : x \in C`Q . \equiv . x \in (R * Q)`x$

***257·123.** $\vdash : R \mathrel{G} Q . \supset . \breve{R}``(R * Q)`x \subset (R * Q)`x$

I.e. if $R \mathrel{G} Q$, $(R * Q)`x$ is hereditary with respect to $R$. The hypothesis $R \mathrel{G} Q$ is required for most of the properties of $(R * Q)`x$.

***257·125.** $\vdash : R \mathrel{G} Q . x \in C`Q . \supset . \overleftarrow{R_*}`x \subset (R * Q)`x$

Thus if $x \in C`Q$, the $R$-posterity of $x$ is contained in $(R * Q)`x$.

***257·13.** $\vdash : \mu \subset (R * Q)`x . \exists ! \mu . \supset . \overrightarrow{\text{lt}_Q}`\mu \subset (R * Q)`x$

***257·14.** $\vdash : R \mathrel{G} Q . \supset . (R * Q)`x \subset \overleftarrow{Q_*}`x$

Thus $(R * Q)`x$ is wholly contained in the Q-posterity of x.

The following propositions (*257·2—·36) are concerned in proving $Q_{Rx} \in \Omega$, with a suitable hypothesis. This hypothesis is

$$Q \in \text{Rl}`J \cap \text{trans} . R \in \text{Rl}`Q \cap \text{Cls} \rightarrow 1 . \text{lt}_Q \restriction \text{Cl ex}`(R * Q)`x \in 1 \rightarrow \text{Cls}.$$

We assume, to begin with, only part of this hypothesis, namely,

$$Q \in \text{Rl}`J \cap \text{trans} . R \in \text{Rl}`Q \cap \text{Cls} \rightarrow 1.$$

Thus to prove $Q_{Rx} \in \text{Ser}$, we only have to prove $Q_{Rx} \in \text{connex}$, *i.e.*

$$y \in (R * Q)`x . \supset . (R * Q)`x \subset \overleftrightarrow{Q}`y,$$

or, what comes to the same thing,

$$(R * Q)`x \subset p`\overleftrightarrow{Q}``(R * Q)`x.$$

Let us put $\qquad \sigma_1 = (R * Q)`x \cap p`\overleftrightarrow{Q}``(R * Q)`x.$

Then any member of σ_1 may be called a "connected term," because it is connected by Q or $\breve{Q}$ with every other term of $(R * Q)`x$. (A connected relation is then a relation whose field consists entirely of connected terms.) We wish to prove that $\sigma_1$ is a transfinitely hereditary class, and therefore equal to $(R * Q)`x$. We do this, not directly, but by combining σ_1 with another class σ_2 defined as follows. Consider those members z of $(R * Q)`x$ which are such that their successors in $Q_{Rx}$ consist of $\breve{R}`z$ and its successors in Q_{Rx}, *i.e.* put

$$\tau = (R * Q)`x \cap \hat{z} \{\overleftarrow{Q_{Rx}}`z = \overleftarrow{(Q_{Rx})_*}`\breve{R}`z\}.$$

It will be observed that, even when Q is transitive, Q_* and $(Q_{Rx})_*$ are still useful. In this case, $(Q_{Rx})_* = Q_{Rx} \cup I \restriction C`Q_{Rx}$, so that $\overleftarrow{(Q_{Rx})_*}`\breve{R}`z$ consists of $\breve{R}`z$ and its successors in Q_{Rx}. We then consider the class σ_2 consisting of those terms y whose predecessors are all members of τ, *i.e.* we put

$$\sigma_2 = (R * Q)`x \cap \hat{y} \{zQy . z \in (R * Q)`x . \supset_z . \overleftarrow{Q_{Rx}}`z = \overleftarrow{(Q_{Rx})_*}`\breve{R}`z\}.$$

Finally we put $\sigma = \sigma_1 \cap \sigma_2$, *i.e.*

$$\sigma = (R * Q)`x \cap p`\overleftrightarrow{Q}``(R * Q)`x \cap \hat{y} \{zQy . z \in (R * Q)`x . \supset_z . \overleftarrow{Q_{Rx}}`z = \overleftarrow{(Q_{Rx})_*}`\breve{R}`z\}.$$

The reason for this process is that it is easier to prove that σ is a transfinitely hereditary class than it is to prove this directly for σ_1; and the result follows immediately for σ_1 when it has been proved for σ.

We have then to prove $\quad \breve{R}\text{‘‘}\sigma \subset \sigma \,.\, \delta_Q\text{‘}\sigma \subset \sigma.$

The first step is to prove

$$y \,\epsilon\, \sigma \,.\, \supset .\, \overleftarrow{Q}_{Rx}\text{‘}y = \overleftarrow{Q}_{Rx}\text{‘}\breve{R}\text{‘}y \cup \iota\text{‘}\breve{R}\text{‘}y.$$

This is proved by transfinite induction, by showing that

$$\overrightarrow{Q}_{*}\text{‘}y \cup \overleftarrow{Q}_{*}\text{‘}\breve{R}\text{‘}y$$

is a transfinitely hereditary class, whence the result, because, by hypothesis,

$$(R*Q)\text{‘}x = \overrightarrow{(Q_{Rx})_{*}}\text{‘}y \cup \overleftarrow{Q}_{Rx}\text{‘}y.$$

The proof that $\overrightarrow{Q}_{*}\text{‘}y \cup \overleftarrow{Q}_{*}\text{‘}\breve{R}\text{‘}y$ is a transfinitely hereditary class is as follows.

If $z \,\epsilon\, \overleftarrow{Q}_{*}\text{‘}\breve{R}\text{‘}y$, $\breve{R}\text{‘}z \,\epsilon\, \overleftarrow{Q}_{*}\text{‘}\breve{R}\text{‘}y$. If $z = y$, $\breve{R}\text{‘}z = \breve{R}\text{‘}y$.

If $z \,\epsilon\, \overrightarrow{Q}_{Rx}\text{‘}y$, then since by the hypothesis $\overleftarrow{Q}_{Rx}\text{‘}z = \overleftarrow{(Q_{Rx})_{*}}\text{‘}\breve{R}\text{‘}z$, we have

$$y \,\epsilon\, \overleftarrow{(Q_{Rx})_{*}}\text{‘}\breve{R}\text{‘}z, \text{ i.e. } \breve{R}\text{‘}z \,\epsilon\, \overrightarrow{Q}_{*}\text{‘}y.$$

Hence $z \,\epsilon\, (R*Q)\text{‘}x \cap (\overrightarrow{Q}_{*}\text{‘}y \cup \overleftarrow{Q}_{*}\text{‘}\breve{R}\text{‘}y) \,.\, \supset .\, \breve{R}\text{‘}z \,\epsilon\, \overrightarrow{Q}_{*}\text{‘}y \cup \overleftarrow{Q}_{*}\text{‘}\breve{R}\text{‘}y.$

We have next to prove

$$\mu \subset (R*Q)\text{‘}x \cap (\overrightarrow{Q}_{*}\text{‘}y \cup \overleftarrow{Q}_{*}\text{‘}\breve{R}\text{‘}y) \,.\, \exists\,!\,\mu \,.\, \supset .\, \overrightarrow{\text{lt}}_Q\text{‘}\mu \subset \overrightarrow{Q}_{*}\text{‘}y \cup \overleftarrow{Q}_{*}\text{‘}\breve{R}\text{‘}y.$$

If $\exists\,!\,\mu \cap \overleftarrow{Q}_{*}\text{‘}\breve{R}\text{‘}y$, then $\overrightarrow{\text{lt}}_Q\text{‘}\mu \subset \overleftarrow{Q}_{*}\text{‘}\breve{R}\text{‘}y$.

If $\mu \subset \overrightarrow{Q}_{*}\text{‘}y \,.\, y \,\epsilon\, \mu$, then $y \,\epsilon\, \overrightarrow{\text{max}}_Q\text{‘}\mu$, and $\overrightarrow{\text{lt}}_Q\text{‘}\mu = \Lambda$.

If $\mu \subset \overrightarrow{Q}\text{‘}y$, we have $y \,\epsilon\, p\text{‘}\overleftarrow{Q}\text{‘‘}\mu$, whence $w \,\text{lt}_Q \mu \,.\, \supset .\, \sim(yQw)$, whence, since y, by hypothesis, is a connected term, $wQ_{*}y$.

Hence in any case $\overrightarrow{\text{lt}}_Q\text{‘}\mu \subset \overrightarrow{Q}_{*}\text{‘}y \cup \overleftarrow{Q}_{*}\text{‘}\breve{R}\text{‘}y$. Hence $\overrightarrow{Q}_{*}\text{‘}y \cup \overleftarrow{Q}_{*}\text{‘}\breve{R}\text{‘}y$ is hereditary, and therefore contains $(R*Q)\text{‘}x$; and hence

$$\overleftarrow{Q}_{Rx}\text{‘}y = \overleftarrow{(Q_{Rx})_{*}}\text{‘}\breve{R}\text{‘}y \,.\, \overrightarrow{(Q_{Rx})_{*}}\text{‘}y = \overrightarrow{Q}_{Rx}\text{‘}\breve{R}\text{‘}y.$$

This shows that $\breve{R}\text{‘}y$ is a member of σ_2. For by hypothesis this holds of all predecessors of y, and we have now shown (1) that it also holds of y, (2) that y is the only predecessor of $\breve{R}\text{‘}y$ which does not precede y. This is the first step towards proving that σ is transfinitely hereditary.

It follows immediately, from what has now been proved, that if $y \,\epsilon\, \sigma$, $\breve{R}\text{‘}y$ (if it exists) is a connected term. For by hypothesis

$$(R*Q)\text{‘}x \subset \overrightarrow{Q}_{*}\text{‘}y \cup \overleftarrow{Q}\text{‘}y,$$

whence, by what we have just proved,

$$(R*Q)\text{‘}x \subset \overrightarrow{Q}\text{‘}\breve{R}\text{‘}y \cup \overleftarrow{Q}_{*}\text{‘}\breve{R}\text{‘}y,$$

whence $\breve{R}`y$ is a connected term. Hence $\breve{R}`y \epsilon \sigma$. Hence $\breve{R}``\sigma \subset \sigma$.

It remains to prove $\delta_Q`\sigma \subset \sigma$.

Just as $\breve{R}``\sigma \subset \sigma$ was proved by proving $\overleftarrow{Q}`y = \overleftarrow{Q_*}`\breve{R}`y$, so $\delta_Q`\sigma \subset \sigma$ is proved by proving

$$p`\overleftarrow{Q}``\mu \subset \breve{Q}_*``\overrightarrow{\text{lt}_Q}`\mu,$$

provided $\mu \subset \sigma \,.\, \exists ! \mu \,.\, \sim \exists ! \overrightarrow{\text{max}_Q}`\mu$;

and this is proved by showing that $Q``\mu \cup \breve{Q}_*``\overrightarrow{\text{lt}_Q}`\mu$ is a transfinitely hereditary class.

To show that $Q``\mu \cup \breve{Q}_*``\overrightarrow{\text{lt}_Q}`\mu$ is a transfinitely hereditary class if

$$\mu \subset \sigma \,.\, \exists ! \mu \,.\, \sim \exists ! \overrightarrow{\text{max}_Q}`\mu,$$

we observe that by hypothesis

$$z \epsilon Q_{Rx}``\mu \,.\, \supset \,.\, \overleftarrow{Q_{Rx}}`z = \overleftarrow{(Q_{Rx})_*}`\breve{R}`z \,.\, \supset \,.\, \exists ! \mu \cap \overleftarrow{(Q_{Rx})_*}`\breve{R}`z.$$

Hence $\breve{R}`z \epsilon (Q_{Rx})_*``\mu$; and hence, since by hypothesis $\mu \subset Q``\mu$,

$$\breve{R}`z \epsilon Q_{Rx}``\mu.$$

Hence $\breve{R}``\{(Q*R)`x \cap Q``\mu\} \subset (Q*R)`x \cap Q``\mu$.

Also obviously $\breve{R}``\breve{Q}_*``\overrightarrow{\text{lt}}`\mu \subset \breve{Q}_*``\overrightarrow{\text{lt}_Q}`\mu$.

Hence putting $\rho = (Q*R)`x \cap (Q``\mu \cup \breve{Q}_*``\overrightarrow{\text{lt}_Q}`\mu)$,

we have $\breve{R}``\rho \subset \rho$.

We have now to prove $\delta_Q`\rho \subset \rho$,

i.e. $\alpha \subset \rho \,.\, \exists ! \alpha \,.\, \sim \exists ! \overrightarrow{\text{max}_Q}`\alpha \,.\, \supset \,.\, \overrightarrow{\text{lt}_Q}`\alpha \subset \rho$.

If $\alpha \subset Q``\mu$, it is obvious (since $\mu$ is composed entirely of connected terms) that $\overrightarrow{\text{seq}_Q}`\alpha \subset Q``\mu \cup \overrightarrow{\text{lt}_Q}`\mu$.

On the other hand, if $\exists ! \alpha \cap \breve{Q}_*``\overrightarrow{\text{lt}_Q}`\mu$, then $\alpha \cap Q``\mu$, if it exists, does not affect the value of the limit of α, which is the limit of $\alpha \cap \breve{Q}_*``\overrightarrow{\text{lt}_Q}`\mu$, which is obviously contained in $\breve{Q}_*``\overrightarrow{\text{lt}_Q}`\mu$. Hence $\delta_Q`\mu \subset \mu$. Hence μ is transfinitely hereditary, and we have

$$\mu \subset \sigma \,.\, \exists ! \mu \,.\, \sim \exists ! \overrightarrow{\text{max}_Q}`\mu \,.\, \supset \,.\, (R*Q)`x \subset Q``\mu \cup \breve{Q}_*``\overrightarrow{\text{lt}_Q}`\mu.$$

At this point it is necessary to assume

$$\text{lt}_Q \upharpoonright \text{Cl ex}`(R*Q)`x \epsilon 1 \rightarrow \text{Cls}.$$

This being assumed, we have, by what has just been proved,

$$\mu \subset \sigma \,.\, \exists ! \mu \,.\, \exists ! \overrightarrow{\text{lt}_Q}`\mu \,.\, \supset \,.\, (R*Q)`x \subset Q``\mu \cup \overleftarrow{Q_*}`\text{lt}_Q`\mu \,.$$
$$\supset \,.\, (R*Q)`x \subset \overrightarrow{Q}`\text{lt}_Q`\mu \cup \overleftarrow{Q_*}`\text{lt}_Q`\mu.$$

Hence $\text{lt}_Q\text{‘}\mu$ is a connected term. Hence

$$\delta_Q\text{‘}\sigma \subset p\text{‘}\overleftrightarrow{Q}\text{“}(R*Q)\text{‘}x.$$

We only require further

$$\mu \subset \sigma \,.\, \exists\,!\,\mu \,.\, \exists\,!\,\overrightarrow{\text{lt}_Q\text{‘}\mu} \,.\, \supset : zQ\,\text{lt}_Q\text{‘}\mu \,.\, z \in (R*Q)\text{‘}x \,.\, \supset_z .\, \overleftarrow{Q_{Rx}}\text{‘}z = \overleftarrow{(Q_{Rx})_*}\text{‘}\breve{R}\text{‘}z.$$

Now by what we have just proved, $zQ\,\text{lt}_Q\text{‘}\mu \,.\, \equiv .\, z \in Q\text{“}\mu$; and by the definition of σ, since $\mu \subset \sigma$, we have

$$z \in Q\text{“}\mu \,.\, \supset .\, \overleftarrow{Q_{Rx}}\text{‘}z = \overleftarrow{(Q_{Rx})_*}\text{‘}\breve{R}\text{‘}z.$$

Hence we arrive at $\delta_Q\text{‘}\sigma \subset \sigma$. Since we have already proved $\breve{R}\text{“}\sigma \subset \sigma$, it follows that σ is hereditary, and $(R*Q)\text{‘}x \subset \sigma$, *i.e.*

$$y \in (R*Q)\text{‘}x : \supset_y : y \in p\text{‘}\overleftrightarrow{Q}\text{“}(R*Q)\text{‘}x : zQ_{Rx}y \,.\, \supset_z .\, \overleftarrow{Q_{Rx}}\text{‘}z = \overleftarrow{(Q_{Rx})_*}\text{‘}\breve{R}\text{‘}z,$$

i.e.
$$Q_{Rx} \in \text{connex} : z \in \text{D}\text{‘}Q_{Rx} \,.\, \supset_z .\, \overleftarrow{Q_{Rx}}\text{‘}z = \overleftarrow{(Q_{Rx})_*}\text{‘}\breve{R}\text{‘}z.$$

Hence $Q_{Rx} \in \text{Ser}$. Hence also the immediate successor of every term z in $\text{D}\text{‘}Q_{Rx}$ is $\breve{R}\text{‘}z$, so that

$$\text{D}\text{‘}Q_{Rx} \subset \text{D}\text{‘}R \,.\, (Q_{Rx})_1 = R \upharpoonright (R*Q)\text{‘}x.$$

To show that $Q_{Rx} \in \Omega$, we observe that every class contained in $\text{D}\text{‘}Q_{Rx}$ has a sequent, namely

$$\text{seq}\,(Q_{Rx})\text{‘}\Lambda = x,$$

$$\alpha \subset \text{D}\text{‘}Q_{Rx} \,.\, \exists\,!\,\overrightarrow{\text{max}_Q\text{‘}\alpha} \,.\, \supset .\, \text{seq}\,(Q_{Rx})\text{‘}\alpha = \breve{R}\text{‘max}_Q\text{‘}\alpha,$$

$$\alpha \subset \text{D}\text{‘}Q_{Rx} \,.\, \exists\,!\,\alpha \,.\, \sim \exists\,!\,\overrightarrow{\text{max}_Q\text{‘}\alpha} \,.\, \supset .\, \text{seq}\,(Q_{Rx})\text{‘}\alpha = \text{lt}_Q\text{‘}\alpha,$$

whence
$$\alpha \subset \text{D}\text{‘}Q_{Rx} \,.\, \supset_\alpha .\, \text{E}\,!\,\text{seq}\,(Q_{Rx})\text{‘}\alpha,$$

which shows that $Q_{Rx} \in \Omega$.

The first derivative of Q_{Rx} is $\delta_Q\text{‘}(Q*R)\text{‘}x$, and its last term, if any, is

$$\breve{\iota}\text{‘}\{(Q*R)\text{‘}x - \text{D}\text{‘}R\},\ \ i.e.\ \ \text{lt}_Q\text{‘}\{(Q*R)\text{‘}x \cap \text{D}\text{‘}R\}.$$

The hypothesis required for $Q_{Rx} \in \Omega$ is the same as for $Q_{Rx} \in \text{Ser}$, namely,

$$Q \in \text{Rl}\text{‘}J \cap \text{trans} \,.\, R \in \text{Rl}\text{‘}Q \cap \text{Cls} \to 1 \,.\, \text{lt}_Q \upharpoonright \text{Cl ex}\text{‘}(R*Q)\text{‘}x \in 1 \to \text{Cls}.$$

In order that Q_{Rx} may not be null, we require further $x \in \text{D}\text{‘}R$.

The next set of propositions (*257·5—·56) are designed to prove that, subject to the above hypothesis together with $x \in \text{D}\text{‘}R$, Q_{Rx} is the only value of P fulfilling the following conditions:

(1) P is transitive.

(2) $C\text{‘}P$ is contained in $(R*Q)\text{‘}x$.

(3) If z is any member of $\text{D}\text{‘}P$, $\breve{R}\text{‘}z$ is its immediate successor.

(4) If α is any existent class contained in $C\text{‘}P$ and having no maximum, $\text{lt}_Q\text{‘}\alpha$ is its P-limit.

This proposition is essential for what may be called "transfinite inductive definitions," *i.e.* definitions of a series by defining the successor of every term, and the successor of every class having no maximum.

The following illustration may make this clear. Suppose R is a many-one relation of classes to individuals; suppose we start with some class α, and proceed to $\alpha \cup \iota`\breve{R}`\alpha$, $\alpha \cup \iota`\breve{R}`\alpha \cup \iota`\breve{R}`(\alpha \cup \iota`\breve{R}`\alpha)$, and so on. At the end of this series we put its sum, *i.e.* its limit with respect to the relation $(\subset \dot{\cap} J)$; let the sum be β. We then proceed with $\beta \cup \iota`\breve{R}`\beta$, and so on, as long as possible. The series ends with a sum which is not a member of $D`R$, if there is such a sum. It is evident that the series is uniquely determined by the above method of generation; the above-mentioned propositions give symbolic expression to the process expressed in words by "and so on, as long as possible."

***257·01.** $(R*Q)`x = C`Q \cap \hat{y}\{x \in \sigma \,.\, \breve{R}``\sigma \cup \delta_Q`\sigma \subset \sigma \,.\supset_\sigma.\, y \in \sigma\}$ Df

***257·02.** $Q_{Rx} = Q(R,x) = Q \upharpoonright (R*Q)`x$ Df

***257·1.** $\vdash :.\, y \in (R*Q)`x \,.\equiv:\, y \in C`Q :\, x \in \sigma \,.\, \breve{R}``\sigma \cup \delta_Q`\sigma \subset \sigma \,.\supset_\sigma.\, y \in \sigma$
[(*257·01)]

***257·101.** $\vdash ::\, y \in (R*Q)`x \,.\equiv:.\, y \in C`Q :.$
$x \in \sigma \,.\, \breve{R}``\sigma \subset \sigma : \mu \subset \sigma \,.\, \exists ! \mu \cap C`Q \,.\supset_\mu.\, \overrightarrow{\text{lt}}_Q`\mu \subset \sigma :\supset_\sigma.\, y \in \sigma$
[*257·1 . *216·1]

***257·102.** $\vdash ::\, y \in (R*Q)`x \,.\equiv:.\, y \in C`Q :.$
$x \in \sigma \,.\, \breve{R}``\sigma \subset \sigma : \mu \subset \sigma \,.\, \exists ! \mu \cap C`Q \,.\, \sim\exists ! \overrightarrow{\max}_Q`\mu \,.\supset_\mu.\, \overrightarrow{\text{seq}}_Q`\mu \subset \sigma :\supset_\sigma.\, y \in \sigma$
[*257·101 . *207·1]

***257·11.** $\vdash : x \in \sigma \,.\, \breve{R}``\sigma \cup \delta_Q`\sigma \subset \sigma \,.\supset.\, (R*Q)`x \subset \sigma$ [*257·1]

Almost all proofs of propositions concerning $(R*Q)`x$ use this proposition.

***257·111.** $\vdash .\, (R*Q)`x \subset C`Q$ [*257·1]

***257·12.** $\vdash : x \in C`Q \,.\equiv.\, x \in (R*Q)`x$ [*257·1]

***257·121.** $\vdash : R \Subset Q \,.\, y \in (R*Q)`x \,.\supset.\, \overleftarrow{R}`y \subset (R*Q)`x$

Dem.

$\vdash .\, *257·1 \,.\supset \vdash :.\, \text{Hp} \,.\, yRz \,.\supset: x \in \sigma \,.\, \breve{R}``\sigma \cup \delta_Q`\sigma \subset \sigma \,.\supset_\sigma.\, y \in \sigma : yRz \,.\, z \in C`Q :$

[*37·1] $\supset : z \in C`Q : x \in \sigma \,.\, \breve{R}``\sigma \subset \sigma \,.\, \delta_Q`\sigma \subset \sigma \,.\supset_\sigma.\, z \in \sigma :$

[*257·1] $\supset : z \in (R*Q)`x :.\supset \vdash .\, \text{Prop}$

***257·122.** $\vdash : R \Subset Q . \mu \subset (R * Q)‘x . \supset . \breve{R}“\mu \subset (R * Q)‘x$ [*257·121]

***257·123.** $\vdash : R \Subset Q . \supset . \breve{R}“(R * Q)‘x \subset (R * Q)‘x$ [*257·122]

***257·124.** $\vdash : R \Subset Q . \supset . \breve{R}_*“(R * Q)‘x \subset (R * Q)‘x$ [*257·123]

***257·125.** $\vdash : R \Subset Q . x \epsilon C‘Q . \supset . \overleftarrow{R_*}‘x \subset (R * Q)‘x$ [*257·12·124]

***257·126.** $\vdash : R \Subset Q . x \epsilon \text{D}‘R . \sim(xRx) . \supset . (R * Q)‘x \sim \epsilon 0 \cup 1$ [*257·125]

***257·13.** $\vdash : \mu \subset (R * Q)‘x . \exists ! \mu . \supset . \overrightarrow{\text{lt}_Q}‘\mu \subset (R * Q)‘x$

Dem.

$\vdash . *257·101 . *10·1 . *22·1 . \supset \vdash :: \mu \subset (R * Q)‘x . \supset :.$

$x \epsilon \sigma . \breve{R}“\sigma \subset \sigma : \nu \subset \sigma . \exists ! \nu \cap C‘Q . \supset_\nu . \overrightarrow{\text{lt}_Q}‘\nu \subset \sigma : \supset . \mu \subset \sigma$ (1)

$\vdash . (1) . \text{Fact} . \supset \vdash :: \text{Hp} . \supset :.$

$x \epsilon \sigma . \breve{R}“\sigma \subset \sigma : \nu \subset \sigma . \exists ! \nu \cap C‘Q . \supset_\nu . \overrightarrow{\text{lt}_Q}‘\nu \subset \sigma : \supset . \mu \subset \sigma . \exists ! \mu$ (2)

$\vdash . *10·1 . *257·111 . \supset$

$\vdash :. \nu \subset \sigma . \exists ! \nu \cap C‘Q . \supset_\nu . \overrightarrow{\text{lt}_Q}‘\nu \subset \sigma : \supset : \text{Hp} . \mu \subset \sigma . y \, \text{lt}_Q \, \mu . \supset . y \epsilon \sigma$ (3)

$\vdash . (2) . (3) . \supset \vdash :: \text{Hp} . y \, \text{lt}_Q \, \mu . \supset :.$

$x \epsilon \sigma . \breve{R}“\sigma \subset \sigma : \nu \subset \sigma . \exists ! \nu \cap C‘Q . \supset_\nu . \overrightarrow{\text{lt}_Q}‘\nu \subset \sigma : \supset . y \epsilon \sigma$ (4)

$\vdash . (4) . *10·11·21 . *257·101 . \supset \vdash : \text{Hp} . y \, \text{lt}_Q \, \mu . \supset . y \epsilon (R * Q)‘\mu : \supset \vdash . \text{Prop}$

***257·131.** $\vdash . \delta_Q‘(R * Q)‘x \subset (R * Q)‘x$ [*257·13 . *216·1]

***257·132.** $\vdash : \kappa \subset \text{Cl ex}‘(R * Q)‘x . \supset . \text{lt}_Q“\kappa \subset (R * Q)‘x$ [*257·13]

***257·14.** $\vdash : R \Subset Q . \supset . (R * Q)‘x \subset \overleftarrow{Q_*}‘x$

Dem.

$\vdash . *90·163 . \supset \vdash : \text{Hp} . \supset . \breve{R}“\overleftarrow{Q_*}‘x \subset \overleftarrow{Q_*}‘x$ (1)

$\vdash . *206·15 . \supset \vdash : \mu \subset \overleftarrow{Q_*}‘x . z \, \text{lt}_Q \, \mu . \exists ! \mu . \supset . z \epsilon p‘\overleftarrow{Q}“\mu . \exists ! \mu . \mu \subset \overleftarrow{Q_*}‘x .$

[*40·61.*90·163] $\supset . z \epsilon \breve{Q}“\mu . \breve{Q}“\mu \subset \overleftarrow{Q_*}‘x .$

[*22·46] $\supset . z \epsilon \overleftarrow{Q_*}‘x$ (2)

$\vdash . (1) . (2) . *257·11 . \supset \vdash : \text{Hp} . x \epsilon C‘Q . \supset . (R * Q)‘x \subset \overleftarrow{Q_*}‘x$ (3)

$\vdash . *37·261·29 . *60·33 . (*216·01) . \supset$

$\vdash : \text{Hp} . \supset . \breve{R}“(-C‘Q) = \Lambda . \delta_Q‘(-C‘Q) = \Lambda$ (4)

$\vdash . (4) . *257·11 . \supset \vdash : \text{Hp} . x \sim \epsilon C‘Q . \supset . (R * Q)‘x \subset -C‘Q .$

[*257·111] $\supset . (R * Q)‘x = \Lambda$ (5)

$\vdash . (3) . (5) . \supset \vdash . \text{Prop}$

***257·141.** $\vdash : R \Subset Q . \supset . \breve{R}“C‘Q \cup \delta_Q‘C‘Q \subset C‘Q$ [*216·111 . *37·201·16]

***257·142.** $\vdash : R \Subset Q . x \in C'Q . \supset . (R * Q)'x = \hat{y}\{x \in \sigma . \breve{R}``\sigma \cup \delta_Q`\sigma \subset \sigma . \supset_\sigma . y \in \sigma\}$

Dem.

$\vdash . *257·141 . \supset \vdash : \text{Hp} . \supset . \hat{y}\{x \in \sigma . \breve{R}``\sigma \cup \delta_Q`\sigma \subset \sigma . \supset_\sigma . y \in \sigma\} \subset C'Q$ (1)

$\vdash . (1) . *257·1 . \supset \vdash . \text{Prop}$

***257·15.** $\vdash : y \in (R * Q)'x . z \in (R * Q)'y . \supset . z \in (R * Q)'x$

Dem.

$\vdash . *257·1 . \supset \vdash :. \breve{R}``\sigma \cup \delta_Q`\sigma \subset \sigma . \supset : x \in \sigma . \supset . y \in \sigma : y \in \sigma . \supset . z \in \sigma :$

[Syll] $\supset : x \in \sigma . \supset . z \in \sigma$ (1)

$\vdash . (1) . *257·1 . \supset \vdash . \text{Prop}$

***257·16.** $\vdash : x \in C'Q - \text{D}'R . \supset . (R * Q)'x = \iota'x$

Dem.

$\vdash . *257·12 . \quad \supset \vdash : \text{Hp} . \supset . x \in (R * Q)'x$ (1)

$\vdash . *37·261·29 . \quad \supset \vdash : \text{Hp} . \supset . \breve{R}``\iota'x = \Lambda$ (2)

$\vdash . *205·18 . \quad \supset \vdash : \text{Hp} . \sim \exists ! \overrightarrow{\max}_Q`\iota'x . \supset . xQx .$

[*206·42] $\supset . \overrightarrow{\text{seq}}_Q`\iota'x = \Lambda$ (3)

$\vdash . (3) . *216·101 . \supset \vdash : \text{Hp} . \supset . \delta_Q`\iota'x = \Lambda$ (4)

$\vdash . (2) . (4) . \quad \supset \vdash : \text{Hp} . \supset . \breve{R}``\iota'x \cup \delta_Q`\iota'x \subset \iota'x .$

[*257·11] $\supset . (R * Q)'x \subset \iota'x$ (5)

$\vdash . (1) . (5) . \supset \vdash . \text{Prop}$

We now begin the proof (completed in *257·34) that under certain circumstances $Q_{Rx} \in \Omega$. We first prove that the class σ introduced in *257·2 is transfinitely hereditary, and this requires as a preliminary the proof that if $y \in \sigma$, the class $\overrightarrow{(Q_{Rx})_*}`y \cup \overleftarrow{(Q_{Rx})_*}`\breve{R}`y$ is transfinitely hereditary. This preliminary is provided by *257·2·21. The hypothesis of *257·2 is not all used in *257·2, but is introduced because it is required in the set of propositions of which this is the first.

***257·2.** $\vdash :. Q \in \text{Rl}'J \cap \text{trans} . R \in \text{Rl}'Q \cap \text{Cls} \to 1 .$

$\sigma = (R * Q)'x \cap p'\overleftrightarrow{Q}``(R * Q)'x \cap \hat{y}\{zQ_{Rx}y . \supset_z . \overleftarrow{Q}_{Rx}`z = \overleftarrow{(Q_{Rx})_*}`\breve{R}`z\} . \supset :$

$y \in \sigma . z \in \overrightarrow{(Q_{Rx})_*}`y \cup \overleftarrow{(Q_{Rx})_*}`\breve{R}`y . z \in \text{D}'R . \supset . \breve{R}`z \in \overrightarrow{(Q_{Rx})_*}`y \cup \overleftarrow{(Q_{Rx})_*}`\breve{R}`y$

Dem.

$\vdash . *90·163 . *37·62 . *257·123 . \supset$

$\vdash :. R \Subset Q . \text{E} ! \breve{R}`z . \supset : z \in \overleftarrow{(Q_{Rx})_*}`\breve{R}`y . \supset . \breve{R}`z \in \overleftarrow{(Q_{Rx})_*}`\breve{R}`y$ (1)

$\vdash . *30·37 . \supset \vdash : \text{E} ! \breve{R}`z . z = y . \supset . \breve{R}`z = \breve{R}`y$ (2)

$\vdash . *201·18 . *91·52 . *32·182 . \supset$

$\vdash : \text{Hp} . y \in \sigma . z \in \overrightarrow{Q}_{Rx}`y . \supset . \overleftarrow{Q}_{Rx}`z = \overleftarrow{(Q_{Rx})_*}`\breve{R}`z . y \in \overleftarrow{Q}_{Rx}`z .$

[*13·13] $\supset . y \in \overleftarrow{(Q_{Rx})_*}`\breve{R}`z .$

[*32·182] $\supset . \breve{R}`z \in \overrightarrow{(Q_{Rx})_*}`y$ (3)

$\vdash . (1) . (2) . (3) . *71·161 . \supset \vdash . \text{Prop}$

***257·21.** $\vdash : \text{Hp} *257\cdot2 . y \in \sigma . \mu \subset \overrightarrow{(Q_{Rx})_*}\text{‘}y \cup \overleftarrow{(Q_{Rx})_*}\text{‘}\breve{R}\text{‘}y . \exists ! \mu . \supset .$

$\overrightarrow{\text{lt}_Q}\text{‘}\mu \subset \overrightarrow{Q_*}\text{‘}y \cup \overleftarrow{Q_*}\text{‘}\breve{R}\text{‘}y$

Dem.

$\vdash . *201\cdot14\cdot15 . *206\cdot134 . \supset$

$\vdash : \text{Hp} . \exists ! \mu \cap \overleftarrow{Q_*}\text{‘}\breve{R}\text{‘}y . \supset . \overrightarrow{\text{lt}_Q}\text{‘}\mu \subset \overleftarrow{Q_*}\text{‘}\breve{R}\text{‘}y$ (1)

$\vdash . *205\cdot38 . \supset \vdash : \text{Hp} . \mu \subset \overrightarrow{Q_*}\text{‘}y . y \in \mu . \supset . y \in \overrightarrow{\max_Q}\text{‘}\mu .$

[*207·11] $\supset . \overrightarrow{\text{lt}_Q}\text{‘}\mu = \Lambda$ (2)

$\vdash . *40\cdot55 . *206\cdot143 . \supset$

$\vdash : \mu \subset \overrightarrow{Q}\text{‘}y . w \, \text{lt}_Q \mu . \supset . y \in p\text{‘}\overleftarrow{Q}\text{“}\mu . w \sim\in \breve{Q}\text{“}p\text{‘}\overleftarrow{Q}\text{“}\mu .$

[*37·1] $\supset . \sim(yQw)$ (3)

$\vdash . *257\cdot13 . \supset \vdash :. \text{Hp}(3) . \text{Hp} . \supset : yQw . \vee . wQ_*y :$

[(3)] $\supset : wQ_*y$ (4)

$\vdash . (1) . (2) . (4) . \supset \vdash . \text{Prop}$

***257·211.** $\vdash : \text{Hp} *257\cdot2 . y \in \sigma . \supset . (R*Q)\text{‘}x \subset \overrightarrow{(Q_{Rx})_*}\text{‘}y \cup \overleftarrow{(Q_{Rx})_*}\text{‘}\breve{R}\text{‘}y$

Dem.

$\vdash . *257\cdot14 . \supset \vdash : \text{Hp} . \supset . x \in \overrightarrow{(Q_{Rx})_*}\text{‘}y$ (1)

$\vdash . (1) . *257\cdot2\cdot21\cdot11 . \supset \vdash . \text{Prop}$

***257·22.** $\vdash : \text{Hp} *257\cdot2 . y \in \sigma . \supset . \overleftarrow{Q_{Rx}}\text{‘}y = \overleftarrow{(Q_{Rx})_*}\text{‘}\breve{R}\text{‘}y . \overrightarrow{(Q_{Rx})_*}\text{‘}y = \overrightarrow{Q_{Rx}}\text{‘}\breve{R}\text{‘}y$

Dem.

$\vdash . *257\cdot211 . \supset \vdash : \text{Hp} . \supset . \overleftarrow{(Q_{Rx})_*}\text{‘}\breve{R}\text{‘}y = (R*Q)\text{‘}x - \overrightarrow{(Q_{Rx})_*}\text{‘}y$

[Hp] $= \overleftarrow{Q_{Rx}}\text{‘}y$ (1)

Similarly $\vdash : \text{Hp} . \supset . \overrightarrow{(Q_{Rx})_*}\text{‘}y = \overrightarrow{Q_{Rx}}\text{‘}\breve{R}\text{‘}y$ (2)

$\vdash . (1) . (2) . \supset \vdash . \text{Prop}$

It is to be understood that $\overleftarrow{(Q_{Rx})_*}\text{‘}\breve{R}\text{‘}y = \Lambda$ if $\sim E ! \breve{R}\text{‘}y$.

***257·23.** $\vdash : \text{Hp} *257\cdot2 . \supset . \breve{R}\text{“}\sigma \subset \sigma$

Dem.

$\vdash . *257\cdot22 . \quad \supset \vdash :. \text{Hp} . y \in \sigma \cap \text{D‘}R . \supset : zQR\text{‘}y . \supset_z . \overleftarrow{Q_{Rx}}\text{‘}z = \overleftarrow{(Q_{Rx})_*}\text{‘}\breve{R}\text{‘}z$ (1)

$\vdash . *257\cdot22\cdot211 . \supset \vdash : \text{Hp} . y \in \sigma \cap \text{D‘}R . \supset . (R*Q)\text{‘}x = \overrightarrow{Q_{Rx}}\text{‘}\breve{R}\text{‘}y \cup \overleftarrow{(Q_{Rx})_*}\text{‘}\breve{R}\text{‘}y$ (2)

$\vdash . (1) . (2) . \quad \supset \vdash : \text{Hp} . y \in \sigma \cap \text{D‘}R . \supset . \breve{R}\text{‘}y \in \sigma : \supset \vdash . \text{Prop}$

The above proposition gives the first stage in the proof that σ is transfinitely hereditary. The second stage, similarly, requires as a preliminary the proof that if μ is an existent sub-class of σ having no maximum, then

$$Q_{Rx}\text{“}\mu \cup (\breve{Q}_{Rx})_*\text{“}\overrightarrow{\text{lt}_Q}\text{‘}\mu$$

is a transfinitely hereditary class. This proof is provided by *257·24·241·242.

***257·24.** $\vdash : \mathrm{Hp} *257{\cdot}2 . \mu \subset \sigma . \exists ! \mu . \sim \exists ! \overrightarrow{\max}_Q\text{‘}\mu . \supset . \breve{R}\text{“}Q_{Rx}\text{“}\mu \subset Q_{Rx}\text{“}\mu$

Dem.

$$\vdash . *91{\cdot}52 . *201{\cdot}18 . \supset \vdash : \mathrm{Hp} . z \in Q_{Rx}\text{“}\mu . \supset . \overleftarrow{Q_{Rx}}\text{‘}z = \overleftarrow{(Q_{Rx})_*}\text{‘}\breve{R}\text{‘}z .$$

$$[*37{\cdot}46 . *13{\cdot}12] \quad \supset . \exists ! \overleftarrow{(Q_{Rx})_*}\text{‘}\breve{R}\text{‘}z \cap \mu .$$

$$[*37{\cdot}46] \quad \supset . \breve{R}\text{‘}z \in (Q_{Rx})_*\text{“}\mu \qquad (1)$$

$$\vdash . *205{\cdot}123 . \quad \supset \vdash : \mathrm{Hp} . \supset . \mu \subset Q_{Rx}\text{“}\mu \qquad (2)$$

$$\vdash . (1) . (2) . \quad \supset \vdash : \mathrm{Hp} . z \in Q_{Rx}\text{“}\mu . \supset . \breve{R}\text{‘}z \in Q_{Rx}\text{“}\mu : \supset \vdash . \mathrm{Prop}$$

***257·241.** $\vdash : \mathrm{Hp} *257{\cdot}24 . \supset . \breve{R}\text{“}\{Q_{Rx}\text{“}\mu \cup (\breve{Q}_{Rx})_*\text{“}\overrightarrow{\mathrm{lt}}_Q\text{‘}\mu\} \subset Q_{Rx}\text{“}\mu \subset (\breve{Q}_{Rx})_*\text{“}\overrightarrow{\mathrm{lt}}_Q\text{‘}\mu$

Dem.

$$\vdash . *90{\cdot}164 . \supset \vdash : R \Subset Q . \supset . \breve{R}\text{“}(\breve{Q}_{Rx})_*\text{“}\overrightarrow{\mathrm{lt}}_Q\text{‘}\mu \subset (\breve{Q}_{Rx})_*\text{“}\overrightarrow{\mathrm{lt}}_Q\text{‘}\mu \qquad (1)$$

$$\vdash . (1) . *257{\cdot}24 . \supset \vdash . \mathrm{Prop}$$

***257·242.** $\vdash : \mathrm{Hp} *257{\cdot}24 . \rho = Q_{Rx}\text{“}\mu \cup (\breve{Q}_{Rx})_*\text{“}\overrightarrow{\mathrm{lt}}_Q\text{‘}\mu .$

$$\alpha \subset \rho . \exists ! \alpha . \sim \exists ! \overrightarrow{\max}_Q\text{‘}\alpha . \supset . \overrightarrow{\mathrm{lt}}_Q\text{‘}\alpha \subset \rho$$

Dem.

$$\vdash . *206{\cdot}15 . \quad \supset \vdash : \mathrm{Hp} . \exists ! \mu \cap p\text{‘}\overleftarrow{Q}\text{“}\alpha . w \,\mathrm{lt}_Q\, \alpha . \supset . \exists ! \mu - \overrightarrow{Q}\text{‘}w \qquad (1)$$

$$\vdash . *201{\cdot}521 . \supset \vdash : \mathrm{Hp} . \mu \subset \sigma . \supset . \mu - \overrightarrow{Q}\text{‘}w \subset \overleftarrow{Q_*}\text{‘}w \qquad (2)$$

$$\vdash . (1) . (2) . \quad \supset \vdash : \mathrm{Hp}(1) . \supset . \exists ! \mu \cap \overleftarrow{Q_*}\text{‘}w \qquad (3)$$

$$\vdash . *205{\cdot}123 . \supset \vdash : \mathrm{Hp} . \supset . \mu \subset Q\text{“}\mu \qquad (4)$$

$$\vdash . (3) . (4) . \quad \supset \vdash : \mathrm{Hp}(1) . \supset . w \in Q_{Rx}\text{“}\mu \qquad (5)$$

$$\vdash . *206{\cdot}24 . \quad \supset \vdash : \mathrm{Hp} . \mu \subset Q\text{“}\alpha . \alpha \subset Q\text{“}\mu . \supset . \overrightarrow{\mathrm{lt}}_Q\text{‘}\alpha = \overrightarrow{\mathrm{lt}}_Q\text{‘}\mu \qquad (6)$$

$$\vdash . *206{\cdot}15 . \quad \supset \vdash : \mathrm{Hp} . \exists ! \alpha \cap (\breve{Q}_{Rx})_*\text{“}\overrightarrow{\mathrm{lt}}_Q\text{‘}\mu . \supset . \overrightarrow{\mathrm{lt}}_Q\text{‘}\alpha \subset (\breve{Q}_{Rx})_*\text{“}\overrightarrow{\mathrm{lt}}_Q\text{‘}\mu \qquad (7)$$

$$\vdash . (5) . (6) . (7) . \supset \vdash . \mathrm{Prop}$$

***257·243.** $\vdash : \mathrm{Hp} *257{\cdot}24 . \supset . (R * Q)\text{‘}x = Q_{Rx}\text{“}\mu \cup p\text{‘}\overleftarrow{Q_{Rx}}\text{“}\mu$ [*40·53 . *205·123]

***257·25.** $\vdash : \mathrm{Hp} *257{\cdot}24 . \supset . (R * Q)\text{‘}x = Q_{Rx}\text{“}\mu \cup (\breve{Q}_{Rx})_*\text{“}\overrightarrow{\mathrm{lt}}_Q\text{‘}\mu$

Dem.

$$\vdash . *257{\cdot}242 . \supset \vdash : \mathrm{Hp} . \supset . \delta_Q\text{‘}\{Q_{Rx}\text{“}\mu \cup (\breve{Q}_{Rx})_*\text{“}\overrightarrow{\mathrm{lt}}_Q\text{‘}\mu\} \subset Q_{Rx}\text{“}\mu \cup (\breve{Q}_{Rx})_*\text{“}\overrightarrow{\mathrm{lt}}_Q\text{‘}\mu \qquad (1)$$

$$\vdash . (1) . *257{\cdot}241 . \supset \vdash . \mathrm{Prop}$$

***257·251.** $\vdash : \mathrm{Hp} *257{\cdot}24 . \supset . (\breve{Q}_{Rx})_*\text{“}\overrightarrow{\mathrm{lt}}_Q\text{‘}\mu = p\text{‘}\overleftarrow{Q_{Rx}}\text{“}\mu$

Dem.

$$\vdash . *257{\cdot}25{\cdot}243 . \supset \vdash : \mathrm{Hp} . \supset . Q_{Rx}\text{“}\mu \cup (\breve{Q}_{Rx})_*\text{“}\overrightarrow{\mathrm{lt}}_Q\text{‘}\mu = Q_{Rx}\text{“}\mu \cup p\text{‘}\overleftarrow{Q_{Rx}}\text{“}\mu .$$

$$[*200{\cdot}53 . *24{\cdot}481] \quad \supset . (\breve{Q}_{Rx})_*\text{“}\overrightarrow{\mathrm{lt}}_Q\text{‘}\mu = p\text{‘}\overleftarrow{Q_{Rx}}\text{“}\mu : \supset \vdash . \mathrm{Prop}$$

***257·252.** $\vdash : \text{Hp} *257\cdot24 \,.\, \exists\,!\, p`\overleftarrow{Q}_{Rx}``\mu \,.\, \supset \,.\, Q_{Rx}``\mu = p`\overrightarrow{Q}_{Rx}``\overrightarrow{\text{lt}}_Q`\mu \,.\, \exists\,!\, \overrightarrow{\text{lt}}_Q`\mu$

Dem.

$\vdash \,.\, *257\cdot251 \,.\, *37\cdot29 \,.\, \supset \vdash : \text{Hp} \,.\, \supset \,.\, \exists\,!\, \overrightarrow{\text{lt}}_Q`\mu$ (1)

$[*200\cdot53 . *40\cdot62] \quad \supset \,.\, p`\overrightarrow{Q}_{Rx}``\overrightarrow{\text{lt}}_Q`\mu \subset (R_*Q)`x - (\breve{Q}_{Rx})_*``\overrightarrow{\text{lt}}_Q`\mu$

$[*257\cdot251] \quad \subset (R_*Q)`x - p`\overleftarrow{Q}_{Rx}``\mu$

$[\text{Hp} . *10\cdot57 . *257\cdot243] \quad \subset Q_{Rx}``\mu$ (2)

$\vdash \,.\, *201\cdot51 \,.\, *40\cdot67 \,.\, \supset \vdash : \text{Hp} \,.\, \supset \,.\, Q_{Rx}``\mu \subset p`\overrightarrow{Q}_{Rx}``\overrightarrow{\text{lt}}_Q`\mu$ (3)

$\vdash \,.\, (1) \,.\, (2) \,.\, (3) \,.\, \supset \vdash \,.\, \text{Prop}$

In order to complete the proof that σ is a hereditary class, we have to introduce the additional hypothesis

$$\text{lt}_Q \upharpoonright \text{Cl ex}`(R_*Q)`x \in 1 \to \text{Cls}.$$

With the help of this hypothesis, the last stage of the proof is provided by the following proposition.

***257·26.** $\vdash : \text{Hp} *257\cdot2 \,.\, \text{lt}_Q \upharpoonright \text{Cl ex}`(R_*Q)`x \in 1 \to \text{Cls} \,.\, \supset \,.\, \delta_Q`\sigma \subset \sigma$

Dem.

$\vdash \,.\, *257\cdot251\cdot252 \,.\, \supset \vdash :. \text{Hp} \,.\, \mu \subset \sigma \,.\, \exists\,!\, \mu \,.\, \exists\,!\, \overrightarrow{\text{lt}}_Q`\mu \,.\, \supset :$

$\quad (R_*Q)`x = \overrightarrow{Q}_{Rx}`\text{lt}_Q`\mu \cup \overleftarrow{(Q_{Rx})_*}`\text{lt}_Q`\mu \,.\, \overrightarrow{Q}_{Rx}`\text{lt}_Q`\mu = Q_{Rx}``\mu :$

$[\text{Hp}] \supset : \text{lt}_Q`\mu \in p`\overleftrightarrow{Q}``(R_*Q)`x : yQ_{Rx}\,\text{lt}_Q`\mu \,.\, \supset_y \,.\, \overleftarrow{Q}_{Rx}`y = \overleftarrow{(Q_{Rx})_*}`\breve{R}`y :$

$[\text{Hp}] \supset : \text{lt}_Q`\mu \in \sigma :. \supset \vdash \,.\, \text{Prop}$

***257·261.** $\vdash : \text{Hp} *257\cdot26 \,.\, \supset \,.\, (R_*Q)`x = \sigma \quad [*257\cdot11\cdot23\cdot26]$

***257·27.** $\vdash : Q \in \text{Rl}`J \cap \text{trans} \,.\, R \in \text{Rl}`Q \cap \text{Cls} \to 1 \,.$

$\quad \text{lt}_Q \upharpoonright \text{Cl ex}`(R_*Q)`x \in 1 \to \text{Cls} \,.\, \supset \,.$

$\quad Q_{Rx} \in \text{Ser} \,.\, Q_{Rx} = (R \mid Q_*) \upharpoonright\!\!\upharpoonright (R_*Q)`x$

Dem.

$\vdash \,.\, *257\cdot261 \,.\, \supset$

$\vdash : \text{Hp} \,.\, \supset \,.\, (R_*Q)`x \subset p`\overleftrightarrow{Q}``(R_*Q)`x \cap \hat{y}\,\{zQ_{Rx}y \,.\, \supset_z \,.\, \overleftarrow{Q}_{Rx}`z = \overleftarrow{(Q_{Rx})_*}`\breve{R}`z\}$ (1)

$\vdash \,.\, (1) \,.\, \supset \vdash :: \text{Hp} \,.\, \supset :. Q_{Rx} \in \text{connex} :. z \in \text{D}`Q_{Rx} \,.\, \supset_z : zQ_{Rx}w \,.\, \equiv_w \,.\, zR \mid (Q_{Rx})_* w :.$

$[*5\cdot32 . *4\cdot71 . *257\cdot121]$

$\quad \supset :. Q_{Rx} \in \text{connex} :. zQ_{Rx}w \,.\, \equiv_{z,w} \,.\, z \in \text{D}`Q_{Rx} \,.\, zR \mid Q_* w \,.\, w \in C`Q_{Rx} :.$

$[*36\cdot13 . *257\cdot121] \supset :. Q_{Rx} \in \text{connex} \,.\, Q_{Rx} = (R \mid Q_*) \upharpoonright\!\!\upharpoonright (R_*Q)`x :: \supset \vdash \,.\, \text{Prop}$

We have thus proved that Q_{Rx} is a series. No additional hypothesis is required to prove that it is well-ordered, as we shall now show.

***257·28.** $\vdash : \text{Hp} *257\cdot27 \,.\, \mu \subset (R_*Q)`x \,.\, \exists\,!\, \mu \,.\, \overrightarrow{\max}_Q`\mu = \Lambda \,.\, \exists\,!\, p`\overleftarrow{Q}_{Rx}``\mu \,.\, \supset \,.$

$\quad p`\overleftarrow{Q}_{Rx}``\mu = \overleftarrow{(\breve{Q}_{Rx})_*}``\text{lt}_Q`\mu \,.\, Q_{Rx}``\mu = p`\overrightarrow{Q}_{Rx}``\overrightarrow{\text{lt}}_Q`\mu \quad [*257\cdot251\cdot27]$

***257·281.** $\vdash : \text{Hp} *257\cdot28 . \text{E}!\,\text{lt}_Q`\mu . \supset .$

$$p`\overleftarrow{Q_{Rx}}``\mu = (\overleftarrow{Q_{Rx}})_*`\text{lt}_Q`\mu . Q_{Rx}``\mu = \overrightarrow{Q_{Rx}}`\text{lt}_Q`\mu \quad [*257\cdot28]$$

***257·29.** $\vdash : \text{Hp} *257\cdot27 . x \in \text{D}`R . \supset . C`Q_{Rx} = (R*Q)`x . B`Q_{Rx} = x$

Dem.

$\vdash . *257\cdot27\cdot126 . *202\cdot55 . \supset \vdash : \text{Hp} . \supset . C`Q_{Rx} = (R*Q)`x$ (1)

$\vdash . *257\cdot14 . \quad \supset \vdash : \text{Hp} . \supset . (R*Q)`x - \iota`x \subset \overleftarrow{Q_{Rx}}`x$ (2)

$\vdash . (1) . (2) . \supset \vdash . \text{Prop}$

***257·291.** $\vdash : \text{Hp} *257\cdot27 . x \sim\in \text{D}`R . \supset . Q_{Rx} = \dot\Lambda \quad [*257\cdot16 . *200\cdot35]$

***257·3.** $\vdash : \text{Hp} *257\cdot27 . \supset . \text{D}`Q_{Rx} = \text{D}`R \cap (R*Q)`x$

Dem.

$\vdash . *257\cdot27 . \supset \vdash :. \text{Hp} . y \in (R*Q)`x . \supset : \exists!\,\overleftarrow{Q}`y . \equiv . \exists!\,\overleftarrow{Q_*}`\breve{R}`y .$

$[*257\cdot141] \quad \equiv . \text{E}!\,\breve{R}`y :. \supset \vdash . \text{Prop}$

***257·31.** $\vdash : \text{Hp} *257\cdot27 . \mu \subset (R*Q)`x . \exists!\,\mu . \sim\exists!\,\overrightarrow{\max_Q}`\mu . \exists!\,p`\overleftarrow{Q_{Rx}}``\mu . \supset .$

$$\text{seq}\,(Q_{Rx})`\mu = \text{lt}_Q`\mu \quad [*257\cdot28]$$

***257·32.** $\vdash : \text{Hp} *257\cdot27 . \mu \subset (R*Q)`x . \exists!\,\overrightarrow{\max_Q}`\mu . \exists!\,p`\overleftarrow{Q_{Rx}}``\mu . \supset .$

$$\text{seq}\,(Q_{Rx})`\mu = \breve{R}`\max\,(Q_{Rx})`\mu$$

Dem.

$\vdash . *257\cdot3 . \supset \vdash : \text{Hp} . \supset . \mu \subset \text{D}`R .$

$[*257\cdot27.\text{Transp}] \quad \supset . \overrightarrow{Q_*}`\max\,(Q_{Rx})`\mu = \overrightarrow{Q}`\breve{R}`\max\,(Q_{Rx})`\mu : \supset \vdash . \text{Prop}$

***257·33.** $\vdash : \text{Hp} *257\cdot27 . \mu \subset (R*Q)`x . \exists!\,\mu . \exists!\,p`\overleftarrow{Q_{Rx}}``\mu . \supset . \text{E}!\,\text{seq}\,(Q_{Rx})`\mu$

$[*257\cdot31\cdot32]$

The above proposition together with *257·27 shows that Q_{Rx} is well-ordered, in virtue of *250·123.

***257·34.** $\vdash : \text{Hp} *257\cdot27 . \supset . Q_{Rx} \in \Omega$

Dem.

$\vdash . *257\cdot291 . \quad \supset \vdash : \text{Hp} . x \sim\in \text{D}`R . \supset . Q_{Rx} \in \Omega$ (1)

$\vdash . *257\cdot29 . *206\cdot14 . \supset \vdash : \text{Hp} . x \in \text{D}`R . \supset . \text{seq}_P`\Lambda = x$ (2)

$\vdash . (2) . *257\cdot33 . \supset$

$\vdash :. \text{Hp} . x \in \text{D}`R . \supset : \mu \subset (R*Q)`x . \exists!\,p`\overleftarrow{Q_{Rx}}``\mu . \supset_\mu . \text{E}!\,\text{seq}\,(Q_{Rx})`\mu :$

$[*257\cdot29.*206\cdot131] \supset : \exists!\,p`\overleftarrow{Q_{Rx}}``(\mu \cap C`Q_{Rx}) . \supset_\mu . \text{E}!\,\text{seq}\,(Q_{Rx})`\mu :$

$[*250\cdot123.*257\cdot27] \supset : Q_{Rx} \in \Omega$ (3)

$\vdash . (1) . (3) . \supset \vdash . \text{Prop}$

***257·35.** $\vdash : \text{Hp} *257\cdot27 . \supset . R \upharpoonleft (R*Q)`x = (Q_{Rx})_1 . R \upharpoonleft (R*Q)`x \in 1 \to 1$

Dem.

$\vdash . *257\cdot32 . \supset \vdash :. \text{Hp} . \supset : y \in \text{D}`Q_{Rx} . \supset . \text{seq}\,(Q_{Rx})`\iota`y = \breve{R}`y$ (1)

$\vdash . (1) . *206\cdot43 . *204\cdot7 . \supset \vdash . \text{Prop}$

***257·36.** $\vdash : \text{Hp} *257\cdot27 . x \in \text{D}`R . \supset .$

$C`Q_{Rx} = (R*Q)`x . \text{Ꮃ}`Q_{Rx} = (R*Q)`x - \iota`x .$

$B`Q_{Rx} = x . \overrightarrow{B}`\breve{Q}_{Rx} = (R*Q)`x - \text{D}`R$ [*257·29·3]

The following propositions are concerned in showing that a relation P which satisfies the hypothesis of *257·5 is identical with Q_{Rx}, thus showing that this hypothesis is sufficient to determine P.

***257·5.** $\vdash : \text{Hp} *257\cdot27 . P \in \text{trans} . C`P \subset (R*Q)`x . P \dot{-} P^2 = R \upharpoonleft (R*Q)`x .$

$\text{lt}_P \upharpoonleft \text{Cl ex}`(R*Q)`x = \text{lt}_Q \upharpoonleft \text{Cl ex}`(R*Q)`x . \supset . P \in J . C`P = (R*Q)`x$

The above hypothesis is not all necessary for the present proposition, but it is necessary for the series of propositions of which this is the first.

Dem.

$\vdash . *37\cdot41 . \supset \vdash :. \text{Hp} . \supset : \text{D}`(P \dot{-} P^2) = R``(R*Q)`x \cap (R*Q)`x$

[*257·36] $= (R*Q)`x \cap \text{D}`R$ (1)

$\vdash . *32\cdot14 . \supset \vdash : \text{Hp} . \supset . \overrightarrow{\text{lt}_P}`\{(R*Q)`x \cap \text{D}`R\} = \overrightarrow{\text{lt}_Q}`\{(R*Q)`x \cap \text{D}`R\}$

[*257·36] $= (R*Q)`x - \text{D}`R$ (2)

$\vdash . (1) . (2) . \supset \vdash : \text{Hp} . \supset . (R*Q)`x \subset C`P .$

[Hp] $\supset . (R*Q)`x = C`P$ (3)

$\vdash . (3) . \quad \supset \vdash : \text{Hp} . \supset : x \in \text{D}`P . \supset . xP \dot{-} P^2 (\breve{R}`x) .$

[*34·5.Transp] $\supset . \sim (xPx)$ (4)

$\vdash . (3) . (4) . \supset \vdash . \text{Prop}$

***257·51.** $\vdash : \text{Hp} *257\cdot5 . \supset . C`P = \overleftarrow{P}_*`x$

Dem.

$\vdash . *257\cdot123 . *90\cdot16 . \supset \vdash : \text{Hp} . \supset . \breve{R}``\overleftarrow{P}_*`x \subset \overleftarrow{P}_*`x$ (1)

$\vdash . *90\cdot13 . \quad \supset \vdash : \text{Hp} . \supset . \text{lt}_Q``\text{Cl ex}`\overleftarrow{P}_*`x = \text{lt}_P``\text{Cl ex}`\overleftarrow{P}_*`x .$

[*90·163.*40·61] $\supset . \text{lt}_Q``\text{Cl ex}`\overleftarrow{P}_*`x \subset \overleftarrow{P}_*`x$ (2)

$\vdash . (1) . (2) . \quad \supset \vdash : \text{Hp} . \supset . (R*Q)`x \subset \overleftarrow{P}_*`x$ (3)

$\vdash . (3) . *257\cdot5 . \supset \vdash . \text{Prop}$

In order to prove $P = Q_{Rx}$ we first prove $P \in \Omega$. The proof proceeds as for Q_{Rx}, but in some points it is easier. It is merely outlined below, as it closely resembles the proof for Q_{Rx}.

***257·52.** $\vdash : \text{Hp} *257\cdot5 .$

$\sigma = C`P \cap p`\overleftrightarrow{P}``C`P \cap \hat{y}(zPy . \supset_z . \overleftarrow{P}`z = \overleftarrow{P}_*`\breve{R}`z) . \supset . \breve{R}``\sigma \subset \sigma$

Dem.

$\vdash . *34{\cdot}5 . \text{Transp} . *201{\cdot}18 . \supset \vdash :. P_1 = R \upharpoonright (R*Q)`x . y \,\epsilon\, p`\overleftrightarrow{P}``C`P . \supset :$

$zP(\breve{R}`y) . \supset . \sim(yPz) : zP_*y . \supset . zP(\breve{R}`y) :$

[Hp] $\supset : zP(\breve{R}`y) . \equiv . zP_*y$ (1)

As in $*257{\cdot}2{\cdot}21$, using $\text{lt}_P \upharpoonright \text{Cl ex}`(R*Q)`x = \text{lt}_Q \upharpoonright \text{Cl ex}`(R*Q)`x$, we prove

$\vdash : \text{Hp} . y \,\epsilon\, \sigma \cap \text{D}`R . \rho = \overrightarrow{P_*}`y \cup \overleftarrow{P_*}`\breve{R}`y . \supset . \breve{R}``\rho \subset \rho . \delta_Q`\rho \subset \rho .$

$\supset . (R*Q)`x = \overrightarrow{P_*}`y \cup \overleftarrow{P_*}`\breve{R}`y$ (2)

$\vdash . (1) . (2) . \supset \vdash : \text{Hp} . y \,\epsilon\, \sigma \cap \text{D}`R . \supset . \overleftarrow{P}`y = \overleftarrow{P_*}`\breve{R}`y$ (3)

$\vdash . (1) . (3) . \supset \vdash : \text{Hp} . y \,\epsilon\, \sigma \cap \text{D}`R . \supset . \breve{R}`y \,\epsilon\, \sigma : \supset \vdash . \text{Prop}$

***257·521.** $\vdash : \text{Hp}\, *257{\cdot}52 . \mu \subset \sigma . \exists ! \mu . \sim \exists ! \overrightarrow{\text{max}_P}`\mu . \supset .$

$(R*Q)`x = P``\mu \cup \breve{P}_*``\overrightarrow{\text{lt}_P}`\mu$

[Proof as in *257·25, by similar stages]

***257·53.** $\vdash :. \text{Hp}\, *257{\cdot}5 . \supset : P \,\epsilon\, \text{Ser} : z \,\epsilon\, \text{D}`P . \supset_z . \overleftarrow{P}`z = \overleftarrow{P_*}`\breve{R}`z$

[Proof as in *257·27]

***257·54.** $\vdash : \text{Hp}\, *257{\cdot}5 . \supset . P \,\epsilon\, \Omega$ [Proof as in *257·34]

***257·55.** $\vdash : \text{Hp}\, *257{\cdot}5 . \sigma = \hat{y}(\overrightarrow{P}`y = \overrightarrow{Q_{Rx}}`y) . \supset . \breve{R}``\sigma \subset \sigma$

Dem.

$\vdash . *257{\cdot}53 . \supset \vdash : \text{Hp} . y \,\epsilon\, C`P . \supset . \overrightarrow{P}`\breve{R}`y = C`P - \overleftarrow{P_*}`\breve{R}`y$

[*257·53] $= C`P - \overleftarrow{P}`y$

[*257·53] $= \overrightarrow{P}`y \cup \iota`y$ (1)

$\vdash . (1) . \supset \vdash : \text{Hp} . y \,\epsilon\, \sigma . \supset . \overrightarrow{P}`\breve{R}`y = \overrightarrow{Q_{Rx}}`y \cup \iota`y$

[*257·22] $= \overrightarrow{Q_{Rx}}`\breve{R}`y : \supset \vdash . \text{Prop}$

***257·551.** $\vdash : \text{Hp}\, *257{\cdot}55 . \supset . \delta_Q`\sigma \subset \sigma$

Dem.

$\vdash . *257{\cdot}53 . \supset$

$\vdash : \text{Hp} . \mu \subset \sigma . \exists ! \mu . z = \text{lt}_Q`\mu . \supset . \overrightarrow{P}`z = \{(R*Q)`x \cap \mu\} \cup P``\mu$

[Hp] $= \{(R*Q)`x \cap \mu\} \cup Q_{Rx}``\mu$

[*257·27] $= \overrightarrow{Q_{Rx}}`z : \supset \vdash . \text{Prop}$

***257·56.** $\vdash : \text{Hp}\, *257{\cdot}5 . \supset . P = Q_{Rx}$

Dem.

$\vdash . *257{\cdot}51{\cdot}54 . \supset \vdash : \text{Hp} . \supset . \overrightarrow{P}`x = \Lambda .$

[*257·36] $\supset . \overrightarrow{P}`x = \overrightarrow{Q_{Rx}}`x$ (1)

$\vdash . (1) . *257{\cdot}55{\cdot}551 . \supset \vdash :. \text{Hp} . \supset : y \,\epsilon\, C`P . \supset_y . \overrightarrow{P}`y = \overrightarrow{Q_{Rx}}`y :. \supset \vdash . \text{Prop}$

This proves that the conditions in the hypothesis of *257·5 are sufficient to determine P.

$*258$. ZERMELO'S THEOREM.

Summary of $*258$.

In this number, we shall first show the applicability of the propositions of $*257$ to the case where the Q of that number is replaced by logical inclusion combined with diversity, *i.e.* by any one of the four relations:

$$\hat{\alpha}\hat{\beta}(\alpha \subset \beta \,.\, \alpha \neq \beta), \quad \hat{\alpha}\hat{\beta}(\beta \subset \alpha \,.\, \alpha \neq \beta),$$

$$\hat{M}\hat{N}(M \subseteq N \,.\, M \neq N), \quad \hat{M}\hat{N}(N \subseteq M \,.\, M \neq N).$$

If we put $\qquad Q = \hat{\alpha}\hat{\beta}(\alpha \subset \beta \,.\, \alpha \neq \beta)$,

and if κ is any class of classes, then $s'\kappa$ is the maximum of κ with respect to Q if $s'\kappa \in \kappa$, and the sequent of κ with respect to Q if $s'\kappa \sim\in \kappa$ ($*258{\cdot}1{\cdot}11$); similarly $p'\kappa$ is the minimum of κ if $p'\kappa \in \kappa$ and the precedent of κ if $p'\kappa \sim\in \kappa$ ($*258{\cdot}101{\cdot}111$). Hence every class of classes has a unique maximum or a unique sequent with respect to Q, and every class of classes has a unique minimum or a unique precedent ($*258{\cdot}12$); we have, moreover,

$$\text{lt}_Q = s \upharpoonright (-\text{G}'\text{max}_Q) \,.\, \text{tl}_Q = p \upharpoonright (-\text{G}'\text{min}_Q) \quad (*258{\cdot}13{\cdot}131).$$

Hence $\text{lt}_Q, \text{tl}_Q \in 1 \rightarrow \text{Cls}$ ($*258{\cdot}14$), and Q and $\breve{Q}$ therefore satisfy the most exacting part of the hypothesis of $*257{\cdot}27$. Also Q and $\breve{Q}$ are Dedekindian relations ($*258{\cdot}14$). (They are not series, because they are not connected.)

An exactly similar argument applies to $\hat{M}\hat{N}(M \subseteq N \,.\, M \neq N)$. Hence if Q is any one of the above four relations, and if R is a many-one contained in Q, it follows from $*257{\cdot}34$ that Q with its field limited to the transfinite posterity of any term is a well-ordered series. If we take $Q = \hat{\alpha}\hat{\beta}(\alpha \subset \beta \,.\, \alpha \neq \beta)$, and take any initial term α, our series proceeds to continually larger classes, proceeding to the limit by taking the logical sum, *i.e.* if κ is any existent sub-class of the posterity of α, $s'\kappa = \text{limax}_Q{}'\kappa = \text{limax}\,(Q_{R\alpha})'\kappa$ ($*258{\cdot}21{\cdot}22$), where $Q_{R\alpha}$ has the meaning defined in $*257$. This process stops with $s'\{\text{D}'R \cap (R{*}Q)'x\}$ if $\text{D}'R \cap (R{*}Q)'x$ has no maximum; otherwise, it stops with the R-successor of this maximum, which is $\text{max}_Q{}'\{C'R \cap (R{*}Q)'x\}$. If, on the other hand, we take Q to be the converse of the above, we proceed to continually smaller classes, and the limit of any set of classes κ having no last term is $p'\kappa$. In this case, if, starting from α, every existent sub-class of α belongs to $\text{D}'R$, the process of diminution cannot stop short of Λ. This is the process applied in Zermelo's theorem. We have the e a class μ, assumed to be not a unit class, and a selective relation S for existent sub-classes of μ, *i.e.* a relation S for which $S \epsilon \epsilon_\Delta$'Cl ex'$\mu$. Then our relation R is the relation of α to $\alpha - \iota$'S'α, *i.e.* the relation of an existent sub-class of μ to the class resulting from taking away its S-representative. Thus $Q_{R\mu}$ is a well-ordered series, which starts from μ and ends with Λ. Omitting the final Λ, S selects a representative from every member of the field of $Q_{R\mu}$, and the series of these representatives, *i.e.* $S;Q_{R\mu}$, is similar to $Q_{R\mu}$ with the final Λ omitted. Moreover every member of μ occurs among these representatives, for, if x be any member of μ, let κ be the class of those members of C'$Q_{R\mu}$ of which x is a member. (There are such classes, because $\mu \epsilon C$'Q_{Rx} and $x \epsilon \mu$.) Then $x \epsilon p$'κ, and by what was said earlier, p'κ is a member of C'$Q_{R\mu}$. Hence, by the definition of κ, p'$\kappa \epsilon \kappa$, and therefore p'$\kappa = \text{max}_Q$'κ. But no class smaller than p'κ can belong to κ, and therefore p'$\kappa - \iota$'S'p'κ is not a member of κ, and therefore x is not a member of p'$\kappa - \iota$'S'p'κ. Hence $x = S$'p'κ, and therefore x occurs among the representatives of members of C'$Q_{R\mu}$, which was to be proved. (The above is an abbreviated rendering of the symbolic proof given below in *258·301.) Hence the field of $S;Q_{R\mu}$ is μ, and therefore there is a well-ordered series having μ for its field, provided ϵ_Δ'Cl ex'μ is not null (*258·32). This is Zermelo's theorem.

The converse of Zermelo's theorem has been already proved (*250·51). Hence the assumption that a selection can be made from all the existent sub-classes of μ is equivalent to the assumption that μ can be well-ordered or is a unit class, *i.e.*

***258·36.** $\vdash : \mu \epsilon C$"$\Omega \cup 1 . \equiv . \exists ! \epsilon_\Delta$'Cl ex'$\mu$

Hence also, by *88·33, the multiplicative axiom is equivalent to the assumption that all classes except unit classes can be well-ordered, *i.e.*

***258·37.** $\vdash$: Mult ax . ≡ . C"$\Omega \cup 1 = \text{Cls}$

Hence also, in virtue of *255·73, the multiplicative axiom implies that of any two unequal existent cardinals one must be the greater, *i.e.*

***258·39.** $\vdash$ :: Mult ax . ⊃ :. $\mu, \nu \epsilon \text{N}_0\text{C} . \supset : \mu \leqslant \nu . \text{v} . \mu > \nu$

***258·1.** $\vdash :. Q = \hat{\alpha}\hat{\beta}(\alpha \subset \beta . \alpha \neq \beta) . \supset : s$'$\kappa \epsilon \kappa . \supset . s$'$\kappa = \text{max}_Q$'$\kappa$

Dem.

$\vdash$. *205·101 . ⊃ $\vdash$ :: Hp . ⊃ :. $\gamma \, \text{max}_Q \kappa . \equiv : \gamma \epsilon \kappa : \alpha \epsilon \kappa . \supset_\alpha . \sim(\gamma \subset \alpha . \gamma \neq \alpha)$:

[Transp] $\equiv : \gamma \epsilon \kappa : \alpha \epsilon \kappa . \alpha \neq \gamma . \supset_\alpha . \sim(\gamma \subset \alpha)$ (1)

$\vdash$. (1) . *10·1 . ⊃ $\vdash$ :: Hp . s'$\kappa \epsilon \kappa$. ⊃ :.

$\gamma \, \text{max}_Q \kappa . \equiv : \gamma \epsilon \kappa : \alpha \epsilon \kappa . \alpha \neq \gamma . \supset_\alpha . \sim(\gamma \subset \alpha) : s$'$\kappa \neq \gamma . \supset . \sim(\gamma \subset s$'$\kappa)$:

[*40·13] $\equiv : \gamma \epsilon \kappa : \alpha \epsilon \kappa . \alpha \neq \gamma . \supset_\alpha . \sim(\gamma \subset \alpha) : s$'$\kappa = \gamma$:

[Transp.*40·13] $\equiv : \gamma \epsilon \kappa . s$'$\kappa = \gamma$:

[Hp] $\equiv : s$'$\kappa = \gamma$ :: ⊃ $\vdash$. Prop

***258·101.** $\vdash : \text{Hp} * 258·1 . p‘\kappa \in \kappa . \supset . p‘\kappa = \min_Q‘\kappa$ [Proof as in *258·1]

***258·11.** $\vdash : \text{Hp} * 258·1 . s‘\kappa \sim\in \kappa . \supset . \text{seq}_Q‘\kappa = s‘\kappa$

Dem.

$\vdash . *40·53 . \supset \vdash : \text{Hp} . \supset . p‘\overleftarrow{Q}‘‘\kappa = \hat{\gamma}(\alpha \in \kappa . \supset_\alpha . \alpha \subset \gamma . \alpha \neq \gamma)$

[Hp.*40·151.*10·29] $= \hat{\gamma}(s‘\kappa \subset \gamma)$ (1)

$\vdash . *40·1 . *22·42·46 . \supset \vdash . s‘\kappa = p‘\hat{\gamma}(s‘\kappa \subset \gamma)$ (2)

$\vdash . (2) . *258·101 . \supset \vdash : \text{Hp} . \supset . s‘\kappa = \min_Q‘\hat{\gamma}(s‘\kappa \subset \gamma)$

[(1)] $= \text{seq}_Q‘\kappa : \supset \vdash . \text{Prop}$

***258·111.** $\vdash : \text{Hp} * 258·1 . p‘\kappa \sim\in \kappa . \supset . \text{prec}_Q‘\kappa = p‘\kappa$ [Proof as in *258·11]

***258·12.** $\vdash :. \text{Hp} * 258·1 . \supset : E ! \max_Q‘\kappa . \vee . E ! \text{seq}_Q‘\kappa :$
$E ! \min_Q‘\kappa . \vee . E ! \text{prec}_Q‘\kappa$ [*258·1·101·11·111]

***258·13.** $\vdash : \text{Hp} * 258·1 . \supset . \text{lt}_Q = s \upharpoonright (-\text{G}‘\max_Q)$

Dem.

$\vdash . *258·1 . \text{Transp} . \supset \vdash : \text{Hp} . \sim \exists ! \overrightarrow{\max_Q}‘\kappa . \supset . s‘\kappa \sim\in \kappa .$

[*258·11] $\supset . \text{lt}_Q‘\kappa = s‘\kappa : \supset \vdash . \text{Prop}$

***258·131.** $\vdash : \text{Hp} * 258·1 . \supset . \text{tl}_Q = p \upharpoonright (-\text{G}‘\min_Q)$ [Proof as in *258·13]

***258·14.** $\vdash : \text{Hp} * 258·1 . \supset . Q, \breve{Q} \in \text{Ded} . \text{lt}_Q, \text{tl}_Q \in 1 \rightarrow \text{Cls}$ [*258·12·13·131]

***258·2.** $\vdash : \text{Hp} * 258·1 . R \in \text{Rl}‘Q \cap \text{Cls} \rightarrow 1 . \supset . Q_{R\alpha} \in \Omega$

Dem.

$\vdash . *258·14 . \supset \vdash : \text{Hp} . \supset . \text{Hp} * 257·27$ (1)

$\vdash . (1) . *257·34 . \supset \vdash . \text{Prop}$

***258·201.** $\vdash : Q = \hat{\alpha}\hat{\beta}(\beta \subset \alpha . \alpha \neq \beta) . R \in \text{Rl}‘Q \cap \text{Cls} \rightarrow 1 . \supset . Q_{R\alpha} \in \Omega$
[Proof as in *258·2]

***258·202.** $\vdash : Q = \hat{M}\hat{N}(M \Subset N . M \neq N) . R \in \text{Rl}‘Q \cap \text{Cls} \rightarrow 1 . \supset . Q_{RX} \in \Omega$

***258·203.** $\vdash : Q = \hat{M}\hat{N}(N \Subset M . M \neq N) . R \in \text{Rl}‘Q \cap \text{Cls} \rightarrow 1 . \supset . Q_{RX} \in \Omega$

***258·21.** $\vdash : \text{Hp} * 258·2 . \kappa \subset (R * Q)‘\alpha . \supset . s‘\kappa = \text{limax}_Q‘\kappa$

Dem.

$\vdash . *258·13 . \supset \vdash : \text{Hp} . \sim \exists ! \overrightarrow{\max_Q}‘\kappa . \supset . s‘\kappa = \text{lt}_Q‘\kappa$ (1)

$\vdash . *258·2 . \supset \vdash :. \text{Hp} . \exists ! \overrightarrow{\max_Q}‘\kappa . \supset : (\exists\gamma) : \gamma \in \kappa : \alpha \in \kappa . \supset_\alpha . \alpha \subset \gamma :$

[*40·151] $\supset : s‘\kappa \in \kappa :$

[*258·1] $\supset : s‘\kappa = \max_Q‘\kappa$ (2)

$\vdash . (1) . (2) . \supset \vdash . \text{Prop}$

***258·211.** $\vdash : \text{Hp} * 258·201 . \kappa \subset (R * Q)‘\alpha . \supset . p‘\kappa = \text{limax}_Q‘\kappa$

***258·22.** $\vdash : \text{Hp} *258\cdot2 . \alpha \epsilon \text{D}`R . \kappa \subset (R*Q)`\alpha . \exists ! \kappa . \supset . s`\kappa = \text{limax}\,(Q_{R\alpha})`\kappa$

Dem.

$\vdash . *258\cdot21 . \supset \vdash : \text{Hp} . s`\kappa \sim \epsilon \kappa . \supset . s`\kappa = \text{lt}_Q`\kappa .$

$[*257\cdot13] \qquad \supset . s`\kappa \epsilon (R*Q)`\alpha .$

$[*210\cdot233] \qquad \supset . s`\kappa = \text{limax}\,(Q_{R\alpha})`\kappa : \supset \vdash . \text{Prop}$

***258·221.** $\vdash : \text{Hp} *258\cdot201 . \alpha \epsilon \text{D}`R . \kappa \subset (R*Q)`\alpha . \supset . p`\kappa = \text{limax}\,(Q_{R\alpha})`\kappa$

***258·23.** $\vdash : \text{Hp} *258\cdot2 . \alpha \epsilon \text{D}`R . \supset . Q_{R\alpha} \epsilon \text{Ded} . s`(R*Q)`\alpha = B`\breve{Q}_{R\alpha}$

$[*258\cdot2\cdot22 . *250\cdot23 . *205\cdot121]$

***258·231.** $\vdash : \text{Hp} *258\cdot201 . \alpha \epsilon \text{D}`R . \supset . Q_{R\alpha} \epsilon \text{Ded} . p`(R*Q)`\alpha = B`\breve{Q}_{R\alpha}$

***258·24.** $\vdash : \text{Hp} *258\cdot2 . \supset .$

$$(R*Q)`\alpha = \hat{\beta}\,(\alpha \epsilon \sigma . \breve{R}``\sigma \subset \sigma . s``\text{Cl ex}`\sigma \subset \sigma . \supset_\sigma . \beta \epsilon \sigma)$$

Dem.

$\vdash . *258\cdot1\cdot13 . *257\cdot1 . \supset$

$\vdash : \text{Hp} . \supset . (R*Q)`\alpha \subset \hat{\beta}\,(\alpha \epsilon \sigma . \breve{R}``\sigma \subset \sigma . s``\text{Cl ex}`\sigma \subset \sigma . \supset_\sigma . \beta \epsilon \sigma)$ (1)

$\vdash . *257\cdot123 . \supset \vdash : \text{Hp} . \supset . \breve{R}``(R*Q)`\alpha \subset (R*Q)`\alpha$ (2)

$\vdash . *258\cdot22 . \supset \vdash : \text{Hp} . \mu \subset (R*Q)`\alpha . \exists ! \mu . \supset . s`\mu \epsilon (R*Q)`\alpha$ (3)

$\vdash . *257\cdot12 . \supset \vdash : \text{Hp} . \supset . \alpha \epsilon (R*Q)`\alpha$ (4)

$\vdash . (2) . (3) . (4) . \supset$

$\vdash :. \text{Hp} : \alpha \epsilon \sigma . \breve{R}``\sigma \subset \sigma . s``\text{Cl ex}`\sigma \subset \sigma . \supset_\sigma . \beta \epsilon \sigma : \supset . \beta \epsilon (R*Q)`x$ (5)

$\vdash . (1) . (5) . \supset \vdash . \text{Prop}$

***258·241.** $\vdash : \text{Hp} *258\cdot201 . \supset .$

$$(R*Q)`\alpha = \hat{\beta}\,(\alpha \epsilon \sigma . \breve{R}``\sigma \subset \sigma . p``\text{Cl ex}`\sigma \subset \sigma . \supset_\sigma . \beta \epsilon \sigma)$$

***258·242.** $\vdash : \text{Hp} *258\cdot202 . \supset .$

$$(R*Q)`X = \hat{Y}\,(X \epsilon \sigma . \breve{R}``\sigma \subset \sigma . \dot{s}``\text{Cl ex}`\sigma \subset \sigma . \supset_\sigma . Y \epsilon \sigma)$$

***258·243.** $\vdash : \text{Hp} *258\cdot203 . \supset .$

$$(R*Q)`X = \hat{Y}\,(X \epsilon \sigma . \breve{R}``\sigma \subset \sigma . \dot{p}``\text{Cl ex}`\sigma \subset \sigma . \supset_\sigma . Y \epsilon \sigma)$$

***258·3.** $\vdash : Q = \hat{\alpha}\hat{\beta}\,(\beta \subset \alpha . \alpha \neq \beta) . S \epsilon \epsilon_\Delta`\text{Cl ex}`\mu .$

$R = \hat{\alpha}\hat{\beta}\,(\alpha \epsilon \text{Cl ex}`\mu . \beta = \alpha - \iota`S`\alpha) . \supset . Q_{R\mu} \epsilon \Omega . S ; Q_{R\mu} \,\text{smor}\, Q_{R\mu} \upharpoonright (-\iota`\Lambda)$

Dem.

$\vdash . *80\cdot14 . \supset \vdash : \text{Hp} . \supset . R \Subset Q . R \epsilon \text{Cls} \to 1 . \text{D}`R = \text{Cl ex}`\mu . C`R = \text{Cl}`\mu$ (1)

$\vdash . (1) . *258\cdot201 . \supset \vdash : \text{Hp} . \supset . Q_{R\mu} \epsilon \Omega$ (2)

$\vdash . *257\cdot35 . \supset \vdash : \text{Hp} . \supset . R \upharpoonright C`Q_{R\mu} \epsilon 1 \to 1 .$

$[(1) . \text{Hp}] \qquad \supset . S \upharpoonright C`Q_{R\mu} \epsilon 1 \to 1$ (3)

$\vdash . *257\cdot14 . \supset \vdash : \text{Hp} . \supset . C`Q_{R\mu} \subset \text{Cl}`\mu$ (4)

$\vdash . *80\cdot14 . \supset \vdash : \text{Hp} . \supset . \text{Cl}`S = \text{Cl ex}`\mu$ (5)

$\vdash . (3) . (4) . (5) . \supset \vdash : \text{Hp} . \supset . S ; Q_{R\mu} \,\text{smor}\, Q_{R\mu} \upharpoonright (-\iota`\Lambda)$ (6)

$\vdash . (2) . (6) . \supset \vdash . \text{Prop}$

***258·301.** $\vdash : \mathrm{Hp} * 258{\cdot}3 \,.\, x \in \mu \,.\, \kappa = C‘Q_{R\mu} \cap \overleftarrow{\epsilon}‘x \,.\, \supset .\, x = S‘p‘\kappa$

Dem.

$\vdash . *257{\cdot}36 . \quad \supset \vdash : \mathrm{Hp} . \supset . \mu \in C‘Q_{R\mu} .$

$[\mathrm{Hp}] \quad \supset . \exists ! \kappa$ (1)

$\vdash . (1) . *258{\cdot}241 . \supset \vdash : \mathrm{Hp} . \supset . p‘\kappa \in (R * Q)‘\mu .$

$[*257{\cdot}36] \quad \supset . p‘\kappa \in C‘Q_{R\mu}$ (2)

$\vdash . *40{\cdot}1 . \quad \supset \vdash : \mathrm{Hp} . \supset . x \in p‘\kappa$ (3)

$\vdash . (2) . (3) . \quad \supset \vdash : \mathrm{Hp} . \supset . p‘\kappa \in \kappa .$

$[*258{\cdot}101] \quad \supset . p‘\kappa = \max_Q‘\kappa$ (4)

$\vdash . (4) . \quad \supset \vdash : \mathrm{Hp} . \supset . (p‘\kappa - \iota‘S‘p‘\kappa) \sim\in \kappa .$

$[*257{\cdot}121 . \mathrm{Hp}] \quad \supset . x \sim\in (p‘\kappa - \iota‘S‘p‘\kappa)$ (5)

$\vdash . (3) . (5) . \quad \supset \vdash : \mathrm{Hp} . \supset . x \in \iota‘S‘p‘\kappa : \supset \vdash . \mathrm{Prop}$

***258·31.** $\vdash : \mathrm{Hp} * 258{\cdot}3 \,.\, \mu \sim\in 1 \,.\, \supset .\, C‘S ; Q_{R\mu} = \mu$

Dem.

$\vdash . *80{\cdot}14 . \supset \vdash : \mathrm{Hp} . \supset . \text{ᗡ}‘S = \mathrm{Cl\,ex}‘\mu .$

$[*150{\cdot}36 . *257{\cdot}14] \quad \supset . S;Q_{R\mu} = S;Q_{R\mu} \upharpoonleft (-\iota‘\Lambda) . C‘Q_{R\mu} \upharpoonleft (-\iota‘\Lambda) \subset \text{ᗡ}‘S .$

$[*150{\cdot}22] \quad \supset . C‘S;Q_{R\mu} = S‘‘C‘Q_{R\mu} \upharpoonleft (-\iota‘\Lambda) .$

$[*202{\cdot}54 . *257{\cdot}125] \quad \supset . C‘S;Q_{R\mu} = S‘‘(C‘Q_{R\mu} - \iota‘\Lambda)$ (1)

$\vdash . *83{\cdot}21 . \supset \vdash : \mathrm{Hp} . \supset . S‘‘C‘Q_{R\mu} \subset \mu$ (2)

$\vdash . *258{\cdot}241{\cdot}301 . \supset \vdash : \mathrm{Hp} . x \in \mu . \supset . x \in S‘‘\{(R * Q)‘\mu - \iota‘\Lambda\} .$

$[*257{\cdot}36] \quad \supset . x \in S‘‘(C‘Q_{R\mu} - \iota‘\Lambda)$ (3)

$\vdash . (2) . (3) . \supset \vdash : \mathrm{Hp} . \supset . S‘‘(C‘Q_{R\mu} - \iota‘\Lambda) = \mu$ (4)

$\vdash . (1) . (4) . \supset \vdash . \mathrm{Prop}$

***258·32.** $\vdash : \mu \sim\in 1 \,.\, \exists ! \epsilon_\Delta‘\mathrm{Cl\,ex}‘\mu \,.\, \supset .\, \mu \in C‘‘\Omega \quad [*258{\cdot}3{\cdot}31]$

This is Zermelo's theorem.

***258·321.** $\vdash : \mathrm{Hp} * 258{\cdot}3 \,.\, \beta Q_{R\mu} \alpha \,.\, \supset .\, S‘\beta \sim\in \alpha$

Dem.

$\vdash . *250{\cdot}242 . \supset \vdash :. \mathrm{Hp} . \supset : \alpha = (\breve{Q}_{R\mu})_1‘\beta . \vee . (\breve{Q}_{R\mu})_1‘\beta Q_{R\mu} \alpha :$

$[*257{\cdot}35 . \mathrm{Hp}] \quad \supset : \alpha \subset \beta - \iota‘S‘\beta :. \supset \vdash . \mathrm{Prop}$

***258·33.** $\vdash : \mathrm{Hp} * 258{\cdot}3 \,.\, \mu \sim\in 1 \,.\, P = S;Q_{R\mu} \,.\, \supset .\, S = \min_P \upharpoonright \mathrm{Cl\,ex}‘\mu$

Dem.

$\vdash . *80{\cdot}14 . \quad \supset \vdash : \mathrm{Hp} . \alpha \subset \mu . \exists ! \alpha . \supset . S‘\alpha \in \alpha$ (1)

$\vdash . *258{\cdot}321 . \quad \supset \vdash : \mathrm{Hp}(1) . x \in \alpha . \supset . \sim(\exists \beta) . \beta Q_{R\mu} \alpha . x = S‘\beta .$

$[*150{\cdot}4 . \mathrm{Hp}] \quad \supset . \sim(x P S‘\alpha)$ (2)

$\vdash . (1) . (2) . *205{\cdot}1 . \supset \vdash : \mathrm{Hp}(1) . \supset . S‘\alpha \min_P \alpha .$

$[*258{\cdot}3] \quad \supset . S‘\alpha = \min_P‘\alpha : \supset \vdash . \mathrm{Prop}$

***258·34.** $\vdash :. \mu \sim \epsilon 1 . \supset :$

$$S \epsilon \epsilon_\Delta \text{‘Cl ex‘} \mu . \equiv . (\exists P) . P \epsilon \Omega . C\text{‘}P = \mu . S = \min_P \upharpoonright \text{Cl ex‘} \mu$$

[*250·5 . *258·33]

***258·35.** $\vdash : \mu \epsilon C\text{“}\Omega . \equiv . \mu \sim \epsilon 1 . \exists ! \epsilon_\Delta \text{‘Cl ex‘} \mu$ [*200·12 . *250·51 . *258·32]

***258·36.** $\vdash : \mu \epsilon C\text{“}\Omega \cup 1 . \equiv . \exists ! \epsilon_\Delta \text{‘Cl ex‘} \mu$ [*258·35 . *60·37 . *83·901]

***258·37.** $\vdash : \text{Mult ax} . \equiv . C\text{“}\Omega \cup 1 = \text{Cls}$ [*258·36 . *88·33]

***258·38.** $\vdash :. \text{Mult ax} . \supset : \text{Nc‘}\alpha < \text{Nc‘}\beta . \vee . \text{Nc‘}\alpha = \text{Nc‘}\beta . \vee . \text{Nc‘}\alpha > \text{Nc‘}\beta$

[*255·73 . *258·37 . *117·54·55]

***258·39.** $\vdash :: \text{Mult ax} . \supset :. \mu, \nu \epsilon N_0C . \supset : \mu \leqslant \nu . \vee . \mu > \nu$ [*258·38]

*259. INDUCTIVELY DEFINED CORRELATIONS.

Summary of *259.

In the theory of well-ordered relations, we often have occasion to define a relation (which is generally of the nature of a correlation) by the following process: Given a relation S, let $W\text{‘}S$ be a relation (generally a couple) which is a function of S. Let us put

$$\breve{A}_W\text{‘}S = S \mathbin{\dot\cup} W\text{‘}S.$$

Then, starting from $\dot\Lambda$, we form the series

$$\dot\Lambda,\ \breve{A}_W\text{‘}\dot\Lambda,\ \breve{A}_W\text{‘}\breve{A}_W\text{‘}\dot\Lambda, \text{ etc.},$$

each of which contains all its predecessors. We proceed to the limit by taking the sum of all these relations, *i.e.* $\dot{s}\text{‘}\overleftarrow{(A_W)}_*\text{‘}\dot\Lambda$; we then proceed to $\breve{A}_W\text{‘}\dot{s}\text{‘}\overleftarrow{(A_W)}_*\text{‘}\dot\Lambda$, and so on, as long as possible. The sum of all the relations so obtained is a function of W, and is often important.

As an example, we may consider the correlation of two well-ordered series P, Q, which is dealt with in *259·2—·25 below. In this case, we put

$$W = \hat{X}\hat{T}\{X = \mathrm{seq}_P\text{‘}\mathrm{D}\text{‘}T \downarrow \mathrm{seq}_Q\text{‘}\text{ᗡ}\text{‘}T\}.$$

Hence
$$W\text{‘}\dot\Lambda = \breve{A}_W\text{‘}\dot\Lambda = B\text{‘}P \downarrow B\text{‘}Q = 1_P \downarrow 1_Q,$$
$$\breve{A}_W\text{‘}\breve{A}_W\text{‘}\dot\Lambda = 1_P \downarrow 1_Q \mathbin{\dot\cup} 2_P \downarrow 2_Q,$$
and so on.

Proceeding in this fashion, we can continue until one at least of the two series P, Q is exhausted. We thus obtain a new proof that, of any two well-ordered series, one must be similar to a section of the other.

For convenience of notation, let us put temporarily

$$A = \hat{S}\hat{T}(S \mathrel{\dot\subset} T \,.\, S \neq T) \quad \text{Df.}$$

We then have $A \in \mathrm{Rl}\text{‘}J \cap \mathrm{trans} \,.\, A_W \in \mathrm{Rl}\text{‘}A \cap \mathrm{Cls} \to 1$, which is part of the hypothesis of *257·27 and following propositions. The rest of this hypothesis follows by analogy from *258·14. We now put

$$W_A = \dot{s}\text{‘}(A_W * A)\text{‘}\dot\Lambda \quad \text{Df.}$$

Then W_A correlates the whole of P with part or the whole of Q, or vice versa. This is proved in *259·25, below.

For other values of W, we get other results, often of a useful kind; for example we shall have occasion to use the methods of this number in $*273$, which deals with series similar to the series of rationals.

The present number gives, first, some elementary properties of $(A_W * A)\text{‘}\dot{\Lambda}$ and W_A for a general relation W, concerning which we only assume that $W\text{‘}S$ is never contained in S, *i.e.* $W \dot{\frown} (\mathrm{G}) = \dot{\Lambda}$ (except in $*259\,121{\cdot}13$, where we also assume $W \in 1 \to \mathrm{Cls}$). We then proceed to deal specially with the case where

$$W = \hat{X}\hat{T}\{X = \mathrm{seq}_P\text{‘}\mathrm{D}\text{‘}T \downarrow \mathrm{seq}_Q\text{‘}\mathrm{Q}\text{‘}T\}$$

as explained above.

$*259{\cdot}01.\quad A = \hat{S}\hat{T}(S \mathrm{G} T \,.\, S \neq T) \quad$ Dft [$*259$]

$*259{\cdot}02.\quad A_W = \hat{S}\hat{T}(T = S \cup W\text{‘}S) \quad$ Dft [$*259$]

$*259{\cdot}03.\quad W_A = \dot{s}\text{‘}(A_W * A)\text{‘}\dot{\Lambda} \quad$ Df

In the following propositions, which result from those of $*258$, it is essential to have $A_W \mathrm{G} A$. For this we require that $W\text{‘}S$, when it exists, shall not be contained in S. It will be observed that, according to the above definition,

$$A_* = \hat{S}\hat{T}(S \mathrm{G} T).$$

Hence instead of using "G" as a relation, which is notationally awkward, we shall use A_*. Thus the condition we wish to impose upon W is that we are never to have $(W\text{‘}S) A_* S$. This is insured by

$$W \dot{\frown} A_* = \dot{\Lambda},$$

which accordingly appears as hypothesis in the following propositions.

$*259{\cdot}1.\quad \vdash : A \in \mathrm{Rl}\text{‘}J \frown \mathrm{trans} \,.\, \mathrm{lt}_A \in 1 \to \mathrm{Cls} :$
$$W \dot{\frown} A_* = \dot{\Lambda} \,.\supset .\, A_W \in \mathrm{Rl}\text{‘}A \frown \mathrm{Cls} \to 1 \,.\, A\,(A_W, \dot{\Lambda}) \in \Omega$$

Dem.

As in $*258{\cdot}14$, $\quad \vdash .\, \mathrm{lt}_A \in 1 \to \mathrm{Cls} \quad (1)$

$\vdash .\, *201{\cdot}18 \,. \quad \supset \vdash :.\, \mathrm{Hp} \,.\supset : MWS \,.\supset .\, \sim (M \mathrm{G} S) \quad (2)$

$\vdash .\, (2) \,.\, (*259{\cdot}02) \,.\supset \vdash :.\, \mathrm{Hp} \,.\supset : SA_W T \,.\supset .\, S \mathrm{G} T \,.\, S \neq T \,.$
$[(*259{\cdot}01)] \quad \supset .\, SAT \quad (3)$

$\vdash .\, (1) \,.\, (3) \,.\, *258{\cdot}202 \,.\supset \vdash .\,$ Prop

In the following proposition, the notation $A\,(A_W, \dot{\Lambda})$ is that defined in $*257{\cdot}02$, adopted because A_W cannot conveniently be used as a suffix.

$*259{\cdot}11.\quad \vdash : \mathrm{E}\,!\, W\text{‘}\dot{\Lambda} \,.\, W \dot{\frown} A_* = \dot{\Lambda} \,.\supset .$
$$W_A = B\text{‘}\mathrm{Cnv}\text{‘}A\,(A_W, \dot{\Lambda}) \,.\, \dot{s}\text{‘‘}\mathrm{Cl}\text{‘}(A_W * A)\text{‘}\dot{\Lambda} \subset (A_W * A)\text{‘}\dot{\Lambda}$$

Dem.

$\vdash .\, *258{\cdot}242 \,.\, *259{\cdot}1 \,.\supset \vdash : \mathrm{Hp} \,.\, \lambda \subset (A_W * A)\text{‘}\dot{\Lambda} \,.\supset .\, \dot{s}\text{‘}\lambda \in (A_W * A)\text{‘}\dot{\Lambda} \quad (1)$

$\vdash .\, (1) \,. \quad \supset \vdash : \mathrm{Hp} \,.\supset .\, W_A \in (A_W * A)\text{‘}\dot{\Lambda} \quad (2)$

$\vdash .\, *41{\cdot}13 \,. \quad \supset \vdash : \mathrm{Hp} \,.\, T \in (A_W * A)\text{‘}\dot{\Lambda} - \iota\text{‘}W_A \,.\supset .\, TAW_A \quad (3)$

$\vdash .\, (1) \,.\, (2) \,.\, (3) \,.\supset \vdash .\,$ Prop

***259·111.** $\vdash :. W \dot{\frown} A_* = \dot{\Lambda} . S, T \in (A_W * A)`\dot{\Lambda} . \supset : S \in T . \vee . T \in S$
[*259·1 . *257·36]

***259·12.** $\vdash : S \in D`A_W . \equiv . E! W`S$ [(*259·02)]

***259·121.** $\vdash : W \in 1 \rightarrow Cls . \supset . D`A_W = \text{Cl}`W$ [*259·12]

***259·122.** $\vdash : W \dot{\frown} A_* = \dot{\Lambda} . x W_A y . \lambda = (A_W * A)`\dot{\Lambda} \frown \hat{T}\{\sim(xTy)\} . \supset . x(W`\dot{s}`\lambda)y$

Dem.

$\vdash . *259·11 . \supset \vdash : Hp . \supset . \dot{s}`\lambda \in (A_W * A)`\dot{\Lambda} .$ (1)

[Hp] $\supset . \dot{s}`\lambda \in \lambda$ (2)

$\vdash . (1) . (2) . *257·3 . \supset \vdash : Hp . \supset . \dot{s}`\lambda \in D`A_W .$

[*259·12] $\supset . E! W`\dot{s}`\lambda$ (3)

$\vdash . (3) . \supset \vdash : Hp . \supset . (\dot{s}`\lambda) A (A_W`\dot{s}`\lambda) .$

[*257·121] $\supset . A_W`\dot{s}`\lambda \in (A_W * A)`\dot{\Lambda} - \lambda .$

[Hp] $\supset . x (A_W`\dot{s}`\lambda) y$ (4)

$\vdash . (2) . (4) . \supset \vdash : Hp . \supset . \sim\{x (\dot{s}`\lambda) y\} . x (A_W`\dot{s}`\lambda) y .$

[(*259·02)] $\supset . x (W`\dot{s}`\lambda) y : \supset \vdash . Prop$

***259·13.** $\vdash : W \dot{\frown} A_* = \dot{\Lambda} . W \in 1 \rightarrow Cls . \supset . W_A = \dot{s}`W``(A_W * A)`\dot{\Lambda}$

Dem.

$\vdash . *259·122 . \supset \vdash : Hp . \supset . W_A \in \dot{s}`W``(A_W * A)`\dot{\Lambda}$ (1)

$\vdash . *257·123 . \supset \vdash : Hp . \supset . \dot{s}`W``(A_W * A)`\dot{\Lambda} \in W_A$ (2)

$\vdash . (1) . (2) . \supset \vdash . Prop$

***259·14.** $\vdash :. W \dot{\frown} A_* = \dot{\Lambda} : S \in (A_W * A)`\dot{\Lambda} \frown 1 \rightarrow Cls \frown \text{Cl}`W . \supset_S .$
$W`S \in 1 \rightarrow Cls . \text{Cl}`S \frown \text{Cl}`W`S = \Lambda : \supset . W_A \in 1 \rightarrow Cls$

Dem.

$\vdash . *71·24 . (*259·02) . \supset \vdash :. Hp . \supset :$

$S \in (A_W * A)`\dot{\Lambda} \frown 1 \rightarrow Cls . \supset . \breve{A}_W`S \in (A_W * A)`\dot{\Lambda} \frown 1 \rightarrow Cls$ (1)

$\vdash . *259·111 . \supset \vdash :. Hp . S, T \in (A_W * A)`\dot{\Lambda} . \supset : S \in T . \vee . T \in S$ (2)

$\vdash . (2) . \supset \vdash : Hp . \lambda \subset (A_W * A)`\dot{\Lambda} . x(\dot{s}`\lambda)z . y(\dot{s}`\lambda)z . \supset . (\exists T) . T \in \lambda . xTz . yTz$ (3)

$\vdash . (3) . \supset \vdash : Hp . \lambda \subset (A_W * A)`\dot{\Lambda} \frown 1 \rightarrow Cls . x(\dot{s}`\lambda) z . y (\dot{s}`\lambda) z . \supset . x = y$ (4)

$\vdash . (4) . \supset \vdash : Hp . \lambda \subset (A_W * A)`\dot{\Lambda} \frown 1 \rightarrow Cls . \supset . \dot{s}`\lambda \in 1 \rightarrow Cls$ (5)

$\vdash . (1) . (5) . *258·242 . \supset \vdash : Hp . \supset . (A_W * A)`\dot{\Lambda} \subset 1 \rightarrow Cls .$

[*259·11] $\supset . W_A \in 1 \rightarrow Cls : \supset \vdash . Prop$

***259·141.** $\vdash :. W \dot{\frown} A_* = \dot{\Lambda} : S \in (A_W * A)`\dot{\Lambda} \frown Cls \rightarrow 1 \frown \text{Cl}`W . \supset_S .$
$W`S \in Cls \rightarrow 1 . D`S \frown D`W`S = \Lambda : \supset . W_A \in Cls \rightarrow 1$

[Proof as in *259·14]

$*259{\cdot}15.\quad \vdash :. W \dot{\cap} A_* = \dot{\Lambda} : S \in (A_W * A)`\dot{\Lambda} \cap 1 \to 1 \cap \text{ᗡ}`W . \supset_S .$

$W`S \in 1 \to 1 . \mathrm{D}`S \cap \mathrm{D}`W`S = \Lambda . \text{ᗡ}`S \cap \text{ᗡ}`W`S = \Lambda : \supset . W_A \in 1 \to 1$

[$*259{\cdot}14{\cdot}141$]

The following proposition is a lemma for $*273{\cdot}23$.

$*259{\cdot}16.\quad \vdash :. W \dot{\cap} A_* = \dot{\Lambda} : T \in (A_W * A)`\dot{\Lambda} \cap \text{ᗡ}`W . P \upharpoonleft \mathrm{D}`T = T ; Q . \supset_T .$

$P \upharpoonleft (\breve{A}_W`T) = (\breve{A}_W`T) ; Q : \supset :$

$P \upharpoonleft \mathrm{D}`W_A = W_A ; Q : T \in (A_W * A)`\dot{\Lambda} . \supset_T . P \upharpoonleft \mathrm{D}`T = T ; Q$

Dem.

$\vdash . *259{\cdot}111 . \supset \vdash :. \mathrm{Hp} . \lambda \subset (A_W * A)`\dot{\Lambda} . \supset :$

$x (P \upharpoonleft \mathrm{D}`\dot{s}`\lambda) y . \equiv . (\exists T) . T \in \lambda . x (P \upharpoonleft \mathrm{D}`T) y \qquad (1)$

$\vdash . (1) . \supset \vdash :. \mathrm{Hp} . \lambda \subset (A_W * A)`\dot{\Lambda} : T \in \lambda . \supset_T . P \upharpoonleft \mathrm{D}`T = T ; Q : \supset :$

$x (P \upharpoonleft \mathrm{D}`\dot{s}`\lambda) y . \equiv . (\exists T) . T \in \lambda . x (T ; Q) y .$

[$*259{\cdot}111$] $\equiv . (\exists S, T) . S, T \in \lambda . x (S \mid Q \mid \breve{T}) y .$

[$*150{\cdot}1$] $\equiv . x \{(\dot{s}`\lambda) ; Q\} y \qquad (2)$

$\vdash . (2) . *258{\cdot}242 . \supset \vdash : \mathrm{Hp} . T \in (A_W * A)`\dot{\Lambda} . \supset . P \upharpoonleft \mathrm{D}`T = T ; Q \qquad (3)$

$\vdash . (3) . *259{\cdot}11 . \supset \vdash . \mathrm{Prop}$

The two following propositions are lemmas for $*273{\cdot}22{\cdot}212$.

$*259{\cdot}17.\quad \vdash :. W \dot{\cap} A_* = \dot{\Lambda} : S \in (A_W * A)`\dot{\Lambda} \cap \text{ᗡ}`W . \supset_S .$

$\text{ᗡ}`S \cap \text{ᗡ}`W`S = \Lambda : \supset . \text{ᗡ} \upharpoonright (A_W * A)`\dot{\Lambda} \in 1 \to 1$

Dem.

$\vdash . *250{\cdot}242 . *257{\cdot}35 . *259{\cdot}1 . \supset$

$\vdash :. \mathrm{Hp} . S, T \in (A_W * A)`\dot{\Lambda} . S \neq T . \supset : A_W`S \mathrel{\mathsf{G}} T . \mathsf{v} . \breve{A}_W`T \mathrel{\mathsf{G}} S :$

[$(*259{\cdot}02)$] $\supset : \text{ᗡ}`W`S \subset \text{ᗡ}`T . \mathsf{v} . \text{ᗡ}`W`T \subset \text{ᗡ}`S :$

[Hp] $\supset : \text{ᗡ}`S \neq \text{ᗡ}`T :. \supset \vdash . \mathrm{Prop}$

$*259{\cdot}171.\quad \vdash :. W \dot{\cap} A_* = \dot{\Lambda} : S \in (A_W * A)`\dot{\Lambda} \cap \text{ᗡ}`W . \supset_S .$

$\mathrm{D}`S \cap \mathrm{D}`W`S = \Lambda : \supset . \mathrm{D} \upharpoonright (A_W * A)`\dot{\Lambda} \in 1 \to 1$

[Proof as in $*259{\cdot}17$]

$*259{\cdot}2.\quad \vdash : W = \hat{X}\hat{T} \{ X = \mathrm{seq}_P`\mathrm{D}`T \downarrow \mathrm{seq}_Q`\text{ᗡ}`T \} . \supset . W_A \in 1 \to 1 . W \dot{\cap} A_* = \dot{\Lambda}$

Dem.

$\vdash . *72{\cdot}182 . \supset \vdash :. \mathrm{Hp} . \supset : T \in \text{ᗡ}`W . \supset . W`T \in 1 \to 1 \qquad (1)$

$\vdash . *206{\cdot}2 . \supset \vdash :. \mathrm{Hp} . \supset : T \in \text{ᗡ}`W . \supset . \mathrm{D}`T \cap \mathrm{D}`W`T = \Lambda . \text{ᗡ}`T \cap \text{ᗡ}`W`T = \Lambda \qquad (2)$

$\vdash . (2) . *55{\cdot}134 . \supset \vdash : \mathrm{Hp} . T \in \text{ᗡ}`W . \supset . \sim (W`T \mathrel{\mathsf{G}} T) \qquad (3)$

$\vdash . (1) . (2) . (3) . *259{\cdot}15 . \supset \vdash . \mathrm{Prop}$

***259·21.** $\vdash : \text{Hp} \ast 259\cdot2 \,.\, Q^2 \Subset J \,.\, \supset \,.\, W_A ; Q \Subset P \,.\, \text{D}`W_A \subset C`P \,.\, \text{Ɑ}`W_A \subset C`Q.$

Dem.

$\vdash \,.\, \ast 206\cdot133 \,.\, \supset \vdash : \text{Hp} \,.\, T \in \text{Ɑ}`W \,.\, \supset \,.\, (W`T) ; Q = \dot{\Lambda}$ (1)

$\vdash \,.\, \ast 206\cdot21 \,.\, \supset \vdash : \text{Hp}\,(1) \,.\, \supset \,.\, \text{seq}_Q`\text{Ɑ}`T \sim \in Q``\text{Ɑ}`T \,.$

$[\ast 37\cdot461] \quad \supset \,.\, (W`T) \,|\, Q \,|\, \breve{T} = \dot{\Lambda}$ (2)

$\vdash \,.\, \ast 206\cdot18 \,.\, \supset \vdash : \text{Hp}\,(1) \,.\, \supset \,.\, \text{D}`A_W \subset C`P$ (3)

$\vdash \,.\, (3) \,.\, \ast 41\cdot43 \,.\, \ast 258\cdot242 \,.\, \supset \vdash : \text{Hp} \,.\, \supset \,.\, \text{D}`W_A \subset C`P$ (4)

Similarly $\quad \vdash : \text{Hp} \,.\, \supset \,.\, \text{Ɑ}`W_A \subset C`Q$ (5)

$\vdash \,.\, (4) \,.\, \ast 206\cdot132 \,.\, \supset \vdash : \text{Hp}\,(1) \,.\, T \in (A_W \ast A)`\dot{\Lambda} \,.\, \supset \,.\, \text{seq}_P`\text{D}`T \in p`\overleftarrow{P}``\text{D}`T \,.$

$[\ast 40\cdot16] \quad \supset \,.\, \text{seq}_P`\text{D}`T \in p`\overleftarrow{P}``T``\overrightarrow{Q}`\text{seq}_Q`\text{Ɑ}`T \,.$

$[\ast 40\cdot67] \quad \supset \,.\, (T``\overrightarrow{Q}`\text{seq}_Q`\text{Ɑ}`T) \uparrow \iota`\text{seq}_P`\text{D}`T \Subset P$ (6)

$\vdash \,.\, (1) \,.\, (2) \,.\, (6) \,.\, \supset \vdash : \text{Hp}\,(1) \,.\, T \in (A_W \ast A)`\dot{\Lambda} \,.\, T ; Q \Subset P \,.\, \supset \,.\, (\breve{A}_W`T) ; Q \Subset P$ (7)

$\vdash \,.\, \ast 259\cdot111 \,.\, \supset \vdash :: \lambda \subset (A_W \ast A)`\dot{\Lambda} \,.\, x \,\{(\dot{s}`\lambda) ; Q\}\, y \,.\, \supset :.$
$(\exists T) \,.\, T \in \lambda \,.\, x\,(T ; Q)\,y :.$

$[\ast 11\cdot62 . \ast 10\cdot23] \quad \supset :. \, T \in \lambda \,.\, \supset_T \,.\, T ; Q \Subset P : \supset \,.\, xPy$ (8)

$\vdash \,.\, (8) \,.\, \text{Comm} \,.\, \supset \vdash :. \, \lambda \subset (A_W \ast A)`\dot{\Lambda} : T \in \lambda \,.\, \supset_T \,.\, T ; Q \Subset P : \supset \,.\, (\dot{s}`\lambda) ; Q \Subset P$ (9)

$\vdash \,.\, (7) \,.\, (9) \,.\, \ast 258\cdot242 \,.\, \supset \vdash :. \, \text{Hp} \,.\, \supset : T \in (A_W \ast A)`\dot{\Lambda} \,.\, \supset \,.\, T ; Q \Subset P :$

$[\ast 259\cdot11] \quad \supset : W_A ; Q \Subset P$ (10)

$\vdash \,.\, (10) \,.\, (4) \,.\, (5) \,.\, \supset \vdash \,.\, \text{Prop}$

***259·211.** $\vdash : \text{Hp} \ast 259\cdot2 \,.\, P^2 \Subset J \,.\, \supset \,.\, \breve{W}_A ; P \Subset Q$ [Proof as in *259·21]

***259·22.** $\vdash : \text{Hp} \ast 259\cdot2 \,.\, P \in \text{connex} \,.\, \supset \,.\, \text{D}``(A_W \ast A)`\dot{\Lambda} \subset \text{sect}`P$

Dem.

$\vdash \,.\, \ast 211\cdot22 \,.\, \supset \vdash : \text{Hp} \,.\, T \in \text{Ɑ}`W \,.\, \text{D}`T \in \text{sect}`P \,.\, \supset \,.\, \text{D}`\breve{A}_W`T \in \text{sect}`P$ (1)

$\vdash \,.\, \ast 211\cdot63 \,.\, \supset \vdash : \text{D}``\lambda \subset \text{sect}`P \,.\, \supset \,.\, \text{D}`\dot{s}`\lambda \in \text{sect}`P$ (2)

$\vdash \,.\, (1) \,.\, (2) \,.\, \ast 258\cdot242 \,.\, \supset \vdash \,.\, \text{Prop}$

***259·221.** $\vdash : \text{Hp} \ast 259\cdot2 \,.\, Q \in \text{connex} \,.\, \supset \,.\, \text{Ɑ}``(A_W \ast A)`\dot{\Lambda} \subset \text{sect}`Q$

***259·222.** $\vdash : \text{Hp} \ast 259\cdot2 \,.\, P \in \text{Ser} \,.\, \text{E}!\, B`P \,.\, Q^2 \Subset J \,.\, T \in (A_W \ast A)`\dot{\Lambda} \,.\, \supset \,.$
$T ; Q \in C`P_s$ [*259·21·22 . *213·161]

***259·223.** $\vdash : \text{Hp} \ast 259\cdot2 \,.\, Q \in \text{Ser} \,.\, \text{E}!\, B`Q \,.\, P^2 \Subset J \,.\, T \in (A_W \ast A)`\dot{\Lambda} \,.\, \supset \,.$
$\breve{T} ; P \in C`Q_s$

***259·23.** $\vdash : \text{Hp} \ast 259\cdot2 \,.\, P, Q \in \text{Ser} \cap \text{Ɑ}`B \,.\, T \in (A_W \ast A)`\dot{\Lambda} \,.\, \supset \,.$
$(\exists M, N) \,.\, M \in C`P_s \,.\, N \in C`Q_s \,.\, T \in M \,\overline{\text{smor}}\, N$ [*259·2·21·222·223]

***259·24.** $\vdash :.\ \mathrm{Hp}\ *259{\cdot}2\ .\ P, Q \in \Omega\ .\ \supset :\ \mathrm{D}`W_A = C`P\ .\ \mathrm{v}\ .\ \text{Ͻ}`W_A = C`Q$

Dem.

$\vdash .\ *206{\cdot}18\ .\ \supset \vdash :\ \mathrm{Hp}\ .\ P = \dot{\Lambda}\ .\ \supset .\ W_A = \dot{\Lambda}$ (1)

$\vdash .\ *206{\cdot}18\ .\ \supset \vdash :\ \mathrm{Hp}\ .\ Q = \dot{\Lambda}\ .\ \supset .\ W_A = \dot{\Lambda}$ (2)

$\vdash .\ (1)\ .\ (2)\ .\ \supset \vdash :.\ \mathrm{Hp} : P = \dot{\Lambda}\ .\ \mathrm{v}\ .\ Q = \dot{\Lambda} : \supset : \mathrm{D}`W_A = C`P\ .\ \mathrm{v}\ .\ \text{Ͻ}`W_A = C`Q$ (3)

$\vdash .\ *259{\cdot}11\ .\ *257{\cdot}36\ .\ \supset \vdash :\ \mathrm{Hp}\ .\ \dot{\exists} \,!\, P\ .\ \dot{\exists} \,!\, Q\ .\ \supset .\ W_A \sim \in \mathrm{D}`A_W\ .$

[*259·12] $\supset .\ \sim(\mathrm{E} \,!\, \mathrm{seq}_P`\mathrm{D}`W_A\ .\ \mathrm{E} \,!\, \mathrm{seq}_Q`\text{Ͻ}`W_A)$ (4)

$\vdash .\ (4)\ .\ *252{\cdot}1\ .\ *259{\cdot}22{\cdot}221\ .\ \supset$

$\vdash :.\ \mathrm{Hp}\ .\ \dot{\exists} \,!\, P\ .\ \dot{\exists} \,!\, Q\ .\ \supset :\ \mathrm{D}`W_A = C`P\ .\ \mathrm{v}\ .\ \text{Ͻ}`W_A = C`Q$ (5)

$\vdash .\ (3)\ .\ (5)\ .\ \supset \vdash .\ \mathrm{Prop}$

***259·25.** $\vdash :.\ \mathrm{Hp}\ *259{\cdot}24\ .\ \supset :\ (\exists\beta)\ .\ \beta \in \mathrm{sect}`Q\ .\ W_A \in P\ \overline{\mathrm{smor}}\ (Q \upharpoonright \beta)\ .\ \mathrm{v}\ .$

$(\exists\alpha)\ .\ \alpha \in \mathrm{sect}`P\ .\ W_A \in (P \upharpoonright \alpha)\ \overline{\mathrm{smor}}\ Q$ [*259·23·24]

The above affords a new proof of *254·37, which asserts that if P and Q are well-ordered series, one must be similar to a section of the other. In virtue of *259·25 (which has been proved without using the propositions of *254), W_A is the correlator which correlates the whole of one series with part or the whole of the other.

It will be observed that the relations $(A_W * A)`\dot{\Lambda}$ are the class of correlators of sections of $P$ with sections of $Q$, provided $P, Q \in \Omega - \iota`\dot{\Lambda}$; *i.e.*

$\vdash :\ \mathrm{Hp}\ *259{\cdot}2\ .\ P, Q \in \Omega - \iota`\dot{\Lambda}\ .\ \supset .$

$$(A_W * A)`\dot{\Lambda} = \hat{T}\{(\exists M, N)\ .\ M \in C`P_\varsigma\ .\ N \in C`Q_\varsigma\ .\ T \in M\ \overline{\mathrm{smor}}\ N\}.$$

SECTION E.

FINITE AND INFINITE SERIES AND ORDINALS.

Summary of Section E.

In the present section we shall be concerned first with the distinction of finite and infinite as applied to series and ordinals. We shall then establish the distinguishing properties of finite ordinals, and shall deal with the smallest of infinite ordinals, namely ω, the ordinal number of a *progression.* Finally we shall briefly consider certain special ordinals, and the series of cardinals applicable to well-ordered infinite series, namely the series of "Alephs," as they are called after Cantor's usage.

In dealing with the finite and the infinite as applied to series, we have constant need of the relation $(P_1)_{po}$, where P is the generating relation of the series. We have

$$x (P_1)_{po} y . \equiv . P (x \mapsto y) \epsilon \text{ Cls induct} - \iota' \Lambda,$$

i.e. "$x (P_1)_{po} y$" holds when, and only when, there is a finite number of intermediaries between x and y. When P is finite, we have

$$P = (P_1)_{po},$$

but we may have this when P is not finite. The infinite series for which this holds are progressions and their converses (which we will call regressions), and series consisting of a regression followed by a progression, of which an instance is afforded by the negative and positive finite integers in order of magnitude.

$*260$. ON FINITE INTERVALS IN A SERIES.

Summary of $*260$.

In the present number we are concerned with the relation which holds between x and y when the interval $P(x \vdash y)$ is an inductive class other than Λ, or when the interval $P(x \mapsto y)$ is an inductive class of at least two terms. This relation holds if x and y have any relation of the class $\text{fin}`P$ (defined in $*121$). We will call this relation P_{fn}. Thus we put

$$P_{\text{fn}} = \dot{s}`\text{fin}`P \quad \text{Df.}$$

Then $xP_{\text{fn}}y$ holds when $xP_\nu y$, where ν is an inductive cardinal other than 0 ($*260{\cdot}1$). This relation will take us from x to any later term which can be reached without passing to the limit. But if in the interval $P(x \dashv y)$ there is any term which has no immediate predecessor, *i.e.* any member of $C`P - \text{G}`P_1$, then we shall not have $xP_{\text{fn}}y$. Thus P_{fn} confines us to terms which are at a finite distance from our starting-point. We shall find that if $P \in \Omega$, a necessary condition for the finitude of P is $P = P_{\text{fn}}$. This is not a *sufficient* condition, since it does not exclude progressions, but these are the only infinite series it admits, and these are excluded by the assumption $\text{E}\,!\,B`\breve{P}$.

Although P_{fn} is not in general serial when P or P_{po} is serial, it becomes serial when confined to the posterity or the ancestry or the family of any term with respect to itself ($*260{\cdot}32{\cdot}4$). When a series P is well-ordered, the whole series can be divided into constituent series, each of which is the family of any one of its members with respect to P_{fn} (except when P has a last term which has no immediate predecessor, in which case this last term must be omitted). (Cf. $*264$.) Each of these series (except the last, possibly) is a progression, and the last is either finite or a progression. Hence every infinite well-ordered series consists of a series of progressions followed by a finite tail (which may be null); hence the cardinal of the field of an infinite well-ordered series is a multiple of $\aleph_0$. These results will be proved later; for the present we are concerned with the proof that the family of any term with respect to P_{fn} is a series of which the generating relation is P_{fn} with its field confined to that family.

In the present number we are chiefly concerned with the relations of P_{fn} to P_1. We have

***260·27.** $\vdash : P_{\text{po}} \epsilon \text{Ser} \,.\supset .\, P_{\text{fn}} = (P_1)_{\text{po}}$

This proposition will be used very frequently throughout this section.

Without any hypothesis we have

***260·12.** $\vdash .\, P_{\text{fn}} \mathrel{\dot\subset} P_{\text{po}}$

We have also

***260·15.** $\vdash .\, P_{\text{fn}} = (P_{\text{po}})_{\text{fn}}$

Hence whatever properties of P_{fn} result from the hypothesis that P is a series will result from the weaker hypothesis that P_{po} is a series.

If P_{po} is a series, P_{fn} is contained in diversity and is transitive (*260·202), but not in general connected.

In comparing P_{fn} and $(P_1)_{\text{po}}$, we constantly need the proposition

***260·22.** $\vdash : P_{\text{po}} \epsilon \text{Ser} \,.\supset .\, (P_1)_1 = P_1 \,.\, P_1 \epsilon 1 \rightarrow 1 \,.\, (P_1)_{\text{po}} \mathrel{\dot\subset} J$

From *260·3 to the end of the number, we are concerned with the result of limiting the field of P_{fn} to the ancestry, posterity or family of some member of its field. We have

***260·33.** $\vdash : P_{\text{po}} \epsilon \text{Ser} \,.\, x \epsilon \text{D}`P_1 \,.\, P_1 = R \,.\supset .$

$$P_{\text{fn}} \mathbin{\upharpoonright\!\upharpoonleft} (\iota`x \cup \overleftarrow{P}_{\text{fn}}`x) = (\overleftarrow{R}_*`x) \upharpoonleft R_{\text{po}} = \{(\overleftarrow{R}_*`x) \upharpoonleft R\}_{\text{po}} = \{R \upharpoonright (\overleftarrow{R}_{\text{po}}`x)\}_{\text{po}}$$

***260·34.** $\vdash : \text{Hp} \,*260{\cdot}33 \,.\supset .\, \{P_{\text{fn}} \mathbin{\upharpoonright\!\upharpoonleft} (\iota`x \cup \overleftarrow{P}_{\text{fn}}`x)\}_1 = (\overleftarrow{R}_*`x) \upharpoonleft R = R \upharpoonright \overleftarrow{R}_{\text{po}}`x$

***260·01.** $P_{\text{fn}} = \dot{s}`\text{fin}`P \quad \text{Df}$

***260·1.** $\vdash : x P_{\text{fn}} y \,.\equiv .\, (\exists \nu) \,.\, \nu \epsilon \text{NC induct} - \iota`0 \,.\, x P_\nu y$

[*121·121 . (*260·01)]

***260·11.** $\vdash : x P_{\text{fn}} y \,.\equiv .\, P(x \mapsto y) \epsilon \text{Cls induct} - 0 - 1$

Dem.

$\vdash .\, *260{\cdot}1 \,.\, *121{\cdot}11 \,.\supset$

$\vdash : x P_{\text{fn}} y \,.\equiv .\, (\exists \nu) \,.\, \nu \epsilon \text{NC induct} - \iota`0 \,.\, P(x \mapsto y) \epsilon \nu +_c 1 \,.$

$[*120{\cdot}472] \equiv .\, (\exists \mu) \,.\, \mu \epsilon \text{NC induct} - \iota`0 - \iota`1 \,.\, P(x \mapsto y) \epsilon \mu \,.$

$[*120{\cdot}2] \quad \equiv .\, P(x \mapsto y) \epsilon \text{Cls induct} - 0 - 1 :\supset \vdash .\, \text{Prop}$

***260·12.** $\vdash .\, P_{\text{fn}} \mathrel{\dot\subset} P_{\text{po}}$

Dem.

$\vdash .\, *121{\cdot}321 \,.\, *117{\cdot}511 \,.\supset \vdash : \nu \epsilon \text{NC induct} - \iota`0 \,.\supset .\, P_\nu \mathrel{\dot\subset} P_{\text{po}} \quad (1)$

$\vdash .\, (1) \,.\, *260{\cdot}1 \,.\supset \vdash .\, \text{Prop}$

***260·13.** $\vdash : xP_{fn}y . \supset . P(x \vdash y), P(x \dashv y) \in \text{Cls induct} - \iota`\Lambda$

Dem.

$\vdash . *260·12 . *121·21·22 . \supset \vdash : \text{Hp} . \supset . P(x \vdash y), P(x \dashv y) \in - \iota`\Lambda$ (1)

$\vdash . *91·54 . (*121·011·012·013) . \supset$

$\vdash . P(x \vdash y) \subset P(x \mapsto y) . P(x \dashv y) \subset P(x \mapsto y) .$

$[*120·481 . *260·11] \supset \vdash : \text{Hp} . \supset . P(x \vdash y), P(x \dashv y) \in \text{Cls induct}$ (2)

$\vdash . (1) . (2) . \supset \vdash . \text{Prop}$

***260·131.** $\vdash :. P_{po} \in J . \supset : xP_{fn}y . \equiv . P(x \vdash y) \in \text{Cls induct} - \iota`\Lambda .$

$\equiv . P(x \dashv y) \in \text{Cls induct} - \iota`\Lambda$

Dem.

$\vdash . *121·22 . \supset \vdash : P(x \vdash y) \in \text{Cls induct} - \iota`\Lambda . \supset . xP_{po}y .$ (1)

$[*121·242 . *91·54] \qquad \supset . P(x \mapsto y) = P(x \vdash y) \cup \iota`y$

$[*120·251] \qquad \supset . P(x \mapsto y) \in \text{Cls induct}$ (2)

$\vdash . (1) . *121·242 . \supset \vdash : \text{Hp} . \text{Hp}(1) . \supset . x, y \in P(x \mapsto y) . x \neq y .$

$[*52·41] \qquad \supset . P(x \mapsto y) \sim \in 0 \cup 1$ (3)

$\vdash . (2) . (3) . *260·11 . \supset \vdash : \text{Hp} . \text{Hp}(1) . \supset . xP_{fn}y$ (4)

Similarly $\vdash : \text{Hp} . P(x \dashv y) \in \text{Cls induct} . \supset . xP_{fn}y$ (5)

$\vdash . (4) . (5) . *260·13 . \supset \vdash . \text{Prop}$

***260·14.** $\vdash : P \in (\text{Cls} \rightarrow 1) \cup (1 \rightarrow \text{Cls}) . P_{po} \in J . \supset . P_{fn} = P_{po}$

Dem.

$\vdash . *121·52 . \supset \vdash : \text{Hp} . \supset . \dot{s}`\text{finid}`P = P_*.$

$[(*260·01)] \qquad \supset . P_{fn} = P_* \dot{-} P_0$

$[*121·302] \qquad = P_* \dot{-} I \upharpoonright C`P$

$[*91·541] \qquad = P_{po} : \supset \vdash . \text{Prop}$

***260·15.** $\vdash . P_{fn} = (P_{po})_{fn}$ $[*260·1 . *121·254]$

***260·16.** $\vdash . (\breve{P})_{fn} = \breve{P}_{fn}$ $[*260·1 . *121·26]$

***260·17.** $\vdash : P_{po} \in \text{Ser} . xP_{po}y . \supset . P(x \mapsto y) = C`\{P_{po} \upharpoonright P(x \mapsto y)\} .$

$x = B`\{P_{po} \upharpoonright P(x \mapsto y)\} . y = B`\text{Cnv}`\{P_{po} \upharpoonright P(x \mapsto y)\}$

Dem.

$\vdash . *121·242 . \supset \vdash : \text{Hp} . \supset . x, y \in P(x \mapsto y) . x \neq y .$ (1)

$[*52·41] \qquad \supset . P(x \mapsto y) \sim \in 1 .$

$[*202·55] \qquad \supset . C`\{P_{po} \upharpoonright P(x \mapsto y)\} = P(x \mapsto y)$ (2)

$\vdash . *91·542 . \supset \vdash :. \text{Hp} . \supset : z \in P(x \mapsto y) . z \neq x . \supset . x \{P_{po} \upharpoonright P(x \mapsto y)\} z :$

$[(1) . *205·35] \qquad \supset : x = \min \{P_{po} \upharpoonright P(x \mapsto y)\}`P(x \mapsto y) :$

$[(2) . *205·12] \qquad \supset : x = B`\{P_{po} \upharpoonright P(x \mapsto y)\}$ (3)

Similarly $\vdash : \text{Hp} . \supset . y = B`\text{Cnv}`\{P_{po} \upharpoonright P(x \mapsto y)\}$ (4)

$\vdash . (2) . (3) . (4) . \supset \vdash . \text{Prop}$

The following propositions are concerned in proving that if $P_{po} \in \text{Ser}$, $P_{fn} = (P_1)_{po}$ and $P_\nu = (P_1)_\nu$. Note that "$x (P_1)_{po} y$" means that we can get from x to y by a finite number of steps from one term to the next, so that the series contains no limit-points between x and y. The relation "$x (P_1)_\nu y$" means that $\nu -_c 1$ intermediate terms

$$z_1, z_2, z_3, \ldots z_{\nu -_c 1}$$

can be found, each of which has the relation P_1 to its neighbour, and such that xP_1z_1 and $z_{\nu -_c 1}P_1y$. Thus we have to prove that, provided P_{po} is a series, this occurs when, and only when, the number of terms in the interval $P(x \mapsto y)$ is $\nu +_c 1$.

***260·2.** $\vdash : P_{po} \in \text{connex} . xP_*y . yP_*z . \supset . P(x \mapsto z) = P(x \mapsto y) \cup P(y \mapsto z)$

Dem.

$\vdash . *201·14·15 . \supset \vdash : \text{Hp} . \supset . P(x \mapsto y) \subset P(x \mapsto z) . P(y \mapsto z) \subset P(x \mapsto z)$ (1)

$\vdash . *202·13·103 . \supset \vdash :. \text{Hp} . xP_*w . \supset : wP_*y . \vee . yP_*w$ (2)

$\vdash . (2) . *121·103 . \supset$

$\vdash :. \text{Hp} . w \in P(x \mapsto z) . \supset : xP_*w . wP_*y . \vee . yP_*w . wP_*z :$

[*121·103] $\supset : w \in P(x \mapsto y) \cup P(y \mapsto z)$ (3)

$\vdash . (1) . (3) . \supset \vdash . \text{Prop}$

***260·201.** $\vdash : P_{po} \in \text{connex} . \supset . P_{fn} \in \text{trans}$

Dem.

$\vdash . *260·12 . \supset \vdash : xP_{fn}y . yP_{fn}z . \supset . xP_*y . yP_*z$ (1)

$\vdash . (1) . *260·2 . \supset$

$\vdash : \text{Hp} . xP_{fn}y . yP_{fn}z . \supset . P(x \mapsto z) = P(x \mapsto y) \cup P(y \mapsto z) .$ (2)

[*260·11.*120·71] $\supset . P(x \mapsto z) \in \text{Cls induct}$ (3)

$\vdash . *60·32·371 . \supset \vdash : \alpha \in 0 \cup 1 . \beta \subset \alpha . \supset . \beta \in 0 \cup 1 :$

[Transp] $\supset \vdash : \beta \sim \in 0 \cup 1 . \beta \subset \alpha . \supset . \alpha \sim \in 0 \cup 1$ (4)

$\vdash . (2) . *260·11 . \supset$

$\vdash : \text{Hp} . xP_{fn}y . yP_{fn}z . \supset . P(x \mapsto y) \sim \in 0 \cup 1 . P(x \mapsto y) \subset P(x \mapsto z) .$

[(4)] $\supset . P(x \mapsto z) \sim \in 0 \cup 1$ (5)

$\vdash . (3) . (5) . *260·11 . \supset \vdash : \text{Hp} . xP_{fn}y . yP_{fn}z . \supset . xP_{fn}z : \supset \vdash . \text{Prop}$

***260·202.** $\vdash : P_{po} \in \text{Ser} . \supset . P_{fn} \in \text{Rl}‘J \cap \text{trans}$

Dem.

$\vdash . *260·12 . \supset \vdash : P_{po} \Subset J . \supset . P_{fn} \Subset J$ (1)

$\vdash . (1) . *260·201 . \supset \vdash . \text{Prop}$

We shall not have in general $P_{po} \in \text{Ser} . \supset . P_{fn} \in \text{Ser}$, because P_{fn} is in general not connected. P_{fn} only relates two terms which are at a finite distance from each other, and hence divides P_{po} into a number of mutually exclusive parts. We shall only have $P_{fn} \in \text{Ser}$ when every interval in the series is finite.

***260·21.** $\vdash : P_{po} \epsilon \text{Ser} . xP_*y . yP_1z . \supset . P(x \mapsto z) = P(x \mapsto y) \cup \iota`z$

Dem.

$\vdash . *121·304 . \supset \vdash : \text{Hp} . \supset . P(y \mapsto z) = \iota`y \cup \iota`z$ (1)

$\vdash . *121·242 . \supset \vdash : \text{Hp} . \supset . y \epsilon P(x \mapsto y)$ (2)

$\vdash . *260·2 . \quad \supset \vdash : \text{Hp} . \supset . P(x \mapsto z) = P(x \mapsto y) \cup P(y \mapsto z)$

$[(1).(2)] \quad = P(x \mapsto y) \cup \iota`z : \supset \vdash . \text{Prop}$

***260·22.** $\vdash : P_{po} \epsilon \text{Ser} . \supset . (P_1)_1 = P_1 . P_1 \epsilon 1 \to 1 . (P_1)_{po} \subseteq J$

Dem.

$\vdash . *121·254 . \quad \supset \vdash . P_1 = (P_{po})_1$ (1)

$\vdash . (1) . *204·7 . \supset \vdash : \text{Hp} . \supset . P_1 \epsilon 1 \to 1$ (2)

$\vdash . *121·305 . \quad \supset \vdash : \text{Hp} . \supset . P_1 \subseteq P .$

$[*91·59] \quad \supset . (P_1)_{po} \subseteq P_{po} .$

$[*204·1] \quad \supset . (P_1)_{po} \subseteq J$ (3)

$\vdash . (1) . (2) . (3) . *121·31 . \supset \vdash . \text{Prop}$

***260·23.** $\vdash : P_{po} \epsilon \text{Ser} . \nu \epsilon \text{NC induct} . \supset . (P_1)_\nu \epsilon 1 \to 1$

$[*121·342 . *260·22]$

***260·24.** $\vdash : P_{po} \epsilon \text{Ser} . \nu \epsilon \text{NC induct} . x(P_1)_\nu y . x(P_1)_{\nu +_c 1} z . \supset . yP_1z$

Dem.

$\vdash . *121·35 . *260·22 . \supset \vdash : \text{Hp} . \supset . x\{(P_1)_\nu \mid P_1\} z .$

$[*34·1] \quad \supset . (\exists w) . x(P_1)_\nu w . wP_1z .$

$[*260·23.\text{Hp}] \quad \supset . yP_1z : \supset \vdash . \text{Prop}$

***260·25.** $\vdash : P_{po} \epsilon \text{Ser} . R = P_1 . xR_*y . \supset . P(x \mapsto y) = R(x \mapsto y)$

Dem.

$\vdash . *260·24 . \supset \vdash : \text{Hp} . \nu \epsilon \text{NC induct} . xR_\nu y . xR_{\nu +_c 1} z . P(x \mapsto y) = R(x \mapsto y) . \supset .$

$yRz . P(x \mapsto y) = R(x \mapsto y) .$

$[*260·21] \quad \supset . P(x \mapsto z) = R(x \mapsto y) \cup \iota`z$

$[*260·22.*121·371·304] \quad = R(x \mapsto z)$ (1)

$\vdash . (1) . \supset \vdash :. \text{Hp} . \nu \epsilon \text{NC induct} : xR_\nu y . \supset_y . P(x \mapsto y) = R(x \mapsto y) : \supset :$

$xR_{\nu +_c 1} z . \supset_z . P(x \mapsto z) = R(x \mapsto z)$ (2)

$\vdash . *121·301·22·242 . \supset \vdash : \text{Hp} . xR_0y . \supset . P(x \mapsto y) = \iota`x = R(x \mapsto y)$ (3)

$\vdash . (2) . (3) . \text{Induct} . \supset$

$\vdash :. \text{Hp} . \supset : \nu \epsilon \text{NC induct} . xR_\nu y . \supset . P(x \mapsto y) = R(x \mapsto y) :$

$[*121·12] \supset : S \epsilon \text{finid}`R . xSy . \supset . P(x \mapsto y) = R(x \mapsto y) :$

$[*121·52.*260·22] \supset : xR_*y . \supset . P(x \mapsto y) = R(x \mapsto y) :. \supset \vdash . \text{Prop}$

In the above proposition, "Induct" refers to *120·13. The "$\phi\xi$" of *120·13 is replaced by

$$xR_\xi y . \supset_y . P(x \mapsto y) = R(x \mapsto y).$$

Thus (2), in the above proof, is (when ν is replaced by ξ)

$$\xi \in \text{NC induct} . \phi\xi . \supset . \phi(\xi +_c 1),$$

and (3) is $\phi 0.$

Hence, by $*120{\cdot}13$, we have

$$\alpha \in \text{NC induct} . \supset . \phi\alpha,$$

i.e. $\nu \in \text{NC induct} . \supset : xR_\nu y . \supset_y . R(x \mapsto y),$

which is the inference drawn in the above proof.

Wherever "Induct" is given as a reference, it indicates a process such as the above, making use of $*120{\cdot}13$ or $*120{\cdot}11$.

$*260{\cdot}251$. $\vdash : P_{po} \in \text{Ser} . \supset . (P_1)_{po} \subseteq P_{fn}$

Dem.

$\vdash . *260{\cdot}25 . \supset \vdash : \text{Hp} . R = P_1 . xR_{po}y . \supset . P(x \mapsto y) = R(x \mapsto y).$ (1)

$[*121{\cdot}45 . *260{\cdot}22]$ $\supset . P(x \mapsto y) \in \text{Cls induct}$ (2)

$\vdash . *121{\cdot}242 . (1) . *260{\cdot}22 . \supset \vdash : \text{Hp}(1) . \supset . x, y \in P(x \mapsto y) . x \neq y .$

$[*52{\cdot}41]$ $\supset . P(x \mapsto y) \sim \in 0 \cup 1$ (3)

$\vdash . (2) . (3) . \supset \vdash : \text{Hp} . x(P_1)_{po}y . \supset . P(x \mapsto y) \in \text{Cls induct} - 0 - 1 .$

$[*260{\cdot}11]$ $\supset . xP_{fn}y : \supset \vdash . \text{Prop}$

$*260{\cdot}26$. $\vdash :. P_{po} \in \text{Ser} . R = P_1 . xR_* y . \supset : xP_\nu y . \equiv . xR_\nu y$

Dem.

$\vdash . *260{\cdot}25 . \supset \vdash :. \text{Hp} . \supset : P(x \mapsto y) = R(x \mapsto y) :$

$[*121{\cdot}11]$ $\supset : xP_\nu y . \equiv . xR_\nu y :. \supset \vdash . \text{Prop}$

$*260{\cdot}261$. $\vdash : P_{po} \in \text{Ser} . \nu \in \text{NC induct} - \iota\text{‘}0 . xP_\nu y . xP_{\nu +_c 1} z . \supset . yP_1 z$

Dem.

$\vdash . *121{\cdot}11 . \supset \vdash : \text{Hp} . \supset . \text{Nc‘}P(x \mapsto y) = \nu +_c 1 . \text{Nc‘}P(x \mapsto z) = \nu +_c 2 .$ (1)

$[*120{\cdot}32]$ $\supset . y \neq z$ (2)

$\vdash . (1) . *120{\cdot}428 . \supset \vdash : \text{Hp} . \supset . \text{Nc‘}P(x \mapsto z) > \text{Nc‘}P(x \mapsto y) .$

$[*117{\cdot}222 . \text{Transp}]$ $\supset . \sim \{P(x \mapsto z) \subset P(x \mapsto y)\} .$

$[*121{\cdot}103 . *201{\cdot}14{\cdot}15]$ $\supset . \sim (zP_* y) .$ (3)

$[*202{\cdot}103]$ $\supset . yP_{po}z .$

$[*202{\cdot}171]$ $\supset . P(x \mapsto z) = P(x \mapsto y) \cup P(y \dashv z) .$

$[*120{\cdot}41 . (1) . (3)]$ $\supset . P(y \dashv z) \in 1 .$

$[*121{\cdot}242 . (2)]$ $\supset . P(y \mapsto z) \in 2 .$

$[*121{\cdot}11]$ $\supset . yP_1 z : \supset \vdash . \text{Prop}$

$*260{\cdot}27$. $\vdash : P_{po} \in \text{Ser} . \supset . P_{fn} = (P_1)_{po}$

Dem.

$\vdash . *260{\cdot}261 . \supset \vdash : \text{Hp} . \nu \in \text{NC induct} - \iota\text{‘}0 . xP_\nu y . xP_{\nu +_c 1} z . x(P_1)_{po} y . \supset .$
$yP_1 z . x(P_1)_{po} y .$

$[*91{\cdot}511]$ $\supset . x(P_1)_{po} z$ (1)

$\vdash . (1) . \supset \vdash :. \text{Hp} . \nu \in \text{NC induct} - \iota`0 : x P_\nu y . \supset_y . x (P_1)_{po} y : \supset :$
$x P_{\nu +_c 1} z . \supset_z . x (P_1)_{po} z$ (2)

$\vdash . *91.502 . \supset \vdash : x P_1 y . \supset . x (P_1)_{po} y$ (3)

$\vdash . (2) \because (3) . *120.47 . \supset \vdash :. \text{Hp} . \supset : \nu \in \text{NC induct} - \iota`0 . \supset_\nu . P_\nu \in (P_1)_{po} :$
[*260.1] $\supset : P_{fn} \in (P_1)_{po}$ (4)

$\vdash . (4) . *260.251 . \supset \vdash . \text{Prop}$

***260.28.** $\vdash : P_{po} \in \text{Ser} . \nu \in \text{NC induct} - \iota`0 . \supset . P_\nu = (P_1)_\nu = (P_{fn})_\nu$

Dem.

$\vdash . *260.26 . \supset \vdash :. \text{Hp} . \supset : x (P_1)_{po} y . x P_\nu y . \equiv . x (P_1)_{po} y . x (P_1)_\nu y$ (1)

$\vdash . *260.1 . \supset \vdash : \text{Hp} . x P_\nu y . \supset . x P_{fn} y .$
[*260.27] $\supset . x (P_1)_{po} y$ (2)

$\vdash . *121.321 . \supset \vdash : \text{Hp} . x (P_1)_\nu y . \supset . x (P_1)_{po} y$ (3)

$\vdash . (1) . (2) . (3) . \supset \vdash :. \text{Hp} . \supset : x P_\nu y . \equiv . x (P_1)_\nu y$ (4)

$\vdash . *121.254 . \supset \vdash . (P_1)_\nu = \{(P_1)_{po}\}_\nu .$
[*260.27] $\supset \vdash : \text{Hp} . \supset . (P_1)_\nu = (P_{fn})_\nu$ (5)

$\vdash . (4) . (5) . \supset \vdash . \text{Prop}$

The above proposition does not hold in general when $\nu = 0$, for if P is a compact series, $P_1 = \dot\Lambda$, so that $(P_1)_0 = \dot\Lambda$, but $P_0 = I \upharpoonright C`P$.

***260.29.** $\vdash : P_{po} \in \text{Ser} . x P_{fn} y . \supset . P (x \mapsto y) = P_1 (x \mapsto y) = P_{fn} (x \mapsto y)$

Dem.

$\vdash . *260.27.25 . \supset \vdash : \text{Hp} . \supset . P (x \mapsto y) = P_1 (x \mapsto y)$
[*121.253.*260.27] $= P_{fn} (x \mapsto y) : \supset \vdash . \text{Prop}$

The following propositions are mainly concerned with the result of confining the field of P_{fn} to the posterity of a single term.

***260.3.** $\vdash : P_{po} \in \text{Ser} . \supset . \text{D}`P_{fn} = \text{D}`P_1 . \text{ᗡ}`P_{fn} = \text{ᗡ}`P_1 . C`P_{fn} = C`P_1$
[*260.27 . *91.504]

***260.31.** $\vdash : P_{po} \in \text{Ser} . x \in \text{D}`P_1 . \supset .$
$C`\{P_{fn} \upharpoonright (\iota`x \cup \overleftarrow{P_{fn}}`x)\} = \overleftarrow{(P_1)_*}`x = \iota`x \cup \overleftarrow{P_{fn}}`x$

Dem.

$\vdash . *260.27 . \supset \vdash : \text{Hp} . \supset . \iota`x \cup \overleftarrow{P_{fn}}`x = \iota`x \cup \overleftarrow{(P_1)_{po}}`x$
[*96.14] $= \overleftarrow{(P_1)_*}`x$ (1)

$\vdash . *260.3 . \supset \vdash : \text{Hp} . \supset . \exists ! \overleftarrow{P_{fn}}`x .$
[*36.13] $\supset . (\exists y) . x \{P_{fn} \upharpoonright (\iota`x \cup \overleftarrow{P_{fn}}`x)\} y$ (2)

$\vdash . *36.13 . \supset \vdash : y \in \overleftarrow{P_{fn}}`x . \supset . x \{P_{fn} \upharpoonright (\iota`x \cup \overleftarrow{P_{fn}}`x)\} y .$
[*10.24] $\supset . (\exists z) . z \{P_{fn} \upharpoonright (\iota`x \cup \overleftarrow{P_{fn}}`x)\} y$ (3)

$\vdash . (2) . (3) . \supset \vdash : \text{Hp} . \supset . \iota`x \cup \overleftarrow{P_{fn}}`x \subset C`\{P_{fn} \upharpoonright (\iota`x \cup \overleftarrow{P_{fn}}`x)\} .$
[*37.41] $\supset . \iota`x \cup \overleftarrow{P_{fn}}`x = C`\{P_{fn} \upharpoonright (\iota`x \cup \overleftarrow{P_{fn}}`x)\}$ (4)

$\vdash . (1) . (4) . \supset \vdash . \text{Prop}$

***260·32.** $\vdash : P_{po} \epsilon \mathrm{Ser} . \supset .$

$$P_{fn} \mathbin{\pounds} (\iota`x \cup \overleftarrow{P}_{fn}`x) = P_{po} \mathbin{\pounds} (\iota`x \cup \overleftarrow{P}_{fn}`x) . P_{fn} \mathbin{\pounds} (\iota`x \cup \overleftarrow{P}_{fn}`x) \epsilon \mathrm{Ser}$$

Dem.

$\vdash . *260{\cdot}12 . \supset \vdash . P_{fn} \mathbin{\pounds} (\iota`x \cup \overleftarrow{P}_{fn}`x) \mathrel{\dot{\subset}} P_{po} \mathbin{\pounds} (\iota`x \cup \overleftarrow{P}_{fn}`x)$ (1)

$\vdash . *260{\cdot}3 . *200{\cdot}35 . \supset$

$\vdash : \mathrm{Hp} . x \sim \epsilon D`P_1 . \supset . P_{fn} \mathbin{\pounds} (\iota`x \cup \overleftarrow{P}_{fn}`x) = \dot{\Lambda} = P_{po} \mathbin{\pounds} (\iota`x \cup \overleftarrow{P}_{fn}`x)$ (2)

$\vdash . *201{\cdot}521 . *260{\cdot}27 . \supset$

$\vdash : \mathrm{Hp} . x \epsilon D`P_1 . \supset . P_{fn} \mathbin{\pounds} (\iota`x \cup \overleftarrow{P}_{fn}`x) = (P_1)_{po} \mathbin{\pounds} \overleftarrow{(P_1)_*}`x .$

$[*202{\cdot}14 . *260{\cdot}22] \supset . P_{fn} \mathbin{\pounds} (\iota`x \cup \overleftarrow{P}_{fn}`x) \epsilon \mathrm{connex} .$

$[*260{\cdot}202] \qquad \supset . P_{fn} \mathbin{\pounds} (\iota`x \cup \overleftarrow{P}_{fn}`x) \epsilon \mathrm{Ser} .$ (3)

$[(1) . *260{\cdot}31 . *204{\cdot}41] \supset . P_{fn} \mathbin{\pounds} (\iota`x \cup \overleftarrow{P}_{fn}`x) = P_{po} \mathbin{\pounds} (\iota`x \cup \overleftarrow{P}_{fn}`x)$ (4)

$\vdash . (2) . (3) . (4) . \supset \vdash . \mathrm{Prop}$

***260·33.** $\vdash : P_{po} \epsilon \mathrm{Ser} . x \epsilon D`P_1 . P_1 = R . \supset .$

$$P_{fn} \mathbin{\pounds} (\iota`x \cup \overleftarrow{P}_{fn}`x) = (\overleftarrow{R}_*`x) \mathbin{\upharpoonleft} R_{po} = \{(\overleftarrow{R}_*`x) \mathbin{\upharpoonleft} R\}_{po} = \{R \upharpoonright (\overleftarrow{R}_{po}`x)\}_{po}$$

Dem.

$\vdash . *260{\cdot}27{\cdot}31 . \supset \vdash : \mathrm{Hp} . \supset . P_{fn} \mathbin{\pounds} (\iota`x \cup \overleftarrow{P}_{fn}`x) = R_{po} \mathbin{\pounds} \overleftarrow{R}_*`x$

$[*96{\cdot}16 . *91{\cdot}602] \qquad = (\overleftarrow{R}_*`x) \mathbin{\upharpoonleft} R_{po}$ (1)

$[*96{\cdot}13] \qquad = \{(\overleftarrow{R}_*`x) \mathbin{\upharpoonleft} R\}_{po}$ (2)

$[*96{\cdot}2 . *260{\cdot}22] \qquad = \{R \upharpoonright (\overleftarrow{R}_{po}`x)\}_{po}$ (3)

$\vdash . (1) . (2) . (3) . \supset \vdash . \mathrm{Prop}$

***260·34.** $\vdash : \mathrm{Hp}\ *260{\cdot}33 . \supset . \{P_{fn} \mathbin{\pounds} (\iota`x \cup \overleftarrow{P}_{fn}`x)\}_1 = (\overleftarrow{R}_*`x) \mathbin{\upharpoonleft} R = R \upharpoonright \overleftarrow{R}_{po}`x$

Dem.

$\vdash . *260{\cdot}33 . *121{\cdot}254 . \supset$

$\vdash : \mathrm{Hp} . \supset . \{P_{fn} \mathbin{\pounds} (\iota`x \cup \overleftarrow{P}_{fn}`x)\}_1 = \{(\overleftarrow{R}_*`x) \mathbin{\upharpoonleft} R\}_1 = \{R \upharpoonright \overleftarrow{R}_{po}`x\}_1$ (1)

$\vdash . (1) . *121{\cdot}31 . *260{\cdot}22 . \supset \vdash . \mathrm{Prop}$

The following propositions are concerned with the result of confining the field of P_{fn} to a single family.

***260·4.** $\vdash : P_{po} \epsilon \mathrm{Ser} . \supset . P_{fn} \mathbin{\pounds} \overleftrightarrow{P}_{fn}`x \epsilon \mathrm{Ser} .$

$$C`(P_{fn} \mathbin{\pounds} \overleftrightarrow{P}_{fn}`x) = \overleftrightarrow{P}_{fn}`x = \overleftrightarrow{(P_1)_*}`x . \overleftrightarrow{P}_{fn}`x \sim \epsilon 1$$

Dem.

$\vdash . *260{\cdot}27 . *97{\cdot}17 . \supset \vdash : \mathrm{Hp} . \supset . P_{fn} \mathbin{\pounds} \overleftrightarrow{P}_{fn}`x = (P_1)_{po} \mathbin{\pounds} \overleftrightarrow{(P_1)_*}`x .$

$[*202{\cdot}15 . *260{\cdot}22] \qquad \supset . P_{fn} \mathbin{\pounds} \overleftrightarrow{P}_{fn}`x \epsilon \mathrm{connex} .$

$[*260{\cdot}202 . *204{\cdot}42] \qquad \supset . P_{fn} \mathbin{\pounds} \overleftrightarrow{P}_{fn}`x \epsilon \mathrm{Ser}$ (1)

$\vdash . *97{\cdot}18 . \supset \vdash . C\text{‘}(P_{\text{fn}} \sqsubset \overleftrightarrow{P}_{\text{fn}}\text{‘}x) = \overleftrightarrow{P}_{\text{fn}}\text{‘}x$ (2)

$\vdash . (2) . *260{\cdot}202 . *200{\cdot}12 . \supset \vdash : \text{Hp} . \supset . \overleftrightarrow{P}_{\text{fn}}\text{‘}x \sim\epsilon\, 1$ (3)

$\vdash . *260{\cdot}27 . *97{\cdot}17 . \supset \vdash : \text{Hp} . \supset . \overleftrightarrow{P}_{\text{fn}}\text{‘}x = (\overleftrightarrow{P_1})_*\text{‘}x$ (4)

$\vdash . (1) . (2) . (3) . (4) . \supset \vdash . \text{Prop}$

***260·41.** $\vdash : P_{\text{po}} \epsilon \text{Ser} . R = P_1 . \supset .$

$$P_{\text{fn}} \sqsubset \overleftrightarrow{P}_{\text{fn}}\text{‘}x = R_{\text{po}} \sqsubset \overleftrightarrow{R}_*\text{‘}x = (\overleftrightarrow{R}_*\text{‘}x) \rceil R_{\text{po}} = R_{\text{po}} \upharpoonright \overleftrightarrow{R}_*\text{‘}x$$

Dem.

$\vdash . *260{\cdot}27 . *97{\cdot}17 . \supset \vdash : \text{Hp} . \supset . P_{\text{fn}} \sqsubset \overleftrightarrow{P}_{\text{fn}}\text{‘}x = R_{\text{po}} \sqsubset \overleftrightarrow{R}_*\text{‘}x$ (1)

$\vdash . *97{\cdot}13 . \supset \vdash : \text{Hp} . y \epsilon \overleftrightarrow{R}_*\text{‘}x . y R_{\text{po}} z . \supset . z \epsilon \breve{R}_{\text{po}}\text{“}\overrightarrow{R}_*\text{‘}x \cup \breve{R}_{\text{po}}\text{“}\overleftarrow{R}_*\text{‘}x .$

$[*92{\cdot}311 . *260{\cdot}22] \quad \supset . z \epsilon \overrightarrow{R}_*\text{‘}x \cup \overleftarrow{R}_*\text{‘}x .$

$[*97{\cdot}13 . *36{\cdot}13] \quad \supset . y (R_{\text{po}} \sqsubset \overleftrightarrow{R}_*\text{‘}x) z$ (2)

$\vdash . *35{\cdot}21{\cdot}441 . \supset \vdash . R_{\text{po}} \sqsubset \overleftrightarrow{R}_*\text{‘}x \mathrel{\dot\subset} (\overleftrightarrow{R}_*\text{‘}x) \rceil R_{\text{po}}$ (3)

$\vdash . (2) . (3) . \quad \supset \vdash : \text{Hp} . \supset . R_{\text{po}} \sqsubset \overleftrightarrow{R}_*\text{‘}x = (\overleftrightarrow{R}_*\text{‘}x) \rceil R_{\text{po}}$ (4)

Similarly $\vdash : \text{Hp} . \supset . R_{\text{po}} \sqsubset \overleftrightarrow{R}_*\text{‘}x = R_{\text{po}} \upharpoonright \overleftrightarrow{R}_*\text{‘}x$ (5)

$\vdash . (1) . (4) . (5) . \supset \vdash . \text{Prop}$

***260·42.** $\vdash : \text{Hp}\, *260{\cdot}41 . \supset . P_{\text{fn}} \sqsubset \overleftrightarrow{P}_{\text{fn}}\text{‘}x = (\overleftrightarrow{R}_*\text{‘}x \rceil R)_{\text{po}} = (R \upharpoonright \overleftrightarrow{R}_*\text{‘}x)_{\text{po}}$

Dem.

$\vdash . *92{\cdot}32 . *260{\cdot}22 . \supset \vdash : \text{Hp} . \supset . \breve{R}\text{“}\overleftrightarrow{R}_*\text{‘}x \subset \overleftrightarrow{R}_*\text{‘}x .$

$[*96{\cdot}111] \quad \supset . (\overleftrightarrow{R}_*\text{‘}x) \rceil R_{\text{po}} = \{(\overleftrightarrow{R}_*\text{‘}x) \rceil R\}_{\text{po}}$ (1)

Similarly $\vdash : \text{Hp} . \supset . R_{\text{po}} \upharpoonright \overleftrightarrow{R}_*\text{‘}x = \{R \upharpoonright \overleftrightarrow{R}_*\text{‘}x\}_{\text{po}}$ (2)

$\vdash . (1) . (2) . *260{\cdot}41 . \supset \vdash . \text{Prop}$

260·43. $\vdash : P_{\text{po}} \epsilon \text{Ser} . \supset .$

$$\{P_{\text{fn}} \sqsubset \overleftrightarrow{P}_{\text{fn}}\text{‘}x\}_1 = P_1 \sqsubset \overleftrightarrow{P}_{\text{fn}}\text{‘}x = (\overleftrightarrow{P}_{\text{fn}}\text{‘}x) \rceil P_1 = P_1 \upharpoonright (\overleftrightarrow{P}_{\text{fn}}\text{‘}x)$$

Dem.

$\vdash . *260{\cdot}42 . *121{\cdot}254 . \supset$

$\vdash : \text{Hp} . R = P_1 . \supset . \{P_{\text{fn}} \sqsubset \overleftrightarrow{P}_{\text{fn}}\text{‘}x\}_1 = \{(\overleftrightarrow{R}_*\text{‘}x) \rceil R\}_1$

$[*121{\cdot}31 . *260{\cdot}22] \quad = (\overleftrightarrow{R}_*\text{‘}x) \rceil R$

$[*97{\cdot}17 . *260{\cdot}27] \quad = (\overleftrightarrow{P}_{\text{fn}}\text{‘}x) \rceil P_1$ (1)

Similarly $\vdash : \text{Hp} . \supset . \{P_{\text{fn}} \sqsubset \overleftrightarrow{P}_{\text{fn}}\text{‘}x\}_1 = P_1 \upharpoonright \overleftrightarrow{P}_{\text{fn}}\text{‘}x$ (2)

$\vdash . (1) . (2) . *35{\cdot}11 . \supset \vdash : \text{Hp} . \supset . \{P_{\text{fn}} \sqsubset \overleftrightarrow{P}_{\text{fn}}\text{‘}x\}_1 = P_1 \sqsubset \overleftrightarrow{P}_{\text{fn}}\text{‘}x$ (3)

$\vdash . (1) . (2) . (3) . \supset \vdash . \text{Prop}$

Observe that the two series $P_{\text{fn}} \sqsubset \overleftrightarrow{P}_{\text{fn}}\text{‘}x$ and $P_{\text{fn}} \sqsubset \overleftrightarrow{P}_{\text{fn}}\text{‘}y$ are either identical or have no common terms in their fields. This results immediately from *97·16, since the fields of the two series are $(\overleftrightarrow{P_1})_*\text{‘}x$ and $(\overleftrightarrow{P_1})_*\text{‘}y$.

$*261$. FINITE AND INFINITE SERIES.

Summary of $*261$.

In this number we define finite and infinite series, and we show that, where well-ordered series are concerned, there is only one kind of finitude, *i.e.* there is not the distinction, which exists in cardinals, between "inductive" and "non-reflexive." We also give various equivalent forms of the distinction between finite and infinite series, and some of the simpler properties of each. The propositions of this number are numerous and important.

We define an infinite series as one whose field is a reflexive class, and a finite series as one which is not infinite. Thus we put

$$\text{Ser infin} = \text{Ser} \cap \breve{C}\text{``Cls refl} \quad \text{Df},$$

$$\Omega\ \text{infin} = \Omega \cap \breve{C}\text{``Cls refl} \quad \text{Df},$$

$$\text{Ser fin} = \text{Ser} - \text{Ser infin} \quad \text{Df},$$

$$\Omega\ \text{fin} = \Omega - \Omega\ \text{infin} \quad \text{Df}.$$

We also put, to begin with,

$$\Omega\ \text{induct} = \Omega \cap \breve{C}\text{``Cls induct} \quad \text{Df},$$

but in the course of this number we prove

$*261\cdot42$. $\vdash . \Omega\ \text{fin} = \Omega\ \text{induct}$

so that the symbol "Ω induct" is not required after the present number.

After some preliminary propositions, we proceed ($*261\cdot2$ ff.) to various criteria of finitude and infinity. We have

$*261\cdot25$. $\vdash :. P \in \text{Ser} . \supset :$

$$C\text{`}P \in \text{Cls induct} - \iota\text{`}\Lambda . \equiv . P = P_{\text{fn}} . \text{E} ! B\text{`}P . \text{E} ! B\text{`}\breve{P}$$

The condition $P = P_{\text{fn}}$ insures that every interval is finite, but this still leaves it possible for our series to be a progression, or its converse, or the converse of a progression followed by a progression (*i.e.* the type of the negative and positive finite integers in order of magnitude). The third of these possibilities is excluded by either $\text{E}\,!\,B\text{‘}P$ or $\text{E}\,!\,B\text{‘}\breve{P}$; the second is excluded by $\text{E}\,!\,B\text{‘}P$, and the first by $\text{E}\,!\,B\text{‘}\breve{P}$. We have

***261·212.** $\vdash :.\, P \in \Omega \,.\supset :\, \text{C}\!\!\text{I}\text{‘}P_1 = \text{C}\!\!\text{I}\text{‘}P \,.\equiv .\, P = (P_1)_{\text{po}} \,.\equiv .\, P = P_{\text{fn}}$

"$\text{C}\!\!\text{I}\text{‘}P_1 = \text{C}\!\!\text{I}\text{‘}P$" means that every term except the first has an immediate predecessor. We have

***261·26.** $\vdash :\, P \in \text{Ser} \,.\, \alpha \subset C\text{‘}P \,.\, \exists !\, \alpha \,.\, \alpha \in \text{Cls induct} \,.\supset .\, \text{E}\,!\,\text{min}_P\text{‘}\alpha \,.\, \text{E}\,!\,\text{max}_P\text{‘}\alpha$

and

***261·27.** $\vdash :.\, P \in \text{Ser} :\, \alpha \subset C\text{‘}P \,.\, \exists !\, \alpha \,.\supset_\alpha .\, \text{E}\,!\,\text{min}_P\text{‘}\alpha \,.\, \text{E}\,!\,\text{max}_P\text{‘}\alpha :\supset .$
$P = P_{\text{fn}} \,.\, C\text{‘}P \in \text{Cls induct}$

whence we obtain

***261·28.** $\vdash ::\, P \in \text{Ser} \,.\supset :.$
$\alpha \subset C\text{‘}P \,.\, \exists !\, \alpha \,.\supset_\alpha .\, \text{E}\,!\,\text{min}_P\text{‘}\alpha \,.\, \text{E}\,!\,\text{max}_P\text{‘}\alpha :\equiv .\, C\text{‘}P \in \text{Cls induct}$

I.e. a series whose field is inductive is one in which every existent sub-class of the field has both a minimum and a maximum.

From the above, together with an inductive proof that every inductive class which is not a unit class is the field of some series, we obtain

***261·29.** $\vdash .\, \text{Cls induct} =$
$1 \cup C\text{“}\hat{P}\{P \in \text{Ser} :\, \alpha \subset C\text{‘}P \,.\, \exists !\, \alpha \,.\supset_\alpha .\, \text{E}\,!\,\text{min}_P\text{‘}\alpha \,.\, \text{E}\,!\,\text{max}_P\text{‘}\alpha\}$
$= 1 \cup C\text{“}(\Omega \cap \text{Cnv}\text{“}\Omega)$

The above proposition is interesting as giving an alternative method of treating inductive classes. Instead of the definitions adopted in *120, we might have taken the above proposition as the definition of inductive classes, putting

$$\text{NC induct} = \text{Nc}\text{“}\text{Cls induct} \quad \text{Df.}$$

We should thus wholly avoid the use of mathematical induction in definitions; hence if such avoidance were in any way desirable, it could be secured by dealing with series before introducing the distinction of finite and infinite, and then defining inductive classes as the fields of series which are well-ordered backwards as well as forwards. The inductive properties of such classes would then be deduced from *261·27, together with *260·27, in virtue of which we have

$$P \in \Omega \cap \text{Cnv}\text{“}\Omega \,.\supset .\, P = (P_1)_{\text{po}},$$

whence, by *91·62,

$$\vdash ::\, P \in \Omega \cap \text{Cnv}\text{“}\Omega \,.\supset :.\, xPy \,.\equiv :\, \breve{P}_1\text{“}\mu \subset \mu \,.\, \breve{P}_1\text{‘}x \in \mu \,.\supset_\mu .\, y \in \mu.$$

In virtue of this proposition, if γ is the field of a well-ordered series P whose converse is well-ordered, then any property which is inherited with respect to P_1 belongs to all the successors of x (where $x \in \gamma$) if it belongs to the immediate successor of x. Hence mathematical induction follows.

From the above we obtain at once

***261·31.** $\vdash :. P \epsilon \text{Ser} . \supset : C`P \epsilon \text{Cls induct} . \equiv . P, \breve{P} \epsilon \Omega$

I.e. series whose fields are inductive are the same as inductive well-ordered series, and are also the same as well-ordered series whose converses are well-ordered. Hence also we obtain

***261·33.** $\vdash : P, Q \epsilon \Omega . Q \subset \breve{P} . \supset . Q \epsilon \Omega \text{ induct}$

I.e. a *descending* well-ordered series of terms chosen out of a well-ordered series must be finite. This proposition, which is due to Cantor, has been used by him in many proofs.

We have

***261·35.** $\vdash :. P \epsilon \Omega . \supset : C`P \epsilon \text{Cls induct} - \iota`\Lambda . \equiv . \text{Cl}`P_1 = \text{Cl}`P . \text{E} ! B`\breve{P}$

In *253·51 and following propositions we have already had the hypothesis $\text{Cl}`P_1 = \text{Cl}`P . \text{E} ! B`\breve{P}$, which now turns out to be equivalent to the hypothesis that our series is finite and not null. Thus we have

***261·36.** $\vdash :. P \epsilon \Omega . \supset : C`P \epsilon \text{Cls induct} - \iota`\Lambda . \equiv . \text{Nr}`P \neq \dot{1} \dot{+} \text{Nr}`P$

*261·4 and following propositions are concerned in proving that a well-ordered series which is not inductive always contains progressions, and in deducing consequences from this. We have

***261·4.** $\vdash : P \epsilon \Omega - \Omega \text{ induct} . \supset . \{\overleftarrow{(P_1)_*}`B`P\} \upharpoonright P_1 \epsilon \text{Prog}$

The above proposition is very important, for many reasons. One of its most important consequences is that, if P is a well-ordered series which is not inductive, its field contains an $\aleph_0$, and is therefore a reflexive class (*261·401). Hence a class which can be well-ordered is either inductive or reflexive (*261·43), and a well-ordered series is either inductive or infinite according to the definitions given above (*261·41). Hence where well-ordered series are concerned, the two ways of defining finite and infinite (namely those in *120 and *124) give equivalent results. This cannot (so far as is known) be proved for classes in general without assuming the multiplicative axiom.

From the above-mentioned propositions it follows that an infinite well-ordered series is one in which P_1 limited to the posterity of $B`P$ with respect to P_1 is a progression in the sense of *122 (*261·44), and that any class contained in a well-ordered series is either inductive or reflexive (*261·46).

The number ends with some propositions in ordinal arithmetic. We prove that P^Q is well-ordered if P is well-ordered and Q is a finite well-ordered series (*261·62); that if R is a finite well-ordered series, and P is less than Q (in the sense of *254), then P^R is less than Q^R; and that a finite well-ordered series is less than an infinite one (*261·65).

***261·01.** $\text{Ser infin} = \text{Ser} \cap \breve{C}``\text{Cls refl}$ Df

***261·02.** $\Omega\ \text{infin} = \Omega \cap \breve{C}``\text{Cls refl}$ Df

***261·03.** $\text{Ser fin} = \text{Ser} - \text{Ser infin}$ Df

***261·04.** $\Omega\ \text{fin} = \Omega - \Omega\ \text{infin}$ Df

***261·05.** $\Omega\ \text{induct} = \Omega \cap \breve{C}``\text{Cls induct}$ Df

***261·1.** $\vdash : P \epsilon \text{Ser infin} . \equiv . P \epsilon \text{Ser} . C`P \epsilon \text{Cls refl}$ [(*261·01)]

***261·11.** $\vdash : P \epsilon \Omega\ \text{infin} . \equiv . P \epsilon \Omega . C`P \epsilon \text{Cls refl}$ [(*261·02)]

***261·12.** $\vdash : P \epsilon \text{Ser fin} . \equiv . P \epsilon \text{Ser} - \text{Ser infin} . \equiv . P \epsilon \text{Ser} . C`P \sim\epsilon \text{Cls refl}$
[(*261·03)]

***261·13.** $\vdash : P \epsilon \Omega\ \text{fin} . \equiv . P \epsilon \Omega - \Omega\ \text{infin} . \equiv . P \epsilon \Omega . C`P \sim\epsilon \text{Cls refl}$
[(*261·04)]

***261·14.** $\vdash : P \epsilon \Omega\ \text{induct} . \equiv . P \epsilon \Omega . C`P \epsilon \text{Cls induct}$ [(*261·05)]

***261·15.** $\vdash : P \epsilon \text{Ser infin} . P \text{ smor } Q . \supset . Q \epsilon \text{Ser infin}$

Dem.

$\vdash . *261{\cdot}1 . \supset \vdash : \text{Hp} . \supset . P \epsilon \text{Ser} . C`P \epsilon \text{Cls refl} . P \text{ smor } Q .$

[*204·21.*151·18] $\supset . Q \epsilon \text{Ser} . C`P \epsilon \text{Cls refl} . C`P \text{ sm } C`Q .$

[*124·18] $\supset . Q \epsilon \text{Ser} . C`Q \epsilon \text{Cls refl} .$

[*261·1] $\supset . Q \epsilon \text{Ser infin} : \supset \vdash . \text{Prop}$

***261·151.** $\vdash : P \epsilon \text{Ser infin} . \supset . \text{Nr}`P \subset \text{Ser infin}$ [*261·15]

***261·152.** $\vdash : P \epsilon \text{Ser infin} . \equiv . \text{N}_0\text{r}`P \subset \text{Ser infin} . \equiv . \exists ! \text{N}_0\text{r}`P \cap \text{Ser infin}$
[*261·151 . *155·12]

***261·153.** $\vdash : P \epsilon \text{Ser infin} . \equiv . (\exists Q) . P \text{ smor } Q . Q \epsilon \text{Ser infin}$
[*261·15 . *151·13]

***261·16.** $\vdash : P \epsilon \Omega\ \text{infin} . P \text{ smor } Q . \supset . Q \epsilon \Omega\ \text{infin}$
[Proof as in *261·15, using *261·11 . *251·111 . *151·18 . *124·18]

***261·161.** $\vdash : P \epsilon \Omega\ \text{infin} . \supset . \text{Nr}`P \subset \Omega\ \text{infin}$ [*261·16]

***261·162.** $\vdash : P \epsilon \Omega\ \text{infin} . \equiv . \text{N}_0\text{r}`P \subset \Omega\ \text{infin} . \equiv . \exists ! \text{N}_0\text{r}`P \cap \text{Ser infin}$
[*261·161 . *155·12]

***261·163.** $\vdash : P \epsilon \Omega\ \text{infin} . \equiv . (\exists Q) . P \text{ smor } Q . Q \epsilon \Omega\ \text{infin}$ [*261·16 . *151·13]

***261·17.** $\vdash : P \epsilon \text{Ser fin} . P \text{ smor } Q . \supset . Q \epsilon \text{Ser fin}$ [*261·15 . Transp]

***261·171.** $\vdash : P \epsilon \text{Ser fin} . \supset . \text{Nr}`P \subset \text{Ser fin}$ [*261·17]

***261·172.** $\vdash : P \epsilon \text{Ser fin} . \equiv . \text{N}_0\text{r}`P \subset \text{Ser fin} . \equiv . \exists ! \text{N}_0\text{r}`P \cap \text{Ser fin}$
[*261·171 . *155·12]

***261·173.** $\vdash : P \epsilon \text{Ser fin} . \equiv . (\exists Q) . P \text{ smor } Q . Q \epsilon \text{Ser fin}$ [*261·17 . *151·13]

***261·18.** $\vdash : P \epsilon \Omega\,\mathrm{fin} \,.\, P \,\mathrm{smor}\, Q \,.\supset .\, Q \epsilon \Omega\,\mathrm{fin}$ [*261·16 . Transp]

***261·181.** $\vdash : P \epsilon \Omega\,\mathrm{fin} \,.\supset .\, \mathrm{Nr}\text{‘}P \subset \Omega\,\mathrm{fin}$ [*261·18]

***261·182.** $\vdash : P \epsilon \Omega\,\mathrm{fin} \,.\equiv .\, \mathrm{N_0r}\text{‘}P \subset \Omega\,\mathrm{fin} \,.\equiv .\, \exists !\, \mathrm{N_0r}\text{‘}P \cap \Omega\,\mathrm{fin}$
[*261·181 . *155·12]

***261·183.** $\vdash : P \epsilon \Omega\,\mathrm{fin} \,.\equiv .\, (\exists Q) \,.\, P \,\mathrm{smor}\, Q \,.\, Q \epsilon \Omega\,\mathrm{fin}$ [*261·18 . *151·13]

***261·19.** $\vdash : P \epsilon \Omega\,\mathrm{induct} \,.\, P \,\mathrm{smor}\, Q \,.\supset .\, Q \epsilon \Omega\,\mathrm{induct}$
[Proof as in *261·16, using *120·214 instead of *124·18]

***261·191.** $\vdash : P \epsilon \Omega\,\mathrm{induct} \,.\supset .\, \mathrm{Nr}\text{‘}P \subset \Omega\,\mathrm{induct}$ [*261·19]

***261·192.** $\vdash : P \epsilon \Omega\,\mathrm{induct} \,.\equiv .\, \mathrm{N_0r}\text{‘}P \subset \Omega\,\mathrm{induct} \,.\equiv .\, \exists !\, \mathrm{N_0r}\text{‘}P \cap \Omega\,\mathrm{induct}$
[*261·191 . *155·12]

***261·193.** $\vdash : P \epsilon \Omega\,\mathrm{induct} \,.\equiv .\, (\exists Q) \,.\, P \,\mathrm{smor}\, Q \,.\, Q \epsilon \Omega\,\mathrm{induct}$
[*261·19 . *151·13]

***261·2.** $\vdash : P_{\mathrm{po}} \epsilon \mathrm{connex} \,.\, (B\text{‘}P)\, P_{\mathrm{fn}}\, (B\text{‘}\breve{P}) \,.\supset .\, C\text{‘}P \epsilon \mathrm{Cls\,induct}$

Dem.

$\vdash .\, *202\cdot181 \,.\supset \vdash : \mathrm{Hp} \,.\supset .\, C\text{‘}P = P(B\text{‘}P \vdash\!\!\dashv B\text{‘}\breve{P}) \,.$

[*260·11.Hp] $\supset .\, C\text{‘}P \epsilon \mathrm{Cls\,induct} : \supset \vdash .\, \mathrm{Prop}$

***261·21.** $\vdash : P \epsilon \mathrm{connex} \,.\, P = P_{\mathrm{fn}} \,.\, \mathrm{E}!\, B\text{‘}P \,.\, \mathrm{E}!\, B\text{‘}\breve{P} \,.\supset .\, C\text{‘}P \epsilon \mathrm{Cls\,induct}$

Dem.

$\vdash .\, *202\cdot103 \,.\, *93\cdot101 \,.\supset \vdash : \mathrm{Hp} \,.\supset .\, (B\text{‘}P)\, P\, (B\text{‘}\breve{P}) \,.$

[Hp] $\supset .\, (B\text{‘}P)\, P_{\mathrm{fn}}\, (B\text{‘}\breve{P}) \,.$

[*261·2] $\supset .\, C\text{‘}P \epsilon \mathrm{Cls\,induct} : \supset \vdash .\, \mathrm{Prop}$

***261·211.** $\vdash : P \epsilon \mathrm{Ser} \,.\supset .\, \overrightarrow{\min}_P\text{‘}\{\overleftarrow{P}\text{‘}x - \overleftarrow{(P_1)_{\mathrm{po}}}\text{‘}x\} \subset \text{Ɑ}\text{‘}P - \text{Ɑ}\text{‘}P_1$

Dem.

$\vdash .\, *91\cdot511 \,.\, *121\cdot305 \,.\supset$

$\vdash :.\, \mathrm{Hp} \,.\supset : y \epsilon \overleftarrow{P}\text{‘}x \cap \overleftarrow{(P_1)_{\mathrm{po}}}\text{‘}x \,.\, yP_1z \,.\supset .\, z \epsilon \overleftarrow{P}\text{‘}x \cap \overleftarrow{(P_1)_{\mathrm{po}}}\text{‘}x :$

[Transp] $\supset : z \epsilon \overleftarrow{P}\text{‘}x - \overleftarrow{(P_1)_{\mathrm{po}}}\text{‘}x \,.\, yP_1z \,.\supset .\, y \epsilon - \overleftarrow{P}\text{‘}x \cup - \overleftarrow{(P_1)_{\mathrm{po}}}\text{‘}x$ (1)

$\vdash .\, *91\cdot502 \,.\supset \vdash :.\, z \epsilon \overleftarrow{P}\text{‘}x - \overleftarrow{(P_1)_{\mathrm{po}}}\text{‘}x \,.\supset : z \epsilon \overleftarrow{P}\text{‘}x - \overleftarrow{P_1}\text{‘}x :$

[*201·63] $\supset : \mathrm{Hp} \,.\supset .\, xP^2z$ (2)

$\vdash .\, *201\cdot63 \,.\supset \vdash : \mathrm{Hp} \,.\, xP^2z \,.\, yP_1z \,.\supset .\, \sim(yPx) \,.\, y \neq x \,.$

[*202·103] $\supset .\, xPy$ (3)

$\vdash .\, (2) \,.\, (3) \,.\supset \vdash : \mathrm{Hp} \,.\, z \epsilon \overleftarrow{P}\text{‘}x - \overleftarrow{(P_1)_{\mathrm{po}}}\text{‘}x \,.\, yP_1z \,.\supset .\, y \epsilon \overleftarrow{P}\text{‘}x \,.$

[(1)] $\supset .\, y \epsilon \overleftarrow{P}\text{‘}x - \overleftarrow{(P_1)_{\mathrm{po}}}\text{‘}x \,.$

[*201·63] $\supset .\, y \epsilon \overrightarrow{P}\text{‘}z \cap \{\overleftarrow{P}\text{‘}x - \overleftarrow{(P_1)_{\mathrm{po}}}\text{‘}x\} \,.$

[*205·14] $\supset .\, z \sim\epsilon \overrightarrow{\min}_P\text{‘}\{\overleftarrow{P}\text{‘}x - \overleftarrow{(P_1)_{\mathrm{po}}}\text{‘}x\}$ (4)

$\vdash .\, (4) \,.\, \mathrm{Transp} \,.\supset$

$\vdash : \mathrm{Hp} \,.\, z \epsilon \overrightarrow{\min}_P\text{‘}\{\overleftarrow{P}\text{‘}x - \overleftarrow{(P_1)_{\mathrm{po}}}\text{‘}x\} \,.\supset .\, \sim(\exists y) \,.\, yP_1z : \supset \vdash .\, \mathrm{Prop}$

***261·212.** $\vdash :. P \in \Omega . \supset : \text{Ɑ‘}P_1 = \text{Ɑ‘}P . \equiv . P = (P_1)_{po} . \equiv . P = P_{fn}$

Dem.

$\vdash . {*}121{\cdot}305 . \supset \vdash : \text{Hp} . \supset . (P_1)_{po} \Subset P$ (1)

$\vdash . (1) . \quad \supset \vdash : \text{Hp} . P \neq (P_1)_{po} . \supset . (\exists x, y) . xPy . \sim \{x (P_1)_{po} y\} .$

$[{*}32{\cdot}18] \quad \supset . (\exists x) . \exists ! \overleftarrow{P}\text{‘}x - \overleftarrow{(P_1)_{po}}\text{‘}x .$

$[{*}250{\cdot}121] \quad \supset . (\exists x) . \text{E} ! \min_P\text{‘}\{\overleftarrow{P}\text{‘}x - \overleftarrow{(P_1)_{po}}\text{‘}x\} .$

$[{*}261{\cdot}211] \quad \supset . \exists ! \text{Ɑ‘}P - \text{Ɑ‘}P_1$ (2)

$\vdash . (2) . \text{Transp} . \supset \vdash : \text{Hp} . \text{Ɑ‘}P = \text{Ɑ‘}P_1 . \supset . P = (P_1)_{po}$ (3)

$\vdash . {*}91{\cdot}504 . \quad \supset \vdash : P = (P_1)_{po} . \supset . \text{Ɑ‘}P = \text{Ɑ‘}P_1$ (4)

$\vdash . (3) . (4) . \quad \supset \vdash :. \text{Hp} . \supset : \text{Ɑ‘}P_1 = \text{Ɑ‘}P . \equiv . P = (P_1)_{po} .$

$[{*}260{\cdot}27] \quad \equiv . P = P_{fn} :. \supset \vdash . \text{Prop}$

***261·22.** $\vdash : P \in \text{Ser} . C\text{‘}P \in \text{Cls induct} . \supset . P = P_{fn} . \text{D‘}P = \text{D‘}P_1 . \text{Ɑ‘}P = \text{Ɑ‘}P_1$

Dem.

$\vdash . {*}260{\cdot}12 . {*}201{\cdot}18 . \supset \vdash : \text{Hp} . \supset . P_{fn} \Subset P$ (1)

$\vdash . {*}121{\cdot}242 . \quad \supset \vdash : \text{Hp} . xPy . \supset . x, y \in P(x \mapsto y) . x \neq y .$

$[{*}52{\cdot}41] \quad \supset . P(x \mapsto y) \sim\in 0 \cup 1$ (2)

$\vdash . {*}120{\cdot}481 . \quad \supset \vdash : \text{Hp} . \supset . P(x \mapsto y) \in \text{Cls induct}$ (3)

$\vdash . (2) . (3) . {*}260{\cdot}11 . \supset \vdash : \text{Hp} . xPy . \supset . xP_{fn}y$ (4)

$\vdash . (1) . (4) . \quad \supset \vdash : \text{Hp} . \supset . P = P_{fn} .$ (5)

$[{*}260{\cdot}3] \quad \supset . \text{D‘}P = \text{D‘}P_1 . \text{Ɑ‘}P = \text{Ɑ‘}P_1$ (6)

$\vdash . (5) . (6) . \supset \vdash . \text{Prop}$

***261·23.** $\vdash : P \in \text{Ser} . \text{D‘}P_1 = \text{D‘}P . \sim \text{E} ! B\text{‘}\breve{P} . \dot{\exists} ! P . \supset . C\text{‘}P \in \text{Cls refl}$

Dem.

$\vdash . {*}91{\cdot}52 . \supset \vdash . \breve{P}_1\text{‘‘}\overleftarrow{(P_1)_*}\text{‘}x = \overleftarrow{(P_1)_{po}}\text{‘}x$ (1)

$\vdash . {*}91{\cdot}54 . {*}260{\cdot}22 . \supset$

$\vdash : \text{Hp} . x \in C\text{‘}P . \supset . \overleftarrow{(P_1)_*}\text{‘}x = \iota\text{‘}x \cup \overleftarrow{(P_1)_{po}}\text{‘}x . x \sim\in \overleftarrow{(P_1)_{po}}\text{‘}x$ (2)

$\vdash . {*}93{\cdot}11 . \supset \vdash : \text{Hp} . \supset . \text{D‘}P_1 = C\text{‘}P .$ (3)

$[{*}90{\cdot}18] \quad \supset . \overleftarrow{(P_1)_*}\text{‘}x \subset \text{D‘}P_1$ (4)

$\vdash . {*}260{\cdot}22 . \supset \vdash : \text{Hp} . \supset . P_1 \in 1 \rightarrow 1$ (5)

$\vdash . (1) . (2) . (4) . (5) . {*}73{\cdot}21 . {*}91{\cdot}74 . \supset$

$\vdash :. \text{Hp} . \supset : x \in C\text{‘}P . \supset . \overleftarrow{(P_1)_*}\text{‘}x \,\text{sm}\, \overleftarrow{(P_1)_{po}}\text{‘}x . \overleftarrow{(P_1)_{po}}\text{‘}x \subset \overleftarrow{(P_1)_*}\text{‘}x .$

$\exists ! \overleftarrow{(P_1)_*}\text{‘}x - \overleftarrow{(P_1)_{po}}\text{‘}x .$

$[{*}124{\cdot}16] \quad \supset . \overleftarrow{(P_1)_*}\text{‘}x \in \text{Cls refl}$ (6)

$\vdash . (6) . (3) . (4) . \supset \vdash : \text{Hp} . \supset . \exists ! \text{Cls refl} \cap \text{Cl‘}C\text{‘}P .$

$[{*}124{\cdot}141] \quad \supset . C\text{‘}P \in \text{Cls refl} : \supset \vdash . \text{Prop}$

***261·24.** $\vdash : P \epsilon \mathrm{Ser} . C`P \epsilon \mathrm{Cls\ induct} - \iota`\Lambda . \supset . E ! B`P . E ! B`\breve{P}$

Dem.

$\vdash . *261·22 . \supset \vdash : \mathrm{Hp} . \supset . D`P = D`P_1 .$

$[*261·23 . \mathrm{Transp}] \quad \supset . E ! B`\breve{P}$ (1)

$\vdash . (1) \frac{\breve{P}}{P} . \quad \supset \vdash : \mathrm{Hp} . \supset . E ! B`P$ (2)

$\vdash . (1) . (2) . \supset \vdash . \mathrm{Prop}$

***261·25.** $\vdash :. P \epsilon \mathrm{Ser} . \supset : C`P \epsilon \mathrm{Cls\ induct} - \iota`\Lambda . \equiv . P = P_{\mathrm{fn}} . E ! B`P . E ! B`\breve{P}$
[*261·22·24·21]

When $P = P_{\mathrm{fn}} . E ! B`P . \sim E ! B`\breve{P}$, P is a progression;
when $P = P_{\mathrm{fn}} . E ! B`\breve{P} . \sim E ! B`P$, P is a regression
(*i.e.* the converse of a progression); and when

$$P = P_{\mathrm{fn}} . \sim E ! B`P . \sim E ! B`\breve{P},$$

P is the sum of a regression and a progression. These propositions will be proved in the next number.

***261·26.** $\vdash : P \epsilon \mathrm{Ser} . \alpha \subset C`P . \exists ! \alpha . \alpha \epsilon \mathrm{Cls\ induct} . \supset . E ! \min_P`\alpha . E ! \max_P`\alpha$

Dem.

$\vdash . *205·17 . \supset \vdash : \mathrm{Hp} . \alpha \epsilon 1 . \supset . E ! \min_P`\alpha . E ! \max_P`\alpha$ (1)

$\vdash . *202·55 . \supset \vdash : \mathrm{Hp} . \alpha \sim \epsilon 1 . \supset . \alpha = C`(P \upharpoonright \alpha) .$

$[*261·24] \quad \supset . E ! B`(P \upharpoonright \alpha) . E ! B`\mathrm{Cnv}`(P \upharpoonright \alpha) .$

$[*205·42] \quad \supset . E ! \min_P`\alpha . E ! \max_P`\alpha$ (2)

$\vdash . (1) . (2) . \supset \vdash . \mathrm{Prop}$

***261·27.** $\vdash :. P \epsilon \mathrm{Ser} : \alpha \subset C`P . \exists ! \alpha . \supset_\alpha . E ! \min_P`\alpha . E ! \max_P`\alpha : \supset .$
$P = P_{\mathrm{fn}} . C`P \epsilon \mathrm{Cls\ induct}$

Dem.

$\vdash . *250·121 . \supset \vdash : \mathrm{Hp} . \supset . P \epsilon \Omega .$

$[*250·21] \quad \supset . D`P = D`P_1 .$

$[*260·3] \quad \supset . D`P = D`P_{\mathrm{fn}}$ (1)

$\vdash . (1) . \supset \vdash : \mathrm{Hp} . x P_{\mathrm{fn}} y . y \epsilon D`P . \supset . y \epsilon D`P_{\mathrm{fn}} . x P_{\mathrm{fn}} y .$

$[*260·201] \quad \supset . y \epsilon P_{\mathrm{fn}}``\overleftarrow{P}_{\mathrm{fn}}`x .$

$[*260·12 . *201·18] \quad \supset . y \epsilon P``\overleftarrow{P}_{\mathrm{fn}}`x .$

$[*205·111] \quad \supset . y \neq \max_P`\overleftarrow{P}_{\mathrm{fn}}`x$ (2)

$\vdash . (1) . (2) . \mathrm{Transp} . \supset \vdash : \mathrm{Hp} . x \epsilon D`P . \supset . \max_P`\overleftarrow{P}_{\mathrm{fn}}`x = B`\breve{P}$ (3)

$\vdash . *250·121·13 . \supset \vdash : \mathrm{Hp} . \dot{\exists} ! P . \supset . E ! B`P .$

$[(3)] \quad \supset . (B`P) P_{\mathrm{fn}} (B`\breve{P}) .$

[*260·11] $\supset . P(B'P \mapsto B'\breve{P}) \in \text{Cls induct} .$

[*202·181] $\supset . C'P \in \text{Cls induct}$ (4)

$\vdash . *120\cdot212 . \supset \vdash : P = \dot{\Lambda} . \supset . C'P \in \text{Cls induct}$ (5)

$\vdash . (4) . (5) . \supset \vdash : \text{Hp} . \supset . C'P \in \text{Cls induct} .$ (6)

[*261·22] $\supset . P = P_{\text{fn}}$ (7)

$\vdash . (6) . (7) . \supset \vdash . \text{Prop}$

***261·28.** $\vdash :: P \in \text{Ser} . \supset :.$

$\alpha \subset C'P . \exists ! \alpha . \supset_\alpha . E ! \min_P{}'\alpha . E ! \max_P{}'\alpha : \equiv . C'P \in \text{Cls induct}$

[*261·26·27]

***261·281.** $\vdash : \gamma \in \text{Cls induct} - 1 . \supset . \gamma \in C``\text{Ser}$

Dem.

$\vdash . *204\cdot24 . \quad \supset \vdash . \Lambda \in C``\text{Ser}$ (1)

$\vdash . *52\cdot22 . \quad \supset \vdash . \Lambda \cup \iota'x \in 1$ (2)

$\vdash . *52\cdot22 . \quad \supset \vdash : x = y . \supset . \iota'x \cup \iota'y \in 1$ (3)

$\vdash . *204\cdot25 . \quad \supset \vdash : x \neq y . \supset . \iota'x \cup \iota'y \in C``\text{Ser}$ (4)

$\vdash . (3) . (4) . \quad \supset \vdash . \iota'x \cup \iota'y \in 1 \cup C``\text{Ser} .$

[*52·1] $\quad \supset \vdash : \gamma \in 1 . \supset . \gamma \cup \iota'y \in 1 \cup C``\text{Ser}$ (5)

$\vdash . *51\cdot2 . \quad \supset \vdash : \gamma \in C``\text{Ser} . y \in \gamma . \supset . \gamma \cup \iota'y \in C``\text{Ser}$ (6)

$\vdash . *204\cdot51 . *161\cdot14 . \supset \vdash : \gamma \in C``\text{Ser} . \exists ! \gamma . y \sim\in \gamma . \supset . \gamma \cup \iota'y \in C``\text{Ser}$ (7)

$\vdash . (6) . (7) . \quad \supset \vdash : \gamma \in C``\text{Ser} . \exists ! \gamma . \supset . \gamma \cup \iota'y \in C``\text{Ser}$ (8)

$\vdash . (2) . (5) . (8) . \quad \supset \vdash : \gamma \in 1 \cup C``\text{Ser} . \supset . \gamma \cup \iota'y \in 1 \cup C``\text{Ser}$ (9)

$\vdash . (1) . (9) . *120\cdot26 . \supset \vdash : \gamma \in \text{Cls induct} . \supset . \gamma \in 1 \cup C``\text{Ser} : \supset \vdash . \text{Prop}$

***261·29.** $\vdash . \text{Cls induct} =$

$1 \cup C``\hat{P}\{P \in \text{Ser} : \alpha \subset C'P . \exists ! \alpha . \supset_\alpha . E ! \min_P{}'\alpha . E ! \max_P{}'\alpha\}$

$= 1 \cup C``(\Omega \cap \text{Cnv}``\Omega)$

Dem.

$\vdash . *261\cdot281 . \supset \vdash :. \gamma \in \text{Cls induct} - 1 . \supset : (\exists P) : P \in \text{Ser} . \gamma = C'P :$

[*261·28]

$\supset : (\exists P) : P \in \text{Ser} : \alpha \subset C'P . \exists ! \alpha . \supset_\alpha . E ! \min_P{}'\alpha . E ! \max_P{}'\alpha : \gamma = C'P :$

[*37·6] $\supset : \gamma \in C``\hat{P}\{P \in \text{Ser} : \alpha \subset C'P . \exists ! \alpha . \supset_\alpha . E ! \min_P{}'\alpha . E ! \max_P{}'\alpha\}$ (1)

$\vdash . *261\cdot28 . \supset \vdash :. P \in \text{Ser} :$

$\alpha \subset C'P . \exists ! \alpha . \supset_\alpha . E ! \min_P{}'\alpha . E ! \max_P{}'\alpha : \gamma = C'P : \supset . \gamma \in \text{Cls induct} :.$

[*37·6] $\supset \vdash : \gamma \in C``\hat{P}(P \in \text{Ser} : \alpha \subset C'P . \exists ! \alpha . \supset_\alpha . E ! \min_P{}'\alpha . E ! \max_P{}'\alpha) . \supset .$

$\gamma \in \text{Cls induct}$ (2)

$\vdash . *120\cdot213 . \supset \vdash . 1 \subset \text{Cls induct}$ (3)

$\vdash . (1) . (2) . (3) . \supset$

$\vdash . \text{Cls induct} = C``\hat{P}\{P \in \text{Ser} : \alpha \subset C'P . \exists ! \alpha . \supset_\alpha . E ! \min_P{}'\alpha . E ! \max_P{}'\alpha\}$

[*250·121] $= C``(\Omega \cap \text{Cnv}``\Omega) . \supset \vdash . \text{Prop}$

The following four propositions are immediate consequences of the propositions already proved.

***261·3.** $\vdash :: P \epsilon \text{Ser} . \supset :.$
$C'P \epsilon \text{Cls induct} . \equiv : P \epsilon \Omega : \alpha \subset C'P . \exists ! \alpha . \supset_\alpha . E ! \max_P{}'\alpha$
[*261·28 . *250·121]

***261·31.** $\vdash :. P \epsilon \text{Ser} . \supset : C'P \epsilon \text{Cls induct} . \equiv . P, \breve{P} \epsilon \Omega$ [*261·3 . *250·121]

***261·32.** $\vdash . \text{Ser} \cap \breve{C}``\text{Cls induct} = \Omega \text{ induct} = \Omega \cap \text{Cnv}``\Omega$ [*261·31·14]

On account of this proposition, we do not introduce the notation "Ser induct" for "Ser $\cap \breve{C}``$Cls induct," because a series whose field is inductive is a well-ordered series, and therefore the notation "Ω induct" gives all that is wanted.

***261·33.** $\vdash : P, Q \epsilon \Omega . Q \in \breve{P} . \supset . Q \epsilon \Omega \text{ induct}$

Dem.

$\vdash . *204·2 . \supset \vdash : \text{Hp} . \supset . \breve{Q} \epsilon \text{Ser} . \breve{Q} \in P .$
[*250·14] $\supset . \breve{Q} \epsilon \text{Ser} \cap \text{Bord} .$
[*250·12] $\supset . \breve{Q} \epsilon \Omega .$
[*261·32] $\supset . Q \epsilon \Omega \text{ induct} : \supset \vdash . \text{Prop}$

This proposition (which is due to Cantor) is of great importance in the theory of well-ordered series. It shows that, however great a well-ordered series may be, any *descending* well-ordered series contained in it must be finite. (A *descending* series in a given series is a series contained in the converse of the given series.)

***261·34.** $\vdash : P \epsilon \Omega . \text{Ɑ}'P_1 = \text{Ɑ}'P . E ! B'\breve{P} . \supset . C'P \epsilon \text{Cls induct}$

Dem.

$\vdash . *250·23 . *214·12 . \supset \vdash :. \text{Hp} . \alpha \subset C'P . \supset : E ! \max_P{}'\alpha . \vee . E ! \text{seq}_P{}'\alpha$ (1)
$\vdash . *206·181 . \supset \vdash : \text{Hp} . \alpha \subset C'P . \exists ! \alpha . E ! \text{seq}_P{}'\alpha . \supset . \text{seq}_P{}'\alpha \epsilon \text{Ɑ}'P_1 .$
[*204·7] $\supset . E ! P_1{}'\text{seq}_P{}'\alpha .$
[*206·451] $\supset . E ! \max_P{}'\alpha$ (2)
$\vdash . (1) . (2) . \supset \vdash :. \text{Hp} . \supset : \alpha \subset C'P . \exists ! \alpha . \supset_\alpha . E ! \max_P{}'\alpha :$
[*261·3] $\supset : C'P \epsilon \text{Cls induct} :. \supset \vdash . \text{Prop}$

***261·35.** $\vdash :. P \epsilon \Omega . \supset : C'P \epsilon \text{Cls induct} - \iota'\Lambda . \equiv . \text{Ɑ}'P_1 = \text{Ɑ}'P . E ! B'\breve{P}$
[*261·22·24·34]

Observe that "$\text{Ɑ}'P_1 = \text{Ɑ}'P . E ! B'\breve{P}$" occurs as hypothesis in *253·51 and some succeeding propositions. Thus this hypothesis is equivalent to the hypothesis that the field of P is an inductive existent class. It follows that if P is an inductive well-ordered series, $\text{Nr}`P_s = \text{Nr}`P$, whereas if P is a well-ordered series which is not inductive, $\text{Nr}`P_s = \text{Nr}`P \dot{+} \dot{1}$; also that

***261·36.** $\vdash :. P \epsilon \Omega . \supset : C`P \epsilon \text{Cls induct} - \iota`\Lambda . \equiv . \text{Nr}`P \neq \dot{1} \dot{+} \text{Nr}`P$
[*253·573 . *261·35]

***261·37.** $\vdash :. P \epsilon \Omega . \supset : C`P \epsilon \text{Cls induct} . \equiv . 1 \dot{+} \text{Nr}`P = \text{Nr}`P \dot{+} \dot{1}$
[*253·574 . *261·35 . *161·2·201]

***261·38.** $\vdash :. P \epsilon \Omega . \supset : C`P \epsilon \text{Cls induct} - \iota`\Lambda . \supset . \text{Nr}`P_s = \text{Nr}`P :$
$C`P \sim \epsilon \text{Cls induct} - \iota`\Lambda . \supset . \text{Nr}`P_s = \text{Nr}`P \dot{+} \dot{1}$

[*253·56 . *261·35]

***261·4.** $\vdash : P \epsilon \Omega - \Omega \text{ induct} . \supset . \{\overleftarrow{(P_1)_*}`B`P\} \upharpoonright P_1 \epsilon \text{Prog}$

Dem.

$\vdash . *204·7 . \quad \supset \vdash : \text{Hp} . R = P_1 . \supset . R \epsilon 1 \rightarrow 1$ (1)

$\vdash . *120·212 . \supset \vdash :. \text{Hp} . \supset : \dot{\exists} ! P :$

[*250·13] $\supset : \text{E} ! B`P :$

[*250·21] $\supset : R = P_1 . \supset . B`P \epsilon \text{D}`R$ (2)

$\vdash . *260·22 . \quad \supset \vdash : \text{Hp} . R = P_1 . \supset . R_{\text{po}} \in J$ (3)

$\vdash . *93·103 . *202·52 . \supset$

$\vdash : P \epsilon \Omega . R = P_1 . \exists ! \overleftarrow{R_*}`B`P - \text{D}`P . \supset . B`\breve{P} \epsilon \overleftarrow{R_*}`B`P .$

[*93·101.*91·54] $\supset . (B`P) R_{\text{po}} (B`\breve{P}) .$

[*260·27] $\supset . (B`P) P_{\text{fn}} (B`\breve{P}) .$

[*261·2] $\supset . C`P \epsilon \text{Cls induct}$ (4)

$\vdash . (4) . \text{Transp} . \supset \vdash : \text{Hp} . R = P_1 . \supset . \overleftarrow{R_*}`B`P \subset \text{D}`P .$

[*250·21] $\supset . \overleftarrow{R_*}`B`P \subset \text{D}`R$ (5)

$\vdash . (1) . (2) . (3) . (5) . \supset \vdash : \text{Hp} . R = P_1 . \supset .$

$R \epsilon 1 \rightarrow 1 . B`P \epsilon \text{D}`R . \sim \{(B`P) R_{\text{po}} (B`P)\} . \overleftarrow{R_*}`B`P \subset \text{D}`R .$

[*122·52] $\supset . (\overleftarrow{R_*}`B`P) \upharpoonright R \epsilon \text{Prog} : \supset \vdash . \text{Prop}$

***261·401.** $\vdash : P \epsilon \Omega - \Omega \text{ induct} . \supset . \exists ! \aleph_0 \cap \text{Cl}`C`P . C`P \epsilon \text{Cls refl}$

Dem.

$\vdash . *261·4 . *123·1 . \supset \vdash : \text{Hp} . \supset . \text{D}`\{\overleftarrow{(P_1)_*}`B`P\} \upharpoonright P_1 \epsilon \aleph_0$ (1)

$\vdash . *121·305 . \quad \supset \vdash : \text{Hp} . \supset . \text{D}`\{\overleftarrow{(P_1)_*}`B`P\} \upharpoonright P_1 \subset C`P$ (2)

$\vdash . (1) . (2) . \quad \supset \vdash : \text{Hp} . \supset . \exists ! \aleph_0 \cap \text{Cl}`C`P .$ (3)

[*124·15] $\supset . C`P \epsilon \text{Cls refl}$ (4)

$\vdash . (3) . (4) . \supset \vdash . \text{Prop}$

$*261{\cdot}41.$ $\vdash . \Omega - \Omega \text{ induct} = \Omega \text{ infin}$ [$*261{\cdot}401 . *261{\cdot}11 . *124{\cdot}271$]

$*261{\cdot}42.$ $\vdash . \Omega \text{ fin} = \Omega \text{ induct}$ [$*261{\cdot}41$. Transp . $*124{\cdot}271$]

We shall henceforth use "Ω fin" in preference to "Ω induct."

$*261{\cdot}43.$ $\vdash . C``\Omega \subset \text{Cls induct} \cup \text{Cls refl}$ [$*261{\cdot}401{\cdot}14$]

$*261{\cdot}431.$ $\vdash : P \in \Omega - \iota`\dot{\Lambda} . \supset .$

$$\{\overleftarrow{(P_1)_*}`B`P\} \upharpoonleft P_1 = P_1 \upharpoonright \overleftarrow{P}_{\text{fn}}`B`P = P_1 \,\text{\textlbrackdbl}\, (\iota`B`P \cup \overleftarrow{P}_{\text{fn}}`B`P)$$
$$= (\iota`B`P \cup \overleftarrow{P}_{\text{fn}}`B`P) \upharpoonleft P_1$$

Dem.

$\vdash . *250{\cdot}13{\cdot}21 . \quad \supset \vdash : \text{Hp} . \supset . B`P \in \text{D}`P_1 .$ (1)

[$*260{\cdot}31$] $\supset . \iota`B`P \cup \overleftarrow{P}_{\text{fn}}`B`P = \overleftarrow{(P_1)_*}`B`P$ (2)

$\vdash . (1) . *260{\cdot}27 . \quad \supset \vdash : \text{Hp} . \supset . \overleftarrow{P}_{\text{fn}}`B`P = \overleftarrow{(P_1)_{\text{po}}}`B`P .$

[$*260{\cdot}34$] $\supset . P_1 \upharpoonright \overleftarrow{P}_{\text{fn}}`B`P = \{\overleftarrow{(P_1)_*}`B`P\} \upharpoonleft P_1$ (3)

[(2)] $= (\iota`B`P \cup \overleftarrow{P}_{\text{fn}}`B`P) \upharpoonleft P_1$ (4)

$\vdash . (3) . (4) . *35{\cdot}11 . \supset \vdash : \text{Hp} . \supset . \{\overleftarrow{(P_1)_*}`B`P\} \upharpoonleft P_1 = P_1 \,\text{\textlbrackdbl}\, (\iota`B`P \cup \overleftarrow{P}_{\text{fn}}`B`P)$ (5)

$\vdash . (3) . (4) . (5) . \supset \vdash . \text{Prop}$

$*261{\cdot}44.$ $\vdash :. P \in \Omega . \supset : P_1 \upharpoonright \overleftarrow{P}_{\text{fn}}`B`P \in \text{Prog} . \equiv . P \in \Omega \text{ infin}$

Dem.

$\vdash . *123{\cdot}1 . \supset \vdash : P \in \Omega . P_1 \upharpoonright \overleftarrow{P}_{\text{fn}}`B`P \in \text{Prog} . \supset . \exists ! \aleph_0 \cap \text{Cl}`C`P .$

[$*124{\cdot}15$] $\supset . C`P \in \text{Cls refl} .$

[$*261{\cdot}1$] $\supset . P \in \Omega \text{ infin}$ (1)

$\vdash . *261{\cdot}4{\cdot}431{\cdot}41 . \supset \vdash : P \in \Omega \text{ infin} . \supset . P_1 \upharpoonright \overleftarrow{P}_{\text{fn}}`B`P \in \text{Prog}$ (2)

$\vdash . (1) . (2) . \supset \vdash . \text{Prop}$

$*261{\cdot}45.$ $\vdash . \Omega \text{ infin} = \Omega \cap \hat{P}\{P_1 \upharpoonright \overleftarrow{P}_{\text{fn}}`B`P \in \text{Prog}\}$ [$*261{\cdot}44$]

$*261{\cdot}46.$ $\vdash : P \in \Omega . \supset . \text{Cl}`C`P \subset \text{Cls induct} \cup \text{Cls refl}$

Dem.

$\vdash . *250{\cdot}141 . *202{\cdot}55 . \supset$

$\vdash : \text{Hp} . \alpha \subset C`P . \alpha \sim \in 1 . \supset . P \,\text{\textlbrackdbl}\, \alpha \in \Omega . \alpha = C`(P \,\text{\textlbrackdbl}\, \alpha) .$

[$*261{\cdot}43$] $\supset . \alpha \in \text{Cls induct} \cup \text{Cls refl}$ (1)

$\vdash . *120{\cdot}213 . \supset \vdash : \alpha \in 1 . \supset . \alpha \in \text{Cls induct}$ (2)

$\vdash . (1) . (2) . \supset \vdash . \text{Prop}$

$*261{\cdot}47.$ $\vdash :. P \in \Omega . \alpha \subset C`P . \supset : \alpha \in \text{Cls induct} . \equiv . \alpha \sim \in \text{Cls refl}$
[$*261{\cdot}46 . *124{\cdot}271$]

$*261{\cdot}6.$ $\vdash :. P \in \Omega . C`P \subset \Omega . \text{Nc}`C`P = \nu . \supset_P . \Pi`P \in \Omega :$

$$\nu \in \text{Nc induct} - \iota`0 - \iota`1 : \supset :$$
$$Q \in \Omega . C`Q \subset \Omega . \text{Nc}`C`Q = \nu +_c 1 . \supset_Q . \Pi`Q \in \Omega$$

Dem.

$\vdash . *204{\cdot}272 . \supset \vdash : \text{Nc}`\text{D}`Q = 1 . Q \in \text{Ser} . \supset . Q \in 2_r .$

[$*56{\cdot}112$] $\supset . C`Q \in 2$ (1)

$\vdash . (1) . \text{Transp} . \supset \vdash : Q \epsilon \Omega . C'Q \subset \Omega . \text{Nc}'C'Q = \nu +_c 1 .$

$\qquad \nu \epsilon \text{NC induct} - \iota'0 - \iota'1 . \supset . \text{D}'Q \sim\epsilon 1 \quad (2)$

$\vdash . *261\cdot24 . \supset \vdash : \text{Hp}(2) . \supset . \text{E} ! B'\breve{Q} .$

$[(2).*204\cdot461] \quad \supset . Q = Q \upharpoonright \text{D}'Q \text{⇸} B'\breve{Q} .$

$[*172\cdot32] \quad \supset . \Pi'Q \text{ smor } \Pi'(Q \upharpoonright \text{D}'Q) \times B'\breve{Q} \quad (3)$

$\vdash . *110\cdot63 . \supset \vdash : \text{Hp}(2) . \supset . \text{Nc}'\text{D}'Q +_c 1 = \nu +_c 1 .$

$[*120\cdot311] \quad \supset . \text{Nc}'\text{D}'Q = \nu \quad (4)$

$\vdash . (4) . \quad \supset \vdash :. \text{Hp}(2) : P \epsilon \Omega . C'P \subset \Omega . \text{Nc}'C'P = \nu . \supset_P . \Pi'P \epsilon \Omega : \supset .$

$\qquad \Pi'(Q \upharpoonright \text{D}'Q) \epsilon \Omega .$

$[(3).*251\cdot55] \quad \supset . \Pi'Q \epsilon \Omega \quad (5)$

$\vdash . (5) . \text{Exp} . \supset$

$\vdash :. \text{Hp} . \supset : Q \epsilon \Omega . C'Q \subset \Omega . \text{Nc}'C'Q = \nu +_c 1 . \supset . \Pi'Q \epsilon \Omega :. \supset \vdash . \text{Prop}$

$*261\cdot61$. $\vdash : P \epsilon \Omega \text{ fin} . C'P \subset \Omega . \supset . \Pi'P \epsilon \Omega$

Dem.

$\vdash . *261\cdot6 . \supset \vdash :: \phi\nu . \equiv_\nu : P \epsilon \Omega . C'P \subset \Omega . \text{Nc}'C'P = \nu . \supset_P . \Pi'P \epsilon \Omega :. \supset :.$

$\qquad \nu \epsilon \text{Nc induct} - \iota'0 - \iota'1 . \supset : \phi\nu . \supset . \phi(\nu +_c 1) \quad (1)$

$\vdash . *200\cdot12 . \supset \vdash . \sim(\exists P) . P \epsilon \Omega . C'P \subset \Omega . \text{Nc}'C'P = 1 .$

$[*10\cdot53] \quad \supset \vdash : \text{Hp}(1) . \supset . \phi 1 \quad (2)$

$\vdash . *172\cdot13 . *250\cdot4 . \quad \supset \vdash : \text{Hp}(1) . \supset . \phi 0 \quad (3)$

$\vdash . *172\cdot23 . *251\cdot55 . \supset \vdash :. Y \neq Z . Y, Z \epsilon \Omega . \supset : \Pi'(Y \downarrow Z), \Pi'(Z \downarrow Y) \epsilon \Omega :$

$[*55\cdot54.*204\cdot13] \quad \supset : P \epsilon \text{Ser} . C'P = \iota'Y \cup \iota'Z . \supset . \Pi'P \epsilon \Omega \quad (4)$

$\vdash . (4) . *54\cdot101 . \supset \vdash : \text{Hp}(1) . \supset . \phi 2 \quad (5)$

$\vdash . (2) . (3) . (5) . \supset \vdash :. \text{Hp}(1) . \supset : \phi 0 : \nu \epsilon \iota'0 \cup \iota'1 . \phi\nu . \supset . \phi(\nu +_c 1) \quad (6)$

$\vdash . (1) . (6) . \quad \supset \vdash :. \text{Hp}(1) . \supset : \nu \epsilon \text{NC induct} . \phi\nu . \supset_\nu . \phi(\nu +_c 1) : \phi 0 :$

$[*120\cdot13] \quad \supset : \alpha \epsilon \text{NC induct} . \supset_\alpha . \phi\alpha \quad (7)$

$\vdash . (7) . *13\cdot191 . \supset \vdash : P \epsilon \Omega . C'P \subset \Omega . \text{Nc}'C'P \epsilon \text{NC induct} . \supset_P . \Pi'P \epsilon \Omega :$

$[*261\cdot14\cdot42] \quad \supset \vdash : P \epsilon \Omega \text{ fin} . C'P \subset \Omega . \supset_P . \Pi'P \epsilon \Omega : \supset \vdash . \text{Prop}$

$*261\cdot62$. $\vdash : P \epsilon \Omega . Q \epsilon \Omega \text{ fin} . \supset . P^Q \epsilon \Omega$

Dem.

$\vdash . *251\cdot51 . \quad \supset \vdash : \text{Hp} . \dot{\exists} ! P . \supset . P \downarrow ; Q \epsilon \Omega \quad (1)$

$\vdash . *165\cdot26 . \quad \supset \vdash : \text{Hp} . \supset . C'P \downarrow ; Q \subset \Omega \quad (2)$

$\vdash . (1) . *165\cdot25 . *261\cdot18 . \supset \vdash : \text{Hp} . \dot{\exists} ! P . \supset . P \downarrow ; Q \epsilon \Omega \text{ fin} \quad (3)$

$\vdash . (1) . (2) . (3) . *261\cdot61 . \supset \vdash : \text{Hp} . \dot{\exists} ! P . \supset . \Pi'P \downarrow ; Q \epsilon \Omega .$

$[*176\cdot181\cdot182] \quad \supset . P^Q \epsilon \Omega \quad (4)$

$\vdash . *176\cdot151 . *250\cdot4 . \quad \supset \vdash : P = \dot{\Lambda} . \supset . P^Q \epsilon \Omega \quad (5)$

$\vdash . (4) . (5) . \supset \vdash . \text{Prop}$

∗261·63. $\vdash : E ! B‘R . P \Subset Q . x \in C‘Q \cap p‘\overleftarrow{Q}“C‘P . \supset .$

$$(\iota‘x) \uparrow C‘R \in C‘Q^R \cap p‘\overleftarrow{Q^R}“C‘P^R$$

Dem.

$\vdash . ∗116·12 . \quad \supset \vdash : \mathrm{Hp} . \supset . (\iota‘x) \uparrow C‘R \in (C‘Q \uparrow C‘R)_\Delta‘C‘R .$

$[∗176·14] \quad \supset . (\iota‘x) \uparrow C‘R \in C‘Q^R \qquad (1)$

$\vdash . ∗116·12 . ∗93·11 . \supset \vdash :. \mathrm{Hp} . S \in (C‘P \uparrow C‘R)_\Delta‘C‘R . T = (\iota‘x) \uparrow C‘R . \supset :$

$(S‘B‘R) \, Q \, (T‘B‘R) : \sim (\exists y) . y R (B‘R) :$

$[∗10·53] \quad \supset : (S‘B‘R) \, Q \, (T‘B‘R) : y R (B‘R) . y \neq B‘R . \supset_y . S‘y = T‘y :$

$[∗176·19.(1)] \supset : S (Q^R) T \qquad (2)$

$\vdash . (2) . ∗176·16 . \supset \vdash :. \mathrm{Hp} . \supset : S \in C‘P^R . \supset . S (Q^R) \{(\iota‘x) \uparrow C‘R\} \qquad (3)$

$\vdash . (1) . (3) . \supset \vdash . \mathrm{Prop}$

∗261·64. $\vdash : R \in \Omega \text{ fin} - \iota‘\dot{\Lambda} . P \text{ less } Q . \supset . P^R \text{ less } Q^R$

Dem.

$\vdash . ∗254·55 . \supset \vdash : \mathrm{Hp} . \supset . (\exists P') . P' \text{ smor } P . P' \Subset Q . \exists ! C‘Q \cap p‘\overleftarrow{Q}“C‘P' .$

$[∗261·63 . ∗250·13] \quad \supset . (\exists P') . P' \text{ smor } P . P' \Subset Q . \exists ! C‘Q^R \cap p‘\overleftarrow{Q^R}“C‘(P')^R .$

$[∗176·35·22] \quad \supset . (\exists M) . M \text{ smor } P^R . M \Subset Q^R . \exists ! C‘Q^R \cap p‘\overleftarrow{Q^R}“C‘M .$

$[∗254·55 . ∗261·62] \quad \supset . P^R \text{ less } Q^R : \supset \vdash . \mathrm{Prop}$

∗261·65. $\vdash : P \in \Omega \text{ infin} . Q \in \Omega \text{ fin} . \supset . Q \text{ less } P$

Dem.

$\vdash . ∗261·11·14·42 . \supset \vdash : \mathrm{Hp} . \supset . C‘P \in \text{Cls refl} . C‘Q \in \text{Cls induct} .$

$[∗124·26] \quad \supset . \mathrm{Nc}‘C‘P > \mathrm{Nc}‘C‘Q .$

$[∗255·75] \quad \supset . Q \text{ less } P : \supset \vdash . \mathrm{Prop}$

*262. FINITE ORDINALS.

Summary of *262.

Finite ordinals are defined as the ordinals of finite well-ordered series; infinite ordinals are defined as the ordinals of infinite well-ordered series. In virtue of *261·42, finite ordinals are those whose members have fields which are inductive, and are also those whose members have fields which are not reflexive. Finite ordinals have the formal properties which cardinals have but which relation-numbers and ordinals in general do not have, *i.e.* their sums and products are commutative, and the distributive law holds in the form

$$\mu \dot{\times} (\nu \dot{+} \varpi) = (\mu \dot{\times} \nu) \dot{+} (\mu \dot{\times} \varpi),$$

as well as in the form

$$(\nu \dot{+} \varpi) \dot{\times} \mu = (\nu \dot{\times} \mu) \dot{+} (\varpi \dot{\times} \mu),$$

which was proved generally in *184·35.

The distinguishing properties of finite ordinals are most readily established by means of their correspondence with inductive cardinals. In general, two well-ordered series whose fields have the same cardinal need not be ordinally similar, but when the cardinal of the fields is inductive, the two series must be ordinally similar. Hence the ordinal of a *finite* well-ordered series is determined by the cardinal of the field of the series. We put generally

$$\mu_r = \Omega \cap \breve{C}``\mu \quad \text{Df.}$$

The result is that, if μ is an inductive cardinal, μ_r is the ordinal of all those series whose fields have μ members. Thus there is a one-one correspondence of inductive cardinals and finite ordinals; and in virtue of this correspondence, the formal properties of finite ordinals can be deduced from those of inductive cardinals.

It will be observed that, according to the definitions already given,

$$\vdash . 0_r = \Omega \cap \breve{C}``\Lambda \text{ by } *250·43,$$

$$\vdash . 2_r = \Omega \cap \breve{C}``2 \text{ by } *250·44.$$

Hence the notations 0_r, 2_r are particular cases of the general notation μ_r. But in virtue of $*200\cdot12$, we have, by the definition of μ_r,

$$\vdash . 1_r = \Lambda,$$

so that 1_r does not take its place in the series of finite ordinals.

Our definitions in this number are

$$\text{NO fin} = \text{N}_0\text{r}``\Omega \text{ fin} \quad \text{Df},$$

$$\text{NO infin} = \text{N}_0\text{r}``\Omega \text{ infin} \quad \text{Df},$$

$$\mu_r = \Omega \cap \breve{C}``\mu \quad \text{Df}.$$

It will be observed that for the sake of convenience we have defined NO fin and NO infin so as to exclude Λ. The definition of μ_r is chiefly useful when μ is an inductive cardinal.

The number begins with various elementary propositions, partly embodying the definitions, partly concerned with μ_r. We have

$*262\cdot12$. $\vdash : P \in \mu_r . \equiv . P \in \Omega . C`P \in \mu$

$*262\cdot18$. $\vdash : \mu \in \text{NC} . \exists ! \mu_r . \supset . \mu = C``\mu_r$

This proposition does not require that μ_r should be a relation-number. If μ is a reflexive cardinal, μ_r is not a relation-number unless it is null, because series of many different relation-numbers can be made with a given cardinal number of terms. When μ is a cardinal, "$\exists ! \mu_r$" means that classes having μ terms can be well-ordered.

$*262\cdot19$. $\vdash :. \mu, \nu \in \text{NC} . \exists ! \mu_r . \supset : \mu = \nu . \equiv . \mu_r = \nu_r$

Thus the relation of μ to μ_r is one-one so long as μ is the cardinal number of a class which can be well-ordered.

We next prove that if μ is an inductive cardinal other than Λ or 1, μ_r is a finite ordinal, and that every finite ordinal is of the form μ_r for an appropriate μ. We have

$*262\cdot21$. $\vdash : \mu \in \text{NC induct} - \iota`\Lambda - \iota`1 . \supset . \exists ! \mu_r$

$*262\cdot24$. $\vdash : \mu \in \text{NC induct} - \iota`\Lambda - \iota`1 . \supset . \mu_r \in \text{NO fin}$

We prove this by means of an inductive proof that two series are similar if their fields are inductive and similar.

$*262\cdot26$. $\vdash : \alpha \in \text{NO fin} . \equiv . (\exists \mu) . \mu \in \text{N}_0\text{C induct} - \iota`1 . \alpha = \mu_r$

Hence we easily obtain the properties of finite ordinals from those of the corresponding cardinals. Assuming that μ, ν are inductive cardinals other than 1, we have

$*262\cdot33$. $\mu_r \dot{+} \nu_r = (\mu +_c \nu)_r$

$*262\cdot35$. $\mu_r \dot{+} \dot{1} = (\mu +_c 1)_r$, if $\mu \neq 0$,

$*262\cdot43$. $\mu_r \dot{\times} \nu_r = (\mu \times_c \nu)_r$

$*262{\cdot}53.\quad \mu_r \exp_r \nu_r = (\mu^\nu)_r$, if $\nu \neq 0$,

$*262{\cdot}7.\quad \mu > \nu . \equiv . \mu_r > \nu_r$

Hence if α, β, γ are finite ordinals,

$*262{\cdot}6.\quad \alpha \dot{+} \beta = \beta \dot{+} \alpha$

$*262{\cdot}61.\quad \alpha \dot{\times} \beta = \beta \dot{\times} \alpha$

$*262{\cdot}62.\quad \alpha \dot{\times} (\beta \dot{+} \gamma) = (\alpha \dot{\times} \beta) \dot{+} (\alpha \dot{\times} \gamma)$

$*262{\cdot}63.\quad (\alpha \dot{\times} \beta) \exp_r \gamma = (\alpha \exp_r \gamma) \dot{\times} (\beta \exp_r \gamma)$

Thus the arithmetic of finite ordinals obeys the same formal laws as the arithmetic of inductive cardinals.

$*262{\cdot}01.\quad \mathrm{NO\,fin} = \mathrm{N_0r}``\Omega\,\mathrm{fin} \qquad$ Df

$*262{\cdot}02.\quad \mathrm{NO\,infin} = \mathrm{N_0r}``\Omega\,\mathrm{infin} \qquad$ Df

$*262{\cdot}03.\quad \mu_r = \Omega \cap \breve{C}``\mu \qquad$ Df

$*262{\cdot}1.\quad \vdash : \alpha \in \mathrm{NO\,fin} . \equiv . (\exists P) . P \in \Omega\,\mathrm{fin} . \alpha = \mathrm{N_0r}`P \qquad [(*262{\cdot}01)]$

$*262{\cdot}11.\quad \vdash : \alpha \in \mathrm{NO\,infin} . \equiv . (\exists P) . P \in \Omega\,\mathrm{infin} . \alpha = \mathrm{N_0r}`P \qquad [(*262{\cdot}02)]$

$*262{\cdot}111.\quad \vdash :. \alpha \in \mathrm{NO\,fin} . \equiv : \alpha \in \mathrm{N_0O} : \alpha \neq \dot{1} \dot{+} \alpha . \mathsf{v} . \alpha = 0_r :$

$\qquad \equiv : \alpha \in \mathrm{NO} : \alpha \neq \dot{1} \dot{+} \alpha . \mathsf{v} . \alpha = 0_r$

Dem.

$\vdash . *262{\cdot}1 . \supset$

$\vdash :. \alpha \in \mathrm{NO\,fin} . \equiv : \alpha \in \mathrm{N_0O} : (\exists P) . P \in \Omega\,\mathrm{fin} . \alpha = \mathrm{Nr}`P :$

$[*261{\cdot}36] \qquad \equiv : \alpha \in \mathrm{N_0O} : (\exists P) : \mathrm{Nr}`P \neq \dot{1} \dot{+} \mathrm{Nr}`P . \mathsf{v} . P = \dot{\Lambda} : \alpha = \mathrm{Nr}`P :$

$[(*255{\cdot}03)] \qquad \equiv : \alpha \in \mathrm{N_0O} : \alpha \neq \dot{1} \dot{+} \alpha . \mathsf{v} . \alpha = 0_r : \qquad (1)$

$[*180{\cdot}4 . *155{\cdot}5] \equiv : \alpha \in \mathrm{NO} : \alpha \neq \dot{1} \dot{+} \alpha . \mathsf{v} . \alpha = 0_r \qquad (2)$

$\vdash . (1) . (2) . \supset \vdash .$ Prop

$*262{\cdot}112.\quad \vdash : \alpha \in \mathrm{NO\,infin} . \equiv . \alpha \in \mathrm{N_0O} - \iota`0_r . \dot{1} \dot{+} \alpha = \alpha$

$\qquad [*262{\cdot}111 . \mathrm{Transp} . *261{\cdot}13]$

$*262{\cdot}12.\quad \vdash : P \in \mu_r . \equiv . P \in \Omega . C`P \in \mu \qquad [(*262{\cdot}03)]$

$*262{\cdot}13.\quad \vdash : \mathrm{Nr}`P \in \mathrm{NO\,fin} . \equiv . P \in \Omega\,\mathrm{fin} . \equiv . P \in \Omega . C`P \in \mathrm{Cls\,induct}$

Dem.

$\vdash . *262{\cdot}1 . \supset \vdash : \mathrm{Nr}`P \in \mathrm{NO\,fin} . \equiv . (\exists Q) . Q \in \Omega\,\mathrm{fin} . \mathrm{Nr}`P = \mathrm{N_0r}`Q .$

$[*152{\cdot}35 . *155{\cdot}13] \qquad \equiv . (\exists Q) . Q \in \Omega\,\mathrm{fin} . P \,\mathrm{smor}\, Q .$

$[*261{\cdot}183] \qquad \equiv . P \in \Omega\,\mathrm{fin} . \qquad (1)$

$[*261{\cdot}42{\cdot}14] \qquad \equiv . P \in \Omega . C`P \in \mathrm{Cls\,induct} \qquad (2)$

$\vdash . (1) . (2) . \supset \vdash .$ Prop

***262·14.** $\vdash : \mathrm{Nr}`P \in \mathrm{NO}\ \mathrm{infin} \,.\equiv.\, P \in \Omega\ \mathrm{infin} \,.\equiv.\, P \in \Omega \,.\, C`P \in \mathrm{Cls}\ \mathrm{refl}$

[Proof as in *262·13]

***262·15.** $\vdash :. \alpha \in \mathrm{N_0O} \,.\supset:\, \alpha \in \mathrm{NO}\ \mathrm{fin} \,.\equiv.\, C``\alpha \in \mathrm{NC}\ \mathrm{induct}$

Dem.

$\vdash . *262{\cdot}13 . *120{\cdot}21 . \supset$

$\vdash : \mathrm{N_0r}`P \in \mathrm{NO}\ \mathrm{fin} \,.\equiv.\, P \in \Omega \,.\, \mathrm{N_0c}`C`P \in \mathrm{NC}\ \mathrm{induct}$ (1)

$\vdash . (1) . *251{\cdot}1 . \supset$

$\vdash :. \mathrm{N_0r}`P \in \mathrm{NO} \,.\supset:\, \mathrm{N_0r}`P \in \mathrm{NO}\ \mathrm{fin} \,.\equiv.\, \mathrm{N_0c}`C`P \in \mathrm{NC}\ \mathrm{induct} \,.$

[*152·7] $\equiv . C``\mathrm{N_0r}`P \in \mathrm{NC}\ \mathrm{induct}$ (2)

$\vdash . (2) . *155{\cdot}2 . \supset \vdash . \mathrm{Prop}$

***262·16.** $\vdash :. \alpha \in \mathrm{N_0O} \,.\supset:$

$\alpha \in \mathrm{NO}\ \mathrm{infin} \,.\equiv.\, C``\alpha \sim\in \mathrm{NC}\ \mathrm{induct} \,.\equiv.\, C``\alpha \in \mathrm{NC}\ \mathrm{refl}$

[Proof as in *262·15]

***262·17.** $\vdash : P \in \Omega \,.\supset.\, P \in (\mathrm{Nc}`C`P)_r$

Dem.

$\vdash . *100{\cdot}3 . \supset \vdash . C`P \in \mathrm{Nc}`C`P$ (1)

$\vdash . (1) . *262{\cdot}12 . \supset \vdash . \mathrm{Prop}$

***262·18.** $\vdash : \mu \in \mathrm{NC} \,.\, \exists ! \mu_r \,.\supset.\, \mu = C``\mu_r$

Dem.

$\vdash . *262{\cdot}12 . \quad \supset \vdash . C``\mu_r \subset \mu$ (1)

$\vdash . *262{\cdot}12 . \quad \supset \vdash : \alpha \in \mu \,.\, P \in \mu_r \,.\supset.\, \alpha, C`P \in \mu$ (2)

$\vdash . (2) . *100{\cdot}5 . \supset \vdash : \mathrm{Hp} \,.\, \alpha \in \mu \,.\, P \in \mu_r \,.\supset.\, \alpha\ \mathrm{sm}\ C`P \,.$

[*73·1] $\supset . (\exists S) . S \in 1 \rightarrow 1 \,.\, \alpha = \mathrm{D}`S \,.\, C`P = \mathrm{C\!\!I}`S \,.$

[*151·1.*150·23] $\supset . (\exists S) . S ; P\ \mathrm{smor}\ P \,.\, C`S;P = \alpha \,.$

[*251·111.*262·12] $\supset . (\exists S) . S;P \in \Omega \,.\, C`S;P = \alpha \,.$

[*262·12.Hp] $\supset . (\exists S) . S;P \in \mu_r \,.\, C`S;P = \alpha \,.$

[*37·6] $\supset . \alpha \in C``\mu_r$ (3)

$\vdash . (3) . *10{\cdot}23 . \supset \vdash : \mathrm{Hp} \,.\supset.\, \mu \subset C``\mu_r$ (4)

$\vdash . (1) . (4) . \supset \vdash . \mathrm{Prop}$

***262·19.** $\vdash :. \mu, \nu \in \mathrm{NC} \,.\, \exists ! \mu_r \,.\supset:\, \mu = \nu \,.\equiv.\, \mu_r = \nu_r$

Dem.

$\vdash . *262{\cdot}12 . \supset \vdash : \mu = \nu \,.\supset.\, \mu_r = \nu_r$ (1)

$\vdash . *262{\cdot}18 . \supset \vdash : \mathrm{Hp} \,.\, \mu_r = \nu_r \,.\supset.\, \mu = C``\nu_r$

[*262·18] $= \nu$ (2)

$\vdash . (1) . (2) . \supset \vdash . \mathrm{Prop}$

***262·2.** $\vdash . \text{Cls induct} - 1 = C``(\Omega \cap \text{Cnv}``\Omega)$

Dem.

$\vdash . *261\cdot29 . \supset \vdash . \text{Cls induct} - 1 = C``(\Omega \cap \text{Cnv}``\Omega) - 1$

[*200·12] $= C``(\Omega \cap \text{Cnv}``\Omega) . \supset \vdash . \text{Prop}$

***262·21.** $\vdash : \mu \in \text{NC induct} - \iota`\Lambda - \iota`1 . \supset . \exists ! \mu_r$

Dem.

$\vdash . *120\cdot2 . *100\cdot43 . \supset \vdash : \text{Hp} . \supset . (\exists\alpha) . \alpha \in \mu . \alpha \in \text{Cls induct} . \alpha \sim \in 1 .$

[*262·2] $\supset . (\exists\alpha, P) . \alpha \in \mu . P \in \Omega . C`P = \alpha .$

[*262·12] $\supset . \exists ! \mu_r : \supset \vdash . \text{Prop}$

***262·211.** $\vdash : \alpha \in \text{Cls induct} - 1 . \supset . \exists ! (\text{Nc}`\alpha)_r \cap t_{00}`\alpha$

Dem.

$\vdash . *262\cdot21 . *103\cdot12 . \supset \vdash : \text{Hp} . \supset . \exists ! (\text{N}_0\text{c}`\alpha)_r . \alpha \in \text{N}_0\text{c}`\alpha .$

[*262·12] $\supset . (\exists P) . P \in (\text{Nc}`\alpha)_r . C`P \in \text{N}_0\text{c}`\alpha . \alpha \in \text{N}_0\text{c}`\alpha .$

[*63·13] $\supset . (\exists P) . P \in (\text{Nc}`\alpha)_r . C`P \in t`\alpha .$

[*64·24.*35·9] $\supset . (\exists P) . P \in (\text{Nc}`\alpha)_r . P \in t`(\alpha \uparrow \alpha) .$

[*64·11] $\supset . \exists ! (\text{Nc}`\alpha)_r \cap t_{00}`\alpha : \supset \vdash . \text{Prop}$

***262·212.** $\vdash : \mu \neq 0 . \mu \neq 1 . P \in (\mu +_c 1)_r . \supset . P \upharpoonright \text{D}`P \in \mu_r$

Dem.

$\vdash . *262\cdot12 . \quad \supset \vdash : \text{Hp} . \supset . C`P \in \mu +_c 1 . P \in \Omega .$ (1)

[*110·4] $\supset . \mu \in \text{NC} - \iota`\Lambda$ (2)

$\vdash . *93\cdot103 . *250\cdot13 . \supset \vdash : \text{Hp} . \supset . C`P = \iota`B`P \cup \text{D}`P . B`P \sim \in \text{D}`P .$

[*110·63] $\supset . \text{Nc}`C`P = \text{Nc}`\text{D}`P +_c 1 .$

[(1).(2)] $\supset . \mu +_c 1 = \text{Nc}`\text{D}`P +_c 1 .$

[*120·311.(1)] $\supset . \mu = \text{Nc}`\text{D}`P . P \in \Omega .$

[*202·55.*250·141] $\supset . \mu = \text{Nc}`C`(P \upharpoonright \text{D}`P) . P \upharpoonright \text{D}`P \in \Omega .$

[*262·12.*100·3.(2)] $\supset . P \upharpoonright \text{D}`P \in \mu_r : \supset \vdash . \text{Prop}$

***262·213.** $\vdash :. \mu \neq 0 . \mu \neq 1 : P, Q \in \mu_r . \supset_{P,Q} . P \text{ smor } Q : \supset :$

$P, Q \in (\mu +_c 1)_r . \supset_{P,Q} . P \text{ smor } Q$

Dem.

$\vdash . *262\cdot212\cdot12 . *120\cdot124 . \supset$

$\vdash : \text{Hp} . P, Q \in (\mu +_c 1)_r . \supset . P \upharpoonright \text{D}`P, Q \upharpoonright \text{D}`Q \in \mu_r . P, Q \in \Omega - \iota`\dot\Lambda .$

[*11·1.Hp] $\supset . P \upharpoonright \text{D}`P \text{ smor } Q \upharpoonright \text{D}`Q . P, Q \in \Omega - \iota`\dot\Lambda .$

[*250·17] $\supset . P \text{ smor } Q : \supset \vdash . \text{Prop}$

***262·22.** $\vdash : \mu \in \mathrm{NC\,induct} \,.\, P, Q \in \mu_r \,.\, \supset .\, P \mathrel{\mathrm{smor}} Q$

Dem.

$\vdash . *153{\cdot}101 . *262{\cdot}12 . \supset \vdash : P, Q \in 0_r . \supset . P \mathrel{\mathrm{smor}} Q$ (1)

$\vdash . *200{\cdot}12 . \quad \supset \vdash . 1_r = \Lambda .$

$[*10{\cdot}53] \quad \supset \vdash : P, Q \in 1_r . \supset . P \mathrel{\mathrm{smor}} Q$ (2)

$\vdash . *153{\cdot}202 . \quad \supset \vdash : P, Q \in 2_r . \supset . P \mathrel{\mathrm{smor}} Q$ (3)

$\vdash . (2) . (3) . *2{\cdot}02 . \quad \supset \vdash :. \mu = 0 . \vee . \mu = 1 :$

$P, Q \in \mu_r . \supset_{P,Q} . P \mathrel{\mathrm{smor}} Q : \supset : P, Q \in (\mu +_c 1)_r . \supset_{P,Q} . P \mathrel{\mathrm{smor}} Q$ (4)

$\vdash . (4) . *262{\cdot}213 . \supset$

$\vdash :. P, Q \in \mu_r . \supset_{P,Q} . P \mathrel{\mathrm{smor}} Q : \supset : P, Q \in (\mu +_c 1)_r . \supset_{P,Q} . P \mathrel{\mathrm{smor}} Q$ (5)

$\vdash . (5) . (1) . \mathrm{Induct} . \supset \vdash . \mathrm{Prop}$

***262·23.** $\vdash :. P, Q \in \Omega \,\mathrm{fin} . \supset : C\text{‘}P \mathrel{\mathrm{sm}} C\text{‘}Q . \equiv . P \mathrel{\mathrm{smor}} Q$

Dem.

$\vdash . *262{\cdot}17{\cdot}13 . \supset$

$\vdash : \mathrm{Hp} . C\text{‘}P \mathrel{\mathrm{sm}} C\text{‘}Q . \supset . P, Q \in (\mathrm{Nc}\text{‘}C\text{‘}P)_r . \mathrm{Nc}\text{‘}C\text{‘}P \in \mathrm{NC\,induct} .$

$[*262{\cdot}22] \quad \supset . P \mathrel{\mathrm{smor}} Q$ (1)

$\vdash . (1) . *151{\cdot}18 . \supset \vdash . \mathrm{Prop}$

The above is the fundamental proposition in the theory of finite ordinals, since it enables us to reduce relations among finite ordinals to relations among the corresponding cardinals.

***262·24.** $\vdash : \mu \in \mathrm{NC\,induct} - \iota\text{‘}\Lambda - \iota\text{‘}1 . \supset . \mu_r \in \mathrm{NO\,fin}$

Dem.

$\vdash . *262{\cdot}21 . \quad \supset \vdash : \mathrm{Hp} . \supset . \exists ! \mu_r$ (1)

$\vdash . *262{\cdot}22 . \quad \supset \vdash : \mathrm{Hp} . P \in \mu_r . \supset . \mu_r \subset \mathrm{Nr}\text{‘}P$ (2)

$\vdash . *262{\cdot}12 . *151{\cdot}18 . \supset \vdash : P \in \mu_r . \supset . \mathrm{Nr}\text{‘}P \subset \mu_r$ (3)

$\vdash . (2) . (3) . \quad \supset \vdash : \mathrm{Hp} . P \in \mu_r . \supset . \mu_r = \mathrm{Nr}\text{‘}P$ (4)

$\vdash . (1) . (4) . \quad \supset \vdash : \mathrm{Hp} . \supset . \mu_r \in \mathrm{NR} - \iota\text{‘}\Lambda$ (5)

$\vdash . *262{\cdot}12 . \quad \supset \vdash : \mathrm{Hp} . P \in \mu_r . \supset . C\text{‘}P \in \mathrm{Cls\,induct} .$

$[*262{\cdot}13.(4).(5)] \quad \supset . \mu_r \in \mathrm{NO\,fin}$ (6)

$\vdash . (1) . (6) . \supset \vdash . \mathrm{Prop}$

***262·241.** $\vdash :. \mu \in \mathrm{NC\,induct} . P \in \Omega . \supset : \mu_r = \mathrm{Nr}\text{‘}P . \equiv . \mu = \mathrm{Nc}\text{‘}C\text{‘}P$

Dem.

$\vdash . *100{\cdot}3 . \quad \supset \vdash : \mathrm{Hp} . \mu = \mathrm{Nc}\text{‘}C\text{‘}P . \supset . C\text{‘}P \in \mu .$

$[*262{\cdot}12] \quad \supset . P \in \mu_r .$

$[*152{\cdot}45 . *262{\cdot}24] \quad \supset . \mu_r = \mathrm{Nr}\text{‘}P$ (1)

$\vdash . *152{\cdot}3 . *262{\cdot}18 . \supset \vdash : \mathrm{Hp} . \mu_r = \mathrm{Nr}\text{‘}P . \supset . \mu = C\text{‘‘}\mathrm{Nr}\text{‘}P$

$[*152{\cdot}7] \quad \supset . \mu = \mathrm{Nc}\text{‘}C\text{‘}P$ (2)

$\vdash . (1) . (2) . \supset \vdash . \mathrm{Prop}$

***262·25.** $\vdash : (\exists \mu) . \mu \in \text{NC induct} - \iota`1 - \iota`\Lambda . \alpha = \mu_r . \equiv . \alpha \in \text{NO fin}$

Dem.

$\vdash . *262·1·13 . \supset$

$\vdash : \alpha \in \text{NO fin} . \supset . (\exists P) . P \in \Omega \text{ fin} . \alpha = \text{Nr}`P . \text{Nc}`C`P \in \text{NC induct} .$

[*262·241] $\supset . (\exists P) . P \in \Omega \text{ fin} . \alpha = \text{Nr}`P . (\text{Nc}`C`P)_r = \text{Nr}`P .$
$\text{Nc}`C`P \in \text{NC induct} .$

[*13·172] $\supset . (\exists P) . \alpha = (\text{Nc}`C`P)_r . \text{Nc}`C`P \in \text{NC induct} .$

[*200·12.*262·1.*155·13] $\supset . (\exists \mu) . \mu \in \text{NC induct} - \iota`1 - \iota`\Lambda . \alpha = \mu_r$ (1)

$\vdash . *264·24 . \supset \vdash : (\exists \mu) . \mu \in \text{NC induct} - \iota`1 - \iota`\Lambda . \alpha = \mu_r . \supset . \alpha \in \text{NO fin}$ (2)

$\vdash . (1) . (2) . \supset \vdash . \text{Prop}$

***262·26.** $\vdash : \alpha \in \text{NO fin} . \equiv . (\exists \mu) . \mu \in \dot{\text{N}}_0\text{C induct} - \iota`1 . \alpha = \mu_r$
[*262·25 . *103·13·34]

***262·27.** $\vdash : \alpha, \beta \in \text{NO fin} . \supset . \alpha \dot{+} \beta \in \text{NO fin}$

Dem.

$\vdash . *180·21 . \supset \vdash : \text{Hp} . P \in \alpha . Q \in \beta . \supset . P + Q \in \alpha \dot{+} \beta$ (1)

$\vdash . *251·24 . \supset \vdash : \text{Hp} . \supset . \alpha \dot{+} \beta \in \text{NO}$ (2)

$\vdash . *180·111 . \supset \vdash : \text{Hp}(1) . \supset . \text{Nc}`C`(P + Q) = \text{Nc}`(C`P + C`Q)$

[*110·3] $= \text{Nc}`C`P +_c \text{Nc}`C`Q$ (3)

$\vdash . *262·13 . \supset \vdash : \text{Hp}(1) . \supset . \text{Nc}`C`P, \text{Nc}`C`Q \in \text{NC induct} .$

[*120·45] $\supset . \text{Nc}`C`P +_c \text{Nc}`C`Q \in \text{NC induct}$ (4)

$\vdash . (1) . (2) . *155·26 . *251·122 . \supset$

$\vdash : \text{Hp}(1) . \supset . P + Q \in \Omega . \alpha \dot{+} \beta = \text{N}_0\text{r}`(P + Q)$ (5)

$\vdash . (3) . (4) . \qquad \supset \vdash : \text{Hp}(1) . \supset . C`(P + Q) \in \text{Cls induct}$ (6)

$\vdash . (5) . (6) . *262·1 . *261·42 . \supset \vdash : \text{Hp}(1) . \supset . \alpha \dot{+} \beta \in \text{NO fin}$ (7)

$\vdash . *262·1 . *155·13 . \qquad \supset \vdash : \text{Hp} . \supset . \exists ! \alpha . \exists ! \beta$ (8)

$\vdash . (7) . (8) . \supset \vdash . \text{Prop}$

***262·271.** $\vdash : \alpha, \beta \in \text{NO fin} . \supset . \alpha \dot{\times} \beta \in \text{NO fin}$
[Proof as in *262·27, using *184·12 . *166·12 . *251·55 . *120·5]

***262·272.** $\vdash : \alpha, \beta \in \text{NO fin} . \supset . \alpha \exp_r \beta \in \text{NO fin}$
[Proof as in *262·27, using *186·1 . *176·14 . *261·62 . *120·52]

***262·31.** $\vdash : \mu, \nu \in \text{NC} . \supset . \mu_r \dot{+} \nu_r \subset (\mu +_c \nu)_r$

Dem.

$\vdash . *180·2 . \supset$

$\vdash :. Z \in \mu_r \dot{+} \nu_r . \equiv : (\exists P, Q) . \mu_r = \text{N}_0\text{r}`P . \nu_r = \text{N}_0\text{r}`Q . Z \text{ smor} (P + Q) :$ (1)

[*180·111.*151·18] $\supset : (\exists P, Q) . \mu_r = \text{N}_0\text{r}`P . \nu_r = \text{N}_0\text{r}`Q . C`Z \text{ sm} (C`P + C`Q) :$

[*155·12] $\supset : (\exists P, Q) . P \in \mu_r . Q \in \nu_r . C`Z \text{ sm} (C`P + C`Q) :$

[*262·12] $\supset : (\exists P, Q) . C`P \in \mu . C`Q \in \nu . C`Z \text{ sm} (C`P + C`Q) :$

[*110·21] $\supset : \text{Hp} . \supset . C`Z \in \mu +_c \nu$ (2)

$\vdash . (1) . *262{\cdot}12 . *155{\cdot}12 . \supset$

$\vdash : Z \in \mu_r \dot{+} \nu_r . \supset . (\exists P, Q) . P, Q \in \Omega . Z \operatorname{smor} (P + Q) .$

$[*251{\cdot}25 . *180{\cdot}11{\cdot}12 . (*180{\cdot}01)] \supset . Z \in \Omega$ (3)

$\vdash . (2) . (3) . *262{\cdot}12 . \supset \vdash :. \mathrm{Hp} . \supset : Z \in \mu_r \dot{+} \nu_r . \supset . Z \in (\mu +_c \nu)_r :. \supset \vdash . \mathrm{Prop}$

***262·32.** $\vdash : \mu, \nu \in \mathrm{NC\,induct} . P \in \mu_r . Q \in \nu_r . \supset . P + Q \in \mu_r \dot{+} \nu_r$

Dem.

$\vdash . *200{\cdot}12 . *262{\cdot}12 . \supset \vdash : \mathrm{Hp} . \supset . \mu, \nu \in - \iota\text{‘}1 - \iota\text{‘}\Lambda .$

$[*262{\cdot}24] \qquad \supset . \mu_r, \nu_r \in \mathrm{NO} .$

$[*180{\cdot}21] \qquad \supset . P + Q \in \mu_r \dot{+} \nu_r : \supset \vdash . \mathrm{Prop}$

***262·33.** $\vdash : \mu, \nu \in \mathrm{NC\,induct} - \iota\text{‘}1 . \supset . \mu_r \dot{+} \nu_r = (\mu +_c \nu)_r$

Dem.

$\vdash . *262{\cdot}12 . \supset \vdash :. \mu = \Lambda . \mathbf{v} . \nu = \Lambda : \supset : \mu_r = \Lambda . \mathbf{v} . \nu_r = \Lambda :$

$[*180{\cdot}4] \qquad \supset : \mu_r \dot{+} \nu_r = \Lambda$ (1)

$\vdash . *110{\cdot}4 . \supset \vdash :. \mu = \Lambda . \mathbf{v} . \nu = \Lambda : \supset . \mu +_c \nu = \Lambda .$

$[*262{\cdot}12] \qquad \supset . (\mu +_c \nu)_r = \Lambda$ (2)

$\vdash . *262{\cdot}32 . \supset \vdash : \mathrm{Hp} . P \in \mu_r . Q \in \nu_r . \supset . P + Q \in \mu_r \dot{+} \nu_r .$ (3)

$[*180{\cdot}42 . *152{\cdot}45] \qquad \supset . \mu_r \dot{+} \nu_r = \mathrm{Nr}\text{‘}(P + Q)$ (4)

$\vdash . (3) . *262{\cdot}31 . \supset \vdash : \mathrm{Hp}(3) . \supset . P + Q \in (\mu +_c \nu)_r .$

$[*120{\cdot}45 . *262{\cdot}24] \qquad \supset . P + Q \in (\mu +_c \nu)_r . (\mu +_c \nu)_r \in \mathrm{NR} .$

$[*152{\cdot}45] \qquad \supset . (\mu +_c \nu)_r = \mathrm{Nr}\text{‘}(P + Q)$ (5)

$\vdash . (4) . (5) . *10{\cdot}23 . *262{\cdot}21 . \supset \vdash : \mathrm{Hp} . \exists ! \mu . \exists ! \nu . \supset . \mu_r \dot{+} \nu_r = (\mu +_c \nu)_r$ (6)

$\vdash . (1) . (2) . (6) . \supset \vdash . \mathrm{Prop}$

The above proposition still holds (as we shall now prove) when one of μ and ν is equal to 1, but not both. When both are equal to 1, $\mu_r \dot{+} \nu_r = \Lambda$, while $(\mu +_c \nu)_r = 2_r$.

***262·34.** $\vdash : \mu \in \mathrm{NC} - \iota\text{‘}0 . \supset . \mu_r \dot{+} \dot{1} \subset (\mu +_c 1)_r$

Dem.

$\vdash . *181{\cdot}2 . \supset \vdash :. Z \in \mu_r \dot{+} \dot{1} . \equiv : (\exists P, x) . \mu_r = \mathrm{N_0r}\text{‘}P . Z \operatorname{smor} (P \dot{\dashv\!\rightarrow} x)$ (1)

$\vdash . *181{\cdot}6 . *152{\cdot}7 . \supset \vdash : \dot{\exists} ! P . \supset . \mathrm{Nc}\text{‘}C\text{‘}(P \dot{\dashv\!\rightarrow} x) = \mathrm{Nc}\text{‘}C\text{‘}P +_c 1$ (2)

$\vdash . (1) . (2) . \supset$

$\vdash :. \mathrm{Hp} . \supset : Z \in \mu_r \dot{+} \dot{1} . \supset . (\exists P) . \mu_r = \mathrm{N_0r}\text{‘}P . \mathrm{Nc}\text{‘}C\text{‘}Z = \mathrm{Nc}\text{‘}C\text{‘}P +_c 1 .$

$[*262{\cdot}241{\cdot}12] \qquad \supset . (\exists P) . \mu_r = \mathrm{N_0r}\text{‘}P . \mathrm{Nc}\text{‘}C\text{‘}Z = \mu +_c 1 .$

$[*100{\cdot}3] \qquad \supset . C\text{‘}Z \in \mu +_c 1$ (3)

$\vdash . (1) . *262{\cdot}12 . *155{\cdot}12 . \supset \vdash : Z \in \mu_r \dot{+} \dot{1} . \supset . (\exists P) . P \in \Omega . \mu_r = \mathrm{N_0r}\text{‘}P .$

$[*251{\cdot}1{\cdot}132] \qquad \supset . \mu_r \dot{+} \dot{1} \in \mathrm{NO} .$

$[*251{\cdot}122] \qquad \supset . Z \in \Omega$ (4)

$\vdash . (3) . (4) . *262{\cdot}12 . \supset \vdash :. \mathrm{Hp} . \supset : Z \in \mu_r \dot{+} \dot{1} . \supset . Z \in (\mu +_c 1)_r :. \supset \vdash . \mathrm{Prop}$

***262·341.** $\vdash : \mu \in \text{NC induct} . P \in \mu_r . \supset . P \dot{+\!\!\rightarrow} x \in \mu_r \dot{+} \dot{1}$

Dem.

$\vdash . *200·12 . *262·12 . \supset \vdash : \text{Hp} . \supset . \mu \in - \iota`1 - \iota`\Lambda .$

[*262·24] $\supset . \mu_r \in \text{NO} .$

[*181·21] $\supset . P \dot{+\!\!\rightarrow} x \in \mu_r \dot{+} \dot{1} : \supset \vdash . \text{Prop}$

***262·35.** $\vdash : \mu \in \text{NC induct} - \iota`0 - \iota`1 . \supset . \mu_r \dot{+} \dot{1} = (\mu +_c 1)_r$

Dem.

$\vdash . *262·12 . \quad \supset \vdash : \mu = \Lambda . \supset . \mu_r = \Lambda .$

[*181·4] $\supset . \mu_r \dot{+} \dot{1} = \Lambda$ (1)

$\vdash . *110·4 . \quad \supset \vdash : \mu = \Lambda . \supset . \mu +_c 1 = \Lambda .$

[*262·12] $\supset . (\mu +_c 1)_r = \Lambda$ (2)

$\vdash . *262·341 . \quad \supset \vdash : \text{Hp} . P \in \mu_r . \supset . P \dot{+\!\!\rightarrow} x \in \mu_r \dot{+} \dot{1} .$ (3)

[*181·42.*152·45] $\supset . \mu_r \dot{+} \dot{1} = \text{Nr}`(P \dot{+\!\!\rightarrow} x)$ (4)

$\vdash . (3) . *262·34 . \supset \vdash : \text{Hp} . P \in \mu_r . \supset . P \dot{+\!\!\rightarrow} x \in (\mu +_c 1)_r .$

[*120·45.*262·24] $\supset . P \dot{+\!\!\rightarrow} x \in (\mu +_c 1)_r . (\mu +_c 1)_r \in \text{NR} .$

[*152·45] $\supset . (\mu +_c 1)_r = \text{Nr}`(P \dot{+\!\!\rightarrow} x)$ (5)

$\vdash . (4) . (5) . \quad \supset \vdash : \text{Hp} . \exists ! \mu_r . \supset . \mu_r \dot{+} \dot{1} = (\mu +_c 1)_r :$

[*262·21] $\supset \vdash : \text{Hp} . \exists ! \mu . \supset . \mu_r \dot{+} \dot{1} = (\mu +_c 1)_r$ (6)

$\vdash . (1) . (2) . (6) . \supset \vdash . \text{Prop}$

***262·36.** $\vdash : \mu \in \text{NC induct} - \iota`0 - \iota`1 . \supset . \dot{1} \dot{+} \mu_r = (1 +_c \mu)_r$

[Proof as in *262·35, by means of analogues of *262·34·341]

***262·41.** $\vdash : \mu, \nu \in \text{NC} . \supset . \mu_r \dot{\times} \nu_r \subset (\mu \times_c \nu)_r$

[Proof as in *262·31, using *184·1·5 . *113·21]

***262·42.** $\vdash : \mu, \nu \in \text{NC induct} . P \in \mu_r . Q \in \nu_r . \supset . P \times Q \in \mu_r \dot{\times} \nu_r$

[Proof as in *262·32, using *184·12]

***262·43.** $\vdash : \mu, \nu \in \text{NC induct} - \iota`1 . \supset . \mu_r \dot{\times} \nu_r = (\mu \times_c \nu)_r$

[Proof as in *262·33, using *184·11 . *113·204 . *184·15 . *120·5]

***262·51.** $\vdash : \mu \in \text{NC} . \nu \in \text{NC induct} . \supset . \mu_r \exp_r \nu_r \subset (\mu^\nu)_r$

Dem.

$\vdash . *186·5 . \supset \vdash : \mu_r, \nu_r \in \text{N}_0\text{R} . \nu \neq 0 . R \in \mu_r \exp_r \nu_r . \supset . C`R \in (C``\mu_r)^{C``\nu_r}$ (1)

$\vdash . *186·11 . \supset \vdash : R \in \mu_r \exp_r \nu_r . \supset . \exists ! \mu_r . \exists ! \nu_r$ (2)

$\vdash . (1) . (2) . *262·18 . \supset \vdash : \text{Hp} . \nu \neq 0 . R \in \mu_r \exp_r \nu_r . \supset . C`R \in \mu^\nu$ (3)

$\vdash . *262·12 . \quad \supset \vdash . \mu_r \subset \Omega .$

[(2).*251·1.*186·11] $\supset \vdash : R \in \mu_r \exp_r \nu_r . \supset . \mu_r \in \text{NO}$ (4)

$\vdash . *262·24 . \quad \supset \vdash : \text{Hp} . \nu \neq 1 . \nu \neq \Lambda . \supset . \nu_r \in \text{NO fin}$ (5)

$\vdash . (2) . (4) . (5) . *261·62 . \supset \vdash : \text{Hp} . \nu \neq 1 . R \in \mu_r \exp_r \nu_r . \supset . R \in \Omega$ (6)

$\vdash . (2) . *200·12 . \supset \vdash : R \in \mu_r \exp_r \nu_r . \supset . \nu \neq 1$ (7)

$\vdash . (3) . (6) . (7) . \supset \vdash :. \text{Hp} . \supset : R \in \mu_r \exp_r \nu_r . \supset . R \in \Omega . C`R \in \mu^\nu .$

[*262·12] $\supset . R \in (\mu^\nu)_r :. \supset \vdash . \text{Prop}$

***262·52.** $\vdash : \mu, \nu \in \text{NC induct} . P \in \mu_r . Q \in \nu_r . \supset . (P \exp Q) \in (\mu_r \exp_r \nu_r)$

Dem.

$\vdash . *200·12 . *262·12 . \supset \vdash : \text{Hp} . \supset . \mu, \nu \in -\iota`1 - \iota`\Lambda .$

[*262·24] $\supset . \mu_r, \nu_r \in \text{NO} .$

[*186·13.*152·45] $\supset . (P \exp Q) \in (\mu_r \exp_r \nu_r) : \supset \vdash . \text{Prop}$

***262·53.** $\vdash : \mu, \nu \in \text{NC induct} - \iota`1 . \nu \neq 0 . \supset . \mu_r \exp_r \nu_r = (\mu^\nu)_r$

Dem.

$\vdash . *262·12 . *186·11 . \supset \vdash :. \mu = \Lambda . \vee . \nu = \Lambda : \supset . \mu_r \exp_r \nu_r = \Lambda$ (1)

$\vdash . *116·204 . *262·12 . \supset \vdash :. \mu = \Lambda . \vee . \nu = \Lambda : \supset . (\mu^\nu)_r = \Lambda$ (2)

$\vdash . *262·52 . \supset \vdash : \text{Hp} . P \in \mu_r . Q \in \nu_r . \supset . (P \exp Q) \in (\mu_r \exp_r \nu_r) .$ (3)

[*186·13.*152·45] $\supset . \text{Nr}`(P \exp Q) = \mu_r \exp_r \nu_r$ (4)

$\vdash . (3) . *262·51 . \supset \vdash : \text{Hp}(3) . \supset . (P \exp Q) \in (\mu^\nu)_r$ (5)

$\vdash . (5) . *120·52 . \supset \vdash : \text{Hp}(3) . \supset . \mu^\nu \in \text{NC induct}$ (6)

$\vdash . (5) . \supset \vdash : \text{Hp}(3) . \supset . \exists ! (\mu^\nu)_r .$

[*200·12.*262·12] $\supset . \mu^\nu \neq 1$ (7)

$\vdash . (6) . (7) . *262·24 . \supset \vdash : \text{Hp} . \supset . (\mu^\nu)_r \in \text{NO}$ (8)

$\vdash . (5) . (8) . *152·45 . \supset \vdash : \text{Hp}(3) . \supset . \text{Nr}`(P \exp Q) = (\mu^\nu)_r .$

[(4)] $\supset . \mu_r \exp_r \nu_r = (\mu^\nu)_r$ (9)

$\vdash . (9) . *262·21 . \supset \vdash : \text{Hp} . \exists ! \mu . \exists ! \nu . \supset . \mu_r \exp_r \nu_r = (\mu^\nu)_r$ (10)

$\vdash . (1) . (2) . (10) . \supset \vdash . \text{Prop}$

We are now in a position to establish the commutative property of addition and multiplication of finite ordinals. This is effected by means of *262·33 and *262·43.

***262·6.** $\vdash : \alpha, \beta \in \text{NO fin} . \supset . \alpha \dot{+} \beta = \beta \dot{+} \alpha$

Dem.

$\vdash . *262·26 . \supset \vdash : \text{Hp} . \supset . (\exists \mu, \nu) . \mu, \nu \in \text{NC induct} - \iota`1 . \alpha = \mu_r . \beta = \nu_r .$

[*13·12] $\supset . (\exists \mu, \nu) . \mu, \nu \in \text{NC induct} - \iota`1 . \alpha \dot{+} \beta = \mu_r \dot{+} \nu_r . \alpha = \mu_r . \beta = \nu_r .$

[*262·33] $\supset . (\exists \mu, \nu) . \mu, \nu \in \text{NC induct} - \iota`1 . \alpha \dot{+} \beta = (\mu +_c \nu)_r . \alpha = \mu_r . \beta = \nu_r .$

[*110·51] $\supset . (\exists \mu, \nu) . \mu, \nu \in \text{NC induct} - \iota`1 . \alpha \dot{+} \beta = (\nu +_c \mu)_r . \alpha = \mu_r . \beta = \nu_r .$

[*262·33] $\supset . (\exists \mu, \nu) . \mu, \nu \in \text{NC induct} - \iota`1 . \alpha \dot{+} \beta = \nu_r \dot{+} \mu_r . \alpha = \mu_r . \beta = \nu_r .$

[*13·22] $\supset . \alpha \dot{+} \beta = \beta \dot{+} \alpha : \supset \vdash . \text{Prop}$

***262·61.** $\vdash : \alpha, \beta \in \text{NO fin} . \supset . \alpha \dot{\times} \beta = \beta \dot{\times} \alpha$

[Proof as in *262·6, using *262·43 and *113·27]

***262·62.** $\vdash : \alpha, \beta, \gamma \in \text{NO fin} . \supset . \alpha \dot{\times} (\beta \dot{+} \gamma) = (\alpha \dot{\times} \beta) \dot{+} (\alpha \dot{\times} \gamma)$

Dem.

$\vdash . *262·27·61 . \supset \vdash : \text{Hp} . \supset . \alpha \dot{\times} (\beta \dot{+} \gamma) = (\beta \dot{+} \gamma) \dot{\times} \alpha$

[*184·35] $= (\beta \dot{\times} \alpha) \dot{+} (\gamma \dot{\times} \alpha)$

[*262·61] $= (\alpha \dot{\times} \beta) \dot{+} (\alpha \dot{\times} \gamma) : \supset \vdash . \text{Prop}$

***262·63.** $\vdash : \alpha, \beta, \gamma \epsilon \text{NO fin} . \supset . (\alpha \dot{\times} \beta) \exp_r \gamma = (\alpha \exp_r \gamma) \dot{\times} (\beta \exp_r \gamma)$

Dem.

$\vdash . *262·26 . \supset$

$\vdash : \text{Hp} . \supset . (\exists \mu, \nu, \varpi) . \mu, \nu, \varpi \epsilon \text{NC induct} - \iota`1 . \alpha = \mu_r . \beta = \nu_r . \gamma = \varpi_r$ (1)

$\vdash . *262·43 . \supset$

$\vdash : \mu, \nu, \varpi \epsilon \text{NC induct} - \iota`1 . \supset . (\mu_r \dot{\times} \nu_r) \exp_r \varpi_r = (\mu \times_c \nu)_r \exp_r \varpi_r$ (2)

$\vdash . *113·602 . \supset \vdash : \mu = 0 . \nu = 0 . \supset . \mu \times_c \nu \neq 1$ (3)

$\vdash . *117·631 . \supset \vdash : \mu, \nu \epsilon \text{NC} - \iota`0 - \iota`1 . \supset . \mu \times_c \nu \neq 1$ (4)

$\vdash . (3) . (4) . \quad \supset \vdash : \text{Hp}(2) . \supset . \mu \times_c \nu \neq 1$ (5)

$\vdash . *120·5 . \quad \supset \vdash : \text{Hp}(2) . \supset . \mu \times_c \nu \epsilon \text{NC induct}$ (6)

$\vdash . (5) . (6) . *262·53 . \supset \vdash : \text{Hp}(2) . \varpi \neq 0_r . \supset . (\mu \times_c \nu)_r \exp_r \varpi_r \doteq \{(\mu \times_c \nu)^\varpi\}_r$

[*116·55] $= (\mu^\varpi \times_c \nu^\varpi)_r$ (7)

$\vdash . *117·652 . \supset \vdash : \text{Hp}(7) . \mu \neq 0_r . \supset . \mu^\varpi \geqslant \mu \times_c \varpi .$

[*117·631] $\supset . \mu^\varpi \neq 1$ (8)

$\vdash . *116·311 . \supset \vdash : \text{Hp}(7) . \mu = 0_r . \supset . \mu^\varpi \neq 1$ (9)

$\vdash . (8) . (9) . \quad \supset \vdash : \text{Hp}(7) . \supset . \mu^\varpi \neq 1$ (10)

Similarly $\vdash : \text{Hp}(7) . \supset . \nu^\varpi \neq 1$ (11)

$\vdash . (10) . (11) . *120·52 . *262·43 . \supset \vdash : \text{Hp}(7) . \supset . (\mu^\varpi \times_c \nu^\varpi)_r = (\mu^\varpi)_r \dot{\times} (\nu^\varpi)_r$

[*262·53] $= (\mu_r \exp_r \varpi_r) \dot{\times} (\nu_r \exp_r \varpi_r)$ (12)

$\vdash . (2) . (7) . (12) . \supset$

$\vdash : \text{Hp}(7) . \supset . (\mu_r \dot{\times} \nu_r) \exp_r \varpi_r = (\mu_r \exp_r \varpi_r) \dot{\times} (\nu_r \exp_r \varpi_r)$ (13)

$\vdash . (1) . (13) . *262·19 . \supset$

$\vdash : \text{Hp} . \gamma \neq 0_r . \supset . (\alpha \dot{\times} \beta) \exp_r \gamma = (\alpha \exp_r \gamma) \dot{\times} (\beta \exp_r \gamma)$ (14)

$\vdash . *186·2 . *184·16 . \supset$

$\vdash : \text{Hp} . \gamma = 0_r . \supset . (\alpha \dot{\times} \beta) \exp_r \gamma = 0_r . (\alpha \exp_r \gamma) \dot{\times} (\beta \exp_r \gamma) = 0_r$ (15)

$\vdash . (14) . (15) . \supset \vdash . \text{Prop}$

***262·64.** $\vdash : \alpha \epsilon \text{NO fin} . \supset . \alpha \dot{+} \dot{1} = \dot{1} \dot{+} \alpha$

Dem.

$\vdash . *262·35·36·26 . *110·51 . \supset \vdash : \text{Hp} . \alpha \neq 0_r . \supset . \alpha \dot{+} \dot{1} = \dot{1} \dot{+} \alpha$ (1)

$\vdash . *161·2·201 . \quad \supset \vdash : \alpha = 0_r . \supset . \alpha \dot{+} \dot{1} = 0_r . \dot{1} \dot{+} \alpha = 0_r$ (2)

$\vdash . (1) . (2) . \supset \vdash . \text{Prop}$

***262·65.** $\vdash : \alpha, \beta \epsilon \text{NO fin} . \beta \neq 0_r . \supset . \alpha \times (\beta \dot{+} \dot{1}) = (\alpha \dot{\times} \beta) \dot{+} \alpha$

Dem.

$\vdash . *262·61 . \supset \vdash : \text{Hp} . \supset . \alpha \dot{\times} (\beta \dot{+} \dot{1}) = (\beta \dot{+} \dot{1}) \dot{\times} \alpha$

[*184·41] $= (\beta \dot{\times} \alpha) \dot{+} \alpha$

[*262·61] $= (\alpha \dot{\times} \beta) \dot{+} \alpha : \supset \vdash . \text{Prop}$

***262·66.** $\vdash : \alpha, \beta \epsilon \text{NO fin} . \beta \neq 0_r . \supset . \alpha \dot{\times} (\dot{1} \dot{+} \beta) = \alpha \dot{+} (\alpha \dot{\times} \beta)$

[Proof as in *262·65]

***262·7.** $\vdash :. \mu, \nu \in \mathrm{NC\ induct} - \iota`1 . \supset : \mu > \nu . \equiv . \mu_r \gtrdot \nu_r$

Dem.

$\vdash . *262\cdot21 . *117\cdot12 . \supset \vdash : \mathrm{Hp} . \mu > \nu . \supset . \exists ! \mu_r . \exists ! \nu_r .$

$[*262\cdot18] \quad \supset . \mu = C``\mu_r . \nu = C``\nu_r . \quad (1)$

$[*255\cdot76 . *262\cdot24] \quad \supset . \mu_r \gtrdot \nu_r \quad (2)$

$\vdash . *120\cdot441 . \supset \vdash : \mathrm{Hp} . \sim(\mu > \nu) . \supset . \mu \leqslant \nu \quad (3)$

$\vdash . (1) . \quad \supset \vdash : \mathrm{Hp} . \mu < \nu . \supset . \mu_r \lessdot \nu_r \quad (4)$

$\vdash . *262\cdot21 . \supset \vdash : \mathrm{Hp} . \mu = \mathrm{sm}``\nu . \supset . (\exists P) . \mu = \mathrm{N_0c}`C`P . \mu = \mathrm{sm}``\nu .$

$[*103\cdot4] \quad \supset . (\exists P) . \mu = \mathrm{N_0c}`C`P . \nu = \mathrm{Nc}`C`P .$

$[*262\cdot241] \quad \supset . (\exists P) . \mu_r = \mathrm{N_0r}`P . \nu_r = \mathrm{Nr}`P .$

$[*155\cdot4] \quad \supset . \mu_r = \mathrm{smor}``\nu \quad (5)$

$\vdash . (4) . (5) . *117\cdot104 . \supset \vdash : \mathrm{Hp} . \mu \leqslant \nu . \supset . \mu_r \mathrel{\underline{\lessdot}} \nu_r \quad (6)$

$\vdash . (3) . (6) . *255\cdot483 . \supset \vdash : \mathrm{Hp} . \sim(\mu > \nu) . \supset . \sim(\mu_r \gtrdot \nu_r) \quad (7)$

$\vdash . (2) . (7) . \supset \vdash . \mathrm{Prop}$

***262·71.** $\vdash : \alpha \in \mathrm{NO\ fin} - \iota`0_r . \supset . (\exists \beta) . \beta \in \mathrm{NO\ fin} - \iota`0_r \cup \iota`\dot{1} . \alpha = \beta \dot{+} \dot{1}$

Dem.

$\vdash . *262\cdot11 . *261\cdot24 . \supset \vdash : \mathrm{Hp} . \supset . \exists ! \alpha \cap \text{ᗡ}`(B \mid \mathrm{Cnv}) \quad (1)$

$\vdash . (1) . *204\cdot483 . (*181\cdot04) . \supset \vdash . \mathrm{Prop}$

***262·8.** $\vdash : \alpha, \beta \in \mathrm{NO} . \gamma \in \mathrm{NO\ fin} . \alpha \lessdot \beta . \supset . \alpha \exp_r \gamma \lessdot \beta \exp_r \gamma \quad [*261\cdot64]$

***262·81.** $\vdash : \alpha\ \beta \in \mathrm{N_0O} . \gamma \in \mathrm{NO\ fin} . \alpha \exp_r \gamma = \beta \exp_r \gamma . \supset . \alpha = \mathrm{smor}``\beta$

Dem.

$\vdash . *262\cdot8 . \mathrm{Transp} . *255\cdot42 . \supset \vdash : \mathrm{Hp} . \supset . \sim(\alpha \lessdot \beta) . \sim(\alpha \gtrdot \beta) .$

$[*255\cdot112] \quad \supset . \alpha = \mathrm{smor}``\beta : \supset \vdash . \mathrm{Prop}$

***262·82.** $\vdash : \alpha \in \mathrm{NO\ fin} . \beta \in \mathrm{NO\ infin} . \supset . \alpha \lessdot \beta \quad [*261\cdot65]$

***262·83.** $\vdash : \alpha \in \mathrm{N_0O} - \iota`0_r . \beta, \gamma \in \mathrm{NO\ fin} . \beta \lessdot \gamma . \supset . \alpha \exp_r \beta \lessdot \alpha \exp_r \gamma$

Dem.

$\vdash . *255\cdot33 . \supset \vdash :. \mathrm{Hp} . \supset : (\exists \varpi) . \varpi \in \mathrm{NO} - \iota`0_r . \gamma = \beta \dot{+} \varpi . \mathrm{v} . \beta \neq 0_r . \gamma = \beta \dot{+} \dot{1} \quad (1)$

$\vdash . *254\cdot51 . \supset \vdash : Q \subset P . \supset . \sim(P \mathrm{\ less\ } Q) \quad (2)$

$\vdash . (2) . *255\cdot1 . \supset \vdash : \gamma = \beta \dot{+} \varpi . \supset . \sim(\gamma \lessdot \varpi) \quad (3)$

$\vdash . (3) . *262\cdot82 . \mathrm{Transp} . \supset \vdash : \mathrm{Hp} . \gamma = \beta \dot{+} \varpi . \supset . \varpi \in \mathrm{NO\ fin} \quad (4)$

$\vdash . *186\cdot14 . \supset \vdash : \mathrm{Hp}(4) . \varpi \neq 0_r . \beta \neq 0_r . \supset . \alpha \exp_r \gamma = (\alpha \exp_r \beta) \dot{\times} (\alpha \exp_r \varpi) \quad (5)$

$\vdash . *262\cdot71\cdot272 . \supset \vdash : \mathrm{Hp}(5) . \supset . (\exists \delta) . \delta \in \mathrm{NR} - \iota`0_r \cup \iota`\dot{1} . \alpha \exp_r \beta = \delta \dot{+} \dot{1} .$

$[(5) . (4) . *255\cdot573] \quad \supset . \alpha \exp_r \gamma \gtrdot \alpha \exp_r \beta \quad (6)$

$\vdash . *255\cdot51 . \supset \vdash : \mathrm{Hp}(4) . \varpi \neq 0_r . \beta = 0_r . \supset . \alpha \exp_r \gamma \gtrdot \alpha \exp_r \beta \quad (7)$

$\vdash . *186\cdot22 . \supset \vdash : \mathrm{Hp} . \beta \neq 0_r . \gamma = \beta \dot{+} \dot{1} . \supset . \alpha \exp_r \gamma = (\alpha \exp_r \beta) \dot{\times} \beta .$

$[*262\cdot71 . *255\cdot573] \quad \supset . \alpha \exp_r \gamma \gtrdot \alpha \exp_r \beta \quad (8)$

$\vdash . (1) . (6) . (7) . (8) . \supset \vdash : \mathrm{Hp} . \supset . \alpha \exp_r \gamma \gtrdot \alpha \exp_r \beta : \supset \vdash . \mathrm{Prop}$

***262·84.** $\vdash : P \in \Omega - \iota`\dot{\Lambda} . Q, R \in \Omega \mathrm{\ fin} . Q \mathrm{\ less\ } R . \supset . P^Q \mathrm{\ less\ } P^R \quad [*262\cdot83]$

*263. PROGRESSIONS.

Summary of *263.

If R is a progression in the sense defined in *122, *i.e.* a one-one relation whose field is the posterity of its first term, then R_{po} is a serial relation, and the series generated by R_{po} is of the type which Cantor calls ω, *i.e.* the smallest of infinite series. It is easy to prove that all progressions are ordinally similar, and that, if all inductive cardinals exist, the series of inductive cardinals in order of magnitude is of the type ω. Thus ω is an ordinal number, which is not null if the axiom of infinity holds.

Most of the properties of ω are easily deduced from the corresponding properties of "Prog," which have been proved in *122. The definition is

$$\omega = \hat{P}\{(\exists R) . R \in \text{Prog} . P = R_{po}\} \quad \text{Df.}$$

The axiom of infinity implies that "less to greater" with its field confined to inductive cardinals is a member of ω, or, what comes to the same thing but is easier to prove, that $\{(\text{NC induct}) \upharpoonright (+_c 1)\}_{po}$ is a member of ω (*263·12). Thus the axiom of infinity for the type of x implies the existence of ω in the type $t^{33}{}^{\prime}x$ (*263·132); and generally the existence of ω in any type of relations is equivalent to the existence of $\aleph_0$ in the type of their fields (*263·131), because $\aleph_0 = \text{D}^{\prime\prime}\omega = C^{\prime\prime}\omega$ (*263·101).

By using the fact that in a progression R (in the sense of *122) all the terms are values of ν_R, where every inductive cardinal occurs as a value of ν (which was proved in *122), we easily deduce that if there are progressions they are the series that are ordinally similar to the series of inductive cardinals (*263·161). Hence both "Prog" and ω are relation-numbers (*263·162·19). Moreover, by *122·21·23, ω consists of well-ordered series (*263·11). Hence ω is an ordinal number (*263·2).

We next prove that progressions are infinite series (*263·23), and that a series contained in a progression is finite if it has a maximum (*263·27), and is a progression if it has no maximum (*263·26). It follows that, assuming the existence of progressions or the axiom of infinity, ω is the smallest ordinal which is greater than all the finite ordinals (*263·31·32). Connected with this is the fact that the predecessors of any term in a progression are an inductive class (*263·412).

$*263\cdot44\cdot48$ give various formulae for ω, any one of which might be taken as the definition. We have

$*263\cdot44$. $\vdash . \omega = \Omega - \iota`\Lambda \cap \hat{P}(\text{Cl}`P_1 = \text{Cl}`P . \sim \text{E} ! B`\breve{P})$

I.e. progressions are existent well-ordered series in which every term except the first has an immediate predecessor, and there is no last term.

$*263\cdot46$. $\vdash . \omega = \Omega \cap \hat{P}(\text{E} ! B`P_1 . \sim \text{E} ! B`\breve{P})$

I.e. progressions are well-ordered series in which there is only one term having an immediate successor but no immediate predecessor, and there is no last term.

$*263\cdot47$. $\vdash . \omega = \Omega \cap \hat{P}\{\alpha \subset C`P . \supset_\alpha : \alpha \in \text{Cls induct} . \equiv . \exists ! C`P \cap p`\overleftarrow{P}``\alpha\}$

I.e. a progression is a well-ordered series in which any sub-class α stops short of some point of the series if α is inductive, but not otherwise. This proposition will be useful in the next section.

$*263\cdot49$. $\vdash . \Omega \text{ fin} \cup \omega = \Omega \cap \hat{P}(\text{Cl}`P_1 = \text{Cl}`P) = \Omega \cap \hat{P}(P = P_{\text{fn}})$

I.e. finite well-ordered series and progressions together are those well-ordered series in which every term except the first has an immediate predecessor, and are also those in which every interval is an inductive class.

From $*261\cdot45$ it follows that, if P is an infinite well-ordered series, P confined to the terms at a finite distance from $B`P$ is a progression, *i.e.*

$*263\cdot5$. $\vdash : P \in \Omega \text{ infin} . \supset . P \upharpoonright (\iota`B`P \cup \overleftarrow{P}_{\text{fn}}`B`P) \in \omega$

Hence it follows at once that an infinite ordinal is at least as great as ω, and therefore infinite ordinals other than ω are greater than ω, *i.e.*

$*263\cdot54$. $\vdash : \alpha \in \text{NO infin} - \iota`\omega . \supset . \alpha > \omega$

The remaining propositions of this number are occupied in proving $\omega \dot{\times} 2_r = \omega$ ($*263\cdot63$) and $\omega \dot{\times} \alpha = \omega$ if α is finite and not zero ($*263\cdot66$). It is not the case that $2_r \dot{\times} \omega = \omega$ or $\alpha \dot{\times} \omega = \omega$.

Cantor has varied his definitions of multiplication as regards the order of the factors. Originally, he adopted the same rule as we have adopted, but in later works he inverted the rule, so that what we call $2_r \dot{\times} \omega$ he calls $\omega \dot{\times} 2_r$, and vice versa. Thus with his definitions in his later works, $2_r \dot{\times} \omega = \omega$ but $\omega \dot{\times} 2_r \neq \omega$. We have reverted to his earlier practice, for various reasons, but chiefly in order to have $\text{Nr}`\Pi`(P \downarrow Q) = \text{Nr}`P \dot{\times} \text{Nr}`Q$ (cf. $*172$). Whichever rule we adopt, there are some inconveniences, so that the question as to which is chosen is not of great importance.

***263·01.** $\omega = \hat{P}\{(\exists R) . R \epsilon \text{Prog} . P = R_{po}\}$ Df

***263·02.** $N = \hat{\mu}\hat{\nu}\{\mu \epsilon \text{NC induct} . \nu = (\mu +_c 1) \cap t_0`\mu\}$ Dft [*263]

The above temporary definition of N is the same as that in *123.

***263·1.** $\vdash : P \epsilon \omega . \equiv . (\exists R) . R \epsilon \text{Prog} . P = R_{po}$ [(*263·01)]

***263·101.** $\vdash . \aleph_0 = \text{D}``\omega = C``\omega$ [*123·1 . *122·141 . *91·504]

***263·11.** $\vdash . \omega \subset \Omega$

Dem.

$\vdash . *122·23·141 . *263·1 . \supset \vdash : P \epsilon \omega . \alpha \subset C`P . \exists ! \alpha . \supset . \text{E} ! \min_P`\alpha$ (1)

$\vdash . (1) . *250·125 . \supset \vdash . \text{Prop}$

***263·12.** $\vdash : \text{Infin ax} . \supset . N_{po} \epsilon \omega$ [*123·25 . *263·1]

***263·13.** $\vdash : \exists ! \aleph_0(x) . \equiv . \exists ! \omega \cap t^{11}`x$

Dem.

$\vdash . *263·101 . (*65·02) . \supset$

$\vdash : \exists ! \aleph_0(x) . \equiv . (\exists P) . P \epsilon \omega . C`P \epsilon t`t`x .$

$[*64·57.*63·5] \equiv . (\exists P) . P \epsilon \omega . P \epsilon t^{11}`x : \supset \vdash . \text{Prop}$

***263·131.** $\vdash : \exists ! (\aleph_0)_\alpha . \equiv . \exists ! \omega \cap t_{00}`\alpha$ [Proof as in *263·13]

***263·132.** $\vdash : \text{Infin ax}(x) . \equiv . \exists ! \omega \cap t^{33}`x .$

Dem.

$\vdash . *125·23 . *263·13 . \supset \vdash : \text{Infin ax}(x) . \equiv . \exists ! \omega \cap t^{11}`t^{2}`x .$

$[(*64·011·014)] \qquad \equiv . \exists ! \omega \cap t^{33}`x : \supset \vdash . \text{Prop}$

This proposition asserts that, if the number of individuals of the same type as x is not an inductive number, then there is a progression whose terms are of the type of $t^2`x$. This progression will be that of the inductive cardinals which are applicable to classes whose terms are of the same type as x.

***263·14.** $\vdash : R \epsilon \text{Prog} . P = R_{po} . \supset . P = P_{fn} = R_{fn} . R = P_1$

Dem.

$\vdash . *121·254 . \supset \vdash : \text{Hp} . \supset . P_1 = R_1 .$

$[*121·31.*122·1·16] \qquad \supset . P_1 = R .$ (1)

$[\text{Hp}] \qquad \supset . (P_1)_{po} = P .$

$[*260·27.*263·11] \qquad \supset . P_{fn} = P .$ (2)

$[*260·15.\text{Hp}] \qquad \supset . R_{fn} = P$ (3)

$\vdash . (1) . (2) . (3) . \supset \vdash . \text{Prop}$

***263·141.** $\vdash : P \epsilon \omega . \supset . P_1 \epsilon \text{Prog} . P = (P_1)_{\text{fn}} = (P_1)_{\text{po}}$

Dem.

$\vdash . *263·1 . \supset \vdash : \text{Hp} . \supset . (\exists R) . R \epsilon \text{Prog} . P = R_{\text{po}} .$

$[*263·14] \quad \supset . (\exists R) . R \epsilon \text{Prog} . P_1 = R . P = R_{\text{fn}} . P = R_{\text{po}} .$

$[*13·195] \quad \supset . P_1 \epsilon \text{Prog} . P = (P_1)_{\text{fn}} = (P_1)_{\text{po}} : \supset \vdash . \text{Prop}$

The above proposition shows that every interval $P(x \mapsto y)$ in a progression is an inductive class.

***263·142.** $\vdash : R, S \epsilon \text{Prog} . R_{\text{po}} = S_{\text{po}} . \supset . R = S$

Dem.

$\vdash . *263·14 . \supset \vdash : \text{Hp} . \supset . R = (S_{\text{po}})_1$

$[*263·14] \quad = S : \supset \vdash . \text{Prop}$

***263·143.** $\vdash : P, Q \epsilon \omega . P_1 = Q_1 . \supset . P = Q$

Dem.

$\vdash . *263·1 . \supset \vdash : \text{Hp} . \supset . (\exists R, S) . R, S \epsilon \text{Prog} . P = R_{\text{po}} . Q = S_{\text{po}} . P_1 = Q_1 .$

$[*263·14] \supset . (\exists R, S) . R, S \epsilon \text{Prog} . P = R_{\text{po}} . Q = S_{\text{po}} . R = P_1 . S = Q_1 . P_1 = Q_1 .$

$[*13·17] \quad \supset . (\exists R, S) . R, S \epsilon \text{Prog} . P = R_{\text{po}} . Q = S_{\text{po}} . R = S .$

$[*13·17] \quad \supset . P = Q : \supset \vdash . \text{Prop}$

***263·15.** $\vdash : R \epsilon \text{Prog} . S = \hat{x} \hat{\nu} \{\nu \epsilon \text{NC induct} . x = (\nu +_c 1)_R\} . \supset . S \epsilon R \,\overline{\text{smor}}\, N$

Dem.

$\vdash . *123·3 . \supset \vdash : \text{Hp} . \supset . S \epsilon 1 \to 1 . \text{D}‘S = \text{D}‘R . \text{C}‘S = \text{NC induct} \quad (1)$

$\vdash . *123·21 . \supset \vdash . \text{NC induct} = C‘N \quad (2)$

$\vdash . *110·56·643 . \supset \vdash : \text{Hp} . (\mu +_c 1) N (\nu +_c 1) . \supset . \nu +_c 1 = \mu +_c 2 \quad (3)$

$\vdash . (3) . \supset \vdash :. \text{Hp} . \supset :$

$x (S ; N) y . \equiv . (\exists \mu) . \mu \epsilon \text{NC induct} . x = (\mu +_c 1)_R . y = (\mu +_c 2)_R .$

$[*121·332·131] \quad \equiv . (\exists \mu) . \mu \epsilon \text{NC induct} . (B‘R) R_\mu x . (B‘R) (R_\mu | R) y .$

$[*122·341 . *121·342] \quad \equiv . xRy \quad (4)$

$\vdash . (1) . (2) . (4) . \supset \vdash . \text{Prop}$

***263·151.** $\vdash : R \epsilon \text{Prog} . \supset . R \text{ smor } N$ [*263·15]

***263·152.** $\vdash : R \epsilon \text{Prog} . Q \text{ smor } R . \supset . Q \epsilon \text{Prog}$ [*123·32]

***263·16.** $\vdash : R \epsilon \text{Prog} . \supset . \text{Prog} = \text{Nr}‘R = \text{Nr}‘N$ [*263·151·152]

***263·161.** $\vdash : \exists ! \text{Prog} . \supset . \text{Prog} = \text{Nr}‘N$ [*263·16]

***263·162.** $\vdash . \text{Prog} \epsilon \text{NR}$ [*263·161 . *154·242]

***263·17.** $\vdash : P \epsilon \omega . \supset . \omega = \text{Nr}`P = \text{Nr}`N_{po}$

Dem.

$\vdash . *263\cdot1 . \supset \vdash : \text{Hp} . \supset . (\exists R) . R \epsilon \text{Prog} . P = R_{po} .$

[*263·151] $\supset . (\exists R) . R \text{ smor } N . P = R_{po} .$

[*151·56] $\supset . P \text{ smor } N_{po} .$ (1)

[*152·321] $\supset . \text{Nr}`P = \text{Nr}`N_{po}$ (2)

$\vdash . *151\cdot59 . \supset \vdash : P \epsilon \omega . Q \text{ smor } P . \supset . Q_1 \text{ smor } P_1 .$

[*263·141·152] $\supset . Q_1 \epsilon \text{Prog}$ (3)

$\vdash . *150\cdot83 . \supset \vdash : P \epsilon \omega . S \epsilon Q \,\overline{\text{smor}}\, P . \supset . (Q_1)_{po} = S ; (P_1)_{po}$

[*263·141] $= S ; P$

[*151·11] $= Q$ (4)

$\vdash . (3) . (4) . *263\cdot1 . \supset \vdash : P \epsilon \omega . Q \text{ smor } P . \supset . Q \epsilon \omega$ (5)

$\vdash . (1) . \supset \vdash : P, Q \epsilon \omega . \supset . P \text{ smor } Q$ (6)

$\vdash . (5) . (6) . \supset \vdash : P \epsilon \omega . \supset . \omega = \text{Nr}`P$ (7)

$\vdash . (7) . (2) . \supset \vdash . \text{Prop}$

***263·18.** $\vdash : \exists ! \omega . \supset . \omega = \text{Nr}`N_{po}$ [*263·17]

***263·19.** $\vdash . \omega \epsilon \text{NR}$ [*263·18 . *154·242]

***263·2.** $\vdash . \omega \epsilon \text{NO}$ [*263·19·11 . *256·54]

***263·22.** $\vdash : P \epsilon \omega . \supset . \text{Ɑ}`P \subset \text{D}`P . \sim \text{E} ! B`\breve{P} . \text{E} ! B`P$
[*122·141 . *263·1 . *122·11]

***263·23.** $\vdash . \omega \subset \Omega \text{ infin}$

Dem.

$\vdash . *261\cdot35 . \text{Transp} . *263\cdot11\cdot22 . \supset \vdash : P \epsilon \omega . \supset . C`P \sim \epsilon \text{ Cls induct} - \iota`\Lambda$ (1)

$\vdash . *263\cdot22 . \supset \vdash : P \epsilon \omega . \supset . \exists ! C`P$ (2)

$\vdash . (1) . (2) . \supset \vdash : P \epsilon \omega . \supset . C`P \sim \epsilon \text{ Cls induct} .$

[*261·14·41.*263·11] $\supset . P \epsilon \Omega \text{ infin} : \supset \vdash . \text{Prop}$

***263·24.** $\vdash : \exists ! \omega . \supset . \omega \epsilon \text{NO infin}$ [*262·14 . *263·17·23]

***263·26.** $\vdash : P \epsilon \omega . \exists ! \alpha \cap C`P . \sim \text{E} ! \max_P`\alpha . \supset . P \upharpoonright \alpha \epsilon \omega$

Dem.

$\vdash . *263\cdot1 . *205\cdot123 . \supset$

$\vdash : \text{Hp} . \supset . (\exists R) . R \epsilon \text{Prog} . P = R_{po} . \exists ! \alpha \cap C`R . \alpha \cap C`R \subset R_{po}``\alpha .$

[*122·442·45] $\supset . (\exists R) . R \epsilon \text{Prog} . P = R_{po} . P \upharpoonright \alpha \dot{-} (P \upharpoonright \alpha)^2 \epsilon \text{Prog} .$

$P \upharpoonright \alpha = \{P \upharpoonright \alpha \dot{-} (P \upharpoonright \alpha)^2\}_{po} .$

[*263·1] $\supset . P \upharpoonright \alpha \epsilon \omega : \supset \vdash . \text{Prop}$

***263·27.** $\vdash : P \epsilon \omega . \text{E} ! \max_P`\alpha . \supset . P \upharpoonright \alpha \epsilon \Omega \text{ fin}$

Dem.

$\vdash . *122\cdot43 . *263\cdot1 . \supset \vdash : \text{Hp} . \supset . \alpha \cap C`P \epsilon \text{ Cls induct} .$

[*37·41.*120·481] $\supset . C`(P \upharpoonright \alpha) \epsilon \text{ Cls induct}$ (1)

$\vdash . *263\cdot11 . *250\cdot141 . \supset \vdash : \text{Hp} . \supset . P \upharpoonright \alpha \epsilon \Omega$ (2)

$\vdash . (1) . (2) . *261\cdot14\cdot42 . \supset \vdash . \text{Prop}$

***263·28.** $\vdash : P \epsilon \omega . \supset . \text{Ser} \cap \text{Rl}`P \subset \omega \cup \Omega \text{ fin}$ [*204·421 . *263·26·27]

***263·29.** $\vdash : P \epsilon \omega . Q \epsilon \Omega \text{ fin} . \supset . Q \text{ less } P$ [*261·65 . *263·23]

***263·3.** $\vdash : P \epsilon \omega . \supset . \overrightarrow{\text{less}}`P = \Omega \text{ fin}$

Dem.

$\vdash . *254{\cdot}1 . *263{\cdot}17 . \supset$

$\vdash : P \epsilon \omega . Q \text{ less } P . \supset . \exists ! \text{Nr}`Q \cap \text{Rl}`P . Q \sim \epsilon \omega . Q \epsilon \Omega .$

[*263·17] $\supset . (\exists R) . R \epsilon \text{Nr}`Q \cap \text{Rl}`P . R \sim \epsilon \omega .$

[*263·28] $\supset . (\exists R) . R \epsilon \text{Nr}`Q \cap \Omega \text{ fin} .$

[*261·183] $\supset . Q \epsilon \Omega \text{ fin}$ (1)

$\vdash . (1) . *263{\cdot}29 . \supset \vdash . \text{Prop}$

***263·31.** $\vdash :. \exists ! \omega . \supset : \alpha \lessdot \omega . \equiv . \alpha \epsilon \text{NO fin}$

Dem.

$\vdash . *255{\cdot}17 . *263{\cdot}17 . \supset \vdash :. P \epsilon \omega . \supset : \text{Nr}`Q \lessdot \omega . \equiv . Q \text{ less } P .$

[*263·3] $\equiv . Q \epsilon \Omega \text{ fin} .$

[*262·13] $\equiv . \text{Nr}`Q \epsilon \text{NO fin} :$

[*152·4] $\supset : \alpha \epsilon \text{NR} . \alpha \lessdot \omega . \equiv . \alpha \epsilon \text{NR} . \alpha \epsilon \text{NO fin} :$

[*255·12.*262·1.*152·4] $\supset : \alpha \lessdot \omega . \equiv . \alpha \epsilon \text{NO fin} :. \supset \vdash . \text{Prop}$

***263·32.** $\vdash :. \text{Infin ax} . \supset : \alpha \lessdot \omega . \equiv . \alpha \epsilon \text{NO fin}$ [*263·31·12]

***263·33.** $\vdash : \alpha \lessdot \omega . \supset . \alpha \epsilon \text{NO fin}$

Dem.

$\vdash . *255{\cdot}1 . *155{\cdot}13 . \supset \vdash : \text{Hp} . \supset . \exists ! \omega$ (1)

$\vdash . (1) . *263{\cdot}31 . \supset \vdash . \text{Prop}$

***263·34.** $\vdash . \dot{1} \dotplus \omega = \omega$

Dem.

$\vdash . *262{\cdot}112 . *263{\cdot}24 . \supset \vdash : \text{Hp} . \exists ! \omega . \supset . \dot{1} \dotplus \omega = \omega$ (1)

$\vdash . *181{\cdot}4 . \supset \vdash : \omega = \Lambda . \supset . \dot{1} \dotplus \omega = \Lambda$ (2)

$\vdash . (1) . (2) . \supset \vdash . \text{Prop}$

***263·35.** $\vdash : \alpha \epsilon \text{NO fin} . \supset . \alpha \dotplus \omega = \omega$

Dem.

$\vdash . *180{\cdot}61 . *263{\cdot}18 . \supset \vdash : \exists ! \omega . \supset . 0_r \dotplus \omega = \omega$ (1)

$\vdash . *180{\cdot}4 . \supset \vdash : \omega = \Lambda . \supset . 0_r \dotplus \omega = \Lambda$ (2)

$\vdash . (1) . (2) . \supset \vdash . 0_r \dotplus \omega = \omega$ (3)

$\vdash . *181{\cdot}57 . *263{\cdot}34 . \supset \vdash . 2_r \dotplus \omega = \dot{1} \dotplus \omega$

[*263·34] $= \omega$ (4)

$\vdash . *262{\cdot}36 . \supset \vdash : \mu \epsilon \text{NC induct} - \iota`0 - \iota`1 . \supset . (\mu +_c 1)_r \dotplus \omega = \mu_r \dotplus \dot{1} \dotplus \omega$

[*263·34.*181·58] $= \mu_r \dotplus \omega$ (5)

$\vdash . (5) . \supset \vdash : \mu \epsilon \text{NC induct} - \iota`0 - \iota`1 . \mu_r \dotplus \omega = \omega . \supset . (\mu +_c 1)_r \dotplus \omega = \omega$ (6)

$\vdash . (4) . (6) . \text{Induct} . \supset \vdash : \mu \epsilon \text{NC induct} - \iota`0 - \iota`1 . \supset . \mu_r \dotplus \omega = \omega$ (7)

$\vdash . (3) . (7) . \supset \vdash : \mu \epsilon \text{NC induct} - \iota`1 . \supset . \mu_r \dotplus \omega = \omega :$

[*262·26] $\supset \vdash : \alpha \epsilon \text{NO fin} . \supset . \alpha \dotplus \omega = \omega : \supset \vdash . \text{Prop}$

***263·4.** $\vdash : P \epsilon \omega . \supset . \text{D}‘P_s \subset \Omega\,\text{fin} . \text{Nr}“\text{D}‘P_s = \text{NO fin}$

Dem.

$\vdash . *254·182 . \supset \vdash : \text{Hp} . \supset . \text{D}‘P_s \subset \overrightarrow{\text{less}}‘P .$

$[*263·3] \qquad \supset . \text{D}‘P_s \subset \Omega\,\text{fin} \qquad (1)$

$\vdash . *263·31 . \supset \vdash :. \text{Hp} . \supset : \alpha \lessdot \text{Nr}‘P . \equiv . \alpha \epsilon \text{NO fin} :$

$[*256·11] \qquad \supset : \alpha \epsilon \text{Nr}“\text{D}‘P_s . \equiv . \alpha \epsilon \text{NO fin} \qquad (2)$

$\vdash . (1) . (2) . \supset \vdash . \text{Prop}$

***263·401.** $\vdash : P \epsilon \omega . \alpha \epsilon \text{sect}‘P - \iota‘\Lambda - \iota‘C‘P . \supset . \text{E} ! \max_P‘\alpha$

Dem.

$\vdash . *250·65 . \supset \vdash : \text{Hp} . \supset . P \upharpoonright \alpha \sim \epsilon \text{Nr}‘P .$

$[*263·17] \qquad \supset . P \upharpoonright \alpha \sim \epsilon \omega .$

$[*263·26.\text{Transp}] \qquad \supset . \text{E} ! \max_P‘\alpha : \supset \vdash . \text{Prop}$

***263·402.** $\vdash : P \epsilon \omega . \supset . \text{sect}‘P - \iota‘\Lambda - \iota‘C‘P = \overrightarrow{P_*}“C‘P$

Dem.

$\vdash . *205·131·22 . *263·401 . \supset$

$\vdash : \text{Hp} . \alpha \epsilon \text{sect}‘P - \iota‘\Lambda - \iota‘C‘P . \supset . \alpha \cup P“\alpha = \overrightarrow{P}‘\max_P‘\alpha \cup \iota‘\max_P‘\alpha .$

$[*211·1.*91·54] \qquad \supset . \alpha = \overrightarrow{P_*}‘\max_P‘\alpha .$

$[*205·111] \qquad \supset . \alpha \epsilon \overrightarrow{P_*}“C‘P \qquad (1)$

$\vdash . *211·3·13 . \qquad \supset \vdash . \overrightarrow{P_*}“C‘P \subset \text{sect}‘P \qquad (2)$

$\vdash . *90·12 . \qquad \supset \vdash . \overrightarrow{P_*}“C‘P \subset - \iota‘\Lambda \qquad (3)$

$\vdash . *205·197 . \qquad \supset \vdash : \text{Hp} . x \epsilon C‘P . \supset . \text{E} ! \max_P‘\overrightarrow{P_*}‘x .$

$[*263·22] \qquad \supset . \overrightarrow{P_*}‘x \neq C‘P \qquad (4)$

$\vdash . (2) . (3) . (4) . \supset \vdash : \text{Hp} . \supset . \overrightarrow{P_*}“C‘P \subset \text{sect}‘P - \iota‘\Lambda - \iota‘C‘P \qquad (5)$

$\vdash . (1) . (5) . \supset \vdash . \text{Prop}$

***263·41.** $\vdash : P \epsilon \omega . \supset . P_s \upharpoonright \text{D}‘P_s = P \upharpoonright ; \overrightarrow{P_*} ; P$

Dem.

$\vdash . *213·11·141·151 . \supset$

$\vdash :. \text{Hp} . \supset : Q (P_s \upharpoonright \text{D}‘P_s) R . \equiv . (\exists \alpha, \beta) . \alpha, \beta \epsilon \text{sect}‘P - \iota‘\Lambda - \iota‘C‘P . \alpha \subset \beta . \alpha \neq \beta .$

$Q = P \upharpoonright \alpha . R = P \upharpoonright \beta .$

$[*263·402]$

$\equiv . (\exists x, y) . x, y \epsilon C‘P . \overrightarrow{P_*}‘x \subset \overrightarrow{P_*}‘y . \overrightarrow{P_*}‘x \neq \overrightarrow{P_*}‘y . Q = P \upharpoonright \overrightarrow{P_*}‘x . R = P \upharpoonright \overrightarrow{P_*}‘y .$

$[*200·391]$

$\equiv . (\exists x, y) . x, y \epsilon C‘P . \overrightarrow{P_*}‘x \subset \overrightarrow{P_*}‘y . x \neq v . Q = P \upharpoonright \overrightarrow{P_*}‘x . R = P \upharpoonright \overrightarrow{P_*}‘y .$

$[*204·32.*90·12]$

$\equiv . (\exists x, y) . x P_* y . x \neq y . \overrightarrow{P_*}‘x \subset \overrightarrow{P_*}‘y . Q = P \upharpoonright \overrightarrow{P_*}‘x . R = P \upharpoonright \overrightarrow{P_*}‘y .$

$[*201{\cdot}14{\cdot}15] \equiv . (\exists x, y) . x P_* y . x \neq y . Q = P \upharpoonright \overrightarrow{P_*}`x . R = P \upharpoonright \overrightarrow{P_*}`y .$

$[*201{\cdot}18] \quad \equiv . (\exists x, y) . x P y . Q = P \upharpoonright \overrightarrow{P_*}`x . R = P \upharpoonright \overrightarrow{P_*}`y .$

$[*150{\cdot}1] \quad \equiv . Q (P \upharpoonright ; \overrightarrow{P_*} ; P) R :. \supset \vdash . \text{Prop}$

***263·411.** $\vdash : P \epsilon \omega . \supset . C``\text{D}`P_s = \overrightarrow{P_*}``\text{Ɑ}`P \cup \iota`\Lambda$

Dem.

$\vdash . *213{\cdot}141 . *263{\cdot}402 . \supset$

$\vdash : \text{Hp} . \supset . C``\text{D}`P_s = C``P \upharpoonright``\overrightarrow{P_*}``C`P$

$[*93{\cdot}103] \quad = C``P \upharpoonright``\overrightarrow{P_*}``\text{Ɑ}`P \cup \iota`C`P \upharpoonright \overrightarrow{P_*}`B`P$

$[*201{\cdot}521 . *202{\cdot}55] = \overrightarrow{P_*}``\text{Ɑ}`P \cup \iota`C`P \upharpoonright \overrightarrow{P_*}`B`P$

$[*201{\cdot}521 . *200{\cdot}35] = \overrightarrow{P_*}``\text{Ɑ}`P \cup \iota`\Lambda : \supset \vdash . \text{Prop}$

***263·412.** $\vdash : P \epsilon \omega . \supset . \overrightarrow{P}`x, \overrightarrow{P_*}`x \epsilon \text{Cls induct}$

Dem.

$\vdash . *205{\cdot}197 . \supset \vdash : \text{Hp} . x \epsilon C`P . \supset . \text{E} ! \max_P`\overrightarrow{P_*}`x .$

$[*263{\cdot}27 . *202{\cdot}55 . *120{\cdot}213] \quad \supset . \overrightarrow{P_*}`x \epsilon \text{Cls induct} . \quad (1)$

$[*120{\cdot}481] \quad \supset . \overrightarrow{P}`x \epsilon \text{Cls induct} \quad (2)$

$\vdash . (1) . (2) . \supset \vdash . \text{Prop}$

***263·42.** $\vdash : P \epsilon \omega . \supset . \text{sgm}`P = \Lambda \downarrow (C`P)$

Dem.

$\vdash . *212{\cdot}21 . *211{\cdot}12 . \supset$

$\vdash :. \text{Hp} . \supset : \alpha (\text{sgm}`P) \beta . \equiv . \alpha = P``\alpha . \beta = P``\beta . \alpha \subset \beta . \alpha \neq \beta \quad (1)$

$\vdash . (1) . *211{\cdot}1 . *205{\cdot}123 . \supset$

$\vdash : \text{Hp} . \alpha (\text{sgm}`P) \beta . \supset . \alpha, \beta \epsilon \text{sect}`P . \sim \text{E} ! \max_P`\alpha . \sim \text{E} ! \max_P`\beta .$

$[*263{\cdot}401] \quad \supset . \alpha, \beta \epsilon \iota`\Lambda \cup \iota`C`P \quad (2)$

$\vdash . (1) . (2) . \supset \vdash : \text{Hp} . \alpha (\text{sgm}`P) \beta . \supset . \alpha = \Lambda . \beta = C`P \quad (3)$

$\vdash . *37{\cdot}29 . \supset \vdash : \alpha = \Lambda . \supset . \alpha = P``\alpha \quad (4)$

$\vdash . *263{\cdot}22 . \supset \vdash : \text{Hp} . \beta = C`P . \supset . \beta = P``\beta \quad (5)$

$\vdash . (1) . (4) . (5) . \supset \vdash : \text{Hp} . \alpha = \Lambda . \beta = C`P . \supset . \alpha (\text{sgm}`P) \beta \quad (6)$

$\vdash . (3) . (6) . \supset \vdash . \text{Prop}$

***263·43.** $\vdash : P \epsilon \omega . \supset . \text{Ɑ}`P_1 = \text{Ɑ}`P$

Dem.

$\vdash . *263{\cdot}141 . \supset \vdash : \text{Hp} . \supset . \text{Ɑ}`P = \text{Ɑ}`(P_1)_{po}$

$[*91{\cdot}504] \quad = \text{Ɑ}`P_1 : \supset \vdash . \text{Prop}$

***263·431.** $\vdash : P \in \Omega - \iota`\dot{\Lambda} . \text{Ɑ}`P_1 = \text{Ɑ}`P . \sim E ! B`\breve{P} . \supset . P \in \omega$

Dem.

$\vdash . *261·35 . \text{Transp} . \supset \vdash : \text{Hp} . \supset . P \in \Omega \text{ infin} .$

$[*261·44] \quad \supset . P_1 \upharpoonright \overleftarrow{P}_{\text{fn}}`B`P \in \text{Prog} .$

$[*261·212] \quad \supset . P_1 \upharpoonright \overleftarrow{P}`B`P \in \text{Prog} .$

$[*202·524] \quad \supset . P_1 \in \text{Prog} \quad (1)$

$\vdash . *261·212 . \quad \supset \vdash : \text{Hp} . \supset . P = (P_1)_{\text{po}} \quad (2)$

$\vdash . (1) . (2) . *263·1 . \supset \vdash . \text{Prop}$

***263·44.** $\vdash . \omega = \Omega - \iota`\dot{\Lambda} \cap \hat{P}(\text{Ɑ}`P_1 = \text{Ɑ}`P . \sim E ! B`\breve{P})$ [*263·43·22·431]

***263·45.** $\vdash . \omega = \Omega - \iota`\dot{\Lambda} \cap \hat{P}(P = P_{\text{fn}} . \sim E ! B`\breve{P})$ [*261·212 . *263·44]

***263·46.** $\vdash . \omega = \Omega \cap \hat{P}(E ! B`P_1 . \sim E ! B`\breve{P})$

Dem.

$\vdash . *121·305 . *93·101 . \supset$

$\vdash : P \in \Omega . \sim E ! B`\breve{P} . \text{Ɑ}`P_1 \neq \text{Ɑ}`P . \supset . \exists ! \text{Ɑ}`P - \text{Ɑ}`P_1 . \text{Ɑ}`P = D`P - \iota`B`P .$

$[*250·21] \quad \supset . \exists ! D`P_1 - \text{Ɑ}`P_1 - \iota`B`P .$

$[*93·101] \quad \supset . \exists ! \overrightarrow{B}`P_1 - \iota`B`P \quad (1)$

$\vdash . *121·305 . *250·21 . \supset \vdash : P \in \Omega - \iota`\dot{\Lambda} . \supset . B`P \in \overrightarrow{B}`P_1 \quad (2)$

$\vdash . (1) . (2) . \quad \supset \vdash : P \in \Omega . \sim E ! B`\breve{P} . \text{Ɑ}`P_1 \neq \text{Ɑ}`P . \supset . \overrightarrow{B}`P_1 \sim \in 1 .$

$[*53·3] \quad \supset . \sim E ! B`P_1 \quad (3)$

$\vdash . (3) . \text{Transp} . \supset \vdash : P \in \Omega . E ! B`P_1 . \sim E ! B`\breve{P} . \supset . \text{Ɑ}`P_1 = \text{Ɑ}`P .$

$[*263·44] \quad \supset . P \in \omega \quad (4)$

$\vdash . *250·21 . *263·44 . \supset \vdash : P \in \omega . \supset . \overrightarrow{B}`P_1 = \overrightarrow{B}`P .$

$[*250·13] \quad \supset . E ! B`P_1 \quad (5)$

$\vdash . (5) . *263·44 . \quad \supset \vdash : P \in \omega . \supset . E ! B`P_1 . \sim E ! B`\breve{P} \quad (6)$

$\vdash . (4) . (6) . \supset \vdash . \text{Prop}$

***263·47.** $\vdash . \omega = \Omega \cap \hat{P} \{\alpha \subset C`P . \supset_\alpha : \alpha \in \text{Cls induct} . \equiv . \exists ! C`P \cap p`\overleftarrow{P}``\alpha\}$

Dem.

$\vdash . *254·52 . \supset \vdash : P \in \omega . \alpha \subset C`P . \exists ! C`P \cap p`\overleftarrow{P}``\alpha . \supset . (P \upharpoonleft \alpha) \text{ less } P .$

$[*263·3] \quad \supset . P \upharpoonleft \alpha \in \Omega \text{ fin} .$

$[*261·42·14] \quad \supset . C`(P \upharpoonleft \alpha) \in \text{Cls induct} .$

$[*202·55 . *120·213] \quad \supset . \alpha \in \text{Cls induct} \quad (1)$

$\vdash . *261·26 . \supset \vdash : P \in \omega . \alpha \subset C`P . \alpha \in \text{Cls induct} . \exists ! \alpha . \supset . E ! \max_P`\alpha .$

$[*263·22] \quad \supset . \exists ! \overleftarrow{P}`\max_P`\alpha .$

$[*205·65 . *40·69] \quad \supset . \exists ! C`P \cap p`\overleftarrow{P}``\alpha \quad (2)$

$\vdash . (1) . (2) . *40\cdot2 . \supset$

$\vdash :. P \epsilon \omega . \alpha \subset C'P . \supset : \alpha \epsilon \text{Cls induct} . \equiv . \exists ! C'P \cap p'\overleftarrow{P}``\alpha$ (3)

$\vdash . *40\cdot2 . *120\cdot212 . \supset$

$\vdash :: P \epsilon \Omega :. \alpha \subset C'P . \supset_\alpha : \alpha \epsilon \text{Cls induct} . \equiv . \exists ! C'P \cap p'\overleftarrow{P}``\alpha :. \supset . \dot{\exists} ! P$ (4)

$\vdash . (4) . *200\cdot51 . \supset \vdash : \text{Hp} (4) . \supset . C'P \sim \epsilon \text{Cls induct}$ (5)

$\vdash . *250\cdot16 . \supset$

$\vdash : \text{Hp} (4) . \exists ! \text{G}'P - \text{G}'P_1 . \supset . \overrightarrow{P}'\min_P{}'(\text{G}'P - \text{G}'P_1) \epsilon \text{Cls induct} .$

[$*261\cdot26$] $\supset . E ! \max_P{}'\overrightarrow{P}'\min_P{}'(\text{G}'P - \text{G}'P_1) .$

[$*205\cdot252$] $\supset . \min_P{}'(\text{G}'P - \text{G}'P_1) \epsilon \text{G}'P_1$ (6)

$\vdash . (6) . \text{Transp} . \quad \supset \vdash : \text{Hp} (4) . \supset . \text{G}'P_1 = \text{G}'P$ (7)

$\vdash . (5) . (7) . *261\cdot34 . \supset \vdash : \text{Hp} (4) . \supset . \sim E ! B'\breve{P}$ (8)

$\vdash . (4) . (7) . (8) . \quad \supset \vdash : \text{Hp} (4) . \supset . P \epsilon \omega$ (9)

$\vdash . (3) . (9) . \supset \vdash . \text{Prop}$

$*263\cdot48$. $\vdash . \omega = \Omega \cap \hat{P} \{\alpha \subset C'P . \supset_\alpha : \alpha \sim \epsilon \text{Cls refl} . \equiv . \exists ! C'P \cap p'\overleftarrow{P}``\alpha\}$
[$*263\cdot47 . *261\cdot47$]

$*263\cdot49$. $\vdash . \Omega \text{ fin} \cup \omega = \Omega \cap \hat{P} (\text{G}'P_1 = \text{G}'P) = \Omega \cap \hat{P} (P = P_{\text{fn}})$

Dem.

$\vdash . *261\cdot22 . *263\cdot44 . \supset \vdash : P \epsilon \Omega \text{ fin} \cup \omega . \supset . \text{G}'P_1 = \text{G}'P$ (1)

$\vdash . *261\cdot34 . *263\cdot44 . \supset \vdash : P \epsilon \Omega . \text{G}'P_1 = \text{G}'P . \supset . P \epsilon \Omega \text{ fin} \cup \omega$ (2)

$\vdash . (1) . (2) . \quad \supset \vdash . \Omega \text{ fin} \cup \omega = \Omega \cap \hat{P} (\text{G}'P_1 = \text{G}'P)$

[$*261\cdot212$] $= \Omega \cap \hat{P} (P = P_{\text{fn}}) . \supset \vdash . \text{Prop}$

$*263\cdot491$. $\vdash : P \epsilon \Omega \text{ fin} \cup \omega . \supset . P = (P_1)_{\text{po}} . P_\sigma = (P_1)_\sigma$

Dem.

$\vdash . *263\cdot49 . *261\cdot212 . \supset \vdash : \text{Hp} . \supset . P = (P_1)_{\text{po}} .$ (1)

[$*91\cdot602 . *121\cdot103$] $\supset . P (x \mapsto y) = P_1 (x \mapsto y) .$

[$*121\cdot11$] $\supset . P_\sigma = (P_1)_\sigma$ (2)

$\vdash . (1) . (2) . \supset \vdash . \text{Prop}$

$*263\cdot5$. $\vdash : P \epsilon \Omega \text{ infin} . \supset . P \upharpoonright (\iota'B'P \cup \overleftarrow{P}_{\text{fn}}{}'B'P) \epsilon \omega$

Dem.

$\vdash . *261\cdot45 . \quad \supset \vdash : \text{Hp} . \supset . P_1 \upharpoonright \overleftarrow{P}_{\text{fn}}{}'B'P \epsilon \text{Prog}$ (1)

$\vdash . *260\cdot33\cdot27 . \supset \vdash : \text{Hp} . \supset . (P_1 \upharpoonright \overleftarrow{P}_{\text{fn}}{}'B'P)_{\text{po}} = P_{\text{fn}} \upharpoonright (\iota'B'P \cup \overleftarrow{P}_{\text{fn}}{}'B'P)$

[$*260\cdot32$] $= P \upharpoonright (\iota'B'P \cup \overleftarrow{P}_{\text{fn}}{}'B'P)$ (2)

$\vdash . (1) . (2) . *263\cdot1 . \supset \vdash . \text{Prop}$

***263·51.** $\vdash : P \in \Omega \text{ infin} . \supset .$

$$\iota'B'P \cup \overleftarrow{P}_{\text{fn}}'B'P \in \text{D}'(P_\epsilon \dot{\cap} I) . \iota'B'P \cup \overleftarrow{P}_{\text{fn}}'B'P \in \text{C}'\text{sgm}'P$$

Dem.

$\vdash . *263{\cdot}5{\cdot}22 . \supset \vdash : \text{Hp} . \supset . \sim \text{E} ! \max_P'(\iota'B'P \cup \overleftarrow{P}_{\text{fn}}'B'P)$ (1)

$\vdash . *260{\cdot}11 . \supset \vdash : \text{Hp} . y \in \text{C}'P - \overleftarrow{P}_{\text{fn}}'B'P . x \in \overleftarrow{P}_{\text{fn}}'B'P . \supset .$

$P(B'P \mapsto y) \sim \in \text{Cls induct} . P(B'P \mapsto x) \in \text{Cls induct} .$

[*120·49] $\supset . \text{Nc}'P(B'P \mapsto y) > \text{Nc}'P(B'P \mapsto x) .$

[*117·222.Transp] $\supset . \sim (yPx)$ (2)

$\vdash . (2) . \text{Transp} . \supset \vdash : \text{Hp} . \supset . P``\overleftarrow{P}_{\text{fn}}'B'P \subset \overrightarrow{B'P} \cup \overleftarrow{P}_{\text{fn}}'B'P$ (3)

$\vdash . (3) . *93{\cdot}101 . \supset \vdash : \text{Hp} . \supset . P``(\iota'B'P \subset \overleftarrow{P}_{\text{fn}}'B'P) \subset \iota'B'P \cup \overleftarrow{P}_{\text{fn}}'B'P$ (4)

$\vdash . (1) . (4) . *211{\cdot}41 . \supset \vdash : \text{Hp} . \supset . \iota'B'P \cup \overleftarrow{P}_{\text{fn}}'B'P \in \text{D}'(P_\epsilon \dot{\cap} I) .$ (5)

[*212·152] $\supset . \iota'B'P \cup \overleftarrow{P}_{\text{fn}}'B'P \in \text{C}'\text{sgm}'P$ (6)

$\vdash . (5) . (6) . \supset \vdash . \text{Prop}$

***263·52.** $\vdash : P \in \Omega \text{ infin} - \omega . \supset . (\exists x) . x \in \text{C}'P . \overleftarrow{P}_{\text{fn}}'B'P \cup \iota'B'P = \overrightarrow{P}'x$

Dem.

$\vdash . *263{\cdot}49 . \text{Transp} . \supset \vdash : \text{Hp} . \supset . \exists ! \text{C}'P - \text{C}'P_1 .$

[*260·27] $\supset . \exists ! \text{C}'P - \overleftarrow{P}_{\text{fn}}'B'P .$

[*250·121] $\supset . \text{E} ! \min_P'(\text{C}'P - \overleftarrow{P}_{\text{fn}}'B'P) .$

[*263·51.*206·25.*211·726] $\supset . (\exists x) . x \in \text{C}'P . \overleftarrow{P}_{\text{fn}}'B'P \cup \iota'B'P = \overrightarrow{P}'x :$

$\supset \vdash . \text{Prop}$

***263·53.** $\vdash : P \in \Omega \text{ infin} - \omega . \supset . \text{Nr}'P \mathrel{\geqslant} \omega$

Dem.

$\vdash . *253{\cdot}13 . *263{\cdot}52 . \supset \vdash : \text{Hp} . \supset . P \upharpoonright (\overleftarrow{P}_{\text{fn}}'B'P \cup \iota'B'P) \in \text{D}'P_s .$

[*263·5] $\supset . \exists ! \omega \cap \text{D}'P_s .$

[*255·17.*263·18] $\supset . \text{Nr}'P \mathrel{\geqslant} \omega : \supset \vdash . \text{Prop}$

The above proposition shows that ω is the smallest of infinite ordinals. The same fact is otherwise expressed by the following proposition.

***263·54.** $\vdash : \alpha \in \text{NO infin} - \iota'\omega . \supset . \alpha \mathrel{\geqslant} \omega$ [*263·53]

***263·55.** $\vdash : P \in \omega . \supset . P_s \in \omega \dot{+} \dot{1} . \varsigma'P \in \omega \dot{+} \dot{1}$

Dem.

$\vdash . *253{\cdot}511 . *263{\cdot}44 . \supset \vdash : \text{Hp} . \supset . P_s \in \omega \dot{+} \dot{1}$ (1)

$\vdash . *252{\cdot}372 . *263{\cdot}44 . \supset \vdash : \text{Hp} . \supset . \varsigma'P \in \omega \dot{+} \dot{1}$ (2)

$\vdash . (1) . (2) . \supset \vdash . \text{Prop}$

The following propositions are lemmas for proving $\omega \dot{\times} 2_r = \omega$ (*263·63).

***263·6.** $\vdash :: P \in \text{Ser} \,.\, x \neq y \,.\, M = P \times (x \downarrow y) \,.\supset :.\, RM_1S \,.\, \equiv :$

$(\exists u) \,.\, u \in C\text{‘}P \,.\, R = x \downarrow u \,.\, S = y \downarrow u \,.\vee .\, (\exists u, v) \,.\, uP_1v \,.\, R = y \downarrow u \,.\, S = x \downarrow v$

Dem.

$\vdash .\, *166\cdot111 \,.\supset \vdash :.\, \text{Hp} \,.\, uPv \,.\, R = x \downarrow u : S = x \downarrow v \,.\vee .\, S = y \downarrow v : \supset .$

$RM(y \downarrow u) \,.\, (y \downarrow u) MS \,.$

$[*201\cdot63 \,.\, *204\cdot55] \qquad \supset .\, \sim(RM_1S)$ (1)

Similarly $\quad \vdash :.\, \text{Hp} \,.\, uPv \,.\, R = y \downarrow u \,.\, S = y \downarrow v \,.\supset .\, \sim(RM_1S)$ (2)

$\vdash .\, *166\cdot111 \,.\supset$

$\vdash : \text{Hp} \,.\, uPw \,.\, wPv \,.\, R = y \downarrow u \,.\, S = x \downarrow v \,.\supset .\, RM(x \downarrow w) \,.\, (x \downarrow w) MS \,.$

$[*201\cdot63 \,.\, *204\cdot55] \qquad \supset .\, \sim(RM_1S)$ (3)

$\vdash .\, (1) \,.\, (2) \,.\, (3) \,.\, \text{Transp} \,.\, *166\cdot111 \,.\supset$

$\vdash :.\, \text{Hp} \,.\, RM_1S \,.\supset : (\exists u) \,.\, R = x \downarrow u \,.\, S = y \downarrow u \,.\, u \in C\text{‘}P \,.\vee .$

$(\exists u, v) \,.\, uP_1v \,.\, R = y \downarrow u \,.\, S = x \downarrow v$ (4)

$\vdash .\, *166\cdot111 \,.\supset \vdash : \text{Hp} \,.\, R = x \downarrow u \,.\, S = y \downarrow u \,.\, RM(x \downarrow v) \,.\supset .\, SM(x \downarrow v)$ (5)

$\vdash .\, *166\cdot111 \,.\supset \vdash :.\, \text{Hp} \,.\, R = x \downarrow u \,.\, S = y \downarrow u \,.\, RM(y \downarrow v) \,.\supset : u = v \,.\vee .\, uPv :$

$[*166\cdot111] \qquad \supset : y \downarrow v = S \,.\vee .\, SM(y \downarrow v)$ (6)

$\vdash .\, *166\cdot111 \,.\supset$

$\vdash : \text{Hp} \,.\, R = y \downarrow u \,.\, S = x \downarrow v \,.\, uP_1v \,.\, RM(y \downarrow w) \,.\supset .\, SM(y \downarrow w)$ (7)

$\vdash .\, *166\cdot111 \,.\supset \vdash :.\, \text{Hp} \,.\, R = y \downarrow u \,.\, S = x \downarrow v \,.\, uP_1v \,.\, RM(x \downarrow w) \,.\supset :$

$x \downarrow w = S \,.\vee .\, SM(x \downarrow w)$ (8)

$\vdash .\, (5) \,.\, (6) \,.\, (7) \,.\, (8) \,.\supset \vdash :.\, \text{Hp} : u \in C\text{‘}P \,.\, R = x \downarrow u \,.\, S = y \downarrow u \,.\vee .$

$uP_1v \,.\, R = y \downarrow u \,.\, S = x \downarrow v : \supset .\, RM_1S$ (9)

$\vdash .\, (4) \,.\, (9) \,.\supset \vdash .\, \text{Prop}$

***263·61.** $\vdash : P \in \text{Ser} \,.\, x \neq y \,.\, M = P \times (x \downarrow y) \,.\supset .\, \text{Ɑ}\text{‘}M_1 = y \downarrow\text{“}C\text{‘}P \cup x \downarrow\text{“}\text{Ɑ}\text{‘}P_1$

$[*263\cdot6]$

***263·62.** $\vdash : P \in \omega \,.\, x \neq y \,.\supset .\, P \times (x \downarrow y) \in \omega$

Dem.

$\vdash .\, *263\cdot61\cdot43 \,.\supset \vdash : \text{Hp} \,.\supset .\, \text{Ɑ}\text{‘}\{P \times (x \downarrow y)\}_1 = y \downarrow\text{“}C\text{‘}P \cup x \downarrow\text{“}\text{Ɑ}\text{‘}P$

$[*166\cdot111] \qquad = \text{Ɑ}\text{‘}\{P \times (x \downarrow y)\}$ (1)

$\vdash .\, *251\cdot55 \,. \quad \supset \vdash : \text{Hp} \,.\supset .\, P \times (x \downarrow y) \in \Omega$ (2)

$\vdash .\, *166\cdot14 \,. \quad \supset \vdash : \text{Hp} \,.\supset .\, P \times (x \downarrow y) \in -\iota\text{‘}\Lambda$ (3)

$\vdash .\, *166\cdot16 \,.\, *263\cdot22 \,.\supset \vdash : \text{Hp} \,.\supset .\, \overrightarrow{B}\text{‘}\text{Cnv}\text{‘}\{P \times (x \downarrow y)\} = \Lambda$ (4)

$\vdash .\, (1) \,.\, (2) \,.\, (3) \,.\, (4) \,.\, *263\cdot44 \,.\supset \vdash : \text{Hp} \,.\supset .\, P \times (x \downarrow y) \in \omega : \supset \vdash .\, \text{Prop}$

***263·63.** $\vdash .\, \omega \dot{\times} 2_r = \omega$

Dem.

$\vdash .\, *263\cdot62\cdot17 \,. \qquad \supset \vdash : P \in \omega \,.\, Q \in 2_r \,.\supset .\, \text{Nr}\text{‘}(P \times Q) = \omega$ (1)

$\vdash .\, *184\cdot13 \,.\, *263\cdot17 \,.\supset \vdash : P \in \omega \,.\, Q \in 2_r \,.\supset .\, \text{Nr}\text{‘}(P \times Q) = \omega \dot{\times} 2_r$ (2)

$\vdash .\, (1) \,.\, (2) \,. \qquad \supset \vdash : \exists ! \omega \,.\, \exists ! 2_r \,.\supset .\, \omega \dot{\times} 2_r = \omega$ (3)

$\vdash .\, *184\cdot11 \,. \qquad \supset \vdash : \omega = \Lambda \,.\supset .\, \omega \dot{\times} 2_r = \Lambda$ (4)

$\vdash . *123\cdot14 . *263\cdot101 . \supset \vdash : \exists ! \omega . \supset . \exists ! 2 .$

$[*262\cdot21] \quad \supset . \exists ! 2_r \quad (5)$

$\vdash . (3) . (4) . (5) . \supset \vdash . \text{Prop}$

The following propositions are lemmas for proving $*263\cdot66$.

***263·64.** $\vdash : P, Q \in \text{Ser} . x \in C\text{‘}P . zQ_1w . M = P \times Q . \supset \because (z \downarrow x) M_1 (w \downarrow x)$

Dem.

$\vdash . *166\cdot111 . \supset \vdash : \text{Hp} . \supset . (z \downarrow x) M (w \downarrow x) \quad (1)$

$\vdash . *166\cdot111 . \supset \vdash :. \text{Hp} . (z \downarrow x) M (u \downarrow y) . \supset : xPy . \lor . x = y . zQu :$

$[*204\cdot71] \quad \supset : xPy . \lor . x = y . u = w . \lor . x = y . wQy :$

$[*166\cdot111] \quad \supset : (w \downarrow x) M (u \downarrow y) . \lor . (w \downarrow x) = (u \downarrow y) \quad (2)$

$\vdash . (2) . *204\cdot55 . \supset \vdash : \text{Hp}(2) . \supset . \sim \{(u \downarrow y) M (w \downarrow x)\} \quad (3)$

$\vdash . (1) . (3) . *201\cdot63 . \supset \vdash . \text{Prop}$

***263·641.** $\vdash : P, Q \in \text{Ser} . z = B\text{‘}\breve{Q} . w = B\text{‘}Q . xP_1y . M = P \times Q . \supset .$
$(z \downarrow x) M_1 (w \downarrow y)$

Dem.

$\vdash . *166\cdot111 . \supset \vdash : \text{Hp} . \supset . (z \downarrow x) M (w \downarrow y) \quad (1)$

$\vdash . *166\cdot111 . \supset \vdash :. \text{Hp} . (z \downarrow x) M (u \downarrow v) . \supset : xPv :$

$[*204\cdot71] \quad \supset : v = y . \lor . yPv \quad (2)$

$\vdash . (2) . *166\cdot111 . \supset$

$\vdash :. \text{Hp} . (z \downarrow x) M (u \downarrow v) . \supset : u \downarrow v = w \downarrow y . \lor . (w \downarrow y) M (u \downarrow v) :$

$[*204\cdot55] \quad \supset : \sim \{(u \downarrow v) M (w \downarrow y)\} \quad (3)$

$\vdash . (1) . (3) . *201\cdot63 . \supset \vdash . \text{Prop}$

***263·642.** $\vdash : P, Q \in \text{Ser} . M = P \times Q . \supset . (C\text{‘}P \times \text{Cl}\text{‘}Q_1) \subset \text{Cl}\text{‘}M_1 \quad [*263\cdot64]$

***263·643.** $\vdash : P, Q \in \text{Ser} . E ! B\text{‘}Q . E ! B\text{‘}\breve{Q} . M = P \times Q . \supset . (B\text{‘}Q) \downarrow\text{“}\text{Cl}\text{‘}P_1 \subset \text{Cl}\text{‘}M_1$
$[*263\cdot64]$

***263·65.** $\vdash : P \in \omega . Q \in \Omega \text{ fin} - \iota\text{‘}\Lambda . \supset . P \times Q \in \omega$

Dem.

$\vdash . *251\cdot55 . \supset \vdash : \text{Hp} . \supset . P \times Q \in \Omega \quad (1)$

$\vdash . *166\cdot14 . \supset \vdash : \text{Hp} . \supset . P \times Q \in - \iota\text{‘}\Lambda \quad (2)$

$\vdash . *263\cdot642\cdot643 . *261\cdot24 . \supset$

$\vdash : \text{Hp} . \supset . (C\text{‘}P \times \text{Cl}\text{‘}Q_1) \cup (B\text{‘}Q) \downarrow\text{“}\text{Cl}\text{‘}P_1 \subset \text{Cl}\text{‘}(P_1 \times Q)_1 .$

$[*263\cdot49] \quad \supset . (C\text{‘}P \times \text{Cl}\text{‘}Q) \cup (B\text{‘}Q) \downarrow\text{“}\text{Cl}\text{‘}P \subset \text{Cl}\text{‘}(P \times Q)_1 .$

$[*166\cdot12\cdot16] \quad \supset . C\text{‘}(P \times Q) - \overrightarrow{B}\text{‘}(P \times Q) \subset \text{Cl}\text{‘}(P \times Q)_1 .$

$[*93\cdot101 . *201\cdot63] \supset . \text{Cl}\text{‘}(P \times Q) = \text{Cl}\text{‘}(P \times Q)_1 \quad (3)$

$\vdash . *166\cdot16 . *263\cdot22 . \supset \vdash : \text{Hp} . \supset . \overrightarrow{B}\text{‘}\text{Cnv}\text{‘}(P \times Q) = \Lambda \quad (4)$

$\vdash . (1) . (2) . (3) . (4) . *263\cdot44 . \supset \vdash . \text{Prop}$

***263·66.** $\vdash : \alpha \in \text{NO fin} - \iota\text{‘}0_r . \supset . \omega \dot{\times} \alpha = \omega \quad [*263\cdot65]$

The proof proceeds as in $*263\cdot63$.

∗264. DERIVATIVES OF WELL-ORDERED SERIES.

Summary of ∗264.

The principal purpose of the present number is to show that every infinite well-ordered series is the sum of a series of progressions followed by a finite tag, which may be null. For this purpose, we proceed as follows: If x is any member of $C'P$, it must belong to the family, with respect to P_1, of some member of $C'P - \text{G}'P_1$, unless $x = B'\breve{P}$ and $B'\breve{P} \sim\epsilon\, \text{G}'P_1$. Assuming that we have either $\sim E!B'\breve{P}$ or $B'\breve{P} \epsilon\, \text{G}'P_1$, and assuming further that P is an infinite well-ordered series other than a progression, it follows that every member of $C'P$ belongs to the family, with respect to P_1, of some member of $C'\nabla'P$, because, by ∗216·611, $C'\nabla'P = \text{D}'P_1 - \text{G}'P_1$ in the circumstances contemplated (∗264·15). Now P limited to any one family with respect to P_1 is a progression, unless that family includes $B'\breve{P}$; and if it includes $B'\breve{P}$, it is finite. Hence our proposition follows.

An important consequence of the above proposition is that every cardinal which is not inductive and is applicable to classes that can be well-ordered is a multiple of $\aleph_0$ (∗264·48).

For the purposes of this number we need a notation for the series of series each of which consists of the family of some member of $C'\nabla'P$. We therefore put

$$P_{\text{pr}} = P \upharpoonright ; \overleftarrow{(P_1)_*} ; \nabla'P \quad \text{Dft [∗264].}$$

Here "pr" is intended to suggest "progression." When $P \epsilon \Omega\,\text{infin} - \omega$, P_{pr} is the series of progressions (possibly ending in a finite tag) whose sum is P (or $P \upharpoonright \text{D}'P$, in one case). Before using this definition, some preliminary considerations are necessary. $\nabla'P$ is the series of limit-points of P, including $B'P$. In order that $\nabla'P$ may exist, there must be at least one limit-point besides $B'P$. Now the limit-points of a series are $C'P - \text{G}'P_1$, *i.e.* the limit-points other than $B'P$ are $\text{G}'P - \text{G}'P_1$ (∗216·21). Hence when $B'P$ exists and $\text{G}'P - \text{G}'P_1$ exists, $\nabla'P$ exists. Hence by ∗263·49,

∗264·13. $\vdash :. P \epsilon \Omega . \supset : \dot{\exists} ! \nabla'P . \equiv . P \epsilon \Omega\,\text{infin} - \omega$

I.e. a well-ordered series whose derivative exists is one which is infinite and not a progression. We have similarly

*264·14. $\vdash : P \epsilon \Omega \text{ infin} - \omega . \supset . C`\nabla`P = C`P - \text{ᗡ}`P_1$

and

*264·12. $\vdash : P \epsilon \Omega . \supset . \text{ᗡ}`\nabla`P = \text{ᗡ}`P - \text{ᗡ}`P_1$

We next proceed (*264·2—·261) to study the posterity of a term x with respect to P_1, *i.e.* the series $P \upharpoonright \overleftarrow{(P_1)_*}`x$. We show that if this series has a last term, it is finite (*264·21), and ends with $B`\breve{P}$ (*264·2), while if not, and if $x \epsilon C`P_1$, *i.e.* if x has either an immediate successor or an immediate predecessor, the series is a progression (*264·22). Hence we have

*264·23. $\vdash :. P \epsilon \Omega . x \epsilon C`\nabla`P \cap C`P_1 . \supset :$

$$\text{E} ! \max_P`\overleftarrow{(P_1)_*}`x . \equiv . x = B`\text{Cnv}`\nabla`P . \text{E} ! B`\breve{P}$$

Moreover, if $x \epsilon C`P_1$, the ancestry of x with respect to P_1 must end with a member of the derivative of P, *i.e.*

*264·233. $\vdash : P \epsilon \Omega \text{ infin} - \omega . x \epsilon C`P_1 . \supset . \min_P`\overrightarrow{(P_1)_*}`x \epsilon C`\nabla`P$

We thus arrive at the result that if P has a last term, so has $\nabla`P$ (*264·24), and if $x$ is any member of the derivative except the last, the series $P \upharpoonright \overleftarrow{(P_1)_*}`x$ is a progression (*264·25), while if x is the last term of the derivative, and the series P has a last term, then $P \upharpoonright \overleftarrow{(P_1)_*}`x$ is finite (*264·252). Moreover the supposition that P ends with a member of the derivative is equivalent to the supposition that P ends with a term which has no immediate predecessor (*264·26).

We now proceed (*264·3—·403) to consider the relation P_{pr} defined above. If we take any term y in a well-ordered series, there is some term x belonging to $C`P - \text{ᗡ}`P_1$ such that the family of y with respect to P_1 is the posterity of x. This results from *264·233 above. Thus we may divide the field of P into mutually exclusive stretches, each of which is the posterity of some member of $C`P - \text{ᗡ}`P_1$ with respect to P_1. The series of series thus obtained is P_{pr}. There is an exceptional case, when the series ends in a term having no immediate predecessor, for then the posterity of this term with respect to P_1 is null, and therefore P_{pr} omits this term. Otherwise, we shall have $\Sigma`P_{pr} = P$; *i.e.* we have

*264·39. $\vdash : P \epsilon \Omega \text{ infin} - \omega . \sim (B`\breve{P} \epsilon C`\nabla`P) . \supset . \Sigma`P_{pr} = P$

*264·391. $\vdash : P \epsilon \Omega . B`\breve{P} \epsilon C`\nabla`P . \supset . \Sigma`P_{pr} = P \upharpoonright \text{D}`P$

Moreover we have

*264·36. $\vdash : P \epsilon \Omega . \supset . P_{pr} \text{ smor } \nabla`P . P_{pr} \epsilon \text{Rel}^2 \text{ excl}$

From what was proved earlier we know that, assuming $P \in \Omega$, we have $D`P_{\mathrm{pr}} \subset \omega$ (*264·401); if $P$ has no last term, $C`P_{\mathrm{pr}} \subset \omega$; if P is infinite and has a last term, $B`\breve{P}_{\mathrm{pr}}$ is finite, and if the last term of $P$ belongs to $C`\nabla`P$, $B`\breve{P}_{\mathrm{pr}} = \dot{\Lambda}$. Hence, using *251·63, which assures us that, in virtue of *264·36 above, if $C`P_{\mathrm{pr}} \subset \omega$, $\Sigma`P_{\mathrm{pr}}$ is a multiple of ω, we find (*264·44) that every well-ordered series has an ordinal number of the form $(\alpha \dot{\times} \omega) \dotplus \beta$, where α and β may be any ordinals, including 0_r and $\dot{1}$ (putting $\dot{1} \dot{\times} \alpha = \alpha$ to avoid exceptional cases). The above account omits the exceptional cases, which require special treatment and render the proof long; but in the end the above simple result is obtained.

Since a multiple of $\aleph_0$ is not increased by the addition of an inductive cardinal, it follows (*264·44) that the cardinal number of the field of an infinite well-ordered series is always a multiple of $\aleph_0$ (*264·47). Hence if all classes can be well-ordered, all cardinals which are not inductive are multiples of $\aleph_0$. In virtue of Zermelo's theorem, the same result follows if the multiplicative axiom is true.

***264·01.** $P_{\mathrm{pr}} = P \upharpoonright ;\overleftarrow{(P_1)_*};\nabla`P$ Dft [*264]

***264·11.** $\vdash :. P \in \Omega . \supset : \dot{\exists} ! \,\mathrm{sgm}`P . \equiv . P \in \Omega\, \mathrm{infin}$

Dem.

$\vdash . *263·51 . \qquad \supset \vdash : P \in \Omega\,\mathrm{infin} . \supset . \dot{\exists} ! \,\mathrm{sgm}`P$ (1)

$\vdash . *212·152 . *211·41 . \supset \vdash : P \in \Omega . \dot{\exists} ! \,\mathrm{sgm}`P . \supset . \exists ! \,\mathrm{sect}`P - \iota`\Lambda - \text{Ɑ}`\mathrm{max}_P .$

[*261·28.Transp] $\qquad \supset . P \in \Omega\,\mathrm{infin}$ (2)

$\vdash . (1) . (2) . \supset \vdash . \mathrm{Prop}$

***264·12.** $\vdash : P \in \Omega . \supset . \text{Ɑ}`\nabla`P = \text{Ɑ}`P - \text{Ɑ}`P_1$

Dem.

$\vdash . *216·61 . \qquad \supset \vdash : \mathrm{Hp} . \dot{\exists} ! P . \supset . \text{Ɑ}`\nabla`P = \text{Ɑ}`P - \text{Ɑ}`P_1$ (1)

$\vdash . *216·612 . *33·241 . \supset \vdash : P = \dot{\Lambda} . \supset . \text{Ɑ}`\nabla`P = \Lambda . \text{Ɑ}`P - \text{Ɑ}`P_1 = \Lambda$ (2)

$\vdash . (1) . (2) . \supset \vdash . \mathrm{Prop}$

***264·13.** $\vdash :. P \in \Omega . \supset : \dot{\exists} ! \nabla`P . \equiv . P \in \Omega\,\mathrm{infin} - \omega$

Dem.

$\vdash . *264·12 . \supset \vdash :. \mathrm{Hp} . \supset : \dot{\exists} ! \nabla`P . \equiv . \exists ! \text{Ɑ}`P - \text{Ɑ}`P_1 .$

[*263·49] $\qquad \equiv . P \in \Omega\,\mathrm{infin} - \omega : \supset \vdash . \mathrm{Prop}$

***264·14.** $\vdash : P \in \Omega\,\mathrm{infin} - \omega . \supset . C`\nabla`P = C`P - \text{Ɑ}`P_1$ [*264·13 . *216·611]

***264·15.** $\vdash :. P \in \Omega\,\mathrm{infin} - \omega : \sim E ! B`\breve{P} . \vee . B`\breve{P} \in \text{Ɑ}`P_1 : \supset . C`\nabla`P = \overrightarrow{B}`P_1$

Dem.

$\vdash . *264·14 . *93·103 . \supset \vdash : \mathrm{Hp} . \sim E ! B`\breve{P} . \supset . C`\nabla`P = C`P - \text{Ɑ}`P_1 . C`P = D`P .$

[*93·101.*250·21] $\qquad \supset . C`\nabla`P = \overrightarrow{B}`P_1$ (1)

$\vdash . *93\cdot101 . \quad \supset \vdash : B`\breve{P} \in \text{G}`P_1 . \supset . C`P - \text{G}`P_1 \subset \text{D}`P$ (2)

$\vdash . (2) . *264\cdot14 . \supset \vdash : \text{Hp} . B`\breve{P} \in \text{G}`P_1 . \supset . C`\nabla`P = \text{D}`P - \text{G}`P_1$

[*93·101.*250·21] $= \overrightarrow{B`P_1}$ (3)

$\vdash . (1) . (3) . \supset \vdash . \text{Prop}$

***264·2.** $\vdash : P \in \Omega . \text{E} ! \max_P`\overleftarrow{(P_1)_*}`x . \supset . \max_P`\overleftarrow{(P_1)_*}`x = B`\breve{P}$

Dem.

$\vdash . *206\cdot42\cdot46 . \supset \vdash : \text{Hp} . \supset . \overrightarrow{\text{seq}_P}`\overleftarrow{(P_1)_*}`x = \overleftarrow{P_1}`\max_P`\overleftarrow{(P_1)_*}`x .$

[*90·16] $\supset . \overrightarrow{\text{seq}_P}`\overleftarrow{(P_1)_*}`x \subset \overleftarrow{(P_1)_*}`x .$

[*206·2] $\supset . \overrightarrow{\text{seq}_P}`\overleftarrow{(P_1)_*}`x = \Lambda .$

[*250·126] $\supset . \max_P`\overleftarrow{(P_1)_*}`x = B`\breve{P} : \supset \vdash . \text{Prop}$

***264·21.** $\vdash : P \in \Omega . \text{E} ! \max_P`\overleftarrow{(P_1)_*}`x . \supset .$

$P \restriction \overleftarrow{(P_1)_*}`x \in \Omega\,\text{fin} . P(x \mapsto B`\breve{P}) \in \text{Cls induct}$

Dem.

$\vdash . *200\cdot35 . \supset \vdash : \text{Hp} . \overleftarrow{(P_1)_*}`x = \iota`x . \supset . P \restriction \overleftarrow{(P_1)_*}`x = \dot{\Lambda}$ (1)

$\vdash . *260\cdot27 . \supset \vdash : \text{Hp} . \overleftarrow{(P_1)_*}`x \neq \iota`x . \supset . xP_{\text{fn}} \max_P`\overleftarrow{(P_1)_*}`x .$

[*260·11] $\supset . P\{x \mapsto \max_P`\overleftarrow{(P_1)_*}`x\} \in \text{Cls induct} .$ (2)

[*205·2] $\supset . C`P \restriction \overleftarrow{(P_1)_*}`x \in \text{Cls induct}$ (3)

$\vdash . (1) . (2) . (3) . *264\cdot2 . \supset \vdash . \text{Prop}$

***264·22.** $\vdash : P \in \Omega . \sim \text{E} ! \max_P`\overleftarrow{(P_1)_*}`x . x \in C`P_1 . \supset . P \restriction \overleftarrow{(P_1)_*}`x \in \omega$

Dem.

$\vdash . *260\cdot32\cdot34\cdot27 . \supset \vdash : \text{Hp} . \supset . \{P \restriction \overleftarrow{(P_1)_*}`x\}_1 = \{\overleftarrow{(P_1)_*}`x\} \uparrow P_1 .$ (1)

[*122·52] $\supset . \{P \restriction \overleftarrow{(P_1)_*}`x\}_1 \in \text{Prog}$ (2)

$\vdash . (1) . *260\cdot33 . \supset \vdash : \text{Hp} . \supset . [\{P \restriction \overleftarrow{(P_1)_*}`x\}_1]_{\text{po}} = P \restriction \overleftarrow{(P_1)_*}`x$ (3)

$\vdash . (2) . (3) . *263\cdot1 . \supset \vdash . \text{Prop}$

***264·221.** $\vdash : P \in \Omega . x(\nabla`P)y . \supset . P(x - y) \sim \in \text{Cls induct}$

Dem.

$\vdash . *207\cdot34 . *216\cdot6 . \supset \vdash : \text{Hp} . \supset . xP^2y . y = \text{lt}_P`\overrightarrow{P}`y .$

[*207·25] $\supset . xP^2y . y = \text{lt}_P`(\overleftarrow{P}`x \cap \overrightarrow{P}`y) .$

[*207·13] $\supset . xP^2y . \sim \text{E} ! \max_P`(\overleftarrow{P}`x \cap \overrightarrow{P}`y) .$

[*261·26] $\supset . \overleftarrow{P}`x \cap \overrightarrow{P}`y \sim \in \text{Cls induct} : \supset \vdash . \text{Prop}$

***264·222.** $\vdash : P \in \Omega . \overleftarrow{P}`x \in \text{Cls induct} . \supset . x \sim \in \text{D}`\nabla`P$ [*264·221 . Transp]

∗264·223. $\vdash : P \in \Omega \,.\, P(x - y) \sim\in \text{Cls induct} \,.\, \supset \,.\, \exists ! \, \text{Ɑ}‘\nabla‘P \cap P(x \dashv y)$

Dem.

$\vdash . *261{\cdot}3 . \supset \vdash : \text{Hp} . \supset . (\exists \alpha) . \alpha \subset P(x-y) . \exists ! \alpha . \sim \text{E} ! \, \text{max}_P‘\alpha .$

$[*250{\cdot}122] \quad \supset . (\exists \alpha) . \alpha \subset P(x-y) . \exists ! \alpha . \text{E} ! \, \text{lt}_P‘\alpha .$

$[*206{\cdot}213] \quad \supset . (\exists \alpha) . \alpha \subset P(x-y) . \exists ! \alpha . \text{lt}_P‘\alpha \in P(x \dashv y) .$

$[*206{\cdot}181] \quad \supset . \exists ! \, \text{D}‘\text{lt}_P \cap \text{Ɑ}‘P \cap P(x \dashv y) .$

$[*216{\cdot}602] \quad \supset . \exists ! \, \text{Ɑ}‘\nabla‘P \cap P(x \dashv y) : \supset \vdash . \text{Prop}$

∗264·224. $\vdash : P \in \Omega . x = B‘\text{Cnv}‘\nabla‘P . \text{E} ! B‘\breve{P} . \supset . \overleftarrow{P}‘x \in \text{Cls induct}$

Dem.

$\vdash . *264{\cdot}223 . \text{Transp} . \supset \vdash : \text{Hp} . \supset . P(x - B‘\breve{P}) \in \text{Cls induct} : \supset \vdash . \text{Prop}$

∗264·225. $\vdash :. P \in \Omega . x \in C‘P_1 . \supset : \text{E} ! \, \text{max}_P‘\overleftarrow{(P_1)_*}‘x . \equiv . \overleftarrow{(P_1)_*}‘x \in \text{Cls induct}$ [∗264·21·22]

∗264·23. $\vdash :. P \in \Omega . x \in C‘\nabla‘P \cap C‘P_1 . \supset :$

$\text{E} ! \, \text{max}_P‘\overleftarrow{(P_1)_*}‘x . \equiv . x = B‘\text{Cnv}‘\nabla‘P . \text{E} ! B‘\breve{P}$

Dem.

$\vdash . *264{\cdot}2 . \quad \supset \vdash : \text{Hp} . \text{E} ! \, \text{max}_P‘\overleftarrow{(P_1)_*}‘x . \supset . \text{E} ! B‘\breve{P} \quad (1)$

$\vdash . *264{\cdot}21{\cdot}222 . \supset \vdash : \text{Hp}(1) . \supset . x \sim\in \text{D}‘\nabla‘P .$

$[*93{\cdot}103] \quad \supset . x = B‘\text{Cnv}‘\nabla‘P \quad (2)$

$\vdash . *264{\cdot}224 . \quad \supset \vdash : \text{Hp} . x = B‘\text{Cnv}‘\nabla‘P . \text{E} ! B‘\breve{P} . \supset . \overleftarrow{P}‘x \in \text{Cls induct} .$

$[*120{\cdot}481{\cdot}251] \quad \supset . \overleftarrow{(P_1)_*}‘x \in \text{Cls induct} .$

$[*90{\cdot}12 . \text{Hp} . *261{\cdot}26] \quad \supset . \text{E} ! \, \text{max}_P‘\overleftarrow{(P_1)_*}‘x \quad (3)$

$\vdash . (1) . (2) . (3) . \supset \vdash . \text{Prop}$

∗264·231. $\vdash : P \in \Omega . x \in C‘\nabla‘P - C‘P_1 . \supset . x = B‘\text{Cnv}‘\nabla‘P = B‘\breve{P}$

Dem.

$\vdash . *250{\cdot}21 . \supset \vdash : \text{Hp} . \supset . x \sim\in \text{D}‘P .$

$[*93{\cdot}103] \quad \supset . x = B‘\breve{P} . \quad (1)$

$[*216{\cdot}6] \quad \supset . x \sim\in \text{D}‘\nabla‘P .$

$[*93{\cdot}103] \quad \supset . x = B‘\text{Cnv}‘\nabla‘P \quad (2)$

$\vdash . (1) . (2) . \supset \vdash . \text{Prop}$

∗264·232. $\vdash :. P \in \Omega . x \in C‘\nabla‘P . \supset :$

$\overleftarrow{(P_1)_*}‘x \in \text{Cls induct} . \equiv . x = B‘\text{Cnv}‘\nabla‘P . \text{E} ! B‘\breve{P}$

This proposition differs from ∗264·23 by not assuming that $x \in C‘P_1$. If $B‘\breve{P}$ has no immediate predecessor, $B‘\breve{P} \in C‘\nabla‘P - C‘P_1$, so that $B‘\breve{P}$ satisfies the hypothesis of ∗264·232, but not that of ∗264·23.

Dem.

$\vdash . *90\cdot13 . \quad \supset \vdash : \mathrm{Hp} . \overleftarrow{(P_1)_*}`x = \Lambda . \supset . x \sim\epsilon C`P_1 .$

$[*264\cdot231] \qquad \supset . x = B`\mathrm{Cnv}`\nabla`P . \mathrm{E} ! B`\breve{P} \qquad (1)$

$\vdash . *120\cdot212 . \supset \vdash : \mathrm{Hp}(1) . \supset . \overleftarrow{(P_1)_*}`x \epsilon \text{Cls induct} \qquad (2)$

$\vdash . *264\cdot225 . \supset$

$\vdash :. \mathrm{Hp} . \exists ! \overleftarrow{(P_1)_*}`x . \supset : \overleftarrow{(P_1)_*}`x \epsilon \text{Cls induct} . \equiv . \mathrm{E} ! \max_P`\overleftarrow{(P_1)_*}`x .$

$[*264\cdot23] \qquad \equiv . x = B`\mathrm{Cnv}`\nabla`P . \mathrm{E} ! B`\breve{P} \qquad (3)$

$\vdash . (1) . (2) . (3) . \supset \vdash . \mathrm{Prop}$

$*264\cdot233 . \quad \vdash : P \epsilon \Omega \,\text{infin} - \omega . x \epsilon C`P_1 . \supset . \min_P`\overrightarrow{(P_1)_*}`x \epsilon C`\nabla`P$

Dem.

$\vdash . *250\cdot121 . \quad \supset \vdash : \mathrm{Hp} . \supset . \mathrm{E} ! \min_P`\overrightarrow{(P_1)_*}`x \qquad (1)$

$\vdash . *90\cdot172 . \quad \supset \vdash : \mathrm{Hp} . y (P_1)_* x . z P_1 y . \supset . z \epsilon \overrightarrow{(P_1)_*}`x \cap \overrightarrow{P}`y .$

$[*205\cdot14] \qquad \supset . y \neq \min_P`\overrightarrow{(P_1)_*}`x \qquad (2)$

$\vdash . (2) . \mathrm{Transp} . \supset \vdash : \mathrm{Hp} . y = \min_P`\overrightarrow{(P_1)_*}`x . \supset . y \sim\epsilon \text{Ɑ}`P_1 .$

$[*264\cdot14] \qquad \supset . y \epsilon C`\nabla`P \qquad (3)$

$\vdash . (1) . (3) . \supset \vdash . \mathrm{Prop}$

$*264\cdot24 . \quad \vdash : P \epsilon \Omega \,\text{infin} . \mathrm{E} ! B`\breve{P} . \supset . \mathrm{E} ! B`\mathrm{Cnv}`\nabla`P$

Dem.

$\vdash . *264\cdot12 . \supset \vdash : \mathrm{Hp} . B`\breve{P} \sim\epsilon C`P_1 . \supset . B`\breve{P} \epsilon C`\nabla`P .$

$[*216\cdot6] \qquad \supset . B`\breve{P} = B`\mathrm{Cnv}`\nabla`P \qquad (1)$

$\vdash . *264\cdot233 . *263\cdot22 . \supset \vdash : \mathrm{Hp} . B`\breve{P} \epsilon C`P_1 . \supset . \min_P`\overrightarrow{(P_1)_*}`B`\breve{P} \epsilon C`\nabla`P \qquad (2)$

$\vdash . *205\cdot55 . \supset \vdash : \mathrm{Hp}(2) . x = \min_P`\overrightarrow{(P_1)_*}`B`\breve{P} . \supset . B`\breve{P} = \max_P`\overleftarrow{(P_1)_*}`x .$

$[*264\cdot23.(2)] \qquad \supset . x = B`\mathrm{Cnv}`\nabla`P \qquad (3)$

$\vdash . (1) . (3) . \supset \vdash . \mathrm{Prop}$

$*264\cdot25 . \quad \vdash : P \epsilon \Omega . x \epsilon \mathrm{D}`\nabla`P . \supset . P \upharpoonright \overleftarrow{(P_1)_*}`x \epsilon \omega$

Dem.

$\vdash . *264\cdot232 . *250\cdot21 . \supset \vdash : \mathrm{Hp} . \supset . \overleftarrow{(P_1)_*}`x \sim\epsilon \text{Cls induct} . x \epsilon \mathrm{D}`P_1 .$

$[*264\cdot225] \qquad \supset . \sim \mathrm{E} ! \max_P`\overleftarrow{(P_1)_*}`x . x \epsilon \mathrm{D}`P_1 .$

$[*264\cdot22] \qquad \supset . P \upharpoonright \overleftarrow{(P_1)_*}`x \epsilon \omega : \supset \vdash . \mathrm{Prop}$

$*264\cdot251 . \quad \vdash : P \epsilon \Omega . \sim \mathrm{E} ! B`\breve{P} . x \epsilon C`\nabla`P . \supset . P \upharpoonright \overleftarrow{(P_1)_*}`x \epsilon \omega$

Dem.

$\vdash . *250\cdot21 . \supset \vdash : \mathrm{Hp} . \supset . x \epsilon \mathrm{D}`P_1 .$

$[*264\cdot23.\mathrm{Hp}] \qquad \supset . \sim \mathrm{E} ! \max_P`\overleftarrow{(P_1)_*}`x . x \epsilon \mathrm{D}`P_1 .$

$[*264\cdot22] \qquad \supset . P \upharpoonright \overleftarrow{(P_1)_*}`x \epsilon \omega : \supset \vdash . \mathrm{Prop}$

***264·252.** $\vdash : P \in \Omega . E ! B`\breve{P} . x = B`\text{Cnv}`\nabla`P . \supset . P \upharpoonright \overleftarrow{(P_1)_*}`x \in \Omega \text{ fin}$

Dem.

$\vdash . *264·23 . \supset \vdash : \text{Hp} . x \in C`P_1 . \supset . E ! \max_P`\overleftarrow{(P_1)_*}`x .$

[*264·21] $\supset . P \upharpoonright \overleftarrow{(P_1)_*}`x \in \Omega \text{ fin}$ (1)

$\vdash . *90·14 . \supset \vdash : x \sim\in C`P_1 . \supset . P \upharpoonright \overleftarrow{(P_1)_*}`x = \dot{\Lambda}$ (2)

$\vdash . (1) . (2) . \supset \vdash . \text{Prop}$

***264·26.** $\vdash :. P \in \Omega . \supset : B`\breve{P} \in C`\nabla`P . \equiv . E ! B`\breve{P} . B`\breve{P} \sim\in \text{ᗡ}`P_1$

Dem.

$\vdash . *14·21 . \supset \vdash : B`\breve{P} \in C`\nabla`P . \supset . E ! B`\breve{P}$ (1)

$\vdash . *264·12 . \supset \vdash : \text{Hp} . B`\breve{P} \in C`\nabla`P . \supset . B`\breve{P} \sim\in \text{ᗡ}`P_1$ (2)

$\vdash . *264·12 . \supset \vdash : \text{Hp} . B`\breve{P} \sim\in \text{ᗡ}`P_1 . \supset . B`\breve{P} \in C`\nabla`P$ (3)

$\vdash . (1) . (2) . (3) . \supset \vdash . \text{Prop}$

***264·261.** $\vdash :. P \in \Omega . \supset : \sim(B`\breve{P} \in C`\nabla`P) . \equiv . C`P = C`P_1$

Dem.

$\vdash . *264·26 . \supset \vdash :: \text{Hp} . \supset :. \sim(B`\breve{P} \in C`\nabla`P) . \equiv : \sim E ! B`\breve{P} . \vee . B`\breve{P} \in \text{ᗡ}`P_1 :$

[*202·52] $\equiv : \overrightarrow{B`}\breve{P} \subset \text{ᗡ}`P_1 :$

[*250·21] $\equiv : C`P \subset C`P_1 :$

[*121·322] $\equiv : C`P = C`P_1 :: \supset \vdash . \text{Prop}$

***264·3.** $\vdash : Q P_{\text{pr}} R . \equiv . (\exists x, y) . x (\nabla`P) y . Q = P \upharpoonright \overleftarrow{(P_1)_*}`x . R = P \upharpoonright \overleftarrow{(P_1)_*}`y$

[(*264·01)]

***264·31.** $\vdash :. P \in \text{Ser} . \supset : Q P_{\text{pr}} R . \equiv .$

$(\exists x, y) . x, y \in C`P - \text{ᗡ}`P_1 . x P y . Q = P \upharpoonright \overleftarrow{(P_1)_*}`x . R = P \upharpoonright \overleftarrow{(P_1)_*}`y$

[*207·35 . *264·3 . *216·6]

***264·32.** $\vdash . C`P_{\text{pr}} = P \upharpoonright ``\overleftarrow{(P_1)_*}``C`\nabla`P$ [*150·22 . (*264·01)]

***264·321.** $\vdash : P \in \text{Ser} . x \in C`\nabla`P . \supset . \overleftarrow{(P_1)_*}`x \sim\in 1$

Dem.

$\vdash . *216·611 . \supset \vdash : \text{Hp} . \supset . x \in C`P - \text{ᗡ}`P_1$ (1)

$\vdash . *90·14 . \supset \vdash : x \sim\in C`P_1 . \supset . \overleftarrow{(P_1)_*}`x = \Lambda$ (2)

$\vdash . *121·305 . \supset \vdash : \text{Hp} . x \in D`P_1 . \supset . \exists ! \overleftarrow{(P_1)_*}`x - \iota`x .$

[*90·12] $\supset . \overleftarrow{(P_1)_*}`x \sim\in 1$ (3)

$\vdash . (1) . (2) . (3) . \supset \vdash . \text{Prop}$

***264·33.** $\vdash : P \in \text{Ser} . \supset . C``C`P_{\text{pr}} = \overleftarrow{(P_1)_*}``C`\nabla`P$

[*264·321 . *202·55 . *264·32]

***264·34.** $\vdash : P \in \Omega \,.\, x, y \in C‘P \,.\, P \upharpoonright \overleftarrow{(P_1)_*}‘x = P \upharpoonright \overleftarrow{(P_1)_*}‘y \,.\, \supset \,.\, x = y$

Dem.

$\vdash \,.\, *264·321 \,.\, *202·55 \,.\, \supset \vdash : \mathrm{Hp} \,.\, \supset \,.\, \overleftarrow{(P_1)_*}‘x = \overleftarrow{(P_1)_*}‘y$ (1)

$\vdash \,.\, (1) \,.\, *90·12 \,.\, \supset \vdash : \mathrm{Hp} \,.\, x \in C‘P_1 \,.\, \supset \,.\, x (P_1)_* y \,.\, y (P_1)_* x \,.$

[*260·22.*91·541] $\supset \,.\, x = y$ (2)

$\vdash \,.\, *250·21 \,.\, \supset \vdash : \mathrm{Hp} \,.\, x \sim\in C‘P_1 \,.\, \supset \,.\, x = B‘\breve{P}$ (3)

$\vdash \,.\, (1) \,.\, *90·12·14 \,.\, \supset \vdash : \mathrm{Hp} \,.\, x \sim\in C‘P_1 \,.\, \supset \,.\, y \sim\in C‘P_1 \,.$

[*250·21] $\supset \,.\, y = B‘\breve{P}$ (4)

$\vdash \,.\, (3) \,.\, (4) \,.\, \supset \vdash : \mathrm{Hp} \,.\, x \sim\in C‘P_1 \,.\, \supset \,.\, x = y$ (5)

$\vdash \,.\, (2) \,.\, (5) \,.\, \supset \vdash \,.\, \mathrm{Prop}$

***264·341.** $\vdash : P \in \mathrm{Ser} \,.\, x, y \in C‘\nabla‘P \,.\, x (P_1)_* y \,.\, \supset \,.\, x = y$

Dem.

$\vdash \,.\, *216·611 \,.\, \supset \vdash : \mathrm{Hp} \,.\, \supset \,.\, y \sim\in \text{Ɑ}‘P_1 \,.$

[*91·504] $\supset \,.\, \sim \{x (P_1)_{\mathrm{po}} y\} \,.$

[*91·54] $\supset \,.\, x = y : \supset \vdash \,.\, \mathrm{Prop}$

***264·35.** $\vdash : P \in \mathrm{Ser} \,.\, x, y \in C‘\nabla‘P \,.\, \exists ! \overleftarrow{(P_1)_*}‘x \cap \overleftarrow{(P_1)_*}‘y \,.\, \supset \,.\, x = y$

Dem.

$\vdash \,.\, *96·302 \,.\, \supset \vdash :. \mathrm{Hp} \,.\, \supset : x (P_1)_* y \,.\, \vee \,.\, y (P_1)_* x :$

[*264·341] $\supset : x = y :. \supset \vdash \,.\, \mathrm{Prop}$

***264·36.** $\vdash : P \in \Omega \,.\, \supset \,.\, P_{\mathrm{pr}} \,\mathrm{smor}\, \nabla‘P \,.\, P_{\mathrm{pr}} \in \mathrm{Rel}^2 \,\mathrm{excl}$ [*264·34·35]

The following propositions lead up to *264·39·391.

***264·37.** $\vdash : P \in \Omega \,\mathrm{infin} - \omega \,.\, \supset \,.\, \dot{s}‘C‘P_{\mathrm{pr}} = P_{\mathrm{fn}}$

Dem.

$\vdash \,.\, *264·32 \,.\, \supset \vdash :. \mathrm{Hp} \,.\, \supset : x (\dot{s}‘C‘P_{\mathrm{pr}}) y \,.\, \equiv \,.\, (\exists a) \,.\, a \in C‘\nabla‘P \,.\, x, y \in \overleftarrow{(P_1)_*}‘a \,.\, xPy \,.$

[*260·32·27] $\equiv \,.\, (\exists a) \,.\, a \in C‘\nabla‘P \,.\, x, y \in \overleftarrow{(P_1)_*}‘a \,.\, x P_{\mathrm{fn}} y \,.$

[*264·233·35] $\equiv \,.\, (\exists a) \,.\, a = \min_P‘\overrightarrow{(P_1)_*}‘x = \min_P‘\overrightarrow{(P_1)_*}‘y \,.\, x P_{\mathrm{fn}} y \,.$

[*13·195] $\equiv \,.\, \min_P‘\overrightarrow{(P_1)_*}‘x = \min_P‘\overrightarrow{(P_1)_*}‘y \,.\, x P_{\mathrm{fn}} y$ (1)

$\vdash \,.\, *260·27 \,.\, \supset \vdash : \mathrm{Hp} \,.\, x P_{\mathrm{fn}} y \,.\, \supset \,.\, \overrightarrow{(P_1)_*}‘x \subset \overrightarrow{(P_1)_*}‘y \,.$

[*205·5] $\supset \,.\, \min_P‘\overrightarrow{(P_1)_*}‘x = \min_P‘\overrightarrow{(P_1)_*}‘y$ (2)

$\vdash \,.\, (1) \,.\, (2) \,.\, \supset \vdash :. \mathrm{Hp} \,.\, \supset : x (\dot{s}‘C‘P_{\mathrm{pr}}) y \,.\, \equiv \,.\, x P_{\mathrm{fn}} y :. \supset \vdash \,.\, \mathrm{Prop}$

***264·371.** $\vdash : P \in \mathrm{Ser} \,.\, a (\nabla‘P) b \,.\, \supset \,.\, \overleftarrow{(P_1)_*}‘a \subset \overrightarrow{P}‘b$

Dem.

$\vdash \,.\, *216·6 \,.\, \supset \vdash : \mathrm{Hp} \,.\, \supset \,.\, a \in \overrightarrow{P}‘b$ (1)

$\vdash \,.\, *204·71 \,.\, \supset \vdash : \mathrm{Hp} \,.\, xPb \,.\, xP_1 y \,.\, \sim (yPb) \,.\, \supset \,.\, y = b \,.$

[*33·14] $\supset \,.\, b \in \text{Ɑ}‘P_1$ (2)

$\vdash \,.\, (2) \,.\, \mathrm{Transp} \,.\, *216·611 \,.\, \supset \vdash :. \mathrm{Hp} \,.\, \supset : xPb \,.\, xP_1 y \,.\, \supset \,.\, yPb$ (3)

$\vdash \,.\, (1) \,.\, (3) \,.\, *90·112 \,.\, \supset \vdash :. \mathrm{Hp} \,.\, \supset : a (P_1)_* x \,.\, \supset \,.\, xPb :. \supset \vdash \,.\, \mathrm{Prop}$

***264·372.** $\vdash : P \in \text{Ser} . \supset . F \stackrel{\text{;}}{} P_{\text{pr}} \subseteq P \dot{-} P_{\text{fn}}$

Dem.

$\vdash . *264·3·321 . *202·55 . \supset$

$\vdash :. \text{Hp} . \supset : x (F ; P_{\text{pr}}) y . \equiv . (\exists a, b) . a (\nabla ‘ P) b . x \in \overleftarrow{(P_1)_*} ‘ a . y \in \overleftarrow{(P_1)_*} ‘ b .$ (1)

[*264·371] $\supset . x P y$ (2)

$\vdash . *264·35 . \supset \vdash : \text{Hp} . a (\nabla ‘ P) b . x \in \overleftarrow{(P_1)_*} ‘ a . y \in \overleftarrow{(P_1)_*} ‘ b . \supset . y \sim \in \overleftarrow{(P_1)_*} ‘ a .$

[*90·17] $\supset . y \sim \in \overleftarrow{(P_1)_*} ‘ x .$

[*260·27] $\supset . \sim (x P_{\text{fn}} y)$ (3)

$\vdash . (1) . (2) . (3) . \supset \vdash : \text{Hp} . \supset . F ; P_{\text{pr}} \subseteq P \dot{-} P_{\text{fn}} : \supset \vdash . \text{Prop}$

***264·373.** $\vdash : P \in \Omega . \sim (B ‘ \breve{P} \in C ‘ \nabla ‘ P) . \supset . P \dot{-} P_{\text{fn}} \subseteq F ; P_{\text{pr}}$

Dem.

$\vdash . *264·261·233 . *263·49 . \supset$

$\vdash : \text{Hp} . x (P \dot{-} P_{\text{fn}}) y . \supset . \text{min}_P ‘ \overrightarrow{(P_1)_*} ‘ x , \text{min}_P ‘ \overrightarrow{(P_1)_*} ‘ y \in C ‘ \nabla ‘ P$ (1)

$\vdash . *96·301 . \supset \vdash :. \text{Hp} . \text{min}_P ‘ \overrightarrow{(P_1)_*} ‘ x = \text{min}_P ‘ \overrightarrow{(P_1)_*} ‘ y . \supset : x (P_1)_* y . \vee . y (P_1)_* x :$

[*260·27] $\supset : x = y . \vee . x P_{\text{fn}} y . \vee . y P_{\text{fn}} x$ (2)

$\vdash . (2) . \text{Transp} . \quad \supset \vdash : \text{Hp} (1) . \supset . \text{min}_P ‘ \overrightarrow{(P_1)_*} ‘ x \neq \text{min}_P ‘ \overrightarrow{(P_1)_*} ‘ y$ (3)

$\vdash . (1) . *264·371 . \supset \vdash : \text{Hp} . \text{min}_P ‘ \overrightarrow{(P_1)_*} ‘ y \, P \, \text{min}_P ‘ \overrightarrow{(P_1)_*} ‘ x . \supset . y P x$ (4)

$\vdash . (4) . \text{Transp} . \quad \supset \vdash : \text{Hp} (1) . \supset . \sim \{ \text{min}_P ‘ \overrightarrow{(P_1)_*} ‘ y \, P \, \text{min}_P ‘ \overrightarrow{(P_1)_*} ‘ x \}$ (5)

$\vdash . (3) . (5) . \supset \vdash : \text{Hp} (1) . \supset . \text{min}_P ‘ \overrightarrow{(P_1)_*} ‘ x \, P \, \text{min}_P ‘ \overrightarrow{(P_1)_*} ‘ y$ (6)

$\vdash . (1) . (6) . \supset \vdash : \text{Hp} (1) . \supset . (\exists a, b) . a (\nabla ‘ P) b . x \in \overleftarrow{(P_1)_*} ‘ a . y \in \overleftarrow{(P_1)_*} ‘ b .$

[*264·3·321.*202·55] $\supset . x (F ; P_{\text{pr}}) y : \supset \vdash . \text{Prop}$

***264·38.** $\vdash : P \in \Omega . \sim (B ‘ \breve{P} \in C ‘ \nabla ‘ P) . \supset . F ; P_{\text{pr}} = P \dot{-} P_{\text{fn}}$ [*264·372·373]

***264·381.** $\vdash : P \in \Omega . B ‘ \breve{P} \in C ‘ \nabla ‘ P . \supset . F ; P_{\text{pr}} = P \upharpoonright D ‘ P \dot{-} P_{\text{fn}}$

Dem.

$\vdash . *264·33 . \supset \vdash : \text{Hp} . \supset . s ‘ C ‘‘ C ‘ P_{\text{pr}} \subset C ‘ P_1 .$

[*264·26.*42·2] $\supset . B ‘ \breve{P} \sim \in C ‘ F ; P_{\text{pr}} .$

[*264·372] $\supset . F ; P_{\text{pr}} \subseteq P \upharpoonright D ‘ P \dot{-} P_{\text{fn}}$ (1)

$\vdash . *250·21 . \supset \vdash : \text{Hp} . x (P \upharpoonright D ‘ P \dot{-} P_{\text{fn}}) y . \supset . x , y \in C ‘ P_1 .$

[*264·233.*263·49] $\supset . \text{min}_P ‘ \overrightarrow{(P_1)_*} ‘ x , \text{min}_P ‘ \overrightarrow{(P_1)_*} ‘ y \in C ‘ \nabla ‘ P$ (2)

Thence as in the proof of *264·373,

$\vdash : \text{Hp} . x (P \upharpoonright D ‘ P \dot{-} P_{\text{fn}}) y . \supset . x (F ; P_{\text{pr}}) y$ (3)

$\vdash . (1) . (3) . \supset \vdash . \text{Prop}$

***264·39.** $\vdash : P \epsilon \Omega \text{ infin} - \omega . \sim (B`\breve{P} \epsilon C`\nabla`P) . \supset . \Sigma`P_{\text{pr}} = P$
[*264·37·38 . *260·12 . *162·1]

***264·391.** $\vdash : P \epsilon \Omega . B`\breve{P} \epsilon C`\nabla`P . \supset . \Sigma`P_{\text{pr}} = P \upharpoonright \text{D}`P$

Dem.

$\vdash . *264{\cdot}13 . \supset \vdash : \text{Hp} . \supset . P \epsilon \Omega \text{ infin} - \omega$ (1)
$\vdash . *260{\cdot}27 . \supset \vdash : \text{Hp} . \supset . P_{\text{fn}} = P_{\text{fn}} \upharpoonright C`P_1$
[*264·26] $= P_{\text{fn}} \upharpoonright \text{D}`P$ (2)
$\vdash . (1) . (2) . *264{\cdot}37 . *260{\cdot}12 . \supset \vdash : \text{Hp} . \supset . \dot{s}`C`P_{\text{pr}} = P_{\text{fn}} . P_{\text{fn}} \subseteq P \upharpoonright \text{D}`P$ (3)
$\vdash . (3) . *264{\cdot}381 . \supset \vdash . \text{Prop}$

***264·4.** $\vdash : P \epsilon \Omega . \sim \text{E!} B`\breve{P} . \supset . C`P_{\text{pr}} \subset \omega$ [*264·251·32]

***264·401.** $\vdash : P \epsilon \Omega . \supset . \text{D}`P_{\text{pr}} \subset \omega$

Dem.

$\vdash . *151{\cdot}5 . *264{\cdot}34 . \supset \vdash : \text{Hp} . \supset . \text{D}`P_{\text{pr}} = P \upharpoonright ``\overleftarrow{(P_1)_*}``\text{D}`\nabla`P$ (1)
$\vdash . (1) . *264{\cdot}25 . \supset \vdash . \text{Prop}$

***264·402.** $\vdash : P \epsilon \Omega \text{ infin} . \text{E!} B`\breve{P} . \supset . B`\breve{P}_{\text{pr}} \epsilon \Omega \text{ fin}$

Dem.

$\vdash . *264{\cdot}24 . \supset \vdash : \text{Hp} . \supset . \text{E!} B`\text{Cnv}`\nabla`P .$
[*151·5.*264·34] $\supset . B`\breve{P}_{\text{pr}} = P \upharpoonright \overleftarrow{(P_1)_*}`B`\text{Cnv}`\nabla`P .$
[*264·252] $\supset . B`\breve{P}_{\text{pr}} \epsilon \Omega \text{ fin} : \supset \vdash . \text{Prop}$

***264·403.** $\vdash : P \epsilon \Omega . B`\breve{P} \epsilon C`\nabla`P . \supset . B`\breve{P}_{\text{pr}} = \dot{\Lambda}$

Dem.

$\vdash . *264{\cdot}26{\cdot}231 . \supset \vdash : \text{Hp} . \supset . B`\breve{P} \sim \epsilon C`P_1 . B`\breve{P} = B`\text{Cnv}`\nabla`P .$
[*90·14] $\supset . \overleftarrow{(P_1)_*}`B`\text{Cnv}`\nabla`P = \Lambda .$
[*151·5.*264·34] $\supset . B`\breve{P}_{\text{pr}} = \dot{\Lambda} : \supset \vdash . \text{Prop}$

The following propositions deal with the various different cases that arise. Their net result is expressed in *264·44.

***264·41.** $\vdash : P \epsilon \Omega \text{ infin} - \omega . \sim \text{E!} B`\breve{P} . \supset . \text{Nr}`P = \text{Nr}`\nabla`P \dot{\times} \omega$

Dem.

$\vdash . *264{\cdot}36{\cdot}4 . \supset \vdash : \text{Hp} . \supset . P_{\text{pr}} \epsilon \text{Rel}^2 \text{excl} \cap \text{Nr}`\nabla`P . C`P_{\text{pr}} \subset \omega .$
[*251·63] $\supset . \Sigma`P_{\text{pr}} \epsilon \text{Nr}`\nabla`P \dot{\times} \omega .$
[*264·39] $\supset . P \epsilon \text{Nr}`\nabla`P \dot{\times} \omega : \supset \vdash . \text{Prop}$

***264·42.** $\vdash : P \epsilon \Omega \,.\, B‘\breve{P} \sim\epsilon\, C‘\nabla‘P \,.\, \nabla‘P \epsilon 2_r \,.\, \supset .\, \text{Nr}‘P = \omega \dot{+} \text{Nr}‘B‘\breve{P}_{\text{pr}}$

Dem.

$\vdash .\, *264{\cdot}36 \,.\, \supset \vdash : \text{Hp} \,.\, \supset .\, P_{\text{pr}} = (B‘P_{\text{pr}}) \downarrow (B‘\breve{P}_{\text{pr}})\,.$

$[*162{\cdot}3 . *264{\cdot}39{\cdot}13] \quad \supset .\, P = B‘P_{\text{pr}} \dagger B‘\breve{P}_{\text{pr}}\,.$

$[*264{\cdot}36{\cdot}401] \quad \supset .\, \text{Nr}‘P = \omega \dot{+} B‘\breve{P}_{\text{pr}} : \supset \vdash .\, \text{Prop}$

***264·421.** $\vdash : P \epsilon \Omega \,.\, B‘\breve{P} \epsilon C‘\nabla‘P \,.\, \nabla‘P \epsilon 2_r \,.\, \supset .\, \text{Nr}‘P = \omega \dot{+} \dot{1}$

Dem.

$\vdash .\, *264{\cdot}36 \,.\, \supset : \text{Hp} \,.\, \supset .\, P_{\text{pr}} = (B‘P_{\text{pr}}) \downarrow (B‘\breve{P}_{\text{pr}})\,.$

$[*162{\cdot}3 . *264{\cdot}391{\cdot}13] \supset .\, P \upharpoonright \text{D}‘P = B‘P_{\text{pr}} \dagger B‘\breve{P}_{\text{pr}}$

$[*264{\cdot}403 . *160{\cdot}21] \quad = B‘P_{\text{pr}}\,.$

$[*264{\cdot}401] \quad \supset .\, P \upharpoonright \text{D}‘P \epsilon \omega\,.$

$[*204{\cdot}461] \quad \supset .\, P \epsilon \omega \dot{+} \dot{1} : \supset \vdash .\, \text{Prop}$

***264·422.** $\vdash : P \epsilon \Omega \,\text{infin} - \omega \,.\, B‘\breve{P} \sim\epsilon\, C‘\nabla‘P \,.\, \nabla‘P \sim\epsilon\, 2_r \,.\, \supset .$

$\text{Nr}‘P = \{\text{Nr}‘(\nabla‘P) \upharpoonright (\text{D}‘\nabla‘P) \dot{\times} \omega\} \dot{+} \text{Nr}‘B‘\breve{P}_{\text{pr}}$

Dem.

$\vdash .\, *264{\cdot}36 \,.\, *204{\cdot}272 \,.\, \supset \vdash : \text{Hp} \,.\, \supset .\, \text{D}‘P_{\text{pr}} \sim\epsilon\, 1\,.$

$[*204{\cdot}461 . *264{\cdot}24{\cdot}36] \quad \supset .\, P_{\text{pr}} = P_{\text{pr}} \upharpoonright \text{D}‘P_{\text{pr}} \nrightarrow B‘\breve{P}_{\text{pr}}\,.$

$[*162{\cdot}43 . *264{\cdot}39] \quad \supset .\, P = \Sigma‘(P_{\text{pr}} \upharpoonright \text{D}‘P_{\text{pr}}) \dagger B‘\breve{P}_{\text{pr}} \quad (1)$

$\vdash .\, *264{\cdot}36{\cdot}401 \,.\, *251{\cdot}63 \,.\, \supset$

$\vdash : \text{Hp} \,.\, \supset .\, \text{Nr}‘\Sigma‘(P_{\text{pr}} \upharpoonright \text{D}‘P_{\text{pr}}) = \text{Nr}‘(\nabla‘P) \upharpoonright (\text{D}‘\nabla‘P) \dot{\times} \omega \quad (2)$

$\vdash .\, (1) \,.\, (2) \,.\, *264{\cdot}36 \,.\, \supset \vdash .\, \text{Prop}$

***264·423.** $\vdash : P \epsilon \Omega \,.\, B‘\breve{P} \epsilon C‘\nabla‘P \,.\, \nabla‘P \sim\epsilon\, 2_r \,.\, \supset .$

$\text{Nr}‘P = \{\text{Nr}‘(\nabla‘P) \upharpoonright (\text{D}‘\nabla‘P) \dot{\times} \omega\} \dot{+} \dot{1}$

Dem.

As in *264·422,

$\vdash : \text{Hp} \,.\, \supset .\, P_{\text{pr}} = P_{\text{pr}} \upharpoonright \text{D}‘P_{\text{pr}} \nrightarrow B‘\breve{P}_{\text{pr}}\,.$

$[*162{\cdot}43 . *264{\cdot}391] \supset .\, P \upharpoonright \text{D}‘P = \Sigma‘(P_{\text{pr}} \upharpoonright \text{D}‘P_{\text{pr}}) \dagger B‘P_{\text{pr}}$

$[*264{\cdot}403] \quad = \Sigma‘(P_{\text{pr}} \upharpoonright \text{D}‘P_{\text{pr}}) \quad (1)$

$\vdash .\, *264{\cdot}36{\cdot}401 \,.\, *251{\cdot}63 \,.\, \supset$

$\vdash : \text{Hp} \,.\, \supset .\, \text{Nr}‘\Sigma‘(P_{\text{pr}} \upharpoonright \text{D}‘P_{\text{pr}}) = \text{Nr}‘(\nabla‘P) \upharpoonright (\text{D}‘\nabla‘P) \dot{\times} \omega \quad (2)$

$\vdash .\, *204{\cdot}461 \,.\, \supset \vdash : \text{Hp} \,.\, \supset .\, \text{Nr}‘P = \text{Nr}‘(P \upharpoonright \text{D}‘P) \dot{+} \dot{1} \quad (3)$

$\vdash .\, (1) \,.\, (2) \,.\, (3) \,.\, \supset \vdash .\, \text{Prop}$

***264·429.** $\dot{1} \dot{\times} \alpha = \alpha$ Df

This definition is merely intended to enable us to include $\dot{1}$ with ordinals in general formulae.

***264·44.** $\vdash : P \epsilon \Omega . \supset . (\exists \alpha, \beta) . \alpha \epsilon \text{NO} \cup \iota`\dot{1} . \beta \epsilon \text{NO fin} \cup \iota`\dot{1} . \text{Nr}`P = (\alpha \dot{\times} \omega) \dot{+} \beta$

Dem.

$\vdash . *160·22 . *166·13 . \supset \vdash : P \epsilon \Omega \text{ fin} . \supset . \text{Nr}`P = (0_r \dot{\times} \omega) \dot{+} \text{Nr}`P$ (1)

$\vdash . *160·21 . \quad \supset \vdash : P = \omega . \supset . \text{Nr}`P = (\dot{1} \dot{\times} \omega) \dot{+} 0_r$ (2)

$\vdash . *264·41 . *160·21 . \supset$

$\vdash : P \epsilon \Omega \text{ infin} - \omega . \sim \text{E} ! B`\breve{P} . \supset . (\exists \alpha) . \alpha \epsilon \text{NO} . \text{Nr}`P = (\alpha \dot{\times} \omega) \dot{+} 0_r$ (3)

$\vdash . *264·42·402 . \supset$

$\vdash : P \epsilon \Omega . B`\breve{P} \sim \epsilon C`\nabla`P . \nabla`P \epsilon 2_r . \supset . (\exists \beta) . \beta \epsilon \text{NO fin} . \text{Nr}`P = (\dot{1} \dot{\times} \omega) \dot{+} \beta$ (4)

$\vdash . *264·421 . \quad \supset \vdash : P \epsilon \Omega . B`\breve{P} \epsilon C`\nabla`P . \nabla`P \epsilon 2_r . \supset . \text{Nr}`P = (\dot{1} \dot{\times} \omega) \dot{+} \dot{1}$ (5)

$\vdash . *264·422·402 . \supset \vdash : P \epsilon \Omega \text{ infin} - \omega . B`\breve{P} \sim \epsilon C`\nabla`P . \nabla`P \sim \epsilon 2_r . \supset .$

$(\exists \alpha, \beta) . \alpha \epsilon \text{NO} . \beta \epsilon \text{NO fin} . \text{Nr}`P = (\alpha \dot{\times} \omega) \dot{+} \beta$ (6)

$\vdash . *264·423 . \supset \vdash : P \epsilon \Omega . B`\breve{P} \epsilon C`\nabla`P . \nabla`P \sim \epsilon 2_r . \supset .$

$(\exists \alpha) . \alpha \epsilon \text{NO} . \text{Nr}`P = (\alpha \dot{\times} \omega) \dot{+} \dot{1}$ (7)

$\vdash . (1) . (2) . (3) . (4) . (5) . (6) . (7) . \supset \vdash . \text{Prop}$

The following propositions apply the above results to the cardinal number of the field of a well-ordered series.

***264·45.** $\vdash : P \epsilon \Omega . \nabla`P \epsilon 2_r . \supset . \text{Nc}`C`P = \aleph_0$

Dem.

$\vdash . *264·42·402 . *180·71 . *152·7 . \supset$

$\vdash : \text{Hp} . B`\breve{P} \sim \epsilon C`\nabla`P . \supset . (\exists \mu) . \mu \epsilon \text{NC induct} . \text{Nc}`C`P = C``\omega +_c \mu .$

$[*263·101 . *123·41] \quad \supset . \text{Nc}`C`P = \aleph_0$ (1)

$\vdash . *264·421 . *181·62 . \supset \vdash : \text{Hp} . B`\breve{P} \epsilon C`\nabla`P . \supset . \text{Nc}`C`P = C``\omega +_c 1$

$[*263·101 . *123·4] \quad = \aleph_0$ (2)

$\vdash . (1) . (2) . \supset \vdash . \text{Prop}$

***264·451.** $\vdash : P \epsilon \Omega \text{ infin} - \omega . \sim \text{E} ! B`\breve{P} . \supset . \text{Nc}`C`P = \text{Nc}`C`\nabla`P \times_c \aleph_0$

Dem.

$\vdash . *264·41 . *184·5 . \supset \vdash : \text{Hp} . \supset . \text{Nc}`C`P = \text{Nc}`C`\nabla`P \times_c C``\omega$

$[*263·101] \quad = \text{Nc}`C`\nabla`P \times_c \aleph_0 : \supset \vdash . \text{Prop}$

***264·452.** $\vdash : P \epsilon \Omega \text{ infin} - \omega . \nabla`P \sim \epsilon 2_r . B`\breve{P} \sim \epsilon C`\nabla`P . \supset .$

$\text{Nc}`C`P = \text{Nc}`\text{D}`\nabla`P \times_c \aleph_0$

Dem.

$\vdash . *264·422 . *184·5 . *180·71 . \supset$

$\vdash : \text{Hp} . \supset . (\exists \mu) . \mu \epsilon \text{NC induct} . \text{Nc}`C`P = (\text{Nc}`\text{D}`\nabla`P \times_c \aleph_0) +_c \mu$ (1)

$\vdash . *123\cdot43 . *117\cdot62 . \supset \vdash : \text{Hp} . \mu \in \text{NC induct} . \supset . \mu < \text{Nc}`\text{D}`\nabla`P \times_c \aleph_0 .$

$[*117\cdot561] \supset . (\text{Nc}`\text{D}`\nabla`P \times_c \aleph_0) +_c \mu \leqslant (\text{Nc}`\text{D}`\nabla`P \times_c \aleph_0) +_c (\text{Nc}`\text{D}`\nabla`P \times_c \aleph_0)$

$[*123\cdot421 . *113\cdot43] \qquad \leqslant \text{Nc}`\text{D}`\nabla`P \times_c \aleph_0$ (2)

$\vdash . (1) . (2) . *117\cdot6\cdot25 . \supset \vdash : \text{Hp} . \supset . \text{Nc}`C`P = \text{Nc}`\text{D}`\nabla`P \times_c \aleph_0 : \supset \vdash . \text{Prop}$

***264·453**. $\vdash : P \in \Omega \text{ infin} - \omega . \text{E} ! B`\breve{P} . \nabla`P \sim \in 2_r . \supset . \text{Nc}`C`P = \text{Nc}`\text{D}`\nabla`P \times_c \aleph_0$

Dem.

As in *264·452,

$\vdash . *264\cdot423 . \supset \vdash : \text{Hp} . B`\breve{P} \in C`\nabla`P . \supset . \text{Nc}`C`P = \text{Nc}`\text{D}`\nabla`P \times_c \aleph_0$ (1)

$\vdash . (1) . *264\cdot452 . \supset \vdash . \text{Prop}$

***264·46**. $\vdash : P \in \Omega \text{ infin} - \omega . \supset . \text{Nc}`C`P = \text{Nc}`C`\nabla`P \times_c \aleph_0$

Dem.

$\vdash . *123\cdot421 . *264\cdot45 . \supset \vdash : \text{Hp} . \nabla`P \in 2_r . \supset . \text{Nc}`C`P = \text{Nc}`C`\nabla`P \times_c \aleph_0$ (1)

$\vdash . *264\cdot453 . \supset$

$\vdash : \text{Hp} . \text{E} ! B`\breve{P} . \nabla`P \sim \in 2_r . \text{Nc}`C`\nabla`P = \mu +_c 1 . \supset . \text{Nc}`C`P = \mu \times_c \aleph_0$

$[*123\cdot421 . *113\cdot43] = (\mu \times_c \aleph_0) +_c (\mu \times_c \aleph_0)$ (2)

$\vdash . *117\cdot571\cdot6 . \supset$

$\vdash : \text{Hp} . \supset . \mu \times_c \aleph_0 \leqslant (\mu +_c 1) \times_c \aleph_0 . (\mu +_c 1) \times_c \aleph_0 \leqslant (\mu \times_c \aleph_0) +_c (\mu \times_c \aleph_0)$ (3)

$\vdash . (2) . (3) . \supset \vdash : \text{Hp} . \supset . \text{Nc}`C`P = (\mu +_c 1) \times_c \aleph_0$

$[\text{Hp}] \qquad = \text{Nc}`C`\nabla`P \times_c \aleph_0$ (4)

$\vdash . (1) . (4) . *264\cdot451 . \supset \vdash . \text{Prop}$

***264·47**. $\vdash : P \in \Omega \text{ infin} . \supset . (\exists \mu) . \mu \in \text{NC} - \iota`0 . \text{Nc}`C`P = \mu \times_c \aleph_0$ [*264·46]

***264·48**. $\vdash : \alpha \in C``\Omega - \text{Cls induct} . \supset . \text{Nc}`\alpha \in \text{D}`(\times_c \aleph_0)$ [*264·47]

$*265$. THE SERIES OF ALEPHS.

Summary of $*265$.

In the present number, we shall confine ourselves to the most elementary properties of the ordinals and cardinals considered. The most important propositions to be proved are the existence-theorems. These all depend upon the axiom of infinity; moreover, as the numbers concerned grow greater, the existence-theorems require continually higher types.

In virtue of the definition in $*262$, $(\aleph_0)_r$ is the class of well-ordered series whose fields have $\aleph_0$ terms. This is not an ordinal number, but the logical sum of a certain class of ordinal numbers, namely of $\mathrm{Nr}``(\aleph_0)_r$.

ω_1 is the smallest ordinal whose field has more than $\aleph_0$ terms. We do not, however, take this as the definition of ω_1: we define ω_1 as the class of relations P such that the relations less than P (in the sense of $*254$) are those well-ordered series which are finite or have $\aleph_0$ terms in their fields, *i.e.*

$$\omega_1 = \hat{P}\{\overrightarrow{\mathrm{less}}`P = (\aleph_0)_r \cup \Omega\,\mathrm{fin}\} \quad \mathrm{Df.}$$

By $*254\cdot401$ it follows immediately that if $P \in \omega_1$, P is a well-ordered series and ω_1 is its ordinal number ($*265\cdot11$). Hence ω_1 is an ordinal number ($*265\cdot12$), though we need the axiom of infinity to show that ω_1 exists.

Assuming the axiom of infinity, the existence-theorem for ω_1 is derived from the series of ordinals which are finite or belong to series of $\aleph_0$ terms For notational convenience, we temporarily define this series as N; thus

$$N = (<_{\cdot}) \upharpoonright \{\mathrm{NO\,fin} \cup \mathrm{Nr}``(\aleph_0)_r\} \quad \mathrm{Dft}\ [*265].$$

It is also convenient temporarily to write M for "$<_{\cdot}$": thus

$$M = <_{\cdot} \quad \mathrm{Dft}\ [*265].$$

It is easy to prove that if $\aleph_0$ exists, N is an ω_1 ($*265\cdot25$). Hence we obtain the existence-theorem for ω_1 in either of the forms:

$*265\cdot27$. $\vdash : \exists ! \aleph_0 \cap t`\alpha . \supset . \exists ! \omega_1 \cap t^{11}`t_{00}`\alpha$

$*265\cdot28$. $\vdash : \mathrm{Infin\,ax}(x) . \supset . \exists ! \omega_1 \cap t^{11}`t^{33}`x$

It is easy to prove that ω_1 is greater than the ordinal number of any series of $\aleph_0$ terms ($*265\cdot3$), and that if ω_1 exists,

$$\overrightarrow{M}`\omega_1 = \mathrm{NO\,fin} \cup \mathrm{Nr}``(\aleph_0)_r \quad (*265\cdot35),$$

i.e. the ordinals less thar ω_1 are those that apply to series of $\aleph_0$ terms or of a finite number of terms.

We define $\aleph_1$ as $C``\omega_1$, *i.e.* as the class of those classes which can be arranged in a series whose ordinal number is ω_1. It follows from $*152\cdot71$ that $\aleph_1$ so defined is a cardinal number ($*265\cdot33$), and that if $\aleph_0$ exists, $\aleph_1 > \aleph_0$ ($*265\cdot34$).

In a precisely analogous fashion we can put

$$\omega_2 = \hat{P}\{\overrightarrow{\text{less}}`P = (\aleph_1)_r \cup (\aleph_0)_r \cup \Omega\,\text{fin}\} \quad \text{Df},$$

$$\aleph_2 = C``\omega_2 \quad \text{Df}.$$

Theorems similar to those mentioned above can be proved for ω_2 and $\aleph_2$ by similar methods. We can proceed to ω_ν and $\aleph_\nu$, where ν is any ordinal number. But our methods of proving existence-theorems fail if ν is not finite, since at each stage the existence-theorem is proved in a higher type and we know of no meaning that can be assigned to types whose order is not finite.

It is easy to prove that the sum of two ordinals which are less than ω_1 is less than ω_1. Much of the accepted theory of $(\aleph_0)_r$ and ω_1 depends upon the proposition that the limit of any progression of ordinals less than ω_1 is less than ω_1, so that in the series N, every progression has a limit within the series. This proposition—or at any rate the current proof of it—depends upon the multiplicative axiom. The proof, in outline, is as follows:

It is easy to prove that an ordinal which has $\aleph_0$ predecessors must be a member of $\text{Nr}``(\aleph_0)_r$, *i.e.* must be, in Cantor's language, an ordinal of the second class. Now consider any progression P contained in N, *i.e.* consider a series $\alpha_1, \alpha_2, \ldots \alpha_\nu, \ldots$ of increasing ordinals of the second class. The interval between any two consecutive terms of this series is either finite or has $\aleph_0$ terms. Hence $N``C`P$, *i.e.* the class of ordinals preceding the limit of our series, is the sum of $\aleph_0$ classes each of which is finite or has $\aleph_0$ terms. It is then argued that, because $\aleph_0 \times_c \aleph_0 = \aleph_0$, the whole class $N``C`P$ must consist of $\aleph_0$ terms. This conclusion, however, except in special cases, requires the multiplicative axiom, since it depends upon $*113\cdot32$, *i.e.*

$$\vdash :. \text{Mult ax} . \supset : \mu, \nu \in \text{NC} . \kappa \in \nu \cap \text{Cl.excl}`\mu . \supset . s`\kappa \in \mu \times_c \nu.$$

It follows that, unless for those who regard the multiplicative axiom as certain, it cannot be regarded as proved that ω_1 is not the limit of a progression of smaller ordinals. With this, much of the recognized theory of ordinals of the second class becomes doubtful. For example, Cantor proceeds to define a host of ordinals of the second class as the limits of given series of such ordinals. It is probable that, in regard to all the ordinals which he has defined in this way, a proof that they belong to the second class can be found, by actually arranging the finite integers in a series of the specified type. But the mere fact that they are limits of progressions of numbers of the second class does not, of itself, suffice to prove that they are of the second class.

As another example we may mention the very interesting work of Hausdorff*, much of which is based upon the proposition that a term which is the limit of an ω_1 chosen out of a given series cannot be the limit of an ω chosen out of the same series. This proposition is a consequence of the proposition that ω_1 is not the limit of a progression of smaller ordinals, and must therefore be regarded as doubtful. Hausdorff constructs by means of it many remarkable series, for example, compact series in which no progression or regression has a limit. The existence of such series appears, however, to be open to question, unless the multiplicative axiom is assumed.

It is not improbable that a proof, independent of the multiplicative axiom, can be found for the proposition that ω_1 is not the limit of a progression; but until such a proof is forthcoming, the proposition cannot be regarded as certain.

***265·01.** $\omega_1 = \hat{P}\{\overrightarrow{\text{less}}\text{‘}P = (\aleph_0)_r \cup \Omega \text{ fin}\}$ Df

***265·02.** $\aleph_1 = C\text{“}\omega_1$ Df

***265·03.** $\omega_2 = \hat{P}\{\overrightarrow{\text{less}}\text{‘}P = (\aleph_1)_r \cup (\aleph_0)_r \cup \Omega \text{ fin}\}$ Df

***265·04.** $\aleph_2 = C\text{“}\omega_2$ Df

etc.

***265·05.** $M = \lessdot$ Dft [*265]

This definition is revived from *256.

***265·06.** $N = M \upharpoonright \{\text{NO fin} \cup \text{Nr“}(\aleph_0)_r\}$ Dft [*265]

The existence-theorem for ω_1 is derived from N, since, if $\aleph_0$ exists, $N \in \omega_1$.

***265·1.** $\vdash :. P \in \omega_1 . \equiv : Q \text{ less } P . \equiv_Q . Q \in \Omega . C\text{‘}Q \in \text{Cls induct} \cup \aleph_0$ [(*265·01)]

***265·11.** $\vdash : P \in \omega_1 . \supset . \omega_1 = \text{Nr‘}P . P \in \Omega$

Dem.

$\vdash . *265·1 . \qquad \supset \vdash : \text{Hp} . \supset . \dot{\Lambda} \text{ less } P .$

[*254·1] $\qquad \supset . P \in \Omega \qquad (1)$

$\vdash . *254·401 . (1) . (*265·01) . \supset \vdash : \text{Hp} . Q \in \omega_1 . \supset . Q \text{ smor } P \qquad (2)$

$\vdash . *254·401 . (1) . (*265·01) . \supset \vdash : \text{Hp} . Q \text{ smor } P . \supset . \overrightarrow{\text{less}}\text{‘}Q = (\aleph_0)_r \cup \Omega \text{ fin} .$

[(*265·01)] $\qquad \supset . Q \in \omega_1 \qquad (3)$

$\vdash . (1) . (2) . (3) . \supset \vdash . \text{Prop}$

* *Untersuchungen über Ordnungstypen.* Berichte der mathematisch-physischen Klasse der Königlich Sächsischen Gesellschaft der Wissenschaften zu Leipzig, Feb. 1906 and Feb. 1907.

***265·12.** $\vdash . \omega_1 \in \mathrm{NO}$ [*265·11 . *256·54]

***265·13.** $\vdash : \alpha \in \mathrm{NO\ infin} . \supset . M \upharpoonright \overrightarrow{M}`\alpha \in \alpha$

Dem.

$\vdash . *256{\cdot}202 . \supset \vdash : P \in \Omega\ \mathrm{infin} . \supset . \mathrm{Nr}`M \upharpoonright (\overrightarrow{M}`\mathrm{Nr}`P) = \mathrm{Nr}`(P \upharpoonright \mathrm{G}`P)$

[*262·112] $= \mathrm{Nr}`P$ (1)

$\vdash . (1) . *262{\cdot}11 . \supset \vdash .$ Prop

***265·2.** $\vdash . \mathrm{G}`N = \mathrm{NO\ fin} - \iota`0_r \cup \mathrm{Nr}``(\aleph_0)_r = \overleftarrow{N}`0_r$ [*255·51]

***265·21.** $\vdash : \exists ! \aleph_0 . \alpha \in \mathrm{NO\ fin} \cup \mathrm{Nr}``(\aleph_0)_r . \supset .$

$M \upharpoonright \overrightarrow{M}`\alpha\ \mathrm{less}\ N . \alpha M (\mathrm{Nr}`N) . \alpha \subset \overrightarrow{\mathrm{less}}`N$

Dem.

$\vdash . *253{\cdot}13 . *265{\cdot}2 . \supset \vdash : \mathrm{Hp} . \alpha \in \mathrm{NO\ fin} \cup \mathrm{Nr}``(\aleph_0)_r . \supset . M \upharpoonright \overrightarrow{M}`\alpha \in \mathrm{D}`N_s .$

[*254·182] $\supset . M \upharpoonright \overrightarrow{M}`\alpha\ \mathrm{less}\ N$ (1)

$\vdash . (1) . *265{\cdot}13 . \quad \supset \vdash : \mathrm{Hp} . \alpha \in \mathrm{Nr}``(\aleph_0)_r . \supset . \alpha M (\mathrm{Nr}`N)$ (2)

$\vdash . (2) . *263{\cdot}31{\cdot}101 . \supset \vdash : \mathrm{Hp} . \alpha \in \mathrm{NO\ fin} . \supset . \alpha M \omega . \omega M (\mathrm{Nr}`N) .$

[*256·1] $\supset . \alpha M (\mathrm{Nr}`N)$ (3)

$\vdash . (2) . (3) . \quad \supset \vdash : \mathrm{Hp} . \alpha \in \mathrm{NO\ fin} \cup \mathrm{Nr}``(\aleph_0)_r . \supset . \alpha M (\mathrm{Nr}`N) .$ (4)

[*255·17] $\supset . \alpha \subset \overrightarrow{\mathrm{less}}`N$ (5)

$\vdash . (1) . (4) . (5) . \supset \vdash .$ Prop

***265·22.** $\vdash : \exists ! \aleph_0 . \supset . \Omega\ \mathrm{fin} \cup (\aleph_0)_r \subset \overrightarrow{\mathrm{less}}`N$ [*265·21]

***265·23.** $\vdash : P \in \mathrm{D}`N_s . \supset . (\exists \alpha) . \alpha \in \mathrm{NO\ fin} \cup \mathrm{Nr}``(\aleph_0)_r . P = M \upharpoonright \overrightarrow{M}`\alpha . \mathrm{Nr}`P = \alpha$
[*265·2 . *253·13 . *265·13 . *262·7 . *120·429]

***265·24.** $\vdash : P \in \mathrm{D}`N_s . \supset . P \in \Omega\ \mathrm{fin} \cup (\aleph_0)_r$ [*265·23]

***265·25.** $\vdash : \exists ! \aleph_0 . \supset . N \in \omega_1$

Dem.

$\vdash . *254{\cdot}41{\cdot}12 . \quad \supset \vdash : P\ \mathrm{less}\ N . \supset . (\exists Q) . Q \in \mathrm{D}`N_s . P\ \mathrm{smor}\ Q .$

[*265·24.*261·18.*151·18] $\supset . P \in \Omega\ \mathrm{fin} \cup (\aleph_0)_r$ (1)

$\vdash . (1) . *265{\cdot}22 . \supset \vdash : \mathrm{Hp} . \supset . \overrightarrow{\mathrm{less}}`N = \Omega\ \mathrm{fin} \cup (\aleph_0)_r .$

[*265·1] $\supset . N \in \omega_1 : \supset \vdash .$ Prop

***265·26.** $\vdash : \alpha \in \aleph_0 . \supset . \mathrm{N_0r} ; (\mathrm{less} \upharpoonright \breve{C}``\mathrm{Cl}`\alpha) \in \omega_1 . \mathrm{N_0r} ; (\mathrm{less} \upharpoonright \breve{C}``\mathrm{Cl}`\alpha) = N$

Dem.

$\vdash . *254{\cdot}431 . *150{\cdot}37 . \supset$

$\vdash . \mathrm{N_0r} ; (\mathrm{less} \upharpoonright \breve{C}``\mathrm{Cl}`\alpha) = (\mathrm{N_0r} ; \mathrm{less}) \upharpoonright \mathrm{N_0r}``(\Omega \cap \breve{C}``\mathrm{Cl}`\alpha)$ (1)

$\vdash . *123{\cdot}16 . \supset \vdash : \alpha \in \aleph_0 . \supset . \mathrm{N_0r}``(\Omega \cap \breve{C}``\mathrm{Cl}`\alpha) \subset \mathrm{NO\ fin} \cup \mathrm{N_0r}``(\aleph_0)_r$ (2)

$\vdash . *123\cdot14 . *262\cdot18\cdot21 . \supset \vdash : \alpha \in \aleph_0 . \mu \in \text{NC induct} - \iota\text{‘}1 . \supset . \exists ! \mu_r \cap \breve{C}\text{‘‘Cl‘}\alpha :$

[*262·25] $\supset \vdash : \alpha \in \aleph_0 . \nu \in \text{NO fin} . \supset . \exists ! \nu \cap \breve{C}\text{‘‘Cl‘}\alpha .$

[*152·45] $\supset . \nu \in \text{N}_0\text{r‘‘}\breve{C}\text{‘‘Cl‘}\alpha$ (3)

$\vdash . *152\cdot7 . \supset \vdash : P \in (\aleph_0)_r . \alpha \in \aleph_0 . \supset . \alpha \in C\text{‘‘N}_0\text{r‘}P .$

[*60·34] $\supset . \text{Nr‘}P \in \text{N}_0\text{r‘‘}\breve{C}\text{‘‘Cl‘}\alpha$ (4)

$\vdash . (3) . (4) . \supset \vdash : \alpha \in \aleph_0 . \supset . \text{NO fin} \cup \text{Nr‘‘}(\aleph_0)_r \subset \text{N}_0\text{r‘‘}(\breve{C}\text{‘‘Cl‘}\alpha \cap \Omega)$ (5)

$\vdash . (2) . (5) . \supset \vdash : \alpha \in \aleph_0 . \supset . \text{NO fin} \cup \text{Nr‘‘}(\aleph_0)_r = \text{N}_0\text{r‘‘}(\breve{C}\text{‘‘Cl‘}\alpha \cap \Omega)$ (6)

$\vdash . (1) . (6) . (*255\cdot01 . *265\cdot05\cdot06) . \supset \vdash : \alpha \in \aleph_0 . \supset . \text{N}_0\text{r};(\text{less} \upharpoonright \breve{C}\text{‘‘Cl‘}\alpha) = N .$

[*265·25] $\supset . \text{N}_0\text{r};(\text{less} \upharpoonright \breve{C}\text{‘‘Cl‘}\alpha) \in \omega_1 : \supset \vdash . \text{Prop}$

***265·27.** $\vdash : \exists ! \aleph_0 \cap t\text{‘}\alpha . \supset . \exists ! \omega_1 \cap t^{11}\text{‘}t_{00}\text{‘}\alpha$

Dem.

$\vdash . *64\cdot55 . \supset \vdash : \beta \in t\text{‘}\alpha . C\text{‘}P \subset \beta . \supset . P \in t_{00}\text{‘}\alpha$ (1)

$\vdash . (1) . \supset \vdash : \beta \in t\text{‘}\alpha . \supset . \breve{C}\text{‘‘Cl‘}\beta \subset t_{00}\text{‘}\alpha .$

[*155·12.*63·5] $\supset . \text{N}_0\text{r‘‘}\breve{C}\text{‘‘Cl‘}\beta \subset t\text{‘}t_{00}\text{‘}\alpha .$

[*64·57] $\supset . \text{N}_0\text{r};(\text{less} \upharpoonright \breve{C}\text{‘‘Cl‘}\beta) \in t^{11}\text{‘}t_{00}\text{‘}\alpha$ (2)

$\vdash . (2) . *265\cdot26 . \supset \vdash . \text{Prop}$

***265·28.** $\vdash : \text{Infin ax}\ (x) . \supset . \exists ! \omega_1 \cap t^{11}\text{‘}t^{33}\text{‘}x$

Dem.

$\vdash . *123\cdot37 . \supset \vdash : \text{Hp} . \supset . \exists ! \aleph_0 \cap t\text{‘}t^{3}\text{‘}x .$

[*265·27] $\supset . \exists ! \omega_1 \cap t^{11}\text{‘}t_{00}\text{‘}t^{3}\text{‘}x .$

[*64·312] $\supset . \exists ! \omega_1 \cap t^{11}\text{‘}t^{33}\text{‘}x : \supset \vdash . \text{Prop}$

Propositions concerning $\aleph_2$ and ω_2, and generally $\aleph_\nu$ and ω_ν, where ν is an inductive cardinal, are proved precisely as the above propositions are proved. There is not, however, so far as we know, any proof of the existence of Alephs and Omegas with infinite suffixes, owing to the fact that the type increases with each successive existence-theorem, and that infinite types appear to be meaningless.

***265·3.** $\vdash : \alpha \in \text{Nr‘‘}(\aleph_0)_r . \supset . \alpha < \omega_1$ [*265·22·25]

***265·31.** $\vdash : \exists ! \aleph_0 . \supset . \aleph_1 \geqslant \aleph_0$

Dem.

$\vdash . *265\cdot25 . \quad \supset \vdash : \text{Hp} . \supset . C\text{‘}N \in \aleph_1$ (1)

$\vdash . *265\cdot2 . \quad \supset \vdash . \text{NO fin} - \iota\text{‘}0_r \subset C\text{‘}N$ (2)

$\vdash . *262\cdot19\cdot21 . *123\cdot27 . \supset \vdash : \text{Hp} . \supset . \text{NO fin} - \iota\text{‘}0_r \in \aleph_0$ (3)

$\vdash . (2) . (3) . \quad \supset \vdash : \text{Hp} . \supset . \text{Nc‘}C\text{‘}N \geqslant \aleph_0$ (4)

$\vdash . (1) . (4) . \supset \vdash . \text{Prop}$

***265·32.** $\vdash : \exists ! \aleph_0 . \supset . \aleph_0 \neq \aleph_1 . \aleph_0 \cap \aleph_1 = \Lambda$

Dem.

$\vdash . *265·3 . \supset \vdash : P \in \Omega . C'P \in \aleph_0 . \supset . P \sim \in \omega_1 .$

$[(*265·02)] \qquad \supset . C'P \sim \in \aleph_1 \qquad (1)$

$\vdash . (1) . *262·18 . (*265·02) . \supset \vdash . \aleph_0 \cap \aleph_1 = \Lambda . \supset \vdash . \text{Prop}$

***265·33.** $\vdash . \aleph_1 \in \text{NC} \qquad [*152·71 . *265·12]$

***265·34.** $\vdash : \exists ! \aleph_0 . \supset . \aleph_1 > \aleph_0 \qquad [*265·31·32·33 . *255·74]$

***265·35.** $\vdash : \exists ! \omega_1 . \supset . \overrightarrow{M}'\omega_1 = \text{NO fin} \cup \text{Nr}''(\aleph_0)_r$

Dem.

$\vdash . *265·3 . *263·31 . \supset \vdash : \text{Hp} . \supset . \text{NO fin} \cup \text{Nr}''(\aleph_0)_r \subset \overrightarrow{M}'\omega_1 \qquad (1)$

$\vdash . *265·11 . \supset \vdash : P \in \omega_1 . \text{Nr}'Q \in \overrightarrow{M}'\omega_1 . \supset . Q \text{ less } P .$

$[*265·1] \qquad \supset . \text{Nr}'Q \in \text{NO fin} \cup \text{Nr}''(\aleph_0)_r \qquad (2)$

$\vdash . (1) . (2) . \supset \vdash . \text{Prop}$

***265·351.** $\vdash : P \in \omega_1 . \equiv . \exists ! \omega_1 . \text{Nr}''\text{D}'P_s = \text{NO fin} \cup \text{Nr}''(\aleph_0)_r$

Dem.

$\vdash . *256·11 . *265·35 . \supset$

$\vdash : \exists ! \omega_1 . \text{Nr}''\text{D}'P_s = \text{NO fin} \cup \text{Nr}''(\aleph_0)_r . \equiv . \exists ! \omega_1 . \overrightarrow{M}'\text{Nr}'P = \overrightarrow{M}'\omega_1 .$

$[*256·1 . *204·34] \qquad \equiv . P \in \omega_1 : \supset \vdash . \text{Prop}$

***265·352.** $\vdash : P \in \omega_1 . \supset . \text{Nr}''\text{D}'P_s = \overrightarrow{M}'\omega_1 \qquad [*265·35·351]$

***265·36.** $\vdash : \alpha, \beta \in \text{Nr}''(\aleph_0)_r . \supset . \alpha \dot{+} \beta \in \text{Nr}''(\aleph_0)_r$

Dem.

$\vdash . *180·71 . \supset \vdash : \text{Hp} . \supset . C''(\alpha \dot{+} \beta) = C''\alpha +_c C''\beta$

$[*262·12] \qquad = \aleph_0 +_c \aleph_0$

$[*123·421] \qquad = \aleph_0 .$

$[*262·12] \qquad \supset . \alpha \dot{+} \beta \in \text{Nr}''(\aleph_0)_r : \supset \vdash . \text{Prop}$

***265·361.** $\vdash . \alpha, \beta \in \text{NO fin} \cup \text{Nr}''(\aleph_0)_r . \supset . \alpha \dot{+} \beta \in \text{NO fin} \cup \text{Nr}''(\aleph_0)_r$

[Proof as in *265·36, using *120·45 and *123·41]

***265·4.** $\vdash : P \in \omega_1 . \alpha \subset C'P . P_*''\alpha \in \text{Cls induct} \cup \aleph_0 . \supset . \exists ! p'\overleftarrow{P}''\alpha$

Dem.

$\vdash . *265·1 . \supset \vdash : \text{Hp} . \supset . (P \upharpoonright P_*''\alpha) \text{ less } P .$

$[*254·51] \qquad \supset . P_*''\alpha \neq C'P .$

$[*202·504] \qquad \supset . \exists ! p'\overleftarrow{P}''\alpha : \supset \vdash . \text{Prop}$

***265·401.** $\vdash : P \in \omega_1 . \alpha \subset C'P . P''\alpha \in \text{Cls induct} \cup \aleph_0 . \supset . \exists ! p'\overleftarrow{P}''\alpha$

Dem.

$\vdash . *205·131 . \supset \vdash : \text{Hp} . \supset . P_*''\alpha = P''\alpha \cup \overrightarrow{\max}_P'\alpha .$

$[*205·3 . *120·251 . *123·4] \supset . P_*''\alpha \in \text{Cls induct} \cup \aleph_0 .$

$[*265·4] \qquad \supset . \exists ! p'\overleftarrow{P}''\alpha : \supset \vdash . \text{Prop}$

∗265·41. $\vdash : P \in \omega_1 . \supset . \overrightarrow{P}``C`P \subset \aleph_0 \cup \text{Cls induct} . \overrightarrow{P_*}``C`P \subset \aleph_0 \cup \text{Cls induct}$

Dem.

$\vdash . ∗254·182 . \quad \supset \vdash :. \text{Hp} . \supset : x \in C`P . \supset . (P \upharpoonright \overrightarrow{P}`x) \text{ less } P .$

$[∗265·1] \quad \supset . \overrightarrow{P}`x \in \aleph_0 \cup \text{Cls induct} \quad (1)$

$\vdash . (1) . ∗120·251 . ∗123·4 . \supset \vdash :. \text{Hp} . \supset : x \in C`P . \supset . \overrightarrow{P_*}`x \in \aleph_0 \cup \text{Cls induct} \quad (2)$

$\vdash . (1) . (2) . \supset \vdash . \text{Prop}$

∗265·42. $\vdash : P \in \omega_1 . \supset . \text{Ɑ}`P \subset \text{D}`P$

Dem.

$\vdash . ∗265·4·41 . \supset \vdash : \text{Hp} . x \in \text{Ɑ}`P . \supset . \exists ! p`\overleftarrow{P}``\iota`x .$

$[∗53·01·31] \quad \supset . x \in \text{D}`P : \supset \vdash . \text{Prop}$

∗265·43. $\vdash : P \in \omega_1 . x \in C`P . \supset . P \upharpoonright \overleftarrow{P}_{\text{fn}}`x \in \omega . \text{E} ! \text{lt}_P`\overleftarrow{P}_{\text{fn}}`x$

Dem.

$\vdash . ∗264·2 . ∗265·42 . \supset \vdash : \text{Hp} . \supset . \sim \text{E} ! \max_P`\overleftarrow{P}_{\text{fn}}`x . \quad (1)$

$[∗264·22] \quad \supset . P \upharpoonright \overleftarrow{P}_{\text{fn}}`x \in \omega \quad (2)$

$\vdash . (2) . ∗265·41 . ∗123·421 . \supset \vdash : \text{Hp} . \supset . P``\overleftarrow{P}_{\text{fn}}`x \in \aleph_0 .$

$[∗265·401] \quad \supset . \exists ! p`\overleftarrow{P}``\overleftarrow{P}_{\text{fn}}`x .$

$[(1).∗250·123] \quad \supset . \text{E} ! \text{lt}_P`\overleftarrow{P}_{\text{fn}}`x \quad (3)$

$\vdash . (2) . (3) . \supset \vdash . \text{Prop}$

∗265·431. $\vdash : P \in \omega_1 . Q \in P . x \in C`Q . \overleftarrow{Q}`x \subset \overleftarrow{P}_{\text{fn}}`x . \supset . \exists ! p`\overleftarrow{P}``C`Q$

Dem.

$\vdash . ∗265·43 . \supset \vdash : \text{Hp} . \supset . C`Q \subset \overrightarrow{P}`\text{lt}_P`\overleftarrow{P}_{\text{fn}}`x : \supset \vdash . \text{Prop}$

∗265·44. $\vdash : P \in \omega_1 . x \in C`P . \supset . P \upharpoonright \overleftarrow{P_*}`x \in \omega_1$

Dem.

$\vdash . ∗253·13 . \supset \vdash : \text{Hp} . \supset . \text{D}`(P \upharpoonright \overleftarrow{P_*}`x)_s = \hat{R}\{(\exists y) . x P_* y . R = P \upharpoonright P(x \mapsto y)\} \quad (1)$

$\vdash . ∗254·101 . \supset \vdash : \text{Hp} . x P_* y . \supset . \text{Nr}`P \upharpoonright P(x \mapsto y) \leqslant \text{Nr}`P \upharpoonright \overrightarrow{P}`y .$

$[∗265·352] \quad \supset . \text{Nr}`P \upharpoonright P(x \mapsto y) \in \overrightarrow{M}`\omega_1 \quad (2)$

$\vdash . ∗265·352 . \supset \vdash : \text{Hp} . \supset . \text{Nr}`P \upharpoonright \overrightarrow{P}`x \in \overrightarrow{M}`\omega_1 \quad (3)$

$\vdash . (3) . ∗265·361·35 . \supset$

$\vdash : \text{Hp} . \alpha \in \overrightarrow{M}`\omega_1 . \supset . \text{Nr}`P \upharpoonright \overrightarrow{P}`x \dotplus \alpha \in \overrightarrow{M}`\omega_1 .$

$[∗265·351] \quad \supset . (\exists y) . \text{Nr}`P \upharpoonright \overrightarrow{P}`x \dotplus \alpha = \text{Nr}`P \upharpoonright \overrightarrow{P}`y .$

$[∗253·47·11] \quad \supset . (\exists y) . x P_* y . \text{Nr}`P \upharpoonright \overrightarrow{P}`x \dotplus \alpha = \text{Nr}`P \upharpoonright \overrightarrow{P}`y .$

$[*204{\cdot}45]\ \supset . (\exists y) . xP_* y . \mathrm{Nr}`P \upharpoonright \overrightarrow{P}`x \dot{+} \alpha = \mathrm{Nr}`P \upharpoonright \overrightarrow{P}`x \dot{+} \mathrm{Nr}`P \upharpoonright P(x \mapsto y) .$

$[*255{\cdot}564]\ \supset . (\exists y) . xP_* y . \alpha = \mathrm{Nr}`P \upharpoonright (x \mapsto y) .$

$[(1)]\ \supset . \alpha \in \mathrm{Nr}``\mathrm{D}`(P \upharpoonright \overleftarrow{P_*}`x)_s$ (4)

$\vdash . (2) . (4) . \supset \vdash : \mathrm{Hp} . \supset . \mathrm{Nr}``\mathrm{D}`(P \upharpoonright \overleftarrow{P_*}`x)_s = \overrightarrow{M}`\omega_1 .$

$[*265{\cdot}35{\cdot}351]\ \supset . P \upharpoonright \overleftarrow{P_*}`x \in \omega_1 : \supset \vdash . \mathrm{Prop}$

***265·441.** $\vdash : P \in \mathrm{Ser} . Q, R \in \omega \cap \mathrm{Rl}`P . R \Subset Q . \supset .$

$P``C`R = P``C`Q . Q``C`R = C`Q$

Dem.

$\vdash . *263{\cdot}27 . \mathrm{Transp} . \supset \vdash : \mathrm{Hp} . \supset . \sim \mathrm{E} ! \max_Q `C`R .$

$[*205{\cdot}123]\ \supset . C`R \subset Q``C`R .$ (1)

$[*37{\cdot}2]\ \supset . P``C`R \subset P``Q``C`R$

$[*37{\cdot}15{\cdot}2]\ \subset P``C`Q$ (2)

$\vdash . *263{\cdot}47 . \mathrm{Transp} . \supset \vdash : \mathrm{Hp} . \supset . p`\overleftarrow{Q}``C`R = \Lambda .$

$[(1).*202{\cdot}51]\ \supset . C`Q = Q``C`R .$ (3)

$[*201{\cdot}5.\mathrm{Hp}]\ \supset . P``C`Q \subset P``C`R .$

$[(2)]\ \supset . P``C`R = P``C`Q$ (4)

$\vdash . (3) . (4) . \supset \vdash . \mathrm{Prop}$

***265·45.** $\vdash :. P \in \omega_1 . Q \Subset P : x \in C`Q . \supset_x . \exists ! \overleftarrow{Q}`x - \overleftarrow{P}_{\mathrm{fn}}`x : Q \in \omega .$

$S = \hat{x}\hat{y} \{x \in C`Q . y = \min_Q `(\overleftarrow{Q}`x - \overleftarrow{P}_{\mathrm{fn}}`x)\} . R = S \upharpoonright \overleftarrow{S_*}`B`Q : \supset .$

$R_{\mathrm{po}} \in \omega . R_{\mathrm{po}} \Subset Q . P``C`R_{\mathrm{po}} = P``C`Q$

Dem.

$\vdash . *32{\cdot}181 . \supset \vdash : \mathrm{Hp} . \supset . S \Subset Q .$ (1)

$[*91{\cdot}59.*201{\cdot}18]\ \supset . R_{\mathrm{po}} \Subset Q$ (2)

$\vdash . *263{\cdot}11 . \supset \vdash :. \mathrm{Hp} . \supset : x \in C`Q . \supset_x . \mathrm{E} ! \breve{S}`x :$

$[*71{\cdot}571]\ \supset : S \in \mathrm{Cls} \to 1 . C`Q \subset \mathrm{D}`S :$

$[(1)]\ \supset : S \in \mathrm{Cls} \to 1 . \mathrm{G}`S \subset \mathrm{D}`S :$

$[*122{\cdot}51.*96{\cdot}21]\ \supset : R \in \mathrm{Prog} :$

$[*263{\cdot}1]\ \supset : R_{\mathrm{po}} \in \omega$ (3)

$\vdash . (2) . (3) . *265{\cdot}441 . \supset \vdash : \mathrm{Hp} . \supset . P``C`R = P``C`Q$ (4)

$\vdash . (2) . (3) . (4) . \supset \vdash . \mathrm{Prop}$

***265·451.** $\vdash :. \mathrm{Hp}\ *265{\cdot}45 . \supset : x \in C`R . \supset . P(x \mapsto \breve{R}_1`x) \in \aleph_0$

Dem.

$\vdash . *265{\cdot}45 . *263{\cdot}14 . \supset \vdash :. \mathrm{Hp} . \supset : x \in C`R . \supset . \breve{R}_1`x = \breve{S}`x .$

$[\mathrm{Hp}]\ \supset . \breve{R}_1`x \in \overleftarrow{P}`x - \overleftarrow{P}_{\mathrm{fn}}`x .$

$[*260{\cdot}131]\ \supset . P(x \mapsto \breve{R}_1`x) \sim \in \mathrm{Cls\,induct}$ (1)

$\vdash . *265{\cdot}41 . \supset \vdash :. \mathrm{Hp} . \supset : x \in C`R . \supset . P(x \mapsto \breve{R}_1`x) \in \aleph_0 \cup \mathrm{Cls\ induct}$ (2)

$\vdash . (1) . (2) . \supset \vdash . \mathrm{Prop}$

***265·452.** $\vdash : \text{Hp} *265\cdot45 . \exists ! P(x \mapsto \breve{R}_1{}^{\backprime}x) \cap P(y \mapsto \breve{R}_1{}^{\backprime}y) . \supset . x = y$

Dem.

$\vdash . *201\cdot18 . \supset \vdash :. \text{Hp} . \supset : xP(\breve{R}_1{}^{\backprime}y) . yP(\breve{R}_1{}^{\backprime}x) :$

[*14·21] $\supset : x, y \in C^{\backprime}R . xP(\breve{R}_1{}^{\backprime}y) . yP(\breve{R}_1{}^{\backprime}x) :$

[*204·41.*265·45] $\supset : xR_{po}(\breve{R}_1{}^{\backprime}y) . yR_{po}(\breve{R}_1{}^{\backprime}x) :$

[*204·71] $\supset : x = y . \vee . xR_{po}y : y = x . \vee . yR_{po}x :$

[*4·41] $\supset : x = y . \vee . xR_{po}y . yR_{po}x :$

[*204·13.*265·45] $\supset : x = y :. \supset \vdash . \text{Prop}$

***265·453.** $\vdash : \text{Hp} *265\cdot45 . \kappa = \hat{\alpha}\{(\exists x) . x \in C^{\backprime}R . \alpha = P(x \mapsto \breve{R}_1{}^{\backprime}x)\} . \supset .$
$\kappa \in \aleph_0 \cap \text{Cl excl}^{\backprime}\aleph_0 . s^{\backprime}\kappa = P^{\backprime\backprime}C^{\backprime}R \cap \breve{P}_*{}^{\backprime\backprime}C^{\backprime}R$ [*265·451·452]

***265·454.** $\vdash :. \text{Hp} *265\cdot453 : \kappa \in \aleph_0 \cap \text{Cl excl}^{\backprime}\aleph_0 . \supset_\kappa . s^{\backprime}\kappa \in \aleph_0 : \supset .$
$P^{\backprime\backprime}C^{\backprime}R \cap \breve{P}_*{}^{\backprime\backprime}C^{\backprime}R \in \aleph_0$ [*265·453]

***265·46.** $\vdash :. P \in \omega_1 . Q \in \omega \cap \text{Rl}^{\backprime}P : x \in C^{\backprime}Q . \supset_x . \exists ! \overleftarrow{Q}{}^{\backprime}x - \overleftarrow{P}_{fn}{}^{\backprime}x :$
$\kappa \in \aleph_0 \cap \text{Cl excl}^{\backprime}\aleph_0 . \supset_\kappa . s^{\backprime}\kappa \in \aleph_0 : \supset . P^{\backprime\backprime}C^{\backprime}Q \in \aleph_0$
[*265·41·454 . *123·421]

***265·461.** $\vdash : \text{Hp} *265\cdot46 . \supset . \exists ! p^{\backprime}\overleftarrow{P}{}^{\backprime\backprime}C^{\backprime}Q$ [*265·46·401]

***265·47.** $\vdash :. P \in \omega_1 . Q \in \omega \cap \text{Rl}^{\backprime}P : \kappa \in \aleph_0 \cap \text{Cl excl}^{\backprime}\aleph_0 . \supset_\kappa . s^{\backprime}\kappa \in \aleph_0 : \supset .$
$\exists ! p^{\backprime}\overleftarrow{P}{}^{\backprime\backprime}C^{\backprime}Q$ [*265·461·431]

***265·48.** $\vdash :. \kappa \in \aleph_0 \cap \text{Cl excl}^{\backprime}\aleph_0 . \supset_\kappa . s^{\backprime}\kappa \in \aleph_0 : \supset : P \in \omega_1 . Q \in \omega \cap \text{Rl}^{\backprime}P . \supset \text{E} ! \text{lt}_P{}^{\backprime}C^{\backprime}Q$
[*265·47 . *250·123]

***265·481.** $\vdash : \text{Mult ax} . \supset . \text{Hp} *265\cdot48$ [*113·32 . *123·52]

***265·49.** $\vdash :. \text{Mult ax} . \supset : P \in \omega_1 . Q \in \omega \cap \text{Rl}^{\backprime}P . \supset . \text{E} ! \text{lt}_P{}^{\backprime}C^{\backprime}Q$ [*265·48·481]

This proposition shows that, assuming the multiplicative axiom, any progression of ordinals of the second class (*i.e.* consisting of series having $\aleph_0$ terms) has a limit in the second class, because $N \in \omega_1$.

***265·5.** $\vdash : P \in \omega_1 . Q \in \omega . C^{\backprime}Q \subset C^{\backprime}P . \sim \text{E} ! \max_P{}^{\backprime}C^{\backprime}Q .$
$R = \hat{x}\hat{y}\{x \in C^{\backprime}Q . y = \min_Q{}^{\backprime}(\overleftarrow{P}{}^{\backprime}x \cap \overleftarrow{Q}{}^{\backprime}x)\} . S = R \upharpoonright \overleftarrow{R}_*{}^{\backprime}B^{\backprime}Q . \supset .$
$S_{po} \in \omega . S_{po} \subseteq P . P^{\backprime\backprime}C^{\backprime}S_{po} = P^{\backprime\backprime}C^{\backprime}Q$

Dem.

$\vdash . *205\cdot11 . \quad \supset \vdash : \text{Hp} . \supset . R \subseteq P . R \subseteq Q . \quad (1)$

$[*201\cdot18] \quad \supset . S_{po} \subseteq P . S_{po} \subseteq Q \quad (2)$

$\vdash . *205\cdot197 . \quad \supset \vdash : \text{Hp} . x \in C^{\backprime}Q . \overleftarrow{Q}_*{}^{\backprime}x \subset \overrightarrow{P}_*{}^{\backprime}x . \supset . x = \max_P{}^{\backprime}\overleftarrow{Q}_*{}^{\backprime}x \quad (3)$

$\vdash . *263\cdot412 . *261\cdot26 . \supset \vdash : \text{Hp} . x \in \text{ᗡ}^{\backprime}Q . \supset . \text{E} ! \max_P{}^{\backprime}\overrightarrow{Q}{}^{\backprime}x \quad (4)$

$\vdash . (3) . (4) . *205\cdot193 . \supset\vdash : \text{Hp} . x \in C`Q . \overleftarrow{Q_*}`x \subset \overrightarrow{P_*}`x . \supset . \text{E} ! \max_P`C`Q$ (5)

$\vdash . (5) . \text{Transp} . \quad \supset\vdash :. \text{Hp} . \supset : x \in C`Q . \supset . \exists ! \overleftarrow{Q_*}`x - \overrightarrow{P_*}`x .$

[$*91\cdot542 . *202\cdot103$] $\quad \supset . \exists ! \overleftarrow{Q}`x \cap \overleftarrow{P}`x .$

[$*250\cdot121$] $\quad \supset . \text{E} ! \breve{R}`x$ (6)

$\vdash . (1) . (6) . *122\cdot51 . \supset\vdash : \text{Hp} . \supset . S \in \text{Prog} .$

[$*263\cdot1$] $\quad \supset . S_{\text{po}} \in \omega$ (7)

$\vdash . (2) . (7) . *265\cdot441 . \supset\vdash : \text{Hp} . \supset . P``C`S_{\text{po}} = P``C`Q$ (8)

$\vdash . (2) . (7) . (8) . \supset\vdash . \text{Prop}$

$*265\cdot51$. $\vdash : \text{Hp} *265\cdot48 . P \in \omega_1 . \alpha \in \aleph_0 \cap \text{Cl}`C`P . \sim \text{E} ! \max_P`\alpha . \supset . \text{E} ! \text{lt}_P`\alpha$

Dem.

$\vdash . *265\cdot5 . \supset\vdash : \text{Hp} . \supset . (\exists S) . S \in \omega \cap \text{Rl}`P . P``C`S = \alpha$ (1)

$\vdash . (1) . *265\cdot48 . \supset\vdash . \text{Prop}$

The following propositions follow easily.

$*265\cdot52$. $\vdash :. \text{Hp} *265\cdot48 . P \in \omega_1 . \supset :$

$\alpha \cap C`P \in \aleph_0 \cup \text{Cls induct} . \equiv . \exists ! C`P \cap p`\overleftarrow{P}``(\alpha \cap C`P)$ [$*265\cdot51\cdot41$]

$*265\cdot53$. $\vdash :: \text{Hp} *265\cdot48 . \supset :. P \in \omega_1 . \equiv :$

$P \in \Omega : \alpha \cap C`P \in \aleph_0 \cup \text{Cls induct} . \equiv_\alpha . \exists ! C`P \cap p`\overleftarrow{P}``(\alpha \cap C`P)$

$*265\cdot54$. $\vdash : P \in \omega_1 . \supset . \text{D}`\nabla`P \subset \text{lt}_P``C``(\omega \cap \text{Rl}`P)$ [$*265\cdot5$]

I.e. every limit-point in an ω_1 is the limit of a progression, which is what (following Hausdorff) may be conveniently called an ω-limit.

$*265\cdot55$. $\vdash : P \in \omega_1 . \supset . \text{D}`\nabla`P = \text{lt}_P``C``(\omega \cap \text{Rl}`P)$ [$*265\cdot54 . *216\cdot602$]

This proposition does not, like $*265\cdot48$, assert that every progression in P has a limit, and therefore it does not require the hypothesis of $*265\cdot48$.

SECTION F.

COMPACT SERIES, RATIONAL SERIES, AND CONTINUOUS SERIES.

Summary of Section F.

A *compact* series is one in which there is a term between any two, *i.e.* in which $P \subset P^2$, where P is the generating relation. We may call any relation P compact when $P \subset P^2$; then a *transitive* compact relation will be one for which $P = P^2$. Hence a serial relation P is compact whenever $P = P^2$. Compact series in general have certain properties, some of which have been already proved; but the majority of the interesting propositions in this subject come from adding some other condition besides compactness. Thus series having *Dedekindian continuity*, which have many important properties, are such as are compact and Dedekindian. *Rational* series (*i.e.* such as are ordinally similar to the series of all rational numbers, positive and negative, or, what is equivalent, to the series of rational proper fractions) are defined as such as are compact, without beginning or end, and consisting of $\aleph_0$ terms. Such series, also, have many important properties. A *continuous* series (in Cantor's sense) is a Dedekindian series containing a rational series in such a way that there are terms of the rational series between any two terms of the given series. This species of compact series also has many important properties. It consists of all series ordinally similar to the series of real numbers including 0 and ∞.

*270. COMPACT SERIES.

Summary of *270.

The propositions of the present number are mostly either obvious or repetitions of previously proved propositions. The latter are repeated here for convenience of reference.

We put $\quad \text{comp} = \hat{P}(P \subseteq P^2) \quad \text{Df},$

so that the class of compact series is Ser ∩ comp. We have

***270·11.** $\vdash :. P \in \text{comp} . \equiv : xPy . \supset_{x,y} . \exists ! \overleftarrow{P}`x \cap \overrightarrow{P}`y$

***270·34.** $\vdash : P \in \text{trans} \cap \text{comp} . \supset . \varsigma`P = \text{sgm}`P$

The proposition $\varsigma`P_* = \text{sgm}`P_*$, which was proved in *212, is a particular case of the above.

***270·41.** $\vdash : P \in \text{Ser} \cap \text{comp} . \supset . \text{Nr}`P \subset \text{Ser} \cap \text{comp}$

I.e. a series which is similar to a compact series is a compact series.

***270·56.** $\vdash : P \in \text{Ser} . Q \in \Omega . \sim \text{E} ! B`\breve{P} . \sim \text{E} ! B`\breve{Q} . \supset . P^Q \in \text{Ser} \cap \text{comp}$

This proposition gives us a means of manufacturing compact series of various types, such as $\omega \exp_r \omega$, $\omega \exp_r \omega_1$, etc.

***270·01.** $\text{comp} = \hat{P}(P \subseteq P^2) \quad \text{Df}$

Here "comp" is an abbreviation for "compact." "Compact" series are the same as the series which Cantor calls "überall dicht."

***270·1.** $\vdash : P \in \text{comp} . \equiv . P \subseteq P^2$ [(*270·01)]

***270·11.** $\vdash :. P \in \text{comp} . \equiv : xPy . \supset_{x,y} . \exists ! \overleftarrow{P}`x \cap \overrightarrow{P}`y$ [*270·1]

***270·12.** $\vdash : P \in \text{comp} . \equiv . \breve{P} \in \text{comp}$ [*270·11]

***270·13.** $\vdash : P \in \text{trans} \cap \text{comp} . \equiv . P = P^2$ [*270·1 . *201·1]

***270·14.** $\vdash : P \in \text{Ser} \cap \text{comp} . \equiv . P \in \text{Rl}`J \cap \text{connex} . P = P^2 . \equiv . P \in \text{Ser} . P = P^2$
[*270·13]

***270·15** $\vdash : P \in \text{Ser} \cap \text{comp} . \equiv . P \in \text{Ser} . P_1 = \dot{\Lambda}$ [*201·65 . *270·14]

$*270\cdot2.\quad \vdash : P \in \text{comp} \,.\supset .\, \sim \exists ! \, \text{max}_P \text{‘} \overrightarrow{P} \text{‘} x \quad [*205\cdot25 \,.\, *270\cdot1]$

$*270\cdot201.\quad \vdash : P \in \text{comp} \,.\supset .\, \sim \exists ! \, \overrightarrow{\text{min}}_P \text{‘}\text{Ꭰ}\text{‘}P \,.\, \sim \exists ! \, \overrightarrow{\text{max}}_P \text{‘}\text{D}\text{‘}P$

Dem.

$\vdash .\, *37\cdot25 . \quad \supset \vdash .\, \overrightarrow{\text{min}}_P \text{‘}\text{Ꭰ}\text{‘}P = \breve{P} \text{“}\text{D}\text{‘}P - (\breve{P}^2)\text{“}\text{D}\text{‘}P \quad (1)$

$\vdash .\, (1) \,.\, *270\cdot1 \,.\supset \vdash : \text{Hp} \,.\supset .\, \overrightarrow{\text{min}}_P \text{‘}\text{Ꭰ}\text{‘}P = \Lambda \quad (2)$

Similarly $\vdash : \text{Hp} \,.\supset .\, \overrightarrow{\text{max}}_P \text{‘}\text{D}\text{‘}P = \Lambda \quad (3)$

$\vdash .\, (2) \,.\, (3) \,.\supset \vdash .\, \text{Prop}$

$*270\cdot202.\quad \vdash : P \in \text{comp} \,.\supset .\, \sim \exists ! \, \overrightarrow{\text{min}}_P \text{‘} \breve{P} \text{“} \alpha \,.\, \sim \exists ! \, \overrightarrow{\text{max}}_P \text{‘} P \text{“} \alpha$
[Proof as in $*270\cdot201$]

$*270\cdot203.\quad \vdash : P \in \text{comp} \,.\supset .\, \sim \exists ! \, \overrightarrow{\text{seq}}_P \text{‘} \iota \text{‘} x \quad [*206\cdot42 \,.\, *270\cdot1]$

$*270\cdot204.\quad \vdash : P \in \text{Ser} \cap \text{comp} \,.\, \text{E} ! \, \text{seq}_P \text{‘} \alpha \,.\supset .\, \sim \text{E} ! \, \text{max}_P \text{‘} \alpha$
$[*206\cdot451 \,.\, *270\cdot15]$

$*270\cdot205.\quad \vdash : P \in \text{Ser} \cap \text{comp} \,.\supset .\, \text{lt}_P = \text{seq}_P \quad [*207\cdot1 \,.\, *270\cdot204]$

$*270\cdot21.\quad \vdash : P \in \text{Rl}\text{‘}J \cap \text{comp} \,.\, x \in C\text{‘}P \,.\supset .\, x \, \text{lt}_P \, (\overrightarrow{P}\text{‘}x) \quad [*207\cdot31 \,.\, *270\cdot1]$

$*270\cdot211.\quad \vdash : P \in \text{Rl}\text{‘}J \cap \text{comp} \,.\supset .\, \text{D}\text{‘}\text{lt}_P = C\text{‘}P \quad [*270\cdot21]$

Thus if a relation is compact and contained in diversity, every member of its field is a limit-point.

$*270\cdot212.\quad \vdash : P \in \text{connex} \,.\, \text{D}\text{‘}\text{lt}_P = C\text{‘}P \,.\supset .\, P \in \text{comp}$

Dem.

$\vdash .\, *207\cdot34 \,.\supset \vdash : \text{Hp} \,.\supset .\, C\text{‘}P \subset - \text{Ꭰ}\text{‘}(P \dot{-} P^2) \,.$

$[*33\cdot251] \quad \supset .\, \text{Ꭰ}\text{‘}(P \dot{-} P^2) = \Lambda \,.$

$[*270\cdot1] \quad \supset .\, P \in \text{comp} : \supset \vdash .\, \text{Prop}$

$*270\cdot22.\quad \vdash :.\, P \in \text{Rl}\text{‘}J \cap \text{connex} \,.\supset : P \in \text{comp} \,.\equiv .\, \text{D}\text{‘}\text{lt}_P = C\text{‘}P \,.\equiv .\, \text{Ꭰ}\text{‘}P \subset \text{D}\text{‘}\text{lt}_P$
$[*270\cdot211\cdot212 \,.\, *207\cdot18]$

$*270\cdot23.\quad \vdash : P \in \text{comp} - \iota\text{‘}\dot{\Lambda} \,.\supset .\, P \sim \in \text{Bord}$

Dem.

$\vdash .\, *270\cdot201 \,.\supset \vdash : \text{Hp} \,.\supset .\, (\exists \alpha) \,.\, \alpha \subset C\text{‘}P \,.\, \exists ! \, \alpha \,.\, \sim \exists ! \, \overrightarrow{\text{min}}_P \text{‘} \alpha \,.$

$[*250\cdot101] \quad \supset .\, P \sim \in \text{Bord} : \supset \vdash .\, \text{Prop}$

$*270\cdot24.\quad \vdash : P \in \text{Ser} \cap \text{comp} - \iota\text{‘}\dot{\Lambda} \,.\supset .\, C\text{‘}P \sim \in \text{Cls induct}$

Dem.

$\vdash .\, *270\cdot23 \,.\supset \vdash : \text{Hp} \,.\supset .\, P \sim \in \Omega \,.$

$[*261\cdot31] \quad \supset .\, C\text{‘}P \sim \in \text{Cls induct} : \supset \vdash .\, \text{Prop}$

$*270\cdot3.\quad \vdash : P \in \text{Ser} \cap \text{comp} \,.\supset .\, \text{sect}\text{‘}P - \text{D}\text{‘}P_\epsilon = P_* \text{“} C\text{‘}P$
$[*211\cdot351 \,.\, *270\cdot15]$

***270·31.** $\vdash : P \in \text{trans} \cap \text{comp} . \supset . \text{D}`P_\epsilon = \text{D}`(P_\epsilon \dot{\cap} I)$ [*211·51 . *270·14]

***270·32.** $\vdash : P \in \text{trans} \cap \text{comp} . \supset . \overrightarrow{P}`x \in \text{D}`(P_\epsilon \dot{\cap} I)$ [*211·452 . *270·1]

***270·321.** $\vdash : \overrightarrow{P}``C`P \subset \text{D}`(P_\epsilon \dot{\cap} I) . \supset . P \in \text{comp}$ [*211·451 . *270·1]

***270·322.** $\vdash :. P \in \text{trans} . \supset : \overrightarrow{P}``C`P \subset \text{D}`(P_\epsilon \dot{\cap} I) . \equiv . P \in \text{comp}$
[*270·32·321]

***270·33.** $\vdash :. P \in \text{Ser} . \supset : P \in \text{comp} . \equiv . \text{Ɑ}`\text{max}_P \cap \text{Ɑ}`\text{seq}_P = \Lambda$
[*211·551 . *270·14]

***270·34.** $\vdash : P \in \text{trans} \cap \text{comp} . \supset . \varsigma`P = \text{sgm}`P$ [*270·31 . (*212·01·02)]

***270·35.** $\vdash :. P \in \text{trans} \cap \text{connex} \cap \text{comp} . \supset : P \in \text{Ded} . \equiv . \text{Ɑ}`\text{max}_P = - \text{Ɑ}`\text{seq}_P$
[*214·4 . *270·13]

***270·351.** $\vdash :. P \in \text{Ser} . \supset : P \in \text{comp} \cap \text{Ded} . \equiv . \text{Ɑ}`\text{max}_P = - \text{Ɑ}`\text{seq}_P$
[*214·41 . *270·14]

A series which is compact and Dedekindian is one which has Dedekindian continuity. Thus the above proposition states that a series which has Dedekindian continuity is a series such that every class has either a maximum or a sequent, but not both.

***270·352.** $\vdash : P \in \text{Ser} \cap \text{comp} \cap \text{Ded} . \alpha \in \text{sect}`P . \supset . \text{limax}_P`\alpha = \text{limin}_P`(C`P - \alpha)$
[*214·42]

***270·36.** $\vdash : P \in \text{Rl}`J \cap \text{comp} . \supset . \delta_P`C`P = \text{Ɑ}`P . \nabla`P = P$
[*216·2 . *270·211 . (*216·05)]

***270·4.** $\vdash : P \in \text{comp} . \supset . \text{Nr}`P \subset \text{comp}$

Dem.

$\vdash . *201{\cdot}2 . \quad \supset \vdash : S \in P \,\overline{\text{smor}}\, Q . \supset . (S ; Q)^2 = S ; Q^2 . P = S ; Q$ (1)

$\vdash . (1) . *270{\cdot}1 . \supset \vdash : P \in \text{comp} . S \in P \,\overline{\text{smor}}\, Q . \supset . S ; Q \subset S ; Q^2 .$

[*150·31] $\supset . \breve{S} ; S ; Q \subset \breve{S} ; S ; Q^2 .$

[*151·252] $\supset . Q \subset Q^2 : \supset \vdash . \text{Prop}$

***270·401.** $\vdash : P \in \text{comp} . \equiv . \text{N}_0\text{r}`P \subset \text{comp}$ [*270·4 . *155·12]

***270·41.** $\vdash : P \in \text{Ser} \cap \text{comp} . \supset . \text{Nr}`P \subset \text{Ser} \cap \text{comp}$ [*270·4 . *204·22]

***270·411.** $\vdash : P \in \text{Ser} \cap \text{comp} . \equiv . \text{N}_0\text{r}`P \subset \text{Ser} \cap \text{comp}$ [*270·41 . *155·12]

***270·42.** $\vdash : P \in \text{comp} . \supset . P \upharpoonright \overleftarrow{P_*}`x , P \upharpoonright \overrightarrow{P_*}`x \in \text{comp}$

Dem.

$\vdash . *270{\cdot}11 . \supset \vdash : \text{Hp} . y, z \in \overleftarrow{P_*}`x . yPz . \supset . (\exists w) . yPw . wPz .$

[*90·16] $\supset . (\exists w) . w \in \overleftarrow{P_*}`x . yPw . wPz$ (1)

$\vdash . (1) . *270{\cdot}11 . \supset \vdash : \text{Hp} . \supset . P \upharpoonright \overleftarrow{P_*}`x \in \text{comp}$ (2)

Similarly $\vdash : \text{Hp} . \supset . P \upharpoonright \overrightarrow{P_*}`x \in \text{comp}$ (3)

$\vdash . (2) . (3) . \supset \vdash . \text{Prop}$

***270·5.** $\vdash : P, Q \in \text{Ser} \cap \text{comp} \,.\, C\text{‘}P \cap C\text{‘}Q = \Lambda \,.\, \sim(\text{E}\,!\,B\text{‘}\breve{P} \,.\, \text{E}\,!\,B\text{‘}Q) \,.\supset.$
$P \ddagger Q \in \text{Ser} \cap \text{comp}$

Dem.

$\vdash .\, *160{\cdot}51 \,.\quad \supset \vdash : \text{Hp} \,.\supset.\, (P \ddagger Q)^2 = P^2 \cup Q^2 \cup \text{D}\text{‘}P \uparrow C\text{‘}Q \cup C\text{‘}P \uparrow \text{Ɑ}\text{‘}Q$

$[*93{\cdot}103.\text{Hp}] \qquad = P^2 \cup Q^2 \cup C\text{‘}P \uparrow C\text{‘}Q \qquad (1)$

$\vdash .\, (1) \,.\, *270{\cdot}1 \,.\supset \vdash : \text{Hp} \,.\supset.\, P \ddagger Q \Subset (P \ddagger Q)^2 \qquad (2)$

$\vdash .\, (2) \,.\, *204{\cdot}5 \,.\supset \vdash .\, \text{Prop}$

***270·51.** $\vdash : P \in \text{Ser} \cap \text{comp} \,.\, C\text{‘}P \subset \text{Ser} \cap \text{comp} \,.\, P \in \text{Rel}^2\,\text{excl} \,.\supset.$
$\Sigma\text{‘}P \in \text{Ser} \cap \text{comp}$

Dem.

$\vdash .\, *204{\cdot}52 \,.\supset \vdash : \text{Hp} \,.\supset.\, \Sigma\text{‘}P \in \text{Ser} \qquad (1)$

$\vdash .\, *162{\cdot}1 \,.\supset$

$\vdash .\, (\Sigma\text{‘}P)^2 = (\dot{s}\text{‘}C\text{‘}P)^2 \cup (F \mathbin{;} P)^2 \cup (\dot{s}\text{‘}C\text{‘}P) \,|\, (F \mathbin{;} P) \cup (F \mathbin{;} P) \,|\, (\dot{s}\text{‘}C\text{‘}P) \qquad (2)$

$\vdash .\, *270{\cdot}1 \,.\supset \vdash : \text{Hp} \,.\, x\, (\dot{s}\text{‘}C\text{‘}P)\, y \,.\supset.\, (\exists Q) \,.\, Q \in C\text{‘}P \,.\, x Q^2 y \,.$

$[*41{\cdot}13] \qquad \supset .\, x\, (\dot{s}\text{‘}C\text{‘}P)^2\, y \qquad (3)$

$\vdash .\, *270{\cdot}1 \,.\supset \vdash : \text{Hp} \,.\, x\, (F \mathbin{;} P)\, y \,.\supset.\, x\, (F \mathbin{;} P^2)\, y \,.$

$[*163{\cdot}12.*201{\cdot}2] \qquad \supset .\, x\, (F \mathbin{;} P)^2\, y \qquad (4)$

$\vdash .\, (2) \,.\, (3) \,.\, (4) \,.\, *162{\cdot}1 \,.\supset \vdash : \text{Hp} \,.\supset.\, \Sigma\text{‘}P \Subset (\Sigma\text{‘}P)^2 \qquad (5)$

$\vdash .\, (1) \,.\, (5) \,.\supset \vdash .\, \text{Prop}$

The hypothesis of *270·51 is in excess of what is required for the conclusion, which only requires, in place of $P \in \text{comp}$, that there should be no two consecutive relations in $C\text{‘}P$ of which the first has a last term while the second has a first term. This is proved in the following proposition.

***270·52.** $\vdash : P \in \text{Ser} \cap \text{Rel}^2\,\text{excl} \,.\, C\text{‘}P \subset \text{Ser} \cap \text{comp} \,.$
$B\text{‘‘}\breve{P}_1\text{‘‘}(C\text{‘}P \cap \text{Cnv}\text{‘‘}\text{Ɑ}\text{‘}B) = \Lambda \,.\supset.\, \Sigma\text{‘}P \in \text{Ser} \cap \text{comp}$

Dem.

$\vdash .\, *270{\cdot}1 \,.\, *163{\cdot}12 \,.\supset \vdash : \text{Hp} \,.\supset.\, \dot{s}\text{‘}C\text{‘}P \Subset (\dot{s}\text{‘}C\text{‘}P)^2 \qquad (1)$

$\vdash .\, *201{\cdot}63 \,. \qquad \supset \vdash : \text{Hp} \,.\supset.\, F \mathbin{;} P = F \mathbin{;} P_1 \cup F \mathbin{;} P^2 \qquad (2)$

$\vdash .\, *93{\cdot}103 \,. \qquad \supset \vdash :.\, \text{Hp} \,.\, Q P_1 R \,.\supset :\, \text{D}\text{‘}Q = C\text{‘}Q \,.\vee.\, \text{Ɑ}\text{‘}R = C\text{‘}R \qquad (3)$

$\vdash .\, (3) \,.\supset \vdash :.\, \text{Hp} \,.\, x\, (F \mathbin{;} P_1)\, y \,.\supset :$

$(\exists Q, R) : x \in \text{D}\text{‘}Q \,.\, y \in C\text{‘}R \,.\vee.\, x \in C\text{‘}Q \,.\, y \in \text{Ɑ}\text{‘}R : Q P_1 R :$

$[*33{\cdot}13{\cdot}131{\cdot}17]$

$\supset : (\exists Q, R, z) : x Q z \,.\, z \in C\text{‘}Q \,.\, y \in C\text{‘}R \,.\vee.\, x \in C\text{‘}Q \,.\, z \in C\text{‘}R \,.\, z R y : Q P_1 R :$

$[*150{\cdot}52.*201{\cdot}63] \quad \supset : x\, \{(\dot{s}\text{‘}C\text{‘}P) \,|\, (F \mathbin{;} P)\}\, y \,.\vee.\, x\, \{(F \mathbin{;} P) \,|\, (\dot{s}\text{‘}C\text{‘}P)\}\, y :$

$[*162{\cdot}1] \qquad \supset : x\, (\Sigma\text{‘}P)^2\, y \qquad (4)$

$\vdash .\, *163{\cdot}12 \,.\, *201{\cdot}2 \,.\supset \vdash : \text{Hp} \,.\supset.\, F \mathbin{;} P^2 = (F \mathbin{;} P)^2 \qquad (5)$

$\vdash .\, (2) \,.\, (5) \,.\, *162{\cdot}1 \,.\supset \vdash : \text{Hp} \,.\supset.\, F \mathbin{;} P \Subset (\Sigma\text{‘}P)^2 \qquad (6)$

$\vdash .\, (1) \,.\, (6) \,.\, *162{\cdot}1 \,.\supset \vdash : \text{Hp} \,.\supset.\, \Sigma\text{‘}P \Subset (\Sigma\text{‘}P)^2 \qquad (7)$

$\vdash .\, (4) \,.\, (7) \,.\, *204{\cdot}52 \,.\supset \vdash .\, \text{Prop}$

∗270·521. $\vdash :. P \in \mathrm{Ser} \cap \mathrm{Rel}^2\,\mathrm{excl}\,.\, C\text{‘}P \subset \mathrm{Ser} \cap \mathrm{comp}:$

$C\text{‘}P \cap \mathrm{Cnv}\text{“}\text{ᗡ}\text{‘}B = \Lambda \,.\vee.\, C\text{‘}P \cap \text{ᗡ}\text{‘}B = \Lambda :\supset .\, \Sigma\text{‘}P \in \mathrm{Ser} \cap \mathrm{comp}$ [∗270·52]

∗270·53. $\vdash : P \in \mathrm{Ser} \,.\, Q \in \mathrm{Ser} \cap \mathrm{comp} \,.\, \sim(\mathrm{E}!\,B\text{‘}Q \,.\, \mathrm{E}!\,B\text{‘}\breve{Q}) \,.\supset.\, P \times Q \in \mathrm{Ser} \cap \mathrm{comp}$

Dem.

$\vdash .\, ∗166·1 \,.\supset\vdash .\, P \times Q = \Sigma\text{‘}Q \underset{;}{\downarrow} ;P$ (1)

$\vdash .\, ∗165·21 \,.\supset\vdash .\, Q \underset{;}{\downarrow} ;P \in \mathrm{Rel}^2\,\mathrm{excl}$ (2)

$\vdash .\, ∗165·25 \,.\, ∗204·21 \,.\supset\vdash : \mathrm{Hp} \,.\, \dot{\exists}!\,P \,.\supset.\, Q \underset{;}{\downarrow} ;P \in \mathrm{Ser}$ (3)

$\vdash .\, ∗165·26 \,.\, ∗270·4 \,.\supset\vdash : \mathrm{Hp} \,.\supset.\, C\text{‘}Q \underset{;}{\downarrow} ;P \subset \mathrm{Ser} \cap \mathrm{comp}$ (4)

$\vdash .\, ∗151·5 \,.\, ∗165·26 \,.\supset\vdash : \mathrm{Hp} \,.\sim \mathrm{E}!\,B\text{‘}Q \,.\supset.\, C\text{‘}Q \underset{;}{\downarrow} ;P \cap \text{ᗡ}\text{‘}B = \Lambda$ (5)

$\vdash .\, ∗151·5 \,.\, ∗165·26 \,.\supset\vdash : \mathrm{Hp} \,.\sim \mathrm{E}!\,B\text{‘}\breve{Q} \,.\supset.\, C\text{‘}Q \underset{;}{\downarrow} ;P \cap \mathrm{Cnv}\text{“}\text{ᗡ}\text{‘}B = \Lambda$ (6)

$\vdash .\, (1) \,.\, (2) \,.\, (3) \,.\, (4) \,.\, (5) \,.\, (6) \,.\, ∗270·521 \,.\supset$

$\vdash : \mathrm{Hp} \,.\, \dot{\exists}!\,P \,.\supset.\, P \times Q \in \mathrm{Ser} \cap \mathrm{comp}$ (7)

$\vdash .\, ∗166·13 \,.\supset\vdash : P = \dot{\Lambda} \,.\supset.\, P \times Q \in \mathrm{Ser} \cap \mathrm{comp}$ (8)

$\vdash .\, (7) \,.\, (8) \,.\supset\vdash .$ Prop

∗270·54. $\vdash : P \in \mathrm{Ser} \cap \mathrm{comp} \,.\sim \mathrm{E}!\,B\text{‘}\breve{P} \,.\, x \sim\in C\text{‘}P \,.\supset.\, P \mapsto x \in \mathrm{Ser} \cap \mathrm{comp}$

Dem.

$\vdash .\, ∗204·51 \,.\quad \supset\vdash : \mathrm{Hp} \,.\supset.\, P \mapsto x \in \mathrm{Ser}$ (1)

$\vdash .\, ∗161·1 \,.\quad \supset\vdash : \mathrm{Hp} \,.\supset.\, (P \mapsto x)^2 = P^2 \cup \mathrm{D}\text{‘}P \uparrow \iota\text{‘}x$

[∗93·103] $\qquad = P^2 \cup C\text{‘}P \uparrow \iota\text{‘}x$ (2)

$\vdash .\, (2) \,.\, ∗270·1 \,.\supset\vdash : \mathrm{Hp} \,.\supset.\, P \mapsto x \in (P \mapsto x)^2 .$ (3)

$\vdash .\, (1) \,.\, (3) \,.\supset\vdash .$ Prop

∗270·541. $\vdash : P \in \mathrm{Ser} \cap \mathrm{comp} \,.\sim \mathrm{E}!\,B\text{‘}P \,.\, x \sim\in C\text{‘}P \,.\supset.\, x \leftarrow\!\!\!+ P \in \mathrm{Ser} \cap \mathrm{comp}$

[Proof as in ∗270·54]

∗270·55. $\vdash : P \in \Omega \,.\, C\text{‘}P \subset \mathrm{Ser} \,.\sim \mathrm{E}!\,B\text{‘}\breve{P} \,.\, C\text{‘}P \cap \mathrm{Cnv}\text{“}\text{ᗡ}\text{‘}B = \Lambda \,.\supset.$

$\Pi\text{‘}P \in \mathrm{Ser} \cap \mathrm{comp}$

Dem.

$\vdash .\, ∗251·3 \,.\supset\vdash : \mathrm{Hp} \,.\supset.\, \Pi\text{‘}P \in \mathrm{Ser}$ (1)

$\vdash .\, ∗250·21 \,.\, ∗93·103 \,.\supset$

$\vdash : \mathrm{Hp} \,.\, Q \in C\text{‘}P \,.\, M \in F_\Delta\text{‘}C\text{‘}P \,.\supset.\, (\exists x) \,.\, (M\text{‘}\breve{P}_1\text{‘}Q)(\breve{P}_1\text{‘}Q)\,x$ (2)

$\vdash .\, ∗200·43 \,.\supset$

$\vdash : \mathrm{Hp}(2) \,.\, (M\text{‘}\breve{P}_1\text{‘}Q)(\breve{P}_1\text{‘}Q)x \,.\, L = M \upharpoonright (-\iota\text{‘}\breve{P}_1\text{‘}Q) \cup x \downarrow (\breve{P}_1\text{‘}Q) \,.\supset.\, M(\Pi\text{‘}P)\,L$ (3)

$\vdash .\, ∗200·43 \,.\supset$

$\vdash : \mathrm{Hp}(3) \,.\, N \in F_\Delta\text{‘}C\text{‘}P \,.\, (M\text{‘}Q)\,Q\,(N\text{‘}Q) \,.\, M \upharpoonright \overrightarrow{P}\text{‘}Q = N \upharpoonright \overrightarrow{P}\text{‘}Q \,.\supset.\, L(\Pi\text{‘}P)\,N$ (4)

$\vdash .\, (2) \,.\, (3) \,.\, (4) \,.\supset$

$\vdash : \mathrm{Hp} \,.\, M, N \in F_\Delta\text{‘}C\text{‘}P \,.\, Q \in C\text{‘}P \,.\, (M\text{‘}Q)\,Q\,(N\text{‘}Q) \,.\, M \upharpoonright \overrightarrow{P}\text{‘}Q = N \upharpoonright \overrightarrow{P}\text{‘}Q \,.\supset.$

$(\exists L) \,.\, M(\Pi\text{‘}P)\,L \,.\, L(\Pi\text{‘}P)\,N$ (5)

$\vdash .\, (5) \,.\, ∗200·43 \,.\supset\vdash : \mathrm{Hp} \,.\supset.\, \Pi\text{‘}P \in (\Pi\text{‘}P)^2$ (6)

$\vdash .\, (1) \,.\, (6) \,.\supset\vdash .$ Prop

$*270\cdot56$. $\vdash : P \in \text{Ser} . Q \in \Omega . \sim E ! B \text{‘} \breve{P} . \sim E ! B \text{‘} \breve{Q} . \supset . P^Q \in \text{Ser} \cap \text{comp}$

Dem.

$\vdash . *176\cdot151 . \quad \supset \vdash : P = \dot{\Lambda} . \supset . P^Q \in \text{Ser} \cap \text{comp}$ (1)

$\vdash . *176\cdot181\cdot182 . \quad \supset \vdash . P^Q \,\text{smor}\, \Pi \text{‘} P \downarrow ; Q$ (2)

$\vdash . *165\cdot25 . *251\cdot121 . \supset \vdash : \text{Hp} . \dot{\exists} ! P . \supset . P \downarrow ; Q \in \Omega$ (3)

$\vdash . *165\cdot26 . *204\cdot21 . \quad \supset \vdash : \text{Hp} . \supset . C \text{‘} P \downarrow ; Q \subset \text{Ser}$ (4)

$\vdash . *165\cdot25 . *151\cdot5 . \quad \supset \vdash : \text{Hp} . \dot{\exists} ! P . \supset . \sim E ! B \text{‘} \text{Cnv} \text{‘} P \downarrow ; Q$ (5)

$\vdash . *165\cdot26 . *151\cdot5 . \quad \supset \vdash : \text{Hp} . \supset . C \text{‘} P \downarrow ; Q \cap \text{Cnv} \text{‘‘} \text{Ƈ} \text{‘} B = \Lambda$ (6)

$\vdash . (3) . (4) . (5) . (6) . *270\cdot55 . \supset \vdash : \text{Hp} . \dot{\exists} ! P . \supset . \Pi \text{‘} P \downarrow ; Q \in \text{Ser} \cap \text{comp} .$

$[(2) . *270\cdot41] \qquad \supset . P^Q \in \text{Ser} \cap \text{comp}$ (7)

$\vdash . (1) . (7) . \supset \vdash . \text{Prop}$

By means of the above proposition, compact series can be manufactured by taking series of such types as $\omega \exp_r \omega$, $\omega \exp_r \omega_1$, $\omega_1 \exp_r \omega$, etc. Any power $\alpha \exp_r \beta$ consists of compact series, if β is an ordinal having no immediate predecessor, and α is any serial number having no immediate predecessor (*i.e.* not formed by adding $\dot{1}$ to a serial number).

$*271$. MEDIAN CLASSES IN SERIES.

Summary of $*271$.

We shall call a class α a "median" class in P if $\alpha \subset C\text{‘}P$ and there is a member of α between any two terms of which one has the relation P to the other. When this is the case, we have

$$xPy \,.\supset_{x,y}.\, (\exists z) \,.\, z \in \alpha \,.\, xPz \,.\, zPy,$$

i.e.

$$P \mathrel{\dot{\subset}} P \upharpoonright \alpha \,|\, P.$$

Thus P cannot contain any median class unless P is compact. Conversely, if P is compact, $C\text{‘}P$ is a median class. Hence relations containing median classes are the same as compact relations. Median classes are important in dealing with rational and continuous series: the rationals are a median class in the series of real numbers, and the series which Cantor calls continuous are characterized by the fact that, in addition to being Dedekindian, they contain a median class which forms a series of the same type as the rationals. If P is a compact series, the class $\overrightarrow{P}\text{‘‘}\text{Ɑ}\text{‘}P$ is a median class in the series $\varsigma\text{‘}P$ ($*271{\cdot}31$). This fact is used in proving that the series of segments of a rational series is a continuous series.

Our definition is

$$\text{med} = \hat{\alpha}\hat{P}(\alpha \subset C\text{‘}P \,.\, P \mathrel{\dot{\subset}} P \upharpoonright \alpha \,|\, P) \quad \text{Df.}$$

Thus $\overrightarrow{\text{med}}\text{‘}P$ will be the median classes of P, and "$P \in \text{Ɑ}\text{‘med}$" means that there are median classes of P. We have $\text{Ɑ}\text{‘med} = \text{comp}$ ($*271{\cdot}18$); also

$*271{\cdot}15$. $\vdash : \alpha \,\text{med}\, P \,.\supset.\, P, P \upharpoonleft \alpha \in \text{comp}$

$*271{\cdot}16$. $\vdash : (\alpha \cap C\text{‘}P) \,\text{med}\, P \,.\equiv.\, (\alpha \cap \text{D}\text{‘}P) \,\text{med}\, P \,.\equiv.\, (\alpha \cap \text{Ɑ}\text{‘}P) \,\text{med}\, P \,.$
$\equiv . (\alpha \cap \text{D}\text{‘}P \cap \text{Ɑ}\text{‘}P) \,\text{med}\, P$

If P is a series, and $\alpha \subset C\text{‘}P$, α is a median class when, and only when, its derivative is $\text{Ɑ}\text{‘}P$, *i.e.*

$*271{\cdot}2$. $\vdash :. P \in \text{Ser} \,.\, \alpha \subset C\text{‘}P \,.\supset : \alpha \,\text{med}\, P \,.\equiv.\, \text{Ɑ}\text{‘}P = \delta_P\text{‘}\alpha$

An important proposition is

$*271{\cdot}39$. $\vdash : P, Q \in \text{Ser} \cap \text{Ded} \,.\, \alpha \,\text{med}\, P \,.\, \beta \,\text{med}\, Q \,.\, (P \upharpoonleft \alpha) \,\text{smor}\, (Q \upharpoonleft \beta) \,.\supset.$
$P \,\text{smor}\, Q$

I.e. if P and Q are Dedekindian series, and α, β are median classes of P and Q respectively, then if $P \upharpoonleft \alpha$ and $Q \upharpoonleft \beta$ are similar, so are P and Q. This proposition is proved by showing that P is similar to the series of segments of $P \upharpoonright \alpha$, the correlator being lt_P with its converse domain limited (∗271·37). Another important proposition is

∗271·4. $\vdash : S \in P \,\overline{\mathrm{smor}}\, Q \,.\, \beta \operatorname{med} Q \,.\, \supset . \, (S``\beta) \operatorname{med} P$

I.e. a correlator of P with Q correlates median classes with median classes.

The above two propositions are used in ∗275·3·31, which prove that two series which are continuous (in Cantor's sense) are similar, and that a series similar to a continuous series is continuous.

∗271·01. $\operatorname{med} = \hat{\alpha}\hat{P}(\alpha \subset C`P \,.\, P \Subset P \upharpoonright \alpha \,|\, P)$ Df

∗271·1. $\vdash :. \alpha \operatorname{med} P \,.\equiv: \alpha \subset C`P \,.\, P \Subset P \upharpoonright \alpha \,|\, P :\equiv:$

$\alpha \subset C`P : xPy \,.\supset_{x,y} .\, \exists ! \alpha \cap \overleftarrow{P}`x \cap \overrightarrow{P}`y$ [(∗271·01)]

∗271·11. $\vdash : \alpha \operatorname{med} P \,.\equiv.\, \alpha \operatorname{med} \breve{P}$ [∗271·1]

∗271·13. $\vdash : \alpha \operatorname{med} P \,.\, \beta \subset C`P \,.\supset.\, (\alpha \cup \beta) \operatorname{med} P$ [∗271·1]

∗271·14. $\vdash : \alpha \operatorname{med} P \,.\supset.\, C`P \upharpoonright \alpha \operatorname{med} (P \upharpoonright \alpha)$

Dem.

$\vdash .$ ∗271·1 $. \supset$

$\vdash :. \alpha \operatorname{med} P \,.\supset: x, y \in \alpha \,.\, xPy \,.\supset_{x,y} .\, (\exists z) \,.\, z \in \alpha \,.\, xPz \,.\, zPy \,.$

[∗35·102] $\supset_{x,y} .\, (\exists z) \,.\, z \in \alpha \,.\, x(P \upharpoonright \alpha)z \,.\, z(P \upharpoonright \alpha)y :$

[∗35·102.∗271·1] $\supset : C`P \upharpoonright \alpha \operatorname{med} (P \upharpoonright \alpha) :. \supset \vdash .$ Prop

∗271·15. $\vdash : \alpha \operatorname{med} P \,.\supset.\, P, P \upharpoonright \alpha \in \mathrm{comp}$

Dem.

$\vdash .$ ∗271·1 $. \quad \supset \vdash : \mathrm{Hp} \,.\supset.\, P \Subset P^2 .$

[∗270·1] $\supset .\, P \in \mathrm{comp}$ (1)

$\vdash . (1) .$ ∗271·14 $. \supset \vdash : \mathrm{Hp} \,.\supset.\, P \upharpoonright \alpha \in \mathrm{comp}$ (2)

$\vdash . (1) . (2) . \supset \vdash .$ Prop

∗271·16. $\vdash : (\alpha \cap C`P) \operatorname{med} P \,.\equiv.\, (\alpha \cap D`P) \operatorname{med} P \,.\equiv.\, (\alpha \cap \text{G}`P) \operatorname{med} P \,.$

$\equiv .\, (\alpha \cap D`P \cap \text{G}`P) \operatorname{med} P$

Dem.

$\vdash .$ ∗271·1 $.$ ∗33·15 $. \supset$

$\vdash :. (\alpha \cap C`P) \operatorname{med} P \,.\equiv: xPy \,.\supset_{x,y} .\, \exists ! \alpha \cap D`P \cap \overleftarrow{P}`x \cap \overrightarrow{P}`y :$

[∗271·1] $\equiv : (\alpha \cap D`P) \operatorname{med} P$ (1)

$\vdash .$ ∗271·1 $.$ ∗33·151 $. \supset \vdash : (\alpha \cap C`P) \operatorname{med} P \,.\equiv.\, (\alpha \cap \text{G}`P) \operatorname{med} P$ (2)

$\vdash .$ ∗271·1 $.$ ∗33·15·151 $. \supset$

$\vdash :. (\alpha \cap C`P) \operatorname{med} P \,.\equiv: xPy \,.\supset_{x,y} .\, \exists ! \alpha \cap D`P \cap \text{G}`P \cap \overleftarrow{P}`x \cap \overrightarrow{P}`y :$

[∗271·1] $\equiv : (\alpha \cap D`P \cap \text{G}`P) \operatorname{med} P$ (3)

$\vdash . (1) . (2) . (3) . \supset \vdash .$ Prop

$*271 \cdot 17.\ \vdash : P \in \text{comp} \,.\supset .\, C\text{‘}P, \text{D‘}P, \text{ᗡ‘}P \in \overrightarrow{\text{med}}\text{‘}P$

Dem.

$\vdash .\, *35 \cdot 452 \,.\, *270 \cdot 1 \,.\supset \vdash : P \in \text{comp} \,.\supset .\, P \subseteq P \upharpoonright \text{ᗡ‘}P \,|\, P \,.$

$[*271 \cdot 1] \qquad \supset .\, \text{ᗡ‘}P \in \overrightarrow{\text{med}}\text{‘}P \,. \qquad (1)$

$[*271 \cdot 13] \qquad \supset .\, C\text{‘}P \in \overrightarrow{\text{med}}\text{‘}P \,. \qquad (2)$

$[*271 \cdot 16] \qquad \supset .\, \text{D‘}P \in \overrightarrow{\text{med}}\text{‘}P \qquad (3)$

$\vdash .\, (1) \,.\, (2) \,.\, (3) \,.\supset \vdash .\, \text{Prop}$

$*271 \cdot 18.\ \vdash .\, \text{ᗡ‘med} = \text{comp} \quad [*271 \cdot 15 \cdot 17]$

$*271 \cdot 2.\ \vdash :.\, P \in \text{Ser} \,.\, \alpha \subset C\text{‘}P \,.\supset : \alpha \,\text{med}\, P \,.\equiv .\, \text{ᗡ‘}P = \delta_P\text{‘}\alpha \quad [*216 \cdot 13 \,.\, *271 \cdot 1]$

$*271 \cdot 3.\ \vdash : P \in \text{Rl‘}J \cap \text{trans} \,.\, \alpha \,\text{med}\, P \,.\supset .\, \overrightarrow{P}\text{‘‘}\alpha \,\text{med}\, (\varsigma\text{‘}P)$

Dem.

$\vdash .\, *271 \cdot 15 \,.\, *270 \cdot 34 \,.\supset \vdash : \text{Hp} \,.\supset .\, \varsigma\text{‘}P = \text{sgm‘}P \,.$

$[*212 \cdot 11] \qquad \supset .\, \varsigma\text{‘}P = \hat{\beta}\hat{\gamma}\{\beta, \gamma \in \text{D‘}(P_\epsilon \dot{\cap} I) \,.\, \exists ! \gamma - \beta\} \qquad (1)$

$\vdash .\, (1) \,.\, *211 \cdot 12 \,.\supset \vdash : \text{Hp} \,.\, \beta (\varsigma\text{‘}P) \gamma \,.\supset .\, \exists ! \gamma - \beta \,.\, P\text{‘‘}\gamma = \gamma \,.\, P\text{‘‘}\beta = \beta \,.$

$[*37 \cdot 1] \qquad \supset .\, (\exists x, y) \,.\, x \in \gamma - \beta \,.\, xPy \,.\, y \in \gamma \,.$

$[*271 \cdot 1] \qquad \supset .\, (\exists x, y, z) \,.\, x \in \gamma - \beta \,.\, xPz \,.\, zPy \,.\, z \in \alpha \,.\, y \in \gamma \,.$

$[*201 \cdot 12] \qquad \supset .\, (\exists x, y, z) \,.\, x \in \gamma - \beta \,.\, xPz \,.\, zPy \,.\, z \in \alpha \,.\, y \in \gamma \,.\, \sim (yPz) \,.$

$[*32 \cdot 18] \qquad \supset .\, (\exists z) \,.\, z \in \alpha \,.\, \exists ! \overrightarrow{P}\text{‘}z - \beta \,.\, \exists ! \gamma - \overrightarrow{P}\text{‘}z \,.$

$[(1) . *270 \cdot 322] \qquad \supset .\, (\exists z) \,.\, z \in \alpha \,.\, \beta (\varsigma\text{‘}P) (\overrightarrow{P}\text{‘}z) \,.\, (\overrightarrow{P}\text{‘}z) (\varsigma\text{‘}P) \gamma \qquad (2)$

$\vdash .\, (2) \,.\, *271 \cdot 1 \,.\supset \vdash .\, \text{Prop}$

$*271 \cdot 31.\ \vdash : P \in \text{Rl‘}J \cap \text{trans} \cap \text{comp} \,.\supset .\, \overrightarrow{P}\text{‘‘ᗡ‘}P \,\text{med}\, (\varsigma\text{‘}P) \quad [*271 \cdot 3 \cdot 17]$

The following propositions lead up to the proposition

$*271 \cdot 37.\ \vdash : P \in \text{Ser} \cap \text{Ded} \,.\, \alpha \,\text{med}\, P \,.\supset .\, \text{lt}_P \upharpoonright C\text{‘}\varsigma\text{‘}(P \upharpoonright \alpha) \in P \,\overline{\text{smor}}\, \{\varsigma\text{‘}(P \upharpoonright \alpha)\}$

whence, if α is a median class of P, P is similar to the series of segments of $P \upharpoonright \alpha$. This proposition is used in proving that every continuous series is similar to the series of segments of a rational series.

$*271 \cdot 32.\ \vdash : P \in \text{Ser} \,.\, R = P \upharpoonright \alpha \,.\, \beta \in \text{D‘}R_\epsilon \,.\, \text{E} ! \,\text{lt}_P\text{‘}\beta \,.\supset .\, \beta = R\text{‘‘}\beta = \alpha \cap \overrightarrow{P}\text{‘lt}_P\text{‘}\beta$

Dem.

$\vdash .\, *205 \cdot 9 \,.\supset \vdash : \text{Hp} \,.\, \alpha \cap C\text{‘}P \sim \in 1 \,.\supset .\, \overrightarrow{\text{max}}_R\text{‘}\beta = \overrightarrow{\text{max}}_P (\alpha \cap \beta)$

$[*37 \cdot 413 . *211 \cdot 11] \qquad = \overrightarrow{\text{max}}_P\text{‘}\beta$

$[*207 \cdot 13] \qquad = \Lambda \qquad (1)$

$\vdash .\, (1) \,.\, *200 \cdot 35 \,.\supset \vdash : \text{Hp} \,.\supset .\, \overrightarrow{\text{max}}_R\text{‘}\beta = \Lambda \,.$

$[*211 \cdot 42 \cdot 12] \qquad \supset .\, \beta = R\text{‘‘}\beta \qquad (2)$

$\vdash .\, *207 \cdot 231 \,. \quad \supset \vdash : \text{Hp} \,.\supset .\, P\text{‘‘}\beta = \overrightarrow{P}\text{‘lt}_P\text{‘}\beta \,.$

$[*37 \cdot 413] \qquad \supset .\, R\text{‘‘}\beta = \alpha \cap \overrightarrow{P}\text{‘lt}_P\text{‘}\beta \qquad (3)$

$\vdash .\, (2) \,.\, (3) \,.\supset \vdash .\, \text{Prop}$

***271·321.** $\vdash : P \in \text{Ser} . R = P \upharpoonleft \alpha . \supset . \text{lt}_P \upharpoonright \text{D}`R_\epsilon \in 1 \to 1$

Dem.

$\vdash . *271\cdot32 . \supset \vdash : \text{Hp} . \beta, \gamma \in \text{D}`R_\epsilon . \text{lt}_P`\beta = \text{lt}_P`\gamma . \supset . \beta = \gamma : \supset \vdash . \text{Prop}$

***271·322.** $\vdash : P \in \text{Ser} . R = P \upharpoonleft \alpha . \supset . \text{lt}_P {}^\text{;} \varsigma`R \Subset P$

Dem.

$\vdash . *212\cdot23 . \supset \vdash :. \text{Hp} . \supset : x (\text{lt}_P {}^\text{;} \varsigma`R) y . \equiv .$
$(\exists \beta, \gamma) . \beta, \gamma \in \text{D}`R_\epsilon . \beta \subset \gamma . \beta \neq \gamma . x = \text{lt}_P`\beta . y = \text{lt}_P`\gamma .$

$[*207\cdot231] \quad \supset . (\exists \beta, \gamma) . \beta, \gamma \in \text{D}`R_\epsilon . \beta \subset \gamma . \beta \neq \gamma . \overrightarrow{P}`x = P``\beta . \overrightarrow{P}`y = P``\gamma .$

$[*37\cdot2 . *271\cdot321] \supset . \overrightarrow{P}`x \subset \overrightarrow{P}`y . x \neq y .$

$[*204\cdot33] \quad \supset . xPy :. \supset \vdash . \text{Prop}$

***271·33.** $\vdash : P \in \text{trans} . \alpha \,\text{med}\, P . \supset . \overrightarrow{P}`x = P``(\alpha \cap \overrightarrow{P}`x)$

Dem.

$\vdash . *201\cdot501 . \supset \vdash : \text{Hp} . \supset . P``\overrightarrow{P}`x \subset \overrightarrow{P}`x .$

$[*37\cdot2] \quad \supset . P``(\alpha \cap \overrightarrow{P}`x) \subset \overrightarrow{P}`x \quad (1)$

$\vdash . *271\cdot1 . \quad \supset \vdash :. \text{Hp} . \supset : yPx . \supset . (\exists z) . yPz . z \in \alpha . zPx .$

$[*37\cdot1] \quad \supset . y \in P``(\alpha \cap \overrightarrow{P}`x) \quad (2)$

$\vdash . (1) . (2) . \supset \vdash . \text{Prop}$

***271·331.** $\vdash : \text{Hp } *271\cdot33 . R = P \upharpoonleft \alpha . \supset . \alpha \cap \overrightarrow{P}`x = R``(\alpha \cap \overrightarrow{P}`x)$

Dem.

$\vdash . *271\cdot33 . \supset \vdash : \text{Hp} . \supset . \alpha \cap \overrightarrow{P}`x = \alpha \cap P``(\alpha \cap \overrightarrow{P}`x)$

$[*37\cdot413] \quad = R``(\alpha \cap \overrightarrow{P}`x) : \supset \vdash . \text{Prop}$

***271·332.** $\vdash : P \in \text{Ser} . \alpha \,\text{med}\, P . x \in C`P . \supset . x = \text{lt}_P`(\alpha \cap \overrightarrow{P}`x)$

Dem.

$\vdash . *271\cdot331 . \supset \vdash : \text{Hp} . \supset . \alpha \cap \overrightarrow{P}`x \subset P``(\alpha \cap \overrightarrow{P}`x) .$

$[*205\cdot123] \quad \supset . \text{max}_P`(\alpha \cap \overrightarrow{P}`x) = \Lambda \quad (1)$

$\vdash . (1) . *271\cdot33 . \supset$

$\vdash : \text{Hp} . \supset . x \in C`P . \overrightarrow{P}`x = P``(\alpha \cap \overrightarrow{P}`x) . \sim \text{E} ! \,\text{max}_P`(\alpha \cap \overrightarrow{P}`x) .$

$[*207\cdot521] \supset . x = \text{lt}_P`(\alpha \cap \overrightarrow{P}`x) : \supset \vdash . \text{Prop}$

***271·34.** $\vdash : P \in \text{Ser} . \alpha \,\text{med}\, P . \supset . P = \text{lt}_P {}^\text{;} \varsigma`(P \upharpoonleft \alpha)$

Dem.

$\vdash . *271\cdot331 . *211\cdot11 . \supset \vdash : \text{Hp} . R = P \upharpoonleft \alpha . \supset . \alpha \cap \overrightarrow{P}`x \in \text{D}`R_\epsilon \quad (1)$

$\vdash . *204\cdot33 . \quad \supset \vdash : \text{Hp} . xPy . \supset . \alpha \cap \overrightarrow{P}`x \subset \alpha \cap \overrightarrow{P}`y \quad (2)$

$\vdash . *271\cdot332 . \supset \vdash : \text{Hp} . xPy . \supset . x = \text{lt}_P`(\alpha \cap \overrightarrow{P}`x) . y = \text{lt}_P`(\alpha \cap \overrightarrow{P}`y) . \quad (3)$

$[*204\cdot1] \quad \supset . \alpha \cap \overrightarrow{P}`x \neq \alpha \cap \overrightarrow{P}`y \quad (4)$

$\vdash . (1) . (2) . (4) . *212\cdot23 . \supset$

$\vdash :. \mathrm{Hp} . R = P \mathbin{\rlap{\rule[0.3ex]{0.35em}{0.4pt}}{\rule{0.4pt}{1.2ex}}} \alpha . \supset : xPy . \supset . (\alpha \cap \overrightarrow{P}{}^{\prime}x) (\mathfrak{s}{}^{\prime}R) (\alpha \cap \overrightarrow{P}{}^{\prime}y)$ (5)

$\vdash . (3) . (5) . \supset \vdash :. \mathrm{Hp} . \supset : xPy . \supset . x \{\mathrm{lt}_P \mathchar"3B \mathfrak{s}{}^{\prime}(P \mathbin{\rlap{\rule[0.3ex]{0.35em}{0.4pt}}{\rule{0.4pt}{1.2ex}}} \alpha)\} y$ (6)

$\vdash . (6) . *271\cdot322 . \supset \vdash . \mathrm{Prop}$

*271·35.　$\vdash : \alpha \operatorname{med} P . \supset . \mathrm{D}{}^{\prime}(P \mathbin{\rlap{\rule[0.3ex]{0.35em}{0.4pt}}{\rule{0.4pt}{1.2ex}}} \alpha)_\epsilon \mathrel{\mathsf{C}} - \mathrm{\mathchar"0104}{}^{\prime}\mathrm{max}_P$

Dem.

$\vdash . *37\cdot413 . *211\cdot11 . \supset$

$\vdash :. \beta \epsilon \mathrm{D}{}^{\prime}(P \mathbin{\rlap{\rule[0.3ex]{0.35em}{0.4pt}}{\rule{0.4pt}{1.2ex}}} \alpha)_\epsilon . \supset : (\mathfrak{g}\rho) . \beta = \alpha \cap P{}^{\prime\prime}(\rho \cap \alpha) :$ (1)

$[*37\cdot1] \qquad\qquad \supset : (\mathfrak{g}\rho) : x \epsilon \beta . \supset_x . (\mathfrak{g}y) . y \epsilon \rho \cap \alpha . xPy$ (2)

$\vdash . (2) . *271\cdot1 . \supset$

$\vdash :. \mathrm{Hp} . \beta \epsilon \mathrm{D}{}^{\prime}(P \mathbin{\rlap{\rule[0.3ex]{0.35em}{0.4pt}}{\rule{0.4pt}{1.2ex}}} \alpha)_\epsilon . \supset : (\mathfrak{g}\rho) : x \epsilon \beta . \supset_x . (\mathfrak{g}y, z) . xPz . z \epsilon \alpha . zPy . y \epsilon \rho \cap \alpha .$

$[(1)] \qquad\qquad\qquad\qquad \supset_x . (\mathfrak{g}z) . xPz . z \epsilon \beta .$

$[*37\cdot1] \qquad\qquad\qquad\qquad \supset_x . x \epsilon P{}^{\prime\prime}\beta$ (3)

$\vdash . (3) . *205\cdot123 . \supset \vdash : \mathrm{Hp} . \beta \epsilon \mathrm{D}{}^{\prime}(P \mathbin{\rlap{\rule[0.3ex]{0.35em}{0.4pt}}{\rule{0.4pt}{1.2ex}}} \alpha)_\epsilon . \supset . \overrightarrow{\mathrm{max}}_P{}^{\prime}\beta = \Lambda : \supset \vdash . \mathrm{Prop}$

*271·36.　$\vdash : P \epsilon \mathrm{Ded} . \alpha \operatorname{med} P . \supset . \mathrm{D}{}^{\prime}(P \mathbin{\rlap{\rule[0.3ex]{0.35em}{0.4pt}}{\rule{0.4pt}{1.2ex}}} \alpha)_\epsilon \mathrel{\mathsf{C}} \mathrm{\mathchar"0104}{}^{\prime}\mathrm{lt}_P$　$[*271\cdot35 . *214\cdot101]$

*271·37.　$\vdash : P \epsilon \mathrm{Ser} \cap \mathrm{Ded} . \alpha \operatorname{med} P . \supset . \mathrm{lt}_P \mathbin{\rlap{\rule[0.3ex]{0.35em}{0.4pt}}{\rule{0.4pt}{1.2ex}}} C{}^{\prime}\mathfrak{s}{}^{\prime}(P \mathbin{\rlap{\rule[0.3ex]{0.35em}{0.4pt}}{\rule{0.4pt}{1.2ex}}} \alpha) \epsilon P \overline{\mathrm{smor}} \{\mathfrak{s}{}^{\prime}(P \mathbin{\rlap{\rule[0.3ex]{0.35em}{0.4pt}}{\rule{0.4pt}{1.2ex}}} \alpha)\}$

$[*271\cdot321\cdot34\cdot36 . *151\cdot22]$

*271·38.　$\vdash : P \epsilon \mathrm{Ser} \cap \mathrm{Ded} . \alpha \operatorname{med} P . \supset . P \operatorname{smor} \{\mathfrak{s}{}^{\prime}(P \mathbin{\rlap{\rule[0.3ex]{0.35em}{0.4pt}}{\rule{0.4pt}{1.2ex}}} \alpha)\}$　$[*271\cdot37]$

*271·39.　$\vdash : P, Q \epsilon \mathrm{Ser} \cap \mathrm{Ded} . \alpha \operatorname{med} P . \beta \operatorname{med} Q . (P \mathbin{\rlap{\rule[0.3ex]{0.35em}{0.4pt}}{\rule{0.4pt}{1.2ex}}} \alpha) \operatorname{smor} (Q \mathbin{\rlap{\rule[0.3ex]{0.35em}{0.4pt}}{\rule{0.4pt}{1.2ex}}} \beta) . \supset .$

$P \operatorname{smor} Q$

Dem.

$\vdash . *212\cdot72 . \supset \vdash : \mathrm{Hp} . \supset . \{\mathfrak{s}{}^{\prime}(P \mathbin{\rlap{\rule[0.3ex]{0.35em}{0.4pt}}{\rule{0.4pt}{1.2ex}}} \alpha)\} \operatorname{smor} \{\mathfrak{s}{}^{\prime}(P \mathbin{\rlap{\rule[0.3ex]{0.35em}{0.4pt}}{\rule{0.4pt}{1.2ex}}} \beta)\}$ (1)

$\vdash . *271\cdot38 . \supset \vdash : \mathrm{Hp} . \supset . P \operatorname{smor} \{\mathfrak{s}{}^{\prime}(P \mathbin{\rlap{\rule[0.3ex]{0.35em}{0.4pt}}{\rule{0.4pt}{1.2ex}}} \alpha)\} . Q \operatorname{smor} \{\mathfrak{s}{}^{\prime}(Q \mathbin{\rlap{\rule[0.3ex]{0.35em}{0.4pt}}{\rule{0.4pt}{1.2ex}}} \beta)\}$ (2)

$\vdash . (1) . (2) . \supset \vdash . \mathrm{Prop}$

This proposition is used in proving that all continuous series are similar, by means of the fact that such series contain rational series as medians, and that all rational series are similar.

*271·4.　$\vdash : S \epsilon P \overline{\mathrm{smor}} Q . \beta \operatorname{med} Q . \supset . (S{}^{\prime\prime}\beta) \operatorname{med} P$

Dem.

$\vdash . *35\cdot354 . *74\cdot14 . \supset \vdash : \mathrm{Hp} . \supset . Q \mathbin{\rlap{\rule[0.3ex]{0.35em}{0.4pt}}{\rule{0.4pt}{1.2ex}}} \beta \mid \breve{S} = Q \mid \breve{S} \mathbin{\rlap{\rule[0.3ex]{0.35em}{0.4pt}}{\rule{0.4pt}{1.2ex}}} S{}^{\prime\prime}\beta .$

$[*150\cdot1] \qquad\qquad \supset . S\mathchar"3B (Q \mathbin{\rlap{\rule[0.3ex]{0.35em}{0.4pt}}{\rule{0.4pt}{1.2ex}}} \beta) = (S\mathchar"3B Q) \mathbin{\rlap{\rule[0.3ex]{0.35em}{0.4pt}}{\rule{0.4pt}{1.2ex}}} S{}^{\prime\prime}\beta .$

$[*151\cdot11] \qquad\qquad \supset . \{S\mathchar"3B (Q \mathbin{\rlap{\rule[0.3ex]{0.35em}{0.4pt}}{\rule{0.4pt}{1.2ex}}} \beta)\} \mid (S\mathchar"3B Q) = (P \mathbin{\rlap{\rule[0.3ex]{0.35em}{0.4pt}}{\rule{0.4pt}{1.2ex}}} S{}^{\prime\prime}\beta) \mid P$ (1)

$\vdash . *72\cdot6 . \qquad\qquad \supset \vdash : \mathrm{Hp} . \supset . (Q \mathbin{\rlap{\rule[0.3ex]{0.35em}{0.4pt}}{\rule{0.4pt}{1.2ex}}} \beta) \mid \breve{S} \mid S = Q \mathbin{\rlap{\rule[0.3ex]{0.35em}{0.4pt}}{\rule{0.4pt}{1.2ex}}} \beta .$

$[*150\cdot1] \qquad\qquad\qquad \supset . \{S\mathchar"3B (Q \mathbin{\rlap{\rule[0.3ex]{0.35em}{0.4pt}}{\rule{0.4pt}{1.2ex}}} \beta)\} \mid (S\mathchar"3B Q) = S \mid Q \mathbin{\rlap{\rule[0.3ex]{0.35em}{0.4pt}}{\rule{0.4pt}{1.2ex}}} \beta \mid Q \mid \breve{S}$ (2)

$\vdash . (2) . *271\cdot1 . \qquad \supset \vdash : \mathrm{Hp} . \supset . S \mid Q \mid \breve{S} \mathrel{\mathsf{C}} \{S\mathchar"3B (Q \mathbin{\rlap{\rule[0.3ex]{0.35em}{0.4pt}}{\rule{0.4pt}{1.2ex}}} \beta)\} \mid (S\mathchar"3B Q) .$

$[*151\cdot11 . (1)] \qquad\qquad \supset . P \mathrel{\mathsf{C}} (P \mathbin{\rlap{\rule[0.3ex]{0.35em}{0.4pt}}{\rule{0.4pt}{1.2ex}}} S{}^{\prime\prime}\beta) \mid P .$

$[*271\cdot1] \qquad\qquad\qquad \supset . (S{}^{\prime\prime}\beta) \operatorname{med} P : \supset \vdash . \mathrm{Prop}$

$*272$. SIMILARITY OF POSITION.

Summary of $*272$.

If P, Q are two serial relations, and T is a correlator which correlates some terms of $C'P$ with some terms of $C'Q$, we say that two terms x and y, of which x belongs to $C'P$ and y to $C'Q$, have similar positions with respect to T if y comes after the correlates of all members of $D'T$ which x comes after, and y comes before the correlates of all members of $D'T$ which x comes before. This notion is useful for inductive definitions of correlations. If we start by correlating any two terms x_1, y_1, and take another term x_2 coming (say) after x_1, a term y_2 having similarity of position with respect to $x_1 \downarrow y_1$ must come after y_1. Suppose now we take x_3 between x_1 and x_2. Then a term y_3 having similarity of position with respect to $x_1 \downarrow y_1 \cup x_2 \downarrow y_2$ must come between y_1 and y_2; and so on. A correlation T constructed in this way will be such that $T;Q \Subset P \,.\, \breve{T};P \Subset Q$. If the whole of $C'P$ and $C'Q$ can be obtained by prolonging the construction long enough, T will at last become a correlator of P and Q. This is the principle of Cantor's proof that any two rational series are similar.

As a rule, when the notion of similarity of position is useful, the relation T will be one-one, but this is not assumed in the definition. We write "$xT_{PQ}y$" for "x and y have similar positions in P and Q respectively with respect to T," or, as we may express it more shortly, "the P-position of x is T-similar to the Q-position of y." The definition is

$$T_{PQ} = \hat{x}\hat{y}\{x \in C'P \,.\, y \in C'Q \,.\, D'T \cap \overrightarrow{P}'x \subset T``\overrightarrow{Q}'y \,.\, D'T \cap \overleftarrow{P}'x \subset T``\overleftarrow{Q}'y \,.\, D'T \cap \iota'x \subset \overrightarrow{T}'y\} \quad \text{Df.}$$

This definition states that the predecessors of x which have T-correlates are to be correlated with predecessors of y, the successors of x which have T-correlates are to be correlated with successors of y, and if x itself has a T-correlate, y is to be a T-correlate of x.

When T is a many-one relation, the definition becomes somewhat simpler. We then have

$*272\cdot13$. $\vdash :: T \in \text{Cls} \to 1 \,.\, \supset :.\, xT_{PQ}y \,.\, \equiv :$

$$x \in C'P \,.\, y \in C'Q : z \in D'T \cap \overrightarrow{P}'x \,.\, \supset_z \,.\, \breve{T}'zQy : z \in D'T \cap \overleftarrow{P}'x \,.\, \supset_z \,.\, yQ\breve{T}'z : x \in D'T \,.\, \supset \,.\, y = \breve{T}'x$$

We have

*272·16. $\vdash . (\text{D}`T) \upharpoonleft T_{PQ} \mathrel{\subseteq} T$

That is, a term which has a correlate cannot have similarity of position with any term except one with which it is correlated. A member of $C`P \cap \text{D}`T$ will have similarity of position with its correlate (assuming $T \in \text{Cls} \to 1$) if $P \upharpoonright \text{D}`T \mathrel{\subseteq} T;Q . \breve{T}``C`P \subset C`Q$ (*272·18).

Under ordinary circumstances, a term which is not a member of $\text{D}`T$ cannot have similarity of position with any member of $\text{G}`T$ (*272·2). When T is many-one and its domain is contained in $C`P$, and P and Q are series, and x has no T-correlate, we have (*272·21)

$$xT_{PQ}y . \equiv : x \in C`P . y \in C`Q : z \in \text{D}`T \cap \overrightarrow{P}`x . \equiv_z . \breve{T}`zQy,$$

i.e. in this case, x and y have similar positions if the predecessors of x which have correlates are the terms whose correlates precede y. In this case, if $x \in C`P$, we have (*272·212)

$$\overleftarrow{T_{PQ}}`x = C`Q \cap \hat{y}(\text{D}`T \cap \overrightarrow{P}`x = T``\overrightarrow{Q}`y) = C`Q \cap \hat{y}(\text{D}`T \cap \overleftarrow{P}`x = T``\overleftarrow{Q}`y).$$

We next investigate the condition for $C`P = \text{D}`T_{PQ}$, *i.e.* the condition required in order that every member of $C`P$ may have similarity of position with some member of $C`Q$. A sufficient condition is

$$P, Q \in \text{Ser} . Q \in \text{comp} . T \in \text{Cls} \to 1 . \text{D}`T \in \text{Cls induct} . P \upharpoonright \text{D}`T \mathrel{\subseteq} T;Q . \dot{\exists}\,!\,Q .$$
$$\breve{T}``C`P \subset \text{D}`Q \cap \text{G}`Q$$

as is proved in *272·34.

We next consider the reversibility of T_{PQ}, *i.e.* the condition that the converse of T_{PQ} should be $(\breve{T})_{QP}$. A sufficient condition is

$$P, Q \in \text{Ser} . T \in 1 \to 1 . \text{D}`T \subset C`P . \text{G}`T \subset C`Q \quad (*272·42).$$

Finally, we have two propositions on the addition of another couple $x \downarrow y$ to T. With the above-mentioned hypothesis of *272·42, if $xT_{PQ}y$ and $T;Q \mathrel{\subseteq} P$, putting $W = T \cup x \downarrow y$, we shall have $P \upharpoonright \text{D}`W = W;Q$ (*272·51), so that the hypothesis we had for T still holds for W.

The propositions of this number are in the nature of lemmas for Cantor's proof that any two rational series are similar, which is given in *273.

---

*272·01. $T_{PQ} = \hat{x}\hat{y}\{x \in C`P . y \in C`Q . \text{D}`T \cap \overrightarrow{P}`x \subset T``\overrightarrow{Q}`y .$
$\text{D}`T \cap \overleftarrow{P}`x \subset T``\overleftarrow{Q}`y . \text{D}`T \cap \iota`x \subset \overrightarrow{T}`y\}$ Df

*272·1. $\vdash : xT_{PQ}y . \equiv . x \in C`P . y \in C`Q . \text{D}`T \cap \overrightarrow{P}`x \subset T``\overrightarrow{Q}`y .$
$\text{D}`T \cap \overleftarrow{P}`x \subset T``\overleftarrow{Q}`y . \text{D}`T \cap \iota`x \subset \overrightarrow{T}`y$ [(*272·01)]

***272·11.** $\vdash : x \in C\text{‘}P \,.\, \supset .$

$$\overleftarrow{T}_{PQ}\text{‘}x = C\text{‘}Q \cap p\text{‘}\breve{Q}\text{‘‘‘}\overleftarrow{T}\text{‘‘}(\mathrm{D}\text{‘}T \cap \overrightarrow{P}\text{‘}x) \cap p\text{‘}Q\text{‘‘‘}\overleftarrow{T}\text{‘‘}(\mathrm{D}\text{‘}T \cap \overleftarrow{P}\text{‘}x)$$
$$\cap\, p\text{‘}\overleftarrow{T}\text{‘‘}(\mathrm{D}\text{‘}T \cap \iota\text{‘}x)$$

Dem.

$\vdash . *272·1 . \supset \vdash : \mathrm{Hp} . \supset .$

$$\overleftarrow{T}_{PQ}\text{‘}x = C\text{‘}Q \cap \hat{y}\{z \in \mathrm{D}\text{‘}T \cap \overrightarrow{P}\text{‘}x \,.\, \supset_z .\, zT \,|\, Qy : z \in \mathrm{D}\text{‘}T \cap \overleftarrow{P}\text{‘}x \,.\, \supset_z .\, zT \,|\, \breve{Q}y :$$
$$z \in \mathrm{D}\text{‘}T \cap \iota\text{‘}x \,.\, \supset_z .\, zTy\}$$

$[*40·51·53]$ $$= C\text{‘}Q \cap p\text{‘}\breve{Q}\text{‘‘‘}\overleftarrow{T}\text{‘‘}(\mathrm{D}\text{‘}T \cap \overrightarrow{P}\text{‘}x) \cap p\text{‘}Q\text{‘‘‘}\overleftarrow{T}\text{‘‘}(\mathrm{D}\text{‘}T \cap \overleftarrow{P}\text{‘}x)$$
$$\cap\, p\text{‘}\overleftarrow{T}\text{‘‘}(\mathrm{D}\text{‘}T \cap \iota\text{‘}x) : \supset \vdash . \mathrm{Prop}$$

***272·111.** $\vdash : x \in C\text{‘}P \,.\, \supset .$

$$\overleftarrow{T}_{PQ}\text{‘}x = C\text{‘}Q \cap p\text{‘}\{\breve{Q}\text{‘‘‘}\overleftarrow{T}\text{‘‘}(\mathrm{D}\text{‘}T \cap \overrightarrow{P}\text{‘}x) \cup Q\text{‘‘‘}\overleftarrow{T}\text{‘‘}(\mathrm{D}\text{‘}T \cap \overleftarrow{P}\text{‘}x) \cup \overleftarrow{T}\text{‘‘}(\mathrm{D}\text{‘}T \cap \iota\text{‘}x)\}$$

[*272·11 . *40·18]

***272·12.** $\vdash :: xT_{PQ}y \,.\, \equiv :. \, x \in C\text{‘}P \,.\, y \in C\text{‘}Q :. \, z \in \mathrm{D}\text{‘}T \,.\, \supset_z : zPx \,.\, \supset .\, zT \,|\, Qy :$
$$z\breve{P}x \,.\, \supset .\, zT \,|\, \breve{Q}y : z = x \,.\, \supset .\, zTy \quad [*272·1]$$

***272·13.** $\vdash :: T \in \mathrm{Cls} \to 1 \,.\, \supset :. \, xT_{PQ}y \,.\, \equiv : x \in C\text{‘}P \,.\, y \in C\text{‘}Q :$

$$z \in \mathrm{D}\text{‘}T \cap \overrightarrow{P}\text{‘}x \,.\, \supset_z .\, \breve{T}\text{‘}zQy : z \in \mathrm{D}\text{‘}T \cap \overleftarrow{P}\text{‘}x \,.\, \supset_z .\, yQ\breve{T}\text{‘}z : x \in \mathrm{D}\text{‘}T \,.\, \supset .\, y = \breve{T}\text{‘}x$$

[*272·12 . *71·701]

***272·131.** $\vdash : T \in \mathrm{Cls} \to 1 \,.\, x \in C\text{‘}P \,.\, \supset .$

$$\overleftarrow{T}_{PQ}\text{‘}x = C\text{‘}Q \cap p\text{‘}\{\overleftarrow{Q}\text{‘‘}\breve{T}\text{‘‘}\overrightarrow{P}\text{‘}x \cup \overrightarrow{Q}\text{‘‘}\breve{T}\text{‘‘}\overleftarrow{P}\text{‘}x \cup \overleftarrow{T}\text{‘‘}(\mathrm{D}\text{‘}T \cap \iota\text{‘}x)\}$$

[*272·111 . *71·613]

***272·14.** $\vdash : x \in C\text{‘}P - \mathrm{D}\text{‘}T \,.\, \supset .$

$$\overleftarrow{T}_{PQ}\text{‘}x = C\text{‘}Q \cap p\text{‘}\breve{Q}\text{‘‘‘}\overleftarrow{T}\text{‘‘}(\mathrm{D}\text{‘}T \cap \overrightarrow{P}\text{‘}x) \cap p\text{‘}Q\text{‘‘‘}\overleftarrow{T}\text{‘‘}(\mathrm{D}\text{‘}T \cap \overleftarrow{P}\text{‘}x)$$

[*272·111 . *40·18]

***272·141.** $\vdash : x \in C\text{‘}P - \mathrm{D}\text{‘}T \,.\, \supset .$

$$\overleftarrow{T}_{PQ}\text{‘}x = C\text{‘}Q \cap \hat{y}\,(\mathrm{D}\text{‘}T \cap \overrightarrow{P}\text{‘}x \subset T\text{‘‘}\overrightarrow{Q}\text{‘}y \,.\, \mathrm{D}\text{‘}T \cap \overleftarrow{P}\text{‘}x \subset T\text{‘‘}\overleftarrow{Q}\text{‘}y)$$

[*272·1]

***272·15.** $\vdash : T \in \mathrm{Cls} \to 1 \,.\, x \in C\text{‘}P - \mathrm{D}\text{‘}T \,.\, \supset .$

$$\overleftarrow{T}_{PQ}\text{‘}x = C\text{‘}Q \cap p\text{‘}\overleftarrow{Q}\text{‘‘}\breve{T}\text{‘‘}\overrightarrow{P}\text{‘}x \cap p\text{‘}\overrightarrow{Q}\text{‘‘}\breve{T}\text{‘‘}\overleftarrow{P}\text{‘}x$$

[*272·131 . *40·18]

***272·16.** $\vdash . (\mathrm{D}\text{‘}T) \upharpoonright T_{PQ} \in T$

Dem.

$\vdash . *272·12 . \supset \vdash : x \in \mathrm{D}\text{‘}T \,.\, xT_{PQ}y \,.\, \supset .\, xTy : \supset \vdash . \mathrm{Prop}$

***272·161.** $\vdash : T \in \text{Cls}\to 1 \,.\, P \upharpoonright \text{D}`T \Subset T\,;Q \,.\, \supset .\, (\text{D}`T) \upharpoonleft T_{PQ} = C`P \upharpoonleft T \upharpoonright C`Q$

Dem.

$\vdash .\, *150{\cdot}41 \,.\qquad \supset \vdash : \text{Hp} \,.\, z \in \text{D}`T \,.\, zPx \,.\, xTy \,.\, \supset .\, \breve{T}`z\dot{Q}y \qquad (1)$

$\vdash .\, *150{\cdot}41 \qquad \supset \vdash : \text{Hp} \,.\, z \in \text{D}`T \,.\, xPz \,.\, xTy \,.\, \supset .\, yQ\breve{T}`z \qquad (2)$

$\vdash .\, (1) \,.\, (2) \,.\, *272{\cdot}13 \,.\, \supset \vdash : \text{Hp} \,.\, xTy \,.\, x \in C`P \,.\, y \in C`Q \,.\, \supset .\, xT_{PQ}y \qquad (3)$

$\vdash .\, (3) \,.\, *272{\cdot}16 \,.\, \supset \vdash .\, \text{Prop}$

***272·17.** $\vdash : T \in \text{Cls}\to 1 \,.\, P \upharpoonright \text{D}`T \Subset T\,;Q \,.\, \text{D}`T \subset C`P \,.\, \text{C}`T \subset C`Q \,.\, \supset .$
$T = (\text{D}`T) \upharpoonleft T_{PQ} \quad [*272{\cdot}161]$

The hypothesis of *272·17 is satisfied in all the important uses of T_{PQ}.

***272·171.** $\vdash : \text{Hp}\ *272{\cdot}17 \,.\, x \in \text{D}`T \,.\, \supset .\, \overleftarrow{T_{PQ}}`x = \iota`\breve{T}`x \quad [*272{\cdot}17]$

***272·18.** $\vdash : T \in \text{Cls}\to 1 \,.\, P \upharpoonright \text{D}`T \Subset T\,;Q \,.\, \breve{T}``C`P \subset C`Q \,.\, x \in C`P \cap \text{D}`T \,.\, \supset .$
$\breve{T}_{PQ}`x = \breve{T}`x$

Dem.

$\vdash .\, *150{\cdot}41 \,.\, \supset \vdash :.\, \text{Hp} \,.\, \supset : z \in \text{D}`T \cap \overrightarrow{P}`x \,.\, \supset_z .\, (\breve{T}`z)\, Q\, (\breve{T}`x) \qquad (1)$

$\vdash .\, *150{\cdot}41 \,.\, \supset \vdash :.\, \text{Hp} \,.\, \supset : z \in \text{D}`T \cap \overleftarrow{P}`x \,.\, \supset_z .\, (\breve{T}`x)\, Q\, (\breve{T}`z) \qquad (2)$

$\vdash .\, *37{\cdot}61 \,.\, \supset \vdash : \text{Hp} \,.\, \supset .\, \breve{T}`x \in C`Q \qquad (3)$

$\vdash .\, (1) \,.\, (2) \,.\, (3) \,.\, *272{\cdot}13 \,.\, \supset \vdash : \text{Hp} \,.\, \supset .\, xT_{PQ}(\breve{T}`x) \qquad (4)$

$\vdash .\, *272{\cdot}13 \,.\, \supset \vdash : \text{Hp} \,.\, xT_{PQ}y \,.\, \supset .\, y = \breve{T}`x \qquad (5)$

$\vdash .\, (4) \,.\, (5) \,.\, \supset \vdash .\, \text{Prop}$

***272·2.** $\vdash : T \in \text{Cls}\to 1 \,.\, \text{D}`T \subset C`P \,.\, P \in \text{connex} \,.\, Q \Subset J \,.\, x \sim\in \text{D}`T \,.\, \supset .$
$\overleftarrow{T_{PQ}}`x \cap \text{C}`T = \Lambda$

Dem.

$\vdash .\, *272{\cdot}13 \,.\, \supset \vdash : \text{Hp} \,.\, xT_{PQ}y \,.\, z \in \text{D}`T \cap \overrightarrow{P}`x \,.\, \supset .\, \breve{T}`z \neq y \qquad (1)$

$\vdash .\, *272{\cdot}13 \,.\, \supset \vdash : \text{Hp} \,.\, xT_{PQ}y \,.\, z \in \text{D}`T \cap \overleftarrow{P}`x \,.\, \supset .\, \breve{T}`z \neq y \qquad (2)$

$\vdash .\, (1) \,.\, (2) \,.\, \supset \vdash : \text{Hp} \,.\, xT_{PQ}y \,.\, z \in \text{D}`T \,.\, \supset .\, \breve{T}`z \neq y : \supset \vdash .\, \text{Prop}$

***272·201.** $\vdash : T \in \text{Cls}\to 1 \,.\, \text{D}`T \subset C`P \,.\, P \in \text{connex} \,.\, \exists !\, \text{D}`T_{PQ} - \text{D}`T \,.\, \supset .$
$\text{C}`T \subset C`Q$

Dem.

$\vdash .\, *202{\cdot}104 \,.\, \supset \vdash :.\, \text{Hp} \,.\, z \in \text{D}`T \,.\, xT_{PQ}y \,.\, x \sim\in \text{D}`T \,.\, \supset : zPx \,.\, \vee \,.\, xPz :$

$[*272{\cdot}13] \qquad \supset : \breve{T}`zQy \,.\, \vee \,.\, yQ(\breve{T}`z) :$

$[*33{\cdot}132] \qquad \supset : \breve{T}`z \in C`Q :.\, \supset \vdash .\, \text{Prop}$

***272·21.** $\vdash :: T \in \text{Cls}\to 1 \,.\, \text{D}`T \subset C`P \,.\, P, Q \in \text{Ser} \,.\, x \sim\in \text{D}`T \,.\, \supset :.$
$xT_{PQ}y \,.\, \equiv : x \in C`P \,.\, y \in C`Q : z \in \text{D}`T \cap \overrightarrow{P}`x \,.\, \equiv_z .\, \breve{T}`zQy$

Dem.

$\vdash .\, *272{\cdot}2 \,.\, \supset \vdash :.\, \text{Hp} \,.\, z \in \text{D}`T \,.\, xT_{PQ}y \,.\, \supset : x \neq z \,.\, y \neq \breve{T}`z :$

$[*204{\cdot}3 . *272{\cdot}201] \qquad \supset : xPz \,.\, \equiv .\, \sim(zPx) : yQ(\breve{T}`z) \,.\, \equiv .\, \sim\{(\breve{T}`z)Qy\} \qquad (1)$

$\vdash . (1) . *272{\cdot}13 . \supset \vdash :::. \text{Hp} . \supset :: xT_{PQ}y . \equiv :.$

$x \in C{}^{\backprime}P . y \in C{}^{\backprime}Q :. z \in \text{D}{}^{\backprime}T . \supset_z : zPx . \supset . \breve{T}{}^{\backprime}zQy : \sim(zPx) . \supset . \sim(\breve{T}{}^{\backprime}z)\, Qy$ (2)

$\vdash . (2) . \supset \vdash :: \text{Hp} . \supset :. xT_{PQ}y . \equiv : x \in C{}^{\backprime}P . y \in C{}^{\backprime}Q : z \in \text{D}{}^{\backprime}T . zPx . \equiv_z . \breve{T}{}^{\backprime}zQy ::$
$\supset \vdash .$ Prop

***272·211.** $\vdash :: \text{Hp}\, *272{\cdot}21 . \supset :. xT_{PQ}y . \equiv :$

$x \in C{}^{\backprime}P . y \in C{}^{\backprime}Q : z \in \text{D}{}^{\backprime}T \cap \overleftarrow{P}{}^{\backprime}x . \equiv_z . yQ(\breve{T}{}^{\backprime}z)$ [Proof as in *272·21]

***272·212.** $\vdash : \text{Hp}\, *272{\cdot}21 . x \in C{}^{\backprime}P . \supset .$

$\overleftarrow{T_{PQ}}{}^{\backprime}x = C{}^{\backprime}Q \cap \hat{y}\,(\text{D}{}^{\backprime}T \cap \overrightarrow{P}{}^{\backprime}x = T{}^{\backprime\backprime}\overrightarrow{Q}{}^{\backprime}y) = C{}^{\backprime}Q \cap \hat{y}\,(\text{D}{}^{\backprime}T \cap \overleftarrow{P}{}^{\backprime}x = T{}^{\backprime\backprime}\overleftarrow{Q}{}^{\backprime}y)$

[*272·21·211]

***272·22.** $\vdash : T \in \text{Cls} \to 1 . P, Q \in \text{trans} . xT_{PQ}y . z, w \in \text{D}{}^{\backprime}T . x \in P(z - w) . \supset .$
$y \in Q(\breve{T}{}^{\backprime}z - \breve{T}{}^{\backprime}w)$

Dem.

$\vdash . *272{\cdot}13 . \supset \vdash : \text{Hp} . \supset . \breve{T}{}^{\backprime}zQy . yQ\breve{T}{}^{\backprime}w : \supset \vdash .$ Prop

***272·221.** $\vdash : T \in \text{Cls} \to 1 . P, Q \in \text{trans} . \exists ! \,\text{D}{}^{\backprime}T_{PQ} \cap P(z - w) . \supset . (\breve{T}{}^{\backprime}z)\, Q\, (\breve{T}{}^{\backprime}w)$
[*272·22] $z, w \in \text{D}{}^{\backprime}T$

***272·23.** $\vdash :. T \in \text{Cls} \to 1 . P, Q \in \text{trans} :$

$z(P \upharpoonright \text{D}{}^{\backprime}T)\, w . \supset_{z,w} . \exists ! \,\text{D}{}^{\backprime}T_{PQ} \cap P(z - w) : \supset . P \upharpoonright \text{D}{}^{\backprime}T \subseteq T \,; Q$

Dem.

$\vdash . *272{\cdot}221 . \supset \vdash :. \text{Hp} . \supset : z(P \upharpoonright \text{D}{}^{\backprime}T)\, w . \supset . (\breve{T}{}^{\backprime}z)\, Q\, (\breve{T}{}^{\backprime}w) .$

[*150·41] $\supset . z(T \,; Q)\, w :. \supset \vdash .$ Prop

***272·24.** $\vdash : \text{D}{}^{\backprime}T \cap C{}^{\backprime}P = \Lambda . \supset . T_{PQ} = C{}^{\backprime}P \uparrow C{}^{\backprime}Q$ [*272·1]

***272·3.** $\vdash : T \in \text{Cls} \to 1 . S \subseteq T . \supset . T_{PQ} \subseteq S_{PQ}$

Dem.

$\vdash . *272{\cdot}13 . \supset \vdash :. \text{Hp} . xT_{PQ}y . \supset : z \in \text{D}{}^{\backprime}T . zPx . \supset . \breve{T}{}^{\backprime}zQy :$

[*72·9] $\supset : z \in \text{D}{}^{\backprime}S . zPx . \supset . \breve{S}{}^{\backprime}zQy$ (1)

Similarly $\vdash :. \text{Hp} . xT_{PQ}y . \supset : z \in \text{D}{}^{\backprime}S . xPz . \supset . yQ\breve{S}{}^{\backprime}z$ (2)

$\vdash . *272{\cdot}13 . \supset \vdash :. \text{Hp} . xT_{PQ}y . \supset : z \in \text{D}{}^{\backprime}T . z = x . \supset . \breve{T}{}^{\backprime}z = y :$

[*72·9] $\supset : z \in \text{D}{}^{\backprime}S . z = x . \supset . \breve{S}{}^{\backprime}z = y$ (3)

$\vdash . (1) . (2) . (3) . *272{\cdot}13 . \supset \vdash : \text{Hp} . xT_{PQ}y . \supset xS_{PQ}y : \supset \vdash .$ Prop

The following propositions lead up to *272·34.

***272·31.** $\vdash : P, Q \in \text{Ser} . T \in \text{Cls} \to 1 . x \sim\in \text{D}{}^{\backprime}T . z = \max_P{}^{\backprime}(\text{D}{}^{\backprime}T \cap \overrightarrow{P}{}^{\backprime}x) .$

$w = \min_P{}^{\backprime}(\text{D}{}^{\backprime}T \cap \overleftarrow{P}{}^{\backprime}x) . P \upharpoonright \text{D}{}^{\backprime}T \subseteq T \,; Q . \supset . \overleftarrow{T_{PQ}}{}^{\backprime}x = Q(\breve{T}{}^{\backprime}z - \breve{T}{}^{\backprime}w)$

Dem.

$\vdash . *205{\cdot}21 . \supset \vdash : \text{Hp} . u \in \text{D}{}^{\backprime}T \cap \overrightarrow{P}{}^{\backprime}x - \iota{}^{\backprime}z . \supset . uPz .$

[*150·41.Hp] $\supset . \breve{T}{}^{\backprime}uQ\breve{T}{}^{\backprime}z$ (1)

$\vdash . (1) . \supset \vdash : \text{Hp} . y \in Q(\breve{T}`z - \breve{T}`w) . u \in \text{D}`T \cap \overrightarrow{P}`x . \supset . \breve{T}`uQy$ (2)

Similarly $\vdash : \text{Hp} . y \in Q(\breve{T}`z - \breve{T}`w) . u \in \text{D}`T \cap \overleftarrow{P}`x . \supset . yQ\breve{T}`u$ (3)

$\vdash . (2) . (3) . *272{\cdot}13 . \supset \vdash : \text{Hp} . y \in Q(\breve{T}`z - \breve{T}`w) . \supset . xT_{PQ}y$ (4)

$\vdash . *272{\cdot}22 . \quad \supset \vdash : \text{Hp} . \supset . \overleftarrow{T_{PQ}}`x \subset Q(\breve{T}`z - \breve{T}`w)$ (5)

$\vdash . (4) . (5) . \supset \vdash . \text{Prop}$

***272·32.** $\vdash : P, Q \in \text{Ser} . T \in \text{Cls}\to 1 . \text{D}`T \subset \overrightarrow{P}`x .$

$P \upharpoonright \text{D}`T \in T;Q . z = \max_P`\text{D}`T . \supset . \overleftarrow{T_{PQ}}`x = \overleftarrow{Q}`\breve{T}`z$

Dem.

$\vdash . *272{\cdot}13 . \supset \vdash :: \text{Hp} . \supset :. xT_{PQ}y . \equiv : u \in \text{D}`T . \supset_u . \breve{T}`uQy$ (1)

$\vdash . *205{\cdot}21 . \supset \vdash : \text{Hp} . u \in \text{D}`T - \iota`z . \supset . uPz .$

$[*150{\cdot}41.\text{Hp}] \quad \supset . \breve{T}`uQ\breve{T}`z$ (2)

$\vdash . (2) . \quad \supset \vdash :. \text{Hp} . y \in \overleftarrow{Q}`\breve{T}`z . \supset : u \in \text{D}`T . \supset_u . \breve{T}`uQy :$

$[(1)] \quad \supset : xT_{PQ}y$ (3)

$\vdash . (1) . \quad \supset \vdash : \text{Hp} . xT_{PQ}y . \supset . \breve{T}`zQy$ (4)

$\vdash . (3) . (4) . \supset \vdash . \text{Prop}$

***272·321.** $\vdash : P, Q \in \text{Ser} . T \in \text{Cls}\to 1 . \text{D}`T \subset \overleftarrow{P}`x .$

$P \upharpoonright \text{D}`T \in T;Q . w = \min_P`\text{D}`T . \supset . \overleftarrow{T_{PQ}}`x = \overrightarrow{Q}`\breve{T}`w$

[Proof as in *272·32]

***272·33.** $\vdash : P, Q \in \text{Ser} . Q \in \text{comp} . T \in \text{Cls}\to 1 . \text{D}`T \in \text{Cls induct} .$

$P \upharpoonright \text{D}`T \in T;Q . \supset . (P``\text{D}`T \cap \breve{P}``\text{D}`T) - \text{D}`T \subset \text{D}`T_{PQ}$

Dem.

$\vdash . *261{\cdot}26 . \supset \vdash : \text{Hp} . \exists ! \text{D}`T \cap \overrightarrow{P}`x . \supset . \text{E} ! \max_P`(\text{D}`T \cap \overrightarrow{P}`x)$ (1)

$\vdash . *261{\cdot}26 . \supset \vdash : \text{Hp} . \exists ! \text{D}`T \cap \overleftarrow{P}`x . \supset . \text{E} ! \min_P`(\text{D}`T \cap \overleftarrow{P}`x)$ (2)

$\vdash . *205{\cdot}11{\cdot}111 . \supset$

$\vdash : \text{Hp} . x \sim\in \text{D}`T . z = \max_P`(\text{D}`T \cap \overrightarrow{P}`x) . w = \min_P`(\text{D}`T \cap \overleftarrow{P}`x) . \supset . zPw .$

$[*150{\cdot}41] \quad \supset . \breve{T}`zQ\breve{T}`w .$

$[*270{\cdot}11] \quad \supset . \exists ! Q(\breve{T}`z - \breve{T}`w) .$

$[*272{\cdot}31] \quad \supset . \exists ! \overleftarrow{T_{PQ}}`x$ (3)

$\vdash . (1) . (2) . (3) . \supset$

$\vdash : \text{Hp} . x \sim\in \text{D}`T . \exists ! \text{D}`T \cap \overrightarrow{P}`x . \exists ! \text{D}`T \cap \overleftarrow{P}`x . \supset . x \in \text{D}`T_{PQ} : \supset \vdash . \text{Prop}$

$*272\cdot331$. $\vdash : \text{Hp}\, *272\cdot33 \,.\, \dot{\exists}\,!\, Q \,.\, \breve{T}\text{‘‘}C\text{‘}P \subset \text{D}\text{‘}Q \,.\supset .\, C\text{‘}P \cap p\text{‘}\overleftarrow{P}\text{‘‘}\text{D}\text{‘}T \subset \text{D}\text{‘}T_{PQ}$

Dem.

$\vdash .\, *261\cdot26 \,.\supset \vdash : \text{Hp} \,.\, \exists\,!\, \text{D}\text{‘}T \cap C\text{‘}P \,.\supset .\, \text{E}\,!\, \text{max}_P\text{‘}\text{D}\text{‘}T$ (1)

$\vdash .\, *272\cdot32 \,.\supset \vdash : \text{Hp} \,.\, x \in p\text{‘}\overleftarrow{P}\text{‘‘}\text{D}\text{‘}T \,.\, z = \text{max}_P\text{‘}\text{D}\text{‘}T \,.\supset .\, \overleftarrow{T}_{PQ}\text{‘}x = \overleftarrow{Q}\text{‘}\breve{T}\text{‘}z \,.$

$[*33\cdot4] \qquad \supset .\, \exists\,!\, \overleftarrow{T}_{PQ}\text{‘}x$ (2)

$\vdash .\, (1) \,.\, (2) \,.\supset \vdash : \text{Hp} \,.\, x \in p\text{‘}\overleftarrow{P}\text{‘‘}\text{D}\text{‘}T \,.\, \exists\,!\, \text{D}\text{‘}T \cap C\text{‘}P \,.\supset .\, x \in \text{D}\text{‘}T_{PQ}$ (3)

$\vdash .\, *35\cdot85 \,.\, *272\cdot24 \,.\supset \vdash : \text{Hp} \,.\, \text{D}\text{‘}T \cap C\text{‘}P = \Lambda \,.\supset .\, C\text{‘}P \subset \text{D}\text{‘}T_{PQ}$ (4)

$\vdash .\, (3) \,.\, (4) \,.\supset \vdash .\, \text{Prop}$

$*272\cdot332$. $\vdash : \text{Hp}\, *272\cdot33 \,.\, \dot{\exists}\,!\, Q \,.\, \breve{T}\text{‘‘}C\text{‘}P \subset \text{Ɑ}\text{‘}Q \,.\supset .\, C\text{‘}P \cap p\text{‘}\overrightarrow{P}\text{‘‘}\text{D}\text{‘}T \subset \text{D}\text{‘}T_{PQ}$

[Proof as in $*272\cdot331$]

$*272\cdot34$. $\vdash : \text{Hp}\, *272\cdot33 \,.\, \dot{\exists}\,!\, Q \,.\, \breve{T}\text{‘‘}C\text{‘}P \subset \text{D}\text{‘}Q \cap \text{Ɑ}\text{‘}Q \,.\supset .\, C\text{‘}P = \text{D}\text{‘}T_{PQ}$

[$*272\cdot33\cdot331\cdot332\cdot18 \,.\, *202\cdot505$]

The following propositions are lemmas for $*272\cdot42$.

$*272\cdot4$. $\vdash : P, Q \in \text{Ser} \,.\, T \in 1 \rightarrow 1 \,.\, \text{D}\text{‘}T \subset C\text{‘}P \,.\, \text{Ɑ}\text{‘}T \subset C\text{‘}Q \,.$

$\qquad x \sim\in \text{D}\text{‘}T \,.\, xT_{PQ}y \,.\supset .\, y(\breve{T})_{QP}x$

Dem.

$\vdash .\, *272\cdot21 \,.\supset \vdash :.\, \text{Hp} \,.\supset : x \in C\text{‘}P \,.\, y \in C\text{‘}Q : z \in \text{D}\text{‘}T \cap \overrightarrow{P}\text{‘}x \,.\equiv_z .\, \breve{T}\text{‘}zQy :$

$[*72\cdot243] \qquad \supset : x \in C\text{‘}P \,.\, y \in C\text{‘}Q : (T\text{‘}w)\, Px \,.\equiv_w .\, w \in \text{Ɑ}\text{‘}T \,.\, wQy :$

$[*272\cdot21] \qquad \supset : y(\breve{T})_{QP}x :.\supset \vdash .\, \text{Prop}$

$*272\cdot41$. $\vdash : P, Q \in \text{Ser} \,.\, T \in 1 \rightarrow 1 \,.\, \text{D}\text{‘}T \subset C\text{‘}I\text{‘} \,.\, \text{Ɑ}\text{‘}T \subset C\text{‘}Q \,.$

$\qquad x \in \text{D}\text{‘}T \,.\, xT_{PQ}y \,.\supset .\, y(\breve{T})_{QP}x$

Dem.

$\vdash .\, *272\cdot13 \,.\supset \vdash :: \text{Hp} \,.\supset :.\, x \in C\text{‘}P \,.\, y = \breve{T}\text{‘}x :$

$\qquad z \in \text{D}\text{‘}T \cap \overrightarrow{P}\text{‘}x \,.\supset_z .\, \breve{T}\text{‘}zQy : z \in \text{D}\text{‘}T \cap \overleftarrow{P}\text{‘}x \,.\supset_z .\, yQ(\breve{T}\text{‘}z) :.$

$[*204\cdot3] \qquad \supset :.\, x \in C\text{‘}P \,.\, y = \breve{T}\text{‘}x : z \in \text{D}\text{‘}T \cap \overrightarrow{P}\text{‘}x \,.\supset_z .\, \breve{T}\text{‘}zQy :$

$\qquad z \in \text{D}\text{‘}T - \iota\text{‘}x - \overrightarrow{P}\text{‘}x \,.\supset_z .\, \breve{T}\text{‘}z \neq y \,.\, \sim\{(\breve{T}\text{‘}z)\, Qy\} :.$

$[\text{Transp}] \qquad \supset :.\, x \in C\text{‘}P \,.\, y = \breve{T}\text{‘}x :.\, z \in \text{D}\text{‘}T - \iota\text{‘}x \,.\supset_z : zPx \,.\equiv .\, (\breve{T}\text{‘}z)Qy :.$

$[*204\cdot1] \qquad \supset :.\, x \in C\text{‘}P \,.\, y = \breve{T}\text{‘}x :.\, z \in \text{D}\text{‘}T \,.\supset_z : zPx \,.\equiv .\, (\breve{T}\text{‘}z)\, Qy :.$

$[*72\cdot243] \qquad \supset :.\, x \in C\text{‘}P \,.\, y = \breve{T}\text{‘}x :.\, (T\text{‘}w)\, Px \,.\equiv_z .\, w \in \text{Ɑ}\text{‘}T \,.\, wQy :.$

$[*71\cdot362] \qquad \supset :.\, y \in C\text{‘}Q \,.\, x = T\text{‘}y :.\, (T\text{‘}w)\, Px \,.\equiv_z .\, w \in \text{Ɑ}\text{‘}T \,.\, wQy :.$

$[*14\cdot21 . *33\cdot43] \supset :.\, y \in C\text{‘}Q \,.\, x = T\text{‘}y :.\, w \in \text{Ɑ}\text{‘}T \,.\supset_w : (T\text{‘}w)\, Px \,.\equiv .\, wQy :.$

$[*204\cdot3] \qquad \supset :.\, y \in C\text{‘}Q \,.\, x = T\text{‘}y :.\, w \in \text{Ɑ}\text{‘}T \cap \overrightarrow{Q}\text{‘}y \,.\supset_w .\, T\text{‘}wPx :$

$\qquad w \in \text{Ɑ}\text{‘}T \cap \overleftarrow{Q}\text{‘}y \,.\supset_w .\, xP(T\text{‘}w) :.$

$[*272\cdot13] \qquad \supset :.\, y(\breve{T})_{QP}x :: \supset \vdash .\, \text{Prop}$

$*272{\cdot}42$. $\vdash : P, Q \in \text{Ser} \,.\, T \in 1 \to 1 \,.\, \text{D}`T \subset C`P \,.\, \text{Ɑ}`T \subset C`Q \,.\supset .\, (\breve{T})_{QP} = \breve{T}_{PQ}$

Dem.

$$\vdash .\, *272{\cdot}4{\cdot}41 \,.\supset \vdash : \text{Hp} \,.\supset .\, \breve{T}_{PQ} \Subset (\breve{T})_{QP} \quad (1)$$

$$\vdash .\, (1) \frac{\breve{T}, Q, P}{T, P, Q} \,.\supset \vdash : \text{Hp} \,.\supset .\, \text{Cnv}`(\breve{T})_{QP} \Subset T_{PQ} \quad (2)$$

$$\vdash .\, (1) \,.\, (2) \,.\supset \vdash \,.\, \text{Prop}$$

$*272{\cdot}43$. $\vdash : P, Q \in \text{Ser} \cap \text{comp} - \iota`\dot{\Lambda} \,.\, T \in 1 \to 1 \,.\, \text{D}`T \subset \text{D}`P \cap \text{Ɑ}`P \,.$
$\text{Ɑ}`T \subset \text{D}`Q \cap \text{Ɑ}`Q \,.\, P \upharpoonleft \text{D}`T = T \mid Q \,.\, \text{D}`T \in \text{Cls induct} \,.\supset .$
$\text{D}`T_{PQ} = C`P \,.\, \text{Ɑ}`T_{PQ} = C`Q$

Dem.

$$\vdash .\, *272{\cdot}34 \,.\supset \vdash : \text{Hp} \,.\supset .\, \text{D}`T_{PQ} = C`P \quad (1)$$

$$\vdash .\, *150{\cdot}36 \,.\supset \vdash .\, T \mid Q = T \mid Q \upharpoonleft \text{Ɑ}`T \,.\, \breve{T} \mid P = \breve{T} \mid P \upharpoonleft \text{D}`T \quad (2)$$

$$\vdash .\, (2) \,. \qquad \vdash : \text{Hp} \,.\supset .\, P \upharpoonleft \text{D}`T = T \mid Q \upharpoonleft \text{Ɑ}`T \,.$$

$$[*151{\cdot}25] \qquad \supset .\, Q \upharpoonleft \text{Ɑ}`T = \breve{T} \mid P \upharpoonleft \text{D}`T$$

$$[(2)] \qquad = \breve{T} \mid P \quad (3)$$

$$\vdash .\, *120{\cdot}214 \,. \qquad \supset \vdash : \text{Hp} \,.\supset .\, \text{Ɑ}`T \in \text{Cls induct} \quad (4)$$

$$\vdash .\, (3) \,.\, (4) \,.\, *272{\cdot}34 \,.\supset \vdash : \text{Hp} \,.\supset .\, C`Q = \text{D}`(\breve{T})_{QP}$$

$$[*272{\cdot}42] \qquad = \text{Ɑ}`T_{PQ} \quad (5)$$

$$\vdash .\, (1) \,.\, (5) \,.\supset \vdash \,.\, \text{Prop}$$

$*272{\cdot}5$. $\vdash : P, Q \in \text{Ser} \,.\, T \in \text{Cls} \to 1 \,.\, \text{D}`T \subset C`P \,.\, x T_{PQ} y \,.\, T \mid Q \Subset P \,.\supset .$
$(T \cup x \downarrow y) \mid Q \Subset P$

Dem.

$$\vdash .\, *150{\cdot}75 \,.\supset$$

$$\vdash : \text{Hp} \,.\supset .\, (T \cup x \downarrow y) \mid Q = T \mid Q \cup T``\overrightarrow{Q}`y \uparrow \iota`x \cup \iota`x \uparrow T``\overleftarrow{Q}`y \quad (1)$$

$$\vdash .\, *272{\cdot}212 \,.\supset \vdash : \text{Hp} \,.\, x \sim\in \text{D}`T \,.\supset .\, T``\overrightarrow{Q}`y \subset \overrightarrow{P}`x \,.\, T``\overleftarrow{Q}`y \subset \overleftarrow{P}`x \quad (2)$$

$$\vdash .\, (1) \,.\, (2) \,. \quad \supset \vdash : \text{Hp} \,.\, x \sim\in \text{D}`T \,.\supset .\, (T \cup x \downarrow y) \mid Q \Subset P \quad (3)$$

$$\vdash .\, *272{\cdot}16 \,. \quad \supset \vdash : x \in \text{D}`T \,.\supset .\, T \cup x \downarrow y = T \quad (4)$$

$$\vdash .\, (3) \,.\, (4) \,.\supset \vdash \,.\, \text{Prop}$$

$*272{\cdot}51$. $\vdash : P, Q \in \text{Ser} \,.\, T \in 1 \to 1 \,.\, \text{D}`T \subset C`P \,.\, \text{Ɑ}`T \subset C`Q \,.$
$x T_{PQ} y \,.\, P \upharpoonleft \text{D}`T = T \mid Q \,.\, W = T \cup x \downarrow y \,.\supset .\, P \upharpoonleft \text{D}`W = W \mid Q$

Dem.

$$\vdash .\, *272{\cdot}5 \,. \qquad \supset \vdash : \text{Hp} \,.\supset .\, W \mid Q \Subset P \quad (1)$$

$$\vdash .\, *272{\cdot}42 \,. \qquad \supset \vdash : \text{Hp} \,.\supset .\, y (\breve{T})_{QP} x \quad (2)$$

$$\vdash .\, *150{\cdot}36 \,.\, *151{\cdot}26 \,.\supset \vdash : \text{Hp} \,.\supset .\, \breve{T} \mid P = Q \upharpoonleft \text{Ɑ}`T \quad (3)$$

$$\vdash .\, (2) \,.\, (3) \ *272{\cdot}5 \,. \quad \supset \vdash : \text{Hp} \,.\supset .\, \breve{W} \mid P \Subset Q \quad (4)$$

$$\vdash .\, (1) \,.\, (4) \,.\, *150{\cdot}36 \,.\supset \vdash : \text{Hp} \,.\supset .\, W \mid Q \Subset P \upharpoonleft \text{D}`W \,.\, \breve{W} \mid (P \upharpoonleft \text{D}`W) \Subset Q \,.$$

$$[*151{\cdot}26] \qquad \supset .\, P \upharpoonleft \text{D}`W = W \mid Q : \supset \vdash \,.\, \text{Prop}$$

*273. RATIONAL SERIES.

Summary of *273.

A "rational series" is a series ordinally similar to the series of all positive and negative rational numbers in order of magnitude, or, what is equivalent, a series ordinally similar to the series of all rational proper fractions (0 excluded). This characteristic of rational series is not, however, the most convenient for purposes of definition. Following Cantor, we define a rational series as one which is compact, has no beginning or end, and has $\aleph_0$ terms in its field. Thus the field of a rational series can be arranged in a progression, and this is the source of the special properties which distinguish rational series from other compact series.

Rational proper fractions can be arranged in a progression in many ways, for example the following: If two fractions (in their lowest terms) have the same denominator, put the one with the smaller numerator first; if they have different denominators, put the one with the smaller denominator first. We thus obtain the series

$$\tfrac{1}{2}, \tfrac{1}{3}, \tfrac{2}{3}, \tfrac{1}{4}, \tfrac{3}{4}, \tfrac{1}{5}, \tfrac{2}{5}, \tfrac{3}{5}, \tfrac{4}{5}, \tfrac{1}{6}, \ldots.$$

This series is a progression, and contains all rational proper fractions.

Conversely, the natural numbers can be arranged in a rational series. Take, *e.g.*, the following arrangement: Express the numbers in the dyadic scale, so that every number is of the form

$$\Sigma\, 2^{\mu}\, (\mu \epsilon \kappa),$$

where κ is a finite class of integers. The relation of the number to κ is one-one. Arrange the various κ's by the principle of first differences, *i.e.* form the series $M_{\text{cl}} \upharpoonright (\text{Cls induct} - \iota^{\prime}\Lambda)$, where M is the relation "less than" among finite integers. The resulting series is a rational series; thus the integers are arranged in a rational series by virtue of their correlation with the classes κ. This arrangement places all the odd numbers before all the even numbers, all numbers of the form $4\nu + 2$ before all numbers of the form 4ν, and so on. If two numbers are expressed in the dyadic scale, their relative position in the series is determined by the first digit (starting from the right) which is not the same in the two numbers: the one in which this digit is 1 precedes the one in which it is 0

The two chief propositions in regard to rational series are (1) that any two rational series are ordinally similar, (2) that if R is a progression, its finite existent sub-classes arranged by the principle of first differences form a rational series. The second of these propositions is proved by showing (a) that the finite existent sub-classes arranged by first differences form a compact series, (b) that the finite existent sub-classes arranged by *last* differences form a progression. By this means, given any progression, we can specify a relation which arranges its terms in a rational series. For if T is a correlator of our progression R with the progression

$$R_{\text{lc}} \upharpoonright (\text{Cls induct} - \iota`\Lambda),$$

then

$$T ; R_{\text{cl}} \upharpoonright (\text{Cls induct} - \iota`\Lambda)$$

is a rational series whose field is $C`R$. Hence rational series exist in any type in which progressions exist.

The arrangement of the finite sub-classes of a progression, with the resultant existence-theorem for rational series, will be dealt with in the following number. In the present number, we shall be concerned with the proof that any two rational series are ordinally similar.

The proof of the similarity of any two rational series is due to Cantor. It is long and rather complicated; in outline, it is as follows.

Let P, Q be two rational series, and R, S two progressions whose fields are $C`P$ and $C`Q$ respectively. Construct a series of correlations of parts of P with parts of Q on the following plan: Begin with $\dot{\Lambda}$, and if T is any correlation, let the next be

$$T \mathbin{\dot{\cup}} \text{seq}_R`\text{D}`T \downarrow \text{min}_S`\overleftarrow{T_{PQ}}`\text{seq}_R`\text{D}`T.$$

Then the sum of all the correlations generated from $\dot{\Lambda}$ by this law of succession will be a correlation of P with Q. It will be seen that, if we put

$$W = \hat{X}\hat{T}\{X = \text{seq}_R`\text{D}`T \downarrow \text{min}_S`\overleftarrow{T_{PQ}}`\text{seq}_R`\text{D}`T\},$$

the relation which is to be shown to be a correlator of P and Q is W_A, in the sense defined in $*259$. Thus we have to prove

$$W_A \in 1 \to 1 \,.\, \text{Cl}`W_A = C`Q \,.\, P = W_A ; Q.$$

$W_A \in 1 \to 1$ results immediately from $*259{\cdot}15$.

$P \upharpoonright \text{D}`W_A = W_A ; Q$ results immediately from $*259{\cdot}16$ and $*272{\cdot}51$.

Thus it remains to prove $\text{D}`W_A = C`P \,.\, \text{Cl}`W_A = C`Q$.

$\text{D}`W_A = C`P$ is easily proved. By induction, if T is one of the series of partial correlators, $\text{D}`T \in \text{Cls induct}$, and therefore $\text{E}\,!\,\text{seq}_R`\text{D}`T$, by $*263{\cdot}47$, and by $*272{\cdot}34$, $C`P = \text{D}`T_{PQ}$; hence $\exists\,!\,\overleftarrow{T_{PQ}}`\text{seq}_R`\text{D}`T$, and therefore, by $*250{\cdot}121$, $\text{E}\,!\,\text{min}_S`\overleftarrow{T_{PQ}}`\text{seq}_R`\text{D}`T$. Hence T has a successor, which correlates

$\text{seq}_R\text{`D`}T$ with $\text{min}_S\text{`}\overleftarrow{T}_{PQ}\text{`seq}_R\text{`D`}T$. Hence the successor, in R, of every member of $C\text{`}R$ which has a correlate, has a correlate; hence by induction every member of $C\text{`}R$ (i.e. of $C\text{`}P$) has a correlate. Hence $\text{D`}W_A = C\text{`}P$.

The proof of $\text{Ꭰ`}W_A = C\text{`}Q$ is more difficult. As before, let T be one of the series of partial correlators. We have to prove that there is a correlator which has $\text{seq}_S\text{`Ꭰ`}T$ in its converse domain; when this is proved, the result follows by induction. To prove this, put

$$x = \text{min}_R\text{`}\overrightarrow{T}_{PQ}\text{`seq}_S\text{`Ꭰ`}T.$$

x exists, in virtue of $*272{\cdot}43$. Also since $\text{D`}W_A = C\text{`}P$, it follows from $*259{\cdot}13$ that there is a partial correlator U such that

$$x = \text{seq}_R\text{`D`}U.$$

We then have to prove $\text{seq}_S\text{`Ꭰ`}T = \text{min}_S\text{`}\overleftarrow{U}_{PQ}\text{`}x.$

Put $y = \text{seq}_S\text{`Ꭰ`}T$. Then $\overrightarrow{S}\text{`}y \subset \text{Ꭰ`}T$. Hence, by $*272{\cdot}2$, $\overrightarrow{S}\text{`}y \cap \overleftarrow{U}_{PQ}\text{`}x = \Lambda$. Thus if $xU_{PQ}y$, it follows that $y = \text{min}_S\text{`}\overleftarrow{U}_{PQ}\text{`}x$. To prove $xU_{PQ}y$, observe that

$$T \mathrel{G} U \,.\, U_{PQ} \mathrel{G} T_{PQ} \,.\, P \upharpoonright \text{D`}U = U \mathbin{;} Q.$$

We have $u \in \text{D`}U \,.\, \supset \,.\, \sim(uT_{PQ}y)$, by $*272{\cdot}2$. Hence, by the definition of $T_{PQ}$, we have, if $u \in \text{D`}U$,

$$(\exists z) \,.\, z \in \text{D`}T \,.\, zPu \,.\, \sim(\breve{T}\text{`}zQy) \,.\, \vee \,.\, (\exists z) \,.\, z \in \text{D`}T \,.\, uPz \,.\, \sim(yQ\breve{T}\text{`}z).$$

In the first case, we have $(\exists z) \,.\, z \in \text{D`}T \,.\, zPu \,.\, \sim(zPx)$, because $xT_{PQ}y$ Hence, since $x \neq z$ because $x \sim\in \text{D`}T$,

$$(\exists z) \,.\, z \in \text{D`}T \,.\, zPu \,.\, xPz.$$

Similarly, in the second case,

$$(\exists z) \,.\, z \in \text{D`}T \,.\, uPz \,.\, zPx.$$

The second case is incompatible with xPu, and the first with uPx. Hence

$$xPu \,.\, \supset \,.\, (\exists z) \,.\, z \in \text{D`}T \,.\, xPz \,.\, zPu : uPx \,.\, \supset \,.\, (\exists z) \,.\, z \in \text{D`}T \,.\, uPz \,.\, zPx.$$

But, since $xT_{PQ}y$, $xPz \,.\, \supset \,.\, yQ(\breve{T}\text{`}z) \,.\, \supset \,.\, yQ(\breve{U}\text{`}z)$, because $T \mathrel{G} U$, and since

$$P \upharpoonright \text{D`}U = U \mathbin{;} Q, \quad zPu \,.\, \supset \,.\, (\breve{U}\text{`}z)\, Q\, (\breve{U}\text{`}u).$$

Hence $xPu \,.\, \supset \,.\, yQ(\breve{U}\text{`}u)$, and similarly $uPx \,.\, \supset \,.\, (\breve{U}\text{`}u)\,Qy$. Hence $xU_{PQ}y$. Hence $y = \text{min}_S\text{`}\overleftarrow{U}_{PQ}\text{`}x$, and therefore y belongs to the converse domain of the next correlator after U. Hence every term of $C\text{`}Q$ belongs to the converse domain of some correlator, and therefore to $\text{Ꭰ`}W_A$. Hence W_A correlates P and Q, and P and Q are ordinally similar.

***273·01.** $\eta = \text{Ser} \cap \text{comp} \cap \breve{C}``\aleph_0 \cap \hat{P}(\text{D}`P = \text{Ꙇ}`P)$ Df

Following Cantor, we use η for the class of rational series.

***273·02.** $R_{SPQ}`T = T \cup \text{seq}_R`\text{D}`T \downarrow \text{min}_S`\overleftarrow{T_{PQ}}`\text{seq}_R`\text{D}`T$ Dft [*273]

***273·03.** $(RS)_{PQ} = \overrightarrow{(R_{SPQ})_*}`\dot{\Lambda}$ Dft [*273]

***273·04.** $T_{RSPQ} = \dot{s}`(RS)_{PQ}$ Dft [*273]

T_{RSPQ} will be shown to be a correlator of P with Q when P and Q are rational series, and R and S are progressions whose fields are $C`P$ and $C`Q$ respectively.

***273·1.** $\vdash : P \in \eta . \equiv . P \in \text{Ser} \cap \text{comp} . C`P \in \aleph_0 . \text{D}`P = \text{Ꙇ}`P$ [(*273·01)]

***273·11.** $\vdash :. P \in \eta . \equiv : P \in \text{Ser} \cap \text{comp} . \text{D}`P = \text{Ꙇ}`P : (\exists R) . R \in \omega . C`P = C`R$
[*273·1 . *263·101]

***273·2.** $\vdash : W = \hat{X}\hat{T}\{X = \text{seq}_R`\text{D}`T \downarrow \text{min}_S`\overleftarrow{T_{PQ}}`\text{seq}_R`\text{D}`T\} . \supset .$
$R_{SPQ} = A_W . (RS)_{PQ} \subset (A_W * A)`\dot{\Lambda} . T_{RSPQ} \mathrel{\dot\subset} W_A . T_{RSPQ} \in (A_W * A)`\dot{\Lambda}$
[*257·125 . *258·242 . (*273·02·03·04 . *259·02·03)]

Here the temporary definitions of *259 are revived.

The second of the above inclusions might be changed into an equality, but it is not necessary for our purposes to prove this.

***273·21.** $\vdash : \text{Hp} \, *273{\cdot}2 . \supset . \text{D}`W_A \subset C`R . \text{Ꙇ}`W_A \subset C`S$

Dem.

$\vdash . *259{\cdot}13 . \supset \vdash : \text{Hp} . \supset . \text{D}`W_A = s`\text{D}``W``(A_W * A)`\dot{\Lambda}$ (1)

$\vdash . *206{\cdot}18 . \supset \vdash : \text{Hp} . X \in \text{D}`W . \supset . \text{D}`X \subset C`R$ (2)

$\vdash . (1) . (2) . \supset \vdash : \text{Hp} . \supset . \text{D}`W_A \subset C`R$ (3)

Similarly $\vdash : \text{Hp} . \supset . \text{Ꙇ}`W_A \subset C`S$ (4)

$\vdash . (3) . (4) . \supset \vdash . \text{Prop}$

***273·211.** $\vdash : \text{Hp} \, *273{\cdot}2 . T \in \text{Ꙇ}`W . \supset . \text{D}`T \cap \text{D}`W`T \mathrel{\dot=} \Lambda$ [*206·2]

***273·212.** $\vdash : \text{Hp} \, *273{\cdot}2 . \supset . W_A \in \text{Cls} \to 1 . \text{D} \upharpoonright (A_W * A)`\dot{\Lambda} \in 1 \to 1$
[*273·211 . *259·141·171]

***273·22.** $\vdash : \text{Hp} \, *273{\cdot}2 . C`P = C`R . P \in \text{connex} . Q \mathrel{\dot\subset} J . \supset .$
$W_A \in 1 \to 1 . \text{Ꙇ} \upharpoonright (A_W * A)`\dot{\Lambda} \in 1 \to 1$

Dem.

$\vdash . *273{\cdot}211{\cdot}212{\cdot}21 . *206{\cdot}2 . (*259{\cdot}03) . \supset$

$\vdash :. \text{Hp} . \supset : T \in (A_W * A)`\dot{\Lambda} \cap \text{Ꙇ}`W . \supset . T \in \text{Cls} \to 1 . \text{D}`T \subset C`P . \text{seq}_R`\text{D}`T \sim\in \text{D}`T .$

[*272·2] $\supset . \text{min}_S`\overleftarrow{T_{PQ}}`\text{seq}_R`\text{D}`T \sim\in \text{Ꙇ}`T$ (1)

$\vdash . (1) . \supset \vdash :. \text{Hp} . \supset : T \in (A_W * A)`\dot{\Lambda} \cap \text{Ꙇ}`W . \supset_T . \text{Ꙇ}`T \cap \text{Ꙇ}`W`T = \Lambda :$

[*259·14·17] $\supset : W_A \in 1 \to \text{Cls} . \text{Ꙇ} \upharpoonright (A_W * A) \in 1 \to 1$ (2)

$\vdash . (2) . *273{\cdot}212 . \supset \vdash . \text{Prop}$

***273·23.** $\vdash : \text{Hp} * 273 \cdot 2 \,.\, P, Q \in \text{Ser} \,.\, C`P = C`R \,.\, C`Q = C`S \,.\, T \in (A_W * A)`\dot\Lambda \,.\supset .$
$P \upharpoonright \text{D}`T = T ; Q$

Dem.

$\vdash . *272 \cdot 51 . *273 \cdot 21 . \supset \vdash : \text{Hp} \,.\, T \in \text{G}`W \,.\supset .\, P \upharpoonright \text{D}`\breve{A}_W`T = (\breve{A}_W`T) ; Q$ (1)

$\vdash . (1) . *259 \cdot 16 . \supset \vdash . \text{Prop}$

***273·24.** $\vdash : T \in (RS)_{PQ} \,.\supset .\, \text{D}`T, \text{G}`T \in \text{Cls induct}$

Dem.

$\vdash . *120 \cdot 251 . \supset$

$\vdash :. \text{Hp} . \supset : T \in \text{D}`A_W \,.\, \text{D}`T \in \text{Cls induct} \,.\supset .\, \text{D}`\breve{A}_W`T \in \text{Cls induct} :$

[*90·112] $\supset : \dot\Lambda \,(A_W)_* \, T \,.\supset .\, \text{D}`T \in \text{Cls induct} :$

[*273·2.(*273·03)] $\supset : T \in (RS)_{PQ} \,.\supset .\, \text{D}`T \in \text{Cls induct}$ (1)

Similarly $\vdash :. \text{Hp} . \supset : T \in (RS)_{PQ} \,.\supset .\, \text{G}`T \in \text{Cls induct}$ (2)

$\vdash . (1) . (2) . \supset \vdash . \text{Prop}$

***273·25.** $\vdash : P, Q \in \eta \,.\, C`P = C`R \,.\, C`Q = C`S \,.\, T \in (RS)_{PQ} \,.\supset .$
$\text{D}`T_{PQ} = C`P \,.\, \text{G}`T_{PQ} = C`Q$

Dem.

$\vdash . *273 \cdot 1 . \supset$

$\vdash : \text{Hp} . \supset .\, P, Q \in \text{Ser} \cap \text{comp} \,.\, C`P = \text{D}`P = \text{G}`P \,.\, C`Q = \text{D}`Q = \text{G}`Q$ (1)

$\vdash . *273 \cdot 1 . *263 \cdot 44 . \supset \vdash : \text{Hp} . \supset .\, \dot{\exists} ! P \,.\, \dot{\exists} ! Q$ (2)

$\vdash . (1) . (2) . *273 \cdot 22 \cdot 23 \cdot 24 . *272 \cdot 43 . \supset \vdash . \text{Prop}$

***273·26.** $\vdash :. P, Q \in \eta \,.\, R, S \in \omega \,.\, C`P = C`R \,.\, C`Q = C`S \,.\supset :$
$T \in (RS)_{PQ} \,.\supset .\, \text{E} ! \,\text{seq}_R`\text{D}`T \,.\, \text{E} ! \,\text{min}_S`\overleftarrow{T_{PQ}}`\text{seq}_R`\text{D}`T$

Dem.

$\vdash . *273 \cdot 21 . *263 \cdot 47 . *273 \cdot 24 . \supset \vdash : \text{Hp} \,.\, T \in (RS)_{PQ} \,.\supset .\, \exists ! \, C`R \cap p`\overleftarrow{R}``\text{D}`T \,.$

[*250·122] $\supset .\, \text{E} ! \,\text{seq}_R`\text{D}`T$ (1)

$\vdash . (1) . *273 \cdot 25 . \supset \vdash : \text{Hp} . \supset .\, \exists ! \, \overleftarrow{T_{PQ}}`\text{seq}_R`\text{D}`T \,.$

[*250·121.*272·1] $\supset .\, \text{E} ! \,\text{min}_S`\overleftarrow{T_{PQ}}`\text{seq}_R`\text{D}`T$ (2)

$\vdash . (1) . (2) . \supset \vdash . \text{Prop}$

***273·27.** $\vdash : \text{Hp} * 273 \cdot 2 \,.\, \text{Hp} * 273 \cdot 26 \,.\supset .\, (RS)_{PQ} \subset \text{G}`W \,.\, (RS)_{PQ} \subset \text{D}`A_W$
[*273·26]

***273·271.** $\vdash : \text{Hp} * 273 \cdot 26 \,.\, T \in (RS)_{PQ} \,.\supset .\, \text{seq}_R`\text{D}`T \in \text{D}`T_{RSPQ}$

Dem.

$\vdash . *273 \cdot 2 . \supset \vdash : \text{Hp} \,.\, \text{Hp} * 273 \cdot 2 \,.\supset .\, T \in (RS)_{PQ} \cap \text{D}`A_W \,.\supset .\, \breve{A}_W`T \in (RS)_{PQ}$ (1)

$\vdash . *273 \cdot 2 . \supset$

$\vdash : \text{Hp} \,.\, \text{Hp} * 273 \cdot 2 \,.\, T \in (RS)_{PQ} \,.\, \text{E} ! \,\breve{A}_W`T \,.\supset .\, \text{seq}_R`\text{D}`T \in \text{D}`\breve{A}_W`T$ (2)

$\vdash . (1) . (2) . *273 \cdot 27 . \supset$

$\vdash : \text{Hp} \,.\, \text{Hp} * 273 \cdot 2 \,.\supset .\, \breve{A}_W`T \in (RS)_{PQ} \,.\, \text{seq}_R`\text{D}`T \in \text{D}`\breve{A}_W`T \,.$

[*273·2.(*273·04)] $\supset .\, \text{seq}_R`\text{D}`T \in \text{D}`T_{RSPQ} : \supset \vdash . \text{Prop}$

***273·272.** $\vdash : \text{Hp} *273{\cdot}26 . \supset . \text{D}``(RS)_{PQ} = \overrightarrow{R}``C`R$

Dem.

$\vdash . *206{\cdot}401 . \supset \vdash : \text{Hp} . T \in (RS)_{PQ} . \text{D}`T = \overrightarrow{R}`x . x \in C`R . \supset . x = \text{seq}_R`\text{D}`T .$

$[*204{\cdot}71 . *250{\cdot}21] \quad \supset . \text{D}`R_{SPQ}`T = \overrightarrow{R}`\breve{R}_1`x$ (1)

$\vdash . *250{\cdot}13 . \supset \vdash : \text{Hp} . \supset . \text{D}`\dot{\Lambda} = \overrightarrow{R}`B`R$ (2)

$\vdash . (1) . (2) . *90{\cdot}131 . \supset \vdash :. \text{Hp} . \supset : T (R_{SPQ})_* \dot{\Lambda} . \supset . \text{D}`T \in \overrightarrow{R}``C`R :$

$[(*273{\cdot}03)] \quad \supset : \text{D}``(RS)_{PQ} \subset \overrightarrow{R}``C`R$ (3)

$\vdash . (1) . (*273{\cdot}03) . \supset$

$\vdash :. \text{Hp} . \supset : x \in C`R . \overrightarrow{R}`x \in \text{D}``(RS)_{PQ} . \supset . \overrightarrow{R}`\breve{R}_1`x \in \text{D}``(RS)_{PQ}$ (4)

$\vdash . (2) . \quad \supset \vdash : \text{Hp} . \supset . \overrightarrow{R}`B`R \in \text{D}``(RS)_{PQ}$ (5)

$\vdash . (4) . (5) . *90{\cdot}112 . \supset \vdash :. \text{Hp} . \supset : x \in \overleftarrow{(R_1)_*}`B`R . \supset . \overrightarrow{R}`x \in \text{D}``(RS)_{PQ}$ (6)

$\vdash . *263{\cdot}43 . *250{\cdot}21 . \supset \vdash : \text{Hp} . \supset . C`R = C`R_1 . B`R = B`R_1$ (7)

$\vdash . (6) . (7) . *263{\cdot}141 . *122{\cdot}1{\cdot}141 . \supset$

$\vdash :. \text{Hp} . \supset : x \in C`R . \supset . \overrightarrow{R}`x \in \text{D}``(RS)_{PQ}$ (8)

$\vdash . (3) . (8) . \supset \vdash . \text{Prop}$

***273·28.** $\vdash : \text{Hp} *272{\cdot}26 . \supset . T_{RSPQ} \in 1 \to 1 . \text{D}`T_{RSPQ} = C`P . P = T_{RSPQ} ; Q$

Dem.

$\vdash . *273{\cdot}2{\cdot}22 . \supset \vdash : \text{Hp} . \supset . T_{RSPQ} \in 1 \to 1$ (1)

$\vdash . *273{\cdot}272 . \supset \vdash : \text{Hp} . \supset . \text{D}`T_{RSPQ} = s`\overrightarrow{R}``C`R$

$[*263{\cdot}22] \quad = C`R$ (2)

$\vdash . *273{\cdot}2{\cdot}23 . \supset \vdash : \text{Hp} . \supset . P \upharpoonright \text{D}`T_{RSPQ} = T_{RSPQ} ; Q .$

$[(2)] \quad \supset . P = T_{RSPQ} ; Q$ (3)

$\vdash . (1) . (2) . (3) . \supset \vdash . \text{Prop}$

In order to prove $T_{RSPQ} \in P \, \overline{\text{smor}} \, Q$, it only remains to prove

$$\text{Cl}`T_{RSPQ} = C`Q.$$

***273·3.** $\vdash :. \text{Hp} *273{\cdot}2 . T, U \in (A_W * A)`\dot{\Lambda} . \supset : \text{D}`T \subset \text{D}`U . \equiv . T \Subset U$

Dem.

$\vdash . *33{\cdot}263 . \quad \supset \vdash : T \Subset U . \supset . \text{D}`T \subset \text{D}`U$ (1)

$\vdash . *259{\cdot}111 . \quad \supset \vdash :. \text{Hp} . \supset : T \Subset U . \vee . U \Subset T$ (2)

$\vdash . *33{\cdot}263 . \quad \supset \vdash : U \Subset T . \text{D}`T \subset \text{D}`U . \supset . \text{D}`T = \text{D}`U$ (3)

$\vdash . (3) . *273{\cdot}212 . \supset \vdash : \text{Hp} . U \Subset T . \text{D}`T \subset \text{D}`U . \supset . T = U$ (4)

$\vdash . (2) . (4) . \quad \supset \vdash : \text{Hp} . \text{D}`T \subset \text{D}`U . \supset . T \Subset U$ (5)

$\vdash . (1) . (5) . \supset \vdash . \text{Prop}$

***273·31.** $\vdash : \mathrm{Hp}\,*273{\cdot}26 \,.\, T \in (RS)_{PQ} \,.\, y \in C'S - \text{Ɑ}'T \,.\, \overrightarrow{S}'y \subset \text{Ɑ}'T \,.\, \supset .$

$$(\exists x, U) \,.\, x = \min_R{}'\overrightarrow{T_{PQ}}'y \,.\, U \in (RS)_{PQ} \,.\, x = \mathrm{seq}_R{}'\mathrm{D}'U$$

Dem.

$\vdash \,.\, *273{\cdot}25 \,.\, *250{\cdot}121 \,.\, \supset \vdash : \mathrm{Hp} \,.\, \supset .\, (\exists x) \,.\, x = \min_R{}'\overrightarrow{T_{PQ}}'y$ (1)

$\vdash \,.\, *273{\cdot}272 \,.\, \supset \vdash : \mathrm{Hp} \,.\, x = \min_R{}'\overrightarrow{T_{PQ}}'y \,.\, \supset .\, (\exists U) \,.\, U \in (RS)_{PQ} \,.\, \mathrm{D}'U = \overrightarrow{R}'x \,.$

[*206·401] $\supset .\, (\exists U) \,.\, U \in (RS)_{PQ} \,.\, x = \mathrm{seq}_R{}'\mathrm{D}'U$ (2)

$\vdash \,.\, (1) \,.\, (2) \,.\, \supset \vdash \,.\,$ Prop

***273·32.** $\vdash : \mathrm{Hp}\,*273{\cdot}31 \,.\, x = \min_R{}'\overrightarrow{T_{PQ}}'y \,.\, U \in (RS)_{PQ} \,.\, x = \mathrm{seq}_R{}'\mathrm{D}'U \,.\, \supset .$

$$x U_{PQ} y \,.\, T \Subset U$$

Dem.

$\vdash \,.\, *205{\cdot}14 \,.\, \supset \vdash :.\, \mathrm{Hp} \,.\, uRx \,.\, \supset : \sim (uT_{PQ}y) :$

[*272·13] $\supset : (\exists z) : z \in \mathrm{D}'T : zPu \,.\, \sim (\breve{T}'zQy) \,.\, \vee \,.\, uPz \,.\, \sim (yQ\breve{T}'z)$ (1)

$\vdash \,.\, *272{\cdot}2{\cdot}42 \,.\, \supset \vdash : \mathrm{Hp} \,.\, \supset .\, x \sim\in \mathrm{D}'T \,.$ (2)

[*273·272] $\supset .\, \mathrm{D}'T \subset \overrightarrow{R}'x$ (3)

$\vdash \,.\, *273{\cdot}272 \,.\, \supset \vdash : \mathrm{Hp} \,.\, \supset .\, \overrightarrow{R}'x = \mathrm{D}'U$ (4)

$\vdash \,.\, (3) \,.\, (4) \,.\, *273{\cdot}3 \,.\, \supset \vdash : \mathrm{Hp} \,.\, \supset .\, T \Subset U$ (5)

$\vdash \,.\, (1) \,.\, *272{\cdot}13 \,.\, \supset$

$\vdash :.\, \mathrm{Hp} \,.\, uRx \,.\, \supset : (\exists z) : z \in \mathrm{D}'T : zPu \,.\, \sim (zPx) \,.\, \vee \,.\, uPz \,.\, \sim (xPz)$ (6)

$\vdash \,.\, *204{\cdot}1 \,.\, \supset \vdash :.\, \mathrm{Hp} \,.\, \supset : uPx \,.\, zPu \,.\, \supset .\, zPx : xPu \,.\, uPz \,.\, \supset .\, xPz$ (7)

$\vdash \,.\, (6) \,.\, (7) \,.\, (4) \,.\, \supset \vdash :.\, \mathrm{Hp} \,.\, u \in \mathrm{D}'U \,.\, \supset : uPx \,.\, \supset .\, (\exists z) \,.\, z \in \mathrm{D}'T \,.\, uPz \,.\, \sim (xPz) :$

$$xPu \,.\, \supset .\, (\exists z) \,.\, z \in \mathrm{D}'T \,.\, zPu \,.\, \sim (zPx) :$$

[(2)] $\supset : uPx \,.\, \supset .\, (\exists z) \,.\, z \in \mathrm{D}'T \,.\, uPz \,.\, zPx :$

$xPu \,.\, \supset .\, (\exists z) \,.\, z \in \mathrm{D}'T \,.\, zPu \,.\, xPz$ (8)

$\vdash \,.\, *272{\cdot}13 \,.\, *273{\cdot}23 \,.\, \supset$

$\vdash : \mathrm{Hp} \,.\, u \in \mathrm{D}'U \,.\, z \in \mathrm{D}'T \,.\, uPz \,.\, zPx \,.\, \supset .\, (\breve{U}'u)\, Q\, (\breve{U}'z) \,.\, (\breve{T}'z)\, Qy \,.$

[(5)] $\supset .\, (\breve{U}'u)\, Qy$ (9)

Similarly $\vdash : \mathrm{Hp} \,.\, u \in \mathrm{D}'U \,.\, z \in \mathrm{D}'T \,.\, zPu \,.\, xPz \,.\, \supset .\, yQ\, (\breve{U}'u)$ (10)

$\vdash \,.\, (8) \,.\, (9) \,.\, (10) \,.\, \supset$

$\vdash :.\, \mathrm{Hp} \,.\, u \in \mathrm{D}'U \,.\, \supset : uPx \,.\, \supset .\, (\breve{U}'u)\, Qy : xPu \,.\, \supset .\, yQ\, (\breve{U}'u)$ (11)

$\vdash \,.\, (11) \,.\, *272{\cdot}13 \,.\, \supset \vdash : \mathrm{Hp} \,.\, \supset .\, xU_{PQ}y$ (12)

$\vdash \,.\, (5) \,.\, (12) \,.\, \supset \vdash \,.\,$ Prop

***273·33.** $\vdash : \text{Hp} *273\cdot32 . \supset . y = \min_S{}^{\backprime}\overleftarrow{U_{PQ}}{}^{\backprime}x . x (R_{SPQ}{}^{\backprime}U) y$

Dem.

$\vdash . *273\cdot32 . \supset \vdash : \text{Hp} . \supset . \overrightarrow{S}{}^{\backprime}y \subset \text{Ꮳ}{}^{\backprime}U .$

$[*272\cdot2\cdot42] \quad \supset . \overrightarrow{S}{}^{\backprime}y \cap \overleftarrow{U_{PQ}}{}^{\backprime}x = \Lambda$ (1)

$\vdash . (1) . *273\cdot32 . *205\cdot14 . \supset \vdash : \text{Hp} . \supset . y = \min_S{}^{\backprime}\overleftarrow{U_{PQ}}{}^{\backprime}x$ (2)

$\vdash . (2) . (*273\cdot02) . \supset \vdash : \text{Hp} . \supset . x (R_{SPQ}{}^{\backprime}U) y : \supset \vdash . \text{Prop}$

***273·34.** $\vdash : \text{Hp} *273\cdot31 . \supset . y \in \text{Ꮳ}{}^{\backprime}T_{RSPQ}$

Dem.

$\vdash . *273\cdot31\cdot33 . \supset \vdash : \text{Hp} . \supset . (\exists U) . U \in (RS)_{PQ} . y \in \text{Ꮳ}{}^{\backprime}R_{SQP}{}^{\backprime}U .$

$[*90\cdot16.(*273\cdot03)] \quad \supset . (\exists W) . W \in (RS)_{PQ} . y \in \text{Ꮳ}{}^{\backprime}W .$

$[(*273\cdot04)] \quad \supset . y \in \text{Ꮳ}{}^{\backprime}T_{RSPQ} : \supset \vdash . \text{Prop}$

***273·35.** $\vdash : \text{Hp} *273\cdot26 . \supset . \text{Ꮳ}{}^{\backprime}T_{RSPQ} = C{}^{\backprime}Q$

Dem.

$\vdash . *273\cdot34 . \supset \vdash : \text{Hp} . y \in C{}^{\backprime}S . \overrightarrow{S}{}^{\backprime}y \subset \text{Ꮳ}{}^{\backprime}T_{RSPQ} . \supset . y \in \text{Ꮳ}{}^{\backprime}T_{RSPQ}$ (1)

$\vdash . (1) . *250\cdot34 . \supset \vdash . \text{Prop}$

***273·36.** $\vdash : \text{Hp} *273\cdot26 . \supset . T_{RSPQ} \in P \,\overline{\text{smor}}\, Q$ [*273·28·35]

***273·4.** $\vdash : P, Q \in \eta . \supset . P \text{ smor } Q$

Dem.

$\vdash . *273\cdot11 . \supset \vdash : \text{Hp} . \supset . (\exists R, S) . R, S \in \omega . C{}^{\backprime}P = C{}^{\backprime}R . C{}^{\backprime}Q = C{}^{\backprime}S .$

$[*273\cdot36] \quad \supset . (\exists R, S) . T_{RSPQ} \in P \,\overline{\text{smor}}\, Q : \supset \vdash . \text{Prop}$

***273·41.** $\vdash : P \in \eta . P \text{ smor } Q . \supset . Q \in \eta$

Dem.

$\vdash . *270\cdot41 . \quad \supset \vdash : \text{Hp} . \supset . Q \in \text{Ser} \cap \text{comp}$ (1)

$\vdash . *151\cdot18 . *123\cdot321 . \supset \vdash : \text{Hp} . \supset . C{}^{\backprime}Q \in \aleph_0$ (2)

$\vdash . *151\cdot5 . \quad \supset \vdash : \text{Hp} . \supset . \text{D}{}^{\backprime}Q = \text{Ꮳ}{}^{\backprime}Q$ (3)

$\vdash . (1) . (2) . (3) . *273\cdot1 . \supset \vdash . \text{Prop}$

***273·42.** $\vdash : P \in \eta . \supset . \eta = \text{Nr}{}^{\backprime}P$ [*273·4·41]

***273·43.** $\vdash . \eta \in \text{NR}$ [*273·42 . *256·54]

The following propositions are easy to prove:

$$\vdash : Q \in \text{Ser} \cap \breve{C}{}^{\backprime\backprime}\aleph_0 . P \in \eta . \supset . Q \times P \in \eta,$$

whence $\vdash : \alpha \in \text{NR} \cap \text{Cl}{}^{\backprime}\text{Ser} . C{}^{\backprime\backprime}\alpha = \aleph_0 . \supset . \alpha \dot{\times} \eta = \eta ;$

and

$$\vdash : P \in \eta . Q \in \text{Ser} \cap \breve{C}{}^{\backprime\backprime}\aleph_0 . x \in C{}^{\backprime}P . \supset . x \downarrow {}^{;}Q \in \text{Nr}{}^{\backprime}Q \cap \text{Rl}{}^{\backprime}(Q \times P) . Q \times P \in \eta,$$

whence, from the fact that all η's are similar,

$$\vdash : P \in \eta . Q \in \text{Ser} \cap \breve{C}{}^{\backprime\backprime}\aleph_0 . \supset . \exists ! \text{Nr}{}^{\backprime}Q \cap \text{Rl}{}^{\backprime}P .$$

Thus an η contains series of all the order-types composed of $\aleph_0$ terms.

*274. ON SERIES OF FINITE SUB-CLASSES OF A SERIES.

Summary of *274.

In the present number, we shall be concerned with the construction of a rational series consisting of the finite existent sub-classes of a progression. When the finite sub-classes of a progression (excluding Λ) are arranged by the principle of first differences, the result is a rational series. When they are arranged by the principle of last differences, the result is a progression. These two propositions, with the consequent existence-theorems, are to be proved in the present number.

We define "P_η" as P_{cl} with its field limited to finite existent classes. (For the definition of P_{cl}, see *170·01.) In the present number, we shall be chiefly concerned with P_η when $P \epsilon \omega$, but it has interesting properties in many other cases.

Our definition is

$$P_\eta = P_{cl} \upharpoonright (\text{Cls induct} - \iota`\Lambda) \quad \text{Df.}$$

We shall be concerned in this number not only with P_η, but also with $P_{1c} \upharpoonright (\text{Cls induct} - \iota`\Lambda)$. This is $\text{Cnv}`(\breve{P})_\eta$. Thus if we put $\breve{P} = Q$, the hypothesis that $P \epsilon \Omega$ as used in studying $P_{1c} \upharpoonright (\text{Cls induct} - \iota`\Lambda)$ is equivalent to the hypothesis that $\breve{Q} \epsilon \Omega$ as used in studying $\text{Cnv}`Q_\eta$, *i.e.* $\breve{Q}_\eta$. Thus the study of P_{cl} and P_{1c} with their fields limited to inductive existent classes may be replaced by the study of P_η in the two cases where (1) $P \epsilon \Omega$, (2) $\breve{P} \epsilon \Omega$. The second case is the simpler, and is considered first. We have first, however, a collection of propositions which only assume that P is a series.

Since an inductive existent class in a series must have a maximum and a minimum, we have

***274·12.** $\vdash :: P \epsilon \text{Ser} . \supset :. \alpha P_\eta \beta . \equiv :$
$$\alpha, \beta \epsilon \text{Cl induct}`C`P - \iota`\Lambda : (\exists z) . z \epsilon \alpha - \beta . \alpha \cap \overrightarrow{P}`z = \beta \cap \overrightarrow{P}`z$$

We have

***274·17.** $\vdash : C`P \sim\epsilon 1 . \supset . C`P_\eta = \text{Cl induct}`C`P - \iota`\Lambda$

Whenever P is a series, P_η is a series (*274·18). If P has a last term, the class consisting of this last term only is the last term of P_η; if P has no last term, P_η has no last term (*274·191). If $C'P$ is an inductive existent class, the first term of P_η is $C'P$ (*274·194); if not, P_η has no first term (*274·195). Hence if P has no last term, P_η has no first or last term, and we have $\text{D}'P_\eta = \text{G}'P_\eta$ (*274·196). Thus of the characteristics used in defining η, we have $P_\eta \in \text{Ser}$ whenever $P \in \text{Ser}$, and $\text{D}'P_\eta = \text{G}'P_\eta$ whenever $\sim \text{E}!\,B'\breve{P}$

We next prove

*274·22. $\vdash : \breve{P} \in \Omega \,.\supset .\, \breve{P}_\eta \in \Omega$

which, in virtue of what was said above, is equivalent to

$$P \in \Omega \,.\supset .\, P_{1c} \upharpoonright (\text{Cls induct} - \iota'\Lambda) \in \Omega,$$

that is: The principle of last differences applied to the inductive existent sub-classes of any well-ordered series gives a well-ordered series.

To prove *274·22, since we already know that P_η is a series, we only have to prove that every existent sub-class of $C'P_\eta$ has a maximum with respect to P_η. This is proved as follows.

Let κ be any existent sub-class of $\text{Cl induct}'C'P - \iota'\Lambda$. Consider the minima of all the members of κ: these minima all exist, because κ is composed of inductive classes. Then in virtue of the nature of the principle of first differences, members of κ which have a later minimum come later than those that have an earlier minimum. Hence if we consider $\text{min}_P{}''\kappa$, the classes whose minimum is the maximum of $\text{min}_P{}''\kappa$ (which exists, because $\breve{P} \in \Omega$) are later than any other members of κ. Put

$$x_1 = \text{max}_P{}'\text{min}_P{}''\kappa \,.\, \kappa_1 = \kappa \cap \overleftarrow{\text{min}_P}{}'x_1.$$

Thus κ_1 consists of those members of κ which have the largest minimum, and members of κ_1 come later than any other members of κ. Similarly the latest members of κ_1 will be those that have the greatest second term. That is, if we take away the (common) first term from each member of κ_1, and if λ_1 is the resulting class of classes, we have to apply to λ_1 precisely the same process as we have already applied to κ. Thus we are led to put

$$x_1 = \text{max}_P{}'\text{min}_P{}''\kappa \,.\, \kappa_1 = \kappa \cap \overleftarrow{\text{min}_P}{}'x_1 \,.\, \lambda_1 = (-\iota'x_1)''\kappa_1,$$

$$x_2 = \text{max}_P{}'\text{min}_P{}''\lambda_1 \,.\, \kappa_2 = \lambda_1 \cap \overleftarrow{\text{min}_P}{}'x_2 \,.\, \lambda_2 = (-\iota'x_2)''\kappa_2,$$

and so on. The series $x_1, x_2, \ldots$ is an ascending series in P, and is therefore finite, by *261·33. It therefore has a last term, say x_ν. Then the class $\iota'x_1 \cup \iota'x_2 \cup \ldots \cup \iota'x_\nu$ is a member of κ, and is easily shown to be its maximum. Hence every existent sub-class κ of $C'P_\eta$ has a maximum, and therefore $\breve{P}_\eta \in \Omega$.

In order to symbolize the above process, we put

$$P_m{}^{\text{‘}}\kappa = \max_P{}^{\text{‘}}\min_P{}^{\text{‘‘}}\kappa \qquad \text{Dft,}$$

$$\breve{T}_P{}^{\text{‘}}\kappa = (-\iota{}^{\text{‘}}P_m{}^{\text{‘}}\kappa){}^{\text{‘‘}}(\kappa \cap \overleftarrow{\min_P}{}^{\text{‘}}P_m{}^{\text{‘}}\kappa) - \iota{}^{\text{‘}}\Lambda \qquad \text{Dft,}$$

$$M_P{}^{\text{‘}}\kappa = P_m{}^{\text{‘‘}}\overleftarrow{(T_P)_*}{}^{\text{‘}}\kappa \qquad \text{Dft.}$$

Then $P_m{}^{\text{‘}}\kappa$ is what we called x_1, $\breve{T}_P{}^{\text{‘}}\kappa$ is what we called λ_1, $\overleftarrow{(T_P)_*}{}^{\text{‘}}\kappa$ is the class $\kappa, \lambda_1, \lambda_2, \dots \lambda_{\nu-1}$, and $M_P{}^{\text{‘}}\kappa$ is the class $x_1, x_2, x_3, \dots x_\nu$. Thus what we have to prove is

$$M_P{}^{\text{‘}}\kappa = \max(P_\eta){}^{\text{‘}}\kappa,$$

which is proved in $*274{\cdot}215$.

We prove next

$*274{\cdot}25.$ $\vdash : \breve{P} \epsilon \omega . \supset . \breve{P}_\eta \epsilon \omega$

For this purpose we use $*263{\cdot}44$, namely

$$\omega = \Omega - \iota{}^{\text{‘}}\dot{\Lambda} \cap \hat{P}(\text{Ɑ}{}^{\text{‘}}P_1 = \text{Ɑ}{}^{\text{‘}}P . \sim \text{E}\,!\, B{}^{\text{‘}}\breve{P}).$$

Thus it only remains to prove

$$\text{D}{}^{\text{‘}}(P_\eta)_1 = \text{D}{}^{\text{‘}}P_\eta . \sim \text{E}\,!\, B{}^{\text{‘}}P_\eta.$$

$\sim \text{E}\,!\, B{}^{\text{‘}}P_\eta$ follows from $*274{\cdot}195$, and $\text{D}{}^{\text{‘}}(P_\eta)_1 = \text{D}{}^{\text{‘}}P_\eta$ is proved without any difficulty; hence our proposition follows.

From $*274{\cdot}25{\cdot}17$, by substituting P for $\breve{P}$, we obtain

$*274{\cdot}26.$ $\vdash : P \epsilon \omega . \supset . P_{1c} \upharpoonright (\text{Cls induct} - \iota{}^{\text{‘}}\Lambda) \epsilon \omega .$

$$C{}^{\text{‘}}P_{1c} \upharpoonright (\text{Cls induct} - \iota{}^{\text{‘}}\Lambda) = \text{Cl induct}{}^{\text{‘}}C{}^{\text{‘}}P - \iota{}^{\text{‘}}\Lambda$$

whence it follows immediately that

$*274{\cdot}27.$ $\vdash : \alpha \epsilon \aleph_0 . \supset . \text{Cl induct}{}^{\text{‘}}\alpha \epsilon \aleph_0 . \text{Cl induct}{}^{\text{‘}}\alpha - \iota{}^{\text{‘}}\Lambda \epsilon \aleph_0$

I.e. a class of $\aleph_0$ terms contains $\aleph_0$ inductive sub-classes.

We now have to prove

$*274{\cdot}33.$ $\vdash : P \epsilon \omega . \supset . P_\eta \epsilon \eta$

In virtue of $*274{\cdot}17{\cdot}27$, we have $C{}^{\text{‘}}P_\eta \epsilon \aleph_0$; and by $*274{\cdot}18$, $P_\eta \epsilon \text{Ser}$. Thus it only remains to prove $P_\eta \epsilon \text{comp} . \text{D}{}^{\text{‘}}P_\eta = \text{Ɑ}{}^{\text{‘}}P_\eta$. The second of these results immediately from $*274{\cdot}196$. As for $P_\eta \epsilon$ comp, if $\alpha P_\eta \beta$, $\alpha \cup \beta \epsilon \text{Cls induct}$, and therefore $\exists\,!\, p{}^{\text{‘}}\overleftarrow{P}{}^{\text{‘‘}}(\alpha \cup \beta)$; but if $x \epsilon p{}^{\text{‘}}\overleftarrow{P}{}^{\text{‘‘}}(\alpha \cup \beta)$, we have $\alpha P_\eta (\beta \cup \iota{}^{\text{‘}}x) . (\beta \cup \iota{}^{\text{‘}}x) P_\eta \beta$; hence $P_\eta \subseteq P_\eta{}^2$. This completes the proof that $P_\eta \epsilon \eta$.

The proposition holds not only if $P \epsilon \omega$, but if P is any series which has no last term and whose field has $\aleph_0$ terms ($*274{\cdot}32$).

Finally, we deal with the existence of η ($*274{\cdot}4$—$\cdot46$). If $P \epsilon \omega$, P is similar to $P_{1c} \upharpoonright (\text{Cls induct} - \iota{}^{\text{‘}}\Lambda)$, by $*274{\cdot}26$; and if T is a correlator of these two, $T;P_\eta$ is an η whose field is $C'P$ (*274·4). Hence the existence of η in any type is equivalent to the existence of ω in that type (*274·41). Hence we have merely to apply previous propositions on the existence of ω.

***274·01.** $P_\eta = P_{cl} \upharpoonright (\text{Cls induct} - \iota'\Lambda)$ Df

***274·02.** $P_m{}'\kappa = \max_P{}'\min_P{}''\kappa$ Dft [*274]

***274·03.** $\breve{T}_P{}'\kappa = (-\iota'P_m{}'\kappa)''(\kappa \cap \overleftarrow{\min}_P{}'P_m{}'\kappa) - \iota'\Lambda$ Dft [*274]

***274·04.** $M_P{}'\kappa = P_m{}''\overleftarrow{(T_P)_*}{}'\kappa$ Dft [*274]

***274·1.** $\vdash : \alpha P_\eta \beta . \equiv . \alpha, \beta \in \text{Cl induct}'C'P - \iota'\Lambda . \exists ! \alpha - \beta - \breve{P}''(\beta - \alpha)$ [*170·1 . (*274·01)]

***274·11.** $\vdash : P \in \text{Ser} . \alpha \in \text{Cl induct}'C'P - \iota'\Lambda . \supset . E ! \min_P{}'\alpha . E ! \max_P{}'\alpha$ [*261·26]

***274·111.** $\vdash : P \in \text{Ser} . \sim E ! B'\breve{P} . \alpha \in \text{Cl induct}'C'P . \supset . \exists ! p'\overleftarrow{P}''\alpha$

Dem.

$\vdash . *274·11 . \supset \vdash : \text{Hp} . \exists ! \alpha . \supset . \max_P{}'\alpha \in D'P .$

[*205·65] $\supset . \exists ! p'\overleftarrow{P}''\alpha$ (1)

$\vdash . (1) . *40·2 . \supset \vdash . \text{Prop}$

***274·12.** $\vdash :: P \in \text{Ser} . \supset :. \alpha P_\eta \beta . \equiv :$

$\alpha, \beta \in \text{Cl induct}'C'P - \iota'\Lambda : (\exists z) . z \in \alpha - \beta . \alpha \cap \overrightarrow{P}'z = \beta \cap \overrightarrow{P}'z$

Dem.

$\vdash . *170·2 . \supset$

$\vdash :. \alpha, \beta \in \text{Cl induct}'C'P - \iota'\Lambda : (\exists z) . z \in \alpha - \beta . \alpha \cap \overrightarrow{P}'z = \beta \cap \overrightarrow{P}'z : \supset . \alpha P_\eta \beta$ (1)

$\vdash . *274·11 . \supset \vdash : \text{Hp} . \alpha P_\eta \beta . \supset . E ! \min_P{}'\{\alpha - \beta - \breve{P}''(\beta - \alpha)\} .$

[*170·23.*205·192] $\supset . (\exists z) . z \in \alpha - \beta . \alpha \cap \overrightarrow{P}'z = \beta \cap \overrightarrow{P}'z$ (2)

$\vdash . (1) . (2) . \supset \vdash . \text{Prop}$

***274·13.** $\vdash . P_{lc} \upharpoonright (\text{Cls induct} - \iota'\Lambda) = \text{Cnv}'(\breve{P})_\eta$ [*170·101 . (*274·01)]

***274·14.** $\vdash :: P \in \text{Ser} . \supset :. \alpha \{P_{lc} \upharpoonright (\text{Cls induct} - \iota'\Lambda)\} \beta . \equiv :$

$\alpha, \beta \in \text{Cl induct}'C'P - \iota'\Lambda : (\exists z) . z \in \beta - \alpha . \alpha \cap \overleftarrow{P}'z = \beta \cap \overleftarrow{P}'z$

[*274·12·13]

***274·15.** $\vdash : \alpha, \beta \in \text{Cl induct}'C'P - \iota'\Lambda . \beta \subset \alpha . \beta \neq \alpha . \supset . \alpha P_\eta \beta$ [*170·16 . *274·1]

***274·151.** $\vdash : \alpha \in \text{Cl induct}'C'P - 1 . x \in \alpha . \supset . \alpha P_\eta (\iota'x)$ [*274·15]

***274·16.** $\vdash : \dot{\exists} ! P_\eta . \equiv . C\text{‘}P \sim\in 0 \cup 1$

Dem.

$\vdash . *274\cdot1 . \quad \supset \vdash : \dot{\exists} ! P_\eta . \supset . \exists ! C\text{‘}P$ (1)

$\vdash . *274\cdot151 . \supset \vdash : C\text{‘}P \sim\in 0 \cup 1 . \supset . \dot{\exists} ! P_\eta$ (2)

$\vdash . *60\cdot38 . \quad \supset \vdash : C\text{‘}P \in 1 . \supset . \sim(\exists\alpha, \beta) . \alpha, \beta \in \mathrm{Cl}\text{‘}C\text{‘}P - \iota\text{‘}\Lambda . \exists ! \alpha - \beta .$

[*274·1] $\qquad \supset . P_\eta = \dot{\Lambda}$ (3)

$\vdash . (1) . (2) . (3) . \supset \vdash . \mathrm{Prop}$

***274·17.** $\vdash : C\text{‘}P \sim\in 1 . \supset . C\text{‘}P_\eta = \mathrm{Cl\ induct}\text{‘}C\text{‘}P - \iota\text{‘}\Lambda$

Dem.

$\vdash . *274\cdot151 . \supset \vdash . \mathrm{Cl\ induct}\text{‘}C\text{‘}P - \iota\text{‘}\Lambda - 1 \subset \mathrm{D}\text{‘}P_\eta$ (1)

$\vdash . *274\cdot151 . \supset \vdash : x \in C\text{‘}P . C\text{‘}P \neq \iota\text{‘}x . \supset . \iota\text{‘}x \in \text{Ɑ}\text{‘}P_\eta$ (2)

$\vdash . (2) . \quad \supset \vdash : \mathrm{Hp} . \supset . \mathrm{Cl}\text{‘}C\text{‘}P \cap 1 \subset \text{Ɑ}\text{‘}P_\eta$ (3)

$\vdash . (1) . (3) . \supset \vdash : \mathrm{Hp} . \supset . \mathrm{Cl\ induct}\text{‘}C\text{‘}P - \iota\text{‘}\Lambda \subset C\text{‘}P_\eta$ (4)

$\vdash . (4) . *274\cdot1 . \supset \vdash . \mathrm{Prop}$

***274·171.** $\vdash : P^2 \Subset J . xPy . \supset . (\iota\text{‘}x) P_\eta (\iota\text{‘}y)$ [*274·1]

***274·18.** $\vdash : P \in \mathrm{Ser} . \supset . P_\eta \in \mathrm{Ser}$

Dem.

$\vdash . *201\cdot14 . \supset$

$\vdash :. \mathrm{Hp} . z \in \alpha - \beta . w \in \beta - \gamma . \alpha \cap \overrightarrow{P}\text{‘}z = \beta \cap \overrightarrow{P}\text{‘}z . \beta \cap \overrightarrow{P}\text{‘}w = \gamma \cap \overrightarrow{P}\text{‘}w . \supset :$

$\qquad zPw . \supset . z \in \alpha - \gamma . \alpha \cap \overrightarrow{P}\text{‘}z = \gamma \cap \overrightarrow{P}\text{‘}z$ (1)

$\vdash . *201\cdot14 . \supset \vdash :. \mathrm{Hp}(1) . \supset : wPz . \supset . w \in \alpha - \gamma . \alpha \cap \overrightarrow{P}\text{‘}w = \gamma \cap \overrightarrow{P}\text{‘}w$ (2)

$\vdash . (1) . (2) . *202\cdot103 . *274\cdot12 . \supset \vdash : \mathrm{Hp} . \alpha P_\eta \beta . \beta P_\eta \gamma . \supset . \alpha P_\eta \gamma$ (3)

$\vdash . *274\cdot11 . \supset$

$\vdash : \mathrm{Hp} . \alpha, \beta \in \mathrm{Cl\ induct}\text{‘}C\text{‘}P - \iota\text{‘}\Lambda . \alpha \neq \beta . \supset . (\exists z) . z = \min_P\text{‘}\{(\alpha - \beta) \cup (\beta - \alpha)\} .$

[*205·14] $\qquad \supset . (\exists z) . z \in (\alpha - \beta) \cup (\beta - \alpha) . \alpha \cap \overrightarrow{P}\text{‘}z = \beta \cap \overrightarrow{P}\text{‘}z .$

[*274·12] $\qquad \supset . \alpha (P_\eta \cup \breve{P}_\eta) \beta$ (4)

$\vdash . (3) . (4) . *170\cdot17 . \supset \vdash . \mathrm{Prop}$

***274·19.** $\vdash : P \in \mathrm{connex} . P^2 \Subset J . \supset . \overrightarrow{B}\text{‘}\breve{P}_\eta = \iota\text{“}\overrightarrow{B}\text{‘}\breve{P}$

Dem.

$\vdash . *274\cdot151 . \qquad \supset \vdash . \mathrm{Cl\ induct}\text{‘}C\text{‘}P - 1 \subset \mathrm{D}\text{‘}P_\eta$ (1)

$\vdash . *274\cdot171 . \qquad \supset \vdash : \mathrm{Hp} . \supset . \iota\text{“}\mathrm{D}\text{‘}P \subset \mathrm{D}\text{‘}P_\eta$ (2)

$\vdash . (1) . (2) . *274\cdot17 . \supset \vdash : \mathrm{Hp} . \supset . \overrightarrow{B}\text{‘}\breve{P}_\eta \subset \iota\text{“}\overrightarrow{B}\text{‘}\breve{P}$ (3)

$\vdash . *202\cdot524 . \supset$

$\vdash : \mathrm{Hp} . x \in \overrightarrow{B}\text{‘}\breve{P} . \beta \in \mathrm{Cl}\text{‘}C\text{‘}P - \iota\text{‘}\Lambda . x \sim\in \beta . \supset . x \in \breve{P}\text{“}(\beta - \iota\text{‘}x)$ (4)

$\vdash . (4) . \supset$

$\vdash : \text{Hp} . x \in \overrightarrow{B}`\breve{P} . \supset . \sim(\exists\beta) . \beta \in \text{Cl induct}`C`P - \iota`\Lambda . \exists ! \iota`x - \beta - \breve{P}``(\beta - \iota`x)$.

[*274·1] $\supset . \iota`x \sim\in \text{D}`P_\eta$ (5)

$\vdash . (5) . *274{\cdot}17 . \supset \vdash : \text{Hp} . \supset . \iota``\overrightarrow{B}`\breve{P} \subset \overrightarrow{B}`\breve{P}_\eta$ (6)

$\vdash . (3) . (6) . \supset \vdash . \text{Prop}$

***274·191.** $\vdash :. P \in \text{connex} . P^2 \Subset J . \supset : \text{E} ! B`\breve{P} . \supset . B`\breve{P}_\eta = \iota`B`\breve{P} :$

$\sim \text{E} ! B`\breve{P} . \supset . \overrightarrow{B}`\breve{P}_\eta = \Lambda$ [*274·19]

***274·192.** $\vdash :. P \in \text{connex} . P^2 \Subset J . \supset : \text{E} ! B`\breve{P} . \equiv . \text{E} ! B`\breve{P}_\eta$ [*274·191]

***274·193.** $\vdash . \overrightarrow{B}`P_\eta = \iota`C`P \cap (\text{Cls induct} - \iota`\Lambda - 1)$

Dem.

$\vdash . *274{\cdot}15{\cdot}1 . \supset \vdash : C`P \in \text{Cls induct} - \iota`\Lambda - 1 . \supset . C`P \in \overrightarrow{B}`P_\eta$ (1)

$\vdash . *274{\cdot}16{\cdot}17 . \supset \vdash : C`P \sim\in (\text{Cls induct} - \iota`\Lambda - 1) . \supset . C`P \sim\in C`P_\eta$ (2)

$\vdash . *274{\cdot}15 . \supset \vdash : \alpha \in \text{Cl induct}`C`P - \iota`\Lambda . x \in C`P - \alpha . \supset . (\alpha \cup \iota`x) \, P_\eta \, \alpha$ (3)

$\vdash . (3) . \supset \vdash . \text{Cl induct}`C`P - \iota`\Lambda - \iota`C`P \subset \text{ᗡ}`P_\eta$ (4)

$\vdash . (4) . \text{Transp} . *274{\cdot}1 . \supset \vdash . \overrightarrow{B}`P_\eta \subset (\text{Cl induct}`C`P - \iota`\Lambda) \cap \iota`C`P$ (5)

$\vdash . (5) . *274{\cdot}16 . \supset \vdash . \overrightarrow{B}`P_\eta \subset (\text{Cls induct} - \iota`\Lambda - 1) \cap \iota`C`P$ (6)

$\vdash . (1) . (2) . (6) . \supset \vdash . \text{Prop}$

***274·194.** $\vdash : C`P \in \text{Cls induct} - \iota`\Lambda - 1 . \supset . B`P_\eta = C`P$ [*274·193]

***274·195.** $\vdash : C`P \sim\in \text{Cls induct} . \supset . \overrightarrow{B}`P_\eta = \Lambda$ [*274·193]

***274·196.** $\vdash : P \in \text{Ser} . \sim \text{E} ! B`\breve{P} . \supset . \text{D}`P_\eta = \text{ᗡ}`P_\eta$

Dem.

$\vdash . *274{\cdot}192 . \supset \vdash : \text{Hp} . \supset . \overrightarrow{B}`\breve{P}_\eta = \Lambda$ (1)

$\vdash . *274{\cdot}195{\cdot}16 . *261{\cdot}24 . \supset \vdash : \text{Hp} . \supset . \overrightarrow{B}`P_\eta = \Lambda$ (2)

$\vdash . (1) . (2) . \supset \vdash . \text{Prop}$

The following propositions give the proof of $\breve{P} \in \Omega . \supset . \breve{P}_\eta \in \Omega$ (*274·22).

***274·2.** $\vdash : \breve{P} \in \Omega . \kappa \subset C`P_\eta . \exists ! \kappa . \supset . \text{E} ! P_m`\kappa . P_m`\kappa \in \min_P``\kappa$

[*274·1·11 . *250·121 . (*274·02)]

***274·201.** $\vdash : \beta \in \breve{T}_P`\kappa . \equiv . (\exists\alpha) . \alpha \in \kappa . \min_P`\alpha = P_m`\kappa . \beta = \alpha - \iota`P_m`\kappa . \exists ! \beta$

[(*274·03)]

***274·202.** $\vdash : \text{E} ! P_m`\kappa . \supset . \text{E} ! \breve{T}_P`\kappa$ [(*274·03) . *14·21]

***274·203.** $\vdash :. \text{Hp} *274{\cdot}2 . \supset : \breve{T}_P`\kappa = \Lambda . \equiv . \kappa \cap \overleftarrow{\min_P}`P_m`\kappa = \iota`\iota`P_m`\kappa$

Dem.

$\vdash . *274{\cdot}2{\cdot}202 . \supset$

$\vdash :: \text{Hp} . \supset :. \breve{T}_P`\kappa = \Lambda . \equiv : \sim(\exists\alpha, \beta) . \alpha \in \kappa . \min_P`\alpha = P_m`\kappa . \beta = \alpha - \iota`P_m`\kappa . \exists ! \beta :$

[*13·191] $\equiv : \alpha \in \kappa \cap \overleftarrow{\min_P}`P_m`\kappa . \supset_\alpha . \alpha - \iota`P_m`\kappa = \Lambda :$

[*274·2] $\equiv : \alpha \in \kappa \cap \overleftarrow{\min_P}`P_m`\kappa . \equiv_\alpha . \alpha = \iota`P_m`\kappa :: \supset \vdash . \text{Prop}$

***274·204.** $\vdash : \kappa \subset C'P_\eta \,.\, \kappa (T_P)_* \lambda \,.\, \supset . \, \lambda \subset C'P_\eta$

Dem.

$\vdash . *120·481 . *274·201 . \supset \vdash : \kappa \subset \text{Cls induct} . E ! \breve{T}_P{}'\kappa . \supset . \breve{T}_P{}'\kappa \subset \text{Cls induct}$ (1)

$\vdash . *274·201 . \supset \vdash : \kappa \subset \text{Cl}'C'P . E ! \breve{T}_P{}'\kappa . \supset . \breve{T}_P{}'\kappa \subset \text{Cl}'C'P - \iota'\Lambda$ (2)

$\vdash . (1) . (2) . *274·16 . \supset \vdash : \kappa \subset C'P_\eta . E ! \breve{T}_P{}'\kappa . \supset . \breve{T}_P{}'\kappa \subset C'P_\eta$ (3)

$\vdash . (3) . \text{Induct} . \supset \vdash . \text{Prop}$

***274·205.** $\vdash : P \in \text{Ser} . E ! P_m{}'\breve{T}_P{}'\lambda . \supset . (P_m{}'\lambda) P (P_m{}'\breve{T}_P{}'\lambda)$

Dem.

$\vdash . *274·201 . *205·21 . \supset \vdash : \text{Hp} . \beta \in \breve{T}_P{}'\lambda . \supset . \beta \subset \overleftarrow{P}'P_m{}'\lambda$ (1)

$\vdash . *205·11 . (*274·02) . \supset \vdash : \text{Hp} . \supset . P_m{}'\breve{T}_P{}'\lambda \in s'\breve{T}_P{}^{\cdot}{}'\lambda$ (2)

$\vdash . (1) . (2) . \supset \vdash . \text{Prop}$

***274·206.** $\vdash : \text{Hp} *274·205 . \kappa (T_P)_* \lambda . \supset . (P_m{}'\kappa) P (P_m{}'\breve{T}_P{}'\lambda)$

Dem.

$\vdash . *14·21 . (*274·02) . \supset \vdash : E ! P_m{}'\breve{T}_P{}'\lambda . \supset . E ! P_m{}'\lambda$ (1)

$\vdash . (1) . \text{Induct} . \quad \supset \vdash : \text{Hp} . \supset . E ! P_m{}'\kappa$ (2)

$\vdash . (2) . *274·205 . \text{Induct} . \supset \vdash . \text{Prop}$

***274·207.** $\vdash : \breve{P} \in \Omega . \kappa (T_P)_* \lambda . P_m{}'\lambda = \max_P{}'M_P{}'\kappa . \supset .$

$\sim E ! P_m{}'\breve{T}_P{}'\lambda . \breve{T}_P{}'\lambda = \Lambda$

Dem.

$\vdash . *274·205 . \text{Transp} . \supset \vdash : \text{Hp} . \supset . \sim E ! P_m{}'\breve{T}_P{}'\lambda .$

$[*274·204·2 . \text{Transp}] \quad \supset . \breve{T}_P{}'\lambda = \Lambda : \supset \vdash . \text{Prop}$

***274·208.** $\vdash :. \breve{P} \in \Omega . \kappa \subset C'P_\eta . \exists ! \kappa . \supset :$

$\Lambda \in \overleftarrow{(T_P)_*}{}'\kappa : (\exists \lambda) . \kappa (T_P)_* \lambda . \lambda \cap \overleftarrow{\min_P}{}'P_m{}'\lambda = \iota'\iota'P_m{}'\lambda . \breve{T}_P{}'\lambda = \Lambda$

Dem.

$\vdash . *250·121 . \supset \vdash : \text{Hp} . \supset . E ! \max_P{}'M_P{}'\kappa$ (1)

$\vdash . (1) . *274·207·203·204 . \supset \vdash . \text{Prop}$

***274·21.** $\vdash : \beta \in \breve{T}_P{}'\kappa . \supset . \beta \cup \iota'P_m{}'\kappa \in \kappa \quad [*274·201]$

***274·211.** $\vdash : \kappa (T_P)_* \lambda . \beta \in \lambda . \supset . \beta \cup P_m{}''T_P (\kappa \vdash \lambda) \in \kappa$

Dem.

$\vdash . *274·21 . \supset \vdash :. \text{Hp} : \beta \in \lambda . \supset_\beta . \beta \cup P_m{}''T_P (\kappa \vdash \lambda) \in \kappa : \supset :$

$\gamma \in \breve{T}_P{}'\lambda . \supset_\gamma . \gamma \cup P_m{}''T_P (\kappa \vdash \breve{T}_P{}'\lambda) \in \kappa$ (1)

$\vdash . *274·21 . (1) . \text{Induct} . \supset \vdash . \text{Prop}$

$*274\cdot212.\ \vdash : \breve{P} \in \Omega \,.\, \kappa \subset C`P_\eta \,.\, \exists ! \kappa \,.\, \supset .\, M_P`\kappa \in \kappa$

Dem.

$\vdash .\, *274\cdot208\cdot211 \,.\, \supset$

$\vdash : \mathrm{Hp} \,.\, \supset .\, (\exists\lambda) .\, \kappa (T_P)_* \lambda \,.\, \breve{T}_P`\lambda = \Lambda \,.\, \iota`P_m`\lambda \in \lambda \,.\, \iota`P_m`\lambda \cup P_m``T_P(\kappa \vdash \lambda) \in \kappa \,.$

$[*121\cdot103] \supset .\, (\exists\lambda) .\, P_m``T_P(\kappa \mapsto \lambda) \in \kappa \,.\, P_m``T_P(\kappa \mapsto \lambda) = P_m``\overleftarrow{(T_P)_*}`\kappa :$

$\supset \vdash .\, \mathrm{Prop}$

$*274\cdot213.\ \vdash : P \in \mathrm{Ser} \,.\, \kappa \subset C`P_\eta \,.\, \alpha \in \kappa \,.\, \kappa (T_P)_* \lambda \,.\, \overrightarrow{P}`P_m`\lambda \cap M_P`\kappa \subset \alpha \,.\, \supset .$

$\alpha - (\overrightarrow{P}`P_m`\lambda \cap M_P`\kappa) \in \lambda$

Dem.

$\vdash .\, *274\cdot201 \,.\, \supset \vdash : \mathrm{Hp} \,.\, \kappa = \lambda \,.\, \supset .\, \alpha - (\overrightarrow{P}`P_m`\lambda \cap M_P`\kappa) = \alpha \,.$

$[*13\cdot12] \qquad \supset .\, \alpha - (\overrightarrow{P}`P_m`\lambda \cap M_P`\kappa) \in \kappa \qquad (1)$

$\vdash .\, *274\cdot206 \,.\, \supset$

$\vdash :.\, \mathrm{Hp} : \beta \in \kappa \,.\, \overrightarrow{P}`P_m`\lambda \cap M_P`\kappa \subset \beta \,.\, \supset_\beta .\, \beta - (\overrightarrow{P}`P_m`\lambda \cap M_P`\kappa) \in \lambda : \supset :$

$\beta \in \kappa \,.\, \overrightarrow{P}`P_m`\breve{T}_P`\lambda \cap M_P`\kappa \subset \beta \,.\, \supset .\, \overrightarrow{P}`P_m`\lambda \cap M_P`\kappa \subset \beta \,.\, P_m`\lambda \in \beta \,.$

$\{\beta - (\overrightarrow{P}`P_m`\lambda \cap M_P`\kappa)\} \in \lambda \,.\, P_m`\lambda \in \{\beta - (\overrightarrow{P}`P_m`\lambda \cap M_P`\kappa)\} \,.$

$[*274\cdot201] \qquad \supset .\, \{\beta - (\overrightarrow{P}`P_m`\lambda \cap M_P`\kappa) - \iota`P_m`\lambda\} \in \breve{T}_P`\lambda \,.$

$[*274\cdot206] \qquad \supset .\, \{\beta - (\overrightarrow{P}`P_m`\breve{T}_P`\lambda \cap M_P`\kappa)\} \in \breve{T}_P`\lambda \qquad (2)$

$\vdash .\, (1) .\, (2) \,.\, \mathrm{Induct} \,.\, \supset \vdash .\, \mathrm{Prop}$

$*274\cdot214.\ \vdash : \breve{P} \in \Omega \,.\, \kappa \subset C`P_\eta \,.\, \alpha \in \kappa - \iota`M_P`\kappa \,.\, \supset .\, \alpha P_\eta (M_P`\kappa)$

Dem.

$\vdash .\, *274\cdot212 \,.\qquad \supset \vdash :.\, \mathrm{Hp} \,.\, \supset : M_P`\kappa \in \mathrm{Cls\,induct} : \qquad (1)$

$[*170\cdot16] \qquad \supset : M_P`\kappa \subset \alpha \,.\, \supset .\, \alpha P_\eta (M_P`\kappa) \qquad (2)$

$\vdash .\, *274\cdot11 \,.\, (1) \,.\, \supset \vdash : \mathrm{Hp} \,.\, \exists ! M_P`\kappa - \alpha \,.\, \supset .\, \mathrm{E} ! \min_P`(M_P`\kappa - \alpha) \,.$

$[*205\cdot14.(*274\cdot04)] \supset .\, (\exists\lambda) .\, \kappa (T_P)_* \lambda \,.\, P_m`\lambda \sim\in \alpha \,.\, \overrightarrow{P}`P_m`\lambda \cap M_P`\kappa \subset \alpha \,.$

$[*274\cdot213] \qquad \supset .\, (\exists\lambda) .\, \kappa (T_P)_* \lambda \,.\, P_m`\lambda \sim\in \alpha \,.\, \alpha - (\overrightarrow{P}`P_m`\lambda \cap M_P`\kappa) \in \lambda \,.$

$\overrightarrow{P}`P_m`\lambda \cap M_P`\kappa \subset \alpha \,.$

$[*274\cdot201] \qquad \supset .\, (\exists\lambda, z) .\, \kappa (T_P)_* \lambda \,.\, z = \min_P`\{\alpha - (\overrightarrow{P}`P_m`\lambda \cap M_P`\kappa)\} \,.$

$zP (P_m`\lambda) \,.\, \overrightarrow{P}`P_m`\lambda \cap M_P`\kappa \subset \alpha \,.$

$[*31\cdot18] \qquad \supset .\, (\exists z) .\, z \in \alpha - M_P`\kappa \,.\, M_P`\kappa \cap \overrightarrow{P}`z \subset \alpha \,.$

$[*170\cdot11] \qquad \supset .\, \alpha P_\eta (M_P`\kappa) \qquad (3)$

$\vdash .\, (2) .\, (3) \,.\, \supset \vdash .\, \mathrm{Prop}$

$*274\cdot215.\ \vdash : \breve{P} \in \Omega \,.\, \kappa \subset C`P_\eta \,.\, \exists ! \kappa \,.\, \supset .\, M_P`\kappa = \max (P_\eta)`\kappa \quad [*274\cdot212\cdot214]$

$*274{\cdot}22$. $\vdash : \breve{P} \in \Omega . \supset . \breve{P}_\eta \in \Omega$

Dem.

$$\vdash . *274{\cdot}215 . \supset \vdash : \text{Hp} . \supset . \text{E}\,!!\, \text{max}\,(P_\eta)\text{‘‘Cl ex‘}C\text{‘}P_\eta .$$

$$[*250{\cdot}125] \qquad \supset . \breve{P}_\eta \in \Omega : \supset \vdash . \text{Prop}$$

The following propositions constitute the proof of

$$\breve{P} \in \omega . \supset . \breve{P}_\eta \in \omega \quad (*274{\cdot}25).$$

$*274{\cdot}221$. $\vdash : P \in \text{Ser} . \overleftarrow{P}\text{‘max}_P\text{‘}\alpha \in \text{Cls induct} . \alpha \in \text{Cl induct‘}C\text{‘}P - \iota\text{‘}\Lambda - \iota\text{‘}\overrightarrow{B}\text{‘}\breve{P} .$
$\beta = (\alpha - \iota\text{‘max}_P\text{‘}\alpha) \cup \overleftarrow{P}\text{‘max}_P\text{‘}\alpha . \supset . \alpha P_\eta \beta$

Dem.

$\vdash . *205{\cdot}55 . \quad \supset \vdash : \text{Hp} . B\text{‘}\breve{P} \in \alpha . \supset . \exists ! \alpha - \iota\text{‘max}_P\text{‘}\alpha \qquad (1)$

$\vdash . *202{\cdot}511 . \quad \supset \vdash : \text{Hp} . B\text{‘}\breve{P} \sim\in \alpha . \supset . B\text{‘}\breve{P} \in \overleftarrow{P}\text{‘max}_P\text{‘}\alpha \qquad (2)$

$\vdash . *93{\cdot}101 . \quad \supset \vdash : \text{Hp} . \sim \text{E}\,!\, B\text{‘}\breve{P} . \supset . \exists ! \overleftarrow{P}\text{‘max}_P\text{‘}\alpha \qquad (3)$

$\vdash . (1) . (2) . (3) . \supset \vdash : \text{Hp} . \supset . \exists ! \beta \qquad (4)$

$\vdash . *120{\cdot}481{\cdot}71 . \supset \vdash : \text{Hp} . \supset . \beta \in \text{Cls induct} \qquad (5)$

$\vdash . *205{\cdot}21 . *200{\cdot}361 . \supset \vdash : \text{Hp} . \supset . \beta \cap \overrightarrow{P}\text{‘max}_P\text{‘}\alpha = \alpha \cap \overrightarrow{P}\text{‘max}_P\text{‘}\alpha \qquad (6)$

$\vdash . (4) . (5) . (6) . \supset \vdash : \text{Hp} . \supset . \alpha, \beta \in \text{Cl induct‘}C\text{‘}P - \iota\text{‘}\Lambda . \text{max}_P\text{‘}\alpha \in \alpha - \beta .$
$\alpha \cap \overrightarrow{P}\text{‘max}_P\text{‘}\alpha = \beta \cap \overrightarrow{P}\text{‘max}_P\text{‘}\alpha .$

$[*274{\cdot}12] \qquad \supset . \alpha P_\eta \beta : \supset \vdash . \text{Prop}$

$*274{\cdot}222$. $\vdash : \text{Hp}\, *274{\cdot}221 . \alpha P_\eta \gamma . \text{max}_P\text{‘}\alpha \in \gamma . \supset . \beta P_\eta \gamma$

Dem.

$\vdash . *274{\cdot}12 . \supset \vdash : \text{Hp} . \supset . (\exists z) . z \in \alpha - \gamma . z \neq \text{max}_P\text{‘}\alpha . \alpha \cap \overrightarrow{P}\text{‘}z = \gamma \cap \overrightarrow{P}\text{‘}z .$

$[*201{\cdot}14 . *205{\cdot}21 . \text{Hp}] \supset . (\exists z) . z \in \beta - \gamma . \beta \cap \overrightarrow{P}\text{‘}z = \gamma \cap \overrightarrow{P}\text{‘}z .$

$[*274{\cdot}12] \qquad \supset . \beta P_\eta \gamma : \supset \vdash . \text{Prop}$

$*274{\cdot}223$. $\vdash : \text{Hp}\, *274{\cdot}221 . \alpha P_\eta \gamma . \text{max}_P\text{‘}\alpha \sim\in \gamma . \gamma \neq \beta . \supset . \beta P_\eta \gamma$

Dem.

$\vdash . *274{\cdot}12 . \supset \vdash :. \text{Hp} . \supset : (\exists z) . z \in \alpha - \gamma - \iota\text{‘max}_P\text{‘}\alpha . \alpha \cap \overrightarrow{P}\text{‘}z = \gamma \cap \overrightarrow{P}\text{‘}z . \vee .$
$\alpha \cap \overrightarrow{P}\text{‘max}_P\text{‘}\alpha = \gamma \cap \overrightarrow{P}\text{‘max}_P\text{‘}\alpha \qquad (1)$

$\vdash . *201{\cdot}14 . *205{\cdot}21 . \supset$

$\vdash :. \text{Hp} : (\exists z) . z \in \alpha - \gamma - \iota\text{‘max}_P\text{‘}\alpha . \alpha \cap \overrightarrow{P}\text{‘}z = \gamma \cap \overrightarrow{P}\text{‘}z : \supset . \beta P_\eta \gamma \qquad (2)$

$\vdash . *205{\cdot}21 . \quad \supset \vdash : \text{Hp} . \alpha \cap \overrightarrow{P}\text{‘max}_P\text{‘}\alpha = \gamma \cap \overrightarrow{P}\text{‘max}_P\text{‘}\alpha . \supset .$
$\alpha - \iota\text{‘max}_P\text{‘}\alpha = \gamma \cap \overrightarrow{P}\text{‘max}_P\text{‘}\alpha \qquad (3)$

$\vdash . *202{\cdot}101 . \supset \vdash : \text{Hp} . \supset . \gamma \subset \overrightarrow{P}\text{‘max}_P\text{‘}\alpha \cup \overleftarrow{P}\text{‘max}_P\text{‘}\alpha \qquad (4)$

$\vdash . (3) . (4) . \quad \supset \vdash :. \text{Hp} . \alpha \cap \overrightarrow{P}\text{‘max}_P\text{‘}\alpha = \gamma \cap \overrightarrow{P}\text{‘max}_P\text{‘}\alpha . \supset : \gamma \subset \beta :$

$[*170{\cdot}16 . (*274{\cdot}01)] \qquad \supset : \gamma \neq \beta . \supset . \beta P_\eta \gamma \qquad (5)$

$\vdash . (1) . (2) . (5) . \supset \vdash . \text{Prop}$

***274·224.** $\vdash : \mathrm{Hp}\ *274\cdot221 . \alpha P_\eta \gamma . \beta \neq \gamma . \supset . \beta P_\eta \gamma$ [*274·222·223]

***274·23.** $\vdash : \mathrm{Hp}\ *274\cdot221 . \supset . \alpha (P_\eta)_1 \beta$ [*274·221·224 . *204·72]

***274·25.** $\vdash : \breve{P} \epsilon \omega . \supset . \breve{P}_\eta \epsilon \omega$

Dem.

$\vdash . *274\cdot22\cdot16 . \supset \vdash : \mathrm{Hp} . \supset . \breve{P}_\eta \epsilon \Omega - \iota`\dot{\Lambda}$ (1)

$\vdash . *274\cdot191\cdot17 . \supset$

$\vdash : \mathrm{Hp} . \alpha \epsilon \mathrm{D}`P_\eta . \supset . \alpha \epsilon \mathrm{Cl\ induct}`C`P - \iota`\Lambda - \iota`\overrightarrow{B}`\breve{P}$ (2)

$\vdash . *263\cdot412 . *274\cdot11 . \supset$

$\vdash : \mathrm{Hp} . \alpha \epsilon \mathrm{Cl\ induct}`C`P - \iota`\Lambda . \supset . \overleftarrow{P}`\mathrm{max}_P`\alpha \epsilon \mathrm{Cls\ induct}$ (3)

$\vdash . (2) . (3) . *274\cdot23 . \supset \vdash : \mathrm{Hp} . \alpha \epsilon \mathrm{D}`P_\eta . \supset . \alpha \epsilon \mathrm{D}`(P_\eta)_1$ (4)

$\vdash . (1) . (4) . *274\cdot195 . *121\cdot323 . \supset$

$\vdash : \mathrm{Hp} . \supset . \breve{P}_\eta \epsilon \Omega - \iota`\dot{\Lambda} . \mathrm{D}`P_\eta = \mathrm{D}`(P_\eta)_1 . \sim \mathrm{E} ! B`P_\eta .$

$[*263\cdot44] \supset . \breve{P}_\eta \epsilon \omega : \supset \vdash . \mathrm{Prop}$

***274·26.** $\vdash : P \epsilon \omega . \supset . P_{1c} \upharpoonright (\mathrm{Cls\ induct} - \iota`\Lambda) \epsilon \omega .$

$C`P_{1c} \upharpoonright (\mathrm{Cls\ induct} - \iota`\Lambda) = \mathrm{Cl\ induct}`C`P - \iota`\Lambda$

Dem.

$\vdash . *274\cdot13 . \supset \vdash : Q = \breve{P} . \supset . P_{1c} \upharpoonright (\mathrm{Cls\ induct} - \iota`\Lambda) = \breve{Q}_\eta$ (1)

$\vdash . *274\cdot25 . \supset \vdash : P \epsilon \omega . Q = \breve{P} . \supset . \breve{Q}_\eta \epsilon \omega$ (2)

$\vdash . *274\cdot17 . \supset \vdash : P \epsilon \omega . Q = \breve{P} . \supset . C`\breve{Q}_\eta = \mathrm{Cl\ induct}`C`P - \iota`\Lambda$ (3)

$\vdash . (1) . (2) . (3) . \supset \vdash . \mathrm{Prop}$

***274·27.** $\vdash : \alpha \epsilon \aleph_0 . \supset . \mathrm{Cl\ induct}`\alpha \epsilon \aleph_0 . \mathrm{Cl\ induct}`\alpha - \iota`\Lambda \epsilon \aleph_0$

Dem.

$\vdash . *263\cdot101 . \supset \vdash : \mathrm{Hp} . \supset . (\exists P) . P \epsilon \omega . \alpha = C`P .$

$[*274\cdot26] \quad \supset . (\exists M) . M \epsilon \omega . \mathrm{Cl\ induct}`\alpha - \iota`\Lambda = C`M .$

$[*263\cdot101] \quad \supset . \mathrm{Cl\ induct}`\alpha - \iota`\Lambda \epsilon \aleph_0 .$ (1)

$[*123\cdot4] \quad \supset . \mathrm{Cl\ induct}`\alpha \epsilon \aleph_0$ (2)

$\vdash . (1) . (2) . \supset \vdash . \mathrm{Prop}$

The following propositions constitute the proof of

$$P \epsilon \omega . \supset . P_\eta \epsilon \eta \quad (*274\cdot33).$$

***274·3.** $\vdash : P \epsilon \mathrm{Ser} . \alpha P_\eta \beta . x \epsilon p`\overleftarrow{P}``(\alpha \cup \beta) . \supset . \alpha P_\eta (\beta \cup \iota`x) . (\beta \cup \iota`x) P_\eta \beta$

Dem.

$\vdash . *200\cdot53 . \quad \supset \vdash : \mathrm{Hp} . z \epsilon \alpha . \supset . \beta \cap \overrightarrow{P}`z = (\beta \cup \iota`x) \cap \overrightarrow{P}`z$ (1)

$\vdash . *200\cdot5 . \quad \supset \vdash : \mathrm{Hp} . z \epsilon \alpha - \beta . \supset . z \epsilon \alpha - (\beta \cup \iota`x)$ (2)

$\vdash . (1) . (2) . *274\cdot12 . \supset \vdash : \mathrm{Hp} . \supset . \alpha P_\eta (\beta \cup \iota`x)$ (3)

$\vdash . *200\cdot5 . *170\cdot16 . \supset \vdash : \mathrm{Hp} . \supset . (\beta \cup \iota`x) P_\eta \beta$ (4)

$\vdash . (3) . (4) . \supset \vdash . \mathrm{Prop}$

***274·31.** $\vdash : P \epsilon \text{Ser} . \sim \text{E} ! B'\breve{P} . \supset . P_\eta \epsilon \text{Ser} \cap \text{comp}$

Dem.

$\vdash . *274·1 . *120·71 . \supset \vdash : \alpha P_\eta \beta . \supset . \alpha \cup \beta \epsilon \text{Cls induct} - \iota'\Lambda$ (1)

$\vdash . (1) . *274·11 . \supset \vdash : \text{Hp} . \alpha P_\eta \beta . \supset . \text{E} ! \max_P'(\alpha \cup \beta) .$

[*93·103] $\supset . \exists ! \overleftarrow{P}'\max_P'(\alpha \cup \beta) .$

[*205·67] $\supset . \exists ! p'\overleftarrow{P}''(\alpha \cup \beta) .$

[*274·3] $\supset . \alpha P_\eta{}^2 \beta$ (2)

$\vdash . (2) . *274·18 . \supset \vdash . \text{Prop}$

***274·32.** $\vdash : P \epsilon \text{Ser} \cap \breve{C}''\aleph_0 . \sim \text{E} ! B'\breve{P} . \supset . P_\eta \epsilon \eta$

Dem.

$\vdash . *274·31 . \supset \vdash : \text{Hp} . \supset . P_\eta \epsilon \text{Ser} \cap \text{comp}$ (1)

$\vdash . *274·196 . \supset \vdash : \text{Hp} . \supset . \text{D}'P_\eta = \text{Cl}'P_\eta$ (2)

$\vdash . *274·27·17 . \supset \vdash : \text{Hp} . \supset . C'P_\eta \epsilon \aleph_0$ (3)

$\vdash . (1) . (2) . (3) . *273·1 . \supset \vdash . \text{Prop}$

***274·33.** $\vdash : P \epsilon \omega . \supset . P_\eta \epsilon \eta$ [*274·32 . *263·101·11·22]

This is the principal proposition of the present number.

***274·34.** $\vdash : \alpha \epsilon \aleph_0 . \supset . \exists ! \eta \cap \overleftarrow{C}'(\text{Cl induct}'\alpha - \iota'\Lambda)$

Dem.

$\vdash . *263·101 . \supset \vdash : \text{Hp} . \supset . (\exists P) . P \epsilon \omega . C'P = \alpha .$

[*274·33·17] $\supset . (\exists M) . M \epsilon \eta . C'M = \text{Cl induct}'\alpha - \iota'\Lambda : \supset \vdash . \text{Prop}$

The following propositions are concerned with the existence-theorem for η. They all follow from *274·33.

***274·4.** $\vdash : P \epsilon \omega . T = \breve{\iota}'P \,\overline{\text{smor}}\, \{P_{1c} \upharpoonright (\text{Cls induct} - \iota'\Lambda)\} . \supset . T ; P_\eta \epsilon \eta \cap \overleftarrow{C}'C'P$

Dem.

$\vdash . *274·26·17 . \supset \vdash : \text{Hp} . \supset . \text{Cl}'T = C'P_\eta$ (1)

$\vdash . (1) . *151·11·131 . \supset \vdash : \text{Hp} . \supset . T ; P_\eta \text{ smor } P_\eta . C'T ; P_\eta = C'P .$

[*274·33.*273·41] $\supset . T ; P_\eta \epsilon \eta . C'T ; P_\eta = C'P : \supset \vdash . \text{Prop}$

***274·41.** $\vdash : \exists ! \omega \cap t'P . \equiv . \exists ! \eta \cap t'P$

Dem.

$\vdash . *274·4 . \supset \vdash : Q \epsilon \omega \cap t'P . \supset . (\exists R) . R \epsilon \eta . C'R = C'Q .$

[*64·24] $\supset . \exists ! \eta \cap t'P$ (1)

$\vdash . *273·11 . \supset \vdash : R \epsilon \eta \cap t'P . \supset . (\exists Q) . Q \epsilon \omega . C'Q = C'R .$

[*64·24] $\supset . \exists ! \omega \cap t'P$ (2)

$\vdash . (1) . (2) . \supset \vdash . \text{Prop}$

***274·42.** $\vdash : \alpha \epsilon \aleph_0 . \supset . \exists ! \eta \cap \overleftarrow{C}'\alpha$ [*274·4·26 . *263·17 . *250·6 . *263·101]

***274·43.** $\vdash . \aleph_0 = C''\eta$ [*273·1 . *274·42]

***274·44.** $\vdash : \exists ! \aleph_0 \cap t'\alpha . \equiv . \exists ! \eta \cap t_{00}'\alpha$ [*263·131 . *274·41]

***274·45.** $\vdash : \exists ! \aleph_0(x) . \equiv . \exists ! \eta \cap t^{11}'x$ [*263·13 . *274·41]

***274·46.** $\vdash : \text{Infin ax}(x) . \equiv . \exists ! \eta \cap t^{33}'x$ [*263·132 . *274·41]

*275. CONTINUOUS SERIES.

Summary of *275.

The definition of continuity to be given in this number is due to Cantor. A different and not equivalent definition was given by Dedekind: series which are continuous in Cantor's sense are also continuous in Dedekind's sense, but not vice versa. Cantor's definition has the advantage (among others) that two series which are continuous in his sense are ordinally similar, which is not necessarily the case with series that are continuous in Dedekind's sense. Dedekind's definition of "continuous series" is, in our language, "series which are compact and Dedekindian." Cantor's definition (after a certain amount of simplification) is "series which are Dedekindian and contain an $\aleph_0$ as a median class." In the case of the real numbers, the rationals are a median class of this sort.

An equivalent definition to the above is that a continuous series is a Dedekindian series whose converse domain is the derivative of a contained rational series (*275·13).

Following Cantor, we shall use θ for the class of continuous series.

In what follows, we prove first that the series of segments of a rational series is a continuous series, *i.e.*

***275·21.** $\vdash : P \in \eta . \supset . \varsigma ` P \in \theta$

The contained $\aleph_0$ is $\overrightarrow{P} `` C ` P$. The proposition follows at once from *271·31. On its importance, see remarks on *275·21 below.

From this proposition, it follows that if η exists in any type, θ exists in the next type (275·22), whence the existence of θ in sufficiently high types follows from the axiom of infinity (*275·25).

To prove that any two continuous series are similar, we use *271·39. By the definition, if P and Q are continuous, they contain respectively two median classes α and β, such that $P \upharpoonright \alpha$ and $Q \upharpoonright \beta$ are rational series. Hence by *273·4, $P \upharpoonright \alpha \operatorname{smor} Q \upharpoonright \beta$, and therefore $P \operatorname{smor} Q$, by *271·39. Also obviously $P \in \theta . P \operatorname{smor} Q . \supset . Q \in \theta$. Hence

***275·32.** $\vdash : P \in \theta . \supset . \theta = \mathrm{Nr} ` P$

and

***275·33.** $\vdash . \theta \in \mathrm{NR}$

***275·01.** $\theta = \text{Ser} \cap \text{Ded} \cap \breve{\text{med}}``\aleph_0$ Df

***275·1.** $\vdash : P \in \theta . \equiv . P \in \text{Ser} \cap \text{Ded} . \exists ! \aleph_0 \cap \overrightarrow{\text{med}}`P$
[(*275·01)]

***275·11.** $\vdash :. P \in \theta . \equiv : P \in \text{Ser} \cap \text{Ded} : (\exists \alpha) . \alpha \in \aleph_0 . \delta_P`\alpha = \text{Ɑ}`P . \alpha \subset C`P$
[*275·1 . *271·2]

***275·12.** $\vdash :: P \in \theta . \equiv :. P \in \text{Ser} \cap \text{Ded} :. (\exists \alpha) : \alpha \in \aleph_0 :$
$xPy . \supset_{x,y} . \exists ! \alpha \cap P(x-y) : \alpha \subset C`P$ [*275·1 . *271·1]

***275·13.** $\vdash :. P \in \theta . \equiv : P \in \text{Ser} \cap \text{Ded} : (\exists R) . R \mathrel{\text{Ⓢ}} P . R \in \eta . \delta_P`C`R = \text{Ɑ}`P$

Dem.

$\vdash . *273\cdot1 . *271\cdot2 . \supset$
$\vdash : P \in \text{Ser} \cap \text{Ded} . R \mathrel{\text{Ⓢ}} P . R \in \eta . \delta_P`C`R = \text{Ɑ}`P . \supset . C`R \in \aleph_0 . C`R \in \overrightarrow{\text{med}}`P .$
[*275·1] $\supset . P \in \theta$ (1)
$\vdash . *271\cdot16 . \supset \vdash : \alpha \,\text{med}\, P . \beta = \alpha \cap \text{D}`P \cap \text{Ɑ}`P . \supset . \beta \,\text{med}\, P .$ (2)
[*271·15] $\supset . P \upharpoonright \beta \in \text{comp}$ (3)
$\vdash . *123\cdot17 . \supset \vdash : \text{Hp}(2) . P \in \text{Ser} . \alpha \in \aleph_0 \cap \text{Cl}`C`P . \supset . \beta \in \aleph_0 \cap \text{Cl}`C`P$ (4)
$\vdash . *271\cdot1 . \supset \vdash : \beta \,\text{med}\, P . \supset . P``\beta = \text{D}`P . \breve{P}``\beta = \text{Ɑ}`P$ (5)
$\vdash . (5) . *37\cdot41 . (2) . \supset \vdash : \text{Hp}(2) . \supset . \text{D}`(P \upharpoonright \beta) = \beta . \text{Ɑ}`(P \upharpoonright \beta) = \beta$ (6)
$\vdash . (3) . (4) . (6) . *273\cdot1 . \supset \vdash : \text{Hp}(4) . \supset . P \upharpoonright \beta \in \eta$ (7)
$\vdash . (2) . *271\cdot2 . \supset \vdash : \text{Hp}(4) . \supset . \delta_P`C`(P \upharpoonright \beta) = \text{Ɑ}`P$ (8)
$\vdash . (7) . (8) . *275\cdot1 . \supset \vdash : P \in \theta . \supset . (\exists \beta) . P \upharpoonright \beta \in \eta . \delta_P`C`(P \upharpoonright \beta) = \text{Ɑ}`P$ (9)
$\vdash . (1) . (9) . \supset \vdash .$ Prop

***275·14.** $\vdash . \theta = \text{Cnv}``\theta$

Dem.

$\vdash . *214\cdot14 . *271\cdot11 . \supset \vdash : P \in \text{Ser} \cap \text{Ded} . \alpha \in \aleph_0 \cap \overrightarrow{\text{med}}`P . \equiv .$
$\breve{P} \in \text{Ser} \cap \text{Ded} . \alpha \in \aleph_0 \cap \overrightarrow{\text{med}}`\breve{P}$ (1)
$\vdash . (1) . *275\cdot1 . \supset \vdash .$ Prop

***275·2.** $\vdash : P \in \eta . \supset . \varsigma`P \in \text{Ser} \cap \text{Ded} . \overrightarrow{P}``C`P \in \aleph_0 . \overrightarrow{P}``C`P \in \overrightarrow{\text{med}}`\varsigma`P$

Dem.

$\vdash . *214\cdot33 . \supset \vdash : \text{Hp} . \supset . \varsigma`P \in \text{Ser} \cap \text{Ded}$ (1)
$\vdash . *204\cdot35 . \supset \vdash : \text{Hp} . \supset . \overrightarrow{P}``C`P \,\text{sm}\, C`P .$
[*273·1.*123·321] $\supset . \overrightarrow{P}``C`P \in \aleph_0$ (2)
$\vdash . *271\cdot31 . *273\cdot1 . \supset \vdash : \text{Hp} . \supset . \overrightarrow{P}``C`P \in \overrightarrow{\text{med}}`\varsigma`P$ (3)
$\vdash . (1) . (2) . (3) . \supset \vdash .$ Prop

***275·21.** $\vdash : P \in \eta . \supset . \varsigma`P \in \theta$ [*275·2·1]

This proposition is of great importance, particularly in the theory of real numbers. We shall define the real numbers as segments of the series of rational numbers, in order to be sure of their existence. Thus if P is the series of rational numbers, $\varsigma`P$, which may be taken to be the series of real numbers, is continuous. If $P$ is the series of rational proper fractions, excluding 0, $\varsigma`P$ is the series of real proper fractions together with 0 and 1: this series is continuous in virtue of the above proposition.

The above proposition is also useful as enabling us to deduce the existence of θ from that of η, and thence from that of $\aleph_0$, and thence from the axiom of infinity. A rise of type is, however, required for the existence-theorems, which are given in the following propositions.

***275·22.** $\vdash : \exists ! \eta \cap t_{00}`\alpha . \supset . \exists ! \theta \cap t^{11}`\alpha$

Dem.

$\vdash . *64·55 . \supset \vdash : \exists ! \eta \cap t_{00}`\alpha . \supset . (\exists P) . P \in \eta . C`P \subset t_0`\alpha .$

[*63·371] $\supset . (\exists P) . P \in \eta . C`P \in t`\alpha .$

[*275·21] $\supset . (\exists Q) . Q \in \theta . C`Q \subset t`\alpha .$

[*64·57] $\supset . \exists ! \theta \cap t^{11}`x : \supset \vdash . \text{Prop}$

***275·23.** $\vdash : \exists ! \aleph_0 \cap t`\alpha . \supset . \exists ! \theta \cap t^{11}`\alpha$ [*274·44 . *275·22]

***275·24.** $\vdash : \exists ! \aleph_0 (x) . \supset . \exists ! \theta \cap t^{22}`x$ [*275·23 . *64·31·312 . (*65·02)]

***275·25.** $\vdash : \text{Infin ax} (x) . \supset . \exists ! \theta \cap t^{44}`x$

Dem.

$\vdash . *123·37 . \supset \vdash : \text{Hp} . \supset . \exists ! \aleph_0 (t^{2}`x) .$

[*275·24] $\supset . \exists ! \theta \cap t^{22}`t^{2}`x .$

[*64·312] $\supset . \exists ! \theta \cap t^{44}`x : \supset \vdash . \text{Prop}$

***275·3.** $\vdash : P, Q \in \theta . \supset . P \text{ smor } Q$

Dem.

$\vdash . *275·13 . \supset \vdash :. \text{Hp} . \supset : P, Q \in \text{Ser} \cap \text{Ded} :$

$(\exists R, S) . R, S \in \eta . R \Subset P . S \Subset Q . C`R \in \overrightarrow{\text{med}}`P . C`S \in \overrightarrow{\text{med}}`Q :$

[*204·41] $\supset : P, Q \in \text{Ser} \cap \text{Ded} : (\exists \alpha, \beta) . \alpha \text{ med } P . \beta \text{ med } Q . P \upharpoonright \alpha, Q \upharpoonright \beta \in \eta :$

[*273·4] $\supset : P, Q \in \text{Ser} \cap \text{Ded} : (\exists \alpha, \beta) . \alpha \text{ med } P . \beta \text{ med } Q . (P \upharpoonright \alpha) \text{ smor } (Q \upharpoonright \beta) :$

[*271·39] $\supset : P \text{ smor } Q :. \supset \vdash . \text{Prop}$

***275·31.** $\vdash : P \in \theta . P \text{ smor } Q . \supset . Q \in \theta$

Dem.

$\vdash . *271·4 . \supset \vdash : P \text{ smor } Q . \exists ! \aleph_0 \cap \overrightarrow{\text{med}}`P . \supset . \exists ! \aleph_0 \cap \overrightarrow{\text{med}}`Q$ (1)

$\vdash . *204·21 . *214·6 . \supset \vdash : P \in \text{Ser} \cap \text{Ded} . P \text{ smor } Q . \supset . Q \in \text{Ser} \cap \text{Ded}$ (2)

$\vdash . (1) . (2) . *275·1 . \supset \vdash . \text{Prop}$

***275·32.** $\vdash : P \in \theta . \supset . \theta = \text{Nr}`P$ [*275·3·31]

***275·33.** $\vdash . \theta \in \text{NR}$ [*275·32 . *256·54]

*276. ON SERIES OF INFINITE SUB-CLASSES OF A SERIES.

Summary of *276.

The subject of the present number bears the same relation to θ as that of *274 bears to η. We shall consider, in the present number, the arrangement of all the *infinite* sub-classes of a series (together with Λ) by the principle of first differences, *i.e.* the relation

$$P_{\text{cl}} \upharpoonright (-\text{Cls induct} \cup \iota`\Lambda),$$

where P is the given series. This relation we will call P_θ. It consists of P_{cl} with its field limited to terms not belonging to $C`P_\eta$ (*276·12). It will (under a certain hypothesis) contain a part similar to $\breve{P}_\eta$, namely $P_{\text{cl}}$ with its field limited to complements of finite sub-classes of $C`P$. Hence if $P \in \omega$, P_θ will contain an η, whose field is composed of the complements of members of $C`P_\eta$ (*276·2). The field of this η will be a median class of P_θ. We shall find, also, that $P_\theta \in \text{Ser}$, if $P \in \Omega$ (*276·14), and $P_\theta \in \text{Ded}$, if $P \in \Omega$ infin (*276·4). Hence

***276·41.** $\vdash : P \in \omega \,.\supset .\, P_\theta \in \theta$

Also, since $P \in \omega \,.\supset .\, \text{Cl}`C`P \in 2^{\aleph_0}$, and since $C`P_\eta \in \aleph_0$, we shall have $C`P_\theta \in 2^{\aleph_0}$ (*276·42). This result is important, since it gives the proposition

***276·43.** $\vdash . C``\theta = 2^{\aleph_0}$

The proof that P_θ is Dedekindian if P is an infinite well-ordered series is somewhat complicated. We proceed by proving that every sub-class of $C`P_\theta$ has a lower limit or a minimum. In this proof, we observe first of all that

$$C`P = B`P_\theta \,.\, \Lambda = B`\breve{P}_\theta \quad (*276·121).$$

Hence $C`P$ is the lower limit of the null-class, and $\Lambda$ is the minimum of $\iota`\Lambda$; also if κ is any existent sub-class of $C`P_\theta$, other than $\iota`\Lambda$, we have

$$\overrightarrow{\text{limin}}\,(P_\theta)`\kappa = \overrightarrow{\text{limin}}\,(P_\theta)`(\kappa - \iota`\Lambda).$$

Hence if we can prove

$$\kappa \subset C`P_\theta \,.\, \exists ! \kappa \,.\, \Lambda \sim\in \kappa \,.\supset_\kappa .\, E!\,\text{limin}\,(P_\theta)`\kappa \qquad \text{(A)},$$

we shall have $\quad \text{Cl ex}`C`P_\theta \subset \text{Cl}`\text{limin}\,(P_\theta),$

whence, by $*214{\cdot}12{\cdot}14$, we shall have $P_\theta \in \mathrm{Ded}$. Thus we have to prove (A), *i.e.* $\kappa \subset D`P_\theta . \exists ! \kappa . \supset_\kappa . E ! \operatorname{limin} (P_\theta)`\kappa$, which is $*276{\cdot}39$. To prove this proposition, consider $\min_P`(s`\kappa - p`\kappa)$. This exists unless $\kappa \in 1$; it is the first term which belongs to some members of $\kappa$ but not to others. Those members of $\kappa$ to which it belongs precede (in the order $P_\theta$) those to which it does not belong. Let us call those to which it belongs $\breve{T}_P`\kappa$, so that

$$T_P = \hat{\kappa}\hat{\lambda} \{\lambda = \kappa \cap \overleftarrow{\epsilon}`\min_P`(s`\kappa - p`\kappa)\}.$$

Put also $$P_m`\kappa = \min_P`(s`\kappa - p`\kappa) \quad \mathrm{Dft},$$

so that we may put $$\breve{T}_P`\kappa = \kappa \cap \overleftarrow{\epsilon}`P_m`\kappa \quad \mathrm{Dft}.$$

Then if we put $A = \hat{\kappa}\hat{\lambda} (\lambda \subset \kappa . \lambda \neq \kappa)$, T_P and A fulfil the hypotheses of $*258$, and we have

$$A (T_P, \kappa) \in \Omega.$$

The series $A (T_P, \kappa)$ proceeds to smaller and smaller sub-classes of κ, of which any one, say λ, consists of terms which come earlier (in the order P_θ) than any other sub-class of κ not belonging to λ. By $*258{\cdot}231$, the series $A (T_P, \kappa)$ has an end, namely

$$p`(T_P * A)`\kappa.$$

If this is not null, it must consist of a single term, which will be the minimum of κ ($*276{\cdot}33$). But if it is null, we proceed as follows. Put

$$P_{tl}`\kappa = s`\hat{\gamma} \{(\exists \lambda) . \lambda \in (T_P * A)`\kappa . \gamma = p`\lambda \cap \overrightarrow{P}`P_m`\lambda\} \quad \mathrm{Dft}.$$

Then $P_{tl}`\kappa$ will be the lower limit of κ.

In the first place, we easily prove that, since $p`(T_P * A)`\kappa = \Lambda$, if

$$\lambda \in (T_P * A)`\kappa - \iota`\Lambda,$$

$P_m`\lambda$ and $\breve{T}_P`\lambda$ both exist ($*276{\cdot}341$). Hence every member of κ has predecessors in κ, and κ has no minimum. In the second place, we show that

$$\lambda \{A (T_P, \kappa)\} \mu . \exists ! \mu . \supset . (P_m`\lambda) P (P_m`\mu) \quad (*276{\cdot}34{\cdot}342),$$

and that $$\alpha \in \lambda . \supset . p`\lambda \cap \overrightarrow{P}`P_m`\lambda = \alpha \cap \overrightarrow{P}`P_m`\lambda \quad (*276{\cdot}353).$$

Hence we find that

$$\begin{aligned} \lambda \{A (T_P, \kappa)\} \mu . \alpha \in \mu . \supset . p`\lambda \cap \overrightarrow{P}`P_m`\lambda = p`\mu \cap \overrightarrow{P}`P_m`\lambda = \alpha \cap \overrightarrow{P}`P_m`\lambda . \\ \supset . p`\lambda \cap \overrightarrow{P}`P_m`\lambda \subset p`\mu \cap \overrightarrow{P}`P_m`\mu . \\ (p`\mu \cap \overrightarrow{P}`P_m`\mu) \cap \overrightarrow{P}`P_m`\lambda = p`\lambda \cap \overrightarrow{P}`P_m`\mu, \end{aligned}$$

whence it follows that

$$\lambda \in (T_P * A)`\kappa - \iota`\Lambda . \supset . p`\lambda \cap \overrightarrow{P}`P_m`\lambda = P_{tl}`\kappa \cap \overrightarrow{P}`P_m`\lambda,$$

whence, by what was stated above,

$$\lambda \in (T_P * A)`\kappa . \alpha \in \lambda . \supset . \alpha \cap \overrightarrow{P}`P_m`\lambda = P_{tl}`\kappa \cap \overrightarrow{P}`P_m`\lambda \quad (*276{\cdot}354).$$

Again, if $\alpha \epsilon \kappa$, the product of all the members of $(T_P * A)`\kappa$ to which $\alpha$ belongs is a member of $(T_P * A)`\kappa$ to which α belongs, but if we call this product λ, $P_m`\lambda \sim\epsilon \alpha$ (because, if $P_m`\lambda \epsilon \alpha$, $\alpha \epsilon \breve{T}_P`\lambda$, which is contrary to the definition of λ). Hence we have

$$\alpha \epsilon \kappa . \supset . (P_{tl}`\kappa) P_\theta \alpha \quad (*276\cdot36).$$

It only remains to prove

$$(P_{tl}`\kappa) P_\theta \beta . \supset . (\exists \alpha) . \alpha \epsilon \kappa . \alpha P_\theta \beta \quad (*276\cdot37).$$

By the hypothesis, and the definition of $P_{tl}`\kappa$, we have

$$(\exists z, \lambda) . \lambda \epsilon (T_P * A)`\kappa . z \epsilon p`\lambda \cap \overrightarrow{P}`P_m`\lambda - \beta . P_{tl}`\kappa \cap \overrightarrow{P}`z = \beta \cap \overrightarrow{P}`z.$$

Since this involves $E ! P_m`\lambda$, it involves $\lambda \neq \Lambda$, hence, by what was stated above, it involves

$$(\exists z, \lambda, \alpha) . \lambda \epsilon (T_P * A)`\kappa . \alpha \epsilon \lambda . z \epsilon \alpha \cap \overrightarrow{P}`P_m`\lambda - \beta . P_{tl}`\kappa \cap \overrightarrow{P}`z = \beta \cap \overrightarrow{P}`z.$$

Hence we obtain $\qquad \beta \cap \overrightarrow{P}`z \subset P_{tl}`\kappa \cap \overrightarrow{P}`P_m`\lambda,$

and $\qquad P_{tl}`\kappa \cap \overrightarrow{P}`P_m`\lambda = \alpha \cap \overrightarrow{P}`P_m`\lambda,$

whence $\qquad \beta \cap \overrightarrow{P}`z \subset \alpha.$

Hence, by $*170\cdot11$, we have $\alpha P_\theta \beta$.

This completes the proof of $P_{tl}`\kappa = \text{tl}(P_\theta)`\kappa$ ($*276\cdot38$). Hence, combining the two cases, we find that κ has a minimum if $\exists ! p`(T_P * A)`\kappa$, and a lower limit if $\sim\exists ! p`(T_P * A)`\kappa$. Hence $E ! \text{limin}(P_\theta)`\kappa$, in either case ($*276\cdot39$).

This completes the proof of $P_\theta \epsilon \text{Ded}$ if $P \epsilon \Omega \text{ infin}$.

***276·01.** $P_\theta = P_{cl} \upharpoonright (-\text{Cls induct} \cup \iota`\Lambda)$ Df

***276·02.** $A = \hat{\alpha}\hat{\beta}(\beta \subset \alpha . \beta \neq \alpha)$ Dft [*276]

***276·03.** $P_m`\lambda = \min_P`(s`\lambda - p`\lambda)$ Dft [*276]

***276·04.** $T_P = \hat{\lambda}\hat{\mu}\{\mu = \lambda \cap \overleftarrow{\epsilon}`P_m`\lambda\}$ Dft [*276]

***276·05.** $P_{tl}`\kappa = s`\hat{\gamma}\{(\exists\lambda) . \lambda \epsilon (T_P * A)`\kappa - \iota`\Lambda . \gamma = p`\lambda \cap \overrightarrow{P}`P_m`\lambda\}$ Dft [*276]

***276·1.** $\vdash : \alpha P_\theta \beta . \equiv . \alpha, \beta \epsilon (\text{Cl}`C`P - \text{Cls induct}) \cup \iota`\Lambda . \exists ! \alpha - \beta - \breve{P}``(\beta - \alpha)$
[*170·1 . (*276·01)]

***276·11.** $\vdash :: P \epsilon \Omega . \supset :. \alpha P_\theta \beta . \equiv : \alpha, \beta \epsilon (\text{Cl}`C`P - \text{Cls induct}) \cup \iota`\Lambda :$
$(\exists z) . z \epsilon \alpha - \beta . \alpha \cap \overrightarrow{P}`z = \beta \cap \overrightarrow{P}`z$ [*251·35 . (*276·01)]

***276·12.** $\vdash : C`P \sim\epsilon 1 . \supset . P_\theta = P_{cl} \upharpoonright (-C`P_\eta)$ [*274·17 . *276·1 . *170·1]

***276·121.** $\vdash : C`P \sim\epsilon \text{Cls induct} . \supset .$
$B`\breve{P}_\theta = \Lambda . B`P_\theta = C`P . C`P_\theta = (\text{Cl}`C`P - \text{Cls induct}) \cup \iota`\Lambda$
[*170·31·32·38 . (*276·01)]

***276·122.** $\vdash : C`P \sim\in 0 \cup 1 . \supset . C`P_\eta \cup C`P_\theta = \text{Cl}`C`P$ [*276·121 . *274·17]

***276·123.** $\vdash : C`P \sim\in \text{Cls induct} . \equiv . \dot{\exists} ! P_\theta$ [*276·1·121]

***276·13.** $\vdash : C`P \sim\in 0 \cup 1 . \supset . \text{Nc}`C`P_\eta +_0 \text{Nc}`C`P_\theta = 2^{\text{Nc}`C`P}$
[*276·122 . *116·72]

***276·14.** $\vdash : P \in \Omega . \supset . P_\theta \in \text{Ser}$ [*251·36 . (*276·01)]

***276·2.** $\vdash : P \in \omega . \supset . (C`P -)``(\text{Cl induct}`C`P - \iota`\Lambda) \in \aleph_0 \cap \overrightarrow{\text{med}}`P_\theta$

Dem.

$\vdash . *24{\cdot}492 . \supset \vdash . (C`P -)``(\text{Cl induct}`C`P - \iota`\Lambda) \text{ sm } (\text{Cl induct}`C`P - \iota`\Lambda)$ (1)

$\vdash . (1) . *274{\cdot}27 . \supset \vdash : \text{Hp} . \supset . (C`P -)``(\text{Cl induct}`C`P - \iota`\Lambda) \in \aleph_0$ (2)

$\vdash . *200{\cdot}361 . *263{\cdot}47 . \supset$

$\vdash : \text{Hp} . \alpha P_\theta \beta . z \in \alpha - \beta . \alpha \cap \overrightarrow{P}`z = \beta \cap \overrightarrow{P}`z . \gamma = (\alpha \cap \overrightarrow{P_*}`z) \cup \overleftarrow{P}`\text{min}_P`(\alpha \cap \overleftarrow{P}`z) .$

$\supset . \text{min}_P`(\alpha \cap \overleftarrow{P}`z) \in \alpha - \gamma . \alpha \cap \overrightarrow{P}`\text{min}_P`(\alpha \cap \overleftarrow{P}`z) = \gamma \cap \overrightarrow{P}`\text{min}_P`(\alpha \cap \overleftarrow{P}`z) .$

$z \in \gamma - \beta . \gamma \cap \overrightarrow{P}`z = \alpha \cap \overrightarrow{P}`z = \beta \cap \overrightarrow{P}`z . \gamma \sim\in \text{Cls induct} .$

[*276·11] $\supset . \alpha P_\theta \gamma . \gamma P_\theta \beta$ (3)

$\vdash . *263{\cdot}47 . \supset \vdash : \text{Hp} (3) . \supset . C`P - \gamma \in \text{Cls induct}$ (4)

$\vdash . (3) . (4) . *276{\cdot}11 . \supset$

$\vdash : \text{Hp} . \alpha P_\theta \beta . \supset . (\exists \gamma) . C`P - \gamma \in \text{Cls induct} . \alpha P_\theta \gamma . \gamma P_\theta \beta$ (5)

$\vdash . *120{\cdot}71 . \text{Transp} . \supset$

$\vdash : \text{Hp} . \alpha \in \text{Cl induct}`C`P - \iota`\Lambda . \supset . (C`P - \alpha) \sim\in \text{Cls induct}$ (6)

$\vdash . (6) . *276{\cdot}121 . \supset \vdash : \text{Hp} . \supset . (C`P -)``(\text{Cl induct}`C`P - \iota`\Lambda) \subset C`P_\theta$ (7)

$\vdash . (2) . (5) . *271{\cdot}1 . (7) . \supset \vdash . \text{Prop}$

The following propositions constitute the proof of

$P \in \Omega \text{ infin} . \supset . P_\theta \in \text{Ded}$ (*276·4).

***276·3.** $\vdash :. \text{E} ! P_m`\lambda . \supset : \alpha \in \breve{T}_P`\lambda . \equiv . \alpha \in \lambda . P_m`\lambda \in \alpha : P_m`\lambda = \text{min}_P`(s`\lambda - p`\lambda)$
[(*276·03·04)]

***276·301.** $\vdash : P \in \Omega . \lambda \subset \text{Cl}`C`P - \iota`\Lambda . \lambda \sim\in 0 \cup 1 . \supset . \text{E} ! P_m`\lambda . \text{E} ! \breve{T}_P`\lambda$

Dem.

$\vdash . *40{\cdot}12{\cdot}13 . \quad \supset \vdash :. p`\lambda = s`\lambda . \supset : \alpha, \beta \in \lambda . \supset_{\alpha,\beta} . \alpha = \beta$ (1)

$\vdash . (1) . \text{Transp} . *40{\cdot}23 . \supset \vdash : \text{Hp} . \supset . \exists ! s`\kappa - p`\kappa .$

[*250·121] $\supset . \text{E} ! \text{min}_P`(s`\kappa - p`\kappa) : \supset \vdash . \text{Prop}$

***276·302.** $\vdash : \text{E} ! P_m`\lambda . \supset . P_m`\lambda \in p`\breve{T}_P`\lambda - p`\lambda$ [*276·3]

***276·303.** $\vdash . T_P \in A . (T_P)_{\text{po}} \in A$

Dem.

$\vdash . *276{\cdot}3 . \quad \supset \vdash : \mu \breve{T}_P \lambda . \supset . \mu \subset \lambda$ (1)

$\vdash . *276{\cdot}302 . \supset \vdash : \mu \breve{T}_P \lambda . \supset . \mu \neq \lambda$ (2)

$\vdash . (1) . (2) . *201{\cdot}18 . \supset \vdash . \text{Prop}$

***276·304.** $\vdash : \mu \{A(T_P, \kappa)\} \lambda . \supset . \mu \subset \lambda . p'\lambda \subset p'\mu . \mu \neq \lambda . p'\lambda \neq p'\mu$
[*276·302·303]

***276·305.** $\vdash . A'(T_P, \kappa) \epsilon \Omega$ [*258·201 . *276·303]

***276·31.** $\vdash : P \epsilon \Omega . \exists ! \lambda . \lambda \subset \text{Cl}'C'P - \iota'\Lambda . \lambda \sim \epsilon \text{D}'T_P . \supset .$
$\lambda \epsilon 1 . s'\lambda = p'\lambda = \breve{\iota}'\lambda$ [*276·301 . Transp]

***276·32.** $\vdash :. P \epsilon \Omega . \lambda \sim \epsilon 0 \cup 1 . \lambda \subset \text{D}'P_\theta . \supset :$
$P_m{}'\lambda \epsilon p'\breve{T}_P{}'\lambda - p'\lambda : \alpha \epsilon \lambda . \supset_\alpha . \alpha \cap \overrightarrow{P}'P_m{}'\lambda = p'\lambda \cap \overrightarrow{P}'P_m{}'\lambda$

Dem.

$\vdash . *276·301 . \supset \vdash : \text{Hp} . \supset . \text{E} ! \breve{T}_P{}'\lambda . \text{E} ! P_m{}'\lambda .$ (1)

[*276·302] $\supset . P_m{}'\lambda \epsilon p'\breve{T}_P{}'\lambda - p'\lambda$ (2)

$\vdash . (1) . *276·3 . \supset \vdash : \text{Hp} . \supset . \overrightarrow{P}'P_m{}'\lambda \cap s'\lambda = \overrightarrow{P}'P_m{}'\lambda \cap p'\lambda$ (3)

$\vdash . (2) . (3) . \supset \vdash . \text{Prop}$

***276·321.** $\vdash : \text{Hp} *276·32 . \alpha \epsilon \breve{T}_P{}'\lambda . \beta \epsilon \lambda - \breve{T}_P{}'\lambda . \supset . \alpha P_\theta \beta$

Dem.

$\vdash . *276·3·32 . \supset \vdash : \text{Hp} . \supset . P_m{}'\lambda \epsilon \alpha - \beta . \alpha \cap \overrightarrow{P}'P_m{}'\lambda = \beta \cap \overrightarrow{P}'P_m{}'\lambda .$

[*276·11] $\supset . \alpha P_\theta \beta : \supset \vdash . \text{Prop}$

***276·322.** $\vdash : \text{Hp} *276·32 . \mu \epsilon (T_P * A)'\lambda . \alpha \epsilon \mu . \beta \epsilon \lambda - \mu . \supset . \alpha P_\theta \beta$

Dem.

$\vdash . *40·23 . \supset \vdash :. \rho \subset (T_P * A)'\lambda . \exists ! \rho : \mu \epsilon \rho . \alpha \epsilon \mu . \beta \epsilon \lambda - \mu . \supset_{\mu, \alpha, \beta} . \alpha P_\theta \beta : \supset :$
$\alpha \epsilon p'\rho . \beta \epsilon \lambda - p'\rho . \supset_{\alpha, \beta} . \alpha P_\theta \beta$ (1)

$\vdash . (1) . *276·321 . *258·241 . \supset \vdash . \text{Prop}$

***276·33.** $\vdash : \text{Hp} *276·32 . \exists ! p'(T_P * A)'\lambda . \supset . \breve{\iota}'p'(T_P * A)'\lambda = \min (P_\theta)'\lambda$

Dem.

$\vdash . *276·31 . *258·231 . \supset \vdash : \text{Hp} . \supset . p'(T_P * A)'\lambda \epsilon 1$ (1)

$\vdash . (1) . *276·322 . \supset \vdash : \text{Hp} . \alpha \epsilon \lambda - p'(T_P * A)'\lambda . \supset . \{\breve{\iota}'p'(T_P * A)'\lambda\} P_\theta \alpha$ (2)

$\vdash . (1) . (2) . \supset \vdash . \text{Prop}$

***276·331.** $\vdash : \text{Hp} *276·32 . \exists ! p'(T_P * A)'\lambda . \supset . \text{E} ! \min (P_\theta)'\lambda$ [*276·33]

***276·34.** $\vdash : \text{Hp} *276·32 . \mu \breve{T}_P \lambda . \mu \epsilon \text{D}'T_P . \supset . (P_m{}'\lambda) P (P_m{}'\mu)$

Dem.

$\vdash . *276·3 . \supset \vdash : \text{Hp} . \supset . P_m{}'\lambda = \min_P{}'(s'\lambda - p'\lambda)$ (1)

$\vdash . *276·3·304 . \supset \vdash : \text{Hp} . \supset . P_m{}'\mu \epsilon (s'\lambda - p'\lambda)$ (2)

$\vdash . *276·302 . \supset \vdash : \text{Hp} . \supset . P_m{}'\lambda \epsilon p'\mu . P_m{}'\mu \sim \epsilon p'\mu .$

[*13·12] $\supset . P_m{}'\lambda \neq P_m{}'\mu$ (3)

$\vdash . (1) . (2) . (3) . \supset \vdash . \text{Prop}$

***276·341.** $\vdash :. \text{Hp} *276\cdot32 . p`(T_P * A)`\lambda = \Lambda . \supset :$

$$P_m``(T_P*A)`\lambda \subset P``P_m``(T_P*A)`\lambda . P_m``(T_P*A)`\lambda \sim\epsilon \text{ Cls induct} :$$
$$\mu \epsilon (T_P*A)`\lambda - \iota`\Lambda . \supset_\mu . E! \breve{T}_P`\mu . E! P_m`\mu$$

Dem.

$\vdash . *258\cdot231 . *276\cdot301 . \supset$

$\vdash :. \text{Hp} . \supset : \mu \epsilon (T_P*A)`\lambda - \iota`p`(T_P*A)`\lambda . \supset . E! \breve{T}_P`\mu . E! P_m`\mu :$

$[*276\cdot34.\text{Hp}] \quad \supset : \mu \epsilon (T_P*A)`\lambda . E! P_m`\mu . \supset . (P_m`\mu) P (P_m`\breve{T}_P`\mu) \quad (1)$

$\vdash . (1) . *261\cdot26 . \text{Transp} . \supset \vdash . \text{Prop}$

***276·342.** $\vdash : \text{Hp} *276\cdot341 . \lambda \{A(T_P, \kappa)\} \mu . E! P_m`\mu . \supset . (P_m`\lambda) P (P_m`\mu)$

Dem.

$\vdash . *276\cdot3 . \supset$

$\vdash :: \text{Hp} : \rho \subset (T_P*A)`\kappa . \exists ! \rho . \exists ! p`\rho : \supset :. P_m`p`\rho \epsilon s`p`\rho - p`p`\rho :.$

$[*40\cdot1\cdot11] \quad \supset :. (\exists\alpha) . \alpha \epsilon p`\rho . P_m`p`\rho \epsilon \alpha : (\exists\alpha) . \alpha \epsilon p`\rho . P_m`p`\rho \sim\epsilon \alpha :.$

$[*40\cdot1.*11\cdot26] \supset :. \lambda \epsilon \rho . \supset_\lambda : (\exists\alpha) . \alpha \epsilon \lambda . P_m`p`\rho \epsilon \alpha : (\exists\alpha) . \alpha \epsilon \lambda . P_m`p`\rho \sim\epsilon \alpha :.$

$[*40\cdot1\cdot11] \quad \supset :. \lambda \epsilon \rho . \supset_\lambda . P_m`p`\rho \epsilon (s`\lambda - p`\lambda) \quad (1)$

$\vdash . (1) . *276\cdot302 . \supset \vdash :. \text{Hp}(1) . \supset :$

$$\breve{T}_P`\lambda \epsilon \rho . \lambda \epsilon \rho . \supset_\lambda . P_m`\lambda \epsilon p`\breve{T}_P`\lambda . P_m`p`\rho \sim\epsilon p`\breve{T}_P`\lambda :$$

$[*13\cdot12] \quad \supset : \breve{T}_P`\lambda \epsilon \rho . \lambda \epsilon \rho . \supset_\lambda . P_m`\lambda \neq P_m`p`\rho \quad (2)$

$\vdash . (1) . (2) . *276\cdot3 . \supset \vdash : \text{Hp}(1) . \breve{T}_P`\lambda \epsilon \rho . \lambda \epsilon \rho . \supset . (P_m`\lambda) P (P_m`p`\rho) \quad (3)$

$\vdash . (3) . *276\cdot34 . *258\cdot241 . \supset \vdash . \text{Prop}$

***276·35.** $\vdash :. P \epsilon \Omega . \kappa \subset D`P_\theta . \exists ! \kappa . p`(T_P*A)`\kappa = \Lambda . \supset :$

$$\lambda \epsilon (T_P*A)`\kappa - \iota`\Lambda . \supset . P_m`\lambda \epsilon p`\breve{T}_P`\lambda \cap \overrightarrow{P}`P_m`\breve{T}_P`\lambda$$

Dem.

$\vdash . *276\cdot341 . \supset \vdash : \text{Hp} . \lambda \epsilon (T_P*A)`\kappa - \iota`\Lambda . \supset . E! \breve{T}_P`\lambda .$

$[*276\cdot302\cdot34] \quad \supset . P_m`\lambda \epsilon p`\breve{T}_P`\lambda \cap \overrightarrow{P}`P_m`\breve{T}_P`\lambda : \supset \vdash . \text{Prop}$

***276·351.** $\vdash : \text{Hp} *276\cdot35 . \supset . P_m``(T_P*A)`\kappa \subset P_{tl}`\kappa$

Dem.

$\vdash . *276\cdot3 . \quad \supset \vdash . \sim E! P_m`\Lambda \quad (1)$

$\vdash . *276\cdot35 . (*276\cdot05) . \supset \vdash : \text{Hp} . \lambda \epsilon (T_P*A)`\kappa - \iota`\Lambda . \supset . P_m`\lambda \epsilon P_{tl}`\kappa \quad (2)$

$\vdash . (1) . (2) . \supset \vdash . \text{Prop}$

***276·352.** $\vdash : \text{Hp} *276\cdot35 . \supset . P_{tl}`\kappa \sim\epsilon \text{ Cls induct}$ $[*276\cdot351\cdot341]$

***276·353.** $\vdash : \text{Hp} *276\cdot35 . \lambda \epsilon (T_P*A)`\kappa . \lambda \{A(T_P, \kappa)\} \mu . \alpha \epsilon \mu . \supset .$

$$p`\lambda \cap \overrightarrow{P}`P_m`\lambda = p`\mu \cap \overrightarrow{P}`P_m`\lambda = \alpha \cap \overrightarrow{P}`P_m`\lambda$$

Dem.

$\vdash . *276\cdot304 . \quad \supset \vdash : \text{Hp} . \supset . \alpha \epsilon \lambda \quad (1)$

$\vdash . *276\cdot35\cdot31 . \text{Transp} . \supset \vdash : \text{Hp} . \supset . E! P_m`\lambda . \lambda \sim\epsilon 0 \cup 1 \quad (2)$

$\vdash . (1) . (2) . *276\cdot32 . \quad \supset \vdash : \text{Hp} . \supset . p`\lambda \cap \overrightarrow{P}`P_m`\lambda = \alpha \cap \overrightarrow{P}`P_m`\lambda \quad (3)$

$\vdash . (3) . \supset \vdash :. \text{Hp} . \supset : \beta \epsilon \mu . \supset_\beta . \alpha \cap \overrightarrow{P}`P_m`\lambda = \beta \cap \overrightarrow{P}`P_m`\lambda$ (4)

$\vdash . (4) . \supset \vdash : \text{Hp} . \supset . \alpha \cap \overrightarrow{P}`P_m`\lambda = p`\mu \cap \overrightarrow{P}`P_m`\lambda$ (5)

$\vdash . (3) . (5) . \supset \vdash . \text{Prop}$

∗276·354. $\vdash : \text{Hp} * 276 \cdot 35 . \lambda \epsilon (T_P * A)`\kappa . \alpha \epsilon \lambda . \supset .$

$$P_{tl}`\kappa \cap \overrightarrow{P}`P_m`\lambda = p`\lambda \cap \overrightarrow{P}`P_m`\lambda = \alpha \cap \overrightarrow{P}`P_m`\lambda$$

Dem.

$\vdash . *276 \cdot 353 . \supset \vdash : \text{Hp} . \exists ! \mu . \lambda \{A(T_P, \kappa)\} \mu . \supset .$

$$p`\mu \cap \overrightarrow{P}`P_m`\lambda = p`\lambda \cap \overrightarrow{P}`P_m`\lambda .$$

[∗22·47] $\supset . (p`\mu \cap \overrightarrow{P}`P_m`\mu) \cap \overrightarrow{P}`P_m`\lambda \subset p`\lambda \cap \overrightarrow{P}`P_m`\lambda$ (1)

$\vdash . *276 \cdot 353 . \supset \vdash : \text{Hp} . \mu \{A(T_P, \kappa)\} \lambda . \supset . p`\mu \cap \overrightarrow{P}`P_m`\mu = p`\lambda \cap \overrightarrow{P}`P_m`\mu$

[∗276·342] $\subset p`\lambda \cap \overrightarrow{P}`P_m`\lambda$ (2)

$\vdash . (1) . (2) . *276 \cdot 305 . \supset$

$\vdash : \text{Hp} . \mu \epsilon (T_P * A)`\kappa - \iota`\Lambda . \supset . (p`\mu \cap \overrightarrow{P}`P_m`\mu) \cap \overrightarrow{P}`P_m`\lambda \subset p`\lambda \cap \overrightarrow{P}`P_m`\lambda$ (3)

$\vdash . (3) . *276 \cdot 32 . (*276 \cdot 05) . \supset \vdash . \text{Prop}$

∗276·355. $\vdash : \text{Hp} * 276 \cdot 35 . \alpha \epsilon \kappa . \supset . (\exists \lambda) . \lambda \epsilon (T_P * A)`\kappa . \alpha \epsilon \lambda . P_m`\lambda \sim \epsilon \alpha$

Dem.

$\vdash . *40 \cdot 1 . \supset \vdash :. \text{Hp} . \supset : (\exists \lambda) . \lambda \epsilon (T_P * A)`\kappa . \alpha \sim \epsilon \lambda :$

[∗276·305] $\supset : (\exists \lambda) : \lambda \epsilon (T_P * A)`\kappa . \alpha \sim \epsilon \lambda : \mu \{A(T_P, \kappa)\} \lambda . \supset_\mu . \alpha \epsilon \mu$ (1)

$\vdash . *40 \cdot 1 . \supset \vdash :. \mu \{A(T_P, \kappa)\} \lambda . \supset_\mu . \alpha \epsilon \mu : \lambda = p`\overrightarrow{A(T_P, \kappa)}`\lambda : \supset . \alpha \epsilon \lambda$ (2)

$\vdash . (1) . (2) . \text{Transp} . \supset$

$\vdash : \text{Hp} . \supset . (\exists \lambda, \mu) . \mu, \lambda \epsilon (T_P * A)`\kappa . \lambda = \breve{T}_P`\mu . \alpha \epsilon \mu . \alpha \sim \epsilon \lambda .$

[∗276·3] $\supset . (\exists \mu) . \mu \epsilon (T_P * A)`\kappa . \alpha \epsilon \mu . P_m`\mu \sim \epsilon \alpha : \supset \vdash . \text{Prop}$

∗276·36. $\vdash : \text{Hp} * 276 \cdot 35 . \alpha \epsilon \kappa . \supset . (P_{tl}`\kappa) P_\theta \alpha$

Dem.

$\vdash . *276 \cdot 351 \cdot 355 \cdot 354 . \supset$

$\vdash : \text{Hp} . \supset . (\exists \lambda) . \lambda \epsilon (T_P * A)`\kappa . P_m`\lambda \epsilon P_{tl}`\kappa - \alpha . P_{tl}`\kappa \cap \overrightarrow{P}`P_m`\lambda = \alpha \cap \overrightarrow{P}`P_m`\lambda .$

[∗276·352] $\supset . (P_{tl}`\kappa) P_\theta \alpha : \supset \vdash . \text{Prop}$

∗276·361. $\vdash : \text{Hp} * 276 \cdot 35 . \supset . \kappa \subset \overleftarrow{P_\theta}`P_{tl}`\kappa$ [∗276·36]

∗276·37. $\vdash : \text{Hp} * 276 \cdot 35 . (P_{tl}`\kappa) P_\theta \beta . \supset . (\exists \alpha) . \alpha \epsilon \kappa . \alpha P_\theta \beta$

Dem.

$\vdash . *276 \cdot 11 . \supset \vdash : \text{Hp} . \supset . (\exists z) . z \epsilon P_{tl}`\kappa - \beta . P_{tl}`\kappa \cap \overrightarrow{P}`z = \beta \cap \overrightarrow{P}`z .$

[(∗276·05)] $\supset . (\exists z, \lambda) . \lambda \epsilon (T_P * A)`\kappa . z \epsilon p`\lambda \cap \overrightarrow{P}`P_m`\lambda - \beta .$

$$P_{tl}`\kappa \cap \overrightarrow{P}`z = \beta \cap \overrightarrow{P}`z .$$

[∗276·354] $\supset . (\exists z, \lambda, \alpha) . \lambda \epsilon (T_P * A)`\kappa . \alpha \epsilon \lambda . z \epsilon \alpha - \beta .$

$$\overrightarrow{P}`z \subset \overrightarrow{P}`P_m`\lambda . \alpha \cap \overrightarrow{P}`P_m`\lambda = \beta \cap \overrightarrow{P}`P_m`\lambda .$$

[Fact.∗276·304] $\supset . (\exists z, \alpha) . \alpha \epsilon \kappa . z \epsilon \alpha - \beta . \beta \cap \overrightarrow{P}`z \subset \alpha .$

[∗170·11] $\supset . (\exists \alpha) . \alpha \epsilon \kappa . \alpha P_\theta \beta : \supset \vdash . \text{Prop}$

***276·38.** $\vdash : P \in \Omega \,.\, \kappa \subset D`P_\theta \,.\, \exists ! \kappa \,.\, p`(T_P * A)`\kappa = \Lambda \,.\, \supset \,.\, P_{tl}`\kappa = \mathrm{tl}\,(P_\theta)`\kappa$ [*276·361·37]

***276·381.** $\vdash : P \in \Omega \,.\, \kappa \subset D`P_\theta \,.\, \exists ! \kappa \,.\, p`(T_P * A)`\kappa = \Lambda \,.\, \supset \,.\, E!\,\mathrm{tl}\,(P_\theta)`\kappa$ [*276·38]

***276·39.** $\vdash : P \in \Omega \,.\, \kappa \subset D`P_\theta \,.\, \exists ! \kappa \,.\, \supset \,.\, E!\,\mathrm{limin}\,(P_\theta)`\kappa$ [*276·331·381]

In the following proposition, the only reason why P has to be infinite is in order that P_θ may exist; for "Ded" was so defined as to exclude $\dot{\Lambda}$.

***276·4.** $\vdash : P \in \Omega\,\mathrm{infin} \,.\, \supset \,.\, P_\theta \in \mathrm{Ded}$

Dem.

$$\vdash . *276{\cdot}121 . *207{\cdot}3 . *205{\cdot}18 . \supset \vdash : \mathrm{Hp} . \supset . \mathrm{limin}_P`\Lambda = C`P \,.\, \mathrm{limin}_P`\iota`\Lambda = \Lambda \quad (1)$$

$$\vdash . *206{\cdot}7 . \quad \supset \vdash : \mathrm{Hp} . \kappa \subset C`P_\theta \,.\, \Lambda \in \kappa \,.\, \kappa \neq \iota`\Lambda . \supset .$$
$$\overrightarrow{\mathrm{prec}}\,(P_\theta)`\kappa = \overrightarrow{\mathrm{prec}}\,(P_\theta)`(\kappa - \iota`\Lambda) \quad (2)$$

$$\vdash . *205{\cdot}192 . \supset \vdash : \mathrm{Hp}\,(2) . \supset . \overrightarrow{\mathrm{min}}\,(P_\theta)`\kappa = \overrightarrow{\mathrm{min}}\,(P_\theta)`(\kappa - \iota`\Lambda) \quad (3)$$

$$\vdash . (2) . (3) . \quad \supset \vdash : \mathrm{Hp}\,(2) . \supset . \overrightarrow{\mathrm{limin}}\,(P_\theta)`\kappa = \overrightarrow{\mathrm{limin}}\,(P_\theta)`(\kappa - \iota`\Lambda) .$$

$$[*276{\cdot}39] \quad \supset . E!\,\mathrm{limin}\,(P_\theta)`\kappa \quad (4)$$

$$\vdash . (1) . (4) . *276{\cdot}39 . \supset \vdash :. \mathrm{Hp} . \supset : \kappa \subset C`P_\theta . \supset_\kappa . E!\,\mathrm{limin}\,(P_\theta)`\kappa :$$

$$[*214{\cdot}12{\cdot}14] \quad \supset : P_\theta \in \mathrm{Ded} :. \supset \vdash . \mathrm{Prop}$$

***276·41.** $\vdash : P \in \omega \,.\, \supset \,.\, P_\theta \in \theta$ [*276·2·4·14 . *275·1]

***276·42.** $\vdash : P \in \omega \,.\, \supset \,.\, C`P_\theta \in 2^{\aleph_0}$

Dem.

$$\vdash . *276{\cdot}13 . *274{\cdot}27 . \supset \vdash : \mathrm{Hp} . \supset . \mathrm{Nc}`C`P_\theta +_c \aleph_0 = 2^{\aleph_0} \quad (1)$$

$$\vdash . *276{\cdot}2 . \quad \supset \vdash : \mathrm{Hp} . \supset . (\exists \mu) . \mathrm{Nc}`C`P_\theta = \mu +_c \aleph_0 .$$

$$[*123{\cdot}421] \quad \supset . \mathrm{Nc}`C`P_\theta +_c \aleph_0 = \mathrm{Nc}`C`P_\theta \quad (2)$$

$$\vdash . (1) . (2) . \supset \vdash . \mathrm{Prop}$$

***276·43.** $\vdash \,.\, C``\theta = 2^{\aleph_0}$

Dem.

$$\vdash . *276{\cdot}42{\cdot}41 . \supset \vdash : \exists ! \omega . \supset . \exists ! C``\theta \cap 2^{\aleph_0} .$$

$$[*100{\cdot}42 . *275{\cdot}33 . *152{\cdot}71] \supset . C``\theta = 2^{\aleph_0} \quad (1)$$

$$\vdash . *275{\cdot}11 . *263{\cdot}101 . \supset \vdash : \omega = \Lambda . \supset . \theta = \Lambda \quad (2)$$

$$\vdash . *263{\cdot}101 . *116{\cdot}204 . \supset \vdash : \omega = \Lambda . \supset . 2^{\aleph_0} = \Lambda \quad (3)$$

$$\vdash . (2) . (3) . \quad \supset \vdash : \omega = \Lambda . \supset . C``\theta = 2^{\aleph_0} \quad (4)$$

$$\vdash . (1) . (4) . \supset \vdash . \mathrm{Prop}$$

The propositions proved in the present number are capable of being to some extent generalized. Also we can prove

$$\vdash . \theta = (\omega \exp_r \omega) \dotplus 1.$$

For this purpose, we prove first that if P, Q are well-ordered series, P^Q is Dedekindian (except that if $\sim E ! B'\breve{P}$, P^Q has no last term); *i.e.* we prove

$$P, Q \epsilon \Omega . \supset : \lambda \subset C'P^Q . \exists ! \lambda . \supset_\lambda . E ! \text{limin}(P^Q)'\lambda.$$

For this purpose, assuming $\lambda \subset C'P^Q . \exists ! \lambda$, put

$$Q_m'\lambda = \min_Q{}'\hat{y}(\dot{s}'\lambda'y \sim \epsilon 0 \cup 1),$$
$$\breve{T}_P'\lambda = \lambda \cap \hat{M}\{M'Q_m'\lambda = \min_P{}'\dot{s}'\lambda'Q_m'\lambda\},$$
$$A = \hat{\lambda}\hat{\mu}(\mu \subset \lambda . \mu \neq \lambda),$$
$$(PQ)'\lambda = \dot{s}'\hat{N}\{(\exists\mu) . \mu \epsilon (T_P * A)'\lambda . N = (\dot{p}'\mu) \upharpoonright \overrightarrow{Q}'Q_m'\mu\}.$$

We can then show, by steps closely analogous to those in the proof of $P_\theta \epsilon \text{Ded}$, that we have

$$\exists ! p'(T_P * A)'\lambda . \supset . \iota'\breve{p}'(T_P * A)'\lambda = \min(P^Q)'\lambda,$$
$$\sim \exists ! p'(T_P * A)'\lambda . \supset . (PQ)'\lambda = \text{prec}(P^Q)'\lambda,$$

whence, in either case, $E ! \text{limin}(P^Q)'\lambda$.

Hence we have

$$\vdash : P, Q \epsilon \Omega . E ! B'\breve{P} . \supset . P^Q \epsilon \text{Ded},$$
$$\vdash : P, Q \epsilon \Omega . \sim E ! B'\breve{P} . Z \sim \epsilon C'P^Q . \supset . P^Q \rightarrow\!\!\!\!\!\!+ Z \epsilon \text{Ded}.$$

We have therefore $\qquad \vdash . (\omega \exp_r \omega) \dot{+} \dot{1} \subset \text{Ded}.$

We now have to prove

$$Q \epsilon (\omega \exp_r \omega) \dot{+} \dot{1} . \supset . \exists ! \aleph_0 \cap \overrightarrow{\text{med}}'Q.$$

For this purpose, it will be sufficient to prove

$$P \epsilon \omega . \supset . \exists ! \aleph_0 \cap \overrightarrow{\text{med}}'(P^P).$$

The $\aleph_0$ in question will be the class of those members of $C'(P^P)$ in which, from a certain point onward, the correlate of every member of $C'P$ is $B'P$. We have

$$M(P^P)N . \equiv : M, N \epsilon (C'P \uparrow C'P)_\Delta{}'C'P :$$
$$(\exists x) . x \epsilon C'P . M \upharpoonright \overrightarrow{P}'x = N \upharpoonright \overrightarrow{P}'x . (M'x) P (N'x).$$

Now consider the relation

$$L = M \upharpoonright \overrightarrow{P_*}'x \cup y \downarrow \breve{P}_1'x \cup (\iota'B'P) \uparrow \overleftarrow{P}'\breve{P}_1'x,$$

where $(M'\breve{P}_1'x) P y$.

Then $M(P^P)L . L(P^P)N$. Also L has $B'P$ for the correlate of every term after $\breve{P}_1'x$. Hence it is determined by the correlates of the terms up to and including $\breve{P}_1'x$. Thus, putting $z = \breve{P}_1'x$, we have to consider the class of relations

$$\mu = \hat{X}\{(\exists z) . z \epsilon \text{ᗡ}'P . X \epsilon 1 \rightarrow \text{Cls} . \text{ᗡ}'X = \overrightarrow{P_*}'z . \text{D}'X \subset C'P\}.$$

If $X \epsilon \mu$, $X \cup (\iota\text{'}B\text{'}P) \uparrow \overleftarrow{P}\text{'}\max_P\text{'}\text{Œ}\text{'}X$ is a member of $C\text{'}P^P$. We have therefore only to show that $\mu \epsilon \aleph_0$.

To show that $\mu \epsilon \aleph_0$, we observe that if $X \epsilon \mu$, $D\text{'}X$ and $\text{Œ}\text{'}X$ are both inductive classes; hence each has a maximum. Let X and X' be two members of μ, and let us put

$$x = \max_P\text{'}D\text{'}X \,.\, x' = \max_P\text{'}D\text{'}X' \,.\, y = \max_P\text{'}\text{Œ}\text{'}X \,.\, y' = \max_P\text{'}\text{Œ}\text{'}X'.$$

If $x = \mu_P$ and $y = \nu_P$, put $x +_P y = (\mu +_c \nu)_P$. Then put X before X' if $(x +_P y) P (x' +_P y')$, or if $x +_P y = x' +_P y' \,.\, yPy'$. But if $x +_P y = x' +_P y'$ and $y = y'$, *i.e.* if $x = x' \,.\, y = y'$, take the immediate predecessors of x, y, x', y' in $D\text{'}X$, $\text{Œ}\text{'}X$, $D\text{'}X'$, $\text{Œ}\text{'}X'$ respectively, and apply the same tests to them, and so on, until we come to a difference. In this way, we obtain an arrangement by last differences (in a slightly extended sense), and this arrangement is easily shown to be an ω. Hence $\mu \epsilon \aleph_0$. Hence the class

$$\nu = \hat{\gamma} \{(\exists X) \,.\, X \epsilon \mu \,.\, \gamma = X \cup (\iota\text{'}B\text{'}P) \uparrow \overleftarrow{P}\text{'}\max_P\text{'}\text{Œ}\text{'}X\}$$

is an $\aleph_0$, and we have already shown that it is a median class of $C\text{'}P^P$. Hence

$$\vdash : P \epsilon \omega \,.\, \supset \,.\, \exists \,! \, \aleph_0 \cap \overrightarrow{\text{med}}\text{'}(P^P).$$

The same class will be a median class of $P^P \nrightarrow Z$, if $Z \sim\epsilon C\text{'}P^P$. Hence

$$\vdash : P \epsilon \omega \,.\, Z \sim\epsilon C\text{'}P^P \,.\, \supset \,.\, \exists \,! \, \aleph_0 \cap \overrightarrow{\text{med}}\text{'}(P^P \nrightarrow Z).$$

Hence, by what was proved earlier,

$$\vdash : P \epsilon \omega \,.\, Z \sim\epsilon C\text{'}P^P \,.\, \supset \,.\, (P^P \nrightarrow Z) \epsilon \theta,$$

i.e. $\vdash \,.\, (\omega \exp_r \omega) \dotplus \dot{1} = \theta.$

PART VI.

QUANTITY.

SUMMARY OF PART VI.

THE purpose of this Part is to explain the kinds of applications of numbers which may be called *measurement*. For this purpose, we have first to consider generalizations of number. The numbers dealt with hitherto have been only integers (cardinal or ordinal); accordingly, in Section A, we consider positive and negative integers, ratios, and real numbers. (Complex numbers are dealt with later, under geometry, because they do not form a one-dimensional series.)

In Section B, we deal with what may be called "kinds" of quantity: thus *e.g.* masses, spatial distances, velocities, each form one kind of quantity. We consider each kind of quantity as what may be called a "vector-family," *i.e.* a class of one-one relations all having the same converse domain, and all having their domain contained in their converse domain. In such a case as spatial distances, the applicability of this view is obvious; in such a case as masses, the view becomes applicable by considering *e.g.* one gramme as + one gramme, *i.e.* as the relation of a mass m to a mass m' when m exceeds m' by one gramme. What is commonly called simply one gramme will then be the mass which has the relation + one gramme to the zero of mass. The reasons for treating quantities as vectors will be explained in Section B. Various different kinds of vector-families will be considered, the object being to obtain families whose members are capable of measurement either by means of ratios or by means of real numbers.

Section C is concerned with measurement, *i.e.* with the discovery of ratios, or of the relations expressed by real numbers, between the members of a vector-family. A family of vectors is measurable if it contains a member T (the unit) such that any other member S has to T a relation which is either a ratio or a real number. It will be shown that certain sorts of vector-families are in this sense measurable, and that measurement so defined has the mathematical properties which we expect it to possess.

Section D deals with *cyclic* families of vectors, such as angles or elliptic straight lines. The theory of measurement as applied to such families presents peculiar features, owing to the fact that any number of complete revolutions may be added to a vector without altering it. Thus there is not a single ratio of two vectors, but many ratios, of which we select one as the *principal* ratio.

SECTION A.

GENERALIZATION OF NUMBER.

Summary of Section A.

In this section, we first define the series of positive and negative integers. If μ is a cardinal, the corresponding positive and negative integers are the relations $+_c \mu$ and $-_c \mu$, or rather $(+_c \mu) \upharpoonright (\text{NC induct} - \iota`\Lambda)$ and $(-_c \mu) \upharpoonright (\text{NC induct} - \iota`\Lambda)$. (It will be observed that a positive integer must not be confounded with the corresponding signless integer, for while the former is a relation, the latter is a class of classes.) We next proceed to numerically-defined powers of relations, *i.e.* to R^ν, where ν is an inductive cardinal. We have already defined R^2 and R^3, but for the definition of ratio it is important to define R^ν generally. If $R \epsilon 1 \rightarrow 1 \,.\, R_{po} \subset J$, we shall have $R^\nu = R_\nu$, and if $R \epsilon \text{Ser}$, we shall have $(R_1)^\nu = R_\nu$. But these equations do not hold in general, and in particular if $R \subset I$ and $\nu \neq 0$, $R^\nu = R$ but $R_\nu = \dot{\Lambda}$. After a number devoted to relative primes, we proceed to the definition of signless ratios, thence to the multiplication and addition of signless ratios, thence to negative ratios, and thence to the generalized addition and multiplication which includes negative ratios. (In the case of ratios, signless ratios are identical with positive ratios. This is possible because signless ratios, unlike signless integers, are already relations.) We then proceed to the definition of real numbers, positive and negative, and to the addition and multiplication of real numbers. At each stage, we prove the commutative, associative, and distributive laws, and whatever else may seem necessary, for the particular kind of addition and multiplication in question.

Great difficulties are caused, in this section, by the existence-theorems and the question of types. These difficulties disappear if the axiom of infinity is assumed, but it seems improper to make the theory of (say) 2/3 depend upon the assumption that the number of objects in the universe is not finite. We have, accordingly, taken pains not to make this assumption, except where, as in the theory of real numbers, it is really essential, and not merely convenient. When the axiom of infinity is required, it is always explicitly stated in the hypothesis, so that our propositions, as enunciated, are true even if the axiom of infinity is false.

$*300$. POSITIVE AND NEGATIVE INTEGERS, AND NUMERICAL RELATIONS.

Summary of $*300$.

In this number, we introduce three definitions. We first define "U" as meaning the relation which holds between $\mu +_c \nu$ and μ whenever μ and ν are existent inductive cardinals of the same type, and $\nu \neq 0$, and $\mu +_c \nu$ exists in this type. Thus U is the relation "greater than" confined to existent inductive cardinals of the same type. The definition is:

$*300\cdot01$. $U = (+_c 1)_{po} \upharpoonright (\text{NC induct} - \iota`\Lambda)$ Df

Then if μ is an inductive cardinal which exists in the type in question, U_μ and $\breve{U}_\mu$ are the corresponding positive and negative integers, where "U_μ" has the meaning defined in $*121$. It will be observed that $0 U_\mu \mu$, so that U_μ exists, when μ exists in the type in question. We prove ($*300\cdot15$) that U is a series, and ($*300\cdot14$) that its field consists of all existent inductive cardinals of the type in question, its domain consists of all its field except 0, and its converse domain of all its field except the greatest (if any). If the axiom of infinity holds, $C`U$ consists of all inductive cardinals.

It will be observed that U arranges the inductive cardinals in *descending* order of magnitude. The reason for choosing this order instead of the converse is that U is less required in its serial use than as leading to the functional relations U_μ. As explained at the end of Part I, Section D, there is a broad difference between functional and serial relations, and this produces, where one relation (or its derivatives) is to have both uses, a certain conflict of convenience as to the *sense* in which the relation is to be taken. Considered as arranging the integers in a series, U would naturally be defined so as to arrange them in *ascending* order of magnitude, as was done with "N" in $*123$. But considered as functional relations, it is more convenient and more natural to take (say) $+_c 1$ as the relation to start with, and $-_c 1$ as its converse. Thus we want $\mu U_1 \nu$ when $\mu = \nu +_c 1$, *i.e.* we want $U_1`\nu = \nu +_c 1$; and this requires the definition of U given above.

We prove in this number ($*300\cdot23$) that $\breve{U}$ is well-ordered, and ($*300\cdot21\cdot22$) is either finite or a progression. We also prove ($*300\cdot17\cdot18$) that, if μ is any typically indefinite inductive cardinal, μ and $\mu +_c 1$ will belong to $C\text{'}U$ if U is taken in a sufficiently high type.

Our other two definitions in this number define two classes of relations which are of vital importance in the theory of ratio. We define *numerical relations,* which are called "Rel num," as one-one relations whose powers are all contained in diversity, *i.e.* we put

***300·02.** Rel num $= (1 \to 1) \cap \hat{R}(\text{Pot}\text{'}R \subset \text{Rl}\text{'}J)$ Df

We thus have (*300·3)

$$\vdash : R \in \text{Rel num} . \equiv . R \in 1 \to 1 . R_{po} \mathrel{\subset} J.$$

It will be remembered that the hypothesis $R \in (\text{Cls} \to 1) \cup (1 \to \text{Cls}) . R_{po} \mathrel{\subset} J$ played a great part in *121, and in all later work which depended upon *121. When both R and $\breve{R}$ fulfil this hypothesis, we have $R \in$ Rel num, and vice versa. We prove (*300·44) that if σ is an inductive cardinal not zero, and P is a series, then P_σ is a numerical relation, and so is $\breve{P}_\sigma$. If P is an endless well-ordered series, finid$\text{'}\breve{P}$ (*i.e.* the class of relations $\breve{P}_\sigma$) is what (in Section B) we shall call a vector-family: $\breve{P}_\sigma$ is the vector which carries a term σ steps along the series.

In order to be able to deal with zero, we have to consider the application of ratios, not only to such relations as are numerical in the above sense, but also to relations contained in identity, because a relation contained in identity may be regarded as a zero vector, so that (*e.g.*) if P is a series, $I \restriction C\text{'}P$ will have a zero ratio to P_σ if σ is an inductive cardinal other than 0.

We therefore introduce a class "Rel num id" consisting of numerical relations together with such as are contained in identity; these may be called *numerical or identical relations.* They may be defined as one-one relations whose powers, other than R_0, are contained in diversity, because, if $R \mathrel{\subset} I$, there are no powers other than R_0. Thus we put

***300·03.** Rel num id $= (1 \to 1) \cap \hat{R}(\text{Potid}\text{'}R - \iota\text{'}R_0 \subset \text{Rl}\text{'}J)$ Df

and we then prove

***300·33.** $\vdash$. Rel num id $= \text{Rl}\text{'}I \cup$ Rel num

For the application of ratio, it is important to know under what circumstances there exists a numerical relation R such that R_σ is not null. We prove (*300·45) that if σ is an inductive cardinal, and P is a series of $\sigma +_c 1$ terms, then $(B\text{'}P)\, P_\sigma\, (B\text{'}\breve{P})$. Now we also prove (*300·44) that if P is a series, and $R = P_1$, $P_\sigma = R_\sigma$ and R is a numerical relation. Hence it follows, by *262·211, that if $\sigma \neq 0$ and α is a class of $\sigma +_c 1$ terms, there is a numerical relation R whose field is of the same type as α and for which R_σ exists. Remembering *300·14 (quoted above), this proposition is:

***300·46.** $\vdash : \sigma \in \text{Ɑ}‘U - \iota‘0 . \supset .$

$$(\exists P, R) . P \in (\sigma +_c 1)_r . R = P_1 . R \in \text{Rel num} . t‘C‘R = t_0‘\sigma . (B‘R) R_\sigma (B‘\breve{R})$$

We have conversely (*300·47)

$$\vdash : R \in \text{Rel num} . \dot{\exists} ! R_\sigma . \supset . \sigma \in \text{NC ind} . \exists ! (\sigma +_c 1) \cap t‘C‘R . \sigma \cap t‘C‘R \in \text{Ɑ}‘U,$$

where "NC ind" has the meaning defined in *126, *i.e.* "$\sigma \in$ NC ind" means that σ is a typically indefinite cardinal.

The number ends by propositions proving (*300·52) that U_μ is a numerical relation, that (*300·57)

$$\dot{\exists} ! (U_\xi)_\nu \dot{\cap} (U_\eta)_\mu . \supset . \xi \times_c \nu \in C‘U . \xi \times_c \nu = \eta \times_c \mu,$$

and analogous theorems.

***300·01.** $U = (+_c 1)_{po} \upharpoonright (\text{NC induct} - \iota‘\Lambda)$ Df

***300·02.** $\text{Rel num} = (1 \to 1) \cap \hat{R}(\text{Pot}‘R \subset \text{Rl}‘J)$ Df

***300·03.** $\text{Rel num id} = (1 \to 1) \cap \hat{R}(\text{Potid}‘R - \iota‘R_0 \subset \text{Rl}‘J)$ Df

***300·1.** $\vdash : \mu U \nu . \equiv . \mu (+_c 1)_{po} \nu . \mu, \nu \in \text{NC induct} - \iota‘\Lambda$ [(*300·01)]

***300·11.** $\vdash :. \mu U \nu . \equiv :$

$$\mu, \nu \in \text{NC induct} - \iota‘\Lambda : (\exists \lambda) . \lambda \in \text{NC induct} - \iota‘0 . \mu = \nu +_c \lambda :$$
$$\equiv : \mu, \nu \in \text{NC induct} - \iota‘\Lambda : (\exists \lambda) . \lambda \neq 0 . \mu = \nu +_c \lambda :$$
$$\equiv : \mu, \nu \in \text{NC induct} - \iota‘\Lambda : (\exists \lambda) . \lambda \in \text{NC} - \iota‘0 . \mu = \nu +_c \lambda$$

[*300·1 . *120·42·428·462·452 . *110·4]

***300·12.** $\vdash : \mu U \nu . \equiv . \mu, \nu \in \text{NC induct} - \iota‘\Lambda . \nu < \mu .$

$$\equiv . \mu, \nu \in \text{NC induct} . \nu < \mu .$$
$$\equiv . \mu \in \text{NC induct} . \nu < \mu$$

[*300·11 . *117·3 . *120·42 . *117·26 . *110·6 . *117·15 . *120·48]

***300·13.** $\vdash . U \in J$ [*300·12 . *117·42]

***300·14.** $\vdash . C‘U = \text{NC induct} - \iota‘\Lambda . \text{D}‘U = \text{NC induct} - \iota‘\Lambda - \iota‘0 .$

$$\text{Ɑ}‘U = \text{NC induct} \cap \hat{\nu}(\exists ! \nu +_c 1) = \hat{\nu}(\nu +_c 1 \in \text{NC induct} - \iota‘\Lambda) .$$
$$B‘\breve{U} = 0$$

[*300·12 . *117·511 . *120·122 . *101·241 . *120·429·422]

***300·15.** $\vdash . U \in \text{Ser}$ [*300·13 . *120·441]

***300·16.** $\vdash : \alpha \in \text{Cls induct} . \supset . \text{N}_0\text{c}‘\alpha \in C‘U \cap t^{2}‘\alpha . \text{N}_0\text{c}‘\alpha \in C‘(U \upharpoonright t^{2}‘\alpha)$

Dem.

$\vdash . *120·21 . \supset \vdash : \text{Hp} . \supset . \text{N}_0\text{c}‘\alpha \in \text{NC induct}$ (1)

$\vdash . *103·13 . \supset \vdash . \text{N}_0\text{c}‘\alpha \neq \Lambda$ (2)

$\vdash . *103·11 . \supset \vdash . \text{N}_0\text{c}‘\alpha \in t^{2}‘\alpha$ (3)

$\vdash . (1) . (2) . (3) . *300·14 . \supset \vdash . \text{Prop}$

***300·17.** $\vdash : \mu \in \mathrm{NC\,ind} \,.\supset .\, (\exists \alpha) \,.\, \mu \cap t`\alpha \in C`U \,.\, \mu \in C`(U \upharpoonright t^2`\alpha)$

Dem.

$\vdash .\, *126\cdot1 \,.\qquad \supset \vdash : \mathrm{Hp} \,.\supset .\, (\exists\alpha) \,.\, \alpha \in \mathrm{Cls\,induct} \,.\, \mu = \mathrm{Nc}`\alpha \,.\, \exists \,!\, \mu \,.$

$[*103\cdot34] \qquad \supset .\, (\exists\alpha) \,.\, \alpha \in \mathrm{Cls\,induct} \,.\, \mu \cap t`\alpha = \mathrm{N_0c}`\alpha \quad (1)$

$\vdash .\, (1) \,.\, *300\cdot16 \,.\supset \vdash : \mathrm{Hp} \,.\supset .\, (\exists\alpha) \,.\, \mu \cap t`\alpha \in C`U \,. \quad (2)$

$[*65\cdot13] \qquad \supset .\, (\exists\alpha) \,.\, \mu \in C`U \,.\, \mu \subset t`\alpha \,.$

$[*63\cdot5] \qquad \supset .\, (\exists\alpha) \,.\, \mu \in C`U \,.\, \mu \in t^2`\alpha \quad (3)$

$\vdash .\, (2) \,.\, (3) \,.\supset \vdash .\, \mathrm{Prop}$

***300·18.** $\vdash : \mu \in \mathrm{NC\,ind} \,.\supset .$

$(\exists\sigma) \,.\, 2^\mu \in C`(U \upharpoonright t^2`\sigma) \,.\, (\mu +_c 1) \cap t`\sigma \in C`U \,.\, \mu \in \text{ᗡ}`(U \upharpoonright t^2`\sigma)$

$[*126\cdot13\cdot15 \,.\, *300\cdot17\cdot14]$

***300·181.** $\vdash : \mu \in \mathrm{NC\,ind} \,.\, \mu \cap t`\alpha \in C`U \,.\supset .$

$2^\mu \cap t^{2}`\alpha \in C`U \,.\, (\mu +_c 1) \cap t^{2}`\alpha \in C`U \,.\, \mu \cap t^{2}`\alpha \in \text{ᗡ}`U$

$[*126\cdot23 \,.\, *300\cdot14]$

***300·2.** $\vdash : \mathrm{Infin\,ax} \,.\supset .\, \breve{U} = \dot{N}_{\mathrm{po}}$

Here $\dot{N}$ has the meaning defined in *263·02.

Dem.

$\vdash .\, *300\cdot1 \,.\, *125\cdot1 \,.\supset \vdash :.\, \mathrm{Hp} \,.\supset : \mu U \nu \,.\equiv .\, \mu, \nu \in \mathrm{NC\,induct} \,.\, \mu\, (+_c 1)_{\mathrm{po}}\, \nu \,.$

$[*120\cdot1 . *91\cdot574] \qquad \equiv .\, \nu\, (+_c 1)_* \, 0 \,.\, \mu\, (+_c 1)_{\mathrm{po}}\, \nu \,.$

$[*96\cdot13] \qquad \equiv .\, \mu \,\{(+_c 1) \upharpoonright \overrightarrow{(+_c 1)_*}`0\}_{\mathrm{po}}\, \nu \,.$

$[(*263\cdot02 . *120\cdot01)] \qquad \equiv .\, \nu \dot{N}_{\mathrm{po}}\, \mu :.\supset \vdash .\, \mathrm{Prop}$

***300·21.** $\vdash : \mathrm{Infin\,ax} \,.\supset .\, \breve{U} \in \omega \quad [*300\cdot2 \,.\, *263\cdot12]$

***300·22.** $\vdash : \sim \mathrm{Infin\,ax} \,.\supset .\, \breve{U} \in \Omega\ \mathrm{induct}$

Dem.

$\vdash .\, *125\cdot16\cdot24 \,.\, \mathrm{Transp} \,.\supset \vdash : \mathrm{Hp} \,.\supset .\, C`U \in \mathrm{Cls\,induct} \quad (1)$

$\vdash .\, (1) \,.\, *300\cdot15 \,.\, *261\cdot32 \,.\supset \vdash .\, \mathrm{Prop}$

***300·23.** $\vdash .\, \breve{U} \in \Omega \quad [*300\cdot21\cdot22]$

***300·231.** $\vdash : \mu U_1 \nu \,.\equiv .\, \mu, \nu \in \mathrm{NC\,induct} - \iota`\Lambda \,.\, \mu = \nu +_c 1 \,.$

$\equiv .\, \mu \in \mathrm{NC\,induct} - \iota`\Lambda \,.\, \mu = \nu +_c 1 \,.$

$\equiv .\, \mu \in \mathrm{NC\,induct} - \iota`\Lambda - \iota`0 \,.\, \nu = \mu -_c 1 \,.$

$\equiv .\, \nu \in \mathrm{NC\,induct} - \iota`\Lambda \,.\, \nu = \mu -_c 1$

Dem.

$\vdash .\, *300\cdot15\cdot12 \,.\, *201\cdot63 \,.\supset$

$\vdash :.\, \mu U_1 \nu \,.\equiv :\, \mu, \nu \in \mathrm{NC\,induct} - \iota`\Lambda \,.\, \nu < \mu : \sim (\exists\lambda) \,.\, \nu < \lambda \,.\, \lambda < \mu :$

$[*120\cdot429] \equiv :\, \mu, \nu \in \mathrm{NC\,induct} - \iota`\Lambda \,.\, \nu < \mu : \nu +_c 1 \geqslant \mu \,.\, \mu \geqslant \nu +_c 1 :$

$[*117\cdot25] \quad \equiv :\, \mu, \nu \in \mathrm{NC\,induct} - \iota`\Lambda \,.\, \mu = \nu +_c 1 \quad (1)$

$\vdash .\, (1) \,.\, *120\cdot422\cdot424\cdot423 \,.\supset \vdash .\, \mathrm{Prop}$

∗300·232. $\vdash : \mu \in \text{NC induct} . \supset .$

$$U_\mu = (+_c \mu) \upharpoonright (\text{NC induct} - \iota`\Lambda) . \breve{U}_\mu = (-_c \mu) \upharpoonright (\text{NC induct} - \iota`\Lambda)$$

For the definition of U_μ, see ∗121·02.

Dem.

$\vdash . ∗121·302 . ∗300·15 . \supset \vdash : \rho U_0 \sigma . \equiv . \sigma \in C`U . \rho = \sigma .$

[∗300·14.∗110·6] $\equiv . \rho, \sigma \in \text{NC induct} - \iota`\Lambda . \rho = \sigma +_c 0$ (1)

$\vdash . ∗260·22·28 . ∗121·332 . \supset$

$\vdash : U_\mu = (+_c \mu) \upharpoonright (\text{NC induct} - \iota`\Lambda) . \supset . U_{\mu +_c 1} = (+_c \mu) \upharpoonright (\text{NC induct} - \iota`\Lambda) \mid U_1$

[∗300·231] $= (+_c \mu) \upharpoonright (\text{NC induct} - \iota`\Lambda) \mid (+_c 1) \upharpoonright (\text{NC induct} - \iota`\Lambda)$

[∗120·45·452] $= \{+_c (\mu +_c 1)\} \upharpoonright (\text{NC induct} - \iota`\Lambda)$ (2)

$\vdash . (1) . (2) . \text{Induct} . \supset \vdash . \text{Prop}$

∗300·24. $\vdash : \mu \in \text{NC induct} . \supset . \text{D}`U_\mu = \overrightarrow{U_*}`\mu = \text{NC induct} \cap \hat{\nu} (\nu \geqslant \mu)$ [∗300·232 . ∗117·31 . ∗120·45]

∗300·25. $\vdash : \mu \in \text{NC induct} . \supset .$

$$\overrightarrow{B}`\breve{U}_\mu = \overleftarrow{U}`\mu = \text{NC induct} \cap \hat{\nu} (\nu < \mu) = \breve{U} (0 \vdash \mu)$$

[∗300·232·24·12]

∗300·26. $\vdash : \mu \in C`U . \equiv . \mu U_\mu 0 . \equiv . \dot{\exists} ! U_\mu \upharpoonright (C`U)$ [∗300·232·14 . ∗110·6]

Here the μ in "U_μ" is of higher type than the μ in "$\mu \in C`U$," because the interval $U (0 \mapsto \mu)$ is composed of members each of which is of the same type as μ.

∗300·3. $\vdash : R \in \text{Rel num} . \equiv . R \in 1 \rightarrow 1 . R_{\text{po}} \subseteq J . \equiv . R \in 1 \rightarrow 1 . \text{Pot}`R \subset \text{Rl}`J$ [(∗300·02)]

∗300·31. $\vdash : R \in \text{Rel num id} . \equiv . R \in 1 \rightarrow 1 . \text{Potid}`R - \iota`R_0 \subset \text{Rl}`J$ [(∗300·03)]

∗300·311. $\vdash : R \subseteq I . \equiv . R_0 = R . \equiv . R = I \upharpoonright C`R$

Dem.

$\vdash . ∗201·13·18 . \supset \vdash :. R \subseteq I . \supset : x \in C`R . \supset . \overleftarrow{R_*}`x \cap \overrightarrow{R_*}`x = \iota`x$ (1)

$\vdash . (1) . ∗121·11 . \supset \vdash : R \subseteq I . \supset . I \upharpoonright C`R \subseteq R_0 .$

[∗121·3] $\supset . R_0 = I \upharpoonright C`R .$

[∗72·92] $\supset . R_0 = R = I \upharpoonright C`R$ (2)

$\vdash . ∗121·3 . \supset \vdash : R_0 = R . \supset . R \subseteq I$ (3)

$\vdash . (2) . (3) . \supset \vdash . \text{Prop}$

∗300·312. $\vdash : R \subseteq I . \supset . \text{Potid}`R = \iota`R = \iota`R_0$ [∗300·311 . ∗50·72 . Induct]

∗300·313. $\vdash : R \in \text{Rel num id} . \supset . R_* \dot{-} R_0 \subseteq J$ [∗300·31 . ∗91·55]

***300·32.** $\vdash : R \in \mathrm{Rel\ num\ id} \,.\supset .\, R_0 = I \upharpoonright C`R$

Dem.

$\vdash . *91\cdot35 .\supset \vdash . I \upharpoonright C`R \in \mathrm{Potid}`R - \mathrm{Rl\ ex}`J$ (1)

$\vdash . (1) . *300\cdot31 .\supset \vdash .$ Prop

***300·321.** $\vdash : R \in \mathrm{Rel\ num\ id} \,.\, R \neq R_0 .\supset . R \Subset J \,.\, \dot{\exists} ! R$ [*300·31]

***300·322.** $\vdash : R \Subset J .\supset . R_{po} \dot{\cap} R_0 = \dot{\Lambda}$

Dem.

$\vdash . *121\cdot3 .\supset \vdash : x R_{po} y \,.\, x \neq y .\supset . \sim (x R_0 y)$ (1)

$\vdash . *50\cdot24 .\supset \vdash :. \mathrm{Hp} .\supset : \sim (x R x) :$ (2)

$[*91\cdot57]$ $\supset : x R_{po} x .\supset . x (R_{po} \mid R) x \,.$

$[*121\cdot103.(2)]$ $\supset . R(x \mapsto x) \neq \iota`x \,.$

$[*121\cdot11]$ $\supset . \sim (x R_0 x)$ (3)

$\vdash . (1) . (3) .\supset \vdash .$ Prop

***300·323.** $\vdash : R \in \mathrm{Rel\ num\ id} \,.\, R \neq R_0 .\supset . R_{po} \Subset J$

Dem.

$\vdash . *300\cdot321\cdot322 .\supset \vdash : \mathrm{Hp} .\supset . R_{po} \dot{\cap} R_0 = \dot{\Lambda} \,.$

$[*300\cdot32]$ $\supset . R_{po} \dot{\cap} I \upharpoonright C`R = \dot{\Lambda} : \supset \vdash .$ Prop

***300·324.** $\vdash :. R \in \mathrm{Rel\ num\ id} .\supset : R \Subset I . \vee . R \in \mathrm{Rel\ num}$

Dem.

$\vdash . *300\cdot311\cdot323 .\supset \vdash :. \mathrm{Hp} .\supset : R \Subset I . \vee . R_{po} \Subset J$ (1)

$\vdash . *300\cdot32 .$ $\supset \vdash : R \in \mathrm{Rel\ num\ id} \,.\, R_{po} \Subset J .\supset . \mathrm{Potid}`R - \iota`R_0 = \mathrm{Pot}`R$ (2)

$\vdash . (2) . *300\cdot31 .$ $\supset \vdash : R \in \mathrm{Rel\ num\ id} \,.\, R_{po} \Subset J .\supset . \mathrm{Pot}`R \subset \mathrm{Rl}`J$ (3)

$\vdash . (1) . (3) . *300\cdot3 .\supset \vdash .$ Prop

***300·325.** $\vdash : R \Subset I .\supset . R \in \mathrm{Rel\ num\ id}$

Dem.

$\vdash . *300\cdot312 .\supset \vdash : \mathrm{Hp} .\supset . \mathrm{Potid}`R - \iota`R_0 = \Lambda$ (1)

$\vdash . (1) . *300\cdot31 .\supset \vdash .$ Prop

***300·326.** $\vdash : R \in \mathrm{Rel\ num} .\supset . R \in \mathrm{Rel\ num\ id}$

Dem.

$\vdash . *121\cdot3 . *300\cdot3 .$ $\supset \vdash : \mathrm{Hp} .\supset . R_0 \sim\in \mathrm{Pot}`R$ (1)

$\vdash . *121\cdot302 . *300\cdot3 .\supset \vdash : \mathrm{Hp} .\supset . R_0 = I \upharpoonright C`R$ (2)

$\vdash . (1) . (2) . *91\cdot35 .$ $\supset \vdash : \mathrm{Hp} .\supset . \mathrm{Potid}`R - \iota`R_0 = \mathrm{Pot}`R$ (3)

$\vdash . (3) . *300\cdot3\cdot31 .\supset \vdash .$ Prop

***300·33.** $\vdash . \mathrm{Rel\ num\ id} = \mathrm{Rl}`I \cup \mathrm{Rel\ num}$ [*300·324·325·326]

***300·34.** $\vdash . \dot{\Lambda} \in \mathrm{Rel\ num}$ [*300·3 . *72·1]

***300·4.** $\vdash . \mathrm{Rel\ num} = \mathrm{Cnv}``\mathrm{Rel\ num}$ [*300·3 . *91·522]

***300·41.** $\vdash . \mathrm{Rel\ num\ id} = \mathrm{Cnv}``\mathrm{Rel\ num\ id}$ [*300·31 . *91·521]

***300·42.** $\vdash : R \epsilon \text{Rel num} . \supset . \text{Pot}`R \subset \text{Rel num}$

Dem.

$\vdash . *91·6 . *92·102 . \supset$

$\vdash : R \epsilon \text{Rel num} . P \epsilon \text{Pot}`R . \supset . P \grave{\epsilon} 1 \to 1 . \text{Pot}`P \subset \text{Rl}`J .$

$[*300·3] \qquad \supset . P \epsilon \text{Rel num} : \supset \vdash . \text{Prop}$

***300·43.** $\vdash : R \epsilon \text{Rel num id} . \supset . \text{Potid}`R \subset \text{Rel num id}$

Dem.

$\vdash . *300·325·312 . \quad \supset \vdash : R \mathrel{G} I . \supset . \text{Potid}`R \subset \text{Rel num id} \quad (1)$

$\vdash . *300·325 . \quad \supset \vdash . I \upharpoonright C`R \epsilon \text{Rel num id} \quad (2)$

$\vdash . (2) . *300·42·326 . \supset \vdash : R \epsilon \text{Rel num} . \supset . \text{Potid}`R \subset \text{Rel num id} \quad (3)$

$\vdash . (1) . (3) . *300·33 . \supset \vdash . \text{Prop}$

***300·44.** $\vdash :. P \epsilon \text{Ser} . \sigma \epsilon \text{NC ind} . \supset :$

$P_\sigma, \breve{P}_\sigma \epsilon \text{Rel num id} : \sigma \neq 0 . \supset . P_\sigma = (P_1)_\sigma . P_\sigma, \breve{P}_\sigma \epsilon \text{Rel num}$

Dem.

$\vdash . *121·302 . *300·325 . \supset \vdash : \text{Hp} . \sigma = 0 . \supset . P_\sigma, \breve{P}_\sigma \epsilon \text{Rel num id} \quad (1)$

$\vdash . *260·28 . \quad \supset \vdash : \text{Hp} . \sigma \neq 0 . \supset . P_\sigma = (P_1)_\sigma \quad (2)$

$\vdash . *300·3 . *260·22 . \quad \supset \vdash :. \text{Hp} . \supset : P_1 \epsilon \text{Rel num} :$

$[*121·5 . *300·42] \qquad \supset : \sigma \neq 0 . \supset . (P_1)_\sigma \epsilon \text{Rel num} .$

$[(2) . *300·4] \qquad \supset . P_\sigma, \breve{P}_\sigma \epsilon \text{Rel num} \quad (3)$

$\vdash . (1) . (2) . (3) . \supset \vdash . \text{Prop}$

***300·45.** $\vdash : \sigma \epsilon \text{NC ind} . P \epsilon (\sigma +_c 1)_r . \supset . (B`P) P_\sigma (B`\breve{P})$

For the definition of $(\sigma +_c 1)_r$, see *262·03.

Dem.

$\vdash . *262·12 . \supset \vdash : \text{Hp} . \supset . P \epsilon \Omega . C`P \epsilon \sigma +_c 1 .$

$[*202·181 . *261·24] \quad \supset . (B`P) P_\sigma (B`\breve{P}) : \supset \vdash . \text{Prop}$

***300·46.** $\vdash : \sigma \epsilon \text{Cl}`U - \iota`0 . \supset .$

$(\exists P, R) . P \epsilon (\sigma +_c 1)_r . R = P_1 . R \epsilon \text{Rel num} . t`C`R = t_0`\sigma . (B`R) R_\sigma (B`\breve{R})$

Dem.

$\vdash . *300·14 . \supset \vdash : \text{Hp} . \supset . (\exists \alpha) . \alpha \epsilon \text{Cls induct} . t`\alpha = t_0`\sigma . \alpha \epsilon \sigma +_c 1 .$

$[*262·211] \qquad \supset . (\exists P) . P \epsilon (\sigma +_c 1)_r . t`C`P = t_0`\sigma .$

$[*300·45] \qquad \supset . (\exists P) . P \epsilon (\sigma +_c 1)_r . t`C`P = t_0`\sigma . (B`P) P_\sigma (B`\breve{P}) .$

$[*300·44 . *261·22] \qquad \supset . (\exists P, R) . P \epsilon (\sigma +_c 1)_r . R = P_1 . R \epsilon \text{Rel num} .$

$t`C`R = t_0`\sigma . (B`R) R_\sigma (B`\breve{R}) : \supset \vdash . \text{Prop}$

***300·47.** $\vdash : R \in \text{Rel num} . \dot{\exists} ! R_\sigma . \supset .$
$\sigma \in \text{NC ind} . \exists ! (\sigma +_c 1) \cap t'C'R . \sigma \cap t'C'R \in \text{D}'U$

Dem.

$\vdash . *121{\cdot}11 . \supset \vdash : \text{Hp} . \supset . (\exists x, y) . R(x \mapsto y) \in \sigma +_c 1 .$

$[*121{\cdot}46] \quad \supset . \sigma +_c 1 \in \text{NC ind} . \exists ! (\sigma +_c 1) \cap t'C'R .$

$[*120{\cdot}422 . *300{\cdot}14] \quad \supset . \sigma \in \text{NC ind} . \exists ! (\sigma +_c 1) \cap t'C'R .$

$\sigma \cap t'C'R \in \text{D}'U : \supset \vdash . \text{Prop}$

***300·48.** $\vdash : R \subset I . \nu \neq 0 . \supset . R_\nu = \dot{\Lambda}$

Dem.

$\vdash . *300{\cdot}312{\cdot}311 . *91{\cdot}55 . \supset \vdash : R \subset I . \supset . R_* = I \upharpoonright C'R \quad (1)$

$\vdash . (1) . *121{\cdot}103 . \supset \vdash : R \subset I . \supset . R(x \mapsto y) = C'R \cap \iota'x \cap \iota'y \quad (2)$

$\vdash . (2) . *121{\cdot}11 . \supset \vdash :. R \subset I . \supset : xR_\nu y . \equiv . C'R \cap \iota'x \cap \iota'y \in \nu +_c 1 .$

$[*117{\cdot}222] \quad \supset . \nu +_c 1 \leqslant \text{Nc}'\iota'x .$

$[*117{\cdot}54 . *120{\cdot}124] \quad \supset . \nu +_c 1 = 1 .$

$[*110{\cdot}641 . *120{\cdot}311] \quad \supset . \nu = 0 \quad (3)$

$\vdash . (3) . \text{Transp} . \supset \vdash . \text{Prop}$

***300·481.** $\vdash : R \in \text{Rel num id} . \nu \neq 0 . \supset . (R_0)_\nu = \dot{\Lambda} . (R_\nu)_0 \subset R_0$

Dem.

$\vdash . *300{\cdot}32{\cdot}48 . \supset \vdash : \text{Hp} . \supset . (R_0)_\nu = \dot{\Lambda} \quad (1)$

$\vdash . *300{\cdot}43{\cdot}32 . \supset \vdash : \text{Hp} . \supset . (R_\nu)_0 = I \upharpoonright C'R_\nu .$

$[*121{\cdot}322 . *300{\cdot}32] \quad \supset . (R_\nu)_0 \subset R_0 \quad (2)$

$\vdash . (1) . (2) . \supset \vdash . \text{Prop}$

***300·49.** $\vdash : R \in \text{Rel num} . \dot{\Lambda} \sim \in \text{Pot}'R . \supset . C'R \sim \in \text{Cls induct}$

Dem.

$\vdash . *121{\cdot}5 . \supset \vdash :. \text{Hp} . \supset : \nu \in \text{NC induct} . \supset . \dot{\exists} ! R_\nu .$

$[*121{\cdot}11] \quad \supset . \exists ! (\nu +_c 1) \cap \text{Cl}'C'R :. \supset \vdash . \text{Prop}$

***300·491.** $\vdash : (\exists R) . R \in \text{Rel num} . \dot{\Lambda} \sim \in \text{Pot}'R . \supset . \text{Infin ax} \quad [*300{\cdot}49]$

***300·5.** $\vdash . U_1 \in \text{Rel num} \quad [*300{\cdot}15{\cdot}44]$

***300·51.** $\vdash . U_0 \in \text{Rel num id} \quad [*300{\cdot}15{\cdot}44]$

***300·511.** $\vdash . U_\sigma = (U_1)_\sigma \quad [*300{\cdot}21{\cdot}22 . *263{\cdot}491]$

***300·52.** $\vdash : \mu \in \text{NC ind} - \iota'0 . \supset . U_\mu \in \text{Rel num} \quad [*300{\cdot}15{\cdot}44]$

***300·53.** $\vdash . (\times_c 1) \upharpoonright C'U \in \text{Rel num id} \quad [*300{\cdot}325 . *113{\cdot}621]$

***300·54.** $\vdash : \text{Infin ax} . \mu \in \text{D}'U - \iota'1 . \supset . (\times_c \mu) \upharpoonright \text{D}'U \in \text{Rel num}$

Dem.

$\vdash . *120{\cdot}51 . \quad \supset \vdash : \text{Hp} . \supset . (\times_c \mu) \upharpoonright \text{D}'U \in 1 \to 1 \quad (1)$

$\vdash . *126{\cdot}51 . *113{\cdot}621 . \supset \vdash :. \text{Hp} . \supset : \rho \{(\times_c \mu) \upharpoonright \text{D}'U\} \sigma . \supset . \rho > \sigma :$

$[*117{\cdot}47{\cdot}42] \quad \supset : \{(\times_c \mu) \upharpoonright \text{D}'U\}_{po} \subset J \quad (2)$

$\vdash . (1) . (2) . *300{\cdot}3 . \supset \vdash . \text{Prop}$

***300·55.** $\vdash : \dot{\exists} ! R_\rho \dot{\wedge} R_\sigma . \supset . \exists ! (\rho +_c 1) \cap t`C`R . \rho = \sigma$ [*121·11 . *120·31]

***300·551.** $\vdash : \dot{\exists} ! R_\rho \dot{\wedge} R_\sigma . \equiv . \dot{\exists} ! R_\rho . \rho = \sigma$ [*300·55]

***300·552.** $\vdash : R \in \text{Rel num} . \supset . (R_\xi)_\nu \subseteq R_{\xi \times_c \nu}$

Dem.

$\vdash . *121·36 . \supset \vdash : \text{Hp} . \xi, \nu \in \text{NC ind} - \iota`0 . \supset . (R_\xi)_\nu = R_{\xi \times_c \nu}$ (1)

$\vdash . *300·481 . \supset \vdash : \text{Hp} . \xi = 0 . \nu \neq 0 . \supset . (R_\xi)_\nu = \dot{\Lambda}$ (2)

$\vdash . *300·32·311 . *113·602 . \supset \vdash : \text{Hp} . \xi = 0 . \nu = 0 . \supset . (R_\xi)_\nu = R_{\xi \times_c \nu}$ (3)

$\vdash . *300·481 . *113·602 . \supset \vdash : \text{Hp} . \xi \neq 0 . \nu = 0 . \supset . (R_\xi)_\nu \subseteq R_{\xi \times_c \nu}$ (4)

$\vdash . *300·47 . \supset \vdash : \text{Hp} . \sim(\xi, \nu \in \text{NC ind}) . \supset . (R_\xi)_\nu = \dot{\Lambda}$ (5)

$\vdash . (1) . (2) . (3) . (4) . (5) . \supset \vdash . \text{Prop}$

***300·56.** $\vdash : R \in \text{Rel num} . \dot{\exists} ! (R_\xi)_\nu \dot{\wedge} (R_\eta)_\mu . \supset .$

$$\xi \times_c \nu = \eta \times_c \mu . (\xi \times_c \nu) \cap t`C`R \in \text{Cl}`U$$

Dem.

$\vdash . *300·552 . \supset \vdash : \text{Hp} . \supset . \dot{\exists} ! R_{\xi \times_c \nu} \dot{\wedge} R_{\eta \times_c \mu}$ (1)

$\vdash . (1) . *300·55 . \supset \vdash . \text{Prop}$

***300·57.** $\vdash : \dot{\exists} ! (U_\xi)_\nu \dot{\wedge} (U_\eta)_\mu . \supset . \xi \times_c \nu \in C`U . \xi \times_c \nu = \eta \times_c \mu$

Dem.

$\vdash . *300·5·511·56·552 . \supset \vdash : \text{Hp} . \supset . \xi \times_c \nu = \eta \times_c \mu . \dot{\exists} ! U_{\xi \times_c \nu}$ (1)

$\vdash . (1) . *300·26 . \supset \vdash . \text{Prop}$

By *300·56, we have, with the above hypothesis, $(\xi \times_c \nu) \cap t`C`U \in \text{Cl}`U$. But here the $U$ in $\text{Cl}`U$ is of higher type than the U in $(\xi \times_c \nu) \cap t`C`U$ or in the hypothesis. In the type of the U in the hypothesis, we have $\xi \times_c \nu \in C`U$, not necessarily $\xi \times_c \nu \in \text{Cl}`U$.

***300·571.** $\vdash :. \xi, \eta \in \text{D}`U . \supset : \dot{\exists} ! (U_\xi)_\nu \dot{\wedge} (U_\eta)_\mu . \equiv . \xi \times_c \nu \in C`U . \xi \times_c \nu = \eta \times_c \mu$

Dem.

$\vdash . *300·26 . \supset \vdash : \xi \times_c \nu \in C`U . \xi \times_c \nu = \eta \times_c \mu . \supset . (\xi \times_c \nu) \{U_{\xi \times_c \nu} \dot{\wedge} U_{\eta \times_c \mu}\} 0$ (1)

$\vdash . *121·36 . \supset \vdash : \text{Hp} . \text{Hp}(1) . \mu \neq 0 . \nu \neq 0 . \supset . U_{\xi \times_c \nu} = (U_\xi)_\nu . U_{\eta \times_c \mu} = (U_\eta)_\mu$ (2)

$\vdash . *300·32 . \supset \vdash : \text{Hp} . \text{Hp}(1) . \nu = 0 . \supset . (U_\xi)_\nu = I \upharpoonright C`U_\xi .$

[*300·26] $\supset . 0 \{(U_\xi)_\nu\} 0$ (3)

Similarly $\vdash : \text{Hp} . \text{Hp}(1) . \mu = 0 . \supset . 0 \{(U_\eta)_\mu\} 0$ (4)

$\vdash . *113·602 . \supset \vdash : \text{Hp} . \text{Hp}(1) . \nu = 0 . \supset . \mu = 0$ (5)

$\vdash . (1) . (2) . (3) . (4) . (5) . \supset \vdash : \text{Hp} . \text{Hp}(1) . \supset . \dot{\exists} ! (U_\xi)_\nu \dot{\wedge} (U_\eta)_\mu$ (6)

$\vdash . (6) . *300·57 . \supset \vdash . \text{Prop}$

***300·572.** $\vdash :. \xi \in \text{D}`U . \supset : \dot{\exists} ! (U_\xi)_\nu . \equiv . \xi \times_c \nu \in C`U$ $\left[*300·571 \dfrac{\xi, \nu}{\eta, \mu}\right]$

$*301$. NUMERICALLY DEFINED POWERS OF RELATIONS.

Summary of $*301$.

In this number, we have to exhibit the powers of a relation R, *i.e.* the various members of Potid'R, as of the form R^σ, where σ is an inductive cardinal. We have already had $R^2 = R \mid R$ and $R^3 = R^2 \mid R$. What we need is a definition which shall give

$$R^{\sigma +_c 1} = R^\sigma \mid R.$$

Now R^σ is a function of R and σ; thus we have to exhibit R^σ in the form $S\text{‘}\sigma$, where S will be a function of R. That is, we have to define the relation S as a relation of R^σ to σ, and S must be such that, if it holds between R^σ and σ, it holds between $R^{\sigma +_c 1}$ and $\sigma +_c 1$. Thus we may take S as a sum of couples, such that if one couple is $R^\sigma \downarrow \sigma$, the next is $(R^\sigma \mid R) \downarrow (\sigma +_c 1)$, *i.e.* such that, if one couple is $Q \downarrow \sigma$, the next is $(Q \mid R) \downarrow (\sigma +_c 1)$. Now

$$(Q \mid R) \downarrow (\sigma +_c 1) = \{(\mid R) \parallel (-_c 1)\}\text{‘}(Q \downarrow \sigma).$$

Hence, since we want to have $R^0 = I \upharpoonright C\text{‘}R$, our class of couples is

$$\hat{M}\,[M\,\{(\mid R) \parallel (-_c 1)\}_* \,\{(I \upharpoonright C\text{‘}R) \downarrow 0\}].$$

Calling this class num (R), we may therefore put

$$R^\sigma = \{\dot{s}\text{‘num}\,(R)\}\text{‘}\sigma \quad \text{Df.}$$

If we put $(\mid R) \parallel (-_c 1) = R_p$, the above definitions are

$$\text{num}\,(R) = \overrightarrow{(R_p)_*}\text{‘}\{(I \upharpoonright C\text{‘}R) \downarrow 0\} \quad \text{Dft},$$

$$R^\sigma = \{\dot{s}\text{‘num}\,(R)\}\text{‘}\sigma \quad \text{Df.}$$

But the above definition of R_p requires some modification before it can be considered quite correct. With the above definition, we have

$$R_p\text{‘}(Q \downarrow \sigma) = (Q \mid R) \downarrow (\sigma +_c 1) \quad (1).$$

Now since num (R) is defined by means of $(R_p)_*$, and since the definition of R_* contains the hypothesis $\breve{R}\text{“}\mu \subset \mu$, it follows that, if num (R) is to be significant, the relation $-_c 1$ which appears in the definition of R_p must be homogeneous, so that, in (1), σ and $\sigma +_c 1$ must be of the same type. Hence σ, though typically ambiguous, cannot be typically indefinite;

therefore, if the axiom of infinity is not true, we shall sooner or later arrive at $\sigma = \Lambda$ as we travel up the inductive cardinals. In that case, we shall have

$$R^{\sigma -_c 1} \downarrow (\sigma -_c 1) \epsilon \operatorname{num}(R) . (R^{\sigma -_c 1} | R) \downarrow \Lambda \epsilon \operatorname{num}(R),$$
$$(R^{\sigma -_c 1} | R | R) \downarrow \Lambda \epsilon \operatorname{num}(R), \text{ etc.}$$

Now if (for example) R is a cyclic relation, such as that of an angle of a polygon to the next angle to the left, we shall not have

$$R^{\sigma -_c 1} = R^{\sigma -_c 1} | R \text{ or } R^{\sigma -_c 1} | R = R^{\sigma -_c 1} | R | R.$$

Hence $\dot{s}$'num (R) will fail to be one-many, and R^σ will fail to exist. Hence it becomes desirable to restrict σ to cardinals which exist in some assigned type, *i.e.* to replace $-_c 1$ by $(-_c 1) \upharpoonright (\text{NC induct} - \iota\text{'}\Lambda)$, *i.e.* by $\breve{U}_1$.

Thus we now put $\qquad R_p = (| R) \| \breve{U}_1 \quad$ Dft.

But even this definition is not quite complete, because the type of U is not assigned. It makes some difference how the type of U is assigned, for if we take as the type of C'U a type lower than that of t'N_0c't'R, we may find that our numbers become Λ before we have ceased to obtain fresh powers of R.

For example, suppose the total number of individuals were four, and that these were a, x, y, z. Let us write $x \downarrow (a, y, \ldots)$ for $x \downarrow a \cup x \downarrow y \cup \ldots$. Then consider the relation $R = x \downarrow (a, y) \cup a \downarrow y \cup y \downarrow (x, z)$. Then

$$R^2 = x \downarrow (x, y, z) \cup a \downarrow (x, z) \cup y \downarrow (a, y),$$
$$R^3 = x \downarrow (a, y, x, z) \cup a \downarrow (a, y) \cup y \downarrow (x, y, z),$$
$$R^4 = x \downarrow (y, x, z, a) \cup a \downarrow (y, x, z) \cup y \downarrow (a, y, x, z),$$
$$R^5 = x \downarrow (a, x, y, z) \cup a \downarrow (a, x, y, z) \cup y \downarrow (a, x, y, z).$$

After this, $R^5 = R^5 | R = R^5 | R^2 =$ etc. But up to R^5, each power of R is different from all its predecessors. If we take t'C'$U = t$'N_0c't'C'R, C'U consists only of the numbers 0, 1, 2, 3, 4, and is thus inadequate to deal with R^5. Hence the type in which we take U must be a sufficiently high type, which must increase with the type of R. Hence we take C'U in the type of t'N_0c't'R, *i.e.* in the type of t^3'R. This is secured by writing $U \upharpoonright t^3$'R in place of U in the definition of R_p. Hence the final definitions for R^σ are:

***301·01.** $\quad R_p = (| R) \| (\breve{U}_1 \upharpoonright t^3\text{'}R) \qquad$ Dft [*301]

***301·02.** $\quad \operatorname{num}(R) = \overrightarrow{(R_p)_*}\text{'}\{(I \upharpoonright C\text{'}R) \downarrow (0 \cap t^2\text{'}R)\} \qquad$ Dft [*301]

***301·03.** $\quad R^\sigma = \{\dot{s}\text{'}\operatorname{num}(R)\}\text{'}\sigma \qquad$ Df

The two temporary definitions *301·01·02 are only to extend to the present number.

With the above definitions we have

***301·16.** $\vdash : \mu \in C\text{`}U \cap t^3\text{`}R . \equiv . E ! R^\mu$

***301·2.** $\vdash . R^0 = I \upharpoonright C\text{`}R . R^1 = R$

***301·21.** $\vdash : \nu \in \text{Cl}\text{`}U \cap t^3\text{`}R . \supset . R^{\nu +_c 1} = R^\nu | R$

***301·23.** $\vdash : \mu +_c \nu \in C\text{`}U \cap t^3\text{`}R . \supset . R^{\mu +_c \nu} = R^\mu | R^\nu = R^\nu | R^\mu$

***301·26.** $\vdash : P \in \text{Potid}\text{`}R . \equiv . (\exists \sigma) . P = R^\sigma$

I.e. the powers of R are the various relations R^σ. This proposition might have been not universally true if we had taken U in a lower type.

***301·3.** $\vdash : R \subseteq I . \sigma \in C\text{`}U \cap t^3\text{`}R . \supset . R^\sigma = R = R_0 = I \upharpoonright C\text{`}R$

It is largely for the sake of this proposition that we require powers of relations in dealing with ratio, rather than finid‘R. For we have $R \subseteq I . \sigma \neq 0 . \supset . R_\sigma = \dot\Lambda$, so that R_σ does not give what is wanted if $R \subseteq I$. On the other hand (*301·41), if $R \in \text{Rel num}$, we have $R^\sigma = R_\sigma$ if $\sigma \in C\text{`}U \cap t^3\text{`}R$. Thus as applied to numerical relations, R_σ may always replace R^σ.

We have, whatever R may be,

***301·504.** $\vdash : \mu, \nu \in C\text{`}U \cap t^2\text{`}C\text{`}R . \nu \neq 0 . \supset . (R^\mu)^\nu = R^{\mu \times_c \nu}$

The importance of this number will appear in connection with ratios.

***301·01.** $R_p = (|R) \| (\breve{U}_1 \upharpoonright t^3\text{`}R)$ Dft [*301]

***301·02.** $\text{num}(R) = \overrightarrow{(R_p)_*}\text{`}\{(I \upharpoonright C\text{`}R) \downarrow (0 \cap t^2\text{`}R)\}$ Dft [*301]

***301·03.** $R^\sigma = \{\dot s\text{`num}(R)\}\text{`}\sigma$ Df

***301·1.** $\vdash : \sigma \in \text{Cl}\text{`}(U \upharpoonright t^3\text{`}R) . \supset . R_p\text{`}(Q \downarrow \sigma) = (Q | R) \downarrow \{(\sigma +_c 1) \cap t^2\text{`}R\}$
[*55·61 . (*301·01)]

***301·101.** $\vdash : \sigma \in \text{Cl}\text{`}(U \upharpoonright t^3\text{`}R) . \equiv . \sigma \in \text{Cl}\text{`}U \cap t^3\text{`}R . \equiv : \sigma \in \text{Cl}\text{`}U . \sigma \subset t^2\text{`}R$
[*63·5]

***301·102.** $\vdash : \sigma \in \text{Cl}\text{`}(U \upharpoonright t^3\text{`}R) . \equiv .$
$(\exists \lambda) . \lambda \in \text{Cls induct} . \exists ! -\lambda . R \in t_0\text{`}\lambda . \sigma = N_0c\text{`}\lambda$
[*300·14 . *103·11]

***301·103.** $\vdash : \sigma \in \text{Cl}\text{`}(U \upharpoonright t^3\text{`}R) . \equiv .$
$(\exists \lambda) . \lambda \in \text{Cls induct} . \exists ! -\lambda . R \in \lambda . \sigma = N_0c\text{`}\lambda$
[*301·102 . *73·71·72]

***301·104.** $\vdash : \sigma \in \text{Cl}\text{`}(U \upharpoonright t^3\text{`}R) . \equiv . (\sigma +_c 1) \cap t^2\text{`}R \in \text{NC induct} - \iota\text{`}\Lambda$
[*301·101 . *300·14]

***301·105.** $\vdash : \sigma \in \text{Cl}\text{`}(U \upharpoonright t^3\text{`}R) . \equiv . (\exists \lambda) . \lambda \in \text{Cls induct} . R \in \lambda . \sigma +_c 1 = N_0c\text{`}\lambda$
[*301·104]

***301·106.** $\vdash : \sigma \in \text{G}'(U \upharpoonleft t^{3}{}'R) . \equiv . (\exists\lambda) . \lambda \in \text{Cls induct} . R \in t_0{}'\lambda . \sigma +_c 1 = \text{N}_0\text{c}'\lambda$
[*301·104]

***301·107.** $\vdash : \sigma \in \text{G}'(U \upharpoonleft t^{3}{}'R) . \equiv . \sigma \in \text{NC ind} . R \in s'(\sigma +_c 1)$
[*301·106 . *126·1]

***301·11.** $\vdash : \sigma \in \text{G}'(U \upharpoonleft t^{3}{}'R) . \equiv . \text{E} ! R_p{}'(Q \downarrow \sigma)$ [*301·1]

***301·12.** $\vdash : M \in \text{num}(R) . \supset . (\exists P, \sigma) . P \in \text{Potid}'R . \sigma \in C'U \cap t^{3}{}'R . M = P \downarrow \sigma$
[*95·22]

***301·13.** $\vdash : P \downarrow 0 \in \text{num}(R) . \supset . P = I \upharpoonright C'R$

Dem.

$\vdash . *90{\cdot}31 . (*301{\cdot}02) . \supset$

$\vdash : P \downarrow \mu \in \text{num}(R) - \iota'\{(I \upharpoonright C'R) \downarrow 0\} . \supset .$

$(P \downarrow \mu) \{(R_p)_* \,|\, R_p\} \{(I \upharpoonright C'R) \downarrow 0\} .$

$[*30{\cdot}33 . *301{\cdot}1] \supset . (P \downarrow \mu) (R_p)_* (R \downarrow 1) .$

$[*95{\cdot}22] \quad \supset . \mu U_* 1 .$

$[*300{\cdot}24] \quad \supset . \mu \neq 0$ (1)

$\vdash . (1) . \text{Transp} . \supset \vdash . \text{Prop}$

***301·14.** $\vdash : P \downarrow \mu, Q \downarrow \mu \in \text{num}(R) . \supset . P = Q$

Dem.

$\vdash . *120{\cdot}124 . *90{\cdot}31 . \supset$

$\vdash : \{S \downarrow (\mu +_c 1)\} (R_p)_* \{(I \upharpoonright C'R) \downarrow 0\} . \supset .$

$\{S \downarrow (\mu +_c 1)\} \{R_p \,|\, (R_p)_*\} \{(I \upharpoonright C'R) \downarrow 0\}$ (1)

$\vdash . (1) . (*301{\cdot}02) . *301{\cdot}12 . *300{\cdot}14 . \supset$

$\vdash : S \downarrow (\mu +_c 1) \in \text{num}(R) . \supset . S \downarrow (\mu +_c 1) \in R_p{}''\text{num}(R) . \exists ! \mu +_c 1 .$

[*301·1]

$\supset . (\exists P, \nu) . P \downarrow \nu \in \text{num}(R) . S \downarrow (\mu +_c 1) = (P \,|\, R) \downarrow (\nu +_c 1) . \exists ! \mu +_c 1 .$

[*55·202 . *120·311]

$\supset . (\exists P) . P \downarrow \mu \in \text{num}(R) . S \downarrow (\mu +_c 1) = (P \,|\, R) \downarrow (\mu +_c 1)$ (2)

$\vdash . (2) . \supset \vdash :. P \downarrow \mu, Q \downarrow \mu \in \text{num}(R) . \supset_{P,Q} . P = Q : \supset :$

$S \downarrow (\mu +_c 1), T \downarrow (\mu +_c 1) \in \text{num}(R) . \supset_{S,T} . S = T$ (3)

$\vdash . (3) . *301{\cdot}12{\cdot}13 . \text{Induct} . \supset \vdash . \text{Prop}$

***301·141.** $\vdash . \text{G}'\dot{s}'\text{num}(R) = C'U \cap t^{3}{}'R$

Dem.

$\vdash . *301{\cdot}1 . \supset$

$\vdash : \sigma \in \text{G}'U \cap t^{3}{}'R . \sigma \in \text{G}'\dot{s}'\text{num}(R) . \supset . (\sigma +_c 1) \in \text{G}'\dot{s}'\text{num}(R)$ (1)

$\vdash . (1) . *300{\cdot}14 . \text{Induct} . \supset \vdash . \text{Prop}$

***301·15.** $\vdash . \dot{s}\text{‘num}(R) \epsilon 1 \to \text{Cls}$

Dem.

$\vdash . *301\cdot14 . \supset \vdash : M, N \epsilon \text{num}(R) . \exists ! \text{D‘}M \cap \text{D‘}N . \supset . M = N$ (1)

$\vdash . (1) . *72\cdot32 . \supset \vdash . \text{Prop}$

***301·16.** $\vdash : \mu \epsilon C\text{‘}U \cap t^3\text{‘}R . \equiv . \text{E} ! R^\mu$ [*301·141·15 . (*301·03)]

***301·2.** $\vdash . R^0 = I \upharpoonright C\text{‘}R . R^1 = R$ [*301·13·16·1 . (*301·03)]

***301·201.** $\vdash : \nu \epsilon C\text{‘}U \cap t^3\text{‘}R . \supset . (R^\nu \downarrow \nu) \epsilon \text{num}(R)$

Dem.

$\vdash . *301\cdot16 . (*301\cdot03) . \supset \vdash : \text{Hp} . \supset . R^\nu \{\dot{s}\text{‘num}(R)\} \nu .$

[*41·11] $\supset . (\exists M) . M \epsilon \text{num}(R) . R^\nu M \nu .$

[*301·12] $\supset . (\exists M, P, \sigma) . M \epsilon \text{num}(R) . M = P \downarrow \sigma . R^\nu M \nu .$

[*55·13] $\supset . (R^\nu \downarrow \nu) \epsilon \text{num}(R) : \supset \vdash . \text{Prop}$

***301·21.** $\vdash : \nu \epsilon \text{D‘}U \cap t^3\text{‘}R . \supset . R^{\nu +_c 1} = R^\nu | R$

Dem.

$\vdash . *301\cdot1\cdot201 . \supset \vdash : \text{Hp} . \supset . R^{\nu +_c 1} \downarrow (\nu +_c 1), (R^\nu | R) \downarrow (\nu +_c 1) \epsilon \text{num}(R) .$

[*301·14] $\supset . R^{\nu +_c 1} = R^\nu | R : \supset \vdash . \text{Prop}$

***301·22.** $\vdash : \text{E} ! R^\nu . \supset . R^\nu \epsilon \text{Potid‘}R$ [*301·201·12·16]

***301·23.** $\vdash : \mu +_c \nu \epsilon C\text{‘}U \cap t^3\text{‘}R . \supset . R^{\mu +_c \nu} = R^\mu | R^\nu = R^\nu | R^\mu$
[*301·21 . Induct]

***301·24.** $\vdash :. \sigma \epsilon \text{NC ind} : \mu \leqslant \sigma . \nu < \mu . \supset_{\mu, \nu} . R^\mu \neq R^\nu : \supset .$
$\hat{P} \{(\exists \mu) . \mu \leqslant \sigma . P = R^\mu\} \epsilon \sigma +_c 1$

Dem.

$\vdash . *120\cdot442 . \supset \vdash : \text{Hp} . \mu \leqslant \sigma . \nu \leqslant \sigma . R^\mu = R^\nu . \supset . \mu = \nu$ (1)

$\vdash . (1) . *73\cdot14 . *301\cdot15 . \supset$

$\vdash : \text{Hp} . \supset . \text{Nc‘}\hat{P} \{(\exists \mu) . \mu \leqslant \sigma . P = R^\mu\} = \text{Nc‘}\hat{\mu}(\mu \leqslant \sigma)$ (2)

$\vdash . (2) . *120\cdot57 . \supset \vdash . \text{Prop}$

***301·241.** $\vdash : \text{Hp } *301\cdot24 . \supset . \sigma \cap t^{2}\text{‘}R \epsilon \text{D‘}(U \upharpoonright t^3\text{‘}R) . R^{\sigma +_c 1} = R^\sigma | R$
[*301·24·104·21]

***301·242.** $\vdash : \sigma \epsilon C\text{‘}U \cap t^3\text{‘}R . \mu \leqslant \sigma . \nu < \mu . R^\mu = R^\nu . \supset . R^\sigma | R = R^{\sigma -_c \mu +_c \nu +_c}$

Dem.

$\vdash . *120\cdot412\cdot416 . \supset \vdash : \text{Hp} . \supset . \sigma = (\sigma -_c \mu) +_c \mu .$

[*301·23] $\supset . R^\sigma = R^{\sigma -_c \mu} | R^\mu .$

[Hp.*301·21] $\supset . R^\sigma | R = R^{\sigma -_c \mu} | R^{\nu +_c 1}$

[*301·23] $= R^{\sigma -_c \mu +_c \nu +_c 1} : \supset \vdash . \text{Prop}$

***301·25.** $\vdash : (\exists \sigma) . P = R^\sigma . \supset . (\exists \tau) . P \mid R = R^\tau$ [*301·16·241·242]

***301·26.** $\vdash : P \in \text{Potid}`R . \equiv . (\exists \sigma) . P = R^\sigma$

Dem.

$\vdash . *301·25·2 . \text{Induct} . \supset \vdash : P \in \text{Potid}`R . \supset . (\exists \sigma) . P = R^\sigma$ (1)

$\vdash . (1) . *301·22 . \supset \vdash . \text{Prop}$

***301·3.** $\vdash : R \mathrel{G} I . \sigma \in C`U \cap t^{3}`R . \supset . R^\sigma = R = R_0 = I \upharpoonright C`R$
[*300·312 . *301·16·26]

***301·31.** $\vdash : R \mathrel{G} I . \sigma \neq 0 . \supset . R_\sigma = \dot{\Lambda}$ [*300·48]

The above proposition is the same as *300·48, but is repeated here to show the relations of R_σ and R^σ.

***301·32.** $\vdash :. R \mathrel{G} I . \dot{\exists} ! R . \supset : \dot{\exists} ! R_\sigma . \equiv . \sigma = 0$ [*300·311 . *301·31]

***301·4.** $\vdash : R \in \text{Rel num} . \sigma \in C`U \cap t^{3}`R . \supset . R_\sigma = R^\sigma$

Dem.

$\vdash . *301·2 . *121·302 . \supset \vdash : \text{Hp} . \supset . R_0 = R^0$ (1)

$\vdash . *301·21 . *121·332 . \supset$

$\vdash :. \text{Hp} . \sigma \in C`U \cap t^{3}`R . \supset : R_\sigma = R^\sigma . \supset . R_{\sigma +_c 1} = R^{\sigma +_c 1}$ (2)

$\vdash . (1) . (2) . \text{Induct} . \supset \vdash . \text{Prop}$

***301·41.** $\vdash : R, S \in \text{Rel num} . \dot{\exists} ! R^\mu \dot{\cap} R^\nu . \supset . \mu = \nu . \exists ! (\mu +_c 1) \cap t`C`R$
[*301·4·16 . *300·55]

***301·5.** $\vdash : \mu \times_c \nu \in C`U \cap t^{3}`R . \mu \neq 0 . \nu \neq 0 . \supset . (R^\mu)^\nu = R^{\mu \times_c \nu}$

Dem.

$\vdash . *117·62·32 . \quad \supset \vdash : \text{Hp} . \supset . \mu, \nu \in C`U \cap t^{3}`R$ (1)

$\vdash . (1) . *301·16·2 . \supset \vdash : \text{Hp} . \supset . (R^\mu)^1 = R^{\mu \times_c 1}$ (2)

$\vdash . *301·23 . \quad \supset \vdash : \nu +_c 1 \in C`U \cap t^{3}`R . \supset . (R^\mu)^{\nu +_c 1} = (R^\mu)^\nu \mid R^\mu$ (3)

$\vdash . (3) . *301·23 . \supset$

$\vdash : (\mu \times_c \nu) +_c \mu \in C`U \cap t^{3}`R . (R^\mu)^\nu = R^{\mu \times_c \nu} . \supset . (R^\mu)^{\nu +_c 1} = R^{(\mu \times_c \nu) +_c \mu}$ (4)

$\vdash . (4) . *113·671 . \supset$

$\vdash :. (R^\mu)^\nu = R^{\mu \times_c \nu} . \supset : \mu \times_c (\nu +_c 1) \in C`U \cap t^{3}`R . \supset . (R^\mu)^{\nu +_c 1} = R^{\mu \times_c (\nu +_c 1)}$ (5)

$\vdash . *117·571·32 . \supset \vdash : \mu \times_c (\nu +_c 1) \in C`U \cap t^{3}`R . \supset . \mu \times_c \nu \in C`U \cap t^{3}`R$ (6)

$\vdash . (5) . (6) . \supset \vdash :. \mu \times_c \nu \in C`U \cap t^{3}`R . \supset . (R^\mu)^\nu = R^{\mu \times_c \nu} : \supset :$

$\mu \times_c (\nu +_c 1) \in C`U \cap t^{3}`R . \supset . (R^\mu)^{\nu +_c 1} = R^{\mu \times_c (\nu +_c 1)}$ (7)

$\vdash . (1) . (2) . (7) . \text{Induct} . \supset \vdash . \text{Prop}$

***301·501.** $\vdash : \mu = 0 . \nu \in C`U \cap t^{3}`R . \supset . (R^\mu)^\nu = R^{\mu \times_c \nu}$ [*301·2·3]

***301·502.** $\vdash : \mu, \nu \in C`U \cap t^{2}`C`R . \supset . \mu \times_c \nu \in C`U \cap t^{3}`R . (\mu \times_c \nu) \cap t^{2}`R \in C`U$

Dem.

$\vdash . *300·14 . *120·5 . \supset \vdash : \text{Hp} . \exists ! (\mu \times_c \nu) \cap t^{2}`R . \supset . (\mu \times_c \nu) \cap t^{2}`R \in C`U$ (1)

$\vdash . *300·14 . \quad \supset \vdash : \text{Hp} . \supset . (\exists \alpha, \beta) . \alpha \in \mu . \beta \in \nu . \alpha, \beta \in t`C`R .$

[*113·251] $\quad \supset . (\exists \alpha, \beta) . \alpha \times \beta \in \mu \times_c \nu . \alpha, \beta \in t`C`R .$

[*113·17.*64·61] $\quad \supset . (\exists \alpha, \beta) . \alpha \times \beta \in (\mu \times_c \nu) \cap t^{2}`R$ (2)

$\vdash . (1) . (2) . *65·13 . \supset \vdash . \text{Prop}$

***301·503.** $\vdash : \nu \in \mathrm{NC\,ind} . \nu \cap t'C'R \in C'U \upharpoonright (t^2{}'C'R) . \supset . \nu \cap t^2{}'R \in C'(U \upharpoonright t^3{}'R)$

Dem.

$\vdash . *300{\cdot}14 . \supset \vdash : \mathrm{Hp} . \supset . (\exists \alpha) . \alpha \in \nu \cap t'C'R .$

$[*106{\cdot}2] \quad \supset . (\exists x, \alpha) . \downarrow x''\alpha \in \nu \cap t^2{}'R \quad (1)$

$\vdash . (1) . *300{\cdot}14 . \supset \vdash . \mathrm{Prop}$

***301·504.** $\vdash : \mu, \nu \in C'U \cap t^2{}'C'R . \nu \neq 0 . \supset . (R^\mu)^\nu = R^{\mu \times_c \nu}$

$[*301{\cdot}5{\cdot}501{\cdot}502{\cdot}503]$

***301·505.** $\vdash :. \xi \in \mathrm{D}'U . \supset : \dot{\exists} ! \{(+_c \xi) \upharpoonright C'U\}^\nu . \equiv . \xi \times_c \nu \in C'U$

Dem.

$\vdash . *120{\cdot}452 . \supset \vdash : \dot{\exists} ! \{(+_c \xi) \upharpoonright C'U\}^\nu . \equiv . \dot{\exists} ! \{(+_c \xi) \upharpoonright C'U\}^\nu . \xi \in C'U .$

$[*300{\cdot}232] \quad \equiv . \dot{\exists} ! (U_\xi)^\nu . \xi \in C'U \quad (1)$

$\vdash . (1) . *300{\cdot}52 . *301{\cdot}4 . \supset$

$\vdash :. \mathrm{Hp} . \supset : \dot{\exists} ! \{(+_c \xi) \upharpoonright C'U\}^\nu . \equiv . \dot{\exists} ! (U_\xi)_\nu . \xi \in C'U .$

$[*300{\cdot}572] \quad \equiv . \xi \times_c \nu \in C'U :. \supset \vdash . \mathrm{Prop}$

***301·51.** $\vdash :. \xi, \eta \in \mathrm{D}'U . \supset : \dot{\exists} ! \{(+_c \xi) \upharpoonright C'U\}^\nu \dot{\cap} \{(+_c \eta) \upharpoonright C'U\}^\mu . \equiv .$

$\xi \times_c \nu \in C'U . \xi \times_c \nu = \eta \times_c \mu$

Dem.

$\vdash . *301{\cdot}505 . *300{\cdot}232 . *301{\cdot}4 . \supset$

$\vdash :. \mathrm{Hp} . \supset : \dot{\exists} ! \{(+_c \xi) \upharpoonright C'U\}^\nu \dot{\cap} \{(+_c \eta) \upharpoonright C'U\}^\mu . \equiv . \dot{\exists} ! (U_\xi)_\nu \dot{\cap} (U_\eta)_\mu .$

$[*300{\cdot}571] \quad \equiv . \xi \times_c \nu \in C'U . \xi \times_c \nu = \eta \times_c \mu :. \supset \vdash . \mathrm{Prop}$

***301·52.** $\vdash : \nu \in \mathrm{D}'U \cap t^3{}'R . \supset . (\times_c \mu)^\nu = \times_c (\mu^\nu)$

Dem.

$\vdash . *301{\cdot}2 . *113{\cdot}204 . *116{\cdot}204{\cdot}321 . \supset \vdash . (\times_c \mu)^1 = \times_c (\mu^1) \quad (1)$

$\vdash . *301{\cdot}21 . \supset \vdash : \nu \in \text{Ɑ}'U \cap t^3{}'R . \supset . (\times_c \mu)^{\nu +_c 1} = (\times_c \mu)^\nu \,|\, (\times_c \mu) \quad (2)$

$\vdash . (2) . \supset \vdash : \nu \in \text{Ɑ}'U \cap t^3{}'R . (\times_c \mu)^\nu = \times_c (\mu^\nu) . \supset . (\times_c \mu)^{\nu +_c 1} = \times_c (\mu^\nu) \,|\, (\times_c \mu)$

$[*116{\cdot}52{\cdot}321] \quad = \times_c (\mu^{\nu +_c 1}) \quad (3)$

$\vdash . (1) . (3) . \mathrm{Induct} . \supset \vdash . \mathrm{Prop}$

*302. ON RELATIVE PRIMES.

Summary of *302.

The present number is merely preparatory for the definition and discussion of ratios. We want, of course, to give a definition of ratio which shall ensure that $\mu/\nu = (\mu \times_c \tau)/(\nu \times_c \tau)$. Hence in defining μ/ν in any given type, we cannot exact that μ and ν themselves should exist in that type, but only that, if ρ/σ is the same ratio in its lowest terms, ρ and σ should exist in that type. Hence, if we are not to assume the axiom of infinity, it is necessary to deal with relative primes before defining ratios.

The theory of relative primes is concerned with typically indefinite inductive cardinals (NC ind). It will be observed that we have three different sorts of inductive cardinals, namely NC ind, NC induct, and C‘U. NC ind consists of typically indefinite cardinals, NC induct consists of all cardinals of some one type, and C‘U consists of all *existent* cardinals of some one type. If the axiom of infinity holds, we have C‘U = NC induct, and NC ind = sm‘‘NC induct. But neither of these is true if the axiom of infinity does not hold. It will be found that, where we require typically definite cardinals, it is C‘U or Ɑ‘U or D‘U that we require, not NC induct; that is to say, we almost always want to exclude Λ, and sometimes we want to exclude the greatest existent cardinal of the type in question, or to exclude 0. Thus "NC induct" will seldom occur in what follows. The cases in which C‘U or D‘U or Ɑ‘U occurs are of two sorts: (1) where we are proving typically definite existent-theorems, (2) where we are concerned with *series*, as *e.g.* in *300, where we considered the series of existent cardinals, or in *304 below, where we shall consider the series of ratios. Wherever *series* are concerned, we must have typical definiteness, because the definition of "$P \epsilon$ Ser" involves C‘P, and therefore only a *homogeneous* relation can be serial. This is a particular instance of the fact that when we require numbers as apparent variables (as *e.g.* in the theory of real numbers), typical definiteness becomes essential. Many propositions containing the hypothesis "$\mu \epsilon$ NC ind" (where μ is a real variable) do not allow of μ being turned into an apparent variable, because this requires that μ should be fixed in one type, and our original proposition may demand that the type in which μ is fixed should be a function of μ. For example, *300·17 states

$$\vdash : \mu \epsilon \text{NC ind} . \supset . (\exists \alpha) . \mu \epsilon C`(U \upharpoonright t^2`\alpha).$$

If we fix the type of μ, we thereby also fix the type of α, and the proposition becomes false unless the axiom of infinity is true. In fact, the proposition demands that, the greater μ becomes, the higher must the type of α become. "NC ind" is not a strictly correct idea, and the primitive proposition *9·13 does not apply without reserve to propositions in which it occurs. We have introduced it because it immensely simplifies the expression of many propositions, and because it is easy to avoid the errors to which it might give rise if used without remembering that it is a concession to convenience.

It will be found that, when we are not concerned with existence-theorems, or with numbers as apparent variables, "NC ind" is almost always the notion required. This applies to all cases where we are only concerned with addition, multiplication, subtraction and division; it applies to ratios except when ratios are considered as forming a series, or when we are investigating their existence. As regards the use of an "NC ind" as an apparent variable, there is a distinction between "all values" and "some value." If we have "$\rho \epsilon$ NC ind," "$(\exists \rho)$" will often be legitimate when "(ρ)" is not. The reason of this is that, if we are to fix upon one typically indefinite cardinal, it will be possible to assign one definite type in which it exists; *e.g.* there are at least two classes four classes of classes, sixteen classes of classes of classes, and so on. But if we are making a statement about *all* typically indefinite inductive cardinals, it will not be true unless there is a type such that our statement holds of all inductive cardinals in this type.

In virtue of *300·17, if we have "$\rho \epsilon$ NC ind," we may replace it by "$\rho \epsilon C`U$" if we may take U in as high a type as we please, or if, on account of the rest of our proposition, ρ cannot be greater than some assigned inductive cardinal so long as the hypothesis of our proposition is true.

The above remarks will enable the reader to test the uses of typically indefinite inductive cardinals as apparent variables, and the passage from propositions concerning NC ind to propositions concerning $C`U$.

We define ρ as prime to σ when both are typically indefinite cardinals and 1 is their only common factor, *i.e.* we put

***302·01.** $\text{Prm} = \hat{\rho}\hat{\sigma} \{\rho, \sigma \epsilon \text{NC ind} : \rho = \xi \times_c \tau . \sigma = \eta \times_c \tau . \supset_{\xi, \eta, \tau} . \tau = 1\}$ Df

In this definition, ξ, η, τ may be taken to be typically indefinite cardinals, because, when $\rho = \xi \times_c \tau . \sigma = \eta \times_c \tau$, we must have $\xi \leqslant \rho . \eta \leqslant \sigma . \tau \leqslant \rho . \tau \leqslant \sigma$, so that ξ, η, τ cannot grow indefinitely (with a given ρ and σ) while the hypothesis remains true.

We define "$(\rho, \sigma) \text{Prm}_\tau (\mu, \nu)$" as meaning that ρ is prime to σ, that τ is not zero, and $\mu = \rho \times_c \tau . \nu = \sigma \times_c \tau$, *i.e.* ρ/σ is μ/ν in its lowest terms, and τ is the highest common factor of μ and ν. The definition is:

***302·02.** $(\rho, \sigma) \operatorname{Prm}_\tau (\mu, \nu) . = .$

$$\rho \operatorname{Prm} \sigma . \tau \epsilon \text{NC ind} - \iota\text{‘}0 . \mu = \rho \times_c \tau . \nu = \sigma \times_c \tau \quad \text{Df}$$

We then put further

***302·03.** $(\rho, \sigma) \operatorname{Prm} (\mu, \nu) . = . (\exists \tau) . (\rho, \sigma) \operatorname{Prm}_\tau (\mu, \nu)$ Df

Here again there is no objection to τ as an apparent variable, because τ must be not greater than μ and ν. "$(\rho, \sigma) \operatorname{Prm} (\mu, \nu)$" secures that ρ/σ is μ/ν in its lowest terms.

We also define, in this number, the lowest common multiple and the highest common factor.

Our definition of "Prm" is so framed that every inductive cardinal is prime to 1 (*302·12), that 1 is the only number which is prime to itself (*302·13), and the only number which is prime to 0 (*302·14).

After a number of preliminary propositions, we arrive at the result that if μ and ν are not both zero, and ξ and η are not both zero, the existence of a couple ρ, σ which is prime both to μ, ν and to ξ, η is equivalent to $\mu \times_c \eta = \nu \times_c \xi$, *i.e.*

***302·34.** $\vdash :. \mu, \nu, \xi, \eta \epsilon \text{NC ind} . \sim (\mu = \nu = 0) . \sim (\xi = \eta = 0) . \supset :$

$$\mu \times_c \eta = \nu \times_c \xi . \equiv . (\exists \rho, \sigma) . (\rho, \sigma) \operatorname{Prm} (\mu, \nu) . (\rho, \sigma) \operatorname{Prm} (\xi, \eta)$$

We have also

***302·33.** $\vdash : \mu, \nu \epsilon \text{NC ind} . \sim (\mu = \nu = 0) . \equiv . (\exists \rho, \sigma) . (\rho, \sigma) \operatorname{Prm} (\mu, \nu)$

***302·38.** $\vdash : (\rho, \sigma) \operatorname{Prm} (\mu, \nu) . (\xi, \eta) \operatorname{Prm} (\mu, \nu) . \supset . \rho = \xi . \sigma = \eta$

I.e. there is only one way of reducing a fraction to its lowest terms.

We prove also (*302·15) that if μ, ν are typically indefinite cardinals, which both exist in the type of λ (*i.e.* $\mu_\lambda, \nu_\lambda \epsilon C\text{‘}U$), then

$$(\rho, \sigma) \operatorname{Prm} (\mu, \nu) . \equiv . (\rho, \sigma) \operatorname{Prm} (\mu_\lambda, \nu_\lambda).$$

This enables us, when we wish, to substitute typically definite cardinals for the typically indefinite μ and ν.

***302·01.** $\operatorname{Prm} = \hat{\rho} \hat{\sigma} \{\rho, \sigma \epsilon \text{NC ind} : \rho = \xi \times_c \tau . \sigma = \eta \times_c \tau . \supset_{\xi, \eta, \tau} . \tau = 1\}$ Df

***302·02.** $(\rho, \sigma) \operatorname{Prm}_\tau (\mu, \nu) . = .$

$$\rho \operatorname{Prm} \sigma . \tau \epsilon \text{NC ind} - \iota\text{‘}0 . \mu = \rho \times_c \tau . \nu = \sigma \times_c \tau \quad \text{Df}$$

Here μ, ν are to be typically indefinite in the same way as $\rho \times_c \tau$ and $\sigma \times_c \tau$. Thus if, in some one type, $\rho \times_c \tau$ and $\sigma \times_c \tau$ are both null, that does not justify us in writing $(\rho, \sigma) \operatorname{Prm}_\tau (\Lambda, \Lambda)$, because there are other types in which $\rho \times_c \tau$ and $\sigma \times_c \tau$ are not null. On this subject, cf. *126.

***302·03.** $(\rho, \sigma) \operatorname{Prm} (\mu, \nu) . = . (\exists \tau) . (\rho, \sigma) \operatorname{Prm}_\tau (\mu, \nu)$ Df

***302·04.** $\text{hcf} (\mu, \nu) = (\imath \tau) \{(\exists \rho, \sigma) . (\rho, \sigma) \operatorname{Prm}_\tau (\mu, \nu)\}$ Df

***302·05.** $\text{lcm} (\mu, \nu) = (\imath \xi) \{(\exists \rho, \sigma, \tau) . (\rho, \sigma) \operatorname{Prm}_\tau (\mu, \nu) . \xi = \rho \times_c \sigma \times_c \tau\}$ Df

***302·1.** $\vdash :. \rho \,\mathrm{Prm}\, \sigma . \equiv : \rho, \sigma \in \mathrm{NC\ ind} : \rho = \xi \times_c \tau . \sigma = \eta \times_c \tau . \supset_{\xi, \eta, \tau} . \tau = 1$ [(*302·01)]

***302·11.** $\vdash : \rho \,\mathrm{Prm}\, \sigma . \equiv . \sigma \,\mathrm{Prm}\, \rho$ [*302·1]

***302·12.** $\vdash : \rho \,\mathrm{Prm}\, 1 . \equiv . \rho \in \mathrm{NC\ ind}$ [*302·1 . *117·631·61]

***302·13.** $\vdash : \rho \,\mathrm{Prm}\, \rho . \equiv . \rho = 1$

Dem.

$\vdash .$ *302·12 $. \supset \vdash : \rho = 1 . \supset . \rho \,\mathrm{Prm}\, \rho$ (1)

$\vdash .$ *302·1 $. \supset \vdash :. \rho \,\mathrm{Prm}\, \rho . \supset : \rho = 1 \times_c \rho . \supset . \rho = 1 :$

[*113·621] $\supset : \rho = 1$ (2)

$\vdash . (1) . (2) . \supset \vdash .$ Prop

***302·14.** $\vdash : 0 \,\mathrm{Prm}\, \mu . \equiv . \mu = 1$

Dem.

$\vdash .$ *302·12 $. \supset \vdash : \mu = 1 . \supset . 0 \,\mathrm{Prm}\, \mu$ (1)

$\vdash .$ *302·1 $. \supset \vdash :. 0 \,\mathrm{Prm}\, \mu . \supset : 0 = 0 \times_c \mu . \mu = 1 \times_c \mu . \supset . \mu = 1 :$

[*113·601·621] $\supset : \mu = 1$ (2)

$\vdash . (1) . (2) . \supset \vdash .$ Prop

***302·15.** $\vdash :. \mu, \nu \in \mathrm{NC\ ind} . \mu_\lambda, \nu_\lambda \in C{\text{‘}}U . \supset :$

$(\rho, \sigma) \,\mathrm{Prm}\, (\mu, \nu) . \equiv . (\rho, \sigma) \,\mathrm{Prm}\, (\mu_\lambda, \nu_\lambda)$

Dem.

$\vdash .$ *126·101 . *300·14 $. \supset$

$\vdash :. \mathrm{Hp} . \supset : \rho \,\mathrm{Prm}\, \sigma . \tau \in \mathrm{NC\ ind} - \iota{\text{‘}}0 . \mu = \rho \times_c \tau . \nu = \sigma \times_c \tau . \equiv .$

$\rho \,\mathrm{Prm}\, \sigma . \tau \in \mathrm{NC\ ind} - \iota{\text{‘}}0 . \mu_\lambda = \rho \times_c \tau . \nu_\lambda = \sigma \times_c \tau$ (1)

$\vdash . (1) .$ (*302·02·03) $. \supset \vdash .$ Prop

***302·2.** $\vdash : \mu, \nu \in C{\text{‘}}U . \sim(\mu = \nu = 0) . \kappa = \hat{\tau}\{(\exists \rho, \sigma) . \mu = \rho \times_c \tau . \nu = \sigma \times_c \tau\} . \supset .$

$\mathrm{E}\,!\, \max(\breve{U}){\text{‘}}\kappa . \max(\breve{U}){\text{‘}}\kappa \in \mathrm{D}{\text{‘}}U$

Dem.

$\vdash .$ *113·621 $. \supset \vdash : \mathrm{Hp} . \supset . 1 \in \kappa$ (1)

$\vdash .$ *117·62 . *113·602 . Transp $. \supset$

$\vdash :. \mathrm{Hp} . \tau \in \kappa . \supset : \tau \leqslant \mu . \vee . \tau \leqslant \nu$ (2)

$\vdash . (1) . (2) .$ *300·21·22 . *261·26 . *300·26 $. \supset \vdash .$ Prop

In the above proposition we write "$\max(\breve{U}){\text{‘}}\kappa$" rather than "$\min(U){\text{‘}}\kappa$," because, since U arranges the natural numbers in *descending* order, "$\min(U){\text{‘}}\kappa$" is the *greatest* number which is a member of κ, and therefore it is less confusing to speak of this number as "$\max(\breve{U}){\text{‘}}\kappa$."

***302·21.** $\vdash : \text{Hp} *302\cdot2 . \tau = \max(\breve{U})`\kappa . \mu = \rho \times_c \tau . \nu = \sigma \times_c \tau . \supset .$
$(\rho, \sigma) \,\text{Prm}_\tau\, (\mu, \nu)$

Dem.

$\vdash . *13\cdot12 . \supset \vdash : \text{Hp} . \rho = \rho' \times_c \tau' . \sigma = \sigma' \times_c \tau' . \supset .$
$\mu = \rho' \times_c \tau' \times_c \tau . \nu = \sigma' \times_c \tau' \times_c \tau .$
$[*113\cdot602.\text{Transp.Hp}] \supset . \tau' \times_c \tau \neq 0 . \tau' \times_c \tau \leqslant \tau .$
$[*120\cdot511.*117\cdot62] \quad \supset . \tau' = 1$ (1)
$\vdash . (1) . *302\cdot1 . \supset \vdash : \text{Hp} . \supset . \rho \,\text{Prm}\, \sigma$ (2)
$\vdash . (2) . *302\cdot2 . (*302\cdot02) . \supset \vdash . \text{Prop}$

***302·22.** $\vdash :. \mu, \nu \in \text{NC ind} . \sim(\mu = \nu = 0) . \supset : (\exists \rho, \sigma, \tau) . (\rho, \sigma) \,\text{Prm}_\tau\, (\mu, \nu) :$
$(\exists \rho, \sigma) . (\rho, \sigma) \,\text{Prm}\, (\mu, \nu)$

$[*302\cdot2\cdot21 . *300\cdot17 . (*302\cdot03)]$

***302·23.** $\vdash :. \mu, \nu \in \text{D}`U . \supset : (\exists \rho, \sigma) : \rho, \sigma \in \text{D}`U . \mu \times_c \sigma = \nu \times_c \rho :$
$\xi, \eta \in \text{D}`U . \mu \times_c \eta = \nu \times_c \xi . \supset_{\xi,\eta} . \xi \geqslant \rho . \eta \geqslant \sigma$

Dem.

$\vdash . *300\cdot23 . *113\cdot27 . \supset$
$\vdash : \text{Hp} . \kappa = \text{D}`U \cap \hat{\rho}\{(\exists \sigma) . \mu \times_c \sigma = \nu \times_c \rho\} . \supset . \text{E}! \min(\breve{U})`\kappa$ (1)
$\vdash . (1) . *300\cdot12 . \supset$
$\vdash :. \text{Hp} . \supset : (\exists \rho, \sigma) : \rho, \sigma \in \text{D}`U . \mu \times_c \sigma = \nu \times_c \rho :$
$\xi, \eta \in \text{D}`U . \mu \times_c \eta = \nu \times_c \xi . \supset_{\xi,\eta} . \xi \geqslant \rho$ (2)
$\vdash . *120\cdot51 . \supset$
$\vdash : \text{Hp} . \rho, \sigma \in \text{D}`U . \mu \times_c \sigma = \nu \times_c \rho . \mu \times_c \eta = \nu \times_c \xi . \supset . \rho \times_c \eta = \sigma \times_c \xi$ (3)
$\vdash . *117\cdot571 . \supset \vdash : \text{Hp}(3) . \xi, \eta \in \text{D}`U . \xi \geqslant \rho . \supset . \xi \times_c \sigma \geqslant \rho \times_c \sigma$ (4)
$\vdash . *126\cdot51 . \supset \vdash : \text{Hp}(4) . \sigma > \eta . \supset . \rho \times_c \sigma > \rho \times_c \eta$ (5)
$\vdash . (4) . (5) . \supset \vdash :. \text{Hp}(4) . \supset : \sigma > \eta . \supset . \xi \times_c \sigma > \rho \times_c \eta :$
$[\text{Transp}] \quad \supset : \xi \times_c \sigma = \rho \times_c \eta . \supset . \eta \geqslant \sigma$ (6)
$\vdash . (2) . (3) . (6) . \supset \vdash . \text{Prop}$

***302·24.** $\vdash :. \mu, \nu, \rho, \sigma \in \text{NC ind} - \iota`0 . \mu \times_c \sigma = \nu \times_c \rho :$
$\mu \times_c \eta = \nu \times_c \xi . \xi, \eta \in \text{D}`U . \supset_{\xi,\eta} . \xi \geqslant \rho . \eta \geqslant \sigma : \supset . \rho \,\text{Prm}\, \sigma$

Dem.

$\vdash . *302\cdot1 . \supset$
$\vdash : \rho, \sigma \in \text{D}`U . \sim(\rho \,\text{Prm}\, \sigma) . \supset . (\exists \xi, \eta, \tau) . \tau \neq 1 . \rho = \xi \times_c \tau . \sigma = \eta \times_c \tau$
$[*113\cdot203\cdot602.*120\cdot511.*117\cdot62]$
$\supset . (\exists \xi, \eta, \tau) . \xi, \eta, \tau \in \text{D}`U - \iota`1 . \xi < \rho . \eta < \sigma . \rho = \xi \times_c \tau . \sigma = \eta \times_c \tau$ (1)
$\vdash . *120\cdot51 . \supset \vdash : \mu, \nu, \rho, \sigma \in \text{D}`U . \mu \times_c \sigma = \nu \times_c \rho . \rho = \xi \times_c \tau . \sigma = \eta \times_c \tau . \supset .$
$\mu \times_c \eta = \nu \times_c \xi$ (2)
$\vdash . (1) . (2) . \supset \vdash : \mu, \nu, \rho, \sigma \in \text{D}`U . \mu \times_c \sigma = \nu \times_c \rho . \sim(\rho \,\text{Prm}\, \sigma) . \supset .$
$(\exists \xi, \eta) . \mu \times_c \eta = \nu \times_c \xi . \xi, \eta \in \text{D}`U . \xi < \rho . \eta < \sigma$ (3)
$\vdash . (3) . \text{Transp} . *300\cdot17 . \supset \vdash . \text{Prop}$

***302·25.** $\vdash : \rho, \xi \in \mathrm{D}`U . \supset . (\exists \alpha, \beta) . \alpha \in C`U . \beta < \xi . \rho = (\alpha \times_c \xi) +_c \beta$

Dem.

$\vdash . *117{\cdot}62 . *120{\cdot}428 . \supset \vdash : \mathrm{Hp} . \supset . \rho < (\rho +_c 1) \times_c \xi$ (1)

$\vdash . (1) . *300{\cdot}23 . \supset \vdash : \mathrm{Hp} . \supset . \mathrm{E} ! \min (\breve{U})`\hat{\alpha} \{\alpha \in C`U . \rho < (\alpha +_c 1) \times_c \xi\} .$

[*120·414·416] $\supset . (\exists \alpha) . \alpha \in C`U . \rho < (\alpha +_c 1) \times_c \xi . \rho \geqslant \alpha \times_c \xi .$

[*117·31.*120·452] $\supset . (\exists \alpha, \beta) . \alpha, \beta \in C`U . \rho < (\alpha +_c 1) \times_c \xi . \rho = (\alpha \times_c \xi) +_c \beta .$

[*113·671] $\supset . (\exists \alpha, \beta) . \alpha, \beta \in C`U . \rho < (\alpha \times_c \xi) +_c \xi . \rho = (\alpha \times_c \xi) +_c \beta .$

[*120·442.*117·561.Transp]

$\supset . (\exists \alpha, \beta) . \alpha \in C`U . \beta < \xi . \rho = (\alpha \times_c \xi) +_c \beta : \supset \vdash . \mathrm{Prop}$

***302·26.** $\vdash : \mathrm{Hp} *302{\cdot}24 . \supset . (\rho, \sigma) \mathrm{Prm} (\mu, \nu)$

Dem.

$\vdash . *302{\cdot}25 . \supset$

$\vdash : \mathrm{Hp} . \supset . (\exists \alpha, \beta, \gamma, \delta) . \mu = (\alpha \times_c \rho) +_c \beta . \nu = (\gamma \times_c \sigma) +_c \delta . \beta < \rho . \delta < \sigma$ (1)

$\vdash . *113{\cdot}43 . \supset$

$\vdash : \mu = (\alpha \times_c \rho) +_c \beta . \nu = (\gamma \times_c \sigma) +_c \delta . \beta < \rho . \delta < \sigma . \mu \times_c \sigma = \nu \times_c \rho . \supset .$

$(\alpha \times_c \rho \times_c \sigma) +_c (\beta \times_c \sigma) = (\gamma \times_c \rho \times_c \sigma) +_c (\delta \times_c \rho) . \beta < \rho . \delta < \sigma .$ (2)

[*117·31.*120·452.*113·671]

$\supset . \alpha \times_c \rho \times_c \sigma < (\gamma +_c 1) \times_c \rho \times_c \sigma . \gamma \times_c \rho \times_c \sigma < (\alpha +_c 1) \times_c \rho \times_c \sigma .$

[*126·51] $\supset . \alpha < \gamma +_c 1 . \gamma < \alpha +_c 1 .$

[*120·429·442.*117·25] $\supset . \alpha = \gamma$ (3)

$\vdash . (2) . (3) . *120{\cdot}41 . \supset \vdash : \mathrm{Hp} (2) . \supset . \beta \times_c \sigma = \delta \times_c \rho . \beta < \rho . \delta < \sigma .$

[Hp] $\supset . \beta = 0 . \delta = 0$ (4)

$\vdash . (3) . (4) . \supset \vdash : \mathrm{Hp} (2) . \supset . \mu = \alpha \times_c \rho . \nu = \alpha \times_c \sigma$ (5)

$\vdash . (1) . (5) . *302{\cdot}24 . \supset \vdash . \mathrm{Prop}$

***302·27.** $\vdash : \mu, \nu, \rho, \sigma, \xi, \eta \in \mathrm{NC\,ind} - \iota`0 . \mu \times_c \sigma = \nu \times_c \rho . \mu \times_c \eta = \nu \times_c \xi . \supset .$
$\xi \times_c \sigma = \eta \times_c \rho$

Dem.

$\vdash . *113{\cdot}27 . \supset \vdash : \mathrm{Hp} . \supset . \xi \times_c \nu \times_c \sigma = \eta \times_c \mu \times_c \sigma$

[Hp] $= \eta \times_c \nu \times_c \rho .$

[*126·41] $\supset . \xi \times_c \sigma = \eta \times_c \rho : \supset \vdash . \mathrm{Prop}$

***302·28.** $\vdash : \mathrm{Hp} *302{\cdot}24 . \xi, \eta \in \mathrm{NC\,ind} - \iota`0 . \mu \times_c \eta = \nu \times_c \xi . \supset .$
$(\rho, \sigma) \mathrm{Prm} (\xi, \eta)$ [*302·26·27 . *300·17]

***302·29.** $\vdash : \mathrm{Hp} *302{\cdot}28 . \xi \mathrm{Prm} \eta . \supset . \xi = \rho . \eta = \sigma$

Dem.

$\vdash . *302{\cdot}28{\cdot}1 . \supset$

$\vdash :. \mathrm{Hp} . \supset : (\exists \alpha) . \xi = \alpha \times_c \rho . \eta = \alpha \times_c \sigma : \xi = \alpha \times_c \rho . \eta = \alpha \times_c \sigma . \supset_\alpha . \alpha = 1 :$

[*14·122] $\supset : \xi = 1 \times_c \rho . \eta = 1 \times_c \sigma :. \supset \vdash . \mathrm{Prop}$

∗302·3. $\vdash : \mu, \nu, \xi, \eta \in \text{NC ind} - \iota`0 \,.\, \mu \times_c \eta = \nu \times_c \xi \,.\, \supset .$

$(\exists \rho, \sigma) \,.\, (\rho, \sigma) \text{ Prm } (\mu, \nu) \,.\, (\rho, \sigma) \text{ Prm } (\xi, \eta)$

Dem.

$\vdash . ∗302·23·24 . \supset$

$\vdash :. \text{Hp} . \supset : (\exists \rho, \sigma) : \rho \text{ Prm } \sigma \,.\, \rho, \sigma \in \text{NC ind} - \iota`0 \,.\, \mu \times_c \sigma = \nu \times_c \rho :$

$\alpha, \beta \in \text{D}`U \,.\, \mu \times_c \beta = \nu \times_c \alpha \,.\, \supset_{\alpha,\beta} .\, \alpha \geqslant \rho \,.\, \beta \geqslant \sigma :$

[∗302·26·28] $\supset : (\exists \rho, \sigma) \,.\, (\rho, \sigma) \text{ Prm } (\mu, \nu) \,.\, (\rho, \sigma) \text{ Prm } (\xi, \eta) :. \supset \vdash . \text{Prop}$

∗302·31. $\vdash : (\rho, \sigma) \text{ Prm } (\mu, \nu) \,.\, \mu \text{ Prm } \nu \,.\, \supset .\, \mu = \rho \,.\, \nu = \sigma$

Dem.

$\vdash . ∗302·1 . (∗302·02·03) . \supset$

$\vdash :. \text{Hp} . \supset : (\exists \tau) \,.\, \mu = \rho \times_c \tau \,.\, \nu = \sigma \times_c \tau : \mu = \rho \times_c \tau \,.\, \nu = \sigma \times_c \tau \,.\, \supset_\tau .\, \tau = 1 :$

[∗14·122] $\supset .\, \mu = \rho \times_c 1 \,.\, \nu = \sigma \times_c 1 :. \supset \vdash . \text{Prop}$

∗302·32. $\vdash : \xi \text{ Prm } \eta \,.\, \mu \text{ Prm } \nu \,.\, \xi \times_c \nu = \eta \times_c \mu \,.\, \supset .\, \xi = \mu \,.\, \eta = \nu$

Dem.

$\vdash . ∗302·3·31 . \supset$

$\vdash : \text{Hp} . \supset . (\exists \rho, \sigma) \,.\, \rho \text{ Prm } \sigma \,.\, \xi = \rho \,.\, \mu = \rho \,.\, \eta = \sigma \,.\, \nu = \sigma : \supset \vdash . \text{Prop}$

∗302·33. $\vdash :. \mu, \nu, \xi, \eta \in \text{NC ind} - \iota`0 \,.\, \supset :$

$\mu \times_c \eta = \nu \times_c \xi \,.\, \equiv .\, (\exists \rho, \sigma) \,.\, (\rho, \sigma) \text{ Prm } (\mu, \nu) \,.\, (\rho, \sigma) \text{ Prm } (\xi, \eta)$

Dem.

$\vdash . \text{Id} . (∗302·02·03) . \supset \vdash : (\rho, \sigma) \text{ Prm } (\mu, \nu) \,.\, (\rho, \sigma) \text{ Prm } (\xi, \eta) \,.\, \supset .$

$(\exists \tau, \tau') \,.\, \tau, \tau' \in \text{D}`U \,.\, \mu = \rho \times_c \tau \,.\, \nu = \sigma \times_c \tau \,.\, \xi = \rho \times_c \tau' \,.\, \eta = \sigma \times_c \tau' .$

[∗113·27] $\supset . (\exists \tau, \tau') \,.\, \mu \times_c \eta = \rho \times_c \sigma \times_c \tau \times_c \tau' = \nu \times_c \xi$ (1)

$\vdash . (1) . ∗302·3 . \supset \vdash . \text{Prop}$

∗302·34. $\vdash :. \mu, \nu, \xi, \eta \in \text{NC ind} \,.\, \sim(\mu = \nu = 0) \,.\, \sim(\xi = \eta = 0) \,.\, \supset :$

$\mu \times_c \eta = \nu \times_c \xi \,.\, \equiv .\, (\exists \rho, \sigma) \,.\, (\rho, \sigma) \text{ Prm } (\mu, \nu) \,.\, (\rho, \sigma) \text{ Prm } (\xi, \eta)$

Dem.

$\vdash . ∗113·602 . \supset \vdash : \text{Hp} \,.\, \mu = 0 \,.\, \nu \neq 0 \,.\, \supset .\, \xi = 0 \,.\, \eta \neq 0$ (1)

$\vdash . ∗113·602·621 . \supset$

$\vdash : \mu = 0 \,.\, \nu \neq 0 \,.\, \xi = 0 \,.\, \eta \neq 0 \,.\, \supset .\, \mu = 0 \times_c \nu \,.\, \nu = 1 \times_c \nu \,.\, \xi = 0 \times_c \eta \,.\, \eta = 1 \times_c \eta .$

[∗302·14] $\supset . (0, 1) \text{ Prm } (\mu, \nu) \,.\, (0, 1) \text{ Prm } (\xi, \eta)$ (2)

$\vdash . (1) . (2) . \supset \vdash : \text{Hp} \,.\, \mu = 0 \,.\, \nu \neq 0 \,.\, \supset .$

$(\exists \rho, \sigma) \,.\, (\rho, \sigma) \text{ Prm } (\mu, \nu) \,.\, (\rho, \sigma) \text{ Prm } (\xi, \eta)$ (3)

Similarly $\vdash : \text{Hp} \,.\, \nu = 0 \,.\, \mu \neq 0 \,.\, \supset .$

$(\exists \rho, \sigma) \,.\, (\rho, \sigma) \text{ Prm } (\mu, \nu) \,.\, (\rho, \sigma) \text{ Prm } (\xi, \eta)$ (4)

$\vdash . (3) . (4) . ∗302·33 . \supset \vdash . \text{Prop}$

∗302·35. $\vdash :. \mu, \nu \in \text{NC ind} \,.\, \sim(\mu = \nu = 0) \,.\, \rho \text{ Prm } \sigma \,.\, \supset :$

$\mu \times_c \sigma = \nu \times_c \rho \,.\, \equiv .\, (\rho, \sigma) \text{ Prm } (\mu, \nu)$ [∗302·34·14·31]

***302·36.** $\vdash : \mu, \nu \in \text{NC ind} . \sim(\mu = \nu = 0) . \equiv . (\exists \rho, \sigma) . (\rho, \sigma) \,\text{Prm}\, (\mu, \nu)$

Dem.

$\vdash . *302{\cdot}14 . \supset \vdash :. (\rho, \sigma) \,\text{Prm}\, (\mu, \nu) . \supset :$

$\rho, \sigma \in \text{NC ind} . \sim(\rho = \sigma = 0) : (\exists \tau) . \tau \in \text{NC ind} - \iota`0 . \mu = \rho \times_c \tau . \nu = \sigma \times_c \tau :$

$[*120{\cdot}5 . *113{\cdot}602] \supset : \mu, \nu \in \text{NC ind} . \sim(\mu = \nu = 0)$ (1)

$\vdash . (1) . *302{\cdot}22 . \supset \vdash . \text{Prop}$

***302·37.** $\vdash : (\rho, \sigma) \,\text{Prm}\, (\mu, \nu) . \equiv .$

$\mu, \nu \in \text{NC ind} . \sim(\mu = 0 . \nu = 0) . \rho \,\text{Prm}\, \sigma . \mu \times_c \sigma = \nu \times_c \rho$ [*302·35·36]

***302·38.** $\vdash : (\rho, \sigma) \,\text{Prm}\, (\mu, \nu) . (\xi, \eta) \,\text{Prm}\, (\mu, \nu) . \supset . \rho = \xi . \sigma = \eta$

Dem.

$\vdash . *302{\cdot}37 . \supset \vdash : \text{Hp} . \supset . \rho \,\text{Prm}\, \sigma . \xi \,\text{Prm}\, \eta . \mu \times_c \sigma = \nu \times_c \rho . \mu \times_c \eta = \nu \times_c \xi .$

$\sim(\mu = 0 . \nu = 0)$ (1)

$\vdash . (1) . *302{\cdot}14 . *113{\cdot}602 . \supset \vdash : \text{Hp} . \mu = 0 . \supset . \rho = 0 . \xi = 0 . \sigma = 1 . \eta = 1$ (2)

$\vdash . (1) . *302{\cdot}14 . *113{\cdot}602 . \supset \vdash : \text{Hp} . \nu = 0 . \supset . \rho = 1 . \xi = 1 . \sigma = 0 . \eta = 0$ (3)

$\vdash . *302{\cdot}27 . \supset \vdash : \text{Hp} . \mu \neq 0 . \nu \neq 0 . \supset . \rho \times_c \eta = \sigma \times_c \xi .$

$[(1) . *302{\cdot}32] \qquad \supset . \rho = \xi . \sigma = \eta$ (4)

$\vdash . (2) . (3) . (4) . \supset \vdash . \text{Prop}$

***302·39.** $\vdash : (\rho, \sigma) \,\text{Prm}\, (\mu, \nu) . \supset . \mu \geqslant \rho . \nu \geqslant \sigma$

Dem.

$\vdash . *302{\cdot}23{\cdot}36 . \supset \vdash :. \mu, \nu \in \text{D}`U . \supset :$

$(\exists \rho, \sigma) : (\rho, \sigma) \,\text{Prm}\, (\mu, \nu) : \xi, \eta \in \text{D}`U . \mu \times_c \eta = \nu \times_c \xi . \supset_{\xi, \eta} . \xi \geqslant \rho . \eta \geqslant \sigma :$

$[*113{\cdot}27] \supset : (\exists \rho, \sigma) . (\rho, \sigma) \,\text{Prm}\, (\mu, \nu) . \mu \geqslant \rho . \nu \geqslant \sigma :$

$[*302{\cdot}38] \supset : (\rho, \sigma) \,\text{Prm}\, (\mu, \nu) . \supset . \mu \geqslant \rho . \nu \geqslant \sigma$ (1)

$\vdash . *302{\cdot}37{\cdot}14 . \supset \vdash : \mu = 0 . (\rho, \sigma) \,\text{Prm}\, (\mu, \nu) . \supset . \nu \neq 0 . \rho = 0 . \sigma = 1$ (2)

Similarly $\vdash : \nu = 0 . (\rho, \sigma) \,\text{Prm}\, (\mu, \nu) . \supset . \mu \neq 0 . \rho = 1 . \sigma = 0$ (3)

$\vdash . (2) . (3) . \supset \quad \vdash :. (\rho, \sigma) \,\text{Prm}\, (\mu, \nu) : \mu = 0 . \vee . \nu = 0 : \supset . \mu \geqslant \rho . \nu \geqslant \sigma$ (4)

$\vdash . (1) . (4) . *302{\cdot}36 . *300{\cdot}17 . \supset \vdash . \text{Prop}$

***302·4.** $\vdash : \mu, \nu \in \text{NC ind} . \sim(\mu = \nu = 0) . \supset . \text{E} ! \,\text{hcf}\, (\mu, \nu)$

Dem.

$\vdash . *302{\cdot}22 . \supset \vdash : \text{Hp} . \supset . (\exists \rho, \sigma, \tau) . (\rho, \sigma) \,\text{Prm}_\tau\, (\mu, \nu)$ (1)

$\vdash . *302{\cdot}38 . (*302{\cdot}02{\cdot}03) . \supset$

$\vdash : (\rho, \sigma) \,\text{Prm}_\tau\, (\mu, \nu) . (\xi, \eta) \,\text{Prm}_\varpi\, (\mu, \nu) . \supset . \rho = \xi . \sigma = \eta . \mu = \rho \times_c \tau . \mu = \xi \times_c \varpi .$

$[*126{\cdot}41] \qquad \supset . \tau = \varpi$ (2)

$\vdash . (1) . (2) . (*302{\cdot}04) . \supset \vdash . \text{Prop}$

***302·41.** $\vdash : \mu, \nu \in \text{NC ind} . \sim(\mu = \nu = 0) . \supset . \text{E} ! \,\text{lcm}\, (\mu, \nu)$

[Proof as in *302·4]

***302·42.** $\vdash : \mu, \nu \in \text{NC ind} . \sim(\mu = \nu = 0) . \supset . \text{hcf}(\mu, \nu) \times_c \text{lcm}(\mu, \nu) = \mu \times_c \nu$

Dem.

$\vdash . *302\cdot4\cdot41 . (*302\cdot04\cdot05) . \supset \vdash : \text{Hp} . \supset .$

$(\exists \rho, \sigma, \tau) . \mu = \rho \times_c \tau . \nu = \sigma \times_c \tau . \text{hcf}(\mu, \nu) = \tau . \text{lcm}(\mu, \nu) = \rho \times_c \sigma \times_c \tau .$

$[*113\cdot27 . *116\cdot34] \supset . (\exists \rho, \sigma, \tau) . \mu \times_c \nu = \rho \times_c \sigma \times_c \tau^2 .$

$\text{hcf}(\mu, \nu) \times_c \text{lcm}(\mu, \nu) = \rho \times_c \sigma \times_c \tau^2 : \supset \vdash . \text{Prop}$

***302·43.** $\vdash : (\rho, \sigma) \text{Prm}(\mu, \nu) . \supset . \rho \times_c \text{hcf}(\mu, \nu) = \mu . \sigma \times_c \text{hcf}(\mu, \nu) = \nu$

[*302·4 . (*302·02·04)]

***302·44.** $\vdash : (\rho, \sigma) \text{Prm}(\mu, \nu) . \supset . \rho \times_c \nu = \text{lcm}(\mu, \nu) = \sigma \times_c \mu$

[*302·41 . (*302·02·05)]

***302·45.** $\vdash : (\rho, \sigma) \text{Prm}(\mu, \nu) . \xi, \eta \in \text{NC ind} . \sim(\xi = \eta = 0) . \mu \times_c \eta = \nu \times_c \xi . \supset .$

$\text{lcm}(\xi, \eta) = \rho \times_c \xi = \sigma \times_c \eta$

Dem.

$\vdash . *302\cdot37 . \supset \vdash : \text{Hp} . \supset . (\rho, \sigma) \text{Prm}(\xi, \eta) \quad (1)$

$\vdash . (1) . *302\cdot44 . \supset \vdash . \text{Prop}$

*303. RATIOS.

Summary of *303.

In this number, we give the definition and elementary properties of the ratio μ/ν. Most of the important applications of ratios are to numerical or identical relations, *i.e.* to relations which may, in a certain sense, be called *vectors*. Neglecting identical relations for the moment, let us consider numerical relations, and to fix our ideas, let us take distances on a line. A distance on a line is a one-one relation whose converse domain (and its domain too) is the whole line. If we call two such distances R and S, we may say that they have the ratio μ/ν if, starting from some point x, ν repetitions of R take us to the same point y as we reach by μ repetitions of S, *i.e.* if $xR^\nu y \,.\, xS^\mu y$. Thus R and S will have the ratio μ/ν if $\exists ! R^\nu \cap S^\mu$. In order, however, to insure that $\mu/\nu = \rho/\sigma$ if $(\rho, \sigma) \operatorname{Prm} (\mu, \nu)$, it is necessary, in general, to substitute $\dot{\exists} ! R^\sigma \dot{\cap} S^\rho$ for $\dot{\exists} ! R^\nu \dot{\cap} S^\mu$. (In the above case of distances on a line, the two are equivalent.) Thus we shall say that R has the ratio μ/ν to S if $(\exists \rho, \sigma) \,.\, (\rho, \sigma) \operatorname{Prm} (\mu, \nu) \,.\, \dot{\exists} ! R^\sigma \dot{\cap} S^\rho$.

If we apply the above definition to identical relations, we find that, if $R \subseteq I \,.\, S \subseteq I$, R has the ratio μ/ν to S provided $\dot{\exists} ! R \dot{\cap} S$, *i.e.* provided $\exists ! C'R \cap C'S$. This application is required for dealing with zero quantities and zero ratios.

Thus we are led to the following definition of ratios:

$$*303\cdot01. \quad \mu/\nu = \hat{R}\hat{S} \{(\exists \rho, \sigma) \,.\, (\rho, \sigma) \operatorname{Prm} (\mu, \nu) \,.\, \dot{\exists} ! R^\sigma \dot{\cap} S^\rho\} \quad \text{Df}$$

This definition, as it stands, requires justification in two respects: (1) we commonly think of ratios as applying to magnitudes other than relations, (2) we should not commonly include as examples of ratio certain cases included in the above definition. These two points must now be considered.

(1) In applying our theory to (say) the ratio of two masses, we note that the idea of quantity (say, of mass) in any usage depends upon a comparison of different quantities. The "vector quantity" R, which relates a quantity m_1 with a quantity m_2, is the relation arising from the existence of some definite physical process of addition by which a body of mass m_1 will be transformed into another body of mass m_2. Thus σ such steps, symbolized by R^σ,

represents the addition of the mass $\sigma(m_2 - m_1)$. Similarly if S is the relation between M_2 and M_1 which arises from the process of addition turning a body of mass M_1 into another body of mass M_2, then S^ρ symbolizes the addition of the mass $\rho(M_2 - M_1)$. Now $\dot{\exists}\,!\,R^\sigma \dot{\cap} S^\rho$ means that there are a pair of masses m and m', such that $mR^\sigma m'$ and $mS^\rho m'$. In other words, if we take a body A of mass m and transform it so as to turn it into another of mass $m + \sigma(m_2 - m_1)$, we obtain a body of the same mass m' as if we proceeded to transform A into a body of mass $m + \rho(M_2 - M_1)$. Hence $\sigma(m_2 - m_1) = \rho(M_2 - M_1)$; that is $(m_2 - m_1)/(M_2 - M_1) = \rho/\sigma$. But in our symbolism the addition of $m_2 - m_1$ is represented by the vector quantity R, and that of $M_2 - M_1$ by the vector quantity S; so in our symbolism R has to S the ratio of ρ to σ.

Thus to say that an entity possesses μ units of quantity means that, taking U to represent the unit vector quantity, U^μ relates the zero of quantity—whatever that may mean in reference to that kind of quantity—with the quantity possessed by that entity.

It can be claimed for this method of symbolizing the ideas of quantity (α) that it is always a possible method of procedure whatever view be taken of it as a representation of first principles, and (β) that it directly represents the principle "No *quantity* of any kind without a comparison of different quantities of that kind."

Furthermore analogously to our treatment of cardinal and ordinal numbers, we can define any definite quantity of some kind, say any definite quantity of mass, as being merely the class of all "bodies of equal mass" with some given body. The zero mass will be the class of all bodies of zero mass; and if there are no bodies with the properties that a body of zero mass should have, this class reduces to Λ in the appropriate type.

Thus the application of our symbolism to concrete cases demands the existence of a determinate test of "equality of quantity" of different entities, and a determinate process of "addition of quantity." The formal properties which the process of addition must possess are discussed in the numbers concerned with vector families.

(2) Having now shown that cases apparently excluded by our definition of ratio can be included, we have to show that no harm is done by our inclusion of cases which would naturally be excluded. In order that ratio may agree with our expectations it is necessary that the two relations R and S, whose ratio we are considering, should have the same converse domain. Otherwise we get such cases as the following: Let P, Q be two series, and suppose* $B'P = B'Q$, $5_P = 6_Q$, $11_P = 9_Q$, $13_P = 25_Q$, but that P and Q have no other terms in common. Then we shall have, if $R = P_1 \,.\, S = Q_1$,

$$(B'P)\, R^4 5_P \,.\, (B'P)\, S^5 5_P,$$

* For notation, cf. *121.

whence it follows that R has to S the ratio 5/4, *i.e.* we have $R(5/4)S$. But we shall also have $R(8/10)S$ and $R(24/12)S$, *i.e.* $R(4/5)S$ and $R(2/1)S$. Thus our definition does not make different ratios incompatible. In practical applications, however, when R and S are confined to one vector-family, different ratios do become incompatible, as will be proved at the beginning of Section C. And so long as we are not concerned with the applications which constitute measurement, the important thing about our definition of ratio is that it should yield the usual arithmetical properties, in particular the fundamental property

$$\mu/\nu = \rho/\sigma \,.\equiv.\, \mu \times_c \sigma = \nu \times_c \rho,$$

which is proved, with our definition, in ∗303·39. Thus any further restriction in the definition would constitute an unnecessary complication.

In virtue of our definition of μ/ν, $\mu/\nu = \dot{\Lambda}$ if μ and ν are not both inductive cardinals, or if $\mu = \nu = 0$ (∗303·11·14). We have (∗303·13) $\vdash . \mu/\nu = \text{Cnv}‘(\nu/\mu)$, *i.e.* the converse of a ratio is its reciprocal. If $\mu = 0$, and $R(\mu/\nu)S$, R must have a part in common with identity (which we may express by saying that R is a zero vector), and S may be any numerical or identical relation whose field has a member which has the relation R to itself (∗303·15). Thus if ν, σ are inductive cardinals other than 0, $0/\nu = 0/\sigma$. The common value of ratios whose numerator is 0 is the zero ratio, which we call 0_q (where "q" is intended to suggest "quantity"). The definition of 0_q is

∗303·02. $0_q = \dot{s}‘0/‘‘\text{NC induct}$ Df

In like manner, if μ and ρ are inductive cardinals other than 0, we have $\mu/0 = \rho/0$. The common value of such ratios we call ∞_q, putting

∗303·03. $\infty_q = \dot{s}‘/0‘‘\text{NC induct}$ Df

The properties of ratios require various existence-theorems, and in establishing existence-theorems without assuming the axiom of infinity, the question of types requires considerable care. We have

∗303·211. $\vdash : (\rho, \sigma) \text{Prm} (\mu, \nu) . \supset . \mu/\nu = \rho/\sigma$

so that the existence of μ/ν does not depend upon μ and ν, but upon ρ and σ, where ρ/σ is μ/ν in its lowest terms. We may, therefore, in considering existence-theorems, confine ourselves, in the first instance, to *prime* ratios.

To prove the existence of $(\rho/\sigma) \upharpoonright t‘R$, when $\rho \,\text{Prm}\, \sigma$, we take two relations R and S both contained in identity. These have the ratio ρ/σ provided their fields have a member in common and $\text{E}!\, R^\sigma . \text{E}!\, S^\rho$. By ∗301·16, this requires $\rho, \sigma \in C‘‘(U \upharpoonright t^3‘R)$. Thus we have

∗303·25. $\vdash :. \rho \,\text{Prm}\, \sigma . \supset :$

$$\dot{\exists}!\, (\rho/\sigma) \upharpoonright t‘R \,.\equiv.\, \rho, \sigma \in C‘‘(U \upharpoonright t^3‘R) \,.\equiv.\, \rho(R), \sigma(R) \in C‘U$$

But this existence-theorem, which is obtained by supposing R and S contained in identity, is not much use in practice: what we require is the existence of a ratio between *numerical* relations. For this purpose, assuming $\rho \geqslant \sigma$ and $\sigma \neq 0$, let λ be a class of such a type that $\text{Nc}`t`\lambda \geqslant \rho +_c 1$. (Such a class can always be found in some type, by ∗300·18.) Then we have $\rho_\lambda \in \text{G}`U$, and we can construct a series $Q$ such that $C`Q$ is of the same type as λ and $\text{Nc}`C`Q = \rho +_c 1$. (This is proved in ∗262·211.) We can then choose out of Q a series P having the same beginning and end, and consisting of $\sigma +_c 1$ terms. We then have

$$(B`Q)(Q_1)^\rho(B`\breve{Q}) \,.\, (B`Q)(P_1)^\sigma(B`\breve{Q}).$$

Hence P_1 and Q_1 have the ratio ρ/σ. A similar argument applies if $\sigma \geqslant \rho$ and $\rho \neq 0$. Thus we arrive at the proposition:

∗303·322. $\vdash : \rho \,\text{Prm}\, \sigma \,.\, \rho_\lambda, \sigma_\lambda \in \text{D}`U \cap \text{G}`U \,.\, \supset \,.\, \dot{\exists}\,!\,(\rho/\sigma) \upharpoonright (\text{Rel num} \cap t_{00}`\lambda)$

I.e. if ρ is prime to σ and neither is 0, and $\rho +_c 1$, $\sigma +_c 1$ both exist in the type of λ, then there are numerical relations having the ratio ρ/σ and having their fields of the same type as λ.

The case when either ρ or σ is 0 requires separate treatment. If R has to S the ratio $0/\sigma$, R must be partly contained in identity (∗303·15); hence we have to find a hypothesis for $\dot{\exists}\,!\,(0/\sigma) \upharpoonright \text{Rel num}$, since $\dot{\exists}\,!\,(0/\sigma) \upharpoonright \text{Rel num}$ is impossible. Since $0/\sigma = 0/1$, we only require the existence of 2 in the appropriate type, *i.e.* we have

∗303·63. $\vdash : \exists\,!\,2_\lambda \,.\, \supset \,.\, \dot{\exists}\,!\,0_q \upharpoonright (\text{Rel num} \cap t_{00}`\lambda)$

It will be remembered that $\exists\,!\,2_\lambda$ is demonstrable except in the lowest type.

In the above propositions, μ and ν and ρ and σ have been typically indefinite. Ratios of typically definite inductive cardinals are dealt with by means of ∗302·15, which gives at once

∗303·27. $\vdash : \mu, \nu \in \text{NC ind} \,.\, \mu_\lambda, \nu_\lambda \in C`U \,.\, \supset \,.\, \mu/\nu = \mu_\lambda/\nu_\lambda$

I.e. a ratio may, without changing its value, have its numerator and denominator specified as belonging to any type in which both exist. This enables us to take ρ and σ as typically definite cardinals in ∗303·322, thus obtaining the proposition

∗303·332. $\vdash :. \rho \,\text{Prm}\, \sigma \,.\, \supset : \dot{\exists}\,!\,(\rho/\sigma) \upharpoonright (\text{Rel num} \cap t_{11}`\rho) \,.\, \equiv \,.\, \rho, \sigma \in \text{D}`U \cap \text{G}`U$

The above existence-theorems are useful in proving

$$\alpha/\beta = \gamma/\delta \,.\, \equiv \,.\, \alpha \times_c \delta = \beta \times_c \gamma.$$

We proceed as follows: We first show (∗303·34) that, if ρ, σ are inductive cardinals other than 0, and $\rho +_c 1$, $\sigma +_c 1$ exist in the type of λ, we can find numerical relations R and S such that $\dot{\exists}\,!\,R^\sigma \dot{\cap} S^\rho$, but $\eta > \sigma \,.\, \supset \,.\, \sim \dot{\exists}\,!\,R^\eta$.

This is done by taking two series P and Q having the same beginning and end, and having $C\text{`}P \in \sigma +_c 1 \,.\, C\text{`}Q \in \rho +_c 1$. Then if $R = P_1$ and $S = Q_1$, we have

$$(B\text{`}P)\, R^\sigma\, (B\text{`}\breve{P}) \,.\, (B\text{`}P)\, S^\rho\, (B\text{`}\breve{P}) : \eta > \sigma \,.\, \supset .\, R^\eta = \Lambda,$$

whence the result. From this proposition it follows immediately that if $\rho \,\text{Prm}\, \sigma \,.\, \xi \,\text{Prm}\, \eta \,.\, \eta > \sigma$, and if $\rho_\lambda, \sigma_\lambda \in \text{D}\text{`}U \cap \text{Ꭰ}\text{`}U$, we can find an R and an S such that $R\,(\rho/\sigma)\,S \,.\, \sim\{R\,(\xi/\eta)\,S\}$. A similar argument applies if $\eta < \sigma$ or $\xi > \rho$ or $\xi < \rho$. Hence we find, by transposition,

***303·341.** $\vdash : \rho_\lambda, \sigma_\lambda \in \text{D}\text{`}U \cap \text{Ꭰ}\text{`}U \,.\, \rho \,\text{Prm}\, \sigma \,.\, \xi \,\text{Prm}\, \eta \,.\, (\rho/\sigma) \upharpoonright t_{00}\text{`}\lambda = (\xi/\eta) \upharpoonright t_{00}\text{`}\lambda \,.\, \supset .$
$\rho = \xi \,.\, \sigma = \eta$

From this point on, the argument offers no difficulty. For if we have

$$\alpha/\beta = \gamma/\delta \,.\, (\rho, \sigma)\, \text{Prm}\, (\alpha, \beta) \,.\, (\xi, \eta)\, \text{Prm}\, (\gamma, \delta),$$

we have, by *303·341·211, $\rho = \xi \,.\, \sigma = \eta$. Hence, by *302·32, we have $\alpha \times_c \delta = \beta \times_c \gamma$. What is approximately the converse, *i.e.*

***303·23.** $\vdash : \mu, \nu, \xi, \eta \in \text{NC ind} \,.$
$\sim(\mu = \nu = 0) \,.\, \sim(\xi = \eta = 0) \,.\, \mu \times_c \eta = \nu \times_c \xi \,.\, \supset .\, \mu/\nu = \xi/\eta$

follows at once from *303·211 and *302·3. Hence, after dealing with special cases, we find

***303·38.** $\vdash :.\, \alpha, \beta, \gamma, \delta \in \text{NC ind} :$
$\alpha_\lambda, \beta_\lambda \in \text{Ꭰ}\text{`}U \,.\, \text{v} \,.\, \gamma_\lambda, \delta_\lambda \in \text{Ꭰ}\text{`}U : \sim(\alpha = \beta = 0) \,.\, \sim(\gamma = \delta = 0) : \supset :$
$(\alpha/\beta) \upharpoonright t_{00}\text{`}\lambda = (\gamma/\delta) \upharpoonright t_{00}\text{`}\lambda \,.\, \equiv .\, \alpha \times_c \delta = \beta \times_c \gamma$

It will be observed that α/β is typically indefinite, like $\text{Nc}\text{`}\xi$. But in order to insure that $\alpha/\beta = \gamma/\delta$ however the type may be determined, it is only necessary to insure that this equation holds in a type in which $(\alpha/\beta) \upharpoonright \text{Rel num}$ exists. When we write simply "$\alpha/\beta = \gamma/\delta$," we shall mean that this equation holds however the type may be determined; in other words, that it holds in a type in which $(\alpha/\beta) \upharpoonright \text{Rel num}$ exists. (There always is such a type, if $\alpha, \beta \in \text{NC ind} - \iota\text{`}0$, in virtue of *303·322 and *300·18.) Thus we have

***303·391.** $\vdash :.\, \alpha, \beta \in \text{NC ind} \,.\, \alpha_\lambda, \beta_\lambda \in \text{Ꭰ}\text{`}U \,.\, \sim(\alpha = \beta = 0) \,.\, \supset :$
$(\alpha/\beta) \upharpoonright t_{00}\text{`}\lambda = (\gamma/\delta) \upharpoonright t_{00}\text{`}\lambda \,.\, \equiv .\, \alpha/\beta = \gamma/\delta \,.\, \equiv .\, \alpha \times_c \delta = \beta \times_c \gamma$

and, in virtue of *303·38, we have

***303·39.** $\vdash :.\, \alpha, \beta, \gamma, \delta \in \text{NC ind} \,.\, \sim(\alpha = \beta = 0) \,.\, \sim(\gamma = \delta = 0) \,.\, \supset :$
$\alpha/\beta = \gamma/\delta \,.\, \equiv .\, \alpha \times_c \delta = \beta \times_c \gamma$

This proposition is, of course, essential to the justification of our definition of ratios.

The remaining propositions of *303 consist (1) of applications of the theory of ratio to powers of a given numerical relation, (2) of properties of 0_q and ∞_q, (3) of a few properties of the class of ratios. This last set of propositions depends upon two new definitions, which must be briefly explained.

We have already explained that μ/ν is typically indefinite. Thus if we call μ/ν a "ratio," ratios are, like "NC ind," not strictly a class, because every class must be confined within some one type. Nevertheless it is convenient, just as in the case of NC ind, to treat ratios as if they formed a class; and, with similar precautions, we can avoid the errors into which we might be led by treating them as a proper class. We therefore put

***303·04.** $\text{Rat} = \hat{X}\{(\exists \mu, \nu) . \mu, \nu \in \text{NC ind} . \nu \neq 0 . X = \mu/\nu\}$ Df

(The condition $\nu \neq 0$ is only introduced because it is usually convenient to exclude ∞_q.) It will be observed that μ/ν is still typically indefinite if μ and ν are typically definite. This results from *303·27. But we often want typically definite ratios. We want these defined in types in which there are numerical relations having the ratios in question. Hence we put

***303·05.** $\text{Rat def} = \hat{X}\{(\exists \mu, \nu) . \mu, \nu \in \text{D}`U \cap \text{G}`U . X = (\mu/\nu) \upharpoonright t_{11}`\mu\}$ Df

Here "def" stands for "definite," and μ, ν are typically definite inductive cardinals. The desired properties of "Rat def" result from *303·322. It should be observed that, besides consisting of typically definite ratios, "Rat def" differs from "Rat" by the exclusion of 0_q. This is merely for reasons of convenience.

The properties of "Rat" and "Rat def" follow immediately from previous propositions. We have

***303·721.** $\vdash : X \in \text{Rat} - \iota`0_q . \supset . (\exists \mu) . X \upharpoonright t_{11}`\mu \in \text{Rat def}$

***303·73.** $\vdash : X \in \text{Rat def} . \supset . \dot{\exists} ! X \upharpoonright \text{Rel num}$

By *303·322; and by *303·391,

***303·76.** $\vdash :. X, Y \in \text{Rat} . X \upharpoonright t_{11}`\rho \in \text{Rat def} . \supset : X \upharpoonright t_{11}`\rho = Y \upharpoonright t_{11}`\rho . \equiv . X = Y$

If the axiom of infinity holds, every member of "Rat" except 0_q becomes a member of "Rat def" as soon as it is made typically definite. Hence

***303·78.** $\vdash : \text{Infin ax} . \supset . \text{Rat def} = \text{Rat} - \iota`0_q$

The uses of "Rat" and "Rat def" differ just as the uses of "NC ind" and "NC induct" differ. The distinction is only important so long as the axiom of infinity is not assumed.

***303·01.** $\mu/\nu = \hat{R}\hat{S}\{(\exists \rho, \sigma) . (\rho, \sigma) \text{Prm} (\mu, \nu) . \dot{\exists} ! R^{\sigma} \dot{\cap} S^{\rho}\}$ Df

In the above definition, ρ, σ, μ, ν are typically ambiguous, but ρ, σ must (by *301·16) exist in the type of $t`R$, while μ, ν need not do so; μ, ν cannot, however, be null in *all* types, by *300·17.

***303·02.** $0_q = \dot{s}`0/``\text{NC induct}$ Df

***303·03.** $\infty_q = \dot{s}`/0``\text{NC induct}$ Df

***303·04.** $\mathrm{Rat} = \hat{X}\{(\exists\mu,\nu).\mu,\nu\in\mathrm{NC\,ind}.\nu\neq 0.X=\mu/\nu\}$ Df

***303·05.** $\mathrm{Rat\,def} = \hat{X}\{(\exists\mu,\nu).\mu,\nu\in\mathrm{D}`U\cap\mathrm{Cl}`U.X=(\mu/\nu)\upharpoonright t_{11}`\mu\}$ Df

***303·1.** $\vdash :. R(\mu/\nu)S.\equiv.(\exists\rho,\sigma).(\rho,\sigma)\,\mathrm{Prm}\,(\mu,\nu).\dot{\exists}!R^\sigma\dot{\cap}S^\rho$ [(*303·01)]

***303·11.** $\vdash :\sim(\mu,\nu\in\mathrm{NC\,ind}).\supset.\mu/\nu=\dot{\Lambda}$ [*303·1 . *302·36]

***303·13.** $\vdash.\mu/\nu=\mathrm{Cnv}`(\nu/\mu)$ [*303·1 . *302·11]

***303·14.** $\vdash.0/0=\dot{\Lambda}$ [*303·1 . *302·36]

***303·15.** $\vdash : R(0/\nu)S.\equiv.\nu\in\mathrm{NC\,ind}-\iota`0.\dot{\exists}!R\dot{\cap}I\upharpoonright C`S.$

$\equiv.\nu\in\mathrm{NC\,ind}-\iota`0.\exists!C`S\cap\hat{x}(xRx)$

Dem.

$\vdash.*302\cdot14\cdot38.*303\cdot1.\supset$

$\vdash : R(0/\nu)S.\equiv.\nu\in\mathrm{NC\,ind}-\iota`0.\dot{\exists}!R^1\dot{\cap}S^0.$

[*301·2] $\equiv.\nu\in\mathrm{NC\,ind}-\iota`0.\dot{\exists}!R\dot{\cap}I\upharpoonright C`S:\supset\vdash.\mathrm{Prop}$

***303·151.** $\vdash :. R,S\in\mathrm{Rel\,num\,id}.\supset: R(0/\nu)S.\equiv.$

$\nu\in\mathrm{NC\,ind}-\iota`0.R\in\mathrm{Rl}`I.S\in\mathrm{Rel\,num\,id}.\exists!C`R\cap C`S$

[*303·15 . *300·324·3]

***303·16.** $\vdash : R(\mu/0)S.\equiv.\mu\in\mathrm{NC\,ind}-\iota`0.\dot{\exists}!S\dot{\cap}I\upharpoonright C`R.$

$\equiv.\mu\in\mathrm{NC\,ind}-\iota`0.\exists!C`R\cap\hat{x}(xSx)$ [*303·15·13]

***303·161.** $\vdash :. R,S\in\mathrm{Rel\,num\,id}.\supset: R(\mu/0)S.\equiv.$

$\mu\in\mathrm{NC\,ind}-\iota`0.R\in\mathrm{Rel\,num\,id}.S\in\mathrm{Rl}`I.\exists!C`R\cap C`S$

[*303·151·13]

***303·17.** $\vdash :. \mu,\nu\in\mathrm{NC\,ind}-\iota`0.R,S\in\mathrm{Rel\,num\,id}.R(\mu/\nu)S.\supset:$

$R,S\in\mathrm{Rl}`I.\lor.R,S\in\mathrm{Rel\,num}$

Dem.

$\vdash.*303\cdot1.*113\cdot602.\supset$

$\vdash :: \mathrm{Hp}.\supset :. R,S\in\mathrm{Rel\,num\,id}:(\exists\rho,\sigma).\rho,\sigma\in\mathrm{NC\,ind}-\iota`0.\dot{\exists}!R^\sigma\dot{\cap}S^\rho :.$

[*300·33.*301·3]

$\supset :. S\in\mathrm{Rel\,num\,id}:. R\in\mathrm{Rl}`I:(\exists\rho).\rho\in\mathrm{NC\,ind}-\iota`0.\dot{\exists}!R\dot{\cap}S^\rho:\lor:$

$R\in\mathrm{Rel\,num}:(\exists\rho,\sigma).\rho,\sigma\in\mathrm{NC\,ind}-\iota`0.\dot{\exists}!R^\sigma\dot{\cap}S^\rho :.$

[*300·3] $\supset :. S\in\mathrm{Rel\,num\,id}:. R\in\mathrm{Rl}`I.\dot{\exists}!I\dot{\cap}S_{po}.\lor.R\in\mathrm{Rel\,num}.\dot{\exists}!J\dot{\cap}S_{po} :.$

[*300·3·33] $\supset :. R,S\in\mathrm{Rl}`I.\lor.R,S\in\mathrm{Rel\,num} :: \supset\vdash.\mathrm{Prop}$

∗303·18. $\vdash :. \mu, \nu \epsilon \text{D}`U \upharpoonright t^{3}`R \,.\, R, S \epsilon \text{Rl}`I \,.\, \supset :$

$$R(\mu/\nu)S \,.\equiv.\, R(0/\nu)S \,.\equiv.\, R(\mu/0)S \,.\equiv.\, \exists ! C`R \cap C`S$$

[∗303·1·151·16 . ∗301·3]

∗303·181. $\vdash : \dot{\exists} ! (\mu/\nu) \,.\equiv.\, (\exists\rho, \sigma) \,.\, (\rho, \sigma) \text{ Prm } (\mu, \nu)$

Dem.

$\vdash .\, ∗303·1 \,.\supset\vdash : \dot{\exists} ! (\mu/\nu) \,.\supset.\, (\exists\rho, \sigma) \,.\, (\rho, \sigma) \text{ Prm } (\mu, \nu)$ (1)

$\vdash .\, ∗301·3 . ∗300·325·17 \,.\supset\vdash : (\rho, \sigma) \text{ Prm } (\mu, \nu) \,.\supset.\, (\exists x) . (x \downarrow x)(\mu/\nu)(x \downarrow x)$ (2)

$\vdash . (1) . (2) . \supset \vdash .$ Prop

In the above proposition, if μ/ν is typically indefinite, so that "$\dot{\exists} ! \mu/\nu$" only asserts existence in a sufficiently high type, ρ, σ may also be typically indefinite. But if μ/ν is to be taken in a definite type, ρ and σ must be taken in the corresponding type, and must not be null in that type. This is proved later.

∗303·182. $\vdash :. 0/0 = \mu/\nu \,.\equiv :\, \sim(\mu, \nu \epsilon \text{NC ind}) \,.\vee.\, \mu = \nu = 0$

Here the equation $0/0 = \mu/\nu$ is assumed to hold in a sufficiently high type.

Dem.

$\vdash .\, ∗303·14 \,.\supset\vdash :. 0/0 = \mu/\nu \,.\supset : \mu/\nu = \dot{\Lambda} :$

[∗303·181.∗302·36] $\supset : \sim(\mu, \nu \epsilon \text{NC ind} - \iota`0) \,.\vee.\, \mu = \nu = 0$ (1)

$\vdash . (1) .\, ∗303·11·14 \,.\supset \vdash .$ Prop

∗303·19. $\vdash : R(\mu/\nu)S \,.\equiv.\, \breve{R}(\mu/\nu)\breve{S}$ [∗303·1 . ∗121·26]

∗303·2. $\vdash :. (\rho, \sigma) \text{ Prm } (\mu, \nu) \,.\supset : R(\mu/\nu)S \,.\equiv.\, \dot{\exists} ! R^{\sigma} \dot{\cap} S^{\rho}$

Dem.

$\vdash .\, ∗303·1 .$ $\supset \vdash : \text{Hp} \,.\, \dot{\exists} ! R^{\sigma} \dot{\cap} S^{\rho} \,.\supset.\, R(\mu/\nu)S$ (1)

$\vdash .\, ∗302·38 . ∗303·1 \,.\supset \vdash : \text{Hp} \,.\, R(\mu/\nu)S \,.\supset.\, \dot{\exists} ! R^{\sigma} \dot{\cap} S^{\rho}$ (2)

$\vdash . (1) . (2) . \supset \vdash .$ Prop

∗303·21. $\vdash :. \rho \text{ Prm } \sigma \,.\supset : R(\rho/\sigma)S \,.\equiv.\, \dot{\exists} ! R^{\sigma} \dot{\cap} S^{\rho}$ [∗302·31 . ∗303·1]

∗303·211. $\vdash : (\rho, \sigma) \text{ Prm } (\mu, \nu) \,.\supset.\, \mu/\nu = \rho/\sigma$ [∗303·2·21]

∗303·22. $\vdash : \rho \text{ Prm } \sigma \,.\, \mu, \nu \epsilon \text{NC ind} \,.\sim(\mu = \nu = 0) \,.\, \mu \times_c \sigma = \nu \times_c \rho \,.\supset.\, \mu/\nu = \rho/\sigma$

[∗302·37 . ∗303·211]

∗303·23. $\vdash : \mu, \nu, \xi, \eta \epsilon \text{NC ind} \,.\sim(\mu = \nu = 0) . \sim(\xi = \eta = 0) \,.\, \mu \times_c \eta = \nu \times_c \xi \,.\supset.$

$\mu/\nu = \xi/\eta$ [∗302·3 . ∗303·211]

∗303·24. $\vdash : \mu, \nu \epsilon \text{NC ind} \,.\sim(\mu = \nu = 0) \,.\supset.\, (\exists\rho, \sigma) \,.\, \rho \text{ Prm } \sigma \,.\, \mu/\nu = \rho/\sigma$

[∗303·211 . ∗302·22]

The following propositions give typically definite existence-theorems for ratios.

***303·25.** $\vdash :. \rho \,\mathrm{Prm}\, \sigma . \supset : \dot{\exists} ! (\rho/\sigma) \upharpoonright t ‘R . \equiv . \rho, \sigma \in C‘(U \upharpoonright t^{3}‘R) . \equiv . \rho(R), \sigma(R) \in C‘U$

I.e. if ρ Prm σ, there are relations of the same type as R and having the ratio ρ/σ when, and only when, the number of relations of the same type as R is at least as great as ρ and at least as great as σ.

Dem.

$\vdash . *303·21 . \supset \vdash :. \mathrm{Hp} . \supset : \dot{\exists} ! (\rho/\sigma) \upharpoonright t‘R . \supset . (\exists S, T) . E ! S^{\sigma} . E ! T^{\rho} . S, T \in t‘R .$

[*301·16] $\supset . \rho, \sigma \in C‘U \upharpoonright t^{3}‘R$ (1)

$\vdash . *301·16·3 . \supset \vdash :. \mathrm{Hp} . \supset :$

$\rho, \sigma \in C‘U \upharpoonright t^{3}‘R . x \in t_0‘C‘R . \supset . (x \downarrow x)^{\rho} = (x \downarrow x)^{\sigma} = x \downarrow x$ (2)

$\vdash . (2) . *303·21 . \supset$

$\vdash :. \mathrm{Hp} . \supset : \rho, \sigma \in C‘U \upharpoonright t^{3}‘R . x \in t_0‘C‘R . \supset . (x \downarrow x) (\rho/\sigma) (x \downarrow x)$ (3)

$\vdash . (1) . (3) . *63·18 . \supset \vdash . \mathrm{Prop}$

***303·251.** $\vdash : \mu, \nu \in C‘U \upharpoonright t^{3}‘R . \sim(\mu = \nu = 0) . \supset . \dot{\exists} ! (\mu/\nu) \upharpoonright t‘R$

Dem.

$\vdash . *302·36·39 . \supset \vdash : \mathrm{Hp} . \supset . (\exists \rho, \sigma) . (\rho, \sigma) \,\mathrm{Prm}\, (\mu, \nu) . \mu \geqslant \rho . \nu \geqslant \sigma .$

[*117·32] $\supset . (\exists \rho, \sigma) . (\rho, \sigma) \,\mathrm{Prm}\, (\mu, \nu) . \rho, \sigma \in C‘U \upharpoonright t^{3}‘R .$

[*303·211·25] $\supset . \dot{\exists} ! (\mu/\nu) \upharpoonright t‘R : \supset \vdash . \mathrm{Prop}$

***303·252.** $\vdash : \mu, \nu \in \mathrm{NC\,ind} \cap C‘U \upharpoonright t^{2}‘C‘R . \sim(\mu = \nu = 0) . \supset . \dot{\exists} ! (\mu/\nu) \upharpoonright t‘R$

Dem.

$\vdash . *64·51·55 . \supset \vdash : \mu = \mathrm{Nc}‘\alpha . \alpha \in t‘C‘R . x \in t_0‘C‘R . \supset . \downarrow x ‘‘\alpha \in \mu \cap t^{2}‘R$ (1)

$\vdash . (1) . *300·14 . \supset \vdash : \mathrm{Hp} . \supset . \mu, \nu \in C‘U \upharpoonright t^{3}‘R$ (2)

$\vdash . (2) . *303·251 . \supset \vdash . \mathrm{Prop}$

In the above proof, μ, ν are assumed to be typically indefinite. If they are typically definite, sm‘‘μ and sm‘‘ν must be substituted for μ and ν on the right-hand side of (1) and (2). The hypothesis "$\mu, \nu \in \mathrm{NC\,ind} \cap C‘U \upharpoonright t^{2}‘C‘R$" is a convenient abbreviation for

"$\mu, \nu \in \mathrm{NC\,ind} . \mu \cap t‘C‘R, \nu \cap t‘C‘R \in C‘U \upharpoonright t^{2}‘C‘R .$"

By *65·13,

$$\mu \cap t‘C‘R \in C‘U \upharpoonright t^{2}‘C‘R . \equiv . \mu \subset t‘C‘R . \mu \in C‘U \upharpoonright t^{2}‘C‘R . \equiv . \mu \in C‘U \upharpoonright t^{2}‘C‘R .$$

But "$\mu \in C‘U \upharpoonright t^{2}‘C‘R$" requires that μ should be typically definite, whereas "$\mu \in \mathrm{NC\,ind}$" requires that μ should be typically indefinite. Hence the hypothesis of *303·252 is only defensible as an abbreviation, meaning "$\mu, \nu \in \mathrm{NC\,ind}$, and if μ, ν are given the suitable typical definition, they become members of $C‘U \upharpoonright t^{2}‘C‘R$."

***303·253.** $\vdash : \mu, \nu \in \mathrm{NC\,ind} \cap C‘U \upharpoonright t^{2}‘\Lambda . \sim(\mu = \nu = 0) . \supset . \dot{\exists} ! (\mu/\nu) \upharpoonright t_{00}‘\Lambda$
[*303·252]

***303·254.** $\vdash : \mu, \nu \in \mathrm{NC\,ind} . \mu_{\Lambda}, \nu_{\Lambda} \in C‘U . \sim(\mu = \nu = 0) . \supset . \dot{\exists} ! (\mu/\nu) \upharpoonright t_{00}‘\Lambda$
[*303·253 . (*65·01)]

***303·26.** $\vdash : \mu, \nu \in \mathrm{NC\,ind} . \sim(\mu = \nu = 0) . \supset . (\exists \lambda) . \dot{\exists} ! (\mu/\nu) \upharpoonleft t_{00}\text{‘}\lambda$
[*303·254 . *300·17]

***303·27.** $\vdash : \mu, \nu \in \mathrm{NC\,ind} . \mu_\lambda, \nu_\lambda \in C\text{‘}U . \supset . \mu/\nu = \mu_\lambda/\nu_\lambda$ [*302·15 . *303·1]

***303·3.** $\vdash : \rho \,\mathrm{Prm}\, \sigma . \dot{\exists} ! P^{\rho \times_c \sigma} . \supset . P^\rho (\rho/\sigma) P^\sigma$

Dem.

$\vdash . *301\cdot16 . *14\cdot21 . \supset \vdash : \mathrm{Hp} . \supset . \rho \times_c \sigma \in C\text{‘}U \cap t^3\text{‘}R$ (1)

$\vdash . (1) . *301\cdot5 . \supset \vdash : \mathrm{Hp} . \rho \neq 0 . \sigma \neq 0 . \supset . (P^\rho)^\sigma = P^{\rho \times_c \sigma} = (P^\sigma)^\rho .$

[*303·21] $\supset . P^\rho (\rho/\sigma) P^\sigma$ (2)

$\vdash . *301\cdot2 . \supset \vdash : \mathrm{Hp} . \rho = 0 . \supset . P^\rho = I \upharpoonright C\text{‘}P = P^{\rho \times_c \sigma} . \dot{\exists} ! I \upharpoonright C\text{‘}P$ (3)

$\vdash . *302\cdot14 . \supset \vdash : \mathrm{Hp} . \rho = 0 . \supset . \sigma = 1 .$

[*301·2] $\supset . P^\sigma = P$ (4)

$\vdash . (3) . (4) . \supset \vdash : \mathrm{Hp} . \rho = 0 . \supset . \dot{\exists} ! (P^\rho)^\sigma \dot{\cap} (P^\sigma)^\rho .$

[*303·21] $\supset . P^\rho (\rho/\sigma) P^\sigma$ (5)

Similarly $\vdash : \mathrm{Hp} . \sigma = 0 . \supset . P^\rho (\rho/\sigma) P^\sigma$ (6)

$\vdash . (2) . (5) . (6) . \supset \vdash . \mathrm{Prop}$

***303·31.** $\vdash : \rho \,\mathrm{Prm}\, \sigma . \rho \neq 0 . \sigma \neq 0 . (\rho \times_c \sigma) \cap t\text{‘}\lambda \in \mathrm{Cl}\text{‘}U . \supset .$
$(\exists P) . P \in \mathrm{Rel\,num} \cap t_{00}\text{‘}\lambda . P^\rho (\rho/\sigma) P^\sigma$

Dem.

$\vdash . *300\cdot46 . *301\cdot4 . \supset \vdash : \mathrm{Hp} . \supset . (\exists P) . P \in \mathrm{Rel\,num} . (B\text{‘}P) P^{\rho \times_c \sigma} (B\text{‘}\breve{P})$ (1)

$\vdash . (1) . *303\cdot3 . \supset \vdash . \mathrm{Prop}$

***303·311.** $\vdash : \rho_\lambda, \sigma_\lambda \in \mathrm{Cl}\text{‘}U - \iota\text{‘}0 . \rho \geqslant \sigma . \supset . (\exists P, Q) . P \in (\rho +_c 1)_r . Q \in (\sigma +_c 1)_r .$
$P, Q \in t_{00}\text{‘}\lambda . Q \Subset P . B\text{‘}P = B\text{‘}Q . B\text{‘}\breve{P} = B\text{‘}\breve{Q}$

Dem.

$\vdash . *262\cdot21 . \supset \vdash : \mathrm{Hp} . \supset . \exists ! (\rho +_c 1)_r \cap t_{00}\text{‘}\lambda$ (1)

$\vdash . *117\cdot22 . \supset \vdash : \mathrm{Hp} . P \in (\rho +_c 1)_r . \supset . (\exists \alpha) . \alpha \subset C\text{‘}P . \alpha \in \sigma +_c 1$ (2)

$\vdash . *261\cdot26 . *205\cdot732 . \supset$

$\vdash : \mathrm{Hp} . P \in (\rho +_c 1)_r . \alpha \subset C\text{‘}P . \alpha \in \sigma +_c 1 .$

$\beta = (\alpha - \iota\text{‘}\mathrm{min}_P\text{‘}\alpha - \iota\text{‘}\mathrm{max}_P\text{‘}\alpha) \cup \iota\text{‘}B\text{‘}P \cup \iota\text{‘}B\text{‘}\breve{P} . \supset . \beta \in \sigma +_c 1 .$

[*250·141.*202·55] $\supset . P \upharpoonleft \beta \in (\sigma +_c 1)_r$ (3)

$\vdash . (1) . (2) . (3) . *205\cdot55 . \supset \vdash . \mathrm{Prop}$

***303·32.** $\vdash : \rho \,\mathrm{Prm}\, \sigma . \rho \geqslant \sigma . \sigma \neq 0 . \rho_\lambda \in \mathrm{Cl}\text{‘}U . \supset .$
$\dot{\exists} ! (\rho/\sigma) \upharpoonleft (\mathrm{Rel\,num} \cap t_{00}\text{‘}\lambda) \dot{\cap} \hat{R}\hat{S} (R_{po} \Subset S_{po})$

Dem.

$\vdash . *303\cdot311 . \supset \vdash : \mathrm{Hp} . \supset . (\exists P, Q) . P \in (\rho +_c 1)_r . Q \in (\sigma +_c 1)_r . P, Q \in t_{00}\text{‘}\lambda .$
$Q \Subset P . B\text{‘}P = B\text{‘}Q . B\text{‘}\breve{P} = B\text{‘}\breve{Q}$ (1)

$\vdash . *300\cdot44\cdot45 . *301\cdot4 . \supset$

$\vdash : \mathrm{Hp} . P \in (\rho +_c 1)_r . S = P_1 . \supset . S \in \mathrm{Rel\,num} . (B\text{‘}P) S^\rho (B\text{‘}\breve{P})$ (2)

Similarly

$\vdash : \text{Hp} . Q \in (\sigma +_c 1)_r . R = Q_1 . \supset . R \in \text{Rel num} . (B`Q) R^\sigma (B`\breve{Q})$ (3)

$\vdash . (1) . (2) . (3) . *261{\cdot}35{\cdot}212 . \supset$

$\vdash : \text{Hp} . \supset . (\exists R, S) . R, S \in \text{Rel num} \cap t_{00}`\lambda . R_{po} \Subset S_{po} . \dot{\exists} ! R^\sigma \dot{\cap} S^\rho$ (4)

$\vdash . (4) . *303{\cdot}21 . \supset \vdash . \text{Prop}$

***303·321.** $\vdash : \rho \text{ Prm } \sigma . \rho \neq 0 . \sigma \neq 0 . \rho_\lambda, \sigma_\lambda \in \text{Ɑ}`U . \supset . \dot{\exists} ! (\rho/\sigma) \upharpoonright (\text{Rel num} \cap t_{00}`\lambda)$
[*303·32·13]

***303·322.** $\vdash : \rho \text{ Prm } \sigma . \rho_\lambda, \sigma_\lambda \in \text{D}`U \cap \text{Ɑ}`U . \supset . \dot{\exists} ! (\rho/\sigma) \upharpoonright (\text{Rel num} \cap t_{00}`\lambda)$
[*303·321]

***303·323.** $\vdash : \mu, \nu \in \text{NC ind} - \iota`0 . \supset . (\exists \lambda) . \dot{\exists} ! (\mu/\nu) \upharpoonright (\text{Rel num} \cap t_{00}`\lambda)$
[*303·322]

***303·324.** $\vdash : \mu, \nu \in \text{NC ind} . \mu_\lambda, \nu_\lambda \in \text{D}`U . \sim(\mu \text{ Prm } \nu) . \supset .$
$\dot{\exists} ! (\mu/\nu) \upharpoonright (\text{Rel num} \cap t_{00}`\lambda)$

Dem.

$\vdash . *302{\cdot}22 . \supset \vdash : \text{Hp} . \supset .$

$(\exists \rho, \sigma, \tau) . \rho \text{ Prm } \sigma . \rho \neq 0 . \sigma \neq 0 . \tau \neq 0 . \tau \neq 1 . \mu = \rho \times_c \tau . \nu = \sigma \times_c \tau . \exists ! \mu_\lambda . \exists ! \nu_\lambda .$

[*303·2·21]

$\supset . (\exists \rho, \sigma) . \rho \text{ Prm } \sigma . \rho \neq 0 . \sigma \neq 0 . \mu/\nu = \rho/\sigma . \exists ! (\rho +_c 1)_\lambda . \exists ! (\sigma +_c 1)_\lambda .$

[*303·321] $\supset . \dot{\exists} ! (\mu/\nu) \upharpoonright \text{Rel num} : \supset \vdash . \text{Prop}$

In order to the existence of $(\mu/\nu) \upharpoonright \text{Rel num}$ in any given type, it is by no means *necessary* to have $\mu, \nu \in \text{D}`U$ in the corresponding type. If $\rho \text{ Prm } \sigma . \rho, \sigma \in \text{D}`U \cap \text{Ɑ}`U$, $(\rho \times_c \tau)/(\sigma \times_c \tau)$ will exist, however great τ may be, because $(\rho \times_c \tau)/(\sigma \times_c \tau) = \rho/\sigma$.

***303·33.** $\vdash : \dot{\exists} ! (\mu/\nu) \upharpoonright (\text{Rel num} \cap t_{00}`\lambda) . \equiv .$
$(\exists \rho, \sigma) . (\rho, \sigma) \text{ Prm } (\mu, \nu) . \rho_\lambda, \sigma_\lambda \in \text{D}`U \cap \text{Ɑ}`U$

Dem.

$\vdash . *303{\cdot}322{\cdot}211 . \supset$

$\vdash : (\rho, \sigma) \text{ Prm } (\mu, \nu) . \rho_\lambda, \sigma_\lambda \in \text{D}`U \cap \text{Ɑ}`U . \supset . \dot{\exists} ! (\mu/\nu) \upharpoonright (\text{Rel num} \cap t_{00}`\lambda)$ (1)

$\vdash . *303{\cdot}181{\cdot}15{\cdot}16{\cdot}211 . \supset$

$\vdash :. \dot{\exists} ! (\mu/\nu) \upharpoonright (\text{Rel num} \cap t_{00}`\lambda) . \supset : (\exists \rho, \sigma) . (\rho, \sigma) \text{ Prm } (\mu, \nu) . \rho \neq 0 . \sigma \neq 0 .$
$\dot{\exists} ! (\rho/\sigma) \upharpoonright (\text{Rel num} \cap t_{00}`\lambda) :$

[*303·21] $\supset : (\exists \rho, \sigma) . (\rho, \sigma) \text{ Prm } (\mu, \nu) . \rho \neq 0 . \sigma \neq 0 :$
$(\exists R, S) . R, S \in \text{Rel num} \cap t_{00}`\lambda . \dot{\exists} ! R^\sigma \dot{\cap} S^\rho :$

[*301·41] $\supset : (\exists \rho, \sigma) . (\rho, \sigma) \text{ Prm } (\mu, \nu) . \rho \neq 0 . \sigma \neq 0 .$
$\exists ! (\rho +_c 1) \cap t_0`\lambda . \exists ! (\sigma +_c 1) \cap t_0`\lambda$ (2)

$\vdash . (1) . (2) . \supset \vdash . \text{Prop}$

***303·331.** $\vdash :. \rho \text{ Prm } \sigma . \supset : \dot{\exists} ! (\rho/\sigma) \upharpoonright (\text{Rel num} \cap t_{00}`\lambda) . \equiv . \rho_\lambda, \sigma_\lambda \in \text{D}`U \cap \text{Ɑ}`U$
[*303·33 . *302·31]

***303·332**. $\vdash :. \rho \operatorname{Prm} \sigma . \supset : \dot{\exists} ! (\rho/\sigma) \upharpoonright (\text{Rel num} \cap t_{11}{}^{\backprime}\rho) . \equiv . \rho, \sigma \in D^{\backprime}U \cap \text{Cl}^{\backprime}U$ [*303·331]

In this proposition, ρ, σ are typically definite cardinals, whereas in *303·331 they are typically indefinite.

***303·34**. $\vdash : \rho, \sigma \in \text{NC ind} . \rho_\lambda, \sigma_\lambda \in D^{\backprime}U \cap \text{Cl}^{\backprime}U . \eta > \sigma . \supset .$

$$(\exists R, S) . R, S \in \text{Rel num} \cap t_{00}{}^{\backprime}\lambda . \dot{\exists} ! R^\sigma \dot{\wedge} S^\rho . \sim \{\dot{\exists} ! R^\eta \dot{\wedge} S^\xi\}$$

Note that $\sim \{\dot{\exists} ! R^\eta \dot{\wedge} S^\xi\}$ does not imply $E ! R^\eta$ or $E ! S^\xi$.

Dem.

$\vdash . *303·311 . \supset \vdash : \text{Hp} . \supset . (\exists P, Q, R, S) . P \in (\rho +_c 1)_r . Q \in (\sigma +_c 1)_r .$

$$P, Q \in t_{00}{}^{\backprime}\lambda . B^{\backprime}P = B^{\backprime}Q . B^{\backprime}\breve{P} = B^{\backprime}\breve{Q} . R = P_1 . S = Q_1 \quad (1)$$

As in *303·32 Dem,

$\vdash . (1) . \supset \vdash : \text{Hp} . \supset . (\exists P, Q, R, S) . P \in (\rho +_c 1)_r . Q \in (\sigma +_c 1)_r . S = P_1 . R = Q_1 .$

$$R, S \in \text{Rel num} . (B^{\backprime}P)(R^\sigma \dot{\wedge} S^\rho)(B^{\backprime}\breve{P}) .$$

[*121·48.*202·181.*301·4.*300·44]

$$\supset . (\exists R, S) . R, S \in \text{Rel num} \cap t_{00}{}^{\backprime}\lambda . \dot{\exists} ! R^\sigma \dot{\wedge} S^\rho . \sim (\dot{\exists} ! R^\eta) : \supset \vdash . \text{Prop}$$

***303·341**. $\vdash : \rho_\lambda, \sigma_\lambda \in D^{\backprime}U \cap \text{Cl}^{\backprime}U . \rho \operatorname{Prm} \sigma . \xi \operatorname{Prm} \eta . (\rho/\sigma) \upharpoonright t_{00}{}^{\backprime}\lambda = (\xi/\eta) \upharpoonright t_{00}{}^{\backprime}\lambda . \supset .$

$$\rho = \xi . \sigma = \eta$$

Dem.

$\vdash . *303·34·21 . \supset \vdash : \rho_\lambda, \sigma_\lambda \in D^{\backprime}U \cap \text{Cl}^{\backprime}U . \rho \operatorname{Prm} \sigma . \xi \operatorname{Prm} \eta . \eta > \sigma . \supset .$

$$(\rho/\sigma) \upharpoonright t_{00}{}^{\backprime}\lambda \neq (\xi/\eta) \upharpoonright t_{00}{}^{\backprime}\lambda \quad (1)$$

$\vdash . (1) . \text{Transp} . *302·1 . \supset \vdash : \text{Hp} . \supset . \eta \leqslant \sigma \quad (2)$

$\vdash . (2) . *303·13 . \quad \supset \vdash : \text{Hp} . \supset . \xi \leqslant \rho \quad (3)$

$\vdash . (2) . (3) . *117·32 . \quad \supset \vdash : \text{Hp} . \supset . \xi_\lambda, \sigma_\lambda \in \text{Cl}^{\backprime}U \quad (4)$

$\vdash . *303·322 . \quad \supset \vdash : \text{Hp} . \supset . \dot{\exists} ! (\xi/\eta) \upharpoonright \text{Rel num} .$

[*303·11·15·16] $\quad \supset . \xi \neq 0 . \eta \neq 0 \quad (5)$

$\vdash . (2) . (4) . (5) . \quad \supset \vdash : \text{Hp} . \supset . \xi_\lambda, \eta_\lambda \in D^{\backprime}U \cap \text{Cl}^{\backprime}U .$

$\left[(2) . (3) . \dfrac{\xi, \eta, \rho, \sigma}{\rho, \sigma, \xi, \eta}\right] \quad \supset . \sigma \leqslant \eta . \rho \leqslant \xi \quad (6)$

$\vdash . (2) . (3) . (6) . \supset \vdash . \text{Prop}$

***303·35**. $\vdash : 1_\lambda \in \text{Cl}^{\backprime}U . \xi \operatorname{Prm} \eta . (0/1) \upharpoonright t_{00}{}^{\backprime}\lambda = (\xi/\eta) \upharpoonright t_{00}{}^{\backprime}\lambda . \supset . \xi = 0 . \eta = 1$

Dem.

$\vdash . *300·14 . \supset \vdash : \text{Hp} . \supset . (\exists x, y) . x \neq y . x, y \in t_0{}^{\backprime}\lambda .$

[*303·15] $\quad \supset . (\exists x, y) . x \neq y . (x \downarrow x)(0/1)(x \downarrow y) . x \downarrow x, x \downarrow y \in t_{00}{}^{\backprime}\lambda .$

[Hp] $\quad \supset . (\exists x, y) . x \neq y . (x \downarrow x)(\xi/\eta)(x \downarrow y) .$

[*303·16·17.Transp] $\quad \supset . \xi = 0 . \quad (1)$

[*302·14] $\quad \supset . \eta = 1 \quad (2)$

$\vdash . (1) . (2) . \supset \vdash . \text{Prop}$

***303·36.** $\vdash :. \rho_\lambda, \sigma_\lambda \in \text{Ɑ}‘U . \mathbf{v} . \xi_\lambda, \eta_\lambda \in \text{Ɑ}‘U : \rho \operatorname{Prm} \sigma . \xi \operatorname{Prm} \eta : \supset :$

$(\rho/\sigma) \upharpoonright t_{00}‘\lambda = (\xi/\eta) \upharpoonright t_{00}‘\lambda . \equiv . \rho = \xi . \sigma = \eta$

Dem.

$\vdash . *300{\cdot}14 . *302{\cdot}14 . \supset$

$\vdash :. \rho_\lambda, \sigma_\lambda \in \text{Ɑ}‘U . \rho \operatorname{Prm} \sigma . \sim(\rho_\lambda, \sigma_\lambda \in \text{D}‘U) . \supset : \rho = 0 . \sigma = 1 . \mathbf{v} . \rho = 1 . \sigma = 0 :$

$[*303{\cdot}35{\cdot}13] \supset : \xi \operatorname{Prm} \eta . (\rho/\sigma) \upharpoonright t_{00}‘\lambda = (\xi/\eta) \upharpoonright t_{00}‘\lambda . \supset . \rho = \xi . \sigma = \eta \quad (1)$

$\vdash . (1) . *303{\cdot}341 . \supset \vdash . \text{Prop}$

***303·37.** $\vdash :. \alpha, \beta \in \text{NC ind} \cap \text{Ɑ}‘(U \upharpoonright t^2‘\lambda) . \sim(\alpha = \beta = 0) . \mathbf{v} .$

$\gamma, \delta \in \text{NC ind} \cap \text{Ɑ}‘(U \upharpoonright t^2‘\lambda) . \sim(\gamma = \delta = 0) : \supset :$

$(\alpha/\beta) \upharpoonright t_{00}‘\lambda = (\gamma/\delta) \upharpoonright t_{00}‘\lambda . \supset . \alpha \times_c \delta = \beta \times_c \gamma$

Dem.

$\vdash . *302{\cdot}36 . *303{\cdot}211 . \supset \vdash : \alpha, \beta \in \text{NC ind} . \alpha_\lambda, \beta_\lambda \in \text{Ɑ}‘U . \sim(\alpha = \beta = 0) . \supset .$

$(\exists \rho, \sigma) . (\rho, \sigma) \operatorname{Prm} (\alpha, \beta) . \rho/\sigma = \alpha/\beta \quad (1)$

$\vdash . (1) . *303{\cdot}254{\cdot}181 . \supset \vdash : \text{Hp}(1) . (\alpha/\beta) \upharpoonright t_{00}‘\lambda = (\gamma/\delta) \upharpoonright t_{00}‘\lambda . \supset .$

$(\exists \xi, \eta) . (\xi, \eta) \operatorname{Prm} (\gamma, \delta) \quad (2)$

$\vdash . (1) . (2) . *302{\cdot}21{\cdot}22 . *303{\cdot}211 . \supset$

$\vdash : \text{Hp}(2) . \supset . (\exists \rho, \sigma, \xi, \eta) . (\rho, \sigma) \operatorname{Prm} (\alpha, \beta) . (\xi, \eta) \operatorname{Prm} (\gamma, \delta) . \rho, \sigma \in \text{Ɑ}‘U .$

$\rho/\sigma = \alpha/\beta = \gamma/\delta = \xi/\eta .$

$[*303{\cdot}36] \quad \supset . (\exists \rho, \sigma) . (\rho, \sigma) \operatorname{Prm} (\alpha, \beta) . (\rho, \sigma) \operatorname{Prm} (\gamma, \delta) .$

$[*302{\cdot}34] \quad \supset . \alpha \times_c \delta = \beta \times_c \gamma \quad (3)$

Similarly

$\vdash : \gamma, \delta \in \text{NC ind} . \gamma_\lambda, \delta_\lambda \in \text{Ɑ}‘U . \sim(\gamma = \delta = 0) . (\alpha/\beta) \upharpoonright t_{00}‘\lambda = (\gamma/\delta) \upharpoonright t_{00}‘\lambda . \supset .$

$\alpha \times_c \delta = \beta \times_c \gamma \quad (4)$

$\vdash . (3) . (4) . \supset \vdash . \text{Prop}$

***303·371.** $\vdash : \alpha, \beta, \gamma, \delta \in \text{NC ind} . \alpha_\lambda, \beta_\lambda, \gamma_\lambda, \delta_\lambda \in C‘U . \sim (\alpha \operatorname{Prm} \beta . \gamma \operatorname{Prm} \delta) .$

$(\alpha/\beta) \upharpoonright t_{00}‘\lambda = (\gamma/\delta) \upharpoonright t_{00}‘\lambda . \supset . \alpha \times_c \delta = \beta \times_c \gamma$

[Proof as in *303·37]

***303·38.** $\vdash :. \alpha, \beta, \gamma, \delta \in \text{NC ind} : \alpha_\lambda, \beta_\lambda \in \text{Ɑ}‘U . \mathbf{v} . \gamma_\lambda, \delta_\lambda \in \text{Ɑ}‘U :$

$\sim(\alpha = \beta = 0) . \sim(\gamma = \delta = 0) : \supset :$

$(\alpha/\beta) \upharpoonright t_{00}‘\lambda = (\gamma/\delta) \upharpoonright t_{00}‘\lambda . \equiv . \alpha \times_c \delta = \beta \times_c \gamma \quad [*303{\cdot}37{\cdot}23]$

***303·381.** $\vdash :. \alpha, \beta, \gamma, \delta \in \text{NC ind} . \alpha_\lambda, \beta_\lambda, \gamma_\lambda, \delta_\lambda \in C‘U . \sim (\alpha \operatorname{Prm} \beta . \gamma \operatorname{Prm} \delta) . \supset :$

$(\alpha/\beta) \upharpoonright t_{00}‘\lambda = (\gamma/\delta) \upharpoonright t_{00}‘\lambda . \equiv . \alpha \times_c \delta = \beta \times_c \gamma \quad [*303{\cdot}371{\cdot}23]$

***303·39.** $\vdash :. \alpha, \beta, \gamma, \delta \in \text{NC ind} . \sim(\alpha = \beta = 0) . \sim(\gamma = \delta = 0) . \supset :$

$\alpha/\beta = \gamma/\delta . \equiv . \alpha \times_c \delta = \beta \times_c \gamma \quad [*303{\cdot}38 . *300{\cdot}18]$

***303·391.** $\vdash :. \alpha, \beta \in \text{NC ind} . \alpha_\lambda, \beta_\lambda \in \text{Ɑ}‘U . \sim(\alpha = \beta = 0) . \supset :$

$(\alpha/\beta) \upharpoonright t_{00}‘\lambda = (\gamma/\delta) \upharpoonright t_{00}‘\lambda . \equiv . \alpha/\beta = \gamma/\delta . \equiv . \alpha \times_c \delta = \beta \times_c \gamma$

[*303·38·254·11·14]

Thus when α/β is used as a typically indefinite symbol, we obtain the same results as if we supposed it defined as of a type $t_{00}\text{'}\lambda$, where $\alpha +_c 1$ and $\beta +_c 1$ both exist in the type of λ, *i.e.* $\mathrm{Nc}\text{'}t_0\text{'}\lambda > \alpha \,.\, \mathrm{Nc}\text{'}t_0\text{'}\lambda > \beta$.

***303·392.** $\vdash :. \alpha, \beta \in \text{Ɑ}\text{'}U \,.\, \sim(\alpha = \beta = 0) \,.\supset: (\alpha/\beta) \upharpoonright t_{11}\text{'}\alpha = (\gamma/\delta) \upharpoonright t_{11}\text{'}\alpha \,.\equiv.$
$\alpha/\beta = \gamma/\delta \,.\equiv.\, \alpha \times_c \delta = \beta \times_c \gamma$ [*303·391·27]

This proposition differs from *303·391 by the fact that α, β have become typically definite. It will be observed that even when α and β are typically definite, α/β, like $\alpha \times_c \beta$, remains typically indefinite.

***303·4.** $\vdash :. \rho \,\mathrm{Prm}\, \sigma \,.\, R \in \mathrm{Rel\,num} \,.\supset: R_\rho (\rho/\sigma) R_\sigma \,.\equiv.\, \dot{\exists} \,!\, R_{\rho \times_c \sigma}$
[*303·3·21 . *301·4]

***303·41.** $\vdash :: \mu, \nu \in \mathrm{NC\,ind} \,.\, \sim(\mu = 0 \,.\, \nu = 0) \,.\supset:.$
$R \in \mathrm{Rel\,num} \,.\, \xi = \mathrm{lcm}(\mu, \nu) \,.\supset: R_\mu (\mu/\nu) R_\nu \,.\equiv.\, \dot{\exists} \,!\, R_\xi$

Dem.

$\vdash .$ *303·2 . *300·44 . $\supset$

$\vdash :. \mathrm{Hp} \,.\, \mu \neq 0 \,.\, \nu \neq 0 \,.\, R \in \mathrm{Rel\,num} \,.\, (\rho, \sigma) \,\mathrm{Prm}_r (\mu, \nu) \,.\supset:$
$R_\mu (\mu/\nu) R_\nu \,.\equiv.\, \dot{\exists} \,!\, R_{\mu \times_c \sigma} \,\dot{\cap}\, R_{\nu \times_c \rho} \,.$

[*302·37] $\equiv .\, \dot{\exists} \,!\, R_{\mu \times_c \sigma}$ (1)

$\vdash . (1) .$ *302·44 $. \supset \vdash :. \mathrm{Hp}(1) \,.\, \xi = \mathrm{lcm}(\mu, \nu) \,.\supset: R_\mu (\mu/\nu) R_\nu \,.\equiv.\, \dot{\exists} \,!\, R_\xi$ (2)

$\vdash . (2) .$ *302·22 . $\supset$

$\vdash :. \mathrm{Hp} \,.\, \mu \neq 0 \,.\, \nu \neq 0 \,.\, R \in \mathrm{Rel\,num} \,.\, \xi = \mathrm{lcm}(\mu, \nu) \,.\supset: R_\mu (\mu/\nu) R_\nu \,.\equiv.\, \dot{\exists} \,!\, R_\xi$ (3)

$\vdash .$ *302·44 . $\supset$

$\vdash :. \mathrm{Hp} \,.\, \mu = 0 \,.\, R \in \mathrm{Rel\,num} \,.\, \xi = \mathrm{lcm}(\mu, \nu) \,.\supset: \xi = 0 :$

[*303·15] $\supset: R_\mu (\mu/\nu) R_\nu \,.\equiv.\, \dot{\exists} \,!\, R_\xi$ (4)

Similarly

$\vdash :. \mathrm{Hp} \,.\, \nu = 0 \,.\, R \in \mathrm{Rel\,num} \,.\, \xi = \mathrm{lcm}(\mu, \nu) \,.\supset: R_\mu (\mu/\nu) R_\nu \,.\equiv.\, \dot{\exists} \,!\, R_\xi$ (5)

$\vdash . (3) . (4) . (5) . \supset \vdash .$ Prop

***303·42.** $\vdash :. \mathrm{Hp}$ *303·41 $.\, \xi = \mathrm{lcm}(\mu, \nu) \,.\supset: U_\mu (\mu/\nu) U_\nu \,.\equiv.\, \mathrm{lcm}(\mu, \nu) \in C\text{'}U$
[*303·41 . *300·26]

***303·43.** $\vdash :. \mathrm{Infin\,ax} \,.\supset: \mu, \nu \in \mathrm{NC\,ind} \,.\, \sim(\mu = \nu = 0) \,.\supset_{\mu, \nu} .\, U_\mu (\mu/\nu) U_\nu$
[*303·42 . *300·14]

***303·44.** $\vdash :. \mathrm{Hp}$ *303·42 $.\, P \in \mathrm{Ser} \,.\supset: P_\mu (\mu/\nu) P_\nu \,.\equiv.\, \dot{\exists} \,!\, P_\xi$
[*303·41 . *300·44]

***303·45.** $\vdash : P \in \Omega\,\mathrm{infin} \quad \mu, \nu \in \mathrm{NC\,ind} \,.\, \sim(\mu = 0 \,.\, \nu = 0) \,.\supset.\, P_\mu (\mu/\nu) P_\nu$
[*300·44 . *303·44]

***303·46.** $\vdash :. (\rho, \sigma) \,\mathrm{Prm}\, (\mu, \nu) \,.\, \xi, \eta \in \mathrm{NC\,ind} \,.\, R \in \mathrm{Rel\,num} \,.\supset:$
$R_\xi (\mu/\nu) R_\eta \,.\equiv.\, \xi \times_c \sigma = \eta \times_c \rho \,.\, \dot{\exists} \,!\, R_{\xi \times_c \sigma}$

Dem.

$\vdash .$ *303·211 . $\supset$

$\vdash :. \mathrm{Hp} \,.\supset: R_\xi (\mu/\nu) R_\eta \,.\equiv.\, R_\xi (\rho/\sigma) R_\eta \,.$

[*303·21] $\equiv .\, \dot{\exists} \,!\, R_{\xi \times_c \sigma} \,\dot{\cap}\, R_{\eta \times_c \rho} \,.$

[*300·55] $\equiv .\, \xi \times_c \sigma = \eta \times_c \rho \,.\, \dot{\exists} \,!\, R_{\xi \times_c \sigma} :. \supset \vdash .$ Prop

***303·461**. $\vdash :. \mu, \nu, \xi, \eta \in \mathrm{NC\,ind} . \sim (\mu = \nu = 0) . \sim (\xi = \eta = 0) . R \in \mathrm{Rel\,num} . \supset :$
$R_\xi (\mu/\nu) R_\eta . \equiv . \xi \times_c \nu = \eta \times_c \mu . \dot{\exists} ! R_{\mathrm{lcm}(\xi, \eta)}$

Dem.

$\vdash . *302{\cdot}45 . \supset$

$\vdash : \mathrm{Hp} . (\rho, \sigma) \mathrm{Prm} (\xi, \eta) . \supset . \xi \times_c \sigma = \mathrm{lcm} (\xi, \eta)$ (1)

$\vdash . *302{\cdot}35 . \supset$

$\vdash : \mathrm{Hp} . (\rho, \sigma) \mathrm{Prm} (\mu, \nu) . \xi \times_c \sigma = \eta \times_c \rho . \supset . (\rho, \sigma) \mathrm{Prm} (\xi, \eta) .$ (2)

[*302·34] $\supset . \xi \times_c \nu = \eta \times_c \mu$ (3)

$\vdash . *302{\cdot}35{\cdot}37 . \supset$

$\vdash : \mathrm{Hp} . (\rho, \sigma) \mathrm{Prm} (\mu, \nu) . \xi \times_c \nu = \eta \times_c \mu . \supset . \xi \times_c \sigma = \eta \times_c \rho$ (4)

$\vdash . (1) . (2) . (3) . (4) . *303{\cdot}42 . \supset \vdash . \mathrm{Prop}$

***303·47**. $\vdash :. \mathrm{Hp}\, *303{\cdot}461 . \dot{\Lambda} \sim \in \mathrm{Pot}`R . \supset : R_\xi (\mu/\nu) R_\eta . \equiv . \xi \times_c \nu = \eta \times_c \mu$
[*303·461]

***303·471**. $\vdash :. \mu, \nu, \xi, \eta \in \mathrm{NC\,ind} . \sim (\mu = \nu = 0) . \sim (\xi = \eta = 0) . P \in \Omega\,\mathrm{infin} . \supset :$
$P_\xi (\mu/\nu) P_\eta . \equiv . \xi \times_c \nu = \eta \times_c \mu$
[*303·47 . *300·44]

***303·48**. $\vdash :. \mu, \nu, \xi, \eta \in \mathrm{NC\,ind} . \sim (\mu = \nu = 0) . \sim (\xi = \eta = 0) . \supset :$
$U_\xi (\mu/\nu) U_\eta . \equiv . \xi \times_c \nu = \eta \times_c \mu . \mathrm{lcm} (\xi, \eta) \in C`U$
[*303·461 . *300·26]

***303·49**. $\vdash :: \mathrm{Infin\,ax} . \supset :. \mu, \nu, \xi, \eta \in \mathrm{NC\,ind} . \sim (\mu = \nu = 0) . \supset :$
$U_\xi (\mu/\nu) U_\eta . \equiv . \xi \times_c \nu = \eta \times_c \mu$

Dem.

$\vdash . *303{\cdot}15 . \supset \vdash :. \mu, \nu, \xi, \eta \in \mathrm{NC\,ind} . \mu = 0 . \nu \neq 0 . \supset :$

$U_\xi (\mu/\nu) U_\eta . \equiv . U_\xi \in \mathrm{Rl}`I . U_\eta \in \mathrm{Rel\,num\,id} .$

[*120·42] $\equiv . \xi = 0 .$

[*113·602] $\equiv . \xi \times_c \nu = \eta \times_c \mu$ (1)

Similarly

$\vdash :. \mu, \nu, \xi, \eta \in \mathrm{NC\,ind} . \mu \neq 0 . \nu = 0 . \supset : U_\xi (\mu/\nu) U_\eta . \equiv . \xi \times_c \nu = \eta \times_c \mu$ (2)

$\vdash . (1) . (2) . *303{\cdot}48 . \supset \vdash . \mathrm{Prop}$

***303·5**. $\vdash : \rho, \sigma \in \mathrm{NC\,ind} - \iota`0 . \exists ! (\rho +_c \sigma)_\lambda . \supset .$
$(\exists P, Q) . P \in (\rho +_c 1)_r . Q \in (\sigma +_c 1)_r . P, Q \in t_{00}`\lambda .$
$B`P = B`Q . B`\breve{P} = B`\breve{Q} . C`P \cap C`Q = \iota`B`P \cup \iota`B`\breve{P}$

Dem.

$\vdash . *110{\cdot}202 . *120{\cdot}417 . \supset$

$\vdash : \mathrm{Hp} . \supset . (\exists \alpha, \beta) . \alpha, \beta \in t_0`\lambda . \alpha \in \rho +_c 1 . \beta \in \sigma -_c 1 . \alpha \cap \beta = \Lambda$ (1)

$\vdash . *262\cdot2 . \supset$

$\vdash : \text{Hp} . \alpha, \beta \in t_0`\lambda . \alpha \in \rho +_c 1 . \beta \in \sigma -_c 1 . \alpha \cap \beta = \Lambda . \sigma \neq 2 . \supset .$

$(\exists P, S) . P, S \in \Omega \cap t_{00}`\lambda . C`P = \alpha . C`S = \beta . \alpha \cap \beta = \Lambda .$

$[*251\cdot131\cdot141] \supset . (\exists P, S, Q) . P, S, Q \in \Omega \cap t_{00}`\lambda . C`P = \alpha . C`S = \beta .$

$Q = B`P \leftarrow\!\!\!+ S \,+\!\!\!\!\rightarrow B`\breve{P} . C`P \cap C`Q = \iota`B`P \cup \iota`B`Q$ (2)

$\vdash . *262\cdot2 . \supset \vdash : \text{Hp} . \alpha, \beta \in t_0`\lambda . \alpha \in \rho +_c 1 . \beta = \iota`x . x \sim \in \alpha . \sigma = 2 . \supset .$

$(\exists P, Q) . P, Q \in t_{00}`\lambda . P \in \Omega . C`P = \alpha . Q = (B`P) \downarrow x \,+\!\!\!\!\rightarrow B`\breve{P}$ (3)

$\vdash . (1) . (2) . (3) . \supset \vdash . \text{Prop}$

***303·51.** $\vdash :. \rho \text{ Prm } \sigma . \rho \neq 0 . \sigma \neq 0 . \exists ! (\rho +_c \sigma)_\lambda . \supset :$

$(\exists R, S) : R, S \in \text{Rel num} \cap t_{00}`\lambda . R (\rho/\sigma) S : \xi/\eta \neq \rho/\sigma . \supset_{\xi, \eta} . \sim R (\xi/\eta) S$

Dem.

$\vdash . *300\cdot44\cdot45 . *301\cdot4 . \supset$

$\vdash : \text{Hp} . P \in (\rho +_c 1)_r . Q \in (\sigma +_c 1)_r . S = P_1 . R = Q_1 .$

$B`P = B`Q . B`\breve{P} = B`\breve{Q} . C`P \cap C`Q = \iota`B`P \cup \iota`B`\breve{P} . \supset . \dot{\exists} ! R^\sigma \dot{\cap} S^\rho$ (1)

$\vdash . *301\cdot41 . \supset \vdash : \text{Hp}(1) . \sim(\xi = \rho . \eta = \sigma) . \supset . R^\eta \dot{\cap} S^\xi = \dot{\Lambda}$ (2)

$\vdash . (1) . (2) . *303\cdot21 . \supset$

$\vdash :. \text{Hp}(1) . \supset : R (\rho/\sigma) S : \xi \text{ Prm } \eta . \sim(\xi = \rho . \eta = \sigma) . \supset_{\xi, \eta} . \sim R (\xi/\eta) S :$

$[*303\cdot36] \quad \supset : R (\rho/\sigma) S : \xi \text{ Prm } \eta . \xi/\eta \neq \rho/\sigma . \supset_{\xi, \eta} . \sim R (\xi/\eta) S :$

$[*302\cdot22 . *303\cdot211]$

$\supset : R (\rho/\sigma) S : \xi, \eta \in C`U . \sim(\xi = \eta = 0) . \xi/\eta \neq \rho/\sigma . \supset_{\xi, \eta} . \sim R (\xi/\eta) S :$

$[*303\cdot182] \supset : R (\rho/\sigma) S : \xi/\eta \neq \rho/\sigma . \supset_{\xi, \eta} . \sim R (\xi/\eta) S$ (3)

$\vdash . (3) . *300\cdot44 . *303\cdot5 . \supset \vdash . \text{Prop}$

***303·52.** $\vdash :. \mu, \nu \in \text{NC ind} - \iota`0 . \exists ! (\mu +_c \nu)_\lambda . \supset :$

$(\exists R, S) : R, S \in t_{00}`\lambda . R (\mu/\nu) S : \xi/\eta \neq \mu/\nu . \supset_{\xi, \eta} . \sim R (\xi/\eta) S$

Dem.

$\vdash . *303\cdot24 . *302\cdot39 . \supset$

$\vdash : \text{Hp} . \supset . (\exists \rho, \sigma) . \rho \text{ Prm } \sigma . \mu/\nu = \rho/\sigma . \rho \neq 0 . \sigma \neq 0 . \exists ! \rho +_c \sigma$ (1)

$\vdash . (1) . *303\cdot51 . \supset \vdash . \text{Prop}$

***303·6.** $\vdash : \nu \in \text{NC ind} - \iota`0 . \supset . 0/\nu = 0_q$ $[*303\cdot15]$

***303·61.** $\vdash : \nu \in \text{NC ind} - \iota`0 . \supset . \nu/0 = \infty_q$ $[*303\cdot16]$

***303·62.** $\vdash . 0_q = \text{Cnv}`\infty_q = \hat{R}\hat{S} (\dot{\exists} ! R \dot{\cap} I \upharpoonright C`S)$ $[*303\cdot6\cdot61\cdot13\cdot15]$

***303·621.** $\vdash . 0_q \upharpoonright \text{Rel num id} = \text{Cnv}`(\text{Rel num id} \upharpoonleft \infty_q)$

$= \hat{R}\hat{S} (R \subseteq I . S \in \text{Rel num id} . \exists ! C`R \cap C`S)$ $[*303\cdot6\cdot61\cdot13\cdot151]$

***303·63.** $\vdash : \exists ! 2_\lambda . \supset . \dot{\exists} ! 0_q \upharpoonright (\text{Rel num} \cap t_{00}{}^\text{‘}\lambda)$

Dem.

$\vdash . *303\cdot15\cdot6 . \supset \vdash : x \neq y . \supset . I0_q (x \downarrow y) : \supset \vdash . \text{Prop}$

***303·631.** $\vdash : \exists ! 2_\lambda . \supset . \dot{\exists} ! (\text{Rel num} \cap t_{00}{}^\text{‘}\lambda) \,\urcorner\, \infty_q$ [*303·63·62]

***303·65.** $\vdash : \exists ! 2_\lambda . \supset . 0_q \upharpoonright t_{00}{}^\text{‘}\lambda \neq \infty_q \upharpoonright t_{00}{}^\text{‘}\lambda$

Dem.

$\vdash . *303\cdot62 . \supset \vdash : x \neq y . \supset . I0_q (x \downarrow y) . \sim \{I \infty_q (x \downarrow y)\} : \supset \vdash . \text{Prop}$

***303·66.** $\vdash :. \exists ! 2_\lambda . \supset : (\mu/\nu) \upharpoonright t_{00}{}^\text{‘}\lambda = 0_q . \equiv . \mu = 0 . \nu \in \text{NC ind} - \iota^\text{‘}0$

Dem.

$\vdash . *303\cdot6 . \supset \vdash : \mu = 0 . \nu \in \text{NC ind} - \iota^\text{‘}0 . \supset . \mu/\nu = 0_q$ (1)

$\vdash . *303\cdot6\cdot15 . \supset$

$\vdash : \mu/\nu = 0_q . \supset . \mu/\nu = \hat{R}\hat{S} (R \in \text{Rl}^\text{‘}I . S \in \text{Rel num id} . \exists ! C^\text{‘}R \cap C^\text{‘}S)$ (2)

$\vdash . *300\cdot3 . \supset \vdash : \text{Hp} . \supset . (\exists x, y) . x \neq y . x \downarrow y \in \text{Rel num} \cap t_{00}{}^\text{‘}\lambda .$

[*10·24] $\supset . \exists ! (\text{Rel num id} - \text{Rl}^\text{‘}I) \cap t_{00}{}^\text{‘}\lambda$ (3)

$\vdash . (2) . (3) . *303\cdot11\cdot17 . \supset$

$\vdash :: \text{Hp} . \supset :. (\mu/\nu) \upharpoonright t_{00}{}^\text{‘}\lambda = 0_q . \supset : \mu, \nu \in \text{NC ind} : \mu = 0 . \vee . \nu = 0$ (4)

$\vdash . (2) . (3) . *303\cdot16 . \supset$

$\vdash :. \text{Hp} . \supset : (\mu/\nu) \upharpoonright t_{00}{}^\text{‘}\lambda = 0_q . \supset . \sim (\mu \neq 0 . \nu = 0)$ (5)

$\vdash . (4) . (5) . \supset \vdash :. \text{Hp} . \supset : (\mu/\nu) \upharpoonright t_{00}{}^\text{‘}\lambda = 0_q . \supset . \mu = 0 . \nu \in \text{NC ind} - \iota^\text{‘}0$ (6)

$\vdash . (1) . (6) . \supset \vdash . \text{Prop}$

***303·67.** $\vdash :. \exists ! 2_\lambda . \supset : (\mu/\nu) \upharpoonright t_{00}{}^\text{‘}\lambda = \infty_q . \equiv . \nu = 0 . \mu \in \text{NC ind} - \iota^\text{‘}0$
[*303·66·62]

***303·7.** $\vdash : X \in \text{Rat} . \equiv . (\exists \mu, \nu) . \mu, \nu \in \text{NC ind} . \nu \neq 0 . X = \mu/\nu$
[(*303·04)]

***303·71.** $\vdash : X \in \text{Rat def} . \equiv . (\exists \mu, \nu) . \mu, \nu \in \text{D}^\text{‘}U \cap \text{Ꭰ}^\text{‘}U . X = (\mu/\nu) \upharpoonright t_{11}{}^\text{‘}\mu$
[(*303·05)]

***303·72.** $\vdash : X \in \text{Rat} . \supset . (\exists \mu) . \dot{\exists} ! X \upharpoonright t_{11}{}^\text{‘}\mu$ [*303·26]

***303·721.** $\vdash : X \in \text{Rat} - \iota^\text{‘}0_q . \supset . (\exists \mu) . X \upharpoonright t_{11}{}^\text{‘}\mu \in \text{Rat def}$
[*300·18 . *303·7·71]

***303·73.** $\vdash : X \in \text{Rat def} . \supset . \dot{\exists} ! X \upharpoonright \text{Rel num}$ [*303·322·324]

***303·731.** $\vdash :. \rho \text{ Prm } \sigma . \supset : (\rho/\sigma) \upharpoonright t_{11}{}^\text{‘}\rho \in \text{Rat def} . \equiv . \rho, \sigma \in \text{D}^\text{‘}U \cap \text{Ꭰ}^\text{‘}U$
[*303·71 . *302·39]

*303·74. $\vdash :. \rho \operatorname{Prm} \sigma . X = (\rho/\sigma) \restriction t_{11}`\rho . \supset : \dot{\exists} ! X \restriction \text{Rel num} . \equiv . \rho, \sigma \in D`U \cap \text{ᗡ}`U$
[*303·332]

*303·75. $\vdash : X \in \text{Rat} . \dot{\exists} ! X \restriction (t_{11}`\mu \cap \text{Rel num}) . \supset . X \restriction t_{11}`\mu \in \text{Rat def}$
[*303·74·71]

*303·76. $\vdash :. X, Y \in \text{Rat} . X \restriction t_{11}`\rho \in \text{Rat def} . \supset : X \restriction t_{11}`\rho = Y \restriction t_{11}`\rho . \equiv . X = Y$
[*303·391]

*303·77. $\vdash :. \text{Infin ax} . \supset : \mu, \nu \in \text{NC ind} - \iota`0 . \supset . \mu/\nu \in \text{Rat def}$
[*300·14 . *303·71]

*303·78. $\vdash : \text{Infin ax} . \supset . \text{Rat def} = \text{Rat} - \iota`0_q$ [*303·7·77]

The above two propositions assume that μ/ν in the first, and "Rat" in the second, have been made typically definite, but they hold however the type may be defined.

$*304$. THE SERIES OF RATIOS.

Summary of $*304$.

In this number we consider the relation of greater and less among ratios, and the series generated by this relation. We need two different notations, one for greater and less between typically indefinite ratios, the other for greater and less between ratios of the same type. The former is more useful where we are dealing merely with inequalities between specified ratios, but the latter is necessary when we wish to consider the *series* of ratios in order of magnitude, since a series must be composed of terms which are all of the same type. We put

$$*304\cdot01.\quad X <_r Y \,.=.\, (\exists \mu, \nu, \rho, \sigma) \,.\, \mu, \nu, \rho, \sigma \,\epsilon\, \text{NC ind} \,.\, \sigma \neq 0 \,.\, \mu \times_c \sigma < \nu \times_c \rho \,.\, X = \mu/\nu \,.\, Y = \rho/\sigma \quad \text{Df}$$

This definition is so framed as to include 0_q but exclude ∞_q. For the relation "less than" among rationals of given type (excluding 0_q), we use the letter H, to suggest η (defined in $*273$), because, if the axiom of infinity holds, the series of rationals of a given type is an η. The definition is

$$*304\cdot02.\quad H = \hat{X}\hat{Y}\{X, Y \,\epsilon\, \text{Rat def} \,.\, X <_r Y\} \quad \text{Df}$$

When we wish to include 0_q in the series, we use the notation H'; thus

$$*304\cdot03.\quad H' = \hat{X}\hat{Y}\{X, Y \,\epsilon\, \text{Rat def} \cup \iota`0_q \,.\, X <_r Y\} \quad \text{Df}$$

(It will be observed that here $\iota`0_q$ acquires typical definiteness through the fact that it must be of the same type as "Rat def" in order to make "Rat def $\cup\, \iota`0_q$" significant.)

If the axiom of infinity does not hold, H and H' will be finite series: if $\nu +_c 1$ is the greatest integer in a given type ($\nu > 1$), the first term of H is $1/\nu$ and the last is $\nu/1$ ($*304\cdot281$). In a higher type, we shall get a larger series for H, but at no stage shall we get an infinite series. If, on the other hand, the axiom of infinity does hold, H is a compact series ($*304\cdot3$) without beginning or end ($*304\cdot31$) and having $\aleph_0$ terms in its field ($*304\cdot32$), *i.e.* H is an η ($*304\cdot33$). In this case, $C`H = D`H = \text{Rat} - \iota`0_q$ ($*304\cdot34$), *i.e.* any rational other than $0_q$, as soon as it is made typically definite, belongs to $C`H$.

Under all circumstances, H is a series (*304·23), and H exists in the type $t_{00}{}^{\backprime}\lambda$ if 3 exists in the type $t^{\backprime}\lambda$ (*304·27). In the same case, $C^{\backprime}H = \text{Rat def}$ (*304·28). Similar propositions hold for H'.

$C^{\backprime}H'$ consists of typically definite ratios, and if X is any ratio, there are types in which X belongs to $C^{\backprime}H'$ (*304·52). If the axiom of infinity holds, every ratio is a member of $C^{\backprime}H'$ in every type (*304·49).

***304·01.** $X <_r Y . = . (\exists \mu, \nu, \rho, \sigma) . \mu, \nu, \rho, \sigma \in \text{NC ind} . \sigma \neq 0 . \mu \times_c \sigma < \nu \times_c \rho .$
$X = \mu/\nu . Y = \rho/\sigma$ Df

***304·02.** $H = \hat{X}\hat{Y}\{X, Y \in \text{Rat def} . X <_r Y\}$ Df

***304·03.** $H' = \hat{X}\hat{Y}\{X, Y \in \text{Rat def} \cup \iota^{\backprime}0_q . X <_r Y\}$ Df

***304·1.** $\vdash : X <_r Y . \equiv . (\exists \mu, \nu, \rho, \sigma) . \mu, \nu, \rho, \sigma \in \text{NC ind} . \mu \times_c \sigma < \nu \times_c \rho .$
$X = \mu/\nu . Y = \rho/\sigma$ [(*304·01)]

***304·11.** $\vdash : \mu/\nu <_r \rho/\sigma . \equiv . \sigma/\rho <_r \nu/\mu$ [*304·1]

***304·12.** $\vdash : X <_r Y . \equiv . \breve{Y} <_r \breve{X}$ [*304·11 . *303·13]

***304·13.** $\vdash : X <_r Y . \supset . X, Y \in \text{Rat} . Y \neq 0_q$

Dem.

$\vdash . *117·5 . \supset \vdash : \mu \times_c \sigma < \nu \times_c \rho . \supset . \nu \times_c \rho \neq 0 .$
[*113·602] $\supset . \nu \neq 0 . \rho \neq 0$ (1)
$\vdash . (1) . *304·1 . *303·7 . \supset \vdash . \text{Prop}$

***304·14.** $\vdash : XHY . \equiv . X, Y \in \text{Rat def} . X <_r Y$ [(*304·02)]

***304·15.** $\vdash : XHY . \equiv . (\exists \mu, \nu, \rho, \sigma) . \mu, \nu, \rho, \sigma \in D^{\backprime}U \cap \text{Ꮖ}^{\backprime}U .$
$X = (\mu/\nu) \upharpoonright t_{11}{}^{\backprime}\mu . Y = (\rho/\sigma) \upharpoonright t_{11}{}^{\backprime}\mu . \mu \times_c \sigma < \nu \times_c \rho$
[*304·14·1 . *303·71]

***304·151.** $\vdash : XHY . \equiv . (\exists M, N, \mu) . M <_r N . M \upharpoonright t_{11}{}^{\backprime}\mu, N \upharpoonright t_{11}{}^{\backprime}\mu \in \text{Rat def} .$
$X = M \upharpoonright t_{11}{}^{\backprime}\mu . Y = N \upharpoonright t_{11}{}^{\backprime}\mu$ [*304·15]

***304·152.** $\vdash :. \mu \,\text{Prm}\, \nu . \rho \,\text{Prm}\, \sigma . \supset : \{(\mu/\nu) \upharpoonright t_{11}{}^{\backprime}\mu\} H \{(\rho/\sigma) \upharpoonright t_{11}{}^{\backprime}\mu\} . \equiv .$
$\mu/\nu <_r \rho/\sigma . \mu, \nu, \rho, \sigma \in D^{\backprime}U \cap \text{Ꮖ}^{\backprime}U$ [*304·151 . *303·731]

***304·16.** $\vdash : (\mu/\nu) H (\rho/\sigma) . \equiv . (\sigma/\rho) H (\nu/\mu)$ [*304·15]

***304·161.** $\vdash : XHY . \equiv . \breve{Y} H \breve{X}$ [*304·12·151]

***304·2.** $\vdash . H \subseteq J$

Dem.

$\vdash . *303·37 . \supset$
$\vdash : \mu, \nu, \rho, \sigma \in D^{\backprime}U \cap \text{Ꮖ}^{\backprime}U . (\mu/\nu) \upharpoonright t_{11}{}^{\backprime}\mu = (\rho/\sigma) \upharpoonright t_{11}{}^{\backprime}\mu . \supset . \mu \times_c \sigma = \nu \times_c \rho .$
[*304·15] $\supset . \sim \{(\mu/\nu) H (\rho/\sigma)\}$ (1)
$\vdash . (1) . \text{Transp} . \supset \vdash . \text{Prop}$

***304·201.** $\vdash . \sim (X <_r X)$ [Proof as in *304·2]

✱304·21. $\vdash . H \in \mathrm{trans}$

Dem.

$\vdash . {*}304{\cdot}15 . \supset \vdash : XHY . YHZ . \supset .$

$(\exists \mu, \nu, \rho, \sigma, \xi, \eta) . \mu, \nu, \rho, \sigma, \xi, \eta \in \mathrm{D}‘U \cap \text{Ɑ}‘U . \mu \times_c \sigma < \nu \times_c \rho .$

$\rho \times_c \eta < \sigma \times_c \xi . X = (\mu/\nu) \upharpoonright t_{11}‘\mu . Y = (\rho/\sigma) \upharpoonright t_{11}‘u . Z = (\xi/\eta) \upharpoonright t_{11}‘\mu$ (1)

$\vdash . {*}117{\cdot}571 . {*}120{\cdot}51 . \supset$

$\vdash : \mu, \nu, \rho, \sigma, \xi, \eta \in \mathrm{D}‘U \cap \text{Ɑ}‘U . \mu \times_c \sigma < \nu \times_c \rho . \rho \times_c \eta < \sigma \times_c \xi . \supset .$

$\mu \times_c \sigma \times_c \eta < \nu \times_c \rho \times_c \eta < \nu \times_c \sigma \times_c \xi .$

$[{*}126{\cdot}51] \supset . \mu \times_c \eta < \nu \times_c \xi$ (2)

$\vdash . (1) . (2) . \supset \vdash .$ Prop

✱304·211. $\vdash : X <_r Y . Y <_r Z . \supset . X <_r Z$ [Proof as in ✱304·21]

✱304·22. $\vdash . H \in \mathrm{connex}$

Dem.

$\vdash . {*}126{\cdot}33 . \supset \vdash :. \mu, \nu, \rho, \sigma \in \mathrm{D}‘U \cap \text{Ɑ}‘U . \supset :$

$\mu \times_c \sigma < \nu \times_c \rho . \vee . \mu \times_c \sigma = \nu \times_c \rho . \vee . \mu \times_c \sigma > \nu \times_c \rho$ (1)

$\vdash . (1) . {*}304{\cdot}15 . \supset \vdash .$ Prop

✱304·221. $\vdash :. X, Y \in \mathrm{Rat} . \supset : X <_r Y . \vee . X = Y . \vee . Y <_r X$ [Proof as in ✱304·22]

✱304·23. $\vdash . H \in \mathrm{Ser}$ [✱304·2·21·22]

✱304·24. $\vdash : \mu, \nu \in \mathrm{D}‘U \cap \text{Ɑ}‘U . \nu \neq 1 . \supset . (\mu/\nu) \, H \, \{\mu/(\nu -_c 1)\}$

Dem.

$\vdash . {*}120{\cdot}414{\cdot}415{\cdot}416 . \supset \vdash : \mathrm{Hp} . \supset . \nu -_c 1 \in \mathrm{D}‘U \cap \text{Ɑ}‘U$ (1)

$\vdash . (1) . {*}304{\cdot}15 . \supset \vdash .$ Prop

✱304·241. $\vdash : \mu \in \mathrm{D}‘U . \mu +_c 1 \in \text{Ɑ}‘U . \supset . (\mu/1) \, H \, \{(\mu +_c 1)/1\}$

Dem.

$\vdash . {*}300{\cdot}14 . \qquad \supset \vdash : \mathrm{Hp} . \supset . \mu, 1 \in \text{Ɑ}‘U$ (1)

$\vdash . {*}300{\cdot}14 . {*}120{\cdot}124 . \supset \vdash : \mathrm{Hp} . \supset . \mu +_c 1 \in \mathrm{D}‘U$ (2)

$\vdash . (1) . (2) . {*}304{\cdot}15 . \supset \vdash .$ Prop

✱304·25. $\vdash : \mu, \nu \in \mathrm{D}‘U \cap \text{Ɑ}‘U . \sim(\mu +_c 1 = B‘U . \nu = 1) . \supset . \mu/\nu \in \mathrm{D}‘H . \nu/\mu \in \text{Ɑ}‘H$
[✱304·24·241·16]

✱304·251. $\vdash : \mu +_c 1 = B‘U . \supset . \mu/1 \sim\in \mathrm{D}‘H$

Dem.

$\vdash . {*}300{\cdot}14 . \supset$

$\vdash : \mathrm{Hp} . \rho, \sigma \in \mathrm{D}‘U \cap \text{Ɑ}‘U . \supset . \rho \leqslant \mu . 1 \leqslant \sigma .$

$[{*}117{\cdot}571] \qquad \supset . \rho \times_c 1 \leqslant \mu \times_c \sigma$ (1)

$\vdash . (1) . {*}304{\cdot}15 . \supset \vdash .$ Prop

✱304·26. $\vdash :. \mu \, \mathrm{Prm} \, \nu . \supset : \mu/\nu \in \mathrm{D}‘H . \equiv . \nu/\mu \in \text{Ɑ}‘H .$

$\equiv . \mu \, \nu \in \mathrm{D}‘U \cap \text{Ɑ}‘U . \sim(\mu +_c 1 = B‘U . \nu = 1)$

[✱302·39 . ✱304·25·251·15·16]

***304·261.** $\vdash . D`H = \hat{X}\{(\exists \mu, \nu) . \mu, \nu \in D`U \cap \text{G}`U . \sim(\mu +_c 1 = B`U . \nu = 1) .$
$X = (\mu/\nu) \upharpoonright t_{11}`\mu\}$ [*304·25·251·15]

***304·262.** $\vdash . \text{G}`H = \hat{X}\{(\exists \mu, \nu) . \mu, \nu \in D`U \cap \text{G}`U . \sim(\mu +_c 1 = B`U . \nu = 1) .$
$X = (\nu/\mu) \upharpoonright t_{11}`\mu\}$ [*304·261·16]

***304·27.** $\vdash : \dot{\exists} ! H . \equiv . \exists ! 3$

Dem.

$\vdash . *300·14 . \supset$

$\vdash :. \exists ! 3 . \supset : \mu = 1 . \nu = 2 . \supset . \mu, \nu \in D`U \cap \text{G}`U . \sim(\mu +_c 1 = B`U . \nu = 1) .$

[*304·25] $\supset . \dot{\exists} ! H$ (1)

$\vdash . *304·261 . \supset$

$\vdash :. \dot{\exists} ! H . \supset : (\exists \mu, \nu) : \mu, \nu \in D`U \cap \text{G}`U : \mu +_c 1 \in \text{G}`U . \vee . \nu \neq 1 :$

[*300·14] $\supset : (\exists \mu) . \mu \geqslant 1 . \exists ! \mu +_c 2 . \vee . (\exists \nu) . \nu > 1 . \exists ! \nu +_c 1 :$

[*117·32] $\supset : \exists ! 3$ (2)

$\vdash . (1) . (2) . \supset \vdash .$ Prop

***304·28.** $\vdash : \exists ! 3 . \supset . C`H = \hat{X}\{(\exists \mu, \nu) . \mu, \nu \in D`U \cap \text{G}`U . X = (\mu/\nu) \upharpoonright t_{11}`\mu\}$
= Rat def

Dem.

$\vdash . *300·14 . \supset \vdash :. \text{Hp} . \supset : \mu +_c 1 = B`U . \supset . \mu > 1$ (1)

$\vdash . (1) . \supset \vdash : \text{Hp} . \supset . \sim(\exists \mu, \nu) . \mu +_c 1 = B`U . \nu = 1 . \nu +_c 1 = B`U . \mu = 1$ (2)

$\vdash . (2) . *304·261·262 . *303·71 . \supset \vdash .$ Prop

***304·281.** $\vdash :. \exists ! 3 . \supset : \mu/\nu = B`H . \equiv . \mu = 1 . \nu +_c 1 = B`U . \equiv . \nu/\mu = B`\breve{H}$
[*304·28·261·262]

***304·282.** $\vdash . 0_q \sim \in C`H$ [*304·27·28 . *303·66]

***304·29.** $\vdash : (\mu/\nu) H (\rho/\sigma) . \mu +_c \rho, \nu +_c \sigma \in \text{G}`U . \supset .$
$(\mu/\nu) H \{(\mu +_c \rho)/(\nu +_c \sigma)\} . \{(\mu +_c \rho)/(\nu +_c \sigma)\} H (\rho/\sigma)$

Dem.

$\vdash . *304·1 . \supset \vdash : \text{Hp} . \supset . \mu \times_c \sigma < \nu \times_c \rho .$

[*126·5] $\supset . \mu \times_c (\nu +_c \sigma) < \nu \times_c (\mu +_c \rho) .$
$(\mu +_c \rho) \times_c \sigma < (\nu +_c \sigma) \times_c \rho .$ (1)

$\vdash . (1) . *304·1 . \supset \vdash .$ Prop

***304·3.** $\vdash : \text{Infin ax} . \supset . H \in \text{Ser} \cap \text{comp}$ [*304·29·23]

***304·31.** $\vdash : \text{Infin ax} . \supset . \sim E ! B`H . \sim E ! B`\breve{H}$ [*304·281 . *300·14]

***304·32.** $\vdash : \text{Infin ax} . \supset . C`H \in \aleph_0$

Dem.

$\vdash . *304·15 . *303·211 . *302·22 . \supset$

$\vdash . \text{Nc}`C`H \leqslant \text{Nc}`\hat{X}\{(\exists \rho, \sigma) . \rho \text{ Prm } \sigma . \rho, \sigma \in D`U \cap \text{G}`U . X = \rho/\sigma\}$

[*303·36] $\leqslant \text{Nc}`\hat{M}\{(\exists \rho, \sigma) . \rho \text{ Prm } \sigma . \rho, \sigma \in D`U \cap \text{G}`U . M = \rho \downarrow \sigma\}$

[*33·161] $\leqslant \text{Nc}`C`U \times_c \text{Nc}`C`U$ (1)

$\vdash . (1) . *123\cdot52 . *300\cdot21 . \supset \vdash : \text{Hp} . \supset . \text{Nc}`C`H \leqslant \aleph_0$ (2)

$\vdash . *304\cdot28 . \supset$

$\vdash : \text{Hp} . \supset . \text{Nc}`C`H \geqslant \text{Nc}`\hat{X}\{(\exists\nu) . \nu \in \text{D}`U \cap \text{Q}`U . X = \nu/1\}$

$[*303\cdot36] \qquad \geqslant \text{Nc}`(\text{D}`U \cap \text{Q}`U)$

$[*300\cdot21] \qquad \geqslant \aleph_0$ (3)

$\vdash . (2) . (3) . *117\cdot23 . \supset \vdash . \text{Prop}$

***304·33.** $\vdash : \text{Infin ax} . \supset . H \in \eta$ [*304·3·31·32 . *273·1]

***304·34.** $\vdash : \text{Infin ax} . \supset . C`H = \text{D}`H = \text{Rat} - \iota`0_q$ [*303·78 . *304·28]

***304·4.** $\vdash : XH'Y . \equiv . X, Y \in \text{Rat def} \cup \iota`0_q . X <_r Y .$

$\equiv . (\exists\mu, \nu, \rho, \sigma) . \mu, \nu, \rho, \sigma \in \text{Q}`U . \nu \neq 0 . \sigma \neq 0 . \mu \times_c \sigma < \nu \times_c \rho .$

$X = (\mu/\nu) \upharpoonright t_{11}`\mu . Y = (\rho/\sigma) \upharpoonright t_{11}`\mu$ [*303·71 . (*304·03)]

***304·401.** $\vdash :. \text{Infin ax} . \supset : X <_r Y . \equiv . XH'Y$ [*304·4 . *303·78]

***304·41.** $\vdash . \text{D}`H' = \hat{X}\{(\exists\mu, \nu) . \mu, \nu \in \text{Q}`U . \nu \neq 0 . \sim(\mu +_c 1 = B`U . \nu = 1) .$

$X = (\mu/\nu) \upharpoonright t_{11}`\mu\}$

[Proof as in *304·261]

***304·42.** $\vdash . \text{Q}`H' = \hat{X}\{(\exists\mu, \nu) . \mu, \nu \in \text{Q}`U . \mu \neq 0 . \nu \neq 0 . X = (\mu/\nu) \upharpoonright t_{11}`\mu\}$

***304·43.** $\vdash : \dot{\exists} ! H' . \equiv . \exists ! 2$ [*304·42]

***304·44.** $\vdash : \exists ! 2 . \supset . C`H' = \hat{X}\{(\exists\mu, \nu) . \mu, \nu \in \text{Q}`U . \nu \neq 0 . X = (\mu/\nu) \upharpoonright t_{11}`\mu\}$

[*304·41·42]

***304·45.** $\vdash : \exists ! 2 . \supset . B`H' = 0_q$ [*304·41·42 . *303·6]

***304·46.** $\vdash : \exists ! 3 . \supset . H' = 0_q \leftarrow\!\!\!+ H$ [*304·45·4·27·1]

***304·47.** $\vdash : \text{Infin ax} . \supset . H' \in \dot{1} + \eta$ [*304·46·33]

***304·48.** $\vdash . H' \in \text{Ser}$

Dem.

$\vdash . *304\cdot4 . \supset \vdash : \exists ! 2 . \sim\exists ! 3 . \supset . H' = 0_q \downarrow (1/1)$ (1)

$\vdash . (1) . *304\cdot43\cdot46\cdot23 . \supset \vdash . \text{Prop}$

***304·49.** $\vdash : \text{Infin ax} . \supset . C`H' = \text{D}`H' = \text{Rat}$ [*304·34·46]

***304·5.** $\vdash : X \in C`H . \supset . \dot{\exists} ! X \upharpoonright \text{Rel num}$ [*303·73 . *304·14]

***304·51.** $\vdash : X \in C`H' . \supset . \dot{\exists} ! X \upharpoonright \text{Rel num}$

Dem.

$\vdash . *303\cdot63 . *304\cdot43 . \supset \vdash :. \text{Hp} . \supset . \dot{\exists} ! 0_q \upharpoonright \text{Rel num}$ (1)

$\vdash . (1) . *303\cdot73 . *304\cdot4 . \supset \vdash . \text{Prop}$

***304·52.** $\vdash : X \in \text{Rat} . \supset . (\exists\mu) . X \upharpoonright t_{11}`\mu \in C`H'$ [*304·44 . *300·18]

***304·53.** $\vdash : X \in \text{Rat} - \iota`0_q . \supset . (\exists\mu) . X \upharpoonright t_{11}`\mu \in C`H$ [*304·28 . *300·18]

$*305$. MULTIPLICATION OF SIMPLE RATIOS.

Summary of $*305$.

The ratios hitherto considered are called "simple" ratios in opposition to "generalized" ratios (introduced in $*307$), which include negative ratios. We deal with multiplication and addition first for simple ratios, and then for generalized ratios. In this number we are only concerned with the multiplication of simple ratios.

In defining multiplication of ratios, we naturally frame our definition so as to secure that the product of μ/ν and ρ/σ shall be $(\mu \times_c \rho)/(\nu \times_c \sigma)$. This is effected by the following definition (where "s" stands for "simple"):

$$*305\cdot01.\quad X \times_s Y = \hat{R}\hat{S}[(\exists \mu, \nu, \rho, \sigma) . \mu, \nu, \rho, \sigma \in \text{NC ind} . \nu \neq 0 . \sigma \neq 0 . X = \mu/\nu . Y = \rho/\sigma . R\{(\mu \times_c \rho)/(\nu \times_c \sigma)\} S] \quad \text{Df}$$

which gives us

$$*305\cdot142.\quad \vdash : \mu, \rho \in \text{NC ind} . \nu \neq 0 . \sigma \neq 0 . \supset . \mu/\nu \times_s \rho/\sigma = (\mu \times_c \rho)/(\nu \times_c \sigma)$$

and

$$*305\cdot144.\quad \vdash : \dot{\exists} ! (\mu/\nu \times_s \rho/\sigma) . \supset . \mu/\nu \times_s \rho/\sigma = (\mu \times_c \rho)/(\nu \times_c \sigma)$$

The reason for the hypotheses in these propositions is that, if μ is a cardinal which is not inductive, while $\rho = 0$ and ν, σ are inductive and not 0, $\mu/\nu = \dot{\Lambda}$ and $\mu/\nu \times_s \rho/\sigma = \dot{\Lambda}$, but $(\mu \times_c \rho)/(\nu \times_c \sigma) = 0_q$.

For the applications of the multiplication of ratios, it is essential that we should have, if R, S, T belong to a suitable vector family,

$$R(\mu/\nu) S . S(\rho/\sigma) T . \supset . R(\mu/\nu \times_s \rho/\sigma) T,$$

e.g. we want two-thirds of five-sevenths of T to be $(2/3 \times_s 5/7)$ of T. It will be shown in Section C that our definition satisfies this requirement.

We prove in this number

$$*305\cdot3.\quad \vdash : X, Y \in \text{Rat} . \equiv . X \times_s Y \in \text{Rat}$$

$$*305\cdot22.\quad \vdash :. X \times_s Y = 0_q . \equiv : X, Y \in \text{Rat} : X = 0_q . \vee . Y = 0_q$$

i.e. a product only vanishes when one of its factors vanishes;

$$*305\cdot301.\quad \vdash : X, Y \in \text{Rat} - \iota`0_q . \equiv . X \times_s Y \in \text{Rat} - \iota`0_q$$

*305·25. $\vdash : \mu, \nu, \rho, \sigma \in \mathrm{D}`U \cap \mathrm{G}`U . \supset . (\mu/\nu \times_s \rho/\sigma) \upharpoonright t_{00}`\mu \in C`H$

Thus a product of two ratios which both exist in a given type exists in the next type, *i.e.*

*305·26. $\vdash : X, Y \in \mathrm{Rat} . X \upharpoonright t_{11}`\mu, Y \upharpoonright t_{11}`\mu \in \mathrm{Rat\ def} . \supset . (X \times_s Y) \upharpoonright t_{00}`\mu \in C`H$

The formal laws offer no difficulty. We prove the commutative law (*305·11) and the associative law (*305·41); we prove that $X \times_s 1/1 = X$ (*305·51) and that $X \times_s \breve{X} = 1/1$ (*305·52). Division results from

*305·61. $\vdash :. A \in \mathrm{Rat} - \iota`0_q . A' \in \mathrm{Rat} . \supset : A \times_s X = A' . \equiv . X = A' \times_s \breve{A}$

and the axiom of Archimedes is given by

*305·7. $\vdash : X, Y \in \mathrm{Rat} - \iota`0_q . \supset . (\exists \alpha) . \alpha \in \mathrm{NC\,ind} . Y <_r (\alpha/1 \times_s X)$

---

*305·01. $X \times_s Y = \hat{R}\hat{S}[(\exists \mu, \nu, \rho, \sigma) . \mu, \nu, \rho, \sigma \in \mathrm{NC\,ind} . \nu \neq 0 . \sigma \neq 0 .$
$X = \mu/\nu . Y = \rho/\sigma . R\{(\mu \times_c \rho)/(\nu \times_c \sigma)\} S]$ Df

*305·1. $\vdash : R(X \times_s Y) S . \equiv . (\exists \mu, \nu, \rho, \sigma) . \mu, \nu, \rho, \sigma \in \mathrm{NC\,ind} . \nu \neq 0 . \sigma \neq 0 .$
$X = \mu/\nu . Y = \rho/\sigma . R\{(\mu \times_c \rho)/(\nu \times_c \sigma)\} S$ [(*305·01)]

*305·11. $\vdash . X \times_s Y = Y \times_s X$ [*305·1]

*305·12. $\vdash : X, Y \sim \in \iota`0_q \cup \iota`\infty_q . \mathrm{Cnv}`(X \times_s Y) = \breve{X} \times_s \breve{Y}$ [*305·1 . *303·13]

*305·13. $\vdash : \mu, \nu, \rho, \sigma \in \mathrm{NC\,ind} - \iota`0 . \mu/\nu = \mu'/\nu' . \rho/\sigma = \rho'/\sigma' . \supset .$
$(\mu \times_c \rho)/(\nu \times_c \sigma) = (\mu' \times_c \rho')/(\nu' \times_c \sigma')$

Dem.

$\vdash . *303·39 . \supset \vdash : \mathrm{Hp} . \supset . \mu \times_c \nu' = \nu \times_c \mu' . \rho \times_c \sigma' = \rho' \times_c \sigma .$
[*120·51] $\supset . \mu \times_c \rho \times_c \nu' \times_c \sigma' = \mu' \times_c \rho' \times_c \nu \times_c \sigma .$
[*303·39] $\supset . (\mu \times_c \rho)/(\nu \times_c \sigma) = (\mu' \times_c \rho')/(\nu' \times_c \sigma') : \supset \vdash . \mathrm{Prop}$

*305·131. $\vdash : \nu, \rho, \sigma \in \mathrm{NC\,ind} - \iota`0 . 0/\nu = \mu'/\nu' . \rho/\sigma = \rho'/\sigma' . \supset .$
$(0 \times_c \rho)/(\nu \times_c \sigma) = (\mu' \times_c \rho')/(\nu' \times_c \sigma')$

Dem.

$\vdash . *303·66 . \supset \vdash : \mathrm{Hp} . \supset . \mu' = 0 . \nu' \in \mathrm{NC\,ind} - \iota`0$ (1)
$\vdash . (1) . *303·6 . \supset \vdash : \mathrm{Hp} . \supset . (0 \times_c \rho)/(\nu \times_c \sigma) = 0_q = (\mu' \times_c \rho')/(\nu' \times_c \sigma') : \supset \vdash . \mathrm{Prop}$

*305·132. $\vdash : \mu, \nu, \rho, \sigma \in \mathrm{NC\,ind} . \nu \neq 0 . \sigma \neq 0 . \mu/\nu = \mu'/\nu' . \rho/\sigma = \rho'/\sigma' . \supset .$
$(\mu \times_c \rho)/(\nu \times_c \sigma) = (\mu' \times_c \rho')/(\nu' \times_c \sigma')$

[*305·13·131]

***305·14.** $\vdash : \mu \neq 0 . \rho \neq 0 . \nu \neq 0 . \sigma \neq 0 . \supset . \mu/\nu \times_s \rho/\sigma = (\mu \times_c \rho)/(\nu \times_c \sigma)$

Dem.

$\vdash . *305·1·132 . \supset$

$\vdash :: \text{Hp} . \supset :. R (\mu/\nu \times_c \rho/\sigma) S . \equiv :$

$(\exists \mu', \nu', \rho', \sigma') . \mu', \nu', \rho', \sigma' \in \text{NC ind} . \mu/\nu = \mu'/\nu' . \rho/\sigma = \rho'/\sigma' . \nu' \neq 0 . \sigma' \neq 0 :$

$R \{(\mu \times_c \rho)/(\nu \times_c \sigma)\} S$ (1)

$\vdash . *303·181 . *302·36 . *120·512 . \supset$

$\vdash : \text{Hp} . R \{(\mu \times_c \rho)/(\nu \times_c \sigma)\} S . \supset . \mu, \nu, \rho, \sigma \in \text{NC ind}$ (2)

$\vdash . (1) . (2) . \supset \vdash . \text{Prop}$

The condition $\mu \neq 0 . \rho \neq 0$ is required in the above proposition because if, *e.g.* $\mu = 0 . \rho \in \text{NC infin}$, we shall have (if $\nu, \sigma \in \text{NC ind} - \iota`0$) $\mu/\nu = 0_q . \rho/\sigma = \dot{\Lambda}$, whence $\mu/\nu \times_c \rho/\sigma = \dot{\Lambda}$, but $(\mu \times_c \rho)/(\nu \times_c \sigma) = 0_q$. If we assume $\mu, \rho \in \text{NC ind}$, it is not necessary to assume $\mu \neq 0 . \rho \neq 0$. This is stated in *305·142.

***305·141.** $\vdash :. \nu = 0 . \vee . \sigma = 0 : \supset . \mu/\nu \times_s \rho/\sigma = \dot{\Lambda}$

Dem.

$\vdash . *303·67·11 . \supset \vdash : \nu = 0 . \mu', \nu' \in \text{NC ind} . \mu/\nu = \mu'/\nu' . \supset . \nu' = 0$ (1)

$\vdash . (1) . *305·1 . \supset \vdash . \text{Prop}$

***305·142.** $\vdash : \mu, \rho \in \text{NC ind} . \nu \neq 0 . \sigma \neq 0 . \supset . \mu/\nu \times_s \rho/\sigma = (\mu \times_c \rho)/(\nu \times_c \sigma)$
[Proof as in *305·14]

***305·143.** $\vdash : \dot{\exists} ! (\mu/\nu \times_s \rho/\sigma) . \supset . \mu, \nu, \rho, \sigma \in \text{NC ind} . \nu \neq 0 . \sigma \neq 0$

Dem.

$\vdash . *305·1 . \supset \vdash : \dot{\exists} ! (\mu/\nu \times_s \rho/\sigma) . \supset . (\exists \mu', \nu') . \mu', \nu' \in \text{NC ind} . \nu' \neq 0 . \mu/\nu = \mu'/\nu' .$

[*303·182·67] $\supset . \mu, \nu \in \text{NC ind} . \nu \neq 0$ (1)

Similarly $\vdash : \dot{\exists} ! (\mu/\nu \times_s \rho/\sigma) . \supset . \rho, \sigma \in \text{NC ind} . \sigma \neq 0$ (2)

$\vdash . (1) . (2) . \supset \vdash . \text{Prop}$

***305·144.** $\vdash : \dot{\exists} ! (\mu/\nu \times_s \rho/\sigma) . \supset . \mu/\nu \times_s \rho/\sigma = (\mu \times_c \rho)/(\nu \times_c \sigma)$ [*305·143·142]

***305·15.** $\vdash :. \sim(\mu, \nu, \rho, \sigma \in \text{NC ind}) . \vee . \nu = 0 . \vee . \sigma = 0 : \supset . \mu/\nu \times_s \rho/\sigma = \dot{\Lambda}$
[*305·143 . Transp]

***305·16.** $\vdash :. \mu, \nu, \rho, \sigma \in \text{NC ind} : \mu = 0 . \vee . \rho = 0 : \nu \neq 0 . \sigma \neq 0 : \supset .$
$\mu/\nu \times_s \rho/\sigma = 0_q$ [*305·142 . *303·6]

***305·17.** $\vdash . X \times_s \infty_q = \dot{\Lambda}$ [*305·141 . *303·67]

***305·2.** $\vdash : \dot{\exists} ! X \times_s Y . \supset . X, Y \in \text{Rat}$

Dem.

$\vdash . *305·1 . \supset$

$\vdash : \text{Hp} . \supset . (\exists \mu, \nu, \rho, \sigma) . \mu, \nu, \rho, \sigma \in \text{NC ind} . \nu \neq 0 . \sigma \neq 0 . X = \mu/\nu . Y = \rho/\sigma .$

[*303·7] $\supset . X, Y \in \text{Rat} : \supset \vdash . \text{Prop}$

***305·21.** $\vdash : X \times_s Y \epsilon \mathrm{Rat} - \iota`0_q \,.\supset.\, X, Y \epsilon \mathrm{Rat} - \iota`0_q$

Dem.

$\vdash . *303·72 . *305·2 . \supset \vdash : \mathrm{Hp} . \supset . X, Y \epsilon \mathrm{Rat}$ (1)

$\vdash . *305·16 . \mathrm{Transp} . \supset \vdash : \mathrm{Hp} . \supset . X \neq 0_q . Y \neq 0_q$ (2)

$\vdash . (1) . (2) . \supset \vdash . \mathrm{Prop}$

***305·22.** $\vdash :. X \times_s Y = 0_q . \equiv : X, Y \epsilon \mathrm{Rat} : X = 0_q . \vee . Y = 0_q$

Dem.

$\vdash . *305·1·2·142 . *303·66 . \supset$

$\vdash :. X \times_s Y = 0_q . \equiv : (\exists \mu, \nu, \rho, \sigma) . X = \mu/\nu . Y = \rho/\sigma . \mu, \nu, \rho, \sigma \epsilon \mathrm{NC\,ind} .$
$\mu \times_c \rho = 0 . \nu \times_c \sigma \neq 0 :$

[*303·66] $\equiv : (\exists \mu, \nu, \rho, \sigma) : X = \mu/\nu . Y = \rho/\sigma . \mu, \nu, \rho, \sigma \epsilon \mathrm{NC\,ind} .$
$\nu \neq 0 . \sigma \neq 0 : \mu/\nu = 0_q . \vee . \rho/\sigma = 0_q :$

[*303·7] $\equiv : X, Y \epsilon \mathrm{Rat} : X = 0_q . \vee . Y = 0_q :. \supset \vdash . \mathrm{Prop}$

***305·222.** $\vdash : X \times_s Y \epsilon \mathrm{Rat} . \supset . X, Y \epsilon \mathrm{Rat}$ [*305·21·22]

The following propositions are lemmas designed to show that if X, Y are ratios which exist in a given type, $X \times_s Y$ exists in the next type.

***305·23.** $\vdash : \mu \epsilon \mathrm{NC\,ind} . \supset . (2 \times_c \mu) +_c 1 < 2^{\mu +_c 1}$ [*117·652 . *120·429]

***305·231.** $\vdash . (\mu +_c 1)^2 = \mu^2 +_c (2 \times_c \mu) +_c 1$ [*116·34 . *113·43·66]

***305·232.** $\vdash : \mu \epsilon \mathrm{NC\,ind} . \supset . \mu^2 < 2^{\mu +_c 1}$

Dem.

$\vdash . *116·311·321 . \supset \vdash . 0^2 < 2^{0 +_c 1}$ (1)

$\vdash . *305·231 . \quad \supset \vdash : \mathrm{Hp} . \mu^2 < 2^{\mu +_c 1} . \supset . (\mu +_c 1)^2 < 2^{\mu +_c 1} +_c (2 \times_c \mu) +_c 1$ (2)

$\vdash . (2) . *305·23 . \supset \vdash : \mu \epsilon \mathrm{NC\,ind} . \mu^2 < 2^{\mu +_c 1} . \supset . (\mu +_c 1)^2 < 2^{\mu +_c 1} +_c 2^{\mu +_c 1} .$

[*113·66.*116·52] $\supset . (\mu +_c 1)^2 < 2^{\mu +_c 2}$ (3)

$\vdash . (1) . (3) . \mathrm{Induct} . \supset \vdash . \mathrm{Prop}$

***305·24.** $\vdash : \mu, \nu, \rho, \sigma \epsilon \mathrm{D}`U \cap \mathrm{Ɑ}`U . \supset .$
$(\mu \times_c \rho) \cap t`\mu, (\nu \times_c \sigma) \cap t`\mu \epsilon \mathrm{D}`U \cap \mathrm{Ɑ}`U$

Dem.

$\vdash . *116·72 . \supset \vdash : \mathrm{Hp} . \supset . (2^{\mu +_c 1} \cap t`\mu) \epsilon C`U .$

[*305·232] $\supset . \mu^2 \cap t`\mu \epsilon \mathrm{Ɑ}`U$ (1)

$\vdash . *116·35 . \supset \vdash : \mathrm{Hp} . \supset . \mu^2 \cap t`\mu \epsilon \mathrm{D}`U$ (2)

Similarly $\vdash : \mathrm{Hp} . \supset . \nu^2 \cap t`\mu, \rho^2 \cap t`\mu, \sigma^2 \cap t`\mu \epsilon \mathrm{D}`U \cap \mathrm{Ɑ}`U$ (3)

$\vdash . *117·571 . \supset$

$\vdash :. \mathrm{Hp} . \supset : \mu \times_c \rho \leqslant \mu^2 . \vee . \mu \times_c \rho \leqslant \rho^2 : \nu \times_c \sigma \leqslant \nu^2 . \vee . \nu \times_c \sigma \leqslant \sigma^2$ (4)

$\vdash . (1) . (2) . (3) . (4) . \supset \vdash . \mathrm{Prop}$

∗305·25. $\vdash : \mu, \nu, \rho, \sigma \in D'U \cap \text{Ɑ}'U . \supset . (\mu/\nu \times_s \rho/\sigma) \upharpoonright t_{00}'\mu \in C'H$

Dem.

$\vdash . ∗305·14 . \supset \vdash : \text{Hp} . \supset . \mu/\nu \times_s \rho/\sigma = (\mu \times_c \rho)/(\nu \times_c \sigma)$ (1)

$\vdash . (1) . ∗304·28 . ∗305·24 . \supset \vdash . \text{Prop}$

∗305·26. $\vdash : X, Y \in \text{Rat} . X \upharpoonright t_{11}'\mu, Y \upharpoonright t_{11}'\mu \in \text{Rat def} . \supset . (X \times_s Y) \upharpoonright t_{00}'\mu \in C'H$
[∗305·25 . ∗304·28]

∗305·27. $\vdash : X, Y \in \text{Rat} - \iota'0_q . \supset . (\exists\mu) . (X \times_s Y) \upharpoonright t_{00}'\mu \in C'H$
[∗305·26 . ∗303·721]

∗305·28. $\vdash : X, Y \in \text{Rat} . \supset . (\exists\mu) . (X \times_s Y) \upharpoonright t_{00}'\mu \in C'H'$ [∗305·27·22]

∗305·3. $\vdash : X, Y \in \text{Rat} . \equiv . X \times_s Y \in \text{Rat}$

Dem.

$\vdash . ∗305·142 . ∗303·7 . \supset \vdash : X, Y \in \text{Rat} . \supset . X \times_s Y \in \text{Rat}$ (1)

$\vdash . (1) . ∗305·222 . \supset \vdash . \text{Prop}$

∗305·301. $\vdash : X, Y \in \text{Rat} - \iota'0_q . \equiv . X \times_s Y \in \text{Rat} - \iota'0_q$
[∗305·142 . ∗303·7 . ∗305·21]

∗305·31. $\vdash : (\exists\mu) . X \upharpoonright t_{11}'\mu, Y \upharpoonright t_{11}'\mu \in C'H . \equiv . (\exists\nu) . (X \times_s Y) \upharpoonright t_{11}'\nu \in C'H$
[∗305·301 . ∗304·53]

∗305·32. $\vdash : (\exists\mu) . X \upharpoonright t_{11}'\mu, Y \upharpoonright t_{11}'\mu \in C'H' . \equiv . (\exists\nu) . (X \times_s Y) \upharpoonright t_{11}'\nu \in C'H'$
[∗305·3 . ∗304·52]

∗305·4. $\vdash : \lambda, \nu, \sigma \in \text{NC ind} . \mu \neq 0 . \rho \neq 0 . \tau \neq 0 . \supset .$

$(\lambda/\mu \times_s \nu/\rho) \times_s (\sigma/\tau) = (\lambda \times_c \nu \times_c \sigma)/(\mu \times_c \rho \times_c \tau) = \lambda/\mu \times_s (\nu/\rho \times_s \sigma/\tau)$ [∗305·142]

∗305·41. $\vdash . (X \times_s Y) \times_s Z = X \times_s (Y \times_s Z)$ [∗305·4·2]

∗305·5. $\vdash : \mu \neq 0 . \supset . (\lambda/\mu) \times_s (1/1) = \lambda/\mu$ [∗305·14·142·15]

∗305·51. $\vdash : X \in \text{Rat} . \supset . X \times_s (1/1) = X$ [∗305·5]

∗305·52. $\vdash : X \in \text{Rat} - \iota'0_q . \supset . X \times_s \breve{X} = 1/1$

Dem.

$\vdash . ∗305·14 . ∗303·13 . \supset$

$\vdash : \text{Hp} . \supset . (\exists\mu, \nu) . \mu, \nu \in \text{NC ind} - \iota'0 . X \times_s \breve{X} = (\mu \times_c \nu)/(\nu \times_c \mu) .$

[∗303·23] $\supset . X \times_s \breve{X} = 1/1 : \supset \vdash . \text{Prop}$

∗305·6. $\vdash :. A \in \text{Rat} - \iota'0_q . X \in \text{Rat} . \supset : A \times_s X = A' . \equiv . X = A' \times_s \breve{A}$

Dem.

$\vdash . ∗304·1·4 . ∗305·32·222 . \supset$

$\vdash : \text{Hp} . \supset . (\exists\mu, \nu, \rho, \sigma, \xi, \eta) . \mu, \nu, \sigma \in \text{NC ind} - \iota'0 . \rho, \xi, \eta \in \text{NC ind} .$

$A = \mu/\nu . X = \rho/\sigma . A' = \xi/\eta$ (1)

$\vdash . *305{\cdot}142 . \supset \vdash :. \mu, \nu, \sigma \in \text{NC ind} - \iota`0 . \rho, \xi, \eta \in \text{NC ind} . \supset :$

$\mu/\nu \times_s \rho/\sigma = \xi/\eta . \equiv . (\mu \times_c \rho)/(\nu \times_c \sigma) = \xi/\eta .$

[*303·38] $\equiv . \mu \times_c \rho \times_c \eta = \nu \times_c \sigma \times_c \xi .$

[*303·38] $\equiv . \rho/\sigma = (\nu \times_c \xi)/(\mu \times_c \eta)$

[*305·142.*303·13] $= \xi/\eta \times_c \text{Cnv}`(\mu/\nu)$ (2)

$\vdash . (1) . (2) . \supset \vdash . \text{Prop}$

***305·61.** $\vdash :. A \in \text{Rat} - \iota`0_q . A' \in \text{Rat} . \supset : A \times_s X = A' . \equiv . X = A' \times_s \breve{A}$
[*305·6·222·32]

***305·7.** $\vdash : X, Y \in \text{Rat} - \iota`0_q . \supset . (\exists \alpha) . \alpha \in \text{NC ind} . Y <_r (\alpha/1 \times_s X)$

Dem.

$\vdash . *117{\cdot}571 . *120{\cdot}511 . *117{\cdot}62 . \supset$

$\vdash : \mu, \nu, \rho, \sigma \in \text{NC ind} - \iota`0 . \xi > \nu . \supset .$

$\mu \times_c \rho \times_c \xi \times_c \sigma > \nu \times_c \rho .$

[*304·1] $\supset . (\rho/\sigma) <_r (\mu \times_c \rho \times_c \xi)/\nu .$

[*305·14] $\supset . (\rho/\sigma) <_r \{\mu/\nu \times_s (\rho \times_c \xi)/1\}$ (1)

$\vdash . (1) . *304{\cdot}1 . *120{\cdot}5 . \supset \vdash . \text{Prop}$

***305·71.** $\vdash :. Z \in \text{Rat} - \iota`0_q . \supset : X <_r Y . \equiv . X \times_s Z <_r Y \times_s Z$

Dem.

$\vdash . *305{\cdot}142 . \supset \vdash : \text{Hp} . X <_r Y . \supset .$

$(\exists \mu, \nu, \rho, \sigma, \xi, \eta) . \mu, \nu, \rho, \sigma, \xi, \eta \in \text{NC ind} . \nu \neq 0 . \sigma \neq 0 . \xi \neq 0 . \eta \neq 0 .$

$X = \mu/\nu . Y = \rho/\sigma . Z = \xi/\eta . \mu \times_c \sigma < \nu \times_c \rho .$

$X \times_s Z = (\mu \times_c \xi)/(\nu \times_c \eta) . Y \times_s Z = (\rho \times_c \xi)/(\sigma \times_c \eta) .$

[*304·1.*126·51] $\supset . X \times_s Z <_r Y \times_s Z$ (1)

$\vdash . (1) . \supset \vdash : \text{Hp} . X \times_s Z <_r Y \times_s Z . \supset . X \times_s Z \times_s \breve{Z} <_r Y \times_s Z \times_s \breve{Z} .$

[*305·51·52] $\supset . X <_r Y$ (2)

$\vdash . (1) . (2) . \supset \vdash . \text{Prop}$

*306. ADDITION OF SIMPLE RATIOS.

Summary of *306.

The addition of simple ratios is treated in a way analogous to that in which their multiplication is treated. We wish to secure that the sum of λ/ν and μ/ν shall be $(\lambda +_c \mu)/\nu$, and that the sum of μ/ν and ρ/σ shall be $\{(\mu \times_c \sigma) +_c (\nu \times_c \rho)\}/(\nu \times_c \sigma)$. This is secured by the definition

***306·01.** $X +_s Y = \hat{R}\hat{S}[(\exists \mu, \nu, \rho) . \mu, \nu, \rho \in \text{NC ind} . \nu \neq 0 .$
$X = \mu/\nu . Y = \rho/\nu . R\{(\mu +_c \rho)/\nu\} S]$ Df

whence we obtain

***306·13.** $\vdash : \nu \neq 0 . \supset . \mu/\nu +_s \rho/\nu = (\mu +_c \rho)/\nu$

***306·14.** $\vdash : \nu \neq 0 . \sigma \neq 0 . \supset . \mu/\nu +_s \rho/\sigma = \{(\mu \times_c \sigma) +_c (\nu \times_c \rho)\}/(\nu \times_c \sigma)$

Our definition is so framed that $\infty_q +_s \infty_q = \dot{\Lambda}$. This is on the whole convenient, though we could, of course, frame our definition so as to have $\infty_q +_s \infty_q = \infty_q$.

In applications, if R, S, T are members of a suitable vector-family, we want to have

$$R(\mu/\nu)T . S(\rho/\sigma)T . \supset . (R \mid S)(\mu/\nu +_s \rho/\sigma)T,$$

e.g. if a vector R is 2/3 of T, and a vector S is 5/7 of T, we want the vector which consists of first travelling a distance R and then travelling a distance S to be $(2/3 +_s 5/7)$ of T. We shall show in Section C that our definition of addition fulfils this requirement.

As in the case of products, the sum of two ratios is a ratio (*306·22), and the sum of two ratios which exist in a given type exists in the next type (*306·64). A ratio is unchanged by the addition of 0_q (*306·24), and a sum of two ratios is only 0_q if both the summands are 0_q (*306·2). No difficulty is offered by the formal laws: we prove the commutative law (*306·11), the associative law (*306·31), and the distributive law (*306·41).

An important proposition is

***306·52.** $\vdash :. X <_r Y . \equiv : X \in \text{Rat} : (\exists Z) . Z \in \text{Rat} - \iota`0_q . X +_s Z = Y$

When the axiom of infinity is assumed, this proposition becomes

$$XH'Y . \equiv : X \in C`H' : (\exists Z) . Z \in C`H . X +_s Z = Y.$$

We prove also the proposition upon which subtraction depends, namely

$*306\cdot54.\ \vdash :. X, Y \epsilon \text{Rat} . \supset : X +_s Y = X +_s Z . \equiv . Y = Z$

$*306\cdot01.\ X +_s Y = \hat{R}\hat{S}[(\exists \mu, \nu, \rho) . \mu, \nu, \rho \epsilon \text{NC ind} . \nu \neq 0 .$
$X = \mu/\nu . Y = \rho/\nu . R\{(\mu +_c \rho)/\nu\} S]$ Df

$*306\cdot1.\ \vdash : R(X +_s Y) S . \equiv . (\exists \mu, \nu, \rho) . \mu, \nu, \rho \epsilon \text{NC ind} . \nu \neq 0 .$
$X = \mu/\nu . Y = \rho/\nu . R\{(\mu +_c \rho)/\nu\} S$ [(*306·01)]

$*306\cdot11.\ \vdash . X +_s Y = Y +_s X$ [*306·1 . *110·51]

$*306\cdot12.\ \vdash : \dot{\exists} ! (X +_s Y) . \supset . X, Y \epsilon \text{Rat}$ [*306·1 . *303·7]

$*306\cdot121.\ \vdash : \mu/\nu = \mu'/\nu' . \rho/\nu = \rho'/\nu' . \supset . (\mu +_c \rho)/\nu = (\mu' +_c \rho')/\nu'$

Dem.

$\vdash . *303\cdot39 . \supset \vdash : \text{Hp} . \mu, \nu, \rho, \mu', \nu', \rho' \epsilon \text{NC ind} . \nu \neq 0 . \nu' \neq 0 . \supset .$

$\mu \times_c \nu' = \mu' \times_c \nu . \rho \times_c \nu' = \rho' \times_c \nu .$

[*113·43] $\supset . (\mu +_c \rho) \times_c \nu' = (\mu' +_c \rho') \times_c \nu .$

[*303·39] $\supset . (\mu +_c \rho)/\nu = (\mu' +_c \rho')/\nu'$ (1)

$\vdash . *303\cdot181 . *302\cdot36 . \supset$

$\vdash : \text{Hp} . \sim(\mu, \nu, \rho, \mu', \nu', \rho' \epsilon \text{NC ind}) . \supset . (\mu +_c \rho)/\nu = \dot{\Lambda} . (\mu' +_c \rho')/\nu' = \dot{\Lambda}$ (2)

$\vdash . (1) . (2) . *303\cdot67 . \supset \vdash . \text{Prop}$

$*306\cdot13.\ \vdash : \nu \neq 0 . \supset . \mu/\nu +_s \rho/\nu = (\mu +_c \rho)/\nu$

Dem.

$\vdash . *306\cdot1 . \supset \vdash : \text{Hp} . \supset . (\mu +_c \rho)/\nu \subseteq \mu/\nu +_s \rho/\nu$ (1)

$\vdash . *306\cdot121 . \supset$

$\vdash : \mu/\nu = \mu'/\nu' . \rho/\nu = \rho'/\nu' . X\{(\mu' +_c \rho')/\nu'\} Y . \supset . X\{(\mu +_c \rho)/\nu\} Y$ (2)

$\vdash . (2) . *306\cdot1 . \supset \vdash . \mu/\nu +_s \rho/\nu \subseteq (\mu +_c \rho)/\nu$ (3)

$\vdash . (1) . (3) . \supset \vdash . \text{Prop}$

$*306\cdot14.\ \vdash : \nu \neq 0 . \sigma \neq 0 . \supset . \mu/\nu +_s \rho/\sigma = \{(\mu \times_c \sigma) +_c (\nu \times_c \rho)\}/(\nu \times_c \sigma)$

Dem.

$\vdash . *303\cdot39 . \supset$

$\vdash : \text{Hp} . \mu, \nu, \rho, \sigma \epsilon \text{NC ind} . \supset . \mu/\nu = (\mu \times_c \sigma)/(\nu \times_c \sigma) . \rho/\sigma = (\nu \times_c \rho)/(\nu \times_c \sigma) .$

[*306·13] $\supset . \mu/\nu +_s \rho/\sigma = \{(\mu \times_c \sigma) +_c (\nu \times_c \rho)\}/(\nu \times_c \sigma)$ (1)

$\vdash . *306\cdot12 . *303\cdot11 . \supset$

$\vdash : \sim(\mu, \nu, \rho, \sigma \epsilon \text{NC ind}) . \supset . \mu/\nu +_s \rho/\sigma = \dot{\Lambda} . \{(\mu \times_c \sigma) +_c (\nu \times_c \rho)\}/(\nu \times_c \sigma) = \dot{\Lambda}$ (2)

$\vdash . (1) . (2) . \supset \vdash . \text{Prop}$

$*306\cdot141.\ \vdash :. \nu = 0 . \vee . \sigma = 0 : \supset . \mu/\nu +_s \rho/\sigma = \dot{\Lambda}$ [*306·12 . Transp . *303·7]

∗306·15. $\vdash : \mu/\nu +_s \rho/\sigma = 0_q \,.\equiv.\, \mu = \rho = 0 \,.\, \nu, \sigma \in \text{NC ind} - \iota`0$

Dem.

$\vdash . *306\cdot14 . *303\cdot66 . \supset \vdash : \mu = \rho = 0 . \nu, \sigma \in \text{NC ind} - \iota`0 . \supset . \mu/\nu +_s \rho/\sigma = 0_q$ (1)

$\vdash . *306\cdot12 . \quad \supset \vdash : \mu/\nu +_s \rho/\sigma = 0_q . \supset . \mu, \nu, \rho, \sigma \in \text{NC ind}$ (2)

$\vdash . *306\cdot141 . \quad \supset \vdash : \mu/\nu +_s \rho/\sigma = 0_q . \supset . \nu \neq 0 . \sigma \neq 0$ (3)

$\vdash . (3) . *306\cdot14 . \supset \vdash : \text{Hp}(3) . \supset . \{(\mu \times_c \sigma) +_c (\nu \times_c \rho)\}/(\nu \times_c \sigma) = 0_q .$

$[*303\cdot66] \quad \supset . (\mu \times_c \sigma) +_c (\nu \times_c \rho) = 0 . \nu \times_c \sigma \neq 0 .$

$[*110\cdot62 . *113\cdot602] \quad \supset . \mu = \rho = 0 . \nu \neq 0 . \sigma \neq 0$ (4)

$\vdash . (1) . (2) . (4) . \supset \vdash . \text{Prop}$

∗306·16. $\vdash . X +_s Y = \hat{R}\hat{S}\,[(\exists \mu, \nu, \rho, \sigma) . \mu, \nu, \rho, \sigma \in \text{NC ind} . \nu \neq 0 . \sigma \neq 0 .$
$X = \mu/\nu . Y = \rho/\sigma . R \{(\overline{\mu \times_c \sigma} +_c \overline{\nu \times_c \rho})/\overline{\nu \times_c \sigma}\} S]$

[∗306·14·12]

∗306·17. $\vdash : \mu = 0 . \nu, \rho, \sigma \in \text{NC ind} . \nu \neq 0 . \sigma \neq 0 . \supset . \mu/\nu +_s \rho/\sigma = \rho/\sigma$

Dem.

$\vdash . *303\cdot6 . \supset \vdash : \text{Hp} . \supset . \mu/\nu = 0/\sigma .$

$[*306\cdot13] \quad \supset . \mu/\nu +_s \rho/\sigma = (0 +_c \rho)/\sigma : \supset \vdash . \text{Prop}$

∗306·2. $\vdash : X +_s Y = 0_q . \equiv . X = 0_q . Y = 0_q$ [∗306·15·12]

∗306·22. $\vdash : X +_s Y \in \text{Rat} . \equiv . X, Y \in \text{Rat}$

Dem.

$\vdash . *306\cdot16 . *303\cdot7 . \supset \vdash : X +_s Y \in \text{Rat} . \equiv .$

$(\exists \mu, \nu, \rho, \sigma) . \mu, \nu, \rho, \sigma \in \text{NC ind} . X = \mu/\nu . Y = \rho/\sigma . \nu \times_c \sigma \neq 0 .$

$[*113\cdot602] \equiv . (\exists \mu, \nu, \rho, \sigma) . \mu, \nu, \rho, \sigma \in \text{NC ind} . X = \mu/\nu . Y = \rho/\sigma . \nu \neq 0 . \sigma \neq 0 .$

$[*303\cdot7] \quad \equiv . X, Y \in \text{Rat} : \supset \vdash . \text{Prop}$

∗306·23 $\vdash : X +_s Y \in \text{Rat} - \iota`0_q . \equiv . X, Y \in \text{Rat} . \sim(X = Y = 0_q)$
[∗306·22 . ∗303·7 . ∗306·2]

∗306·24. $\vdash : X \in \text{Rat} . \supset . X +_s 0_q = X$ [∗306·17·11]

∗306·25. $\vdash : X +_s Y \in \text{Rat} . \equiv . \dot{\exists}\,!\,(X +_s Y) . \equiv . X, Y \in \text{Rat}$
[∗306·12·22 . ∗303·26 . ∗306·14]

Here $X +_s Y$ must be taken in a sufficiently high type, otherwise $X +_s Y$ may be null when $X, Y \in \text{Rat}$.

∗306·3. $\vdash . (\lambda/\mu +_s \nu/\rho) +_s \sigma/\tau = \lambda/\mu +_s (\nu/\rho +_s \sigma/\tau)$

Dem.

$\vdash . *306\cdot14 . \supset \vdash : \mu \neq 0 . \rho \neq 0 . \tau \neq 0 . \supset . (\lambda/\mu +_s \nu/\rho) +_s \sigma/\tau$

$= \{(\lambda \times_c \rho) +_c (\mu \times_c \nu)\}/(\mu \times_c \rho) +_s \sigma/\tau$

$[*306\cdot14] = \{(\lambda \times_c \rho \times_c \tau) +_c (\mu \times_c \nu \times_c \tau) +_c (\mu \times_c \rho \times_c \sigma)\}/(\mu \times_c \rho \times_c \tau)$

$[*113\cdot43] = [\{\lambda \times_c (\rho \times_c \tau)\} +_c \{\mu \times_c ((\nu \times_c \tau) +_c (\rho \times_c \sigma))\}]/\{\mu \times_c (\rho \times_c \tau)\}$

$[*306\cdot14] = \lambda/\mu +_s \{(\nu \times_c \tau) +_c (\rho \times_c \sigma)\}/(\rho \times_c \tau)$

$[*306\cdot14] = \lambda/\mu +_s (\nu/\rho +_s \sigma/\tau)$ (1)

$\vdash . (1) . *306\cdot12 . \supset \vdash . \text{Prop}$

∗306·31. $\vdash . (X +_s Y) +_s Z = X +_s (Y +_s Z)$

Dem.

$\vdash . ∗306·3 . \supset \vdash : X = \lambda/\mu . Y = \nu/\rho . Z = \sigma/\tau . \supset .$

$(X +_s Y) +_s Z = X +_s (Y +_s Z)$ (1)

$\vdash . ∗306·25 . \supset \vdash : \sim (\exists \lambda, \mu, \nu, \rho, \sigma, \tau) . X = \lambda/\mu . Y = \nu/\rho . Z = \sigma/\tau . \supset .$

$(X +_s Y) +_s Z = \dot{\Lambda} . X +_s (Y +_s Z) = \dot{\Lambda}$ (2)

$\vdash . (1) . (2) . \supset \vdash .$ Prop

∗306·4. $\vdash . \lambda/\mu \times_s (\nu/\rho +_s \sigma/\tau) = (\lambda/\mu \times_s \nu/\rho) +_s (\lambda/\mu \times_s \sigma/\tau)$

Dem.

$\vdash . ∗306·14 . \supset \vdash : \lambda, \mu, \nu, \rho, \sigma, \tau \epsilon \text{NC ind} . \mu \neq 0 . \nu \neq 0 . \sigma \neq 0 . \supset .$

$\lambda/\mu \times_s (\nu/\rho +_s \sigma/\tau) = \lambda/\mu \times_s \{(\nu \times_c \tau) +_c (\rho \times_c \sigma)\}/(\rho \times_c \tau)$

[∗305·14] $= [\lambda \times_c \{(\nu \times_c \tau) +_c (\rho \times_c \sigma)\}]/(\mu \times_c \rho \times_c \tau)$

[∗303·23] $= [\lambda \times_c \mu \times_c \{(\nu \times_c \tau) +_c (\rho \times_c \sigma)\}]/(\mu \times_c \rho \times_c \mu \times_c \tau)$

[∗113·43] $= \{(\lambda \times_c \mu \times_c \nu \times_c \tau) +_c (\lambda \times_c \mu \times_c \rho \times_c \sigma)\}/(\mu \times_c \rho \times_c \mu \times_c \tau)$

[∗306·14] $= (\lambda \times_c \nu)/(\mu \times_c \rho) +_s (\lambda \times_c \sigma)/(\mu \times_c \tau)$

[∗305·14] $= (\lambda/\mu \times_s \nu/\rho) +_s (\lambda/\mu \times_s \sigma/\tau)$ (1)

$\vdash . ∗305·2 . ∗306·22 . \supset \vdash : \dot{\exists} ! \lambda/\mu \times_s (\nu/\rho +_s \sigma/\tau) . \supset . \lambda/\mu, \nu/\rho, \sigma/\tau \epsilon \text{Rat} .$

[∗303·7] $\supset . \text{Hp} (1)$ (2)

$\vdash . ∗306·12 . ∗305·143 . \supset$

$\vdash : \dot{\exists} ! \{(\lambda/\mu \times_s \nu/\rho) +_s (\lambda/\mu \times_s \sigma/\tau)\} . \supset . \lambda/\mu, \nu/\rho, \sigma/\tau \epsilon \text{Rat} .$

[∗303·7] $\supset . \text{Hp} (1)$ (3)

$\vdash . (2) . (3) . \supset$

$\vdash : \sim \text{Hp} (1) . \supset . \lambda/\mu \times_s (\nu/\rho +_s \sigma/\tau) = \dot{\Lambda} = (\lambda/\mu \times_s \nu/\rho) +_s (\lambda/\mu \times_s \sigma/\tau)$ (4)

$\vdash . (1) . (4) . \supset \vdash .$ Prop

∗306·41. $\vdash . X \times_s (Y +_s Z) = (X \times_s Y) +_s (X \times_s Z)$ [∗306·4·25 . ∗305·2]

∗306·51. $\vdash . X +_s (\nu/1 \times_s X) = (\nu +_c 1)/1 \times_s X$

Dem.

$\vdash . ∗306·12 . \supset \vdash :. \dot{\exists} ! \{X +_s (\nu/1 \times_s X)\} . \supset : X, \nu/1 \times_s X \epsilon \text{Rat} :$

[∗305·3 . ∗303·7] $\supset : \nu \epsilon \text{NC ind} : (\exists \rho, \sigma) . \rho, \sigma \epsilon \text{NC ind} . \sigma \neq 0 . X = \rho/\sigma$ (1)

$\vdash . ∗305·2 . \supset \vdash :. \dot{\exists} ! \{(\nu +_c 1)/1 \times_s X\} . \supset : (\nu +_c 1)/1, X \epsilon \text{Rat} :$

[∗303·7 . ∗126·31] $\supset : \nu \epsilon \text{NC ind} : (\exists \rho, \sigma) . \rho, \sigma \epsilon \text{NC ind} . \sigma \neq 0 . X = \rho/\sigma$ (2)

$\vdash . ∗305·142 . \supset \vdash : \nu, \rho, \sigma \epsilon \text{NC ind} . \sigma \neq 0 . \supset . \nu/1 \times_s \rho/\sigma = (\nu \times_c \rho)/\sigma .$

[∗306·13] $\supset . \rho/\sigma +_s (\nu/1 \times_s \rho/\sigma) = \{\rho +_c (\nu \times_c \rho)\}/\sigma$

[∗113·671] $= . \{(\nu +_c 1) \times_c \rho\}/\sigma$

[∗305·14] $= (\nu +_c 1)/1 \times_s \rho/\sigma$ (3)

$\vdash . (1) . (2) . (3) . \supset \vdash .$ Prop

***306·52.** $\vdash :. X <_r Y . \equiv : X \epsilon \mathrm{Rat} : (\exists Z) . Z \epsilon \mathrm{Rat} - \iota\text{‘}0_q . X +_s Z = Y$

Dem.

$\vdash . *306\cdot13 . *119\cdot34 . \supset$

$\vdash : \mu, \nu, \rho, \sigma \epsilon \mathrm{NC\,ind} . \nu \neq 0 . \sigma \neq 0 . X = \mu/\nu . Y = \rho/\sigma . \mu \times_c \sigma < \nu \times_c \rho .$

$\xi = (\nu \times_c \rho) -_c (\mu \times_c \sigma) . Z = \xi/(\nu \times_c \sigma) . \supset . X +_s Z = (\nu \times_c \rho)/(\nu \times_c \sigma)$

[*303·23] $= \rho/\sigma$

[Hp] $= Y$ (1)

$\vdash . (1) . *304\cdot1\cdot13 . \supset$

$\vdash :. X <_r Y . \supset : X \epsilon \mathrm{Rat} : (\exists Z) . Z \epsilon \mathrm{Rat} - \iota\text{‘}0_q . X +_s Z = Y$ (2)

$\vdash . *306\cdot14 . \supset$

$\vdash : \mu, \nu, \rho, \sigma \epsilon \mathrm{NC\,ind} . \nu \neq 0 . \rho \neq 0 . \sigma \neq 0 . X = \mu/\nu . Z = \rho/\sigma . Y = X +_s Z . \supset .$

$Y = \{(\mu \times_c \sigma) +_c (\nu \times_c \rho)\}/(\nu \times_c \sigma) . [\{(\mu \times_c \sigma) +_c (\nu \times_c \rho)\} \times_c \nu] > \mu \times_c (\nu \times_c \sigma) .$

[*304·1] $\supset . X <_r Y$ (3)

$\vdash . (3) . *304\cdot1 . \supset \vdash : X \epsilon \mathrm{Rat} . Z \epsilon \mathrm{Rat} - \iota\text{‘}0_q . X +_s Z = Y . \supset . X <_r Y$ (4)

$\vdash . (2) . (4) . \supset \vdash . \mathrm{Prop}$

The above proposition requires that X and Y should be taken in a sufficiently high type, namely at least in a type in which, if $X = \mu/\nu$ and $Y = \rho/\sigma$, where $\mu \,\mathrm{Prm}\, \nu$ and $\rho \,\mathrm{Prm}\, \sigma$, $(\nu \times_c \rho) +_c 1$ and $(\mu \times_c \sigma) +_c 1$ are not null. Otherwise there may be no Z such that $X +_s Z = Y$.

***306·53.** $\vdash :. \mu, \nu \epsilon \mathrm{NC\,ind} . \nu \neq 0 . \sigma \neq 0 . \eta \neq 0 . \supset :$

$\mu/\nu +_s \rho/\sigma = \mu/\nu +_s \xi/\eta . \equiv . \rho/\sigma = \xi/\eta$

Dem.

$\vdash . *306\cdot12 . \supset \vdash : \mathrm{Hp} . \mu/\nu +_s \rho/\sigma = \mu/\nu +_s \xi/\eta . \sim(\rho, \sigma \epsilon \mathrm{NC\,ind}) . \supset .$

$\mu/\nu +_s \xi/\eta = \dot{\Lambda} . \rho/\sigma = \dot{\Lambda} .$ (1)

[*306·25] $\supset . \sim \{\mu/\nu, \xi/\eta \epsilon \mathrm{Rat}\} .$

[Hp.*303·7] $\supset . \sim(\xi, \eta \epsilon \mathrm{NC\,ind}) .$

[*303·11.(1)] $\supset . \xi/\eta = \rho/\sigma$ (2)

$\vdash . *306\cdot25 . \supset \vdash : \mathrm{Hp} . \mu/\nu +_s \rho/\sigma = \mu/\nu +_s \xi/\eta . \rho, \sigma \epsilon \mathrm{NC\,ind} . \supset .$

$\xi, \eta \epsilon \mathrm{NC\,ind}$ (3)

$\vdash . (3) . *306\cdot14 . *303\cdot39 . \supset$

$\vdash : \mathrm{Hp}\,(3) . \supset . \{(\mu \times_c \sigma) +_c (\nu \times_c \rho)\} \times_c \nu \times_c \eta = \{(\mu \times_c \eta) +_c (\nu \times_c \xi)\} \times_c \nu \times_c \sigma .$

[*113·43]

$\supset . (\mu \times_c \sigma \times_c \nu \times_c \eta) +_c (\nu^2 \times_c \rho \times_c \eta) = (\mu \times_c \sigma \times_c \nu \times_c \eta) +_c (\nu^2 \times_c \xi \times_c \sigma) .$

[*126·4] $\supset . \nu^2 \times_c (\rho \times_c \eta) = \nu^2 \times_c (\xi \times_c \sigma) .$

[*303·39] $\supset . \rho/\sigma = \xi/\eta$ (4)

$\vdash . (2) . (4) . \supset \vdash :. \mathrm{Hp} . \supset : \mu/\nu +_s \rho/\sigma = \mu/\nu +_s \xi/\eta . \supset . \rho/\sigma = \xi/\eta$ (5)

$\vdash . *306\cdot1 . \supset \vdash : \rho/\sigma = \xi/\eta . \supset . \mu/\nu +_s \rho/\sigma = \mu/\nu +_s \xi/\eta$ (6)

$\vdash . (5) . (6) . \supset \vdash . \mathrm{Prop}$

***306·54.** $\vdash :. X, Y \epsilon \text{Rat} . \supset : X +_s Y = X +_s Z . \equiv . Y = Z$

Dem.

$\vdash . *306·25 . \supset \vdash :. \text{Hp} . \supset : X +_s Y \epsilon \text{Rat} :$

[*306·25] $\supset : X +_s Y = X +_s Z . \supset . Z \epsilon \text{Rat}$ (1)

$\vdash . (1) . *306·53 . *303·7 . \supset \vdash . \text{Prop}$

***306·55.** $\vdash : Y <_r X . \supset . \sim(\exists Z) . X +_s Z = Y$

Dem.

$\vdash . *117·291 . *304·1 . \supset \vdash : \text{Hp} . \supset . \sim(X <_r Y) .$

[*306·52] $\supset . \sim(\exists Z) . Z \epsilon \text{Rat} - \iota \text{`} 0_q . X +_s Z = Y$ (1)

$\vdash . *306·24 . *304·1 . \supset \vdash : \text{Hp} . \supset . \sim(X +_s 0_q = Y)$ (2)

$\vdash . *306·25 . \supset \vdash : \text{Hp} . X +_s Z = Y . \supset . Z \epsilon \text{Rat}$ (3)

$\vdash . (1) . (2) . (3) . \supset \vdash . \text{Prop}$

The following propositions are concerned with the existence of $X +_s Y$ in definite types. It will be shown that if X, Y exist in a given type, $X +_s Y$ exists in the next type, *i.e.* if $X \upharpoonright t_{11}\text{`}\mu$ and $Y \upharpoonright t_{11}\text{`}\mu$ exist, then $(X +_s Y) \upharpoonright t_{00}\text{`}\mu$ exists, where X, Y are rationals.

***306·6.** $\vdash : \mu, \rho \epsilon \text{D`}U \cap \text{G`}U . \supset . (\mu +_c \rho) \cap t\text{`}\mu \epsilon \text{D`}U \cap \text{G`}U$

Dem.

$\vdash . *305·23 . \supset \vdash : \text{Hp} . \mu \leqslant \rho . \supset . \mu +_c \rho < 2^{\rho +_c 1}$ (1)

Similarly $\vdash : \text{Hp} . \rho \leqslant \mu . \supset . \mu +_c \rho < 2^{\mu +_c 1}$ (2)

$\vdash . (1) . (2) . *116·72 . \supset \vdash . \text{Prop}$

***306·61.** $\vdash : \mu, \nu, \rho \epsilon \text{D`}U \cap \text{G`}U . \supset . (\mu/\nu +_s \rho/\nu) \cap t_{00}\text{`}\mu \epsilon \text{Rat def}$

Dem.

$\vdash . *306·13·6 . \supset \vdash : \text{Hp} . \supset . \mu/\nu +_s \rho/\nu = (\mu +_c \rho)/\nu . (\mu +_c \rho) \cap t\text{`}\mu, \nu \cap t\text{`}\mu \epsilon \text{D`}U \cap \text{G`}U .$

[*303·71] $\supset . (\mu/\nu +_s \rho/\nu) \cap t_{00}\text{`}\mu \epsilon \text{Rat def} : \supset \vdash . \text{Prop}$

***306·62.** $\vdash : \mu, \nu, \rho \epsilon \text{D`}U \cap \text{G`}U . \supset . (\mu/\nu +_s \rho/\rho) \cap t_{00}\text{`}\mu \epsilon \text{Rat def}$

Dem.

$\vdash . *303·39 . \supset \vdash : \text{Hp} . \supset . \mu/\nu +_s \rho/\rho = \mu/\nu +_s \nu/\nu$ (1)

$\vdash . (1) . *306·61 . \supset \vdash . \text{Prop}$

***306·621.** $\vdash : \sigma \epsilon \text{NC ind} . \supset . \sigma^2 -_c \sigma +_c 1 \leqslant 2^\sigma$

Dem.

$\vdash . *116·301·311 . \supset \vdash . 0^2 -_c 0 +_c 1 \leqslant 2^0$ (1)

$\vdash . *116·321·331 . \supset \vdash . 1^2 -_c 1 +_c 1 \leqslant 2^1$ (2)

$\vdash . *117·55 . *126·5 . \supset \vdash . 2^2 -_c 2 +_c 1 \leqslant 2^2$ (3)

$\vdash . *305·231 . \supset \vdash : \text{Hp} . \sigma > 1 . \sigma^2 -_c \sigma +_c 1 \leqslant 2^\sigma . \supset .$

$(\sigma +_c 1)^2 -_c (\sigma +_c 1) +_c 1 \leqslant 2^\sigma +_c (2 \times_c \sigma) .$

[*117·652.*116·52] $\supset . (\sigma +_c 1)^2 -_c (\sigma +_c 1) +_c 1 \leqslant 2^{\sigma +_c 1}$ (4)

$\vdash . (1) . (2) . (3) . (4) . \text{Induct} . \supset \vdash . \text{Prop}$

***306·622.** $\vdash : \mu \in \text{NC ind} - \iota\text{'}0 . \supset . (\mu -_c 1)^2 = \mu^2 -_c (2 \times_c \mu) +_c 1$

Dem.

$\vdash . *305{\cdot}231 \dfrac{\mu -_c 1}{\mu} . \quad \supset \vdash : \text{Hp} . \supset . (\mu -_c 1)^2 +_c \{2 \times_c (\mu -_c 1)\} +_c 1 = \mu^2$ (1)

$\vdash . *113{\cdot}43 . *120{\cdot}416 . \supset \vdash : \text{Hp} . \supset . \{2 \times_c (\mu -_c 1)\} +_c 2 = 2 \times_c \mu$ (2)

$\vdash . (1) . (2) . \quad \supset \vdash : \text{Hp} . \supset . (\mu -_c 1)^2 +_c (2 \times_c \mu) = \mu^2 +_c 1$ (3)

$\vdash . (3) . *119{\cdot}32 . \supset \vdash . \text{Prop}$

***306·623.** $\vdash : \mu, \nu, \rho \in \text{NC ind} . \nu < \mu . \rho \leqslant \mu . \supset . (\mu \times_c \mu) +_c (\nu \times_c \rho) < 2^{\mu +_c 1}$

Dem.

$\vdash . *120{\cdot}429 . \supset \vdash : \text{Hp} . \supset . (\mu \times_c \mu) +_c (\nu \times_c \rho) \leqslant \mu^2 +_c (\mu -_c 1)^2 .$

$[*120{\cdot}429 . *306{\cdot}622] \quad \supset . (\mu \times_c \mu) +_c (\nu \times_c \rho) < (2 \times_c \mu^2) -_c (2 \times_c \mu) +_c 2$

$[*306{\cdot}621 . *126{\cdot}51] \quad < 2^{\mu +_c 1} : \supset \vdash . \text{Prop}$

***306·624.** $\vdash : \mu, \nu, \rho, \sigma \in \text{NC ind} . \nu < \mu . \rho \leqslant \mu . \sigma \leqslant \mu . \supset .$
$(\mu \times_c \sigma) +_c (\nu \times_c \rho) < 2^{\mu +_c 1}$ [*306·623]

***306·63.** $\vdash : \mu, \nu, \rho, \sigma \in \text{D'}U \cap \text{G'}U . \supset . (\mu/\nu +_s \rho/\sigma) \upharpoonright t_{00}\text{'}\mu \in \text{Rat def}$

Dem.

$\vdash . *306{\cdot}62 . \supset \vdash : \text{Hp} . \nu = \mu . \supset . (\mu/\nu +_s \rho/\sigma) \upharpoonright t_{00}\text{'}\mu \in \text{Rat def}$ (1)

$\vdash . *306{\cdot}624 . *305{\cdot}24 . *303{\cdot}71 . \supset$

$\vdash : \text{Hp} . \nu < \mu . \rho \leqslant \mu . \sigma \leqslant \mu . \supset . (\mu/\nu +_s \rho/\sigma) \upharpoonright t_{00}\text{'}\mu \in \text{Rat def}$ (2)

Similarly

$\vdash : \text{Hp} . \nu < \mu . \mu \leqslant \rho . \sigma \leqslant \mu . \supset . (\mu/\nu +_s \rho/\sigma) \upharpoonright t_{00}\text{'}\mu \in \text{Rat def}$ (3)

$\vdash . (2) . (3) . \supset$

$\vdash : \text{Hp} . \nu < \mu . \sigma \leqslant \mu . \supset . (\mu/\nu +_s \rho/\sigma) \upharpoonright t_{00}\text{'}\mu \in \text{Rat def}$ (4)

Similarly

$\vdash : \text{Hp} . \mu > \nu . \sigma \leqslant \mu . \supset . (\mu/\nu +_s \rho/\sigma) \upharpoonright t_{00}\text{'}\mu \in \text{Rat def}$ (5)

$\vdash . (1) . (4) . (5) . \supset \vdash : \text{Hp} . \sigma \leqslant \mu . \supset . (\mu/\nu +_s \rho/\sigma) \upharpoonright t_{00}\text{'}\mu \in \text{Rat def}$ (6)

Similarly $\quad \vdash : \text{Hp} . \mu \leqslant \sigma . \supset . (\mu/\nu +_s \rho/\sigma) \upharpoonright t_{00}\text{'}\mu \in \text{Rat def}$ (7)

$\vdash . (6) . (7) . \supset \vdash . \text{Prop}$

The following propositions are immediate consequences of *306·63.

***306·64.** $\vdash : (\mu/\nu) \upharpoonright t_{11}\text{'}\mu, (\rho/\sigma) \upharpoonright t_{11}\text{'}\mu \in \text{Rat def} . \supset . (\mu/\nu +_s \rho/\sigma) \upharpoonright t_{00}\text{'}\mu \in \text{Rat def}$

***306·65.** $\vdash : X, Y \in \text{Rat def} . \supset . (X +_s Y) \upharpoonright t_{00}\text{'}C\text{''}C\text{'}X \in \text{Rat def}$

***306·66.** $\vdash : X, Y \in C\text{'}H . \supset . (X +_s Y) \upharpoonright t_{00}\text{'}C\text{''}C\text{'}X \in C\text{'}H$

***306·67.** $\vdash : X, Y \in C\text{'}H' . \supset . (X +_s Y) \upharpoonright t_{00}\text{'}C\text{''}C\text{'}X \in C\text{'}H'$

*307. GENERALIZED RATIOS.

Summary of *307.

In this number we introduce negative ratios. If X is a ratio, what would ordinarily be called $-X$ is $X \mid \text{Cnv}$. This may be seen as follows. Suppose we have RXS. We then have $R(X \mid \text{Cnv})\breve{S}$. Now if R and S are vectors which carry us in the same direction, R and $\breve{S}$ are vectors which carry us in opposite directions, *i.e.* their ratio is negative. Hence calling the class of negative ratios "Rat_n," we may put

***307·01.** $\text{Rat}_n = \mid \text{Cnv}``\text{Rat}$ Df

The sum of "Rat" and "Rat_n" we will call "Rat_g," where "g" stands for "generalized." Thus we put

***307·011.** $\text{Rat}_g = \text{Rat} \cup \text{Rat}_n$ Df

If $\mu/\nu <_r \rho/\sigma$, we have $\{(\mu/\nu) \mid \text{Cnv}\} (\mid \text{Cnv} ; <_r) \{(\rho/\sigma) \mid \text{Cnv}\}$. Hence we put

***307·02.** $<_n = \mid \text{Cnv} ; <_r$ Df

***307·021.** $>_n = \text{Cnv}`<_n$ Df

If X and Y are generalized ratios, we consider X less than Y if either X, Y are both positive and $X <_r Y$, or X, Y are both negative and $X >_n Y$, or X is negative and Y is positive or zero. Hence we put

***307·03.** $<_g = (>_n) \cup (<_r) \cup (\text{Rat}_n - \iota`0_q) \uparrow \text{Rat}$ Df

On the analogy of $<_n$ and $<_g$, we put

***307·04.** $H_n = \mid \text{Cnv} ; H$ Df

***307·05.** $H_g = \breve{H}_n \ddagger H'$ Df

We prove in this number that if X is a ratio, $X \mid \text{Cnv} = \text{Cnv} \mid X$, and $\text{Cnv}`(X \mid \text{Cnv}) = \breve{X} \mid \text{Cnv}$ (*307·21·22). We prove also

***307·25.** $\vdash . C`H \cap C`H_n = \Lambda$

We prove that 0_q and ∞_q are their own negatives, but are not the negatives of anything else (*307·26·27·31). We prove $\text{Nr}`H_n = \text{Nr}`H$ (*307·41) and Infin ax $. \supset . H_g \in \eta$ (*307·46). None of the propositions of this number offer any difficulty.

***307·01.** $\text{Rat}_n = |\,\text{Cnv}``\text{Rat}$ Df

***307·011.** $\text{Rat}_g = \text{Rat} \cup \text{Rat}_n$ Df

***307·02.** $<_n = |\,\text{Cnv};<_r$ Df

***307·021.** $>_n = \text{Cnv}`<_n$ Df

***307·03.** $<_g = (>_n) \uplus (<_r) \uplus (\text{Rat}_n - \iota`0_q) \uparrow \text{Rat}$ Df

***307·031.** $>_g = \text{Cnv}`<_g$ Df

***307·04.** $H_n = |\,\text{Cnv};H$ Df

***307·05.** $H_g = \breve{H}_n \Uparrow H'$ Df

***307·1.** $\vdash : R(X\,|\,\text{Cnv})S \,.\equiv .\, RX\breve{S}$ [*71·7]

***307·11.** $\vdash : R(|\,\text{Cnv};X)S \,.\equiv .\, \breve{R}X\breve{S}$ [*307·1]

***307·12.** $\vdash .\, X\,|\,\text{Cnv}\,|\,\text{Cnv} = X$ [*307·1]

***307·13.** $\vdash : X\,|\,\text{Cnv} = Y\,|\,\text{Cnv} \,.\equiv .\, X = Y$ [*307·12]

***307·14.** $\vdash : Y = X\,|\,\text{Cnv} \,.\equiv .\, X = Y\,|\,\text{Cnv}$ [*307·12]

***307·15.** $\vdash : \dot{\exists} \,!\, X \upharpoonright \kappa \,.\equiv .\, \dot{\exists} \,!\, \kappa \urcorner (X\,|\,\text{Cnv}) \upharpoonright (\text{Cnv}``\kappa)$ [*307·1]

***307·16.** $\vdash :. \kappa = \text{Cnv}``\kappa \,.\supset : \dot{\exists} \,!\, X \upharpoonright \kappa \,.\equiv .\, \dot{\exists} \,!\, (X\,|\,\text{Cnv}) \upharpoonright \kappa$ [*307·15]

***307·2.** $\vdash .\, (\mu/\nu)\,|\,\text{Cnv} = \text{Cnv}\,|\,(\mu/\nu)$ [*307·1 . *303·19]

***307·21.** $\vdash : X \in \text{Rat} \cup \iota`\infty_q \,.\supset .\, X\,|\,\text{Cnv} = \text{Cnv}\,|\,X$ [*307·2 . *303·7·67]

***307·22.** $\vdash : X \in \text{Rat} \cup \iota`\infty_q \,.\supset .\, \text{Cnv}`(X\,|\,\text{Cnv}) = \breve{X}\,|\,\text{Cnv}$ [*307·21]

***307·23.** $\vdash .\, \text{Cnv}``C`H_n = C`H_n$ [*304·28 . *303·13 . *307·22]

***307·24.** $\vdash : \mu, \nu, \rho, \sigma \in \text{NC}`U \,.\, \mu \text{ Prm } \nu \,.\, \rho \text{ Prm } \sigma \,.\, \rho \geqslant \sigma \,.\, \sigma \neq 0 \,.\supset .$
$\dot{\exists} \,!\, (\rho/\sigma) \dot{\wedge} (\mu/\nu)\,|\,\text{Cnv}$

Dem.

$\vdash .\, *303·32 \,.\supset \vdash :.\, \text{Hp} \,.\supset : (\exists P, Q) \,.\, P, Q \in \text{Rel num} \,.\, P_{po} \mathrel{G} Q_{po} \,.\, P(\rho/\sigma)Q :$

[*303·21] $\supset : (\exists P, Q) \,.\, P, Q \in \text{Rel num} \,.\, P_{po} \mathrel{G} Q_{po} \,.\, \dot{\exists} \,!\, P^\sigma \dot{\wedge} Q^\rho :$

[*300·3] $\supset : (\exists P, Q) \,.\, P, Q \in \text{Rel num} \,.\, \dot{\exists} \,!\, P^\sigma \dot{\wedge} Q^\rho \,.\, P^\nu \dot{\wedge} \breve{Q}^\mu = \dot{\Lambda} :$

[*303·21] $\supset : (\exists P, Q) \,.\, P(\rho/\sigma)Q \,.\sim \{P(\mu/\nu)\breve{Q}\} :. \supset \vdash .$ Prop

***307·25.** $\vdash .\, C`H \cap C`H_n = \Lambda$

Dem.

$\vdash .\, *307·24 \,.\, *303·13 \,.\supset$

$\vdash : \mu, \nu, \rho, \sigma \in \text{NC}`U \,.\, \mu \text{ Prm } \nu \,.\, \rho \text{ Prm } \sigma \,.\supset .\, \mu/\nu \neq (\rho/\sigma)\,|\,\text{Cnv}$ (1)

$\vdash .\, *302·22 \,.\, *303·211 \,.\, *304·27·28 \,.\supset \vdash : X, Y \in C`H \,.\supset .$

$(\exists \mu, \nu, \rho, \sigma) \,.\, \mu, \nu, \rho, \sigma \in \text{NC}`U \,.\, \mu \text{ Prm } \nu \,.\, \rho \text{ Prm } \sigma \,.\, X = \mu/\nu \,.\, Y = \rho/\sigma$ (2)

$\vdash .\, (1) \,.\, (2) \,.\supset \vdash : X, Y \in C`H \,.\supset .\, X \neq Y\,|\,\text{Cnv} : \supset \vdash .$ Prop

***307·26.** $\vdash . 0_q \mid \mathrm{Cnv} = 0_q = \mathrm{Cnv} \mid 0_q$

Dem.

$$\vdash . *307{\cdot}2 . \qquad \supset \vdash . 0_q \mid \mathrm{Cnv} = \mathrm{Cnv} \mid 0_q \qquad (1)$$

$$\vdash . *303{\cdot}6{\cdot}15 . *307{\cdot}1 . \supset \vdash : R \,(0_q \mid \mathrm{Cnv})\, S . \equiv . \dot{\exists} ! R \dot{\cap} I \upharpoonright C\text{‘}\breve{S} .$$

$$[*33{\cdot}22] \qquad \equiv . \dot{\exists} ! R \dot{\cap} \breve{I} \upharpoonright C\text{‘}S .$$

$$[*303{\cdot}15] \qquad \equiv . R 0_q S \qquad (2)$$

$$\vdash . (1) . (2) . \supset \vdash . \mathrm{Prop}$$

***307·27.** $\vdash . \infty_q \mid \mathrm{Cnv} = \infty_q = \mathrm{Cnv} \mid \infty_q$ [*307·26 . *303·62]

***307·3.** $\vdash : X \in C\text{‘}H . \supset . \dot{\exists} ! (X \mid \mathrm{Cnv}) \downharpoonleft \mathrm{Rel\,num}$ [*304·5 . *307·16 . *300·4]

***307·31.** $\vdash : X \in \mathrm{Rat} - \iota\text{‘}0_q . \supset . X \mid \mathrm{Cnv} \neq 0_q . X \mid \mathrm{Cnv} \neq \infty_q$
[*307·3 . *304·53 . *303·62]

***307·4.** $\vdash : X H_n Y . \equiv . (X \mid \mathrm{Cnv})\, H \,(Y \mid \mathrm{Cnv})$ [*150·41 . (*307·04)]

***307·41.** $\vdash . \mathrm{Nr}\text{‘}H_n = \mathrm{Nr}\text{‘}H$ [*307·13 . (*307·04)]

***307·42.** $\vdash : \mathrm{Infin\ ax} . \supset . \mathrm{Nr}\text{‘}H_n = \mathrm{Nr}\text{‘}\breve{H}_n = \eta$ [*307·41 . *304·33]

***307·43.** $\vdash : X \in C\text{‘}H_n . \supset . \dot{\exists} ! X \downharpoonleft \mathrm{Rel\,num}$ [*307·3]

***307·44.** $\vdash . 0_q, \infty_q \sim\in C\text{‘}H_n$ [*307·31]

***307·45.** $\vdash . \mathrm{Nr}\text{‘}H_g = \mathrm{Nr}\text{‘}\breve{H} \dot{+} \dot{1} \dot{+} \mathrm{Nr}\text{‘}H$ [*307·25·41 . (*307·05)]

***307·46.** $\vdash : \mathrm{Infin\ ax} . \supset . H_g \in \eta$ [*307·45 . *304·33]

This proposition requires $\eta \dot{+} \dot{1} \dot{+} \eta = \eta$, which is easily proved.

$*308$. ADDITION OF GENERALIZED RATIOS.

Summary of $*308$.

In this number we have to extend addition so as to include negative ratios as addenda, and for this purpose we have to define subtraction of simple ratios. This is defined as follows:

$$*308\cdot01.\quad X -_s Y = \hat{R}\hat{S}\{(\exists Z) : X, Y, Z \in \text{Rat} : Z +_s Y = X \,.\, RZS \,.\, \text{v} \,.\, Z +_s X = Y \,.\, RZ\breve{S}\} \quad \text{Df}$$

That is to say, if $Y <_r X$, $X -_s Y$ is the ratio which must be added to Y to give X, while if $X <_r Y$, $X -_s Y$ is the negative of the ratio which must be added to X to give Y. Thus we have

$$*308\cdot13.\quad \vdash :. Y <_r X \,.\, \text{v} \,.\, Y \in \text{Rat} \,.\, Y = \dot{X} : \supset . X -_s Y = (\iota Z)(Z +_s Y = X)$$

$$*308\cdot14.\quad \vdash :. X <_r Y \,.\, \text{v} \,.\, X \in \text{Rat} \,.\, Y = X : \supset . X -_s Y = \{(\iota Z)(Z +_s X = Y)\} \,|\, \text{Cnv}$$

We have, of course, $X -_s 0_q = X$ ($*308\cdot22$), $0_q -_s X = X \,|\, \text{Cnv}$ ($*308\cdot23$), and $X -_s X = 0_q$ ($*308\cdot12$). Existence-theorems for $X -_s Y$ are closely analogous to those for $X +_s Y$ and $X \times_s Y$. Also we have

$$*308\cdot2.\quad \vdash : X, Y \in \text{Rat} \,.\, \equiv . X -_s Y \in \text{Rat}_g$$

We define the sum of two generalized ratios by means of the sums and differences of simple ratios, as follows:

$$*308\cdot02.\quad X +_g Y = (X +_s Y) \cup (X -_s Y \,|\, \text{Cnv}) \cup (Y -_s X \,|\, \text{Cnv}) \cup (X \,|\, \text{Cnv} +_s Y \,|\, \text{Cnv}) \,|\, \text{Cnv} \quad \text{Df}$$

Of the four relations which occur in the above definition, all but one must be null if neither X nor Y is 0_q. Thus if X and Y are positive, $X -_s Y \,|\, \text{Cnv}$, $Y -_s X \,|\, \text{Cnv}$, and $X \,|\, \text{Cnv} +_s Y \,|\, \text{Cnv}$ are null; if X is positive and Y negative, $X +_s Y$, $Y -_s X \,|\, \text{Cnv}$, and $X \,|\, \text{Cnv} +_s Y \,|\, \text{Cnv}$ are null; if X and Y are both negative, $X +_s Y$, $X -_s Y \,|\, \text{Cnv}$, and $Y -_s X \,|\, \text{Cnv}$ are null.

If X is 0_q and Y is positive,

$$X +_s Y = Y -_s X \,|\, \text{Cnv} \,.\, X -_s Y \,|\, \text{Cnv} = (X \,|\, \text{Cnv} +_s Y \,|\, \text{Cnv}) \,|\, \text{Cnv} = \dot{\Lambda}.$$

If both X and Y are 0_q, all four relations are 0_q.

Hence we find

***308·32.** $\vdash : X, Y \epsilon \text{Rat} . \supset . X +_g Y = X +_s Y$

***308·321.** $\vdash : X \epsilon \text{Rat} . Y \epsilon \text{Rat}_n . \supset . X +_g Y = X -_s Y | \text{Cnv}$

***308·322.** $\vdash : Y \epsilon \text{Rat} . X \epsilon \text{Rat}_n . \supset . X +_g Y = Y -_s X | \text{Cnv}$

***308·323.** $\vdash : X, Y \epsilon \text{Rat}_n . \supset . X +_g Y = (X | \text{Cnv} +_s Y | \text{Cnv}) | \text{Cnv}$

The existence-theorems for $X +_g Y$ are closely analogous to those for $X +_s Y$, and the formal laws offer no difficulty. We have

***308·52.** $\vdash :. X, Y \epsilon \text{Rat}_g . \supset : X +_g Y = X +_g Z . \equiv . Y = Z$

***308·54.** $\vdash : X, Y \epsilon \text{Rat}_g . \supset . (\exists Z) . Z \epsilon \text{Rat}_g . X +_g Z = Y$

***308·56.** $\vdash :. X <_g Y . \equiv : X \epsilon \text{Rat}_g : (\exists Z) . Z \epsilon \text{Rat} - \iota ‘0_q . X +_g Z = Y$

***308·72.** $\vdash : (X +_g Z) <_g (X +_g Z') . \equiv . X \epsilon \text{Rat}_g . Z <_g Z'$

***308·01.** $X -_s Y = \hat{R}\hat{S} \{(\exists Z) : X, Y, Z \epsilon \text{Rat} : Z +_s Y = X . RZS . \mathbf{v} .$
$Z +_s X = Y . RZ\breve{S}\}$ Df

***308·02.** $X +_g Y = (X +_s Y) \cup (X -_s Y | \text{Cnv}) \cup$
$(Y -_s X | \text{Cnv}) \cup (X | \text{Cnv} +_s Y | \text{Cnv}) | \text{Cnv}$ Df

***308·1.** $\vdash : Y <_r X . \supset . X -_s Y = \hat{R}\hat{S} \{(\exists Z) . Z \epsilon \text{Rat} . Z +_s Y = X . RZS\}$

Dem.

$\vdash . *306·55 . \supset \vdash : \text{Hp} . \supset . \sim (\exists Z) . Z +_s X = Y$ (1)

$\vdash . (1) . (*308·01) . \supset \vdash . \text{Prop}$

***308·11.** $\vdash : X <_r Y . \supset . X -_s Y = \hat{R}\hat{S} \{(\exists Z) . Z \epsilon \text{Rat} . Z +_s X = Y . RZ\breve{S}\}$

Dem.

$\vdash . *306·55 . \supset \vdash : \text{Hp} . \supset . \sim (\exists Z) . Z +_s Y = X$ (1)

$\vdash . (1) . (*308·01) . \supset \vdash . \text{Prop}$

***308·12.** $\vdash : X \epsilon \text{Rat} . X = Y . \supset . X -_s Y = 0_q$ [*306·54·24]

***308·13.** $\vdash :. Y <_r X . \mathbf{v} . Y \epsilon \text{Rat} . Y = X : \supset . X -_s Y = (\iota Z)(Z +_s Y = X)$

Dem.

$\vdash . *306·52·24 . \supset \vdash : \text{Hp} . \supset . (\exists Z) . Z +_s Y = X . Z \epsilon \text{Rat}$ (1)

$\vdash . *306·54 . \supset \vdash : \text{Hp} . Z +_s Y = X . Z' +_s Y = X . \supset . Z = Z'$ (2)

$\vdash . (1) . (2) . *308·1·12 . \supset \vdash . \text{Prop}$

***308·14.** $\vdash :. X <_r Y . \mathbf{v} . X \epsilon \text{Rat} . X = Y : \supset . X -_s Y = \{(\iota Z)(Z +_s X = Y)\} | \text{Cnv}$
[Proof as in *308·13]

***308·15.** $\vdash : \sim (X, Y \epsilon \text{Rat}) . \supset . X -_s Y = \dot{\Lambda}$ [(*308·01)]

***308·16.** $\vdash : X, Y \epsilon \text{Rat} . Y +_s Z = X . \supset . X -_s Y = Z$

Dem.

$\vdash . *306·55 . *304·221 . \supset \vdash :. \text{Hp} . \supset : Y <_r X . \mathbf{v} . Y \epsilon \text{Rat} . Y = X$ (1)

$\vdash . (1) . *308·13 . \supset \vdash . \text{Prop}$

***308·17.** $\vdash : X, Y \in \mathrm{Rat} . X +_s Z = Y . \supset . X -_s Y = Z | \mathrm{Cnv}$ [*306·55.*308·14]

***308·18.** $\vdash : Y <_r X . \supset . X -_s Y \in \mathrm{Rat} - \iota`0_q$

Dem.

$\vdash . *306·52 . \supset \vdash : \mathrm{Hp} . \supset . (\exists Z) . Z \in \mathrm{Rat} - \iota`0_q . Y +_s Z = X$ (1)

$\vdash . (1) . *308·13 . \supset \vdash . \mathrm{Prop}$

***308·19.** $\vdash : X <_r Y . \supset . X -_s Y \in \mathrm{Rat}_n - \iota`0_q$

Dem.

$\vdash . *306·52 . \supset \vdash : \mathrm{Hp} . \supset . (\exists Z) . Z \in \mathrm{Rat} - \iota`0_q . X +_s Z = Y$ (1)

$\vdash . (1) . *308·14 . \supset \vdash . \mathrm{Prop}$

***308·2.** $\vdash : X, Y \in \mathrm{Rat} . \equiv . X -_s Y \in \mathrm{Rat}_g$ [*308·12·18·19·15]

***308·21.** $\vdash : X -_s Y = (Y -_s X) | \mathrm{Cnv} = \mathrm{Cnv} | (Y -_s X)$

Dem.

$\vdash . *308·13·14 . \supset$

$\vdash :. X <_r Y . \vee . X \in \mathrm{Rat} - \iota`0_q . X = Y : \supset . X -_s Y = (Y -_s X) | \mathrm{Cnv}$ (1)

$\vdash . *308·13·14 . *307·12 . \supset$

$\vdash :. Y <_r X . \vee . Y \in \mathrm{Rat} - \iota`0_q . Y = X : \supset . X -_s Y = (Y -_s X) | \mathrm{Cnv}$ (2)

$\vdash . (1) . (2) . *304·221 . \supset \vdash : X, Y \in \mathrm{Rat} . \supset . X -_s Y = (Y -_s X) | \mathrm{Cnv}$ (3)

[*307·21.*308·2] $= \mathrm{Cnv} | (Y -_s X)$ (4)

$\vdash . (3) . (4) . *308·15 . \supset \vdash . \mathrm{Prop}$

***308·22.** $\vdash : X \in \mathrm{Rat} . \supset . X -_s 0_q = X$ [*306·24 . *308·13]

***308·23.** $\vdash : X \in \mathrm{Rat} . \supset . 0_q -_s X = X | \mathrm{Cnv}$ [*308·21·22]

***308·24.** $\vdash : (\nu/\rho) <_r (\lambda/\mu) . \supset . \lambda/\mu -_s \nu/\rho = \{(\lambda \times_c \rho) -_c (\mu \times_c \nu)\}/(\mu \times_c \rho)$

Dem.

$\vdash . *304·1 . \supset \vdash : \mathrm{Hp} . \supset . \lambda \times_c \rho > \mu \times_c \nu$ (1)

$\vdash . *303·23 . *306·13 . (1) . \supset$

$\vdash : \mathrm{Hp} . \supset . \{(\lambda \times_c \rho) - (\mu \times_c \nu)\}/(\mu \times_c \rho) +_s \nu/\rho =$

$[\{(\lambda \times_c \rho) - (\mu \times_c \nu)\} +_c (\mu \times_c \nu)]/(\mu \times_c \rho)$

[*303·23.*119·34] $= \lambda/\mu$ (2)

$\vdash . (1) . (2) . *308·16 . \supset \vdash . \mathrm{Prop}$

***308·241.** $\vdash : (\lambda/\mu) <_r (\nu/\rho) . \supset . \lambda/\mu -_s \nu/\rho = [\{(\mu \times_c \nu) -_c (\lambda \times_c \rho)\}/(\mu \times_c \rho)] | \mathrm{Cnv}$
[*308·24·21]

***308·25.** $\vdash : \lambda, \mu, \nu, \rho \in \mathrm{D}`U \cap \mathrm{G}`U . \nu/\rho <_r \lambda/\mu . \supset . (\lambda/\mu -_s \nu/\rho) \upharpoonright t_{00}`\mu \in C`H$

Dem.

$\vdash . *305·24 . \supset$

$\vdash : \mathrm{Hp} . \supset . \{(\lambda \times_c \rho) -_c (\mu \times_c \nu)\} \cap t`\mu, (\mu \times_c \rho) \cap t`\mu \in \mathrm{D}`U \cap \mathrm{G}`U$ (1)

$\vdash . (1) . *308·24 . *304·28 . \supset \vdash . \mathrm{Prop}$

***308·251.** $\vdash : \lambda, \mu, \nu, \rho \in \text{D}`U \cap \text{Cl}`U . \lambda/\mu <_r \nu/\rho . \supset . (\lambda/\mu -_s \nu/\rho) \upharpoonright t_{00}`\mu \in C`H_n$
[*305·24 . *308·241]

***308·252.** $\vdash : \lambda, \mu, \nu, \rho \in \text{D}`U \cap \text{Cl}`U . \supset . (\lambda/\mu -_s \nu/\rho) \upharpoonright t_{00}`\mu \in C`H_g$
[*308·25·251·12]

***308·26.** $\vdash : X, Y \in \text{Rat} . X \upharpoonright t_{11}`\mu, Y \upharpoonright t_{11}`\mu \in C`H' . \supset . (X -_s Y) \upharpoonright t_{00}`\mu \in C`H_q$
[*308·252 . *304·28]

***308·261.** $\vdash : X, Y \in C`H' . \supset . (X -_s Y) \upharpoonright t_{00}`C``C`X \in C`H_g$ [*308·26]

***308·3.** $\vdash : \dot{\exists} ! (X -_s Y | \text{Cnv}) . \supset . X \in \text{Rat} . Y \in \text{Rat}_n$
[*308·15 . *307·12]

***308·301.** $\vdash : \dot{\exists} ! (X | \text{Cnv} +_s Y | \text{Cnv}) . \supset . X, Y \in \text{Rat}_n$ [*306·12 . *307·23·12]

***308·31.** $\vdash : \dot{\exists} ! (X +_g Y) . \supset . X, Y \in \text{Rat}_g$ [*306·12 . *308·3·301 . (*308·02)]

***308·32.** $\vdash : X, Y \in \text{Rat} . \supset . X +_g Y = X +_s Y$

Dem.

$\vdash . *308·3·301 . *307·25 . (*308·02) . \supset$
$\vdash : X, Y \in \text{Rat} - \iota`0_q . \supset . X +_g Y = X +_s Y$ (1)
$\vdash . *306·24 . *308·22·3·301 . \supset$
$\vdash : X \in \text{Rat} - \iota`0_q . Y = 0_q . \supset . X +_g Y = X = X +_s Y$ (2)
$\vdash . *306·24 . *308·3·301 . \supset \vdash : X = 0_q . Y = 0_q . \supset . X +_g Y = 0_q = X +_s Y$ (3)
$\vdash . (2) . (3) . \supset$
$\vdash :. X \in \text{Rat} . Y = 0_q . \vee . Y \in \text{Rat} . X = 0_q : \supset . X +_g Y = X +_s Y$ (4)
$\vdash . (1) . (4) . \supset \vdash . \text{Prop}$

***308·321.** $\vdash : X \in \text{Rat} . Y \in \text{Rat}_n . \supset . X +_g Y = X -_s Y | \text{Cnv}$
[*306·12 . *308·3·301 . *307·25 . (*308·02)]

***308·322.** $\vdash : Y \in \text{Rat} . X \in \text{Rat}_n . \supset . X +_g Y = Y -_s X | \text{Cnv}$
[*306·12 . *308·3·301 . *307·25 . (*308·02)]

***308·323.** $\vdash : X, Y \in \text{Rat}_n . \supset . X +_g Y = (X | \text{Cnv} +_s Y | \text{Cnv}) | \text{Cnv}$
[*306·12 . *308·3·301 . *307·25 . (*308·02)]

***308·33.** $\vdash : X +_g Y \in \text{Rat}_g . \equiv . X, Y \in \text{Rat}_g$
[*306·22 . *308·2·32·31]

***308·4.** $\vdash . X +_g Y = Y +_g X$ [*306·11 . (*308·02)]

***308·41.** $\vdash . X +_g Y = (X | \text{Cnv} +_g Y | \text{Cnv}) | \text{Cnv}$

Dem.

$\vdash . *307·12 . *34·26 . (*308·02) . \supset$
$\vdash . (X | \text{Cnv} +_g Y | \text{Cnv}) | \text{Cnv} = (X | \text{Cnv} +_s Y | \text{Cnv}) | \text{Cnv} \cup (X | \text{Cnv} -_s Y) | \text{Cnv}$
$\cup (Y | \text{Cnv} -_s X) | \text{Cnv} \cup (X +_s Y)$
[*308·21] $= (X | \text{Cnv} \cup Y | \text{Cnv}) | \text{Cnv} \cup (Y -_s X | \text{Cnv})$
$\cup (X -_s Y | \text{Cnv}) \cup (X +_s Y)$
[(*308·02)] $= X +_g Y . \supset \vdash . \text{Prop}$

***308·411.** $\vdash . (X +_g Y) | \mathrm{Cnv} = X | \mathrm{Cnv} +_g Y | \mathrm{Cnv}$ [*308·41 . *307·12]

***308·412.** $\vdash : X | \mathrm{Cnv} +_g Y | \mathrm{Cnv} = Z | \mathrm{Cnv} . \equiv . X +_g Y = Z$
[*308·411 . *307·13]

***308·42.** $\vdash : X, Y \epsilon \mathrm{Rat} . \supset . (X -_s Y) +_g Y = X$

Dem.

$\vdash . *308{\cdot}12{\cdot}32 . *306{\cdot}24 . \supset \vdash : \mathrm{Hp} . X = Y . \supset . (X -_s Y) +_g Y = X$ (1)

$\vdash . *308{\cdot}18{\cdot}32 . \supset \vdash : \mathrm{Hp} . Y <_r X . \supset . (X -_s Y) +_g Y = (X -_s Y) +_s Y$

[*308·13] $= X$ (2)

$\vdash . *308{\cdot}19{\cdot}322 . \supset \vdash : \mathrm{Hp} . X <_r Y . \supset . (X -_s Y) +_g Y = Y -_s (X -_s Y) | \mathrm{Cnv}$

[*308·21] $= Y -_s (Y -_s X)$ (3)

$\vdash . *308{\cdot}13 . \supset \vdash : \mathrm{Hp}(3) . \supset . X +_s (Y -_s X) = Y .$

[*308·16·18] $\supset . X = Y -_s (Y -_s X)$ (4)

$\vdash . (3) . (4) . \supset \vdash : \mathrm{Hp} . X <_r Y . \supset . (X -_s Y) +_g Y = X$ (5)

$\vdash . (1) . (2) . (5) . *304{\cdot}221 . \supset \vdash . \mathrm{Prop}$

***308·43.** $\vdash : X, Y \epsilon \mathrm{Rat} . \supset . (X +_g Y) -_s Y = X$

Dem.

$\vdash . *308{\cdot}32 . \supset \vdash : \mathrm{Hp} . \supset . X +_g Y = X +_s Y .$

[*308·16.*306·22] $\supset . (X +_g Y) -_s Y = X : \supset \vdash . \mathrm{Prop}$

***308·44.** $\vdash :. X, Z \epsilon \mathrm{Rat} . \supset : X -_s Z = Y -_s Z . \equiv . X = Y$

Dem.

$\vdash . *308{\cdot}13{\cdot}14{\cdot}15 . \supset \vdash : X = Y . \supset . X -_s Z = Y -_s Z$ (1)

$\vdash . *308{\cdot}2 . \supset \vdash : \mathrm{Hp} . X -_s Z = Y -_s Z . \supset . Y \epsilon \mathrm{Rat} .$

[*308·42] $\supset . (Y -_s Z) +_s Z = Y .$

[Hp] $\supset . (X -_s Z) +_s Z = Y .$

[*308·42] $\supset . X = Y$ (2)

$\vdash . (1) . (2) . \supset \vdash . \mathrm{Prop}$

***308·45.** $\vdash :. X, Z \epsilon \mathrm{Rat} . \supset : Z -_s X = Z -_s Y . \equiv . X = Y$
[*308·44·21 . *307·13]

***308·46.** $\vdash : X, Y \epsilon \mathrm{Rat} . Y \neq 0_q . \supset . (X -_s Y) <_g X$

Dem.

$\vdash . *308{\cdot}19 . \supset \vdash : X <_r Y . \supset . (X -_s Y) \epsilon \mathrm{Rat}_n - \iota`0_q . X \epsilon \mathrm{Rat} .$

[(*307·03)] $\supset . (X -_s Y) <_g X$ (1)

$\vdash . *308{\cdot}12 . \supset \vdash : \mathrm{Hp} . X = Y . \supset . X -_s Y = 0_q .$

[*304·46.(*307·03)] $\supset . (X -_s Y) <_g X$ (2)

$\vdash . *308{\cdot}13{\cdot}18 . \supset \vdash : \mathrm{Hp} . Y <_r X . \supset . (X -_s Y) +_s Y = X . X -_s Y \epsilon \mathrm{Rat} - \iota`0_q .$

[*306·52] $\supset . (X -_s Y) <_r X .$

[(*307·03)] $\supset . (X -_s Y) <_g X$ (3)

$\vdash . (1) . (2) . (3) . \supset \vdash . \mathrm{Prop}$

***308·47.** $\vdash : X \epsilon \text{Rat} . Y, Z \epsilon \text{Rat} - \iota`0_q . \supset . X -_s Y \neq X +_s Z$

Dem.

$\vdash . *306·52 . *308·46 . \supset \vdash : \text{Hp} . \supset . (X -_s Y) <_r (X +_s Z) .$

[*304·201] $\supset . X -_s Y \neq X +_s Z : \supset \vdash . \text{Prop}$

***308·51.** $\vdash :. X \epsilon \text{Rat}_g . \supset : X +_g Y = X . \equiv . Y = 0_q$

Dem.

$\vdash . *308·33 . \supset \vdash :. \text{Hp} . \supset : X +_g Y = X . \supset . Y \epsilon \text{Rat}_g$ (1)

$\vdash . *308·32 . \supset \vdash : X \epsilon \text{Rat} . Y = 0_q . \supset . X +_g Y = X +_s Y$

[*306·24] $= X$ (2)

$\vdash . *308·322 . \supset \vdash : X \epsilon \text{Rat}_n . Y = 0_q . \supset . X +_g Y = Y -_s X | \text{Cnv}$

[*308·23.*307·12] $= X$ (3)

$\vdash . (2) . (3) . \supset \vdash :. \text{Hp} . \supset : Y = 0_q . \supset . X +_g Y = X$ (4)

$\vdash . *308·32 . \supset \vdash : X, Y \epsilon \text{Rat} . X +_g Y = X . \supset . X +_s Y = X .$

[*306·24·54] $\supset . Y = 0_q$ (5)

$\vdash . *308·321 . \supset \vdash : X \epsilon \text{Rat} . Y \epsilon \text{Rat}_n . X +_g Y = X . \supset . X -_s Y | \text{Cnv} = X .$

[*308·22·45] $\supset . Y | \text{Cnv} = 0_q .$

[*307·2] $\supset . Y = 0_q$ (6)

$\vdash . *308·322 . \supset \vdash : X \epsilon \text{Rat}_n . Y \epsilon \text{Rat} . X +_g Y = X . \supset . Y -_s X | \text{Cnv} = X$

[*308·23.*307·12] $= 0_q -_s X | \text{Cnv} .$

[*308·44] $\supset . Y = 0_q$ (7)

$\vdash . *308·323 . *307·14 . \supset$

$\vdash : X, Y \epsilon \text{Rat}_n . X +_g Y = X . \supset . X | \text{Cnv} +_s Y | \text{Cnv} = X | \text{Cnv} .$

[(5).*307·26] $\supset . Y = 0_q$ (8)

$\vdash . (1) . (5) . (6) . (7) . (8) . \supset \vdash :. \text{Hp} . \supset : X +_g Y = X . \supset . Y = 0_q$ (9)

$\vdash . (4) . (9) . \supset \vdash . \text{Prop}$

***308·52.** $\vdash :. X, Y \epsilon \text{Rat}_g . \supset : X +_g Y = X +_g Z . \equiv . Y = Z$

Dem.

$\vdash . *308·321·47 . \supset \vdash : X, Y \epsilon \text{Rat} . Y \neq 0_q . X +_g Y = X +_g Z . \supset . Z \sim \epsilon \text{Rat}_n$ (1)

$\vdash . *308·51 . \supset \vdash : X \epsilon \text{Rat}_g . Y = 0_q . X +_g Y = X +_g Z . \supset . Z = 0_q$ (2)

$\vdash . (1) . (2) . *308·33 . \supset \vdash : X, Y \epsilon \text{Rat} . X +_g Y = X +_g Z . \supset . Z \epsilon \text{Rat}$ (3)

$\vdash . (3) . *308·32 . \supset \vdash : X, Y \epsilon \text{Rat} . X +_g Y = X +_g Z . \supset . X +_s Y = X +_s Z .$

[*306·54] $\supset . Y = Z$ (4)

$\vdash . (4) . *308·323 . *307·13 . \supset \vdash : X, Y \epsilon \text{Rat}_n . X +_g Y = X +_g Z . \supset . Y = Z$ (5)

$\vdash . *308·321·32·47 . \supset$

$\vdash : X \epsilon \text{Rat} . Y \epsilon \text{Rat}_n . X +_g Y = X +_g Z . \supset . Z \sim \epsilon \text{Rat} - \iota`0_q$ (6)

$\vdash . (2) \dfrac{Z, Y}{Y, Z} . \text{Transp} . \supset$

$\vdash : X \epsilon \text{Rat} . Y \epsilon \text{Rat}_n - \iota`0_q . X +_g Y = X +_g Z . \supset . Z \neq 0_q$ (7)

$\vdash . (6) . (7) . *308{\cdot}33 . \supset$

$\vdash : X \epsilon \text{Rat} . Y \epsilon \text{Rat}_n - \iota`0_q . X +_g Y = X +_g Z . \supset . Z \epsilon \text{Rat}_n$ (8)

$\vdash . (8) . *308{\cdot}321 . \supset \vdash : \text{Hp}(8) . \supset . X -_s Y | \text{Cnv} = X -_s Z | \text{Cnv} .$

[*308·45.*307·13] $\supset . Y = Z$ (9)

$\vdash . (9) . *308{\cdot}411 . *307{\cdot}13 . \supset$

$\vdash : X \epsilon \text{Rat}_n . Y \epsilon \text{Rat} . X +_g Y = X +_g Z . \supset . Y = Z$ (10)

$\vdash . (4) . (5) . (9) . (10) . \supset \vdash : \text{Hp} . X +_g Y = X +_g Z . \supset . Y = Z$ (11)

$\vdash . (11) . (*308{\cdot}02) . \supset \vdash . \text{Prop}$

***308·53.** $\vdash : X, Y \epsilon \text{Rat}_g . \supset . X +_g (Y +_g X | \text{Cnv}) = Y$

Dem.

$\vdash . *308{\cdot}321 . *307{\cdot}12 . \supset \vdash : X, Y \epsilon \text{Rat} . \supset . X +_g (Y +_g X | \text{Cnv}) = X +_g (Y -_s X)$

[*308·4·42] $= Y$ (1)

$\vdash . *308{\cdot}32 . \supset$

$\vdash : X \epsilon \text{Rat}_n . Y \epsilon \text{Rat} . \supset . X +_g (Y +_g X | \text{Cnv}) = X +_g (Y +_s X | \text{Cnv})$

[*308·4·321.*306·22] $= (Y +_s X | \text{Cnv}) -_s X | \text{Cnv}$

[*308·43·32] $= Y$ (2)

$\vdash . *308{\cdot}323 . *307{\cdot}12 . \supset$

$\vdash : X \epsilon \text{Rat} . Y \epsilon \text{Rat}_n . \supset . X +_g (Y +_g X | \text{Cnv}) = X +_g (Y | \text{Cnv} +_s X) | \text{Cnv}$

[*308·321.*306·22] $= X -_s (Y | \text{Cnv} +_s X)$

[*308·17.*307·12] $= Y$ (3)

$\vdash . (1) . \supset \vdash : X, Y \epsilon \text{Rat}_n . \supset . X | \text{Cnv} +_g (Y | \text{Cnv} +_g X | \text{Cnv} | \text{Cnv}) = Y | \text{Cnv} .$

[*308·411] $\supset . X | \text{Cnv} +_g (Y +_g X | \text{Cnv}) | \text{Cnv} = Y | \text{Cnv} .$

[*308·412] $\supset . X +_g (Y +_g X | \text{Cnv}) = Y$ (4)

$\vdash . (1) . (2) . (3) . (4) . \supset \vdash . \text{Prop}$

***308·54.** $\vdash : X, Y \epsilon \text{Rat}_g . \supset . (\exists Z) . Z \epsilon \text{Rat}_g . X +_g Z = Y$ [*308·53·33]

***308·55.** $\vdash :. X, Y, Z \epsilon \text{Rat}_g . \supset : X +_g Z = Y . \equiv . X = Y +_g Z | \text{Cnv}$

Dem.

$\vdash . *308{\cdot}53{\cdot}52{\cdot}4 . \supset \vdash : \text{Hp} . X +_g Z = Y . \supset . Y +_g Z | \text{Cnv} = X$ (1)

$\vdash . *308{\cdot}53{\cdot}4 . \quad \supset \vdash : \text{Hp} . Y +_g Z | \text{Cnv} = X . \supset . X +_g Z = Y$ (2)

$\vdash . (1) . (2) . \supset \vdash . \text{Prop}$

***308·56.** $\vdash :. X <_g Y . \equiv : X \epsilon \text{Rat}_g : (\exists Z) . Z \epsilon \text{Rat} - \iota`0_q . X +_g Z = Y$

Dem.

$\vdash . *306{\cdot}52 . *308{\cdot}32 . \supset$

$\vdash :. X <_r Y . \equiv : X \epsilon \text{Rat} : (\exists Z) . Z \epsilon \text{Rat} - \iota`0_q . X +_g Z = Y :$ (1)

[*306·52·25] $\supset : Y \epsilon \text{Rat} : (\exists Z) . Z \epsilon \text{Rat} - \iota`0_q . X +_g Z = Y$ (2)

$\vdash . (2) \dfrac{Y | \text{Cnv}, X | \text{Cnv}}{X, Y} . \supset$

$\vdash :. X >_n Y . \supset : X \epsilon \text{Rat}_n : (\exists Z) . Z \epsilon \text{Rat} - \iota`0_q . Y | \text{Cnv} +_g Z = X | \text{Cnv} :$

[*308·55·412] $\supset : X \epsilon \text{Rat}_n : (\exists Z) . Z \epsilon \text{Rat} - \iota`0_q . X +_g Z = Y$ (3)

$\vdash . *308{\cdot}32{\cdot}53 . *306{\cdot}23 . \supset \vdash : X \epsilon \text{Rat}_n . Y \epsilon \text{Rat} . \supset .$

$Y +_g X \mid \text{Cnv} \epsilon \text{Rat} - \iota`0_q . X +_g (Y +_g X \mid \text{Cnv}) = Y$ (4)

$\vdash . (1) . (2) . (3) . (4) . (*307{\cdot}03) . \supset$

$\vdash :. X <_g Y . \supset : X \epsilon \text{Rat}_g : (\exists Z) . Z \epsilon \text{Rat} - \iota`0_q . X +_g Z = Y$ (5)

$\vdash . *35{\cdot}103 . (*307{\cdot}03) . \supset \vdash : X \epsilon \text{Rat}_n - \iota`0_q . Y \epsilon \text{Rat} . \supset . X <_g Y$ (6)

$\vdash . *308{\cdot}55{\cdot}412 . \supset$

$\vdash : X, Y \epsilon \text{Rat}_n . Z \epsilon \text{Rat} - \iota`0_q . X +_g Z = Y . \supset . X \mid \text{Cnv} = Y \mid \text{Cnv} +_s Z .$

[*306·52] $\supset . X >_n Y$ (7)

$\vdash . (6) . (7) . \supset \vdash :. X \epsilon \text{Rat}_n : (\exists Z) . Z \epsilon \text{Rat} - \iota`0_q . X +_g Z = Y : \supset . X <_g Y$ (8)

$\vdash . (1) . (8) . \supset \vdash :. X \epsilon \text{Rat}_g : (\exists Z) . Z \epsilon \text{Rat} - \iota`0_q . X +_g Z = Y : \supset . X <_g Y$ (9)

$\vdash . (5) . (9) . \supset \vdash . \text{Prop}$

***308·561.** $\vdash :. X <_g Y . \equiv : Y \epsilon \text{Rat}_g : (\exists Z) . Z \epsilon \text{Rat} - \iota`0_q . X +_g Z = Y$
[*308·56·33]

***308·57.** $\vdash : X <_g Y . \equiv . X \epsilon \text{Rat}_g . Y +_g X \mid \text{Cnv} \epsilon \text{Rat} - \iota`0_q .$
$\equiv . Y \epsilon \text{Rat}_g . Y +_g X \mid \text{Cnv} \epsilon \text{Rat} - \iota`0_q$

Dem.

$\vdash . *308{\cdot}55{\cdot}56{\cdot}4 . \supset$

$\vdash :. X <_g Y . \equiv : X \epsilon \text{Rat}_g : (\exists Z) . Z \epsilon \text{Rat} - \iota`0_q . Z = Y +_g X \mid \text{Cnv}$ (1)

$\vdash . *308{\cdot}55{\cdot}561{\cdot}4 . \supset$

$\vdash :. X <_g Y . \equiv : Y \epsilon \text{Rat}_g : (\exists Z) . Z \epsilon \text{Rat} - \iota`0_q . Z = Y +_g X \mid \text{Cnv}$ (2)

$\vdash . (1) . (2) . \supset \vdash . \text{Prop}$

***308·6.** $\vdash : X, Y, Z \epsilon \text{Rat} . \supset . (X +_g Y) +_g Z = X +_g (Y +_g Z)$
[*308·32 . *306·22·31]

***308·601.** $\vdash : X, Y, Z \epsilon \text{Rat}_n . \supset . (X +_g Y) +_g Z = X +_g (Y +_g Z)$

Dem.

$\vdash . *308{\cdot}323 . *307{\cdot}12$

$\vdash : \text{Hp} . \supset . (X +_g Y) +_g Z = (X \mid \text{Cnv} +_s Y \mid \text{Cnv}) \mid \text{Cnv} +_g (Z \mid \text{Cnv}) \mid \text{Cnv}$

[*308·411] $= \{(X \mid \text{Cnv} +_s Y \mid \text{Cnv}) +_g Z \mid \text{Cnv}\} \mid \text{Cnv}$

[*308·6.*306·22] $= \{X \mid \text{Cnv} +_g (Y \mid \text{Cnv} +_g Z \mid \text{Cnv})\} \mid \text{Cnv}$

[*308·411] $= X +_g (Y \mid \text{Cnv} +_g Z \mid \text{Cnv}) \mid \text{Cnv}$

[*308·323] $= X +_g (Y +_g Z) : \supset \vdash . \text{Prop}$

***308·602.** $\vdash : \lambda, \mu, \nu, \rho, \sigma, \tau \epsilon \text{NC ind} . \mu, \rho, \tau \sim \epsilon \iota`0 . \supset .$

$(\lambda/\mu +_s \nu/\rho) -_s \sigma/\tau = (\lambda/\mu -_s \sigma/\tau) +_g \nu/\rho$

Dem.

$\vdash . *308{\cdot}24 . \supset \vdash : \text{Hp} . \sigma/\tau <_r \lambda/\mu . \supset .$

$(\lambda/\mu +_s \nu/\rho) -_s \sigma/\tau = \{(\lambda \times_c \rho \times_c \tau) +_c (\mu \times_c \nu \times_c \tau) -_c (\mu \times_c \rho \times_c \sigma)\}/(\mu \times_c \rho \times_c \tau) .$

$(\lambda/\mu -_s \sigma/\tau) +_s \nu/\rho = \{(\lambda \times_c \rho \times_c \tau) -_c (\mu \times_c \rho \times_c \sigma) +_c (\mu \times_c \nu \times_c \tau)\}/(\mu \times_c \rho \times_c \tau)$ (1)

$\vdash . *308\cdot241 . \supset \vdash : \text{Hp} . \lambda/\mu +_s \nu/\rho <_r \sigma/\tau . \supset . (\lambda/\mu +_s \nu/\rho) -_s \sigma/\tau$

$= [\{(\mu \times_c \rho \times_c \sigma) - (\lambda \times_c \rho \times_c \tau) - (\mu \times_c \nu \times_c \tau)\}/(\mu \times_c \rho \times_c \tau)] \mid \text{Cnv} .$

$(\lambda/\mu -_s \sigma/\tau) +_g \nu/\rho = [\{(\mu \times_c \tau) -_s (\lambda \times_c \sigma)\}/(\mu \times_c \tau)] \mid \text{Cnv} +_g \nu/\rho$

[$*308\cdot322\cdot21$]

$= [\{(\mu \times_c \rho \times_c \sigma) - (\lambda \times_c \rho \times_c \tau) - (\mu \times_c \nu \times_c \tau)\}/(\mu \times_c \rho \times_c \tau)] \mid \text{Cnv}$ (2)

$\vdash . *308\cdot24\cdot241 . \supset \vdash : \text{Hp} . \lambda/\mu <_r \sigma/\tau . \sigma/\tau <_r \lambda/\mu +_s \nu/\rho . \supset .$

$(\lambda/\mu +_s \nu/\rho) -_s \sigma/\tau = \{(\lambda \times_c \rho \times_c \tau) +_c (\mu \times_c \nu \times_c \tau) -_c (\mu \times_c \rho \times_c \sigma)\}/(\mu \times_c \rho \times_c \tau) .$

$(\lambda/\mu -_s \sigma/\tau) +_g \nu/\rho = [\{(\mu \times_c \sigma) -_c (\lambda \times_c \tau)\}/(\mu \times_c \tau)] \mid \text{Cnv} +_g \nu/\rho$

[$*308\cdot322\cdot21$] $= \{(\lambda \times_c \rho \times_c \tau) +_c (\mu \times_c \nu \times_c \tau) -_c (\mu \times_c \rho \times_c \sigma)\}/(\mu \times_c \rho \times_c \tau)$ (3)

$\vdash . *308\cdot16\cdot12 . \supset$

$\vdash : \text{Hp} . \lambda/\mu = \sigma/\tau . \supset . (\lambda/\mu +_s \nu/\rho) -_s \sigma/\tau = \nu/\rho = (\lambda/\mu -_s \sigma/\tau) +_g \nu/\rho$ (4)

$\vdash . *308\cdot12\cdot53\cdot17 . \supset$

$\vdash : \text{Hp} . \lambda/\mu +_c \nu/\rho = \sigma/\tau . \supset . (\lambda/\mu +_s \nu/\rho) -_s \sigma/\tau = 0_q = (\lambda/\mu -_s \sigma/\tau) +_g \nu/\rho$ (5)

$\vdash . (1) . (2) . (3) . (4) . (5) . \supset \vdash . \text{Prop}$

$*308\cdot61$. $\vdash : X, Y, Z \in \text{Rat} . \supset . (X +_g Y) -_s Z = (X -_s Z) +_g Y$

[$*308\cdot602\cdot32$]

$*308\cdot62$. $\vdash : X, Y \in \text{Rat} . Z \in \text{Rat}_n . \supset . (X +_g Y) +_g Z = X +_g (Y +_g Z)$

Dem.

$\vdash . *308\cdot33\cdot321 . \supset \vdash : \text{Hp} . \supset . (X +_g Y) +_g Z = (X +_g Y) -_s Z \mid \text{Cnv}$

[$*308\cdot4$] $= (Y +_g X) -_s Z \mid \text{Cnv}$

[$*308\cdot61$] $= (Y -_s Z \mid \text{Cnv}) +_g X$

[$*308\cdot4$] $= X +_g (Y -_s Z \mid \text{Cnv})$

[$*308\cdot321$] $= X +_g (Y +_a Z) : \supset \vdash . \text{Prop}$

$*308\cdot621$. $\vdash : X, Y \in \text{Rat}_n . Z \in \text{Rat} . \supset . (X +_g Y) +_g Z = X +_g (Y +_g Z)$

Dem.

$\vdash . *308\cdot62 . \supset$

$\vdash : \text{Hp} . \supset . (X \mid \text{Cnv} +_g Y \mid \text{Cnv}) +_g Z \mid \text{Cnv} = X \mid \text{Cnv} +_g (Y \mid \text{Cnv} +_g Z \mid \text{Cnv}) .$

[$*308\cdot411$] $\supset . (X +_g Y) \mid \text{Cnv} +_g Z \mid \text{Cnv} = X \mid \text{Cnv} +_g (Y +_g Z) \mid \text{Cnv}$

[$*308\cdot411$] $= \{X +_g (Y +_g Z)\} \mid \text{Cnv} .$

[$*308\cdot412$] $\supset . (X +_g Y) +_g Z = X +_g (Y +_g Z) : \supset \vdash . \text{Prop}$

$*308\cdot63$. $\vdash . (X +_g Y) +_g Z = X +_g (Y +_g Z)$

Dem.

$\vdash . *308\cdot6\cdot601\cdot62\cdot621 . \supset$

$\vdash : X, Y, Z \in \text{Rat}_g . \supset . (X +_g Y) +_g Z = X +_g (Y +_g Z)$ (1)

$\vdash . *308\cdot31\cdot33 . \supset$

$\vdash : \sim(X, Y, Z \in \text{Rat}_g) . \supset . (X +_g Y) +_g Z = \dot\Lambda . X +_g (Y +_g Z) = \dot\Lambda$ (2)

$\vdash . (1) . (2) . \supset \vdash . \text{Prop}$

∗308·71. $\vdash : X \epsilon \text{Rat}_g \,.\, Z <_g Z' \,.\, \supset .\, (X +_g Z) <_g (X +_g Z')$

Dem.

$\vdash . ∗308·57 . \supset \vdash : \text{Hp} . \supset . Z' +_g Z | \text{Cnv} \epsilon \text{Rat} - \iota ' 0_q .$

[∗308·56] $\supset . (X +_g Z) <_g \{(X +_g Z) +_g (Z' +_g Z | \text{Cnv})\} .$

[∗308·63·53] $\supset . (X +_g Z) <_g (X +_g Z') : \supset \vdash .$ Prop

∗308·72. $\vdash : (X +_g Z) <_g (X +_g Z') . \equiv . X \epsilon \text{Rat}_g . Z <_g Z'$

Dem.

$\vdash . ∗308·33 . \supset \vdash : (X +_g Z) <_g (X +_g Z') . \supset . X, Z, Z' \epsilon \text{Rat}_g$ (1)

$\vdash . ∗308·57 . \supset$

$\vdash : (X +_g Z) <_g (X +_g Z') . \supset . \{(X +_g Z') +_g (X +_g Z) | \text{Cnv}\} \epsilon \text{Rat} - \iota ' 0_q .$

[∗308·411·63·53] $\supset . (Z' +_g Z | \text{Cnv}) \epsilon \text{Rat} - \iota ' 0_q$ (2)

$\vdash . (1) . (2) . ∗308·57 . \supset \vdash : (X +_g Z) <_g (X +_g Z') . \supset . Z <_g Z'$ (3)

$\vdash . (1) . (3) . ∗308·71 . \supset \vdash .$ Prop

∗308·8. $\vdash : X, Y \epsilon \text{Rat}_g . X \upharpoonright t_{11} ' \mu, Y \upharpoonright t_{11} ' \mu \epsilon C ' H_g . \supset . (X +_g Y) \upharpoonright t_{00} ' \mu \epsilon C ' H_g$
[∗308·32·321·322·323 . ∗306·64 . ∗308·26]

∗308·81. $\vdash : X, Y \epsilon C ' H_g . \supset . (X +_g Y) \upharpoonright t_{00} ' C '' C ' X \epsilon C ' H_g$ [∗308·8]

*309. MULTIPLICATION OF GENERALIZED RATIOS.

Summary of *309.

The subject of this number is simpler than that of *308, because it requires nothing analogous to the consideration of subtraction. The product of two generalized ratios is defined as follows:

***309·01.** $X \times_g Y = (X \times_s Y) \cup (X \,|\, \mathrm{Cnv} \times_s Y \,|\, \mathrm{Cnv})$
$\cup (X \times_s Y \,|\, \mathrm{Cnv}) \,|\, \mathrm{Cnv} \cup (X \,|\, \mathrm{Cnv} \times_s Y) \,|\, \mathrm{Cnv}$ Df

As in *308, three of the four products concerned in this definition will be null in any given case (unless $X = 0_q$ or $Y = 0_q$). Hence

***309·14.** $\vdash : X, Y \in \mathrm{Rat} \,.\, \supset .\, X \times_g Y = X \times_s Y$

***309·141.** $\vdash : X \in \mathrm{Rat} \,.\, Y \in \mathrm{Rat}_n \,.\, \supset .\, X \times_g Y = (X \times_s Y \,|\, \mathrm{Cnv}) \,|\, \mathrm{Cnv}$

***309·142.** $\vdash : Y \in \mathrm{Rat} \,.\, X \in \mathrm{Rat}_n \,.\, \supset .\, X \times_g Y = (X \,|\, \mathrm{Cnv} \times_s Y) \,|\, \mathrm{Cnv}$

***309·143.** $\vdash : X, Y \in \mathrm{Rat}_n \,.\, \supset .\, X \times_g Y = X \,|\, \mathrm{Cnv} \times_s Y \,|\, \mathrm{Cnv}$

The propositions of this number are merely generalizations of those of *305. The proofs of the formal laws are straightforward, but the proof of the distributive law (*309·37) is long, because of the multiplicity of different cases.

***309·01.** $X \times_g Y = (X \times_s Y) \cup (X \,|\, \mathrm{Cnv} \times_s Y \,|\, \mathrm{Cnv})$
$\cup (X \times_s Y \,|\, \mathrm{Cnv}) \,|\, \mathrm{Cnv} \cup (X \,|\, \mathrm{Cnv} \times_s Y) \,|\, \mathrm{Cnv}$ Df

***309·1.** $\vdash .\, X \times_g Y = (X \times_s Y) \cup (X \,|\, \mathrm{Cnv} \times_s Y \,|\, \mathrm{Cnv})$
$\cup (X \times_s Y \,|\, \mathrm{Cnv}) \,|\, \mathrm{Cnv} \cup (X \,|\, \mathrm{Cnv} \times_s Y) \,|\, \mathrm{Cnv}$ [(*309·01)]

***309·101.** $\vdash : X \in \mathrm{Rat} - \iota ‘ 0_q \,.\, \supset .\, X \,|\, \mathrm{Cnv} \times_s Y = \dot{\Lambda}$ [*305·2 . *307·25]

***309·102.** $\vdash : X \in \mathrm{Rat}_n - \iota ‘ 0_q \,.\, \supset .\, X \times_s Y = \dot{\Lambda}$ [*305·2 . *307·25]

***309·11.** $\vdash : \dot{\exists} ! \, X \times_g Y \,.\, \supset .\, X, Y \in \mathrm{Rat}_g$ [*305·2 . *309·1]

***309·12.** $\vdash .\, X \times_g Y = Y \times_g X$ [*305·11 . *309·1]

***309·121.** $\vdash .\, X \times_g Y = X \,|\, \mathrm{Cnv} \times_g Y \,|\, \mathrm{Cnv}$
$= (X \times_g Y \,|\, \mathrm{Cnv}) \,|\, \mathrm{Cnv} = (X \,|\, \mathrm{Cnv} \times_g Y) \,|\, \mathrm{Cnv}$ [*309·1 . *307·12]

***309·122.** $\vdash . X \times_g Y | \text{Cnv} = X | \text{Cnv} \times_g Y = (X \times_g Y) | \text{Cnv}$
[*309·121 . *307·12]

***309·13.** $\vdash : X, Y \epsilon \text{Rat} - \iota`0_q . \supset . X \times_g Y = X \times_s Y$ [*309·1·101·12]

***309·131.** $\vdash :. X = 0_q . Y \epsilon \text{Rat} - \iota`0_q . \vee . Y = 0_q . X \epsilon \text{Rat} - \iota`0_q : \supset .$
$X \times_g Y = X \times_s Y = 0_q$

Dem.

$\vdash . *309·101 . \supset$
$\vdash : X = 0_q . Y \epsilon \text{Rat} - \iota`0_q . \supset . X \times_g Y = (X \times_s Y) \cup (X | \text{Cnv} \times_s Y) | \text{Cnv} .$
[*307·26.*305·22] $\supset . X \times_g Y = X \times_s Y = 0_q$ (1)
$\vdash . (1) . *309·12 . \supset \vdash : Y = 0_q . X \epsilon \text{Rat} - \iota`0_q . \supset . X \times_g Y = X \times_s Y = 0_q$ (2)
$\vdash . (1) . (2) . \supset \vdash .$ Prop

***309·133.** $\vdash : X = 0_q . Y = 0_q . \supset . X \times_g Y = X \times_s Y = 0_q$
[*309·1 . *307·26 . *305·22]

***309·14.** $\vdash : X, Y \epsilon \text{Rat} . \supset . X \times_g Y = X \times_s Y$ [*309·13·131·133]

***309·141.** $\vdash : X \epsilon \text{Rat} . Y \epsilon \text{Rat}_n . \supset . X \times_g Y = (X \times_s Y | \text{Cnv}) | \text{Cnv}$
[*309·121·14]

***309·142.** $\vdash : Y \epsilon \text{Rat} . X \epsilon \text{Rat}_n . \supset . X \times_g Y = (X | \text{Cnv} \times_s Y) | \text{Cnv}$
[*309·141·12]

***309·143.** $\vdash : X, Y \epsilon \text{Rat}_n . \supset . X \times_g Y = X | \text{Cnv} \times_s Y | \text{Cnv}$ [*309·14·121]

***309·15.** $\vdash : X, Y \epsilon \text{Rat}_g . \equiv . X \times_g Y \epsilon \text{Rat}_g$

Dem.

$\vdash . *305·3 . *309·14·143 . \supset$
$\vdash :. X, Y \epsilon \text{Rat} . \vee . X, Y \epsilon \text{Rat}_n : \supset . X \times_g Y \epsilon \text{Rat}$ (1)
$\vdash . *305·3 . *309·141·142 . \supset$
$\vdash :. X \epsilon \text{Rat} . Y \epsilon \text{Rat}_n . \vee . X \epsilon \text{Rat}_n . Y \epsilon \text{Rat} : \supset . X \times_g Y \epsilon \text{Rat}_n$ (2)
$\vdash . (1) . (2) .$ $\supset \vdash : X, Y \epsilon \text{Rat}_g . \supset . X \times_g Y \epsilon \text{Rat}_g$ (3)
$\vdash . *303·72 . (*307·01·011) . \supset \vdash : X \times_g Y \epsilon \text{Rat}_g . \supset . \dot{\exists} ! X \times_g Y$ (4)
$\vdash . (4) . *309·11 .$ $\supset \vdash : X \times_g Y \epsilon \text{Rat}_g . \supset . X, Y \epsilon \text{Rat}_g$ (5)
$\vdash . (3) . (5) . \supset \vdash .$ Prop

***309·16.** $\vdash . (X \times_g Y) \times_g Z = X \times_g (Y \times_g Z)$ [*305·41 . *309·1]

***309·17.** $\vdash : X, Y \sim \epsilon \iota`0_q \cup \iota`\infty_q . \supset . \breve{X} \times_g \breve{Y} = \text{Cnv}`(X \times_g Y)$

Dem.

$\vdash . *309·1 . \supset \vdash . \breve{X} \times_g \breve{Y} = (\breve{X} \times_s \breve{Y}) \cup (\breve{X} | \text{Cnv} \times_s \breve{Y} | \text{Cnv})$
$\cup (\breve{X} \times_s \breve{Y} | \text{Cnv}) | \text{Cnv} \cup (\breve{X} | \text{Cnv} \times_s \breve{Y}) | \text{Cnv}$ (1)

$\vdash . *305{\cdot}12 . \supset \vdash : \text{Hp} . \supset . \breve{X} \times_s \breve{Y} = \text{Cnv}'(X \times_s Y)$ (2)

$\vdash . *307{\cdot}22 . \supset \vdash : X \in \text{Rat} . \supset . \breve{X} | \text{Cnv} = \text{Cnv}'(X | \text{Cnv})$ (3)

$\vdash . (3) . \quad \supset \vdash : Z \in \text{Rat} . X = Z | \text{Cnv} . \supset . \breve{X} | \text{Cnv} = (\breve{Z} | \text{Cnv}) | \text{Cnv}$

[*307·12] $= \breve{Z}$

[*307·14] $= \text{Cnv}'(X | \text{Cnv})$ (4)

$\vdash . (3) . (4) . \supset \vdash : X \in \text{Rat}_g . \supset . \breve{X} | \text{Cnv} = \text{Cnv}'(X | \text{Cnv})$ (5)

$\vdash . (2) . (5) . \supset \vdash : \text{Hp} . X, Y \in \text{Rat}_g . \supset .$

$\breve{X} | \text{Cnv} \times_s \breve{Y} | \text{Cnv} = \text{Cnv}'(X | \text{Cnv} \times_s Y | \text{Cnv}) .$

$\breve{X} \times_s \breve{Y} | \text{Cnv} = \text{Cnv}'(X \times_s Y | \text{Cnv}) .$

$\breve{X} | \text{Cnv} \times_s \breve{Y} = \text{Cnv}'(X | \text{Cnv} \times_s Y)$ (6)

$\vdash . (1) . (2) . (6) . *309{\cdot}1 . \supset \vdash : \text{Hp} . X, Y \in \text{Rat}_g . \supset . \breve{X} \times_g \breve{Y} = \text{Cnv}'(X \times_g Y)$ (7)

$\vdash . *303{\cdot}13{\cdot}7 . \quad \supset \vdash : X, Y \in \text{Rat}_g - \iota'0_q . \equiv . \breve{X}, \breve{Y} \in \text{Rat}_g - \iota'0_q$ (8)

$\vdash . (8) . *309{\cdot}11 . \supset$

$\vdash : \sim(X, Y \in \text{Rat}_g \cup \iota'\infty_q) . \supset . \breve{X} \times_g \breve{Y} = \dot{\Lambda} . \text{Cnv}'(X \times_g Y) = \dot{\Lambda}$ (9)

$\vdash . (7) . (9) . \supset \vdash . \text{Prop}$

***309·21.** $\vdash :. X, Y \in \text{Rat}_g : X = 0_q . \vee . Y = 0_q : \equiv . X \times_g Y = 0_q$

Dem.

$\vdash . *309{\cdot}14{\cdot}141 . *305{\cdot}22 . *307{\cdot}26 . \supset \vdash : X \in \text{Rat}_g . Y = 0_q . \supset . X \times_g Y = 0_q$ (1)

$\vdash . *309{\cdot}15 . \quad \supset \vdash : X \times_g Y = 0_q . \supset . X, Y \in \text{Rat}_g$ (2)

$\vdash . (2) . *309{\cdot}14{\cdot}141{\cdot}142{\cdot}143 . *307{\cdot}26 . \supset$

$\vdash :. X \times_g Y = 0_q . \supset : X \times_s Y = 0_q . \vee . X | \text{Cnv} \times_s Y | \text{Cnv} = 0_q .$

$\vee . X \times_s Y | \text{Cnv} = 0_q . \vee . X | \text{Cnv} \times_s Y = 0_q :$

[*305·22.*307·26] $\supset : X = 0_q . \vee . Y = 0_q$ (3)

$\vdash . (1) . (2) . (3) . \supset \vdash . \text{Prop}$

***309·22.** $\vdash : X, Y \in \text{Rat}_g - \iota'0_q . \equiv . X \times_g Y \in \text{Rat}_g - \iota'0_q$ [*309·21 . Transp]

***309·23.** $\vdash : X \in \text{Rat}_g - \iota'0_q . \supset . X \times_g \breve{X} = 1/1$

Dem.

$\vdash . *309{\cdot}13 . \quad \supset \vdash : X \in \text{Rat} - \iota'0_q . \supset . X \times_g \breve{X} = X \times_s \breve{X}$

[*305·52] $= 1/1$ (1)

$\vdash . *309{\cdot}121 . *307{\cdot}22 . \supset \vdash : Y \in \text{Rat} - \iota'0_q . X = Y | \text{Cnv} . \supset . X \times_g \breve{X} = Y \times_g \breve{Y}$

[(1)] $= 1/1$ (2)

$\vdash . (1) . (2) . \supset \vdash . \text{Prop}$

***309·24.** $\vdash : X \in \text{Rat}_g . \supset . X \times_g 1/1 = X$

Dem.

$\vdash . *309{\cdot}14 . \quad \supset \vdash : X \in \text{Rat} . \supset . X \times_g 1/1 = X \times_s 1/1$

[*305·51] $= X$ (1)

$\vdash . (1) . *309{\cdot}142 . \supset \vdash : X \in \text{Rat}_n . \supset . X \times_g 1/1 = (X | \text{Cnv}) | \text{Cnv}$

[*307·12] $= X$ (2)

$\vdash . (1) . (2) . \supset \vdash . \text{Prop}$

***309·25.** $\vdash :. X, A \in \mathrm{Rat}_g . A \neq 0_q . \supset : X \times_g A = A' . \equiv . X = A' \times_g \breve{A}$

Dem.

$\vdash . *309·23·24·16 . \quad \supset \vdash : \mathrm{Hp} . \supset . X = X \times_g A \times_g \breve{A}$ (1)

$\vdash . (1) . \quad \supset \vdash : \mathrm{Hp} . X \times_g A = A' . \supset . X = A' \times_g \breve{A}$ (2)

$\vdash . (1) \frac{A', \breve{A}}{X, A} . *309·15 . \supset \vdash : \mathrm{Hp} . \supset . A' = A' \times_g \breve{A} \times_g A$ (3)

$\vdash . (3) . \quad \supset \vdash : \mathrm{Hp} . X = A' \times_g \breve{A} . \supset . X \times_g A = A'$ (4)

$\vdash . (2) . (4) . \supset \vdash . \mathrm{Prop}$

***309·251.** $\vdash :. X, A' \in \mathrm{Rat}_g . A \neq 0_q . \supset : X \times_g A = A' . \equiv . X = A' \times_g \breve{A}$
[*309·25·15]

***309·26.** $\vdash : X, Y \in \mathrm{Rat}_g . X \neq 0_q . \supset . (\exists Z) . Z \in \mathrm{Rat}_g . X \times_g Z = Y$

Dem.

$\vdash . *309·25 . \supset \vdash : \mathrm{Hp} . Z = Y \times_g \breve{X} . \supset . Z \times_g X = Y$ (1)

$\vdash . (1) . *309·15·12 . \supset \vdash . \mathrm{Prop}$

***309·31** $\vdash : X, Y \in \mathrm{Rat} . Z \in \mathrm{Rat}_g . \supset . (X +_g Y) \times_g Z = (X \times_g Z) +_g (Y \times_g Z)$

Dem.

$\vdash . *308·32 . *309·14 . \supset$

$\vdash : \mathrm{Hp} . Z \in \mathrm{Rat} . \supset . (X +_g Y) \times_g Z = (X +_s Y) \times_s Z .$
$X \times_g Z = X \times_s Z . Y \times_g Z = Y \times_s Z .$

[*306·41] $\supset . (X +_g Y) \times_g Z = (X \times_g Z) +_g (Y \times_g Z)$ (1)

$\vdash . *309·122 . \supset$

$\vdash : \mathrm{Hp} . W \in \mathrm{Rat} . Z = W | \mathrm{Cnv} . \supset . (X +_g Y) \times_g Z = \{(X +_g Y) \times_g W\} | \mathrm{Cnv}$

[(1)] $= \{(X \times_g W) +_g (Y \times_g W)\} | \mathrm{Cnv}$

[*308·411.*309·122] $= (X \times_g Z) +_g (Y \times_g Z)$ (2)

$\vdash . (1) . (2) . \supset \vdash . \mathrm{Prop}$

***309·311.** $\vdash : X, Y \in \mathrm{Rat}_n . Z \in \mathrm{Rat}_g . \supset . (X +_g Y) \times_g Z = (X \times_g Z) +_g (Y \times_g Z)$

Dem.

$\vdash . *308·41 . *309·122 . \supset$

$\vdash : \mathrm{Hp} . \supset . (X +_g Y) \times_g Z = \{(X | \mathrm{Cnv} +_g Y | \mathrm{Cnv}) \times_g Z\} | \mathrm{Cnv}$

[*309·31] $= \{(X | \mathrm{Cnv} \times_g Z) +_g (Y | \mathrm{Cnv} \times_g Z)\} | \mathrm{Cnv}$

[*309·122.*308·41] $= (X \times_g Z) +_g (Y \times_g Z) : \supset \vdash . \mathrm{Prop}$

***309·32.** $\vdash : (\nu/\rho) <_r (\lambda/\mu) . \sigma/\tau \in \mathrm{Rat} . \supset .$
$(\lambda/\mu -_s \nu/\rho) \times_g \sigma/\tau = \{((\lambda \times_c \rho) -_c (\mu \times_c \nu)) \times_c \sigma\}/(\mu \times_c \rho \times_c \tau)$

Dem.

$\vdash . *308·24 . \supset \vdash : \mathrm{Hp} . \supset . \lambda/\mu -_s \nu/\rho = ((\lambda \times_c \rho) -_c (\mu \times_c \nu))/\mu \times_c \rho$ (1)

$\vdash . (1) . *309·14 . *305·142 . \supset \vdash . \mathrm{Prop}$

***309·33.** $\vdash : \lambda/\mu, \nu/\rho, \sigma/\tau \in \text{Rat} . \supset .$
$$(\lambda/\mu -_s \nu/\rho) \times_g (\sigma/\tau) = (\lambda/\mu \times_g \sigma/\tau) -_s (\nu/\rho \times_g \sigma/\tau)$$

Dem.

$\vdash . *309{\cdot}14 . \supset \vdash : \text{Hp} . \supset . \lambda/\mu \times_g \sigma/\tau = \lambda/\mu \times_s \sigma/\tau . \nu/\rho \times_g \sigma/\tau = \nu/\rho \times_s \sigma/\tau .$

$[*305{\cdot}142] \supset . \lambda/\mu \times_g \sigma/\tau = (\lambda \times_c \sigma)/(\mu \times_c \tau) . \nu/\rho \times_g \sigma/\tau = (\nu \times_c \sigma)/(\rho \times_c \tau)$ (1)

$\vdash . (1) . *308{\cdot}24 . \supset$

$\vdash : \text{Hp} . (\nu/\rho) <_r (\lambda/\mu) . \supset . (\lambda/\mu \times_g \sigma/\tau) -_s (\nu/\rho \times_g \sigma/\tau) =$
$$\{(\lambda \times_c \sigma) \times_c (\rho \times_c \tau) -_c (\mu \times_c \tau) \times_c (\nu \times_c \sigma)\}/(\mu \times_c \rho \times_c \tau^2)$$

$[*303{\cdot}38] \quad = \{(\lambda \times_c \sigma \times_c \rho) - (\mu \times_c \nu \times_c \sigma)\}/(\mu \times_c \rho \times_c \tau)$

$[*309{\cdot}32] \quad = (\lambda/\mu -_s \nu/\rho) \times_g \sigma/\tau$ (2)

$\vdash . (2) . \supset \vdash : \text{Hp} . (\lambda/\mu) <_r (\nu/\rho) . \supset .$
$$(\nu/\rho \times_g \sigma/\tau) -_s (\lambda/\mu \times_g \sigma/\tau) = (\nu/\rho -_s \lambda/\mu) \times_g \sigma/\tau .$$

$[*308{\cdot}21 . *309{\cdot}122] \quad \supset . (\lambda/\mu \times_g \sigma/\tau) -_s (\nu/\rho \times_g \sigma/\tau) = (\lambda/\mu -_s \nu/\rho) \times_g \sigma/\tau$ (3)

$\vdash . *308{\cdot}12 . *309{\cdot}21 . \supset$

$\vdash : \text{Hp} . \lambda/\mu = \nu/\rho . \supset . (\lambda/\mu -_s \nu/\rho) \times_g \sigma/\tau = 0_q .$
$$(\lambda/\mu \times_g \sigma/\tau) -_s (\nu/\rho \times_g \sigma/\tau) = 0_q$$ (4)

$\vdash . (2) . (3) . (4) . \supset \vdash . \text{Prop}$

***309·34.** $\vdash : X, Y, Z \in \text{Rat} . \supset . (X -_s Y) \times_g Z = (X \times_g Z) -_s (Y \times_g Z)$
[*309·33]

***309·35.** $\vdash : X, Z \in \text{Rat} . Y \in \text{Rat}_n . \supset . (X +_g Y) \times_g Z = (X \times_g Z) +_g (Y \times_g Z)$

Dem.

$\vdash . *308{\cdot}321 . \supset \vdash : \text{Hp} . \supset . X +_g Y = X -_s Y \,|\, \text{Cnv} .$
$$(X \times_g Z) +_g (Y \times_g Z) = (X \times_g Z) -_s (Y \,|\, \text{Cnv} \times_g Z)$$ (1)

$\vdash . (1) . *309{\cdot}34 . \supset \vdash . \text{Prop}$

***309·36.** $\vdash : X, Z \in \text{Rat}_n . Y \in \text{Rat} . \supset . (X +_g Y) \times_g Z = (X \times_g Z) +_g (Y \times_g Z)$

Dem.

$\vdash . *308{\cdot}41 . *309{\cdot}121 . \supset$

$\vdash : \text{Hp} . \supset . X +_g Y = (X \,|\, \text{Cnv} +_g Y \,|\, \text{Cnv}) \,|\, \text{Cnv} . X \times_g Z = X \,|\, \text{Cnv} \times_g Z \,|\, \text{Cnv} .$
$$Y \times_g Z = Y \,|\, \text{Cnv} \times_g Z \,|\, \text{Cnv} .$$

$[*309{\cdot}122] \supset . (X +_g Y) \times_g Z = (X \,|\, \text{Cnv} +_g Y \,|\, \text{Cnv}) \times_g Z \,|\, \text{Cnv} .$
$$(X \times_g Z) +_g (Y \times_g Z) = (X \,|\, \text{Cnv} \times_g Z \,|\, \text{Cnv}) +_g (Y \,|\, \text{Cnv} \times_g Z \,|\, \text{Cnv})$$ (1)

$\vdash . (1) . *309{\cdot}35 . \supset \vdash . \text{Prop}$

***309·361.** $\vdash : X \in \text{Rat}_g . Y \in \text{Rat}_n . Z \in \text{Rat} . \supset .$
$$(X +_g Y) \times_g Z = (X \times_g Z) +_g (Y \times_g Z)$$ [*309·311·36]

***309·362.** $\vdash : X, Z \epsilon \text{Rat}_g . Y \epsilon \text{Rat}_n . \supset . (X +_g Y) \times_g Z = (X \times_g Z) +_g (Y \times_g Z)$

Dem.

$\vdash . *309·122 . *308·41 . \supset$

$\vdash . (X +_g Y) \times_g Z = \{(X +_g Y) \times_g Z \mid \text{Cnv}\} \mid \text{Cnv} .$

$(X \times_g Z) +_g (Y \times_g Z) = \{(X \times_g Z \mid \text{Cnv}) +_g (Y \times_g Z \mid \text{Cnv})\} \mid \text{Cnv}$ (1)

$\vdash . *309·361 . \supset$

$\vdash : \text{Hp} . Z \epsilon \text{Rat}_n . \supset . (X +_g Y) \times_g Z \mid \text{Cnv}$

$= (X \times_g Z \mid \text{Cnv}) +_g (Y \times_g Z \mid \text{Cnv})$ (2)

$\vdash . (1) . (2) . \supset \vdash : \text{Hp} . Z \epsilon \text{Rat}_n . \supset . (X +_g Y) \times_g Z = (X \times_g Z) +_g (Y \times_g Z)$ (3)

$\vdash . (3) . *309·361 . \supset \vdash . \text{Prop}$

***309·363.** $\vdash : X, Y, Z \epsilon \text{Rat}_g . \supset . (X +_g Y) \times_g Z = (X \times_g Z) +_g (Y \times_g Z)$

Dem.

$\vdash . *309·35·12 . *308·4 . \supset$

$\vdash : Y, Z \epsilon \text{Rat} . X \epsilon \text{Rat}_n . \supset . (X +_g Y) \times_g Z = (X \times_g Z) +_g (Y \times_g Z)$ (1)

$\vdash . *309·36 . \supset$

$\vdash : Y \epsilon \text{Rat} . X, Z \epsilon \text{Rat}_n . \supset . (X +_g Y) \times_g Z = (X \times_g Z) +_g (Y \times_g Z)$ (2)

$\vdash . (1) . (2) . \supset$

$\vdash : X \epsilon \text{Rat}_n . Y \epsilon \text{Rat} . Z \epsilon \text{Rat}_g . \supset . (X +_g Y) \times_g Z = (X \times_g Z) +_g (Y \times_g Z)$ (3)

$\vdash . (3) . *309·31 . \supset$

$\vdash : X \epsilon \text{Rat}_g . Y \epsilon \text{Rat} . Z \epsilon \text{Rat}_g . \supset . (X +_g Y) \times_g Z = (X \times_g Z) +_g (Y \times_g Z)$ (4)

$\vdash . (4) . *309·362 . \supset \vdash . \text{Prop}$

***309·37.** $\vdash . (X +_g Y) \times_g Z = (X \times_g Z) +_g (Y \times_g Z)$
[*309·363·11·15 . *308·31·33]

***309·41.** $\vdash :. A \epsilon \text{Rat} - \iota‘0_q . \supset : (A \times_g X) <_g Y . \equiv . X <_g (Y \times_g \breve{A})$

Dem.

$\vdash . *308·56 . \supset \vdash :. (A \times_g X) <_g Y . \equiv :$

$A \times_g X \epsilon \text{Rat}_g : (\exists Z) . Z \epsilon \text{Rat} - \iota‘0_q . (A \times_g X) +_g Z = Y$ (1)

$\vdash . (1) . *309·15 . \supset \vdash :: \text{Hp} . \supset :. (A \times_g X) <_g Y . \equiv :$

$X \epsilon \text{Rat}_g : (\exists Z) . Z \epsilon \text{Rat} - \iota‘0_q . (A \times_g X) +_g Z = Y :$

[*309·25·37·23·24] $\supset : X \epsilon \text{Rat}_g : (\exists Z) . Z \epsilon \text{Rat} - \iota‘0_q . X +_g (Z \times_g \breve{A}) = Y \times_g \breve{A} :$

[*305·31.*309·13] $\supset : X \epsilon \text{Rat}_g : (\exists Z') . Z' \epsilon \text{Rat} - \iota‘0_q . X +_g Z' = Y \times_g \breve{A} :$

[*308·56] $\supset : X <_g (Y \times_g \breve{A})$ (2)

Similarly $\vdash :. \text{Hp} . \supset : X <_g (Y \times_g \breve{A}) . \supset . (A \times_g X) <_g Y$ (3)

$\vdash . (2) . (3) . \supset \vdash . \text{Prop}$

***309·42.** $\vdash :. A \in \mathrm{Rat}_n - \iota`0_q . \supset : (A \times_g X) <_g Y . \equiv . (Y \times_g \breve{A}) <_g X$

Dem.

$\vdash . *307{\cdot}4 . *309{\cdot}122 . \supset$

$\vdash :. \mathrm{Hp} . \supset : (A \times_g X) <_g Y . \equiv . (Y \,|\, \mathrm{Cnv}) <_g (A \,|\, \mathrm{Cnv} \times_g X) .$

$[*309{\cdot}41 . *307{\cdot}22] \qquad \equiv . (Y \,|\, \mathrm{Cnv} \times_g \breve{A} \,|\, \mathrm{Cnv}) <_g X .$

$[*309{\cdot}121] \qquad \equiv . (Y \times_g \breve{A}) <_g X :. \supset \vdash . \mathrm{Prop}$

***309·5.** $\vdash : X, Y \in \mathrm{Rat}_g . X \upharpoonright t_{11}`\mu , Y \upharpoonright t_{11}`\mu \in C`H_g . \supset . (X \times_g Y) \upharpoonright t_{00}`\mu \in C`H_g$

[*309·14·141·142·143 . *305·26]

***309·51.** $\vdash : X, Y \in C`H_g . \supset . (X \times_g Y) \upharpoonright t_{00}`C``C`X \in C`H_g$ [*309·5]

$*310$. THE SERIES OF REAL NUMBERS.

Summary of $*310$.

Real numbers, as opposed to ratios, are required primarily in order to obtain a Dedekindian series, so as to secure limits to sets of rationals having no *rational* limit. If rationals and irrationals are to form one series, it is necessary to give some definition of "rationals" other than "ratios," since the series of ratios (assuming the axiom of infinity) is not Dedekindian, and is not part of any arithmetically definable Dedekindian series. But in virtue of the propositions of $*212$, the series of segments of the series of ratios, *i.e.* the series $\varsigma\text{‘}H$, is Dedekindian, and this series contains a series, namely $\overrightarrow{H};H$, which is ordinally similar to H. Thus the properties which we desire real numbers to have will result if we identify them* with segments of H, and give the name "rational real numbers" to segments of the form $\overrightarrow{H}\text{‘}X$, *i.e.* to segments which have ratios as limits. Thus $\overrightarrow{H}\text{‘}X$ is the rational real number corresponding to the ratio X, and a real number in general is of the form $H\text{“}\lambda$, where λ is a class of ratios. $H\text{“}\lambda$ will be *irrational* when λ has no limit or maximum in H.

Since real numbers involve *classes* of ratios, the ratios concerned must be of some one type, and cannot be typically indefinite. Thus, as might be expected, hardly any of the properties of real numbers can be proved without assuming the axiom of infinity. In the present number, however, we shall be mainly concerned with just those few simple properties which are independent of the axiom of infinity.

The series $\varsigma\text{‘}H$, by which real numbers are to be defined, has both a beginning and an end, namely Λ and $\text{D}\text{‘}H$ (which $= C\text{‘}H$ if the axiom of infinity holds). $\text{D}\text{‘}H$ will be infinity among real numbers. It is not convenient to include it in the series of real numbers as defined, just as it was not convenient to include ∞_q in the series H or H'. Again Λ is not naturally to be taken as the zero of real numbers, which should rather be taken as being $\iota\text{‘}0_q$. Thus we are led to the two following definitions, in which Θ is the series of positive real numbers other than zero and infinity,

* On this definition of real numbers, cf. *Principles of Mathematics*, Chap. XXXIII.

while Θ' is the series of zero and the positive real numbers other than infinity:

***310·01.** $\Theta = (\varsigma`H) \upharpoonright (-\iota`\Lambda - \iota`\mathrm{D}`H)$ Df

***310·011.** $\Theta' = \iota`0_q \leftarrow\!\!\!\!+ \Theta$ Df

These notations are framed on the analogy of H and H', the letter Θ being chosen to suggest θ, the relation-number of the continuum. Although we do not have $\mathrm{Nr}`\Theta = \theta$, we have $\mathrm{Nr}`\varsigma`H = \theta$, and therefore (*310·15) $\dot{1} \dotplus \mathrm{Nr}`\Theta \dotplus \dot{1} = \theta$, and $\mathrm{Nr}`\Theta' \dotplus \dot{1} = \theta$ (assuming the axiom of infinity). Thus the relation-number of Θ is simply that of a θ with the ends cut off.

We put further, on the analogy of H_n, H_g,

***310·02.** $\Theta_n = (\varsigma`H_n) \upharpoonright (-\iota`\Lambda - \iota`\mathrm{D}`H_n)$ Df

***310·021.** $\Theta'_n = \iota`0_q \leftarrow\!\!\!\!+ \Theta_n$ Df

***310·03.** $\Theta_g = \breve{\Theta}_n \ddagger \Theta'$ Df

Thus Θ_n is the series of negative real numbers, Θ'_n the series of zero and the negative real numbers, Θ_g the series of negative and positive real numbers including zero (infinity always excluded). The *class* of positive real numbers is $C`\Theta$, of negative real numbers $C`\Theta_n$, of all real numbers (excluding infinity) $C`\Theta \cup \iota`\iota`0_q \cup C`\Theta_n$. If ν is a positive real number, $|\mathrm{Cnv}``\nu$ is the corresponding negative real number (*310·16). The properties of Θ, Θ_n, Θ_g in respect of limits, continuity, etc., result from the properties of θ as proved in *275, and from the properties of series of segments as proved in *212.

Instead of taking the series of segments as constituting the real numbers, it is possible to take the series of their relational sums, *i.e.* $\dot{s};\Theta$. This depends on the fact that $\dot{s};\Theta \; \mathrm{smor} \; \Theta$ (*310·33). The chief advantage of $\dot{s};\Theta$ is that it is of the same type as the series of ratios. We shall show in *314 how to construct the arithmetic of real numbers defined as the relational sums of segments; until then, we shall regard real numbers as segments of the series of ratios.

***310·01.** $\Theta = (\varsigma`H) \upharpoonright (-\iota`\Lambda - \iota`\mathrm{D}`H)$ Df

***310·011.** $\Theta' = \iota`0_q \leftarrow\!\!\!\!+ \Theta$ Df

***310·02.** $\Theta_n = (\varsigma`H_n) \upharpoonright (-\iota`\Lambda - \iota`\mathrm{D}`H_n)$ Df

***310·021.** $\Theta'_n = \iota`0_q \leftarrow\!\!\!\!+ \Theta_n$ Df

***310·03.** $\Theta_g = \breve{\Theta}_n \ddagger \Theta'$ Df

***310·1.** $\vdash . \Theta, \Theta', \Theta_n, \Theta'_n, \Theta_g \in \mathrm{Ser}$ [*304·23 . *307·41·25 . *204·5 . *212·31]

***310·11.** $\vdash : \mu \Theta \nu . \equiv . \mu, \nu \in \mathrm{D}`H_\epsilon - \iota`\Lambda - \iota`\mathrm{D}`H . \mu \subset \nu . \mu \neq \nu .$

$\equiv . \mu, \nu \in \mathrm{D}`H_\epsilon . \exists ! \mu . \exists ! \mathrm{D}`H - \nu . \exists ! \nu - \mu .$

$\equiv . \mu, \nu \in \mathrm{D}`\varsigma`H \cap \mathrm{G}`\varsigma`H . \mu \subset \nu . \mu \neq \nu$

[*212·23·132 . *211·61 . (*310·01)]

***310·111.** $\vdash : \mu \Theta_n \nu . \equiv . \mu, \nu \in D`(H_n)_\epsilon - \iota`\Lambda - \iota`D`H_n . \mu \subset \nu . \mu \neq \nu .$

$\equiv . \mu, \nu \in D`(H_n)_\epsilon . \exists ! \mu . \exists ! D`H_n - \nu . \exists ! \nu - \mu .$

$\equiv . \mu, \nu \in D`s`H_n \cap \text{Ɑ}`s`H_n . \mu \subset \nu . \mu \neq \nu$ [(*310·02)]

***310·112.** $\vdash :. \mu \Theta_g \nu . \equiv : \mu \breve{\Theta}_n \nu . \vee . \mu \Theta \nu . \vee .$

$\mu \in C`\Theta_n . \nu \in \iota`\iota`0_q \cup C`\Theta . \vee . \mu = \iota`0_q . \nu \in C`\Theta$ [(*310·03)]

***310·113.** $\vdash :. \mu \Theta' \nu . \equiv : \mu = \iota`0_q . \nu \in C`\Theta . \vee . \mu \Theta \nu$ [(*310·011)]

***310·114.** $\vdash :. \mu \Theta'_n \nu . \equiv : \mu = \iota`0_q . \nu \in C`\Theta_n . \vee . \mu \Theta_n \nu$ [(*310·021)]

***310·12.** $\vdash . C`\Theta = D`s`H \cap \text{Ɑ}`s`H = D`H_\epsilon - \iota`\Lambda - \iota`D`H .$

$C`\Theta_n = D`s`H_n \cap \text{Ɑ}`s`H_n = D`(H_n)_\epsilon - \iota`\Lambda - \iota`D`H_n$ [*212·132]

***310·121.** $\vdash . C`\Theta \subset \text{Cl ex}`D`H . C`\Theta_n \subset \text{Cl ex}`D`H_n$ [*310·12]

***310·122.** $\vdash : \exists ! 3 . \equiv . \dot{\exists} ! \Theta . \equiv . \dot{\exists} ! \Theta' . \equiv . \dot{\exists} ! \Theta_n . \equiv . \dot{\exists} ! \Theta'_n . \equiv . \dot{\exists} ! \Theta_g$
[*212·14 . *161·13 . *304·27]

***310·123.** $\vdash : \exists ! 3 . \supset . C`\Theta' = \iota`\iota`0_q \cup C`\Theta . C`\Theta'_n = \iota`\iota`0_q \cup C`\Theta_n .$

$C`\Theta_g = C`\Theta_n \cup \iota`\iota`0_q \cup C`\Theta$ [*310·122 . *161·14]

***310·13.** $\vdash . C`\Theta \cap C`\Theta_n = \Lambda . s`C`\Theta \cap s`C`\Theta_n = \Lambda$

Dem.

$\vdash . *310·11·111 . \supset \vdash : \mu \in C`\Theta . \nu \in C`\Theta_n . \supset . \mu \subset D`H . \nu \subset D`H_n . \exists ! \mu . \exists ! \nu .$

[*307·25] $\supset . \mu \neq \nu . \mu \cap \nu = \Lambda : \supset \vdash . \text{Prop}$

***310·131.** $\vdash . \iota`0_q \sim\in C`\Theta \cup C`\Theta_n$ [*304·282]

***310·14.** $\vdash . \Theta_n \text{ smor } \Theta$ [*212·72 . *307·41]

***310·15.** $\vdash : \text{Infin ax} . \supset . \Theta' \dashrightarrow C`H, \Theta'_n \dashrightarrow C`H_n, C`H_n \leftarrow \Theta_g \dashrightarrow C`H \in \theta$
[*304·33 . *310·14 . *275·21]

***310·151.** $\vdash : \text{Infin ax} . \supset . \Theta', \Theta'_n \in \text{Ser} \cap \text{comp} \cap \text{semi Ded}$
[*310·15 . *275·1 . *271·18 . *214·74]

***310·16.** $\vdash : \nu \in C`\Theta . \equiv . | \text{Cnv}``\nu \in C`\Theta_n$ [*310·12 . (*307·04)]

***310·17.** $\vdash . | \text{Cnv}`` | \text{Cnv}``\nu = \nu$ [*307·12]

***310·18.** $\vdash : \mu = | \text{Cnv}``\nu . \equiv . \nu = | \text{Cnv}``\mu$ [*310·17]

***310·19.** $\vdash : \mu = \nu . \equiv . | \text{Cnv}``\mu = | \text{Cnv}``\nu$ [*310·17]

***310·31.** $\vdash : \mu \in C`\Theta \cup C`\Theta_n . \supset . \dot{\exists} ! (\dot{s}`\mu) \upharpoonright \text{Rel num}$ [*304·5 . *310·121]

∗310·32. $\vdash :. \mu, \nu \epsilon C`\Theta_g . \supset : \dot{s}`\mu = \dot{s}`\nu . \equiv . \mu = \nu$

Dem.

$\vdash . {*}310{\cdot}31 . {*}303{\cdot}62 . \supset$

$\vdash : \mu \epsilon C`\Theta \cup C`\Theta_n . \nu = \iota`0_q . \supset . \dot{\exists} ! (\dot{s}`\mu) \upharpoonright \text{Rel num} . \sim \dot{\exists} ! (\dot{s}`\nu) \upharpoonright \text{Rel num} .$

$\supset . \dot{s}`\mu \neq \dot{s}`\nu$ (1)

$\vdash . {*}310{\cdot}12{\cdot}31 . {*}307{\cdot}25 . \supset \vdash : \mu \epsilon C`\Theta . \nu \epsilon C`\Theta_n . \supset . \dot{s}`\mu \neq \dot{s}`\nu$ (2)

$\vdash . {*}310{\cdot}11 . \supset \vdash :. \mu \Theta \nu . \supset : \exists ! \nu - \mu :$

$[{*}310{\cdot}121] \supset : (\exists \rho, \sigma) : \rho/\sigma \epsilon \nu : \xi/\eta \epsilon \mu . \supset_{\xi,\eta} . \xi/\eta \neq \rho/\sigma :$

$[{*}303{\cdot}52] \supset : (\exists \rho, \sigma, R, S) : \rho/\sigma \epsilon \nu . R(\rho/\sigma) S : \xi/\eta \epsilon \mu . \supset_{\xi,\eta} . \sim \{R(\xi/\eta) S\} :$

$[{*}41{\cdot}11] \supset : \dot{\exists} ! \dot{s}`\nu \dot{-} \dot{s}`\mu$ (3)

$\vdash . (3) . {*}310{\cdot}1 . \supset \vdash : \mu, \nu \epsilon C`\Theta . \mu \neq \nu . \supset . \dot{s}`\mu \neq \dot{s}`\nu$ (4)

Similarly $\vdash : \mu, \nu \epsilon C`\Theta_n . \mu \neq \nu . \supset . \dot{s}`\mu \neq \dot{s}`\nu$ (5)

$\vdash . (1) . (2) . (4) . (5) . \supset \vdash :. \text{Hp} . \supset : \mu \neq \nu . \supset . \dot{s}`\mu \neq \dot{s}`\nu$ (6)

$\vdash . (6) . \text{Transp} . \supset \vdash . \text{Prop}$

∗310·33. $\vdash . \dot{s};\Theta \text{ smor } \Theta . \dot{s};\Theta_n \text{ smor } \Theta_n . \dot{s};\Theta_g \text{ smor } \Theta_g$ [∗310·32]

*311. ADDITION OF CONCORDANT REAL NUMBERS.

Summary of *311.

We define a set of real numbers as *concordant* when all are positive or zero, or all are negative or zero, *i.e.* when all belong to $C`\Theta'$ or all belong to $C`\Theta'_n$. Given two concordant real numbers μ and ν, we define the sum of μ and ν as the class of sums, in the sense of *308, of a member of μ and a member of ν, *i.e.* as

$$\hat{W}\{(\exists M, N) . M \epsilon \mu . N \epsilon \nu . W = M +_g N\},$$

i.e. as $s`\mu \underset{,,}{+_g}``\nu$, in virtue of *40·7. It is easy to prove that, assuming the axiom of infinity, the sum so defined has the properties we require of a sum. We denote the sum so defined by "$\mu +_p \nu$." In order to insure that $\mu +_p \nu$ shall be Λ unless μ, ν are concordant real numbers, we put

*311·02. $\mu +_p \nu = \hat{X}\{\text{concord}(\mu, \nu) . X \epsilon s`\mu \underset{,,}{+_g}``\nu\}$ Df

Thus if μ, ν are concordant real numbers, $\mu +_p \nu = s`\mu \underset{,,}{+_g}``\nu$ (*311·11); if not, $\mu +_p \nu = \Lambda$ (*311·1). A definition of addition which applies to real numbers of opposite sign will be given in *312.

The commutative and associative laws for $+_p$ (*311·12·121) follow at once from the corresponding laws for $+_g$. Assuming the axiom of infinity, we prove without much difficulty that the sum of two positive real numbers is a positive real number (*311·27), and the sum of two negative real numbers is a negative real number (*311·42). In these proofs, when propositions of previous numbers involving "Rat" are used, "Rat" is replaced by $C`H'$ and "Rat $- \iota`0_q$" by $C`H$. This is legitimate in virtue of *304·49·34. In *311·511 we prove (assuming the axiom of infinity) that if ξ is a positive real number, and Y is any positive ratio, however small, there are members X of ξ such that $Y +_g X$ is not a member of ξ, *i.e.* given any positive real number, there are rationals differing from it by less than any assigned positive rational. This proposition is useful, and is used in proving that if ξ, η are positive real numbers, each is less than $\xi +_p \eta$ (*311·52). The converse of this proposition, *i.e.* the proposition that, if $\mu \Theta \nu$, there is a positive real number

λ such that $\nu = \mu +_p \lambda$, is proved in $*311{\cdot}621{\cdot}64$, after a considerable amount of work. Thus we have

***311·65.** $\vdash :: \text{Infin ax} . \supset :. \mu \Theta \nu . \equiv : \mu, \nu \in C{`}\Theta : (\exists \lambda) . \lambda \in C{`}\Theta . \nu = \mu +_p \lambda$

We have, of course, a corresponding proposition for Θ_n ($*311{\cdot}66$). From $*311{\cdot}65$ we deduce without difficulty that if μ is less than ν (μ, ν being positive real numbers), then $\lambda +_p \mu$ is less than $\lambda +_p \nu$ (λ being a positive real number), *i.e.*

***311·73.** $\vdash : \text{Infin ax} . \lambda \in C{`}\Theta . \mu \Theta \nu . \supset . (\lambda +_p \mu) \Theta (\lambda +_p \nu)$

whence (with the corresponding proposition for Θ_n) we deduce

***311·75.** $\vdash :. \text{Infin ax} . \text{concord}(\lambda, \mu) . \supset : \lambda +_p \mu = \lambda +_p \nu . \equiv . \mu = \nu$

which secures the uniqueness of subtraction.

***311·01.** $\text{concord}(\mu, \nu, \ldots) . = : \mu, \nu, \ldots \in C{`}\Theta' . \vee . \mu, \nu, \ldots \in C{`}\Theta'_n$ Df

***311·02.** $\mu +_p \nu = \hat{X} \{\text{concord}(\mu, \nu) . X \in s{`}\mu \underset{,,}{+_g}{``}\nu\}$ Df

***311·1.** $\vdash : \sim \text{concord}(\mu, \nu) . \supset . \mu +_p \nu = \Lambda$ [($*311{\cdot}02$)]

***311·11.** $\vdash : \text{concord}(\mu, \nu) . \supset .$

$$\mu +_p \nu = s{`}\mu \underset{,,}{+_g}{``}\nu = \hat{W}\{(\exists M, N) . M \in \mu . N \in \nu . W = M +_g N\}$$

[($*311{\cdot}02$)]

***311·12.** $\vdash . \mu +_p \nu = \nu +_p \mu$ [$*311{\cdot}1{\cdot}11 . *308{\cdot}4$]

***311·121.** $\vdash . (\lambda +_p \mu) +_p \nu = \lambda +_p (\mu +_p \nu)$ [$*311{\cdot}1{\cdot}11 . *308{\cdot}63$]

***311·13.** $\vdash : \text{concord}(\mu, \nu) . \equiv . \text{concord}(|\text{Cnv}{``}\mu, |\text{Cnv}{``}\nu)$
[$*310{\cdot}16$. ($*311{\cdot}01$)]

***311·14.** $\vdash : \text{concord}(\mu, |\text{Cnv}{``}\nu) . \equiv . \text{concord}(|\text{Cnv}{``}\mu, \nu)$ [$*311{\cdot}13 . *310{\cdot}17$]

***311·15.** $\vdash : \text{concord}(\mu, |\text{Cnv}{``}\nu) . \supset . \sim \text{concord}(\mu, \nu)$ [$*310{\cdot}13{\cdot}16$]

***311·2.** $\vdash : \text{Infin ax} . \xi \subset C{`}H . X \in C{`}H . \supset . X +_g{``}H{``}\xi = H{``}X +_g{``}\xi \cap \overleftarrow{H}{`}X$

Dem.

$\vdash . *308{\cdot}72 . *304{\cdot}34{\cdot}401 . \supset \vdash :. \text{Hp} . \supset : Y \in X +_g{``}H{``}\xi . \equiv .$

$(\exists Z, Z') . Z' \in \xi . Z \in C{`}H . Y = X +_g Z . (X +_g Z) H (X +_g Z') .$

[$*37{\cdot}6$] $\equiv . (\exists Z, Y') . Z \in C{`}H . Y = X +_g Z . Y' \in X +_g{``}\xi . Y H Y' .$

[$*306{\cdot}52$] $\equiv . Y \in H{``}X +_g{``}\xi . X H Y :. \supset \vdash . \text{Prop}$

***311·21.** $\vdash : \text{Infin ax} . \xi \subset C{`}H . \exists ! \xi . X \in C{`}H . \supset . \overrightarrow{H_*}{`}X \subset H{``}X +_g{``}\xi$

Dem.

$\vdash . *306{\cdot}52 . *304{\cdot}401 . \supset \vdash :. \text{Hp} . \supset : Y \in \xi . \supset . X H (X +_g Y) :$

[$*40{\cdot}51{\cdot}61$] $\supset : X \in H{``}X +_g{``}\xi$ (1)

$\vdash . (1) . *304{\cdot}23 . \supset \vdash . \text{Prop}$

***311·22.** $\vdash : \text{Infin ax} \,.\, \xi \subset C`H \,.\, \exists ! \xi \,.\, X \in C`H \,.\, \supset .$

$$H``X +_g``\xi = \overrightarrow{H}_*`X \cup X +_g``H``\xi$$

Dem.

$\vdash . *304·23 . \supset \vdash . H``X +_g``\xi = (H``X +_g``\xi \cap \overrightarrow{H}_*`X) \cup (H``X +_g``\xi \cap \overleftarrow{H}`X)$ (1)

$\vdash . (1) . *311·2·21 . \supset \vdash . \text{Prop}$

***311·23.** $\vdash : \text{Infin ax} \,.\, \xi \in C`\Theta \,.\, X \in C`H \,.\, \supset .\, H``X +_g``\xi = \overrightarrow{H}_*`X \cup X +_g``H``\xi$

[*311·22 . *310·12]

***311·24.** $\vdash :. \text{Infin ax} \,.\, \xi \in C`\Theta \,.\, Y \in C`H \,.\, \supset :$

$$(\exists Z) \,.\, ZHY \,.\, Y \in Z +_g``\xi : Y \in s`\xi \underset{,,}{+}_g``\overrightarrow{H}`Y$$

Dem.

$\vdash . *304·31 . \supset \vdash : \text{Hp} . \supset . (\exists W) . W \in \xi . WHY .$

[*306·52] $\supset . (\exists Z, W) . W \in \xi . ZHY . Y = Z +_g W : \supset \vdash . \text{Prop}$

***311·25.** $\vdash : \text{Infin ax} \,.\, \xi, \eta \in C`\Theta \,.\, \supset .\, \xi \subset \xi +_p \eta \,.\, \eta \subset \xi +_p \eta$

Dem.

$\vdash . *310·12 .$ $\supset \vdash : \text{Hp} . Y \in \eta . \supset . \overrightarrow{H}`Y \subset \eta .$

[*311·24] $\supset . Y \in s`\xi \underset{,,}{+}_g``\eta$ (1)

$\vdash . (1) . *311·11 . \supset \vdash : \text{Hp} . \supset . \eta \subset \xi +_p \eta$ (2)

$\vdash . (2) . *311·12 . \supset \vdash : \text{Hp} . \supset . \xi \subset \xi +_p \eta$ (3)

$\vdash . (2) . (3) . \supset \vdash . \text{Prop}$

***311·26.** $\vdash : \text{Infin ax} \,.\, \xi, \eta \in C`\Theta \,.\, \supset .\, H``(\xi +_p \eta) = \xi +_p \eta$

Dem.

$\vdash . *311·23 . \supset \vdash :. \text{Hp} . \supset : Y \in \eta . \supset . H``(\xi \underset{,,}{+}_g Y) = \overrightarrow{H}_*`Y \cup (H``\xi) \underset{,,}{+}_g Y :$

[*311·11.*310·12] $\supset : H``(\xi +_p \eta) = H_*``\eta \cup (\xi +_p \eta)$

[*311·25.*310·12] $= \xi +_p \eta :. \supset \vdash . \text{Prop}$

***311·27.** $\vdash : \text{Infin ax} \,.\, \xi, \eta \in C`\Theta \,.\, \supset .\, \xi +_p \eta \in C`\Theta$

Dem.

$\vdash . *311·25 . *310·12 . \supset \vdash : \text{Hp} . \supset . \exists ! \xi +_p \eta .$

[*311·26.*310·12] $\supset . \xi +_p \eta \in C`\Theta \cup \iota`\text{D}`H$ (1)

$\vdash . *310·12 . *211·703 . \supset$

$\vdash : \text{Hp} . \supset . (\exists M, N) . M, N \in \text{D}`H . M \in p`\overleftarrow{H}``\xi . N \in p`\overleftarrow{H}``\eta .$

[*308·32·72.*306·23] $\supset . (\exists M, N) . M +_g N \in p`\overleftarrow{H}``(\xi +_p \eta) \cap \text{D}`H$ (2)

$\vdash . (2) . *200·5 . \supset \vdash : \text{Hp} . \supset . \xi +_p \eta \neq \text{D}`H$ (3)

$\vdash . (1) . (3) . \supset \vdash . \text{Prop}$

The axiom of infinity is essential to the truth of the above proposition, for if it fails we have $\text{E} ! B`H . B`H \sim\in \xi +_p \eta$, while $\mu \in C`\Theta . \supset . B`H \in \mu$.

***311·31.** $\vdash . \mid \text{Cnv}``(\mu +_p \nu) = (\mid \text{Cnv}``\mu) +_p (\mid \text{Cnv}``\nu)$

Dem.

$\vdash . *311·13·1 . \supset$

$\vdash : \sim \text{concord}(\mu, \nu) . \supset . \mid \text{Cnv}``(\mu +_p \nu) = \Lambda . (\mid \text{Cnv}``\mu) +_p (\mid \text{Cnv}``\nu) = \Lambda$ (1)

$\vdash . *311·13·11 . \supset \vdash : \text{concord}(\mu, \nu) . \supset . \mid \text{Cnv}``(\mu +_p \nu) = \mid \text{Cnv}``s`\mu \underset{,,}{+_g}``\nu$

$[*308·411] = s`(\mid \text{Cnv}``\mu) \underset{,,}{+_g}``(\mid \text{Cnv}``\nu)$ (2)

$\vdash . (1) . (2) . \supset \vdash . \text{Prop}$

***311·32.** $\vdash . \mid \text{Cnv}``(\mu +_p \mid \text{Cnv}``\nu) = (\mid \text{Cnv}``\mu) +_p \nu$ [*311·31 . *310·17]

***311·33.** $\vdash . \mu +_p \nu = \mid \text{Cnv}``\{(\mid \text{Cnv}``\mu) +_p (\mid \text{Cnv}``\nu)\}$ [*311·31 . *310·18]

***311·41.** $\vdash : \text{Infin ax} . \mu, \nu \in C`\Theta_n . \supset . \mu \subset \mu +_p \nu . \nu \subset \mu +_p \nu$

Dem.

$\vdash . *311·25 . *310·16 . \supset \vdash : \text{Hp} . \supset . \mid \text{Cnv}``\mu \subset (\mid \text{Cnv}``\mu) +_p (\mid \text{Cnv}``\nu) .$

$[*311·33 . *310·17] \quad \supset . \mu \subset \mu +_p \nu$ (1)

Similarly $\vdash : \text{Hp} . \supset . \nu \subset \mu +_p \nu$ (2)

$\vdash . (1) . (2) . \supset \vdash . \text{Prop}$

***311·42.** $\vdash : \text{Infin ax} . \mu, \nu \in C`\Theta_n . \supset . \mu +_p \nu \in C`\Theta_n$

Dem.

$\vdash . *311·27 . *310·16 . \supset \vdash : \text{Hp} . \supset . (\mid \text{Cnv}``\mu) +_p (\mid \text{Cnv}``\nu) \in C`\Theta .$

$[*311·33 . *310·16] \quad \supset . \mu +_p \nu \in C`\Theta_n : \supset \vdash . \text{Prop}$

***311·43.** $\vdash : \mu \in C`\Theta_g . \supset . \mu +_p \iota`0_q = \mu$

Dem.

$\vdash . *311·11 . \supset \vdash : \text{Hp} . \supset . \mu +_p \iota`0_q = \hat{W}\{(\exists M) . M \in \mu . W = M +_g 0_q\}$

$[*308·51] \quad = \mu : \supset \vdash . \text{Prop}$

***311·44.** $\vdash : \text{Infin ax} . \text{concord}(\mu, \nu) . \supset . \mu +_p \nu \in C`\Theta_g$ [*311·27·42·43]

***311·45.** $\vdash :. \text{Infin ax} . \text{concord}(\mu, \nu) : \mu \neq \iota`0_q . \vee . \nu = \iota`0_q : \supset . \mu \subset \mu +_p \nu$

[*311·25·41·43]

***311·51.** $\vdash : \text{Infin ax} . \xi \in \text{D}`H_\epsilon - \iota`\Lambda . Y \in C`H . Y +_g``\xi \subset \xi . \supset . \xi = C`H = \text{D}`H$

Dem.

$\vdash . *38·13 . \supset \vdash : \text{Hp} . X \in \xi . \supset . Y +_g X \in \xi .$

$[*306·52] \quad \supset . Y \in \xi$ (1)

$\vdash . *306·51 . \supset$

$\vdash : \text{Hp} . \nu \in \text{NC ind} . X \in \xi . Y +_g (\nu/1 \times_s X) \in \xi . \supset . Y +_g \{(\nu +_c 1)/1 \times_s X\} \in \xi$ (2)

$\vdash . (1) . (2) . \text{Induct} . \supset \vdash : \text{Hp} . \nu \in \text{NC ind} . X \in \xi . \supset . Y +_g (\nu/1 \times_s X) \in \xi$ (3)

$\vdash . *305·7 . *306·52 . \supset$

$\vdash : \text{Hp} . X \in \xi . Z \in C`H . \supset . (\exists \nu) . \nu \in \text{NC ind} . ZH\{Y +_g (\nu/1 \times_s X)\}$ (4)

$\vdash . (3) . (4) . \supset \vdash : \text{Hp} . Z \in C`H . \supset . Z \in \xi : \supset \vdash . \text{Prop}$

***311·511.** $\vdash :$ Infin ax . $\xi \epsilon C`\Theta \,.\, Y \epsilon C`H \,.\, \supset .\, (\exists X) \,.\, X \epsilon \xi \,.\, Y +_g X \sim\epsilon \xi$
[*311·51 . Transp]

***311·52.** $\vdash :$ Infin ax . $\xi, \eta \epsilon C`\Theta \,.\, \supset .\, \xi \Theta (\xi +_p \eta)$

Dem.

$\vdash .$ *311·511 . $\supset \vdash :.$ Hp . $\supset : Y \epsilon C`H \,.\, \supset .\, (\exists X) \,.\, X \epsilon \xi \,.\, X +_g Y \sim\epsilon \xi :$
[*311·11] $\supset : (\exists X, Y) \,.\, X +_g Y \epsilon (\xi +_p \eta) - \xi :$
[*310·11.*311·27] $\supset : \xi \Theta (\xi +_p \eta) :. \supset \vdash .$ Prop

***311·53.** $\vdash :$ Infin ax . $\xi, \eta \epsilon C`\Theta_n \,.\, \supset .\, \xi \Theta_n (\xi +_p \eta)$ [*311·52·33]

***311·56.** $\vdash :.$ Infin ax . $\xi \epsilon C`\Theta_g \,.\, \supset : \xi = \xi +_p \eta \,.\, \equiv .\, \eta = \iota`0_q$ [*311·1·43·52·53]

***311·57.** $\vdash ::$ Infin ax . $\supset :.\, \xi = \xi +_p \eta \,.\, \equiv : \xi = \Lambda \,.\, \mathbf{v} \,.\, \xi \epsilon C`\Theta_g \,.\, \eta = \iota`0_q$
[*311·56·1]

***311·58.** $\vdash :$ Infin ax . $\mu \epsilon C`\Theta \,.\, \supset .\, \mu = H``\mu$ [*304·3 . *270·31]

***311·6.** $\vdash :$ Infin ax . $\mu \Theta \nu \,.\, X, Y \epsilon \nu - \mu \,.\, XHY \,.\, M \epsilon \mu \,.\, \supset .\, M +_g (Y -_s X) \epsilon \nu$

Dem.

$\vdash .$ *310·11 . $\supset \vdash :$ Hp . $\supset .\, MHX$.
[*308·42·72] $\supset .\, \{M +_g (Y -_s X)\} HY$ (1)
$\vdash .$ (1) . *311·58 . $\supset \vdash .$ Prop

***311·61.** $\vdash :$ Infin ax . $\mu \Theta \nu$.
$\lambda = \hat{L} \{(\exists X, Y) \,.\, X, Y \epsilon \nu - \mu \,.\, XHY \,.\, L = Y -_s X\} \,.\, \supset .$
$s`\mu \underset{\prime\prime}{+_g} ``\lambda \subset \nu$ [*311·6]

***311·62.** $\vdash :$ Infin ax . $\mu \Theta \nu \,.\, X \epsilon \nu - \mu \,.\, \supset .\, (\exists Y) \,.\, Y \epsilon \nu - \mu \,.\, XHY$

Dem.

$\vdash .$ *311·58 . $\supset \vdash :$ Hp . $\supset .\, X \epsilon H``\nu - H``\mu : \supset \vdash .$ Prop

***311·621.** $\vdash :$ Hp *311·61 . $\supset .\, \lambda \epsilon C`\Theta$

Dem.

$\vdash .$ *311·62 . $\supset \vdash :$ Hp . $\supset .\, \exists ! \lambda$ (1)
$\vdash .$ *308·46 . $\supset \vdash :$ Hp . $\supset .\, \lambda \subset H``\nu$ (2)
$\vdash .$ *311·62 . $\supset \vdash :$ Hp . $X, Y \epsilon \nu - \mu \,.\, XHY \,.\, \supset .\, (\exists Z) \,.\, Z \epsilon \nu - \mu \,.\, YHZ$.
[*308·42·72] $\supset .\, (\exists Z) \,.\, Z \epsilon \nu - \mu \,.\, (Y -_s X) H (Z -_s X)$ (3)
$\vdash .$ (3) . *37·1 . $\supset \vdash :$ Hp . $\supset .\, \lambda \subset H``\lambda$ (4)
$\vdash .$ *308·56·42·72 . $\supset$
$\vdash :$ Hp . $X, Y \epsilon \nu - \mu \,.\, XHY \,.\, LH (Y -_s X) \,.\, \supset .\, XH (X +_g L) \,.\, (X +_g L) HY$.
[*310·11.*308·43] $\supset .\, L \epsilon \lambda$ (5)
$\vdash .$ (5) . *37·1 . $\supset \vdash :$ Hp . $\supset .\, H``\lambda \subset \lambda$ (6)
$\vdash .$ (1) . (2) . (4) . (6) . $\supset \vdash :$ Hp . $\supset .\, \lambda \epsilon \mathrm{D}`H_\epsilon - \iota`\Lambda - \iota`\mathrm{D}`H$.
[*310·12] $\supset .\, \lambda \epsilon C`\Theta : \supset \vdash .$ Prop

$*311{\cdot}63$. $\vdash : \text{Infin ax} . \nu \in C`\Theta . X \in \nu . N \in C`H . \supset . (\exists L) . LHN . X +_g L \in \nu$

Dem.

$\vdash . *311{\cdot}58 . \supset \vdash : \text{Hp} . \supset . (\exists Y) . Y \in \nu . XHY$ (1)

$\vdash . *308{\cdot}42 . \supset \vdash : \text{Hp} . Y \in \nu . XHY . Z = Y -_s X . ZHN . \supset . ZHN . X +_g Z \in \nu$ (2)

$\vdash . *308{\cdot}42{\cdot}72 . \supset$

$\vdash : \text{Hp} . Y \in \nu . XHY . Z = Y -_s X . NH_* Z . LHN . \supset . LHN . X +_g L \in \nu$ (3)

$\vdash . (3) . *311{\cdot}58 . \supset$

$\vdash : \text{Hp} . Y \in \nu . XHY . Z = Y -_s X . NH_* Z . \supset . (\exists L) . LHN . X +_g L \in \nu$ (4)

$\vdash . (1) . (2) . (4) . \supset \vdash . \text{Prop}$

$*311{\cdot}631$. $\vdash : \text{Infin ax} . \mu \Theta \nu . N \in \mu . \supset .$

$(\exists M, X, Y) . M \in \mu . X, Y \in \nu - \mu . XHY . N = M +_g (Y -_s X)$

Dem.

$\vdash . *311{\cdot}58 . *308{\cdot}72 . \supset$

$\vdash : \text{Hp} . X \in \nu - \mu . LHN . X +_g L \in \nu . Y = X +_g L . M = N -_g L . \supset .$

$M \in \mu . X, Y \in \nu - \mu . XHY . N = M +_g (Y -_s X)$ (1)

$\vdash . (1) . *311{\cdot}63 . \supset \vdash . \text{Prop}$

$*311{\cdot}632$. $\vdash : \text{Infin ax} . \mu \Theta \nu . N \in \nu - \mu . \supset .$

$(\exists M, W) . M \in \mu . M +_g W, N +_g W \in \nu - \mu . (M +_g W) H (N +_g W)$

Dem.

$\vdash . *306{\cdot}52 . *311{\cdot}63{\cdot}58 . \supset \vdash : \text{Hp} . \supset . (\exists W) . W \in C`H . N +_g W \in \nu - \mu$ (1)

$\vdash . *311{\cdot}511 . \supset \vdash : \text{Hp} . W \in C`H . \supset . (\exists M) . M \in \mu . M +_g W \sim\in \mu$ (2)

$\vdash . *311{\cdot}58 . \supset \vdash : \text{Hp} . M \in \mu . N \in \nu - \mu . W \in C`H . \supset . MHN . W \in C`H .$

[$*308{\cdot}72$] $\supset . (M +_g W) H (N +_g W)$ (3)

$\vdash . (3) . *311{\cdot}58 . \supset \vdash : \text{Hp}(3) . N +_g W \in \nu . \supset . M +_g W \in \nu$ (4)

$\vdash . (2) . (4) . \supset$

$\vdash : \text{Hp} . W \in C`H . N +_g W \in \nu - \mu . \supset . (\exists M) . M \in \mu . M +_g W \in \nu - \mu$ (5)

$\vdash . (1) . (3) . (5) . \supset \vdash . \text{Prop}$

$*311{\cdot}633$. $\vdash : \text{Infin ax} . \mu \Theta \nu . N \in \nu . \supset .$

$(\exists M, X, Y) . M \in \mu . X, Y \in \nu - \mu . XHY . N = M +_g (Y -_s X)$

Dem.

$\vdash . *308{\cdot}61{\cdot}4{\cdot}63 . \supset$

$\vdash : \text{Hp} . MHN . X = M +_g W . Y = N +_g W . \supset . N = M +_g (Y -_s X)$ (1)

$\vdash . *311{\cdot}632 . *308{\cdot}72 . \supset \vdash : \text{Hp} . N \sim\in \mu . \supset . (\exists M, W, X, Y) .$

$M \in \mu . X = M +_g W . Y = N +_g W . XHY . MHN . X, Y \in \nu - \mu$ (2)

$\vdash . (1) . (2) . \supset \vdash : \text{Hp} . N \sim\in \mu . \supset .$

$(\exists M, X, Y) . M \in \mu . X, Y \in \nu - \mu . XHY . N = M +_g (Y -_s X)$ (3)

$\vdash . (3) . *311{\cdot}631 . \supset \vdash . \text{Prop}$

***311·64.** $\vdash : \text{Hp} *311\cdot61 . \supset . \nu = \mu +_p \lambda$

Dem.

$\vdash . *311\cdot633 . \supset . \nu \subset s`\mu \underset{,,}{+_g}``\lambda$ (1)

$\vdash . (1) . *311\cdot621\cdot61 . \supset \vdash : \text{Hp} . \supset . \lambda \in C`\Theta . \nu = s`\mu \underset{,,}{+_g}``\lambda .$

[*311·11] $\supset . \nu = \mu +_p \lambda : \supset \vdash . \text{Prop}$

***311·65.** $\vdash :: \text{Infin ax} . \supset :. \mu \Theta \nu . \equiv : \mu, \nu \in C`\Theta : (\exists \lambda) . \lambda \in C`\Theta . \nu = \mu +_p \lambda$
[*311·52·64]

***311·66.** $\vdash :: \text{Infin ax} . \supset :. \mu \Theta_n \nu . \equiv : \mu, \nu \in C`\Theta_n : (\exists \lambda) . \lambda \in C`\Theta_n . \nu = \mu +_p \lambda$

Dem.

$\vdash . *310\cdot11\cdot111 . \supset \vdash : \mu \Theta_n \nu . \equiv . (| \text{Cnv}``\mu) \Theta (| \text{Cnv}``\nu)$ (1)

$\vdash . (1) . *311\cdot65 . \supset \vdash :: \text{Hp} . \supset :.$

$\mu \Theta_n \nu . \equiv : | \text{Cnv}``\mu \in C`\Theta : (\exists \lambda) . \lambda \in C`\Theta . | \text{Cnv}``\nu = | \text{Cnv}``\mu +_p \lambda :$

[*311·32.*310·16·19] $\equiv : \mu \in C`\Theta_n : (\exists \lambda) . \lambda \in C`\Theta_n . \nu = \mu +_p \lambda :: \supset \vdash . \text{Prop}$

***311·73.** $\vdash : \text{Infin ax} . \lambda \in C`\Theta . \mu \Theta \nu . \supset . (\lambda +_p \mu) \Theta (\lambda +_p \nu)$

Dem.

$\vdash . *311\cdot65 . \supset \vdash : \text{Hp} . \supset . (\exists \rho) . \rho \in C`\Theta . \nu = \mu +_p \rho .$

[*311·121] $\supset . (\exists \rho) . \rho \in C`\Theta . \lambda +_p \nu = (\lambda +_p \mu) +_p \rho$ (1)

$\vdash . *311\cdot27 . \supset \vdash : \text{Hp} . \supset . \lambda +_p \mu, \lambda +_p \nu \in C`\Theta$ (2)

$\vdash . (1) . (2) . *311\cdot65 . \supset \vdash . \text{Prop}$

***311·731.** $\vdash : \text{Infin ax} . \lambda \in C`\Theta_n . \mu \Theta_n \nu . \supset . (\lambda +_p \mu) \Theta_n (\lambda +_p \nu)$ [*311·73]

***311·74.** $\vdash :. \text{Infin ax} : \lambda, \mu \in C`\Theta . \vee . \lambda, \mu \in C`\Theta_n : \supset : \lambda +_p \mu = \lambda +_p \nu . \equiv . \mu = \nu$

Dem.

$\vdash . *311\cdot27\cdot1 . \supset \vdash : \lambda, \mu \in C`\Theta . \lambda +_p \mu = \lambda +_p \nu . \supset . \nu \in C`\Theta$ (1)

$\vdash . *311\cdot73 . \text{Transp} . \supset \vdash : \text{Hp}(1) . \supset . \sim(\mu \Theta \nu) . \sim(\nu \Theta \mu)$ (2)

$\vdash . (1) . (2) . *310\cdot1 . \supset \vdash : \text{Hp}(1) . \supset . \mu = \nu$ (3)

Similarly $\vdash : \lambda, \mu \in C`\Theta_n . \lambda +_p \mu = \lambda +_p \nu . \supset . \mu = \nu$ (4)

$\vdash . (3) . (4) . \supset \vdash . \text{Prop}$

***311·75.** $\vdash :. \text{Infin ax} . \text{concord}(\lambda, \mu) . \supset : \lambda +_p \mu = \lambda +_p \nu . \equiv . \mu = \nu$
[*311·74·43]

*312. ALGEBRAIC ADDITION OF REAL NUMBERS.

Summary of *312.

In this number we extend the definition of addition so as to apply to real numbers of opposite sign. As in *308, this requires a previous definition of subtraction. We define subtraction as follows: If there is a λ such that $\nu +_p \lambda = \mu$, then $\mu -_p \nu$ is λ; if there is a λ such that $\mu +_p \lambda = \nu$, then $\mu -_p \nu$ is $|\,\text{Cnv}``\lambda$, *i.e.* the negative of λ; in any other case, $\mu -_p \nu = \Lambda$. The formal definition is:

***312·01.** $\mu -_p \nu = \hat{X}\{(\exists\lambda) : \lambda, \mu, \nu \in C`\Theta_g :$
$$\nu +_p \lambda = \mu \,.\, X \in \lambda \,.\vee.\, \mu +_p \lambda = \nu \,.\, X \in |\,\text{Cnv}``\lambda\} \quad \text{Df}$$

Hence assuming the axiom of infinity we have

$$\nu\,(\Theta \cup \Theta_n)\,\mu \,.\supset.\, \mu -_p \nu = (\imath\lambda)\,(\nu +_p \lambda = \mu) \quad (*312\cdot18),$$
$$\mu\,(\Theta \cup \Theta_n)\,\nu \,.\supset.\, \mu -_p \nu = (\imath\lambda)\,(\mu +_p |\,\text{Cnv}``\lambda = \nu) \quad (*312\cdot181),$$
$$\lambda \in C`\Theta_g \,.\supset.\, \lambda -_p \lambda = \iota`0_q \quad (*312\cdot191).$$

The algebraic sum of μ and ν is defined as $\mu +_p \nu$ if μ and ν are of the same sign, and as $\mu -_p |\,\text{Cnv}``\nu$ if μ and ν are of opposite signs; *i.e.* we put

***312·02.** $\mu +_a \nu = (\mu +_p \nu) \cup (\mu -_p |\,\text{Cnv}``\nu)$ Df

This definition is justified because either $\mu +_p \nu$ or $\mu -_p |\,\text{Cnv}``\nu$ must always be Λ. Thus we have

***312·32.** $\vdash :\text{concord}\,(\mu, \nu) \,.\supset.\, \mu +_a \nu = \mu +_p \nu$

***312·33.** $\vdash : \sim\text{concord}\,(\mu, \nu) \,.\supset.\, \mu +_a \nu = \mu -_p |\,\text{Cnv}``\nu$

The propositions proved are analogous to those of previous numbers, and offer no difficulty.

***312·01.** $\mu -_p \nu = \hat{X}\{(\exists\lambda) : \lambda, \mu, \nu \in C`\Theta_g :$
$$\nu +_p \lambda = \mu \,.\, X \in \lambda \,.\vee.\, \mu +_p \lambda = \nu \,.\, X \in |\,\text{Cnv}``\lambda\} \quad \text{Df}$$

***312·02.** $\mu +_a \nu = (\mu +_p \nu) \cup (\mu -_p |\,\text{Cnv}``\nu)$ Df

***312·1.** $\vdash :. X \epsilon \mu -_p \nu . \equiv : \mu, \nu \epsilon C\text{‘}\Theta_g : (\exists\lambda) : \lambda \epsilon C\text{‘}\Theta_g :$
$\nu +_p \lambda = \mu . X \epsilon \lambda . \vee . \mu +_p \lambda = \nu . X \epsilon | \text{Cnv}\text{“}\lambda$ [(*311·01)]

***312·11.** $\vdash : \sim \text{concord}(\mu, \nu) . \supset . \mu -_p \nu = \Lambda$ [*311·1·27·42·43]

***312·12.** $\vdash : \text{Infin ax} . \nu \Theta \mu . \supset .$
$$\mu -_p \nu = \hat{X} \{(\exists\lambda) . \lambda \epsilon C\text{‘}\Theta . \nu +_p \lambda = \mu . X \epsilon \lambda\} = (\iota\lambda)(\nu +_p \lambda = \mu)$$

Dem.

$\vdash . *311·1·65 . \supset \vdash : \text{Hp} . \supset . \sim (\exists\lambda) . \mu +_p \lambda = \nu$ (1)

$\vdash . (1) . *312·1 . \supset \vdash : \text{Hp} . \supset . \mu -_p \nu = \hat{X} \{(\exists\lambda) . \lambda \epsilon C\text{‘}\Theta . \nu +_p \lambda = \mu . X \epsilon \lambda\}$ (2)

$\vdash . (2) . *311·74 . \supset \vdash . \text{Prop}$

***312·13.** $\vdash : \text{Infin ax} . \mu \Theta \nu . \supset .$
$$\mu -_p \nu = \hat{X} \{(\exists\lambda) . \lambda \epsilon C\text{‘}\Theta . \mu +_p \lambda = \nu . X \epsilon | \text{Cnv}\text{“}\lambda\}$$
$$= | \text{Cnv}\text{“}(\iota\lambda)(\mu +_p \lambda = \nu)$$ [Proof as in *312·12]

***312·14.** $\vdash : \text{Infin ax} . \nu \Theta_n \mu . \supset .$
$$\mu -_p \nu = \hat{X} \{(\exists\lambda) . \lambda \epsilon C\text{‘}\Theta_n . \nu +_p \lambda = \mu . X \epsilon \lambda\}$$
$$= (\iota\lambda)(\nu +_p \lambda = \mu)$$ [Proof as in *312·12]

***312·15.** $\vdash : \text{Infin ax} . \mu \Theta_n \nu . \supset .$
$$\mu -_p \nu = \hat{X} \{(\exists\lambda) . \lambda \epsilon C\text{‘}\Theta_n . \mu +_p \lambda = \nu . X \epsilon | \text{Cnv}\text{“}\lambda\}$$
$$= | \text{Cnv}\text{“}(\iota\lambda)(\mu +_p \lambda = \nu)$$ [Proof as in *312·12]

***312·16.** $\vdash : \mu \epsilon C\text{‘}\Theta_g . \supset . \mu -_p \iota\text{‘}0_q = \mu$ [*312·1 . *311·43]

***312·17.** $\vdash : \mu \epsilon C\text{‘}\Theta_g . \supset . \iota\text{‘}0_q -_p \mu = | \text{Cnv}\text{“}\mu$ [*312·1 . *311·43]

***312·18.** $\vdash : \text{Infin ax} . \nu (\Theta \cup \Theta_n) \mu . \supset . \mu -_p \nu = (\iota\lambda)(\nu +_p \lambda = \mu)$ [*312·12·14]

***312·181.** $\vdash : \text{Infin ax} . \mu (\Theta \cup \Theta_n) \nu . \supset . \mu -_p \nu = | \text{Cnv}\text{“}(\iota\lambda)(\mu +_p \lambda = \nu)$
$= (\iota\lambda)(\mu +_p | \text{Cnv}\text{“}\lambda = \nu)$ [*312·13·15]

***312·19.** $\vdash : \text{Infin ax} . \text{concord}(\lambda, \mu) . \supset . (\lambda +_p \mu) -_p \lambda = \mu$
[*312·18 . *311·65·66·43]

***312·191.** $\vdash : \text{Infin ax} . \lambda \epsilon C\text{‘}\Theta_g . \supset . \lambda -_p \lambda = \iota\text{‘}0_q$ [*311·52·53·43]

***312·2.** $\vdash . | \text{Cnv}\text{“}(\mu -_p \nu) = | \text{Cnv}\text{“}\mu -_p | \text{Cnv}\text{“}\nu$

Dem.

$\vdash . *312·1 . *310·16 . \supset$

$\vdash :. X \epsilon | \text{Cnv}\text{“}\mu -_p | \text{Cnv}\text{“}\nu . \equiv : \mu, \nu \epsilon C\text{‘}\Theta_g :$
$(\exists\lambda) : \lambda \epsilon C\text{‘}\Theta_g : | \text{Cnv}\text{“}\nu +_p \lambda = | \text{Cnv}\text{“}\mu . X \epsilon \lambda . \vee .$
$| \text{Cnv}\text{“}\mu +_p \lambda = | \text{Cnv}\text{“}\nu . X \epsilon | \text{Cnv}\text{“}\lambda :$

[*311·32] $\equiv : \mu, \nu \epsilon C\text{‘}\Theta_g : (\exists\lambda) : \lambda \epsilon C\text{‘}\Theta_g :$
$\nu +_p | \text{Cnv}\text{“}\lambda = \mu . X \epsilon \lambda . \vee . \mu +_p | \text{Cnv}\text{“}\lambda = \nu . X \epsilon | \text{Cnv}\text{“}\lambda :$

[*312·1.*310·16] $\equiv : X \epsilon | \text{Cnv}\text{“}(\mu -_p \nu) :. \supset \vdash . \text{Prop}$

***312·201.** $\vdash . \mu -_p | \text{Cnv}\text{“}\nu = | \text{Cnv}\text{“}(| \text{Cnv}\text{“}\mu -_p \nu)$ [*312·2]

***312·21.** $\vdash . \mid \text{Cnv}``(\nu -_p \mu) = \mu -_p \nu$

Dem.

$\vdash . *312·1 . \supset \vdash :: X \in \mid \text{Cnv}``(\nu -_p \mu) . \equiv :. (\exists Y) :. \mu, \nu \in C`\Theta_g :.$
$(\exists \lambda) : \lambda \in C`\Theta_g : \mu +_p \lambda = \nu . Y \in \lambda . X = Y \mid \text{Cnv} . \vee .$
$\nu +_p \lambda = \mu . Y \in \mid \text{Cnv}``\lambda . X = Y \mid \text{Cnv} :.$

[*310·16] $\equiv :. \mu, \nu \in C`\Theta_g :. (\exists \lambda) : \lambda \in C`\Theta_g : \mu +_p \lambda = \nu . X \in \mid \text{Cnv}``\lambda . \vee .$
$\nu +_p \lambda = \mu . X \in \lambda :.$

[*312·1] $\equiv :. X \in \mu -_p \nu :: \supset \vdash . \text{Prop}$

***312·211.** $\vdash . \mu -_p \mid \text{Cnv}``\nu = \nu -_p \mid \text{Cnv}``\mu$ [*312·201·21]

***312·22.** $\vdash : \text{Infin ax} . \nu (\Theta \cup \breve{\Theta}_n) \mu . \supset . \mu -_p \nu \in C`\Theta$

Dem.

$\vdash . *311·65 . *312·12 . \supset \vdash : \text{Hp} . \nu \Theta \mu . \supset . \mu -_p \nu \in C`\Theta$ (1)

$\vdash . *311·66 . *312·15 . \supset \vdash : \text{Hp} . \mu \Theta_n \nu . \supset . \mid \text{Cnv}``(\mu -_p \nu) \in C`\Theta_n .$

[*310·16] $\supset . \mu -_p \nu \in C`\Theta$ (2)

$\vdash . (1) . (2) . \supset \vdash . \text{Prop}$

***312·23.** $\vdash : \text{Infin ax} . \mu (\Theta \cup \breve{\Theta}_n) \nu . \supset . \mu -_p \nu \in C`\Theta_n$ [*312·21·22 . *310·16]

***312·3.** $\vdash . \mu +_a \nu = (\mu +_p \nu) \cup (\mu -_p \mid \text{Cnv}``\nu)$ [(*312·02)]

***312·31.** $\vdash : \sim (\mu, \nu \in C`\Theta_g) . \supset . \mu +_a \nu = \Lambda$ [*312·3·11 . *311·1]

***312·32.** $\vdash : \text{concord}(\mu, \nu) . \supset . \mu +_a \nu = \mu +_p \nu$ [*312·3·11 . *311·15]

***312·33.** $\vdash : \sim \text{concord}(\mu, \nu) . \supset . \mu +_a \nu = \mu -_p \mid \text{Cnv}``\nu$ [*312·3 . *311·1]

***312·34.** $\vdash : \text{Infin ax} . \mu, \nu \in C`\Theta_g . \supset . \mu +_a \nu \in C`\Theta_g$
[*312·32·33·22·23 . *311·44]

***312·41.** $\vdash . \mu +_a \nu = \nu +_a \mu$

Dem.

$\vdash . *312·32 . *311·12 . \supset \vdash : \text{concord}(\mu, \nu) . \supset . \mu +_a \nu = \nu +_a \mu$ (1)

$\vdash . *312·33·21 . \supset \vdash : \sim \text{concord}(\mu, \nu) . \supset . \mu +_a \nu = \mid \text{Cnv}``(\mid \text{Cnv}``\nu -_p \mu)$

[*312·201] $= \nu -_p \mid \text{Cnv}``\mu$

[*312·33] $= \nu +_a \mu$ (2)

$\vdash . (1) . (2) . \supset \vdash . \text{Prop}$

***312·42.** $\vdash : \text{Infin ax} . \text{concord}(\lambda, \mu, \nu) . \supset . (\lambda +_p \mu) -_p (\lambda +_p \nu) = \mu -_p \nu$

Dem.

$\vdash . *311·27·42·43 . \supset \vdash :. \text{Hp} . \supset : \text{concord}(\lambda +_p \mu, \lambda +_p \nu, \lambda, \mu, \nu) :$

[*311·75] $\supset : \lambda +_p \rho = \mu . \equiv . (\lambda +_p \rho) +_p \nu = \mu +_p \nu .$

[*311·12·121] $\equiv . (\lambda +_p \nu) +_p \rho = \mu +_p \nu$ (1)

Similarly $\vdash :. \text{Hp} . \supset : \mu +_p \rho = \lambda . \equiv . (\mu +_p \nu) +_p \rho = \lambda +_p \nu$ (2)

$\vdash . (1) . (2) . *312·1 . \supset \vdash . \text{Prop}$

***312·43.** $\vdash :$ Infin ax . concord $(\lambda, \mu, \nu) . \nu (\Theta \cup \Theta_n) \mu . \supset .$

$$(\lambda +_p \mu) -_p \nu = \lambda +_p (\mu -_p \nu)$$

Dem.

$\vdash . *311·65·66 . \supset \vdash : \text{Hp} . \supset . (\exists \rho) . \rho \in C\text{‘}\Theta_g . \mu = \nu +_p \rho .$

$[*312·12·13·19] \supset . (\exists \rho) . \rho \in C\text{‘}\Theta_g . (\lambda +_p \mu) -_p \nu = \lambda +_p \rho . \mu -_p \nu = \rho : \supset \vdash . \text{Prop}$

***312·44.** $\vdash :$ Infin ax . concord $(\lambda, \mu, \nu) . \mu (\Theta \cup \Theta_n) \nu . \supset .$

$$(\lambda +_p \mu) -_p \nu = \lambda -_p (\nu -_p \mu)$$

Dem.

$\vdash . *311·65·66 . \supset \vdash : \text{Hp} . \supset . (\exists \rho) . \rho \in C\text{‘}\Theta_g . \nu = \mu +_p \rho .$

$[*312·42·19] \supset . (\exists \rho) . \rho \in C\text{‘}\Theta_g . (\lambda +_p \mu) -_p \nu = \lambda -_p \rho . \rho = \nu -_p \mu : \supset \vdash . \text{Prop}$

***312·45.** $\vdash :$ Infin ax . concord $(\lambda, \mu) . \supset . (\lambda +_p \mu) -_p \mu = \lambda +_p (\mu -_p \mu)$

Dem.

$\vdash . *312·19 . *311·43 . \supset \vdash : \text{Hp} . \supset . \mu -_p \mu = \iota\text{‘}0_q .$

$[*311·43] \qquad \supset . \lambda +_p (\mu -_p \mu) = \lambda$

$[*312·19] \qquad = (\lambda +_p \mu) -_p \mu : \supset \vdash . \text{Prop}$

***312·451.** $\vdash :$ Infin ax . concord $(\lambda, \mu, \nu) . \supset .$

$$(\lambda +_p \mu) -_p \nu = (\lambda +_a \mu) +_a | \text{Cnv}\text{“}\nu = \lambda +_a (\mu +_a | \text{Cnv}\text{“}\nu)$$

Dem.

$\vdash . *312·43 . \supset \vdash : \text{Hp} . \nu (\Theta \cup \Theta_n) \mu . \supset . (\lambda +_p \mu) -_p \nu = \lambda +_p (\mu -_p \nu)$

$[*312·33] \qquad = \lambda +_p (\mu +_a | \text{Cnv}\text{“}\nu)$

$[*312·32·12·14] \qquad = \lambda +_a (\mu +_a | \text{Cnv}\text{“}\nu) \quad (1)$

$\vdash . *312·44 . \supset \vdash : \text{Hp} . \mu (\Theta \cup \Theta_n) \nu . \supset . (\lambda +_p \mu) -_p \nu = \lambda -_p (\nu -_p \mu)$

$[*312·21] \qquad = \lambda -_p | \text{Cnv}\text{“}(\mu -_p \nu)$

$[*312·33·12·14] \qquad = \lambda +_a (\mu -_p \nu)$

$[*312·33] \qquad = \lambda +_a (\mu +_a | \text{Cnv}\text{“}\nu) \quad (2)$

$\vdash . *312·45 . \supset \vdash : \text{Hp} . \mu = \nu . \supset . (\lambda +_p \mu) -_p \nu = \lambda +_p (\mu -_p \nu)$

$[*312·33·32] \qquad = \lambda +_a (\mu +_a | \text{Cnv}\text{“}\nu) \quad (3)$

$\vdash . (1) . (2) . (3) . *312·32 . *311·43 . \supset \vdash . \text{Prop}$

***312·46.** $\vdash :$ Infin ax . concord $(\lambda, \mu) . \supset . (\lambda +_a \mu) +_a \nu = \lambda +_a (\mu +_a \nu)$

Dem.

$\vdash . *312·32 . *311·65·66·43 . \supset \vdash : \text{Hp} . \text{concord} (\lambda, \mu, \nu) . \supset .$

$$(\lambda +_a \mu) +_a \nu = (\lambda +_p \mu) +_p \nu . \lambda +_a (\mu +_a \nu) = \lambda +_p (\mu +_p \nu) \quad (1)$$

$\vdash . *312·451 . \supset$

$\vdash : \text{Hp} . \text{concord} (\lambda, \mu, | \text{Cnv}\text{“}\nu) . \supset . (\lambda +_a \mu) +_a \nu = \lambda +_a (\mu +_a \nu) \quad (2)$

$\vdash . *312·31 . \supset \vdash : \nu \sim \in C\text{‘}\Theta_g . \supset . (\lambda +_a \mu) +_a \nu = \Lambda . \lambda +_a (\mu +_a \nu) = \Lambda \quad (3)$

$\vdash . (1) . (2) . (3) . *311·121 . \supset \vdash . \text{Prop}$

∗312·461. $\vdash : \text{Infin ax} . \text{concord}(\mu, \nu) . \supset . (\lambda +_a \mu) +_a \nu = \lambda +_a (\mu +_a \nu)$

Dem.

$\vdash . ∗312·46 . \supset \vdash : \text{Hp} . \supset . (\nu +_a \mu) +_a \lambda = \nu +_a (\mu +_a \lambda)$ (1)

$\vdash . (1) . ∗312·41 . \supset \vdash . \text{Prop}$

∗312·47. $\vdash : \text{Infin ax} . \text{concord}(\lambda, \nu) . \supset . (\lambda +_a \mu) +_a \nu = \lambda +_a (\mu +_a \nu)$

Dem.

$\vdash . ∗312·461 . \supset \vdash : \text{Hp} . \supset . (\mu +_a \lambda) +_a \nu = \mu +_a (\lambda +_a \nu) .$

[∗312·41] $\supset . (\lambda +_a \mu) +_a \nu = \mu +_a (\lambda +_a \nu)$

[∗312·41] $= (\lambda +_a \nu) +_a \mu$

[∗312·46] $= \lambda +_a (\nu +_a \mu)$

[∗312·41] $= \lambda +_a (\mu +_a \nu) : \supset \vdash . \text{Prop}$

∗312·48. $\vdash : \text{Infin ax} . \supset . (\lambda +_a \mu) +_a \nu = \lambda +_a (\mu +_a \nu)$

Dem.

$\vdash . ∗312·31 . \supset$

$\vdash : \sim \{\lambda, \mu, \nu \in C‘\Theta_g\} . \supset . (\lambda +_a \mu) +_a \nu = \Lambda . \lambda +_a (\mu +_a \nu) = \Lambda$ (1)

$\vdash . ∗310·12 . \supset \vdash :. \lambda, \mu, \nu \in C‘\Theta_g . \supset : \text{concord}(\lambda, \mu) . \vee . \text{concord}(\lambda, \nu) :$

[∗312·46·47] $\supset : (\lambda +_a \mu) +_a \nu = \lambda +_a (\mu +_a \nu)$ (2)

$\vdash . (1) . (2) . \supset \vdash . \text{Prop}$

∗312·51. $\vdash : \lambda \in C‘\Theta_g . \supset . \lambda +_a \iota‘0_q = \lambda$ [∗312·32 . ∗311·43]

∗312·52. $\vdash : \text{Infin ax} . \lambda \in C‘\Theta_g . \supset . \lambda +_a |\,\text{Cnv}“\lambda = \iota‘0_q$

Dem.

$\vdash . ∗312·33 . \supset \vdash : \text{Hp} . \supset . \lambda +_a |\,\text{Cnv}“\lambda = \lambda -_p \lambda$

[∗312·191] $= \iota‘0_q : \supset \vdash . \text{Prop}$

∗312·53. $\vdash :. \text{Infin ax} . \lambda, \mu, \nu \in C‘\Theta_g . \supset : \lambda +_a \mu = \nu . \equiv . \lambda = \nu +_a |\,\text{Cnv}“\mu$ [∗312·48·51·52]

∗312·54. $\vdash : \text{Infin ax} . \lambda, \mu \in C‘\Theta_g . \supset . (\exists \sigma) . \sigma \in C‘\Theta_g . \lambda +_a \sigma = \mu$

Dem.

$\vdash . ∗312·48·51·52 . \supset \vdash : \text{Hp} . \supset . \lambda +_a (|\,\text{Cnv}“\lambda +_a \mu) = \mu$ (1)

$\vdash . ∗312·34 . \quad \supset \vdash : \text{Hp} . \supset . |\,\text{Cnv}“\lambda +_a \mu \in C‘\Theta_g$ (2)

$\vdash . (1) . (2) . \supset \vdash . \text{Prop}$

∗312·55. $\vdash :. \text{Infin ax} . \lambda, \mu, \nu \in C‘\Theta_g . \supset : \lambda +_a \mu = \lambda +_a \nu . \equiv . \mu = \nu$

Dem.

$\vdash . ∗312·41·53 . \supset \vdash :. \text{Hp} . \supset : \lambda +_a \mu = \lambda +_a \nu . \equiv . \mu = (\lambda +_a \nu) +_a |\,\text{Cnv}“\lambda .$

[∗312·41·48] $\equiv . \mu = \nu +_a (\lambda +_a |\,\text{Cnv}“\lambda) .$

[∗312·51·52] $\equiv . \mu = \nu :. \supset \vdash . \text{Prop}$

***312·56.** $\vdash :.$ Infin ax . concord $(\lambda, \mu) . \supset : \lambda \Theta_g \mu . \equiv . (\exists \sigma) . \sigma \epsilon C`\Theta . \lambda +_a \sigma = \mu$

Dem.

$\vdash .$ *311·65 . *312·32 . $\supset$

$\vdash :.$ Hp . $\lambda, \mu \epsilon C`\Theta . \supset : \lambda \Theta_g \mu . \equiv . (\exists \sigma) . \sigma \epsilon C`\Theta . \lambda +_a \sigma = \mu$ (1)

$\vdash .$ *311·66 . *310·16 . $\supset$

$\vdash :.$ Hp . $\lambda, \mu \epsilon C`\Theta_n . \supset : \lambda \Theta_g \mu . \equiv . (\exists \sigma) . \sigma \epsilon C`\Theta . \mu +_p | \text{Cnv}``\sigma = \lambda .$

[*312·53·32] $\equiv . (\exists \sigma) . \sigma \epsilon C`\Theta . \lambda +_a \sigma = \mu$ (2)

$\vdash .$ *312·51 . $\supset \vdash :.$ Hp . $\lambda = \iota`0_q . \supset : \lambda \Theta_g \mu . \equiv . (\exists \sigma) . \sigma \epsilon C`\Theta . \lambda +_a \sigma = \mu$ (3)

$\vdash .$ *312·53·51 . $\supset \vdash :.$ Hp . $\mu = \iota`0_q . \supset : \lambda \Theta_g \mu . \equiv . (\exists \sigma) . \sigma \epsilon C`\Theta . \lambda +_a \sigma = \mu$ (4)

$\vdash .$ (1) . (2) . (3) . (4) . $\supset \vdash .$ Prop

***312·57.** $\vdash :.$ Infin ax . $\lambda, \mu \epsilon C`\Theta_g . \sim$ concord $(\lambda, \mu) . \supset :$

$\lambda \Theta_g \mu . \equiv . (\exists \sigma) . \sigma \epsilon C`\Theta . \lambda +_a \sigma = \mu$

Dem.

$\vdash .$ *312·48·51·52 . $\supset \vdash : \lambda \epsilon C`\Theta_n . \mu \epsilon C`\Theta . \supset . \mu = \lambda +_a (| \text{Cnv}``\lambda +_a \mu)$ (1)

$\vdash .$ *312·32 . *311·27 . $\supset \vdash :$ Hp (1) . $\supset . (| \text{Cnv}``\lambda +_a \mu) \epsilon C`\Theta$ (2)

$\vdash .$ (1) . (2) . $\supset \vdash : \lambda \epsilon C`\Theta_n . \mu \epsilon C`\Theta . \supset . (\exists \sigma) . \sigma \epsilon C`\Theta . \lambda +_a \sigma = \mu$ (3)

$\vdash .$ *312·32 . *311·27 . *310·13 . $\supset$

$\vdash : \lambda \epsilon C`\Theta . \mu \epsilon C`\Theta_n . \supset . \sim (\exists \sigma) . \sigma \epsilon C`\Theta . \lambda +_a \sigma = \mu$ (4)

$\vdash .$ (3) . (4) . $\supset$

$\vdash :.$ Hp . $\supset : \lambda \epsilon C`\Theta_n . \mu \epsilon C`\Theta . \equiv . (\exists \sigma) . \sigma \epsilon C`\Theta . \lambda +_a \sigma = \mu :. \supset \vdash .$ Prop

***312·58.** $\vdash :.$ Infin ax . $\lambda, \mu \epsilon C`\Theta_g . \supset :$

$\lambda \Theta_g \mu . \equiv . (\exists \sigma) . \sigma \epsilon C`\Theta . \lambda +_a \sigma = \mu$ [*312·56·57]

$*313$. MULTIPLICATION OF REAL NUMBERS.

Summary of $*313$.

Multiplication of real numbers is simpler than addition, because it is not necessary to distinguish between factors of the same sign and factors of opposite signs. Thus we put

$*313\cdot01.\quad \mu \times_a \nu = \hat{X}\{\mu, \nu \in C\text{‘}\Theta_g \,.\, X \in s\text{‘}\mu \underset{,,}{\times_g}\text{‘‘}\nu\}$ Df

Thus if μ, ν are real numbers, their product is the class of products (in the sense of $*309$) of members of μ and members of ν; otherwise their product is Λ. The propositions of this number are analogous to those of previous numbers, and the proofs are as a rule analogous to those of $*311$, except in the case of the distributive law ($*313\cdot55$).

$*313\cdot01.\quad \mu \times_a \nu = \hat{X}\{\mu, \nu \in C\text{‘}\Theta_g \,.\, X \in s\text{‘}\mu \underset{,,}{\times_g}\text{‘‘}\nu\}$ Df

Proofs in this number are mostly analogous to those for addition, and are therefore often omitted.

$*313\cdot11.\quad \vdash : \sim(\mu, \nu \in C\text{‘}\Theta_g) \,.\supset .\, \mu \times_a \nu = \Lambda$

$*313\cdot12.\quad \vdash : \mu, \nu \in C\text{‘}\Theta_g \,.\supset .\, \mu \times_a \nu = s\text{‘}\mu \underset{,,}{\times_g}\text{‘‘}\nu$

$*313\cdot21.\quad \vdash : \mu, \nu \in C\text{‘}\Theta \cup \iota\text{‘}\iota\text{‘}0_q \,.\supset .\, \mu \times_a \nu = s\text{‘}\mu \underset{,,}{\times_s}\text{‘‘}\nu$

$*313\cdot22.\quad \vdash : \mu, \nu \in C\text{‘}\Theta_n \cup \iota\text{‘}\iota\text{‘}0_q \,.\supset .\, \mu \times_a \nu = s\text{‘}(|\,\mathrm{Cnv}\text{‘‘}\mu) \underset{,,}{\times_s}\text{‘‘}(|\,\mathrm{Cnv}\text{‘‘}\nu)$

$*313\cdot23.\quad \vdash : \mu \in C\text{‘}\Theta_n \,.\, \nu \in C\text{‘}\Theta \,.\supset .\, \mu \times_a \nu = |\,\mathrm{Cnv}\text{‘‘}s\text{‘}(|\,\mathrm{Cnv}\text{‘‘}\mu) \underset{,,}{\times_s}\text{‘‘}\nu$

$*313\cdot24.\quad \vdash : \mu \in C\text{‘}\Theta \,.\, \nu \in C\text{‘}\Theta_n \,.\supset .\, \mu \times_a \nu = |\,\mathrm{Cnv}\text{‘‘}s\text{‘}(\mu \underset{,,}{\times_s})\text{‘‘}|\,\mathrm{Cnv}\text{‘‘}\nu$

$*313\cdot25.\quad \vdash .\, \mu \times_a \nu = |\,\mathrm{Cnv}\text{‘‘}(|\,\mathrm{Cnv}\text{‘‘}\mu \times_a \nu) = |\,\mathrm{Cnv}\text{‘‘}\mu \times_a |\,\mathrm{Cnv}\text{‘‘}\nu$

$*313\cdot26.\quad \vdash .\, \mu \times_a |\,\mathrm{Cnv}\text{‘‘}\nu = |\,\mathrm{Cnv}\text{‘‘}\mu \times_a \nu = |\,\mathrm{Cnv}\text{‘‘}(\mu \times_a \nu)$

$*313\cdot31.\quad \vdash : \mathrm{Infin\ ax} \,.\, \xi \in C\text{‘}\Theta \,.\, X \in C\text{‘}H \,.\supset .\, X \times_g\text{‘‘}\xi \subset H\text{‘‘}X \times_g\text{‘‘}\xi$

$*313\cdot32.\quad \vdash : \mathrm{Infin\ ax} \,.\, \xi \in C\text{‘}\Theta \,.\, X \in C\text{‘}H \,.\supset .\, X \times_g\text{‘‘}\xi = H\text{‘‘}X \times_g\text{‘‘}\xi$

$*313\cdot33.\quad \vdash : \mathrm{Infin\ ax} \,.\, \xi \in C\text{‘}\Theta \,.\, X \in C\text{‘}H \,.\supset .\, X \times_g\text{‘‘}\xi \in C\text{‘}\Theta$

$*313\cdot34.\quad \vdash : \mathrm{Infin\ ax} \,.\, \xi \in C\text{‘}\Theta_n \,.\, X \in C\text{‘}H_n \,.\supset .\, X \times_g\text{‘‘}\xi \in C\text{‘}\Theta$

$*313\cdot35.\ \vdash : \text{Infin ax} . \xi \in C`\Theta . X \in C`H_n . \supset . X \times_g`` \xi \in C`\Theta_n$

$*313\cdot351.\ \vdash : \text{Infin ax} . \xi \in C`\Theta_n . X \in C`H . \supset . X \times_g`` \xi \in C`\Theta_n$

$*313\cdot36.\ \vdash : \xi \in C`\Theta_g . \supset . 0_q \times_g`` \xi = \iota`0_q$

$*313\cdot37.\ \vdash : X \in C`H_g . \supset . X \times_g`` \iota`0_q = \iota`0_q$

$*313\cdot38.\ \vdash : \text{Infin ax} . \xi \in C`\Theta_g . X \in C`H_g . \supset . X \times_g`` \xi \in C`\Theta_g$

$*313\cdot41.\ \vdash : \text{Infin ax} . \text{concord}(\mu, \nu) . \mu \neq \iota`0_q . \nu \neq \iota`0_q . \supset . \mu \times_a \nu \in C`\Theta$

$*313\cdot42.\ \vdash : \text{Infin ax} . \sim \text{concord}(\mu, \nu) . \mu, \nu \in C`\Theta_g . \supset . \mu \times_a \nu \in C`\Theta_n$

$*313\cdot43.\ \vdash :. \mu = \iota`0_q . \vee . \nu = \iota`0_q : \mu, \nu \in C`\Theta_g : \supset . \mu \times_a \nu = \iota`0_q$

$*313\cdot44.\ \vdash : \text{Infin ax} . \mu, \nu \in C`\Theta_g . \supset . \mu \times_a \nu \in C`\Theta_g$

$*313\cdot45.\ \vdash . \mu \times_a \nu = \nu \times_a \mu$

$*313\cdot46.\ \vdash : \text{Infin ax} . \supset . (\lambda \times_a \mu) \times_a \nu = \lambda \times_a (\mu \times_a \nu)$

The following propositions are concerned with the proof of the distributive law.

$*313\cdot51.\ \vdash : \text{Infin ax} . \text{concord}(\lambda, \mu, \nu) . \supset . (\nu \times_a \lambda) +_a (\nu \times_a \mu) =$
$\hat{M}[(\exists X, Y, Z, Z') . X \in \lambda . Y \in \mu . Z, Z' \in \nu . M = (Z \times_g X) +_g (Z' \times_g Y)]$
[$*313\cdot12 . *312\cdot32 . *311\cdot11 . *313\cdot41$]

$*313\cdot511.\ \vdash : \text{Infin ax} . \lambda, \mu \in C`\Theta . Z, Z' \in \mu . ZHZ' . X \in \lambda . \supset . Z \times_g \breve{Z}' \times_g X \in \lambda$

Dem.

$\vdash . *304\cdot1\cdot401 . *305\cdot14 . \supset \vdash : \text{Hp} . \supset . (Z \times_g X) H (Z' \times_g X) .$
[$*309\cdot41$] $\supset . (Z \times_g \breve{Z}' \times_g X) HX .$
[$*311\cdot58$] $\supset . Z \times_g \breve{Z}' \times_g X \in \lambda : \supset \vdash . \text{Prop}$

$*313\cdot52.\ \vdash : \text{Infin ax} . \text{concord}(\lambda, \mu, \nu) . \supset . (\nu \times_a \lambda) +_a (\nu \times_a \mu) = \nu \times_a (\lambda +_a \mu)$

Dem.

$\vdash . *313\cdot51\cdot511 . \supset \vdash : \text{Hp} . \supset .$
$(\nu \times_a \lambda) +_a (\nu \times_a \mu) = \hat{M}[(\exists X, Y, Z) . X \in \lambda . Y \in \mu . Z \in \nu . M = (Z \times_g X) +_g (Z \times_g Y)]$
[$*309\cdot37$] $= \hat{M}[(\exists X, Y, Z) . X \in \lambda . Y \in \mu . Z \in \nu . M = Z \times_g (X +_g Y)]$
[$*313\cdot12 . *312\cdot32 . *311\cdot11$] $= \nu \times_a (\lambda +_a \mu) : \supset \vdash . \text{Prop}$

$*313\cdot53.\ \vdash : \text{Infin ax} . \text{concord}(\lambda, \mu) . \sim \text{concord}(\lambda, \nu) . \nu \in C`\Theta_g . \supset .$
$(\nu \times_a \lambda) +_a (\nu \times_a \mu) = \nu \times_a (\lambda +_a \mu)$

Dem.

$\vdash . *313\cdot25 . \supset \vdash . (\lambda +_a \mu) \times_a \nu = |\,\text{Cnv}``\{(\lambda +_a \mu) \times_a |\,\text{Cnv}``\nu\}$ (1)
$\vdash . *313\cdot52 . \supset \vdash : \text{Hp} . \supset . (\lambda +_a \mu) \times_a |\,\text{Cnv}``\nu = (\lambda \times_a |\,\text{Cnv}``\nu) +_a (\mu \times_a |\,\text{Cnv}``\nu)$
[$*313\cdot26 . *311\cdot31$] $= \text{Cnv}``\{(\lambda \times_a \nu) +_a (\mu \times_a \nu)\}$ (2)
$\vdash . (1) . (2) . \supset \vdash . \text{Prop}$

***313·54.** $\vdash$: Infin ax . concord (λ, ν) . $\sim$ concord (λ, μ) . $\mu \epsilon C\text{‘}\Theta_g$. $\supset$.
$$\nu \times_a (\lambda +_a \mu) = (\nu \times_a \lambda) +_a (\nu \times_a \mu)$$

Dem.

$\vdash$. *312·33·34 . $\supset \vdash$:. Hp . $\lambda +_a \mu = \rho$. $\supset$: concord (λ, ρ) . $\vee$. concord (μ, ρ) (1)

$\vdash$. *313·52 . $\supset \vdash$: Hp (1) . concord (λ, ρ) . $\supset$.
$$(\rho \times_a \nu) +_a (|\,\text{Cnv}\text{‘‘}\mu \times_a \nu) = (\rho +_a |\,\text{Cnv}\text{‘‘}\mu) \times_a \nu$$

[*312·53] $= \lambda \times_a \nu$.

[*312·53.*313·26] $\supset . \rho \times_a \nu = (\lambda \times_a \nu) +_a (\mu \times_a \nu)$ (2)

Similarly $\vdash$: Hp (1) . concord (μ, ρ) . $\supset . \rho \times_a \nu = (\lambda \times_a \nu) +_a (\mu \times_a \nu)$ (3)

$\vdash$. (1) . (2) . (3) . $\supset \vdash$. Prop

***313·55.** $\vdash$: Infin ax . $\supset . (\nu \times_a \lambda) +_a (\nu \times_a \mu) = \nu \times_a (\lambda +_a \mu)$
[*313·52·53·54·11 . *312·31]

$*314$. REAL NUMBERS AS RELATIONS.

Summary of $*314$.

In this number we take up the definition of real numbers suggested in $*310$, namely $\dot{s}``C`\Theta_g$ instead of $C`\Theta_g$. The series of real numbers is now $\dot{s};\Theta_g$ instead of Θ_g. Everything in this number depends upon

$*310\cdot32$. $\vdash :. \mu, \nu \in C`\Theta_g . \supset : \dot{s}`\mu = \dot{s}`\nu . \equiv . \mu = \nu$

In consequence of this proposition, $\dot{s} \upharpoonright C`\Theta_g$ is a correlation of the two sorts of real numbers, and the properties of the relational sort can be immediately deduced from the propositions of previous numbers. We define addition and multiplication of relational real numbers so as to secure that, if μ, ν are real numbers of our previous sort, the arithmetical sum of $\dot{s}`\mu$ and $\dot{s}`\nu$ is $\dot{s}`(\mu +_a \nu)$ and their product is $\dot{s}`(\mu \times_a \nu)$. This is effected by putting

$*314\cdot01$. $X +_r Y = \hat{R}\hat{S}[(\exists \mu, \nu) . X = \dot{s}`\mu . Y = \dot{s}`\nu . R \{\dot{s}`(\mu +_a \nu)\} S]$ Df

with a similar definition for $X \times_r Y$. The zero of real numbers is now 0_q instead of $\iota`0_q$, and the negative of a real number X is $X \mid \text{Cnv}$. The fundamental propositions are

$*314\cdot13$. $\vdash : \mu, \nu \in C`\Theta_g . \supset . \dot{s}`\mu +_r \dot{s}`\nu = \dot{s}`(\mu +_a \nu)$

$*314\cdot14$. $\vdash : \mu, \nu \in C`\Theta_g . \supset . \dot{s}`\mu \times_r \dot{s}`\nu = \dot{s}`(\mu \times_a \nu)$

in virtue of which the arithmetical properties of relational real numbers follow at once from those of real numbers as segments.

Relational real numbers are useful in applying measurement by means of real numbers to vector-families, since it is convenient to have real numbers of the same type as ratios.

For some purposes, a somewhat different definition of real numbers as relations is more convenient. Instead of deriving our relations from Θ_g, we may derive them from $\varsigma`H_g$, *i.e.* we may consider the relations $\dot{s}``C`\varsigma`H_g$ instead of the relations $\dot{s}``C`\Theta_g$. In virtue of $*217\cdot43$, $(\varsigma`H_g) \upharpoonright (-\iota`\Lambda - \iota`C`H_g)$ is ordinally similar to Θ_g; hence the requisite properties of $\dot{s}``C`\varsigma`H_g$ follow at once.

***314·01.** $X +_r Y = \hat{R}\hat{S}\,[(\exists \mu, \nu) \,.\, X = \dot{s}`\mu \,.\, Y = \dot{s}`\nu \,.\, R\,\{\dot{s}`(\mu +_a \nu)\}\,S]$ Df

***314·02.** $X \times_r Y = \hat{R}\hat{S}\,[(\exists \mu, \nu) \,.\, X = \dot{s}`\mu \,.\, Y = \dot{s}`\nu \,.\, R\,\{\dot{s}`(\mu \times_a \nu)\}\,S]$ Df

***314·03.** $\text{♂} = (\breve{H}_n)_\epsilon \,|\, (C`H_n -) \upharpoonright \{\mathrm{D}`(H_n)_\epsilon - \iota`\Lambda - \iota`C`H_n\}$
$\qquad \dot{\cup}\, (C`H_n) \downarrow (\iota`0_q) \,\dot{\cup}\, (C`H_n \cup) \upharpoonright (\mathrm{D}`H_\epsilon - \iota`\Lambda - \iota`C`H)$ Df

***314·04.** $M +_\sigma N = \hat{R}\hat{S}\,[(\exists \mu, \nu) \,.\, M = \dot{s}`\text{♂}`\mu \,.\, N = \dot{s}`\text{♂}`\nu \,.\, R\,\{\dot{s}`\text{♂}`(\mu +_a \nu)\}\,S]$ Df

***314·05.** $M \times_\sigma N = \hat{R}\hat{S}\,[(\exists \mu, \nu) \,.\, M = \dot{s}`\text{♂}`\mu \,.\, N = \dot{s}`\text{♂}`\nu \,.\, R\,\{\dot{s}`\text{♂}`(\mu \times_a \nu)\}\,S]$ Df

***314·1.** $\vdash : \dot{\exists} \,!\, X +_r Y \,.\supset .\, X, Y \,\epsilon\, \dot{s}``C`\Theta_g$ [*312·31 . (*314·01)]

***314·11.** $\vdash :.\, \text{Infin ax} \,.\supset :\, \dot{\exists} \,!\, X +_r Y \,.\equiv .\, X, Y \,\epsilon\, \dot{s}``C`\Theta_g$ [*314·1 . *312·34]

***314·12.** $\vdash :.\, \text{Infin ax} \,.\supset :\, \dot{\exists} \,!\, X \times_r Y \,.\equiv .\, X, Y \,\epsilon\, \dot{s}``C`\Theta_g$

***314·13.** $\vdash : \mu, \nu \,\epsilon\, C`\Theta_g \,.\supset .\, \dot{s}`\mu +_r \dot{s}`\nu = \dot{s}`(\mu +_a \nu)$

Dem.

$\vdash .\, *314{\cdot}1 \,.\, (*314{\cdot}01) \,.\supset \vdash : R\,\{\dot{s}`\mu +_r \dot{s}`\nu\}\,S \,.\equiv .$
$\qquad (\exists \rho, \sigma) \,.\, \rho, \sigma \,\epsilon\, C`\Theta_g \,.\, \dot{s}`\mu = \dot{s}`\rho \,.\, \dot{s}`\nu = \dot{s}`\sigma \,.\, R\,\{\dot{s}`(\rho +_a \sigma)\}\,S$ (1)

$\vdash .\, (1) \,.\, *310{\cdot}32 \,.\supset \vdash .\, \text{Prop}$

***314·14.** $\vdash : \mu, \nu \,\epsilon\, C`\Theta_g \,.\supset .\, \dot{s}`\mu \times_r \dot{s}`\nu = \dot{s}`(\mu \times_a \nu)$

***314·2.** $\vdash : R \,\epsilon\, \dot{s}``(C`\Theta_g - \iota`\iota`0_q) \,.\supset .\, \dot{\exists} \,!\, R \upharpoonright \text{Rel num}$ [*310·31]

***314·21.** $\vdash :.\, \text{Infin ax} \,.\supset :\, R, S \,\epsilon\, \dot{s}``C`\Theta_g \,.\equiv .\, R +_r S \,\epsilon\, \dot{s}``C`\Theta_g \,.$
$\qquad \equiv .\, R \times_r S \,\epsilon\, \dot{s}``C`\Theta_g$

Dem.

$\vdash .\, *314{\cdot}13{\cdot}14 \,.\, *312{\cdot}34 \,.\, *313{\cdot}44 \,.\supset$
$\vdash : \text{Hp} \,.\, R, S \,\epsilon\, \dot{s}``C`\Theta_g \,.\supset .\, R +_r S, R \times_r S \,\epsilon\, \dot{s}``C`\Theta_g$ (1)
$\vdash .\, (1) \,.\, *314{\cdot}11{\cdot}12 \,.\supset \vdash .\, \text{Prop}$

***314·22.** $\vdash : R \,\epsilon\, \dot{s}``C`\Theta_g \,.\supset .\, R +_r 0_q = R \,.\, R \times_r 0_q = 0_q$

Dem.

$\vdash .\, *314{\cdot}13{\cdot}14 \,.\supset$
$\vdash : \mu \,\epsilon\, C`\Theta_g \,.\supset .\, \dot{s}`\mu +_r 0_q = \dot{s}`(\mu +_a \iota`0_q) \,.\, \dot{s}`\mu \times_r 0_q = \dot{s}`(\mu \times_a \iota`0_q) \,.$
$[*312{\cdot}51 . *313{\cdot}43] \supset .\, \dot{s}`\mu +_r 0_q = \dot{s}`\mu \,.\, \dot{s}`\mu \times_r 0_q = 0_q : \supset \vdash .\, \text{Prop}$

***314·23.** $\vdash : \text{Infin ax} \,.\, R \,\epsilon\, \dot{s}``C`\Theta_g \,.\supset .\, R +_r R \,|\, \text{Cnv} = 0_q$

Dem.

$\vdash .\, *314{\cdot}13 \,.\supset \vdash : \mu \,\epsilon\, C`\Theta_g \,.\supset .\, \dot{s}`\mu +_r \dot{s}`|\,\text{Cnv}``\mu = \dot{s}`(\mu +_a |\,\text{Cnv}``\mu) \,.$
$[*43{\cdot}421] \qquad \supset .\, \dot{s}`\mu +_r (\dot{s}`\mu)\,|\,\text{Cnv} = \dot{s}`(\mu +_a |\,\text{Cnv}``\mu)$
$[*312{\cdot}52] \qquad\qquad = 0_q : \supset \vdash .\, \text{Prop}$

***314·24.** $\vdash . R +_r S = S +_r R$ [*312·41 . (*314·01)]

***314·25.** $\vdash . R \times_r S = S \times_r R$ [*313·45 . (*314·02)]

***314·26.** $\vdash : \text{Infin ax} . \supset . (R +_r S) +_r T = R +_r (S +_r T)$

Dem.

$$\vdash . *314\cdot13 . \supset \vdash : \text{Hp} . \rho, \sigma, \tau \in C\text{‘}\Theta_g . R = \dot{s}\text{‘}\rho . S = \dot{s}\text{‘}\sigma . T = \dot{s}\text{‘}\tau . \supset .$$
$$(R +_r S) +_r T = \dot{s}\text{‘}\{(\rho +_a \sigma) +_a \tau\}$$
$$[*312\cdot48] \quad = \dot{s}\text{‘}\{\rho +_a (\sigma +_a \tau)\}$$
$$[*314\cdot13] \quad = R +_r (S +_r T) \qquad (1)$$
$$\vdash . *314\cdot11\cdot21 . \supset$$
$$\vdash : \sim(\exists \rho, \sigma, \tau) . \rho, \sigma, \tau \in C\text{‘}\Theta_g . R = \dot{s}\text{‘}\rho . S = \dot{s}\text{‘}\sigma . T = \dot{s}\text{‘}\tau . \supset .$$
$$(R +_r S) +_r T = \dot{\Lambda} . R +_r (S +_r T) = \dot{\Lambda} \qquad (2)$$
$$\vdash . (1) . (2) . \supset \vdash . \text{Prop}$$

***314·27.** $\vdash : \text{Infin ax} . \supset . (R \times_r S) \times_r T = R \times_r (S \times_r T)$
[*314·14 . *313·46 . *314·12·21]

***314·28.** $\vdash : \text{Infin ax} . \supset . (R \times_r S) +_r (R \times_r T) = R \times_r (S +_r T)$

Dem.

$$\vdash . *314\cdot13\cdot14 . \supset \vdash : \text{Hp} . \rho, \sigma\, \tau \in C\text{‘}\Theta_g . R = \dot{s}\text{‘}\rho . S = \dot{s}\text{‘}\sigma . T = \dot{s}\text{‘}\tau . \supset .$$
$$(R \times_r S) +_r (R \times_r T) = \dot{s}\text{‘}(\rho \times_a \sigma) +_r \dot{s}\text{‘}(\rho \times_a \tau)$$
$$[*314\cdot21\cdot13] \quad = \dot{s}\text{‘}\{(\rho \times_a \sigma) +_a (\rho \times_a \tau)\}$$
$$[*313\cdot55] \quad = \dot{s}\text{‘}\{\rho \times_a (\sigma +_a \tau)\}$$
$$[*314\cdot21\cdot14] \quad = \dot{s}\text{‘}\rho \times_r \dot{s}\text{‘}(\sigma +_a \tau)$$
$$[*314\cdot13] \quad = \dot{s}\text{‘}\rho \times_r (\dot{s}\text{‘}\sigma +_r \dot{s}\text{‘}\tau)$$
$$[\text{Hp}] \quad = R \times_r (S +_r T) \qquad (1)$$
$$\vdash . *314\cdot21\cdot11\cdot12 . \supset$$
$$\vdash . \sim(\exists \rho, \sigma, \tau) . \rho, \sigma, \tau \in C\text{‘}\Theta_g . R = \dot{s}\text{‘}\rho . S = \dot{s}\text{‘}\sigma . T = \dot{s}\text{‘}\tau . \supset .$$
$$(R \times_r S) +_r (R \times_r T) = \dot{\Lambda} . R \times_r (S +_r T) = \dot{\Lambda} \qquad (2)$$
$$\vdash . (1) . (2) . \supset \vdash . \text{Prop}$$

***314·4.** $\vdash : \text{Infin ax} . \supset . ♂ \in \{(\varsigma\text{‘}H_g) \upharpoonleft (-\iota\text{‘}\Lambda - \iota\text{‘}C\text{‘}H_g)\} \,\overline{\text{smor}}\, \Theta_g$
[*217·43 . *304·31·282·23 . *307·41·44·46·25 . (*310·01·011·02·03)]

***314·41.** $\vdash . \dot{s} \upharpoonright (C\text{‘}\varsigma\text{‘}H_g) \in 1 \to 1$ [The proof is analogous to that of *310·32]

***314·42.** $\vdash : \text{Infin ax} . \supset . \dot{s}\,;♂\,;\Theta_g \text{ smor } \Theta_g$ [*314·4·41]

***314·5.** $\vdash :. \text{Infin ax} . \supset :$
$$\dot{\exists} \,!\, M +_\sigma N . \equiv . \dot{\exists} \,!\, M \times_\sigma N . \equiv . M, N \in \dot{s}\text{‘‘}(\text{D}\text{‘}\varsigma\text{‘}H_g - \iota\text{‘}\Lambda)$$
[*312·34 . *313·44 . *314·42 . (*314·04·05)]

***314·51.** $\vdash : \text{Infin ax} . \mu, \nu \in C\text{‘}\Theta_g . \supset .$
$$\dot{s}\text{‘}♂\text{‘}\mu +_\sigma \dot{s}\text{‘}♂\text{‘}\nu = \dot{s}\text{‘}♂\text{‘}(\mu +_a \nu) . \dot{s}\text{‘}♂\text{‘}\mu \times_\sigma \dot{s}\text{‘}♂\text{‘}\nu = \dot{s}\text{‘}♂\text{‘}(\mu \times_a \nu)$$
[*314·42 . (*314·04·05)]

The properties of $M +_\sigma N$ and $M \times_\sigma N$ result from this proposition exactly as those of $X +_r Y$ and $X \times_r Y$ result from *314·13·14.

SECTION B.

VECTOR-FAMILIES.

Summary of Section B.

The present Section is concerned with the theory of magnitude, so far as this can be developed without measurement. Measurement—*i.e.* the application of ratios and real numbers to magnitudes—will be dealt with in Section C; for the present, we shall confine ourselves to those properties of magnitude which are presupposed in measurement. But throughout this Section, measurement is the goal: the hypotheses introduced and the propositions proved will be such as are relevant to the possibility of measurement.

We conceive a magnitude as a vector, *i.e.* as an operation, *i.e.* as a descriptive function in the sense of ∗30. Thus for example, we shall so define our terms that 1 gramme would not be a magnitude, but the difference between 2 grammes and 1 gramme would be a magnitude, *i.e.* the relation "+1 gramme" would be a magnitude. On the other hand a centimetre and a second will both be magnitudes according to our definition, because distances in space and time are vectors. It will be remembered that we defined ratios as relations between relations; hence if ratios are to hold between magnitudes, magnitudes must be taken as relations.

We demand of a vector (1) that it shall be a one-one relation, (2) that it shall be capable of indefinite repetition, *i.e.* that if the vector takes us from a to b, there shall always be a point c such that the vector takes us from b to c. If R is the vector, the point to which it takes us from a is R‘a; thus the above requisite is expressed by "$\mathrm{E} ! R‘a \,.\supset_a .\, \mathrm{E} ! R‘R‘a$," *i.e.* by "$\mathrm{D}‘R \subset \mathrm{Cl}‘R$." It will be observed that the points which are starting-points of the vector form the class $\mathrm{Cl}‘R$, *i.e.* the class of possible arguments to R considered as a descriptive function, while the points which are the end-points of the vector form the class $\mathrm{D}‘R$, *i.e.* the class of values of R considered as a descriptive function. Since $\mathrm{D}‘R \subset \mathrm{Cl}‘R$, we have $\mathrm{Cl}‘R = C‘R$; thus the field of the vector consists of all points from which the vector can start. By assuming $\text{D}‘R \subset \text{Ɑ}‘R$, we exclude magnitudes of kinds which have a definite maximum, unless they are circular, like the angles at a point or the distances on an elliptic straight line; but, except when they are circular, such magnitudes are of little importance.

According to what has just been said, if R is a vector whose field is α, we have

$$R \epsilon 1 \rightarrow 1 \,.\, \text{Ɑ}‘R = \alpha \,.\, \text{D}‘R \subset \alpha.$$

A relation which fulfils this hypothesis is called a "correspondence" of α, because it makes a part of α correspond with α. The class of correspondences of α we denote by "$\text{cr}‘\alpha$," which is the cardinal correlative of "$\text{cror}‘P$," defined in $*208$. Thus we put

$$\text{cr}‘\alpha = (1 \rightarrow 1) \cap \overleftarrow{\text{Ɑ}}‘\alpha \cap \breve{\text{D}}‘‘\text{Cl}‘\alpha \quad \text{Df.}$$

We proceed next to define a "vector-family of α." This we define as an existent sub-class of $\text{cr}‘\alpha$ such that, if R and S are any two members of it, $R \,|\, S = S \,|\, R$. We define a class of relations as "Abelian" when the relative product of any two members of the class is commutative, *i.e.* we put

$$\text{Abel} = \hat{\kappa}\,(R, S \epsilon \kappa \,.\, \supset_{R,S} .\, R \,|\, S = S \,|\, R) \quad \text{Df.}$$

Thus a vector-family of α is an existent Abelian sub-class of $\text{cr}‘\alpha$, *i.e.* writing "$\text{fm}‘\alpha$" for "vector-family of α," we put

$$\text{fm}‘\alpha = \text{Abel} \cap \text{Cl ex}‘\text{cr}‘\alpha \quad \text{Df.}$$

The class of vector-families is then defined as everything which is a vector-family of some α, *i.e.* we put

$$FM = s‘\text{D}‘\text{fm} \quad \text{Df.}$$

Thus a vector-family is an existent Abelian class of one-one relations which all have the same converse domain, and all have their domains contained in this common converse domain. If κ is a vector-family, the common converse domain is $\breve{\iota}‘\text{Ɑ}‘‘\kappa$, which is identical with $s‘\text{Ɑ}‘‘\kappa$, and will be called the "field" of the family. Thus we have

$$\vdash :\, \kappa \epsilon FM \,.\equiv.\, \kappa \epsilon \text{Abel} \,.\, \kappa \subset 1 \rightarrow 1 \,.\, \text{Ɑ}‘‘\kappa \epsilon 1 \,.\, s‘\text{D}‘‘\kappa \subset s‘\text{Ɑ}‘‘\kappa.$$

A vector-family may be regarded as a kind of magnitude. In order to render measurement possible, we require various hypotheses as to the nature of the family. Measurement within a given family κ is obtained by limiting the fields of ratios to κ, *i.e.* by considering $X \upharpoonright \kappa$ where X is a ratio, or $Z \upharpoonright \kappa$ where Z is a relational real number of the kind defined in $*314$. In order to make measurement possible, we wish κ to be such that, if X is a ratio, $X \upharpoonright \kappa$ shall be one-one; again, if R, S, T are members of κ, and R has the ratio X to S, while S has the ratio Y to T, we wish R to have the ratio $X \times_s Y$ to T, *i.e.* we wish to have

$$X \upharpoonright \kappa \,|\, Y \upharpoonright \kappa \in (X \times_s Y) \upharpoonright \kappa\,;$$

again, if R has the ratio X to T, and S has the ratio Y to T, we wish $R \mid S$ (which represents the "sum" of R and S) to have the ratio $X +_s Y$ to T, *i.e.* we wish to have

$$(X \upharpoonright \kappa`T) \mid (Y \upharpoonright \kappa`T) \subset (X +_s Y) \upharpoonright \kappa`T.$$

The above and other similar properties will be proved, with suitable hypotheses, in Section C; for the present, we shall proceed with the theory of vector-families without explicit regard to measurement.

The first and most important hypothesis as to a family which we consider is the hypothesis that it is "connected," *i.e.* that there is at least one member of its field from which we can reach any member of the field by a vector belonging to the family or by the converse of a vector belonging to the family. Such a member of the field of κ we shall call a "connected point" of κ; the class of such points will be denoted by "$\text{conx}`\kappa$"; the definition is

$$\text{conx}`\kappa = s`\text{C}``\kappa \cap \hat{a}(\overrightarrow{\dot{s}`\kappa}`a \cup \overleftarrow{\dot{s}`\kappa}`a = s`\text{C}``\kappa) \quad \text{Df.}$$

It will be observed that $\overrightarrow{\dot{s}`\kappa}`a$ are the points to which there is a vector from a, while $\overleftarrow{\dot{s}`\kappa}`a$ are the points from which there is a vector to a. The definition states that these two classes together make up the whole field of the family. We define a connected family as one which has at least one connected point, *i.e.* we put

$$FM\,\text{conx} = FM \cap \hat{\kappa}(\exists\,!\,\text{conx}`\kappa) \quad \text{Df.}$$

The properties of connected families are many and important. Among these may be mentioned the following: If κ is a connected family, the logical product of any two different members of κ is null, *i.e.* if $P, Q \in \kappa \,.\, P \neq Q$, then $P \dot{\cap} Q = \dot{\Lambda}$, or, what comes to the same thing, if $P, Q \in \kappa$, and if we ever have $P`x = Q`x$, then $P = Q$; if $P \in \kappa$, all the powers of P are either members of κ or the converses of members; if $P, Q \in \kappa$, then $P \mid Q$ is either a member of κ or the converse of a member. A connected family may not form a group, *i.e.* we do not necessarily have

$$P, Q \in \kappa \,.\, \supset_{P,Q} .\, P \mid Q \in \kappa,$$

but we shall show at a later stage (*354) that a group can be derived from a connected family κ by merely adding to it the converses of those members of κ (if any) whose domains are equal to their converse domains. The result of this addition is to give us a connected family which is a group.

Another important property of a connected family κ is that $I \upharpoonright s`\text{C}``\kappa$ is always a member of it. $I \upharpoonright s`\text{C}``\kappa$ is the zero vector. In a connected family, every vector except $I \upharpoonright s`\text{C}``\kappa$ is contained in diversity. For many purposes, the class of vectors excluding $I \upharpoonright s`\text{C}``\kappa$ is important. We therefore put

$$\kappa_\partial = \kappa - \text{Rl}`I \quad \text{Df.}$$

In the study of a vector-family κ, an important derived class of relations is the class of all relations of the form $\breve{R} | S$, where $R, S \epsilon \kappa$. The operation $\breve{R} | S$ consists of an S-step forward, followed by an R-step backward; that is to say, if $\breve{R}`S`a$ exists, it is obtained by moving a distance S forward from a to $S`a$, and then a distance $R$ backward from $S`a$ to $\breve{R}`S`a$. The class of such relations as $\breve{R} | S$, where $R, S \epsilon \kappa$, we call κ_ι; *i.e.* we put

$$\kappa_\iota = s`(\text{Cnv}``\kappa) \mid_{\prime\prime} ``\kappa \quad \text{Df.}$$

The class κ_ι will have different properties according to the nature of κ. We may distinguish three cases:

(1) The field of κ may have a first term, *i.e.* there may be a member of $s`\text{Ɑ}``\kappa$ which is not a member of $s`\text{D}``\kappa_\partial$. This case is illustrated, *e.g.* by a family of distances from left to right on the portion of a given line not lying to the left of a given point. This given point will then belong to $s`\text{Ɑ}``\kappa$, since there are vectors which start from it, but it will not belong to $s`\text{D}``\kappa_\partial$, since there are no vectors which end at it except the zero vector. A connected point a which belongs to $s`\text{Ɑ}``\kappa$ but not to $s`\text{D}``\kappa_\partial$ is called the "initial" point, and a family which has an initial point is called an "initial" family. A family cannot have more than one initial point. Thus we put

$$\text{init}`\kappa = \breve{\iota}`(\text{conx}`\kappa - s`\text{D}``\kappa_\partial) \quad \text{Df},$$

$$FM\,\text{init} = FM \cap \text{Ɑ}`\text{init} \quad \text{Df.}$$

(2) It may happen that, even if κ is not an initial family, none of the converses of members of κ_∂ are members of κ. (If κ is an initial family, this must happen.) This case is illustrated by the case of all distances towards the right on a straight line. It is also illustrated by the family of vectors of the form $(+_s X) \upharpoonright C`H$, where $X \epsilon C`H'$. In this case, as in (1), it is possible, by adding suitable hypotheses, to secure that $\dot{s}`\kappa_\partial$ shall be a series. This case divides into two, which are illustrated by the above two instances: it may happen, as in our first instance, that the domain of a vector is always equal to its converse domain, *i.e.* $\text{D}``\kappa = \text{Ɑ}``\kappa$; or it may happen, as in our second instance, that the domain is only part of the converse domain. (The domain of $(+_s X) \upharpoonright C`H$ consists of all ratios greater than X.)

(3) It may happen that κ_∂ contains pairs of vectors which are each other's converses. In this case, it is obvious that $\dot{s}`\kappa_\partial$ cannot be serial, since $R, \breve{R} \epsilon \kappa_\partial \,.\supset.\, \breve{R} | R = I \upharpoonright s`\text{Ɑ}``\kappa \,.\, \breve{R} | R \in (\dot{s}`\kappa_\partial)^2$, so that $(\dot{s}`\kappa_\partial)^2$ is not contained in diversity (except in the trivial case $\kappa = \iota`\dot{\Lambda}$).

In considering κ_ι, we do not at first explicitly introduce any of the above possibilities, but it is necessary to bear them in mind in order to realize the purpose of the propositions proved concerning κ_ι. If L is a member of κ_ι, and $L = \breve{R} | S$, where $R, S \in \kappa$, then if a is a connected point, and $L‘a$ exists, it follows that there is a member T of $\kappa \cup \text{Cnv}“\kappa$ such that $L‘a = T‘a$. It is easy to deduce from this that $L = T$, hence $L \in \kappa \cup \text{Cnv}“\kappa$. The same holds if $\breve{L}‘a$ exists. Hence if $E ! L‘a \,.\, \text{v} \,.\, E ! \breve{L}‘a$, *i.e.* if $a \in C‘L$, L is a member of $\kappa \cup \text{Cnv}“\kappa$. Thus if a belongs to the field of every member of κ_ι, we shall have $\kappa_\iota = \kappa \cup \text{Cnv}“\kappa$. We say that a family "has connexity" (not to be confounded with "being connected") if $\exists ! \text{conx}‘\kappa \cap p‘C“\kappa_\iota$; thus we put

$$FM\,\text{connex} = FM \cap \hat{\kappa}\,(\exists ! \text{conx}‘\kappa \cap p‘C“\kappa_\iota) \quad \text{Df}$$

and by what has just been said we have

$$\vdash : \kappa \in FM\,\text{connex} \,.\, \supset .\, \kappa_\iota = \kappa \cup \text{Cnv}“\kappa.$$

We also have $\qquad \vdash : \kappa \in FM\,\text{connex} \,.\, \supset .\, \dot{s}‘\kappa_\partial \in \text{connex}$

and $\qquad \vdash :. \,\kappa \in FM\,\text{conx} \,.\, \supset : \kappa \in FM\,\text{connex} \,.\, \equiv .\, \dot{s}‘\kappa_\partial \in \text{connex}.$

It is these propositions that justify the notation "FM connex."

It is obvious that we shall have $\exists ! p‘C“\kappa_\iota$ if $D“\kappa = \text{Cl}“\kappa$, unless $\kappa = \iota‘\dot{\Lambda}$.

Some illustrations will serve to make clearer the nature of the hypothesis $\exists ! p‘C“\kappa_\iota$. This hypothesis states that there is at least one term a in the field of κ such that, if R, S are any two members of κ, we can either take an R-step forward from a, followed by an S-step backward, or we can take an S-step forward followed by an R-step backward. Suppose, for example, that our family consists of all vectors of the form $(+_c \mu) \restriction \text{NC induct}$, where $\mu \in \text{NC induct}$. Then if R is the operation of adding μ, and S is the operation of adding ν, $\breve{R} | S$ is the operation of adding $\nu -_c \mu$ if $\nu > \mu$, and is the operation of subtracting $\mu -_c \nu$ if $\mu > \nu$. In the former case $\breve{R} | S \in \kappa$, while in the latter case $\breve{S} | R \in \kappa$. In the former case, if ϖ is any inductive cardinal, $(\breve{R} | S)‘\varpi = \nu -_c \mu +_c \varpi$; in the latter case, $(\breve{S} | R)‘\varpi = \mu -_c \nu +_c \varpi$. Thus in either case $\varpi \in C‘(\breve{R} | S)$. Thus the family in question has connexity, and $\kappa_\iota = \kappa \cup \text{Cnv}“\kappa$.

But now consider the family consisting of all vectors of the form $(\times_c \mu) \restriction (\text{NC induct} - \iota‘0)$, where $\mu \in \text{NC induct} - \iota‘0$. This is an initial family, its initial point being 1. But it does not have connexity. If $R = (\times_c \mu) \restriction (\text{NC induct} - \iota‘0)$ and $S = (\times_c \nu) \restriction (\text{NC induct} - \iota‘\Lambda)$, $\breve{R} | S$ is the operation of multiplying by ν and dividing by μ, with its field confined to inductive cardinals other than 0. If ν is prime to μ, this relation has only multiples of μ in its converse domain and only multiples of ν in its domain. Hence its field consists of multiples of μ together with multiples of ν. Thus no member of κ_ι except $I \restriction s‘\text{Cl}“\kappa$, *i.e.* $(\times_c 1) \restriction (\text{NC induct} - \iota‘0)$, has the whole of $s‘\text{Cl}“\kappa$ for its field, and there is no number which belongs to the field of every member of κ_ι. The above family may be usefully borne in mind in considering κ_ι, since it affords good illustrations of most of the general theorems concerning κ_ι.

If κ is any family except ι'Λ, any finite number of members of κ_ι have an existent relative product, and their converse domains have an existent logical product. If κ is a connected family, any two members L, M of κ_ι whose logical product exists, *i.e.* for which $(\exists y) . L\text{‘}y = M\text{‘}y$, are identical, and if x, y are any two members of $s\text{‘}\text{C}\text{‘‘}\kappa$, there is just one member of κ_ι such that $x = L\text{‘}y$. If $M \epsilon \kappa_\iota$ and P is a power of M, there is some member L of κ_ι such that $P \subset L$. But P is not in general itself a member of κ_ι. For the application of ratio, the member of κ_ι which contains P is important. We call it the "representative" of P. The general definition of a representative is

$$\text{rep}_\kappa\text{‘}P = \dot{s}\text{‘}(\kappa_\iota \cap \overleftarrow{\subset}\text{‘}P) \quad \text{Df.}$$

In a connected family, $\kappa_\iota \cap \overleftarrow{\subset}\text{‘}P$ cannot have more than one member; hence if there is any member of κ_ι which contains P, that member is $\text{rep}_\kappa\text{‘}P$, and if there is no member of κ_ι which contains P, $\text{rep}_\kappa\text{‘}P = \dot{\Lambda}$.

If $\breve{P} \mid Q$ is any member of κ_ι (where $P, Q \epsilon \kappa$), we shall have

$$\text{rep}_\kappa\text{‘}(\breve{P} \mid Q)^\rho = \breve{P}^\rho \mid Q^\rho ;$$

and if $L, M \epsilon \kappa_\iota$, we shall have

$$\text{rep}_\kappa\text{‘}(L \mid M)^\rho = \text{rep}_\kappa\text{‘}(L^\rho \mid M^\rho) = \text{rep}_\kappa\text{‘}\{(\text{rep}_\kappa\text{‘}L^\rho) \mid (\text{rep}_\kappa\text{‘}M^\rho)\}.$$

These two formulae are the most useful in determining representatives.

In order to apply the above theory to the measurement of vectors, it is necessary to distinguish between open and cyclic families. An open family is one in which, if $M \epsilon \kappa_\iota - \text{Rl}\text{‘}I$, $M_{\text{po}} \subset J$, *i.e.* one in which no number of repetitions of a non-zero member of κ_ι will bring us back to our starting-point. If this condition fails, as in the case of angles, or distances on the elliptic straight line, the problem of measurement is more complicated, since, if θ is a measure of an angle, so is $2\nu\pi + \theta$ for any integral ν. The case of cyclic families will be considered in Section D; for the present, we proceed to consider open families, and we shall still be concerned almost exclusively with open families in Section C. It should be observed that in cyclic families, as we shall define them, members of κ_∂ return into themselves, whereas in open families, not merely no member of κ_∂, but no member of $\kappa_\iota - \text{Rl}\text{‘}I$, returns into itself. In most of the families that naturally occur, it happens either that no member of $\kappa_\iota - \text{Rl}\text{‘}I$ returns into itself, or that there are members of κ_∂ which do so. But there is no logical necessity in this, as the following instance shows: Consider the family consisting of positive and negative integral multipliers other than -1, with their fields confined to positive and negative integers other than -1. Then 1 is a connected point of this family, in fact the initial point. Multiplication by -1 is a member of κ_ι, since it can be obtained by multiplying by any integer μ and then dividing by $-\mu$. Also the square of multiplication by -1 is contained in identity, and is the zero vector of our family. Hence there is a member of $\kappa_\iota - \text{Rl}'I$ whose square is contained in identity, although no power of any member of κ_∂ is contained in identity.

In order to avoid brackets, we put

$$\kappa_{\iota\partial} = (\kappa_\iota)_\partial \quad \text{Df},$$

i.e.

$$\kappa_{\iota\partial} = \kappa_\iota - \text{Rl}'I.$$

Then the definition of open families is

$$FM\,\text{ap} = FM \cap \hat{\kappa}\,(s'\text{Pot}''\kappa_{\iota\partial} \subset \text{Rl}'J) \quad \text{Df.}$$

Hence $\quad \vdash :. \kappa \in FM\,\text{ap} \,.\equiv : \kappa \in FM : M \in \kappa_{\iota\partial} \,.\supset_M .\, M_{\text{po}} \Subset J.$

It will be observed that if κ is an open family, κ_ι is contained in Rel num id (cf. $*300$), and $\kappa_{\iota\partial} \subset$ Rel num. Hence if $M \in \kappa_{\iota\partial}$, $M^\nu = M_\nu$ (cf. $*121$), and the propositions on intervals in $*121$ become available. Also if $M \in \kappa_{\iota\partial}$, and $a \in s'\text{C}''\kappa$, we have

$$\breve{M} \upharpoonright \overrightarrow{M_*}'a \in \text{Prog} \,.\, \breve{M}_{\text{po}} \upharpoonright \overrightarrow{M_*}'a \in \omega.$$

The chief use of these facts is to show that the existence of open families implies the axiom of infinity and the existence of $\aleph_0$. Hence as applied to open families, the theory of ratio undergoes the very great simplification which results from the axiom of infinity.

If κ is open and connected, and $L, M \in \kappa_\iota$, and σ is any inductive cardinal other than 0, we shall have $L = M$ if $L^\sigma = M^\sigma$ or $\text{rep}_\kappa{}'L^\sigma = \text{rep}_\kappa{}'M^\sigma$ or $\dot{\exists} ! L^\sigma \dot{\cap} M^\sigma$. If ρ, τ are also inductive cardinals other than 0, we shall have $\text{rep}_\kappa{}'L^\rho = \text{rep}_\kappa{}'M^\sigma$ if $L^{\rho \times_c \tau} = M^{\sigma \times_c \tau}$, or if $\text{rep}_\kappa{}'L^{\rho \times_c \tau} = \text{rep}_\kappa{}'M^{\sigma \times_c \tau}$, or if $\dot{\exists} ! L^{\rho \times_c \tau} \dot{\cap} M^{\sigma \times_c \tau}$. We have in fact

$$\text{rep}_\kappa{}'L^\rho = \text{rep}_\kappa{}'M^\sigma \,.\equiv .\, \dot{\exists} ! L^\rho \dot{\cap} M^\sigma$$

$$\equiv .\, \dot{\exists} ! L^{\rho \times_c \tau} \dot{\cap} M^{\sigma \times_c \tau}$$

and $\quad \text{rep}_\kappa{}'M^\rho = \text{rep}_\kappa{}'M^\sigma \,.\equiv .\, M^\rho = M^\sigma \,.\equiv .\, \rho = \sigma.$

On applying the definition of ratio ($*303{\cdot}01$), we see from the above propositions that, with the above hypothesis,

$$M(\rho/\sigma)N \,.\equiv .\, \dot{\exists} ! M^\sigma \dot{\cap} N^\rho \,.\equiv :.\, \text{rep}_\kappa{}'M^\sigma = \text{rep}_\kappa{}'N^\rho,$$

while if R, T are members of κ,

$$R(\rho/\sigma)S \,.\equiv .\, R^\sigma = S^\rho.$$

Further, we have, in virtue of the above propositions,

$$\dot{\exists} ! L^\sigma \dot{\cap} M^\rho \,.\, \dot{\exists} ! L^\nu \dot{\cap} M^\mu \,.\supset .\, \mu \times_c \sigma = \nu \times_c \rho,$$

whence $\quad X, Y \in C'H' \,.\, \dot{\exists} ! X \upharpoonright \kappa_{\iota\partial} \dot{\cap} Y \upharpoonright \kappa_{\iota\partial} \,.\supset .\, X = Y.$

These propositions, together with

$$X \epsilon C\text{‘}H . \supset . X \upharpoonright \kappa_\iota \epsilon 1 \to 1,$$

belong to Section C. They are mentioned here as showing why the propositions of this Section are useful in connection with measurement.

We next proceed to consider serial families, which are those in which $\dot{s}\text{‘}\kappa_\partial$ is an existent serial relation. For this purpose we require the definition of "*FM* connex" already given, and also the definition of "transitive" families. We define a as a "transitive point" of κ if

$$(\dot{s}\text{‘}\kappa_\partial)\text{‘‘}\overrightarrow{\dot{s}\text{‘}\kappa_\partial}\text{‘}a \subset \overrightarrow{\dot{s}\text{‘}\kappa_\partial}\text{‘}a,$$

i.e. if any point which can be reached from a in two non-null steps can also be reached in one non-null step. We define a family as transitive when it has at least one transitive point. If $\kappa \epsilon FM$ conx, the hypothesis that κ is transitive is equivalent to the hypothesis that κ_∂ forms a group, and implies that κ forms a group. We define a serial family as one which is transitive and has connexity, *i.e.* we put

$$FM\,\text{sr} = FM\,\text{trs} \cap FM\,\text{connex} \quad \text{Df.}$$

Then if $\kappa \epsilon FM$ sr, $\dot{s}\text{‘}\kappa_\partial$ is a serial relation, so that the points of the field of κ are arranged in a series by means of relations of distance.

When a family is serial, the vectors also can be arranged in a series, by means of a relation which may be regarded as that of greater and less. After a short number on initial families (explained above), we proceed to the consideration of greater and less (as it may be called) among vectors. We may call a point y "earlier" than a point z when there is a non-null vector which goes from y to z, *i.e.* when $z\,(\dot{s}\text{‘}\kappa_\partial)\,y$. If $M, N \epsilon \kappa_\iota$, we then say that N is "less" than M if the N-step from some point x takes us to an earlier point than the M-step. Writing V_κ for "greater than" among members of κ_ι, our definition is

$$V_\kappa = \hat{M}\hat{N}\,\{M, N \epsilon \kappa_\iota : (\exists x) . (M\text{‘}x)\,(\dot{s}\text{‘}\kappa_\partial)\,(N\text{‘}x)\} \quad \text{Df.}$$

For the same relation confined to members of κ, we use the notation U_κ; thus

$$U_\kappa = V_\kappa \upharpoonright \kappa \quad \text{Df.}$$

If $\kappa \epsilon FM$ conx, we have

$$U_\kappa = \hat{P}\hat{Q}\,\{P, Q \epsilon \kappa : (\exists T) . T \epsilon \kappa_\partial . P = T \mid Q\};$$

this is generally the most serviceable formula for U_κ.

If κ is a serial family, U_κ and V_κ are series; and if κ is an initial family, U_κ is similar to $\dot{s}\text{‘}\kappa_\partial$.

The last number in this Section is concerned with the axiom of Archimedes and with the existence of sub-multiples of vectors. The axiom of Archimedes will be expressed by saying that if a is any member of the field of κ, and R is any vector, then R^{ν}'a, for a sufficiently great finite ν, will be later than any assigned member of the field of κ. In other words, putting $P = \mathrm{Cnv}$'$\dot{s}$'κ_∂, we wish to have

$$x \in C\text{'}P \,.\, \supset_x .\, (\exists \nu) \,.\, \nu \in \mathrm{NC\,ind} - \iota\text{'}0 \,.\, xP\,(R^{\nu}\text{'}a),$$

or, what comes to the same thing,

$$P\text{''}\overrightarrow{R_*}\text{'}a = C\text{'}P.$$

This will hold if κ is a serial family and P is semi-Dedekindian (cf. *214). If, further, P is compact (*i.e.* $P^2 = P$), then all finite sub-multiples of a given vector exist, *i.e.*

$$S \in \kappa \,.\, \nu \in \mathrm{NC\,ind} - \iota\text{'}0 \,.\, \supset .\, (\exists L) \,.\, L \in \kappa \,.\, S = L^{\nu}.$$

It will be observed that, according to our definition of ratio, if $S = L^{\nu}$ and $S \neq \dot{\Lambda}$, L has to S the ratio $1/\nu$, so that L is the νth sub-multiple of S.

Instead of treating vector-families by the method we have adopted, we might have started from a double descriptive function, which we may denote by $x + y$, and concerning which we should make various hypotheses. By the general notation of *38, we obtain various relations of the form $+\,y$ or $x\,+$. These relations may replace the κ employed in our method. For convenience of notation, we may put

$$\overrightarrow{+}\text{'}y = +\,y \quad \mathrm{Df},$$

$$\overleftarrow{+}\text{'}x = x\,+ \quad \mathrm{Df}.$$

Then if $+$ has suitable properties, and γ is a suitable class, $\overrightarrow{+}\text{''}\gamma$ will be a vector family.

Let us assume that $x + y$ exists when, and only when, x and y both belong to the class γ, and that when x and y both belong to the class γ, $x + y$ also belongs to this class. Then if $x + y$ exists, so does $x + y + y$; hence $D\text{'}+y \subset \text{ₐ}\text{'}+y$. Further, by our assumptions, if $x, y \in \gamma$, $x + y$ exists, and therefore $x \in \text{ₐ}\text{'}+y$. Hence $y \in \gamma \,.\, \supset .\, \text{ₐ}\text{'}+y = \gamma$. Hence if γ exists,

$$\text{ₐ}\text{''}\overrightarrow{+}\text{''}\gamma \in 1 \,.\, s\text{'}D\text{''}\overrightarrow{+}\text{''}\gamma \subset s\text{'}\text{ₐ}\text{''}\overrightarrow{+}\text{''}\gamma.$$

If we now assume $\quad y + x = z + x \,.\, \supset_{x,y,z} .\, y = z,$

then $\overrightarrow{+}\text{''}\gamma \subset 1 \rightarrow 1$. Hence we now have

$$\overrightarrow{+}\text{''}\gamma \in \mathrm{Cl\ ex}\text{'}\mathrm{cr}\text{'}\gamma.$$

In order to obtain the Abelian property, we require

$$(x + y) + z = (x + z) + y,$$

which holds if $+$ obeys the permutative and associative laws. Thus in this case,

$$\overrightarrow{+}\text{''}\gamma \in \mathrm{fm}\text{'}\gamma.$$

In order that $\overrightarrow{+}$"γ may be a *connected* family, we require

$$(\exists a) :. z \epsilon \gamma . \supset_z : (\exists y) : a = z + y . \vee . z = a + y.$$

A sufficient, though not a necessary, condition for this is that there should be a zero, *i.e.*

$$(\exists a) : z \epsilon \gamma . \supset_z . z = a + z.$$

In this case, $+a$ is the zero vector, and if a is not the sum of two terms other than itself, a is the initial point of the family.

The condition that if x, y are members of γ so is $x + y$ secures that $\overrightarrow{+}$"γ is a group. Families which are groups we denote by "*FM* grp."

Thus collecting what has been said, we find that

$$\overrightarrow{+}\text{“}\gamma \, \epsilon \, FM \text{ conx grp}$$

if + fulfils the following conditions:

(1) $x + y$ exists when, and only when, $x, y \epsilon \gamma$;

(2) $x, y \epsilon \gamma . \supset_{x,y} . x + y \epsilon \gamma$;

(3) $x + y = x + z . \supset_{x,y,z} . y = z$;

(4) $x + y = y + x$;

(5) $(x + y) + z = x + (y + z)$;

(6) $(\exists a) : z \epsilon \gamma . \supset_z . z = a + z$.

From (3) and (4) it follows that the a of (6) is unique, *i.e.* there cannot be more than one zero.

In order to insure that our family shall have connexity, we require further

(7) $x, y \epsilon \gamma . \supset_{x,y} : (\exists z) : z \epsilon \gamma : x + z = y . \vee . y + z = x$;

(8) in order that our family may be an initial family we require that $x + y$ shall only be zero when x and y are zero.

With this further condition, our family becomes serial.

The above is only a sketch of one of the simplest ways of generating families by means of double descriptive functions. Other ways are possible, and by greater complication greater generality can be obtained.

There are some advantages in the above manner of treatment. First, it is possible to take our magnitudes as being the x and y which appear in "$x + y$," instead of having to take them as the vectors $+y$ or $x+$. Secondly, our vector-family derives unity from the fact of being generated by the single operation +. Thirdly, the method is more in agreement with current conceptions of quantity than the method we have adopted. The choice between the two methods is a matter of taste; but it would seem that the method we have adopted is capable of somewhat greater generality than the other, and that it requires less new technical apparatus than the other. We have not elsewhere had occasion to treat of double descriptive functions which only exist when their arguments belong to assigned classes, though it is to be observed that our definitions of various kinds of addition and multiplication might quite easily have been so framed as to give this result. For instance, we might have put

$$\mu +_{c} \nu = (\imath\varpi)\{(\exists\alpha, \beta) . \mu = N_0c`\alpha . \nu = N_0c`\beta . \varpi = Nc`(\alpha + \beta)\} \quad \text{Df.}$$

In that case, $E ! (\mu +_c \nu)$ would have implied $\mu, \nu \epsilon N_0C$, whereas with our definition it is only $\exists ! (\mu +_c \nu)$ that implies $\mu, \nu \epsilon N_0C$. The general treatment of double functions which only exist in certain cases would require a considerable logical apparatus not required elsewhere in our work, and this is, for us, a reason against adopting the method of treating vector-families which derives them, as in the above sketch, from a single function $x + y$.

$*$330. ELEMENTARY PROPERTIES OF VECTOR-FAMILIES.

Summary of $*$330.

In this number, we begin by defining the class of "correspondences" of α. A "correspondence" of α is a one-one relation R which makes every member of α correspond to an α, *i.e.* which is such that, if $x \in \alpha$, $R`x$ always exists and is a member of α. Thus, for example, if μ is an inductive number, $+_c \mu$, with its field limited to inductive numbers, is a correspondence of the class of inductive numbers, provided the axiom of infinity holds. (Otherwise, $(+_c \mu) \upharpoonright \text{NC induct}$ is not one-one.) The definition of correspondences of α is

$*$330·01. $\text{cr}`\alpha = (1 \rightarrow 1) \cap \overleftarrow{\text{Ɑ}}`\alpha \cap \breve{\text{D}}``\text{Cl}`\alpha$ Df

I.e. a correspondence of α is a one-one relation whose converse domain is α and whose domain is contained in α. The definition should be compared with the definition of "$\text{cror}`P$" in $*$208.

It will be seen that if $R \in \text{cr}`\alpha$ and $x \in \alpha$, $R`x$ exists and is an α, and therefore $R`R`x$ exists and is an α, and so on. Hence all the powers of R exist ($*$330·23). Similarly if $R, S, T, \ldots$ are any finite number of correspondences of α, $R \,|\, S \,|\, T \,|\, \ldots$ exists. This is proved for two and three factors in $*$330·21·22.

We define a "vector-family of α" as an existent Abelian class of correspondences of α, where an Abelian class of relations is defined as one such that the relative product of any two of its members is commutative. Thus we put

$*$330·02. $\text{Abel} = \hat{\kappa}(R, S \in \kappa \,.\supset_{R,S}.\, R \,|\, S = S \,|\, R)$ Df

$*$330·03. $\text{fm}`\alpha = \text{Abel} \cap \text{Cl ex}`\text{cr}`\alpha$ Df

$*$330·04. $FM = s`\text{D}`\text{fm}$ Df

It will be remembered that $\text{Potid}`P$ and (for certain kinds of relations) $\text{finid}`P$ are Abelian classes of relations ($*$91·34 and $*$121·352). If $P \in 1 \rightarrow 1$, $\text{Potid}`P$ will be a vector-family of $C`P$, and if further $P_{\text{po}} \subseteq J$, $\text{finid}`P$ will be the same vector-family.

One other definition belongs to this number, namely

$*$330·05. $\kappa_\iota = s`(\text{Cnv}``\kappa) \underset{\prime\prime}{|} ``\kappa$ Df

This definition has been sufficiently discussed in the summary of the present Section.

After some preliminary propositions on Cl ex‘cr‘α (*330·1—·32) and on κ_ι (*330·4—·43), we proceed to such properties of families as do not require any further hypothesis as to the nature of the family concerned. These properties are mainly such as assert the existence of relative products, and of logical products of converse domains, or such as assert commutativeness of the relative product under certain circumstances. The earlier propositions deal with members of κ, the later propositions mainly with members of κ_ι. The most useful propositions are:

***330·54.** $\vdash : \kappa \epsilon FM \,.\, Q, R \epsilon \kappa \,.\, E\,!\,\breve{R}\text{‘}x \,.\, \supset \,.\, E\,!\,\breve{R}\text{‘}Q\text{‘}x$

***330·56.** $\vdash : \kappa \epsilon FM \,.\, Q, R \epsilon \kappa \,.\, E\,!\,\breve{R}\text{‘}a \,.\, \supset \,.\, \breve{R}\text{‘}Q\text{‘}a = Q\text{‘}\breve{R}\text{‘}a$

***330·61.** $\vdash : \kappa \epsilon FM - \iota\text{‘}\iota\text{‘}\dot{\Lambda} \,.\, L, M \epsilon \kappa_\iota \,.\, \supset .$

$\exists\,!\,\text{Ɑ}\text{‘}L \cap \text{Ɑ}\text{‘}M \,.\, \exists\,!\,\text{D}\text{‘}L \cap \text{Ɑ}\text{‘}M \,.\, \exists\,!\,\text{Ɑ}\text{‘}L \cap \text{D}\text{‘}M \,.\, \exists\,!\,\text{D}\text{‘}L \cap \text{D}\text{‘}M$

***330·611.** $\vdash : \kappa \epsilon FM - \iota\text{‘}\iota\text{‘}\dot{\Lambda} \,.\, L, M \epsilon \kappa_\iota \,.\, \supset \,.\, \dot{\exists}\,!\,L \,|\, M$

***330·624.** $\vdash : \kappa \epsilon FM - \iota\text{‘}\iota\text{‘}\dot{\Lambda} \,.\, L \epsilon \kappa_\iota \,.\, \supset \,.\, \dot{\Lambda} \sim\epsilon \mathrm{Pot}\text{‘}L$

***330·63.** $\vdash : \kappa \epsilon FM \,.\, L, M \epsilon \kappa_\iota \,.\, E\,!\,L\text{‘}x \,.\, E\,!\,L\text{‘}M\text{‘}x \,.\, \supset \,.\, L\text{‘}M\text{‘}x = M\text{‘}L\text{‘}x$

***330·642.** $\vdash : \kappa \epsilon FM - \iota\text{‘}\iota\text{‘}\dot{\Lambda} \,.\, L, M \epsilon \kappa_\iota \,.\, \supset \,.\, (\exists x) \,.\, E\,!\,L\text{‘}x \,.\, E\,!\,L\text{‘}M\text{‘}x$

***330·71.** $\vdash : \kappa \epsilon FM \,.\, P, Q \epsilon \kappa \,.\, \rho \epsilon \mathrm{NC\,ind} - \iota\text{‘}0 \,.\, E\,!\,\breve{P}^{\rho}\text{‘}x \,.\, \supset \,.\, E\,!\,(\breve{P} \,|\, Q)^{\rho}\text{‘}x$

***330·72.** $\vdash : \kappa \epsilon FM - \iota\text{‘}\iota\text{‘}\dot{\Lambda} \,.\, L, M \epsilon \kappa_\iota \,.\, \rho, \sigma \epsilon \mathrm{NC\,induct} \,.\, \supset \,.\, \exists\,!\,\text{Ɑ}\text{‘}L^{\rho} \cap \text{Ɑ}\text{‘}M^{\sigma}$

***330·73.** $\vdash : \kappa \epsilon FM \,.\, P, Q \epsilon \kappa \,.\, \rho \epsilon \mathrm{NC\,ind} \,.\, E\,!\,(\breve{P} \,|\, Q)^{\rho}\text{‘}x \,.\, \supset \,.\, (\breve{P} \,|\, Q)^{\rho}\text{‘}x = \breve{P}^{\rho}\text{‘}Q^{\rho}\text{‘}x$

***330·01.** $\mathrm{cr}\text{‘}\alpha = (1 \to 1) \cap \overleftarrow{\text{Ɑ}}\text{‘}\alpha \cap \breve{\text{D}}\text{‘‘}\mathrm{Cl}\text{‘}\alpha$ Df

***330·02.** $\mathrm{Abel} = \hat{\kappa}\,(R, S \epsilon \kappa \,.\, \supset_{R,S} \,.\, R \,|\, S = S \,|\, R)$ Df

***330·03.** $\mathrm{fm}\text{‘}\alpha = \mathrm{Abel} \cap \mathrm{Cl\,ex}\text{‘}\mathrm{cr}\text{‘}\alpha$ Df

***330·04.** $FM = s\text{‘}\text{D}\text{‘}\mathrm{fm}$ Df

***330·05.** $\kappa_\iota = s\text{‘}(\mathrm{Cnv}\text{‘‘}\kappa) \underset{''}{|}\text{‘‘}\kappa$ Df

***330·1.** $\vdash : \kappa \epsilon \mathrm{Cl\,ex}\text{‘}\mathrm{cr}\text{‘}\alpha \,.\, \equiv \,.\, \kappa \subset 1 \to 1 \,.\, \text{Ɑ}\text{‘‘}\kappa = \iota\text{‘}\alpha \,.\, \text{D}\text{‘‘}\kappa \subset \mathrm{Cl}\text{‘}\alpha$ [(*330·01)]

***330·11.** $\vdash :. (\exists\alpha) \,.\, \kappa \epsilon \mathrm{Cl\,ex}\text{‘}\mathrm{cr}\text{‘}\alpha \,.\, \equiv : \kappa \subset 1 \to 1 : (\exists\alpha) \,.\, \text{Ɑ}\text{‘‘}\kappa = \iota\text{‘}\alpha \,.\, s\text{‘}\text{D}\text{‘‘}\kappa \subset \alpha$
[*330·1]

***330·12.** $\vdash : \kappa \epsilon \mathrm{Cl\,ex}\text{‘}\mathrm{cr}\text{‘}\alpha \,.\, \supset \,.\, s\text{‘}\text{Ɑ}\text{‘‘}\kappa = \alpha$ [*330·1 . *53·02]

***330·13.** $\vdash : \kappa \epsilon \mathrm{Cl\,ex}\text{‘}\mathrm{cr}\text{‘}\alpha \,.\, \supset \,.\, \text{D}\text{‘‘}\kappa \subset \mathrm{Cl}\text{‘}s\text{‘}\text{Ɑ}\text{‘‘}\kappa \,.\, s\text{‘}\text{D}\text{‘‘}\kappa \subset s\text{‘}\text{Ɑ}\text{‘‘}\kappa$ [*330·1·12]

***330·131.** $\vdash : (\exists\alpha) \,.\, \kappa \epsilon \mathrm{Cl\,ex}\text{‘}\mathrm{cr}\text{‘}\alpha \,.\, \equiv \,.\, \kappa \subset 1 \to 1 \,.\, \text{Ɑ}\text{‘‘}\kappa \epsilon 1 \,.\, s\text{‘}\text{D}\text{‘‘}\kappa \subset s\text{‘}\text{Ɑ}\text{‘‘}\kappa$
[*330·11·12]

***330·14.** $\vdash : \kappa \epsilon \mathrm{Cl\,ex}\text{‘}\mathrm{cr}\text{‘}\alpha \,.\, \supset \,.\, \text{D}\text{‘‘}\kappa \subset \mathrm{Nc}\text{‘}\alpha$ [*330·1]

***330·15.** $\vdash . \text{Cl ex}`\text{cr}`\Lambda = \iota`\iota`\dot{\Lambda}$ [*330·1]

***330·151.** $\vdash : \exists ! \alpha . \kappa \in \text{Cl ex}`\text{cr}`\alpha . \supset . \dot{\Lambda} \sim \in \kappa$ [*330·14]

***330·16.** $\vdash :. (\exists \alpha) . \kappa \in \text{Cl ex}`\text{cr}`\alpha : \kappa \neq \iota`\dot{\Lambda} : \supset . \dot{\Lambda} \sim \in \kappa$ [*330·15·151]

***330·17.** $\vdash : \exists ! \alpha . \kappa \in \text{Cl ex}`\text{cr}`\alpha . \supset . \text{D}``\kappa \subset \text{Cl ex}`s`\text{Ɑ}``\kappa$ [*330·13·151]

***330·18.** $\vdash :. (\exists \alpha) . \kappa \in \text{Cl ex}`\text{cr}`\alpha : \kappa \neq \iota`\dot{\Lambda} : \supset . \text{D}``\kappa \subset \text{Cl ex}`s`\text{Ɑ}``\kappa$ [*330·15·17]

***330·19.** $\vdash . \iota`(I \upharpoonright \alpha) \in \text{Cl ex}`\text{cr}`\alpha$ [*330·1]

***330·2.** $\vdash : \kappa \in \text{Cl ex}`\text{cr}`\alpha . R \in \kappa . \exists ! \text{D}`M \cap s`\text{Ɑ}``\kappa . \supset . \dot{\exists} ! R | M$

Dem.

$\vdash . *330·1·12 . \supset \vdash : \text{Hp} . \supset . \exists ! \text{D}`M \cap \text{Ɑ}`R : \supset \vdash . \text{Prop}$

***330·21.** $\vdash : \kappa \in \text{Cl ex}`\text{cr}`\alpha . \kappa \neq \iota`\dot{\Lambda} . R, S \in \kappa . \supset . \dot{\exists} ! R | S$

Dem.

$\vdash . *330·18 . \supset \vdash : \text{Hp} . \supset . \exists ! \text{D}`S \cap s`\text{Ɑ}``\kappa$ (1)

$\vdash . (1) . *330·2 . \supset \vdash . \text{Prop}$

***330·22.** $\vdash : \kappa \in \text{Cl ex}`\text{cr}`\alpha . \kappa \neq \iota`\dot{\Lambda} . R, S, T \in \kappa . \supset . \dot{\exists} ! R | S | T$

Dem.

$\vdash . *330·21·18 . \supset \vdash : \text{Hp} . \supset . \dot{\exists} ! \text{D}`(S | T) \cap s`\text{Ɑ}``\kappa$ (1)

$\vdash . (1) . *330·2 . \supset \vdash . \text{Prop}$

***330·23.** $\vdash : \kappa \in \text{Cl ex}`\text{cr}`\alpha . \kappa \neq \iota`\dot{\Lambda} . R \in \kappa . \supset . \dot{\Lambda} \sim \in \text{Potid}`R$

Dem.

$\vdash . *330·16 . \supset \vdash : \text{Hp} . \supset . \dot{\exists} ! I \upharpoonright C`R$ (1)

$\vdash . *330·18 . \supset \vdash : \text{Hp} . P \in \text{Potid}`R . \dot{\exists} ! P . \supset . \exists ! \text{D}`P \cap s`\text{Ɑ}``\kappa .$

[*330·2] $\supset . \dot{\exists} ! R | P$ (2)

$\vdash . (1) . (2) . \text{Induct} . \supset \vdash . \text{Prop}$

***330·3.** $\vdash : \kappa \in \text{Cl ex}`\text{cr}`\alpha . I \upharpoonright \alpha \in \kappa . \supset . \kappa \subset s`\kappa_{|}``\kappa$

Dem.

$\vdash . *330·1 . \supset \vdash :. \text{Hp} . \supset : R \in \kappa . \supset . R = R | I \upharpoonright \alpha :. \supset \vdash . \text{Prop}$

***330·31.** $\vdash : \kappa \in \text{Cl ex}`\text{cr}`\alpha . R \in \kappa . \supset . \breve{R} | R = I \upharpoonright s`\text{Ɑ}``\kappa$ [*330·1]

***330·32.** $\vdash :. \kappa \in \text{Cl ex}`\text{cr}`\alpha . R, S \in \kappa . \supset : \breve{R} | S = I \upharpoonright s`\text{Ɑ}``\kappa . \equiv . R = S$

Dem.

$\vdash . *330·31 . \supset \vdash :. \text{Hp} . \supset : R = S . \supset . \breve{R} | S = I \upharpoonright s`\text{Ɑ}``\kappa$ (1)

$\vdash . *330·1 . \supset \vdash : \text{Hp} . \supset . R | \breve{R} | S = (\text{D}`R) \upharpoonleft S$ (2)

$\vdash . (2) . \supset \vdash :. \text{Hp} . \supset : \breve{R} | S = I \upharpoonright s`\text{Ɑ}``\kappa . \supset . R = (\text{D}`R) \upharpoonleft S .$

[*72·92] $\supset . R = S \upharpoonright \text{Ɑ}`R .$

[*330·1] $\supset . R = S$ (3)

$\vdash . (1) . (3) . \supset \vdash . \text{Prop}$

***330·4.** $\vdash : M \epsilon \kappa_\iota . \equiv . (\exists R, S) . R, S \epsilon \kappa . M = \breve{R} | S$ [(*330·05)]

***330·41.** $\vdash . \mathrm{Cnv}``\kappa_\iota = \kappa_\iota$ [*330·4]

***330·42.** $\vdash : \kappa \epsilon \mathrm{Cl\,ex}`\mathrm{cr}`\alpha . I \upharpoonright \alpha \epsilon \kappa . \supset . \kappa \cup \mathrm{Cnv}``\kappa \subset \kappa_\iota$

Dem.

$\vdash . *330·1 . *50·5·51 . \supset \vdash : \mathrm{Hp} . R \epsilon \kappa . \supset . R = (I \upharpoonright \alpha) | R . I \upharpoonright \alpha \epsilon \mathrm{Cnv}``\kappa$ (1)

$\vdash . (1) . *330·4·41 . \supset \vdash . \mathrm{Prop}$

***330·43.** $\vdash : \kappa \epsilon \mathrm{Cl\,ex}`\mathrm{cr}`\alpha . \supset . I \upharpoonright s`\mathrm{Cl}``\kappa \epsilon \kappa_\iota$ [*330·31·4]

***330·5.** $\vdash :. \kappa \epsilon \mathrm{Abel} . \equiv : R, S \epsilon \kappa . \supset_{R,S} . R | S = S | R$ [(*330·02)]

***330·51.** $\vdash : \kappa \epsilon \mathrm{fm}`\alpha . \equiv . \kappa \epsilon \mathrm{Abel} \cap \mathrm{Cl\,ex}`\mathrm{cr}`\alpha$ [(*330·03)]

***330·52.** $\vdash : \kappa \epsilon FM . \equiv . (\exists \alpha) . \kappa \epsilon \mathrm{Abel} \cap \mathrm{Cl\,ex}`\mathrm{cr}`\alpha .$

$\equiv . \kappa \epsilon \mathrm{Abel} . \kappa \subset 1 \rightarrow 1 . \mathrm{Cl}``\kappa \epsilon 1 . s`\mathrm{D}``\kappa \subset s`\mathrm{Cl}``\kappa$

[*330·51·131 . (*330·04)]

***330·53.** $\vdash : \kappa \epsilon FM . Q, R \epsilon \kappa . \mathrm{E} ! \breve{R}`\breve{Q}`x . \supset . \mathrm{E} ! \breve{Q}`x . \mathrm{E} ! \breve{R}`x$

Dem.

$\vdash . *330·5 . \supset \vdash : \mathrm{Hp} . \supset . \mathrm{E} ! \breve{Q}`\breve{R}`x$ (1)

$\vdash . (1) . *30·5 . \supset \vdash . \mathrm{Prop}$

***330·54.** $\vdash : \kappa \epsilon FM . Q, R \epsilon \kappa . \mathrm{E} ! \breve{R}`x . \supset . \mathrm{E} ! \breve{R}`Q`x$

Dem.

$\vdash . *330·31·52 . \supset \vdash : \mathrm{Hp} . \supset . \breve{R}`x = \breve{R}`\breve{Q}`Q`x$ (1)

$\vdash . (1) . *330·53 . \supset \vdash . \mathrm{Prop}$

***330·541.** $\vdash : \kappa \epsilon FM . Q, R \epsilon \kappa . \supset . Q``\mathrm{D}`R \subset \mathrm{D}`R$ [*330·54]

***330·542.** $\vdash : \kappa \epsilon FM . R \epsilon \kappa . \supset . \mathrm{D}`R \epsilon \mathrm{sect}`\dot{s}`\kappa$ [*330·541 . *211·1]

***330·55.** $\vdash : \kappa \epsilon FM - \iota`\iota`\dot{\Lambda} . Q, R \epsilon \kappa . \supset . \exists ! \mathrm{D}`Q \cap \mathrm{D}`R . \exists ! Q``\mathrm{D}`R$

Dem.

$\vdash . *330·54 . \supset \vdash :. \mathrm{Hp} . \supset : x \epsilon \mathrm{D}`R . \supset . Q`x \epsilon \mathrm{D}`R :$

[*33·43] $\supset : \exists ! \mathrm{D}`R . \supset . \exists ! \mathrm{D}`Q \cap \mathrm{D}`R$ (1)

$\vdash . (1) . *330·16 . \supset \vdash : \mathrm{Hp} . \supset . \exists ! \mathrm{D}`Q \cap \mathrm{D}`R$ (2)

$\vdash . *330·11·16 . \supset \vdash : \mathrm{Hp} . \supset . \mathrm{D}`R \subset \mathrm{Cl}`Q . \exists ! \mathrm{D}`R .$

[*37·43] $\supset . \exists ! Q``\mathrm{D}`R$ (3)

$\vdash . (2) . (3) . \supset \vdash . \mathrm{Prop}$

***330·551.** $\vdash : \mathrm{Hp} *330·55 . \supset . \dot{\exists} ! Q | R$ [*330·55 . *37·32]

***330·56.** $\vdash : \kappa \in FM \,.\, Q, R \in \kappa \,.\, E \,!\, \breve{R}‘a \,.\, \supset \,.\, \breve{R}‘Q‘a = Q‘\breve{R}‘a$

Dem.

$\vdash \,.\, *330·5·11 \,.\, \supset \vdash : \text{Hp} \,.\, \supset \,.\, Q‘R‘\breve{R}‘a = R‘Q‘\breve{R}‘a \,.$

[*72·24] $\supset \,.\, Q‘a = R‘Q‘\breve{R}‘a \,.$

[*330·31·54] $\supset \,.\, \breve{R}‘Q‘a = Q‘\breve{R}‘a : \supset \vdash \,.\, \text{Prop}$

***330·561.** $\vdash : \kappa \in FM \,.\, Q, R \in \dot{\kappa} \,.\, \supset \,.\, \breve{R} \,|\, Q \upharpoonright \text{D}‘R = Q \,|\, \breve{R}$ [*330·56]

***330·562.** $\vdash : \kappa \in FM \,.\, Q, R \in \kappa \,.\, \supset \,.\, R ; Q \Subset Q$ [*330·561]

***330·563.** $\vdash : \kappa \in FM \,.\, R \in \kappa \,.\, \lambda \subset \kappa \,.\, \supset \,.\, R ; \dot{s}‘\lambda \Subset \dot{s}‘\lambda$ [*330·562]

***330·57.** $\vdash : \kappa \in \text{Abel} \,.\, R, S \in \kappa \,.\, \nu \in \text{NC induct} \,.\, \supset \,.\, R^\nu | S^\nu = (R|S)^\nu \,.\, R | S^\nu = S^\nu | R$

Dem.

$\vdash \,.\, *301·2 \,.\, \quad \supset \vdash \,.\, R^0 | S^0 = (R|S)^0 \,.\, R | S^0 = S^0 | R$ (1)

$\vdash \,.\, *330·5 \,.\, *301·21 \,.\, \supset \vdash : \text{Hp} \,.\, R | S^\nu = S^\nu | R \,.\, \supset \,.\, R | S^{\nu +_c 1} = S^{\nu +_c 1} | R$ (2)

$\vdash \,.\, (1) \,.\, (2) \,.\, \text{Induct} \,.\, \supset \vdash : \text{Hp} \,.\, \supset \,.\, R | S^\nu = S^\nu | R$ (3)

$\vdash \,.\, (3) \,.\, *301·21 \,.\, \supset \vdash : \text{Hp} \,.\, \supset \,.\, R^{\nu +_c 1} | S^{\nu +_c 1} = R^\nu | S^\nu | R | S$ (4)

$\vdash \,.\, (4) \,.\, *301·21 \,.\, \supset \vdash : \text{Hp} \,.\, R^\nu | S^\nu = (R|S)^\nu \,.\, \supset \,.\, R^{\nu +_c 1} | S^{\nu +_c 1} = (R|S)^{\nu +_c 1}$ (5)

$\vdash \,.\, (1) \,.\, (5) \,.\, \text{Induct} \,.\, \supset \vdash : \text{Hp} \,.\, \supset \,.\, R^\nu | S^\nu = (R|S)^\nu$ (6)

$\vdash \,.\, (3) \,.\, (6) \,.\, \supset \vdash \,.\, \text{Prop}$

***330·6.** $\vdash : \kappa \in FM - \iota‘\iota‘\dot{\Lambda} \,.\, L \in \kappa_\iota \,.\, \supset \,.\, \dot{\exists} \,!\, L$

Dem.

$\vdash \,.\, *330·16·4 \,.\, \supset \vdash : \text{Hp} \,.\, \supset \,.\, (\exists Q, R) \,.\, Q, R \in \kappa \,.\, \dot{\exists} \,!\, R \,.\, L = \breve{R} \,|\, Q \,.$

[*330·54] $\supset \,.\, (\exists Q, R, x) \,.\, Q, R \in \kappa \,.\, E \,!\, \breve{R}‘Q‘x \,.\, L = \breve{R} \,|\, Q \,.$

[*34·41] $\supset \,.\, \dot{\exists} \,!\, L : \supset \vdash \,.\, \text{Prop}$

***330·61.** $\vdash : \kappa \in FM - \iota‘\iota‘\dot{\Lambda} \,.\, L, M \in \kappa_\iota \,.\, \supset \,.$

$\exists \,!\, \text{ꓷ}‘L \cap \text{ꓷ}‘M \,.\, \exists \,!\, \text{D}‘L \cap \text{ꓷ}‘M \,.\, \exists \,!\, \text{ꓷ}‘L \cap \text{D}‘M \,.\, \exists \,!\, \text{D}‘L \cap \text{D}‘M$

Dem.

$\vdash \,.\, *330·55·4 \,.\, \supset$

$\vdash : \text{Hp} \,.\, \supset \,.\, (\exists Q, R, S, T) \,.\, Q, R, S, T \in \kappa \,.\, L = \breve{R} \,|\, Q \,.\, M = \breve{T} \,|\, S \,.\, \exists \,!\, \text{D}‘R \cap \text{D}‘T \,.$

[*330·54]

$\supset \,.\, (\exists Q, R, S, T, x) \,.\, Q, R, S, T \in \kappa \,.\, L = \breve{R} \,|\, Q \,.\, M = \breve{T} \,|\, S \,.\, E \,!\, \breve{R}‘Q‘x \,.\, E \,!\, \breve{T}‘S‘x \,.$

[*34·41] $\supset \,.\, (\exists x) \,.\, E \,!\, L‘x \,.\, E \,!\, M‘x \,.$

[*33·43] $\supset \,.\, \exists \,!\, \text{ꓷ}‘L \cap \text{ꓷ}‘M$ (1)

$\vdash \,.\, (1) \,.\, *330·41 \,.\, \supset \vdash \,.\, \text{Prop}$

***330·611.** $\vdash : \kappa \epsilon FM - \iota\text{‘}\iota\text{‘}\dot{\Lambda} \,.\, L, M \epsilon \kappa_\iota \,.\, \supset \,.\, \dot{\exists} \,!\, L \,|\, M$ [*330·61 . *34·3]

***330·612.** $\vdash : \kappa \epsilon FM - \iota\text{‘}\iota\text{‘}\dot{\Lambda} \,.\, L, M, N \epsilon \kappa_\iota \,.\, \supset \,.\, \exists \,!\, \text{Ɑ}\text{‘}L \cap \text{Ɑ}\text{‘}M \cap \text{Ɑ}\text{‘}N$

Dem.

$\vdash \,.\, *330{\cdot}22{\cdot}4 \,.\, \supset$

$\vdash : \text{Hp} \,.\, \supset \,.\, (\exists P, Q, R, S, T, W) \,.\, P, Q, R, S, T, W \epsilon \kappa \,.$

$$L = \breve{P} \,|\, Q \,.\, M = \breve{R} \,|\, S \,.\, N = \breve{T} \,|\, W \,.\, \dot{\exists} \,!\, P \,|\, R \,|\, T \,.$$

[*330·53] $\supset \,.\, (\exists P, Q, R, S, T, W, x) \,.\, P, Q, R, S, T, W \epsilon \kappa \,.$

$$L = \breve{P} \,|\, Q \,.\, M = \breve{R} \,|\, S \,.\, N = \breve{T} \,|\, W \,.\, E \,!\, \breve{P}\text{‘}x \,.\, E \,!\, \breve{R}\text{‘}x \,.\, E \,!\, \breve{T}\text{‘}x \,.$$

[*330·54] $\supset \,.\, (\exists x) \,.\, E \,!\, L\text{‘}x \,.\, E \,!\, M\text{‘}x \,.\, E \,!\, N\text{‘}x : \supset \vdash \,.\,$ Prop

***330·613.** $\vdash : \kappa \epsilon FM - \iota\text{‘}\iota\text{‘}\dot{\Lambda} \,.\, L, M, N \epsilon \kappa_\iota \,.\, \supset \,.\, \dot{\exists} \,!\, L \,|\, M \,|\, N$

Dem.

$\vdash \,.\, *330{\cdot}22{\cdot}4 \,.\, \supset$

$\vdash : \text{Hp} \,.\, \supset \,.\, (\exists P, Q, R, S, T, W, x) \,.\, P, Q, R, S, T, W \epsilon \kappa \,.$

$$L = \breve{P} \,|\, Q \,.\, M = \breve{R} \,|\, S \,.\, N = \breve{T} \,|\, W \,.\, E \,!\, \breve{P}\text{‘}\breve{R}\text{‘}\breve{T}\text{‘}x \,.$$

[*330·54] $\supset \,.\, (\exists P, Q, R, S, x) \,.\, P, Q, R, S \epsilon \kappa \,.$

$$L = \breve{P} \,|\, Q \,.\, M = \breve{R} \,|\, S \,.\, E \,!\, \breve{P}\text{‘}\breve{R}\text{‘}(N\text{‘}x) \,.$$

[*330·54] $\supset \,.\, (\exists P, Q) \,.\, P, Q \epsilon \kappa \,.\, L = \breve{P} \,|\, Q \,.\, E \,!\, \breve{P}\text{‘}(M\text{‘}N\text{‘}x) \,.$

[*330·54] $\supset \,.\, (\exists x) \,.\, E \,!\, L\text{‘}M\text{‘}N\text{‘}x : \supset \vdash \,.\,$ Prop

***330·62.** $\vdash : \kappa \epsilon FM \,.\, L \epsilon \kappa_\iota \,.\, S \epsilon \kappa \,.\, \supset \,.\, S \,|\, L \Subset L \,|\, S$

Dem.

$\vdash \,.\, *330{\cdot}561 \,.\, \supset \vdash : \text{Hp} \,.\, P, Q \epsilon \kappa \,.\, L = \breve{P} \,|\, Q \,.\, \supset \,.\, S \,|\, \breve{P} \Subset \breve{P} \,|\, S \,.$

[*330·5] $\supset \,.\, S \,|\, \breve{P} \,|\, Q \Subset \breve{P} \,|\, Q \,|\, S : \supset \vdash \,.\,$ Prop

***330·621.** $\vdash :. \kappa \epsilon FM - \iota\text{‘}\iota\text{‘}\dot{\Lambda} \,.\, L \epsilon \kappa_\iota \,.\, C\text{‘}P \subset s\text{‘}\text{Ɑ}\text{‘‘}\kappa \,.\, \dot{\exists} \,!\, P :$

$$S \epsilon \kappa \,.\, \supset_S \,.\, S \,|\, P \Subset P \,|\, S : \supset \,.\, \dot{\exists} \,!\, P \,|\, L$$

Dem.

$\vdash \,.\, *330{\cdot}11 \,.\, \supset \vdash :. \text{Hp} \,.\, Q, R \epsilon \kappa \,.\, L = \breve{Q} \,|\, R \,.\, \supset :$

$$xPy \,.\, \supset \,.\, (\exists u, z) \,.\, uRx \,.\, zQy \,.\, xPy \,.$$

[*34·1] $\supset \,.\, \dot{\exists} \,!\, R \,|\, P \,|\, \breve{Q} \,.$

[*330·5] $\supset \,.\, \dot{\exists} \,!\, P \,|\, R \,|\, \breve{Q} \,.$

[*330·561] $\supset \,.\, \dot{\exists} \,!\, P \,|\, \breve{Q} \,|\, R \,.$

[Hp] $\supset \,.\, \dot{\exists} \,!\, P \,|\, L :. \supset \vdash \,.\,$ Prop

***330·622.** $\vdash : \mathrm{Hp} *330{\cdot}621 . \supset . \dot{\exists} ! L | P$

Dem.

$\vdash . *330{\cdot}11 . *72{\cdot}59 . \supset \vdash :: \mathrm{Hp} . Q, R \in \kappa . \dot{L} = \breve{Q} | R . \supset . P \subset \breve{Q} | P | Q .$

$[*72{\cdot}59] \quad \supset . P | \breve{Q} \subset \breve{Q} | P .$

$[*330{\cdot}621] \quad \supset . \dot{\exists} ! \breve{Q} | P | R .$

$[*330{\cdot}5] \quad \supset . \dot{\exists} ! \breve{Q} | R | P .$

$[\mathrm{Hp}] \quad \supset . \dot{\exists} ! L | P : \supset \vdash . \mathrm{Prop}$

***330·623.** $\vdash : \kappa \in FM . S \in \kappa . L \in \kappa_\iota . M \in \mathrm{Pot}‘L . \supset . S | M \subset M | S$

Dem.

$\vdash . *34{\cdot}34 . \supset \vdash : \mathrm{Hp} . S | M \subset M | S . \supset . S | M | L \subset M | S | L .$

$[*330{\cdot}62] \quad \supset . S | M | L \subset M | L | S \quad (1)$

$\vdash . (1) . *330{\cdot}62 . \mathrm{Induct} . \supset \vdash . \mathrm{Prop}$

***330·624.** $\vdash : \kappa \in FM - \iota‘\iota‘\dot{\Lambda} . L \in \kappa_\iota . \supset . \dot{\Lambda} \sim\in \mathrm{Pot}‘L$

Dem.

$\vdash . *330{\cdot}6 . \quad \supset \vdash : \mathrm{Hp} . \supset . \dot{\exists} ! L \quad (1)$

$\vdash . *330{\cdot}622{\cdot}623 . \quad \supset \vdash : \mathrm{Hp} . M \in \mathrm{Pot}‘L . \dot{\exists} ! M . \supset . \dot{\exists} ! M | L \quad (2)$

$\vdash . (1) . (2) . \mathrm{Induct} . \supset \vdash :. \mathrm{Hp} . \supset : M \in \mathrm{Pot}‘L . \supset_M . \dot{\exists} ! M :. \supset \vdash . \mathrm{Prop}$

***330·625.** $\vdash : \kappa \in FM . L, M \in \kappa_\iota . Q \in \mathrm{Pot}‘(L | M) . S \in \kappa . \supset . S | Q \subset Q | S$

Dem.

$\vdash . *330{\cdot}62 . \supset \vdash : \mathrm{Hp} . \supset . S | L | M \subset L | M | S \quad (1)$

$\vdash . *34{\cdot}34 . \supset$

$\vdash : \mathrm{Hp} . R \in \mathrm{Pot}‘(L | M) . S | R \subset R | S . \supset . S | R | L | M \subset R | S | L | M$

$[(1)] \quad \subset \dot{R} | L | M | S \quad (2)$

$\vdash . (1) . (2) . \mathrm{Induct} . \supset \vdash . \mathrm{Prop}$

***330·626.** $\vdash : \kappa \in FM - \iota‘\iota‘\dot{\Lambda} . L, M \in \kappa_\iota . \supset . \dot{\Lambda} \sim\in \mathrm{Pot}‘(L | M)$

Dem.

$\vdash . *330{\cdot}611 . \quad \supset \vdash : \mathrm{Hp} . \supset . \dot{\exists} ! L | M \quad (1)$

$\vdash . *330{\cdot}621{\cdot}625 . \supset \vdash : \mathrm{Hp} . Q \in \mathrm{Pot}‘(L | M) . \dot{\exists} ! Q . \supset . \dot{\exists} ! Q | L \quad (2)$

$\vdash . *330{\cdot}625 . \quad \supset \vdash : \mathrm{Hp} . Q \in \mathrm{Pot}‘(L | M) . S \in \kappa . \supset . S | Q | L \subset Q | S | L$

$[*330{\cdot}62] \quad \subset Q | L | S \quad (3)$

$\vdash . (2) . (3) . *330{\cdot}621 . \supset \vdash : \mathrm{Hp} . Q \in \mathrm{Pot}‘(L | M) . \dot{\exists} ! Q . \supset . \dot{\exists} ! Q | L | M \quad (4)$

$\vdash . (1) . (4) . \mathrm{Induct} . \supset \vdash . \mathrm{Prop}$

***330·627.** $\vdash : \kappa \in FM - \iota\text{‘}\iota\text{‘}\dot{\Lambda} \,.\, L, M \in \kappa_\iota \,.\, P \in \text{Pot}\text{‘}M \,.\supset .\, \dot{\exists} ! P | L \,.\, \dot{\exists} ! L | P$

Dem.

$\vdash . *330\cdot611 . \quad \supset \vdash : \text{Hp} . \supset . \dot{\exists} ! M | L . \dot{\exists} ! L | M \qquad (1)$

$\vdash . *330\cdot623 . \quad \supset \vdash : \text{Hp} . S \in \kappa . \supset . S | P | L \subset P | S | L .$

$[*330\cdot62] \qquad \supset . S | P | L \subset P | L | S \qquad (2)$

$\vdash . (2) . *330\cdot622 . \quad \supset \vdash : \text{Hp} . \dot{\exists} ! P | L . \supset . \dot{\exists} ! M | P | L \qquad (3)$

$\vdash . (1) . (3) . \text{Induct} . \supset \vdash : \text{Hp} . \supset . \dot{\exists} ! P | L \qquad (4)$

$\vdash . (2) . *330\cdot621 . \quad \supset \vdash : \text{Hp} . \dot{\exists} ! L | P . \supset . \dot{\exists} ! L | P | M \qquad (5)$

$\vdash . (1) . (5) . \text{Induct} . \supset \vdash : \text{Hp} . \supset . \dot{\exists} ! L | P \qquad (6)$

$\vdash . (4) . (6) . \supset \vdash . \text{Prop}$

***330·63.** $\vdash : \kappa \in FM \,.\, L, M \in \kappa_\iota \,.\, E ! L\text{‘}x \,.\, E ! L\text{‘}M\text{‘}x \,.\supset .\, L\text{‘}M\text{‘}x = M\text{‘}L\text{‘}x$

Dem.

$\vdash . *330\cdot56 . \supset \vdash : \text{Hp} . Q, R, S, T \in \kappa . L = \breve{Q} | R . M = \breve{S} | T . \supset .$

$\breve{Q}\text{‘}R\text{‘}\breve{S}\text{‘}T\text{‘}x = \breve{Q}\text{‘}\breve{S}\text{‘}R\text{‘}T\text{‘}x$

$[*330\cdot5] \qquad = \breve{S}\text{‘}\breve{Q}\text{‘}T\text{‘}R\text{‘}x$

$[*330\cdot56 . \text{Hp}] \qquad = \breve{S}\text{‘}T\text{‘}\breve{Q}\text{‘}R\text{‘}x : \supset \vdash . \text{Prop}$

***330·64.** $\vdash :. \kappa \in FM \,.\, L, M \in \kappa_\iota \,.\supset :$

$E ! L\text{‘}x \,.\, E ! L\text{‘}M\text{‘}x \,.\equiv .\, E ! M\text{‘}x \,.\, E ! M\text{‘}L\text{‘}x \qquad [*330\cdot63]$

***330·641.** $\vdash :. \kappa \in FM \,.\, L, M \in \kappa_\iota \,.\, E ! L\text{‘}x \,.\, E ! M\text{‘}x \,.\supset :$

$E ! L\text{‘}M\text{‘}x \,.\equiv .\, E ! M\text{‘}L\text{‘}x \,.\equiv .\, L\text{‘}M\text{‘}x = M\text{‘}L\text{‘}x \qquad [*330\cdot63\cdot64]$

***330·642.** $\vdash : \kappa \in FM - \iota\text{‘}\iota\text{‘}\dot{\Lambda} \,.\, L, M \in \kappa_\iota \,.\supset .\, (\exists x) \,.\, E ! L\text{‘}x \,.\, E ! L\text{‘}M\text{‘}x$

Dem.

$\vdash . *330\cdot21 . \supset$

$\vdash : \text{Hp} . \supset . (\exists P, Q, R, S, x) . P, Q, R, S \in \kappa . L = \breve{P} | Q . M = \breve{R} | S . E ! \breve{P}\text{‘}\breve{R}\text{‘}x .$

$[*330\cdot53\cdot54] \supset . (\exists P, Q, R, S, x) . P, Q, R, S \in \kappa . L = \breve{P} | Q . M = \breve{R} | S .$

$E ! \breve{P}\text{‘}Q\text{‘}x . E ! \breve{P}\text{‘}Q\text{‘}\breve{R}\text{‘}S\text{‘}x : \supset \vdash . \text{Prop}$

***330·643.** $\vdash : \kappa \in FM \,.\, P \in \kappa \,.\, L \in \kappa_\iota \,.\, E ! L\text{‘}x \,.\supset .\, P\text{‘}L\text{‘}x = L\text{‘}P\text{‘}x \qquad [*330\cdot56\cdot5]$

***330·65.** $\vdash : \kappa \in FM \,.\, Q, R, S, T \in \kappa \,.\, \breve{R}\text{‘}Q\text{‘}x = \breve{T}\text{‘}S\text{‘}x \,.\supset .\, T\text{‘}Q\text{‘}x = R\text{‘}S\text{‘}x$

Dem.

$\vdash . *72\cdot24 . \supset \vdash : \text{Hp} . \supset . Q\text{‘}x = R\text{‘}\breve{T}\text{‘}S\text{‘}x$

$[*330\cdot56] \qquad = \breve{T}\text{‘}R\text{‘}S\text{‘}x .$

$[*72\cdot24] \qquad \supset . T\text{‘}Q\text{‘}x = R\text{‘}S\text{‘}x : \supset \vdash . \text{Prop}$

***330·66.** $\vdash :. \kappa \in FM \,.\, Q, R, S, T \in \kappa \,.\, E\,!\, \breve{R}‘Q‘x \,.\, E\,!\, \breve{T}‘S‘x \,.\, \supset :$

$$\breve{R}‘Q‘x = \breve{T}‘S‘x \,.\equiv.\, T‘Q‘x = R‘S‘x$$

Dem.

$\vdash \,.\, *330·56 \,.\, \supset \vdash : \mathrm{Hp} \,.\, T‘Q‘x = R‘S‘x \,.\supset.\, T‘\breve{R}‘Q‘x = \breve{R}‘R‘S‘x$

[*72·241] $= S‘x \,.$

[*72·241] $\supset .\, \breve{R}‘Q‘x = \breve{T}‘S‘x$ (1)

$\vdash \,.\, (1) \,.\, *330·65 \,.\, \supset \vdash \,.\,$ Prop

***330·7.** $\vdash : \kappa \in FM \,.\, P, Q \in \kappa \,.\, \rho \in \mathrm{NC\,ind} - \iota‘0 \,.\, E\,!\, Q‘(\breve{P} \,|\, Q)^{\rho -_c 1}‘\breve{P}‘x \,.\supset .$

$$Q‘(\breve{P} \,|\, Q)^{\rho -_c 1}‘\breve{P}‘x = (\breve{P} \,|\, Q)^{\rho}‘x$$

Dem.

$\vdash \,.\, *330·56 \,.\, *301·2 \,.\, \supset$

$\vdash : \mathrm{Hp} \,.\, E\,!\, Q‘(\breve{P} \,|\, Q)^{0}‘\breve{P}‘x \,.\supset.\, Q‘(\breve{P} \,|\, Q)^{0}‘\breve{P}‘x = (\breve{P} \,|\, Q)^{1}‘x$ (1)

$\vdash \,.\, *330·56 \,.\, *301·21 \,.\, \supset$

$\vdash :. \mathrm{Hp} : E\,!\, Q‘(\breve{P} \,|\, Q)^{\rho -_c 1}‘\breve{P}‘x \,.\supset_x .\, Q‘(\breve{P} \,|\, Q)^{\rho -_c 1}‘\breve{P}‘x = (\breve{P} \,|\, Q)^{\rho}‘x : \supset :$

$$E\,!\, Q‘(\breve{P} \,|\, Q)^{\rho}‘\breve{P}‘x \,.\supset.\, Q‘(\breve{P} \,|\, Q)^{\rho}‘\breve{P}‘x = (\breve{P} \,|\, Q)^{\rho}‘Q‘\breve{P}‘x$$

[*330·56.*301·21] $= (\breve{P} \,|\, Q)^{\rho + 1}‘x$ (2)

$\vdash \,.\, (1) \,.\, (2) \,.\,$ Induct $.\, \supset \vdash \,.\,$ Prop

***330·71.** $\vdash : \kappa \in FM \,.\, P, Q \in \kappa \,.\, \rho \in \mathrm{NC\,ind} - \iota‘0 \,.\, E\,!\, \breve{P}^{\rho}‘x \,.\supset .\, E\,!\, (\breve{P} \,|\, Q)^{\rho}‘x$

Dem.

$\vdash \,.\, *330·54 \,.\, \supset \vdash : \mathrm{Hp} \,.\, E\,!\, \breve{P}^{1}‘x \,.\supset.\, E\,!\, (\breve{P} \,|\, Q)^{1}‘x$ (1)

$\vdash \,.\, *301·21 \,.\, \supset \vdash :. \mathrm{Hp} : E\,!\, \breve{P}^{\rho}‘x \,.\supset_x .\, E\,!\, (\breve{P} \,|\, Q)^{\rho}‘x : \supset :$

$$E\,!\, \breve{P}^{\rho +_c 1}‘x \,.\supset.\, E\,!\, (\breve{P} \,|\, Q)^{\rho}‘\breve{P}‘x \,.$$

[*330·52] $\supset .\, E\,!\, Q‘(\breve{P} \,|\, Q)^{\rho}‘\breve{P}‘x \,.$

[*330·7] $\supset .\, E\,!\, (\breve{P} \,|\, Q)^{\rho +_c 1}‘x$ (2)

$\vdash \,.\, (1) \,.\, (2) \,.\,$ Induct $.\, \supset \vdash \,.\,$ Prop

***330·711.** $\vdash : \kappa \in FM \,.\, Q \in s‘\mathrm{Pot}“\kappa \,.\supset .\, \text{Ɑ}‘Q = s‘\text{Ɑ}“\kappa$

Dem.

$\vdash \,.\, *330·52 \,.\, \supset \vdash : \mathrm{Hp} \,.\, P \in \kappa \,.\supset.\, \text{Ɑ}‘P = s‘\text{Ɑ}“\kappa$ (1)

$\vdash \,.\, *37·322 \,.\, \supset$

$\vdash : \mathrm{Hp} \,.\, P \in \kappa \,.\, Q \in \mathrm{Pot}‘P \,.\, \text{Ɑ}‘Q = s‘\text{Ɑ}“\kappa \,.\supset.\, \text{Ɑ}‘(Q \,|\, P) = s‘\text{Ɑ}“\kappa$ (2)

$\vdash \,.\, (1) \,.\, (2) \,.\,$ Induct $.\, \supset \vdash \,.\,$ Prop

∗330·72. $\vdash : \kappa \in FM - \iota`\iota`\Lambda \,.\, L, M \in \kappa_\iota \,.\, \rho, \sigma \in \text{NC induct} \,.\supset .\, \exists ! \,\text{G}`L^\rho \cap \text{G}`M^\sigma$

Dem.

$\vdash . ∗330·711·23 . \supset$

$\vdash : \text{Hp} \,.\, P, R \in \kappa \,.\supset .\, (\exists a) \,.\, E ! R^{\sigma}`a \,.\, R^{\sigma}`a \in \text{G}`P^\sigma \,.$

[∗330·52] $\supset .\, (\exists a) \,.\, E ! P^{\sigma}`R^{\sigma}`a$ (1)

$\vdash . ∗330·57 . \supset \vdash : \text{Hp}\,(1) \,.\, x = P^{\sigma}`R^{\sigma}`a \,.\supset .\, E ! \breve{P}^{\sigma}`x \,.\, E ! \breve{R}^{\sigma}`x$ (2)

$\vdash . (2) . ∗330·71 . \supset$

$\vdash : \text{Hp}\,(2) \,.\, Q, S \in \kappa \,.\, L = \breve{P} \,|\, Q \,.\, M = \breve{R} \,|\, S \,.\supset .\, E ! L^{\rho}`x \,.\, E ! M^{\sigma}`x \,.$

[∗33·43] $\supset .\, x \in \text{G}`L^\rho \cap \text{G}`M^\sigma$ (3)

$\vdash . (1) . (3) . \supset \vdash . \text{Prop}$

We have "NC induct" in the above proposition, not "NC ind," because it is necessary to have $E ! L^\rho \,.\, E ! M^\sigma$, and by ∗301·16 this may fail if either ρ or σ is null in the type of L and M. The existence of a family does not imply the axiom of infinity, since the family may be cyclic.

∗330·73. $\vdash : \kappa \in FM \,.\, P, Q \in \kappa \,.\, \rho \in \text{NC ind} \,.\, E ! (\breve{P} \,|\, Q)^{\rho}`x \,.\supset .$

$$(\breve{P} \,|\, Q)^{\rho}`x = \breve{P}^{\rho}`Q^{\rho}`x$$

Dem.

$\vdash . ∗330·56 . \supset \vdash : \text{Hp} \,.\, E ! \breve{P}`y \,.\supset .\, Q`\breve{P}`y = \breve{P}`Q`y$ (1)

$\vdash . (1) . \supset \vdash : \text{Hp} \,.\, Q`\breve{P}^{\rho -_c 1}`x = \breve{P}^{\rho -_c 1}`Q`x \,.\, E ! \breve{P}^{\rho}`y \,.\supset .\, Q`\breve{P}^{\rho}`y = \breve{P}`Q`\breve{P}^{\rho -_c 1}`y$

[Hp] $= \breve{P}`\breve{P}^{\rho -_c 1}`Q`y$

[∗301·23] $= \breve{P}^{\rho}`Q`y$ (2)

$\vdash . (1) . (2) . \text{Induct} . \supset \vdash : \text{Hp} \,.\, E ! \breve{P}^{\rho}`y \,.\supset .\, Q`\breve{P}^{\rho}`y = \breve{P}^{\rho}`Q`y$ (3)

$\vdash . ∗301·23 . \supset \vdash : \text{Hp} \,.\, (\breve{P} \,|\, Q)^{\rho}`x = \breve{P}^{\rho}`Q^{\rho}`x \,.\, E ! (\breve{P} \,|\, Q)^{\rho +_c 1}`x \,.\supset .$

$(\breve{P} \,|\, Q)^{\rho +_c 1}`x = \breve{P}`Q`\breve{P}^{\rho}`Q^{\rho}`x$

[(3)] $= \breve{P}`\breve{P}^{\rho}`Q`Q^{\rho}`x$

[∗301·23] $= \breve{P}^{\rho +_c 1}`Q^{\rho +_c 1}`x$ (4)

$\vdash . (4) . \text{Induct} . \supset \vdash . \text{Prop}$

*331. CONNECTED FAMILIES.

Summary of *331.

A "connected point" of a family κ is a point of the field of κ from which every member of the field can be reached by a member of κ or the converse of a member. That is, if a is a connected point, we are to have

$$x \in s`\text{ᗡ}``\kappa \,.\supset_x .\, (\exists R) \,.\, R \in \kappa \,.\, x (R \cup \breve{R})\, a$$

as well as $a \in s`\text{ᗡ}``\kappa$. This amounts to saying that every member of $s`\text{ᗡ}``\kappa$ is of the form $R`a$ or $\breve{R}`a$, where $R \in \kappa$. The definition is

***331·01.** $\text{conx}`\kappa = s`\text{ᗡ}``\kappa \cap \hat{a}(\overrightarrow{\dot{s}`\kappa}`a \cup \overleftarrow{\dot{s}`\kappa}`a = s`\text{ᗡ}``\kappa)$ Df

Here we include the factor $s`\text{ᗡ}``\kappa$ in the definition, in order to exclude the case when $\kappa = \iota`\dot{\Lambda}$. If $s`\text{ᗡ}``\kappa$ were not included, we should have $\text{conx}`\iota`\dot{\Lambda} = \text{V}$, whereas with the above definition $\text{conx}`\iota`\dot{\Lambda} = \Lambda$.

In the case of any other family, the factor $s`\text{ᗡ}``\kappa$ makes no difference, since if $s`\text{ᗡ}``\kappa$ exists,

$$\overrightarrow{\dot{s}`\kappa}`a \cup \overleftarrow{\dot{s}`\kappa}`a = s`\text{ᗡ}``\kappa \,.\supset .\, a \in C`\dot{s}`\kappa,$$

and if κ is a family, $C`\dot{s}`\kappa = s`\text{ᗡ}``\kappa$. But in the case of $\iota`\dot{\Lambda}$, the factor $s`\text{ᗡ}``\kappa$ insures that no connected point exists, thus securing, conversely, that a family which has a connected point is not $\iota`\dot{\Lambda}$. This is convenient, since the case of $\iota`\dot{\Lambda}$, which is trivial, would often otherwise have to be explicitly excluded.

The definition would be more analogous to the definition of a connected relation in *202 if we put

$$\text{conx}`\kappa = s`\text{ᗡ}``\kappa \cap \hat{a}(\overrightarrow{\dot{s}`\kappa_\partial}`a \cup \overleftarrow{\dot{s}`\kappa_\partial}`a \cup \iota`a = s`\text{ᗡ}``\kappa) \quad \text{Df.}$$

But this definition fails to give us the information that there is a member of κ which relates a to itself, whereas our definition does give this information, and hence leads to the proof that $I \upharpoonright s`\text{ᗡ}``\kappa \in \kappa$, *i.e.* that there is a zero vector.

We say that a family "is connected" when it has at least one connected point, *i.e.* we put

***331·02.** $FM\,\text{conx} = FM \cap \hat{\kappa}(\exists\,!\,\text{conx}`\kappa)$ Df

When *all* points of the field are connected points, the family "has connexity" (cf. $*334{\cdot}27$), provided $\kappa \neq \iota'\dot{\Lambda}$. For the present, we only assume that at least one of the points of the field is a connected point. To take an illustration: the family whose members are of the form $(\times_0 \mu) \upharpoonright (\text{NC induct} - \iota'0)$, where $\mu \in \text{NC induct} - \iota'0$, has only one connected point, namely 1. If we had taken positive and negative integers, both as multipliers and as constituting the field, we should have had two connected points, namely 1 and -1.

Almost all our future propositions on vector-families will be confined to *connected* families. In the present number, we prove first that in a connected family κ, the vector which relates a connected point to itself also relates any other member of the field to itself ($*331{\cdot}2$), whence it follows that $I \upharpoonright s'\mathrm{C}``\kappa$ is a member of $\kappa$ ($*331{\cdot}22$), and that every other member of $\kappa$ is wholly contained in diversity ($*331{\cdot}23$), and that $\kappa \cup \text{Cnv}``\kappa \subset \kappa_\iota$ ($*331{\cdot}24$). We next prove that the product of two members of κ is a member of κ or of $\text{Cnv}``\kappa$ ($*331{\cdot}33$). We then proceed to consider $\kappa_\iota$, and prove at once the two fundamental properties of $\kappa_\iota$ in a connected family, namely (1) that between any two members of $s'\mathrm{C}``\kappa$ there is a relation which is a member of κ_ι ($*331{\cdot}4$), and (2) that two members of κ_ι whose logical product exists are identical ($*331{\cdot}42$). From these two propositions it follows that there is just one member of κ_ι which relates any two members of $s'\mathrm{C}``\kappa$ ($*331{\cdot}43$). Finally we prove that any power of a member of $\kappa$ is a member of $\kappa \cup \text{Cnv}``\kappa$ ($*331{\cdot}54$), and that any power of a member of κ_ι is contained in some member of κ_ι ($*331{\cdot}56$).

Stated symbolically, the above propositions are as follows:

$*331{\cdot}2$. $\vdash :. \kappa \in FM \,.\, a \in \text{conx}'\kappa \,.\, x \in s'\mathrm{C}``\kappa \,.\, R \in \kappa \,.\, \supset : R'a = a \,.\equiv.\, R'x = x$

$*331{\cdot}22$. $\vdash : \kappa \in FM\,\text{conx} \,.\supset.\, I \upharpoonright s'\mathrm{C}``\kappa \in \kappa$

$*331{\cdot}23$. $\vdash : \kappa \in FM\,\text{conx} \,.\supset.\, \kappa \subset \text{Rl}'I \cup \text{Rl}'J$

$*331{\cdot}24$. $\vdash : \kappa \in FM\,\text{conx} \,.\supset.\, \kappa \cup \text{Cnv}``\kappa \subset \kappa_\iota$

$*331{\cdot}33$. $\vdash : \kappa \in FM\,\text{conx} \,.\supset.\, s'\kappa \mathbin{|}_{''} {}``\kappa \subset \kappa \cup \text{Cnv}``\kappa$

$*331{\cdot}4$. $\vdash : \kappa \in FM\,\text{conx} \,.\, x, y \in s'\mathrm{C}``\kappa \,.\supset.\, (\exists L) \,.\, L \in \kappa_\iota \,.\, x = L'y$

$*331{\cdot}42$. $\vdash :. \kappa \in FM\,\text{conx} \,.\, L, M \in \kappa_\iota \,.\supset : \dot{\exists} \,!\, L \dot{\cap} M \,.\equiv.\, L = M$

$*331{\cdot}43$. $\vdash : \kappa \in FM\,\text{conx} \,.\, x, y \in s'\mathrm{C}``\kappa \,.\supset.\, \hat{M}(M \in \kappa_\iota \,.\, xMy) \in 1$

$*331{\cdot}54$. $\vdash : \kappa \in FM\,\text{conx} \,.\, P \in \kappa \,.\supset.\, \text{Pot}'P \subset \kappa \cup \text{Cnv}``\kappa$

$*331{\cdot}56$. $\vdash : \kappa \in FM\,\text{conx} \,.\, L \in \kappa_\iota \,.\, M \in \text{Pot}'L \,.\supset.\, (\exists N) \,.\, N \in \kappa_\iota \,.\, M \Subset N$

$*331{\cdot}01$. $\text{conx}'\kappa = s'\mathrm{C}``\kappa \cap \hat{a}(\overrightarrow{s'\kappa}'a \cup \overleftarrow{s'\kappa}'a = s'\mathrm{C}``\kappa)$ Df

$*331{\cdot}02$. $FM\,\text{conx} = FM \cap \hat{\kappa}(\exists \,!\, \text{conx}'\kappa)$ Df

$*331{\cdot}1$. $\quad \vdash : a \,\epsilon\, \text{conx}'\kappa \,.\, \equiv \,.\, a \,\epsilon\, s'\overrightarrow{\mathrm{D}}''\kappa \,.\, \overrightarrow{s}'\kappa'a \,\cup\, \overleftarrow{s}'\kappa'a = s'\mathrm{D}''\kappa \quad [(*331{\cdot}01)]$

$*331{\cdot}11$. $\quad \vdash :.\, a \,\epsilon\, \text{conx}'\kappa \,.\, \equiv \,:\, a \,\epsilon\, s'\mathrm{D}''\kappa : x \,\epsilon\, s'\mathrm{D}''\kappa \,.\, \supset_x .\, (\exists R) \,.\, R \,\epsilon\, \kappa \,.\, x (R \cup \breve{R}) a$
$\qquad [*331{\cdot}1]$

$*331{\cdot}12$. $\quad \vdash :\, \exists\,!\, \text{conx}'\kappa \,.\, \supset .\, \kappa \,\neq\, \iota'\dot{\Lambda} \quad [*331{\cdot}1]$

$*331{\cdot}13$. $\quad \vdash :.\, \kappa \,\epsilon\, \text{Cl ex}'\text{cr}'\alpha \,.\, \supset :\, a \,\epsilon\, \text{conx}'\kappa \,.\, \equiv \,.\, \kappa \,\neq\, \iota'\dot{\Lambda} \,.\, \overrightarrow{s}'\kappa'a \,\cup\, \overleftarrow{s}'\kappa'a = s'\mathrm{D}''\kappa$
$\quad$ *Dem.*

$\vdash .\, *53{\cdot}24 .\, \supset \vdash : \text{Hp} .\, \kappa \,\neq\, \iota'\dot{\Lambda} .\, \overrightarrow{s}'\kappa'a \,\cup\, \overleftarrow{s}'\kappa'a = s'\mathrm{D}''\kappa .\, \supset .\, \exists\,!\, \overrightarrow{s}'\kappa'a \,\cup\, \overleftarrow{s}'\kappa'a .$
$[*330{\cdot}13] \hspace{8cm} \supset .\, a \,\epsilon\, s'\mathrm{D}''\kappa \qquad (1)$
$\vdash .\, (1) .\, *331{\cdot}1{\cdot}12 .\, \supset \vdash .\, \text{Prop}$

$*331{\cdot}131$. $\quad \vdash :: \kappa \,\epsilon\, \text{Cl ex}'\text{cr}'\alpha \,.\, \supset :.\, a \,\epsilon\, \text{conx}'\kappa \,.\, \equiv \,:\, \kappa \,\neq\, \iota'\dot{\Lambda} : x \,\epsilon\, s'\mathrm{D}''\kappa \,.\, \supset_x .$
$\qquad\qquad\qquad (\exists R) \,.\, R \,\epsilon\, \kappa \,.\, x (R \cup \breve{R}) a \quad [*331{\cdot}13]$

$*331{\cdot}14$. $\quad \vdash :.\, \lambda = \kappa \,\cup\, \text{Cnv}''\kappa \,.\, \supset :\, a \,\epsilon\, \text{conx}'\kappa \,.\, \equiv \,.\, a \,\epsilon\, s'\mathrm{D}''\kappa \,.\, \overrightarrow{s}'\lambda'a = s'\mathrm{D}''\kappa$
$\qquad [*331{\cdot}1]$

$*331{\cdot}2$. $\quad \vdash :.\, \kappa \,\epsilon\, FM \,.\, a \,\epsilon\, \text{conx}'\kappa \,.\, x \,\epsilon\, s'\mathrm{D}''\kappa \,.\, R \,\epsilon\, \kappa \,.\, \supset :\, R'a = a \,.\, \equiv \,.\, R'x = x$
$\quad$ *Dem.*

$\vdash .\, *331{\cdot}11 . \hspace{2cm} \supset \vdash : \text{Hp} .\, \supset .\, (\exists S) \,.\, S \,\epsilon\, \kappa \,.\, x (S \cup \breve{S}) a \qquad (1)$
$\vdash .\, *330{\cdot}5 . \hspace{2cm} \supset \vdash : \text{Hp} .\, S \,\epsilon\, \kappa \,.\, x = S'a \,.\, R'a = a \,.\, \supset .\, R'x = S'R'a$
$[\text{Hp}] \hspace{8cm} = S'a$
$[\text{Hp}] \hspace{8cm} = x \qquad (2)$
$\vdash .\, *330{\cdot}56 . \hspace{1.5cm} \supset \vdash : \text{Hp} .\, S \,\epsilon\, \kappa \,.\, x = \breve{S}'a \,.\, R'a = a \,.\, \supset .\, R'x = \breve{S}'R'a$
$[\text{Hp}] \hspace{8cm} = \breve{S}'a$
$[\text{Hp}] \hspace{8cm} = x \qquad (3)$
$\vdash .\, (1) .\, (2) .\, (3) .\, \supset \vdash :.\, \text{Hp} .\, \supset :\, R'a = a \,.\, \supset .\, R'x = x \qquad (4)$
$\text{Similarly} \hspace{2cm} \vdash :.\, \text{Hp} .\, \supset :\, R'x = x \,.\, \supset .\, R'a = a \qquad (5)$
$\vdash .\, (4) .\, (5) .\, \supset \vdash .\, \text{Prop}$

$*331{\cdot}21$. $\quad \vdash :.\, \kappa \,\epsilon\, FM \,.\, a \,\epsilon\, \text{conx}'\kappa \,.\, R \,\epsilon\, \kappa \,.\, \supset :\, R'a = a \,.\, \equiv \,.\, I \,{\upharpoonright}\, s'\mathrm{D}''\kappa = R$
$\quad$ *Dem.*

$\vdash .\, *331{\cdot}2 .\, \supset \vdash : \text{Hp} .\, R'a = a \,.\, \supset .\, I \,{\upharpoonright}\, s'\mathrm{D}''\kappa = R \qquad (1)$
$\vdash .\, *331{\cdot}1 .\, \supset \vdash : \text{Hp} .\, I \,{\upharpoonright}\, s'\mathrm{D}''\kappa = R \,.\, \supset .\, R'a = a \qquad (2)$
$\vdash .\, (1) .\, (2) .\, \supset \vdash .\, \text{Prop}$

$*331{\cdot}22$. $\quad \vdash :\, \kappa \,\epsilon\, FM \,\text{conx} \,.\, \supset .\, I \,{\upharpoonright}\, s'\mathrm{D}''\kappa \,\epsilon\, \kappa$
$\quad$ *Dem.*

$\vdash .\, *331{\cdot}11 .\, \supset \vdash : \text{Hp} .\, a \,\epsilon\, \text{conx}'\kappa \,.\, \supset .\, (\exists R) \,.\, R \,\epsilon\, \kappa \,.\, R'a = a \qquad (1)$
$\vdash .\, (1) .\, *331{\cdot}21 .\, \supset \vdash .\, \text{Prop}$

∗331·23. $\vdash : \kappa \in FM \text{ conx} . \supset . \kappa \subset \text{Rl}`I \cup \text{Rl}`J$

Dem.

$\vdash . ∗331·2·21 . \supset \vdash : \text{Hp} . R \in \kappa . \dot{\exists} ! R \dot{\cap} I . \supset . R \mathrel{G} I : \supset \vdash . \text{Prop}$

∗331·24. $\vdash : \kappa \in FM \text{ conx} . \supset . \kappa \cup \text{Cnv}``\kappa \subset \kappa_\iota$ [∗330·42 . ∗331·22]

∗331·25. $\vdash : \kappa \in FM \text{ conx} - 1 . \supset . \exists ! \kappa \cap \text{Rl}`J$ [∗331·22·23]

∗331·26. $\vdash : \kappa \in FM \text{ conx} - 1 . \supset . \dot{s}`\kappa, \dot{s}`\kappa_\iota \sim\in \kappa_\iota$

Dem.

$\vdash . ∗331·22·25 . \supset \vdash : \text{Hp} . \supset . (\exists a, R, S, x) . R, S \in \kappa . aRa . aSx . a \neq x .$

[∗71·172.∗41·11] $\supset . \dot{s}`\kappa \sim\in 1 \rightarrow 1 .$ (1)

[∗331·24] $\supset . \dot{s}`\kappa_\iota \sim\in 1 \rightarrow 1$ (2)

$\vdash . (1) . (2) . ∗330·52 . \supset \vdash . \text{Prop}$

∗331·31. $\vdash :. \kappa \in FM . a \in \text{conx}`\kappa . x \in s`\text{C}``\kappa . P \in \kappa . N \in \kappa_\iota . \supset :$

$P`a = N`a . \equiv . P`x = N`x$

Dem.

$\vdash . ∗331·11 . ∗330·4 . \supset$

$\vdash : \text{Hp} . \supset . (\exists Q, R, S) . Q, R, S \in \kappa . x (Q \cup \breve{Q}) a . N = \breve{R} | S$ (1)

$\vdash . ∗330·5 . \supset$

$\vdash : \text{Hp} . Q, R, S \in \kappa . x = Q`a . N = \breve{R} | S . P`a = N`a . \supset . P`x = Q`\breve{R}`S`a$

[∗330·56] $= \breve{R}`Q`S`a$

[∗330·5] $= \breve{R}`S`Q`a$

[Hp] $= N`x$ (2)

$\vdash . ∗330·56 . \supset$

$\vdash : \text{Hp} . Q, R, S \in \kappa . x = \breve{Q}`a . N = \breve{R} | S . P`a = N`a . \supset . P`x = \breve{Q}`\breve{R}`S`a$

[∗330·5] $= \breve{R}`\breve{Q}`S`a$

[∗330·56.Hp] $= \breve{R}`S`\breve{Q}`a$

[Hp] $= N`x$ (3)

$\vdash . (1) . (2) . (3) . \supset \vdash : \text{Hp} . P`a = N`a . \supset . P`x = N`x$ (4)

Similarly $\vdash : \text{Hp} . P`x = N`x . \supset . P`a = N`a$ (5)

$\vdash . (4) . (5) . \supset \vdash . \text{Prop}$

∗331·32. $\vdash :. \kappa \in FM \text{ conx} . P \in \kappa . N \in \kappa_\iota . \supset : \dot{\exists} ! P \dot{\cap} N . \equiv . P = N$

Dem.

$\vdash . ∗331·31 . \supset \vdash :: \text{Hp} . a \in \text{conx}`\kappa . \supset :. x, y \in s`\text{C}``\kappa . \supset :$

$P`x = N`x . \equiv . P`a = N`a . \equiv . P`y = N`y$ (1)

$\vdash . (1) . (∗331·02) . \supset \vdash :. \text{Hp} . \supset : x, y \in s`\text{C}``\kappa . P`x = N`x . \supset . P`y = N`y :$

[∗33·45.∗72·94] $\supset : \dot{\exists} ! P \dot{\cap} N . \supset . P = N$ (2)

$\vdash . ∗331·12 . ∗330·16 . \supset \vdash :. \text{Hp} . \supset : P = N . \supset . \dot{\exists} ! P \dot{\cap} N$ (3)

$\vdash . (2) . (3) . \supset \vdash . \text{Prop}$

***331·321.** $\vdash :. \kappa \in FM \text{ conx} . P, Q \in \kappa . \supset : \dot{\exists} ! P \dot{\frown} Q . \equiv . P = Q$ [*331·32·24]

***331·33.** $\vdash : \kappa \in FM \text{ conx} . \supset . s`\kappa \,|\,``\kappa \subset \kappa \cup \text{Cnv}``\kappa$

Dem.

$\vdash . *331{\cdot}11 . \supset \vdash :. \text{Hp} . \supset : (\exists a) : P, Q \in \kappa . \supset_{P,Q} . (\exists R) . (P`Q`a)(R \cup \breve{R})\, a$ (1)

$\vdash . *330{\cdot}5 . \supset$

$\vdash : \text{Hp} . P, Q, R \in \kappa . P`Q`a = R`a . S \in \kappa . y = S`a . \supset . P`Q`y = S`P`Q`a$

[Hp] $= S`R`a$

[*330·5.Hp] $= R`y$ (2)

$\vdash . *330{\cdot}56 . \supset$

$\vdash : \text{Hp} . P, Q, R \in \kappa . P`Q`a = R`a . S \in \kappa . y = \breve{S}`a . \supset . P`Q`y = \breve{S}`P`Q`a$

[Hp] $= \breve{S}`R`a$

[*330·56.Hp] $= R`y$ (3)

$\vdash . (2) . (3) . *331{\cdot}11 . \supset \vdash : \text{Hp} . P, Q, R \in \kappa . P`Q`a = R`a . \supset . P \,|\, Q = R$ (4)

Similarly $\vdash : \text{Hp} . P, Q, R \in \kappa . P`Q`a = \breve{R}`a . \supset . P \,|\, Q = \breve{R}$ (5)

$\vdash . (1) . (4) . (5) . \supset$

$\vdash :. \text{Hp} . P, Q \in \kappa . \supset : (\exists R) : R \in \kappa : P \,|\, Q = R . \vee . P \,|\, Q = \breve{R} :. \supset \vdash . \text{Prop}$

***331·4.** $\vdash : \kappa \in FM \text{ conx} . x, y \in s`\text{C}``\kappa . \supset . (\exists L) . L \in \kappa_\iota . x = \dot{L}`y$

Dem.

$\vdash . *331{\cdot}11 . \supset \vdash : \text{Hp} . \supset . (\exists a, R, S) . R, S \in \kappa . x (R \cup \breve{R})\, a . y (S \cup \breve{S})\, a$ (1)

$\vdash . *330{\cdot}56 . \supset \vdash : \text{Hp} . R, S \in \kappa . x = R`a . y = S`a . \supset . x = \breve{S}`R`y .$

[*330·4] $\supset . (\exists L) . L \in \kappa_\iota . x = L`y$ (2)

$\vdash . *331{\cdot}24{\cdot}33 . \supset$

$\vdash : \text{Hp} . R, S \in \kappa . x = R`a . y = \breve{S}`a . \supset . R \,|\, S \in \kappa_\iota . x = (R \,|\, S)`y$ (3)

$\vdash . *331{\cdot}24{\cdot}33 . \supset$

$\vdash : \text{Hp} . R, S \in \kappa . x = \breve{R}`a . y = S`a . \supset . \breve{R} \,|\, \breve{S} \in \kappa_\iota . x = (\breve{R} \,|\, \breve{S})`y$ (4)

$\vdash . *330{\cdot}4 . \supset$

$\vdash : \text{Hp} . R, S \in \kappa . x = \breve{R}`a . y = \breve{S}`a . \supset . \breve{R} \,|\, S \in \kappa_\iota . x = (\breve{R} \,|\, S)`y$ (5)

$\vdash . (1) . (2) . (3) . (4) . (5) . \supset \vdash . \text{Prop}$

***331·41.** $\vdash : \kappa \in FM \text{ conx} . \supset . \dot{s}`\kappa_\iota = (s`\text{C}``\kappa) \uparrow (s`\text{C}``\kappa)$ [*331·4]

***331·42.** $\vdash :. \kappa \in FM \text{ conx} . L, M \in \kappa_\iota . \supset : \dot{\exists} ! L \dot{\frown} M . \equiv . L = M$

Dem.

$\vdash . *330{\cdot}6 . *331{\cdot}12 . \supset \vdash : \text{Hp} . L = M . \supset . \dot{\exists} ! L \dot{\frown} M$ (1)

$\vdash . *331{\cdot}4 . \supset$

$\vdash : \text{Hp} . L`x = M`x . \text{E} ! L`y . \supset . (\exists N) . N \in \kappa_\iota . N`x = y . \text{E} ! L`y .$

[*330·63] $\supset . (\exists N) . N \in \kappa_\iota . N\text{‘}x = y . L\text{‘}y = N\text{‘}L\text{‘}x$

[Hp] $= N\text{‘}M\text{‘}x$

[*330·63] $= M\text{‘}N\text{‘}x$

[*13·12] $\supset . L\text{‘}y = M\text{‘}y$ (2)

Similarly $\vdash : \mathrm{Hp} . L\text{‘}x = M\text{‘}x . \mathrm{E} ! M\text{‘}y . \supset . L\text{‘}y = M\text{‘}y$ (3)

$\vdash . (2) . (3) . *71·35 . \supset \vdash : \mathrm{Hp} . \dot{\exists} ! L \dot{\cap} M . \supset . L = M$ (4)

$\vdash . (1) . (4) . \supset \vdash . \mathrm{Prop}$

***331·43.** $\vdash : \kappa \in FM \,\mathrm{conx} . x, y \in s\text{‘}\text{Ɑ}\text{“}\kappa . \supset . \hat{M}(M \in \kappa_\iota . xMy) \in 1$

Dem.

$\vdash . *331·4 . \supset \vdash : \mathrm{Hp} . \supset . (\exists M) . (M \in \kappa_\iota . xMy)$ (1)

$\vdash . *331·42 . \supset \vdash : \mathrm{Hp} . L, M \in \kappa_\iota . xMy . xLy . \supset . L = M$ (2)

$\vdash . (1) . (2) . \supset \vdash . \mathrm{Prop}$

***331·44.** $\vdash :. \kappa \in FM \,\mathrm{conx} . P, Q \in \kappa . \supset : \dot{\exists} ! P \dot{\cap} Q . \equiv . P = Q$ [*331·42·24]

***331·45.** $\vdash :. \kappa \in FM \,\mathrm{conx} . L, M, N \in \kappa_\iota . \supset :$

$\dot{\exists} ! L | M \dot{\cap} N . \equiv . L | M = N \upharpoonright \text{Ɑ}\text{‘}(L | M)$

Dem.

$\vdash . *330·611 . \supset \vdash : \mathrm{Hp} . L | M = N \upharpoonright \text{Ɑ}\text{‘}(L | M) . \supset . \dot{\exists} ! L | M \dot{\cap} N$ (1)

$\vdash . *330·63 . \supset \vdash : \mathrm{Hp} . L\text{‘}M\text{‘}x = N\text{‘}x . \mathrm{E} ! L\text{‘}M\text{‘}y . X \in \kappa_\iota . y = X\text{‘}x . \supset .$

$L\text{‘}M\text{‘}y = L\text{‘}X\text{‘}M\text{‘}x . \mathrm{E} ! L\text{‘}M\text{‘}x . \mathrm{E} ! L\text{‘}X\text{‘}M\text{‘}x . \mathrm{E} ! X\text{‘}x .$

[*330·63] $\supset . L\text{‘}M\text{‘}y = X\text{‘}L\text{‘}M\text{‘}x . \mathrm{E} ! X\text{‘}x .$

[Hp] $\supset . L\text{‘}M\text{‘}y = X\text{‘}N\text{‘}x . \mathrm{E} ! X\text{‘}x .$

[*330·63] $\supset . L\text{‘}M\text{‘}y = N\text{‘}X\text{‘}x$

[Hp] $= N\text{‘}y$ (2)

$\vdash . (2) . *331·4 . \supset \vdash : \mathrm{Hp} . L\text{‘}M\text{‘}x = N\text{‘}x . y \in \text{Ɑ}\text{‘}(L | M) . \supset . L\text{‘}M\text{‘}y = N\text{‘}y$ (3)

$\vdash . (1) . (3) . \supset \vdash . \mathrm{Prop}$

***331·46.** $\vdash :. \mathrm{Hp}\, *331·45 . \supset : M | L = N \upharpoonright \text{Ɑ}\text{‘}(M | L) . \equiv . L | M = N \upharpoonright \text{Ɑ}\text{‘}(L | M)$

Dem.

$\vdash . *330·642·63 . \supset \vdash : \mathrm{Hp} . L | M = N \upharpoonright \text{Ɑ}\text{‘}(L | M) . \supset . (\exists x) . M\text{‘}L\text{‘}x = N\text{‘}x .$

[*331·45] $\supset . M | L = N \upharpoonright \text{Ɑ}\text{‘}(M | L)$ (1)

Similarly $\vdash : \mathrm{Hp} . M | L = N \upharpoonright \text{Ɑ}\text{‘}(M | L) . \supset . L | M = N \upharpoonright \text{Ɑ}\text{‘}(L | M)$ (2)

$\vdash . (1) . (2) . \supset \vdash . \mathrm{Prop}$

***331·47.** $\vdash : \kappa \in FM \,\mathrm{conx} . L, M \in \kappa_\iota . \supset . (\exists N) . N \in \kappa_\iota . L | M \subseteq N . M | L \subseteq N$ [*331·46·45·4]

***331·48.** $\vdash : \kappa \in FM . L \in \kappa_\iota . \exists ! \mathrm{conx}\text{‘}\kappa \cap C\text{‘}L . \supset . L \in \kappa \cup \mathrm{Cnv}\text{“}\kappa$

Dem.

$\vdash . *330·41 . \supset \vdash :. \mathrm{Hp} . a \in \mathrm{conx}\text{‘}\kappa \cap C\text{‘}L . \supset : L, \breve{L} \in \kappa_\iota : \mathrm{E} ! L\text{‘}a . \vee . \mathrm{E} ! \breve{L}\text{‘}a :$

[*331·11] $\supset : L, \breve{L} \in \kappa_\iota : (\exists R) : R \in \kappa \cup \mathrm{Cnv}\text{“}\kappa : L\text{‘}a = R\text{‘}a . \vee . \breve{L}\text{‘}a = R\text{‘}a :$

[*331·24·42] $\supset : (\exists R) : R \in \kappa \cup \mathrm{Cnv}\text{“}\kappa : L = R . \vee . \breve{L} = R :. \supset \vdash . \mathrm{Prop}$

***331·5.** $\vdash : \kappa \epsilon FM \text{ conx} . P \epsilon \kappa . L \epsilon \kappa_\iota . \supset . L | P, \breve{P} | L \epsilon \kappa_\iota$

Dem.

$\vdash . *331{\cdot}33 . \supset$

$\vdash : \text{Hp} . Q, R \epsilon \kappa . L = \breve{Q} | R . \supset . (\exists S) . S \epsilon \kappa \cup \text{Cnv}``\kappa . L | P = \breve{Q} | S$ (1)

$\vdash . *330{\cdot}4 . \supset \vdash : \text{Hp}(1) . S \epsilon \kappa . L | P = \breve{Q} | S . \supset . L | P \epsilon \kappa_\iota$ (2)

$\vdash . *34{\cdot}2 . \supset$

$\vdash : \text{Hp}(1) . S \epsilon \text{Cnv}``\kappa . L | P = \breve{Q} | S . \supset . (\exists T) . T \epsilon \kappa . L | P = \text{Cnv}`(T | Q) .$

[*331·33] $\supset . L | P \epsilon \kappa \cup \text{Cnv}``\kappa .$

[*331·24] $\supset . L | P \epsilon \kappa_\iota$ (3)

$\vdash . (1) . (2) . (3) . *330{\cdot}41 . \supset \vdash . \text{Prop}$

***331·51.** $\vdash : \kappa \epsilon FM \text{ conx} . P \epsilon \kappa . \supset . \text{Pot}`P \subset \kappa_\iota$ [*331·5 . Induct]

***331·52.** $\vdash : \kappa \epsilon FM \text{ conx} . P, Q \epsilon \kappa . L \epsilon \kappa_\iota . \supset . \breve{P} | L | Q \epsilon \kappa_\iota$ [*331·5]

***331·53.** $\vdash : \kappa \epsilon FM \text{ conx} . P, Q \epsilon \kappa . \rho, \sigma \epsilon \text{NC induct} . \supset . \breve{P}^\rho | Q^\sigma \epsilon \kappa_\iota$
[*331·5 . Induct . *331·51 . *330·43]

***331·54.** $\vdash : \kappa \epsilon FM \text{ conx} . P \epsilon \kappa . \supset . \text{Pot}`P \subset \kappa \cup \text{Cnv}``\kappa$

Dem.

$\vdash . *330{\cdot}711 . \supset \vdash : \text{Hp} . a \epsilon \text{conx}`\kappa . Q \epsilon \text{Pot}`P . \supset . E ! Q`a .$

[*331·11] $\supset . (\exists T) . T \epsilon \kappa \cup \text{Cnv}``\kappa . Q`a = T`a .$

[*331·51·42·24] $\supset . Q \epsilon \kappa \cup \text{Cnv}``\kappa : \supset \vdash . \text{Prop}$

***331·55.** $\vdash : \kappa \epsilon FM \text{ conx} . P, Q \epsilon \kappa_\iota . \rho \epsilon \text{NC induct} . \supset .$
$(\breve{P} | Q)^\rho \in \breve{P}^\rho | Q^\rho . \breve{P}^\rho | Q^\rho \epsilon \kappa_\iota$ [*330·73 . *331·53]

***331·56.** $\vdash : \kappa \epsilon FM \text{ conx} . L \epsilon \kappa_\iota . M \epsilon \text{Pot}`L . \supset . (\exists N) . N \epsilon \kappa_\iota . M \in N$
[*331·55 . *330·4]

*332. ON THE REPRESENTATIVE OF A RELATION IN A FAMILY.

Summary of *332.

We saw at the end of the last number (*331·56) that any power of a member of κ_ι is contained in a member of κ_ι. When a relation is contained in a member of κ_ι, we call this member the "representative" of the relation in the family. For purposes connected with the application of ratio, the "representative" is an important function of a relation, especially when the relation concerned is a power of a member of κ_ι. By the definition of ratio (*303·01), we shall have $L(\rho/\sigma)M$ if $\dot{\exists}\,!\,L^\sigma \dot{\cap} M^\rho$ and $\rho\,\text{Prm}\,\sigma$. Now if L^σ and M^ρ each have a representative, then they must have the *same* representative if $\dot{\exists}\,!\,L^\sigma \dot{\cap} M^\rho$ (by *331·42). Hence we are enabled to substitute an equality for $\dot{\exists}\,!\,L^\sigma \dot{\cap} M^\rho$ in dealing with ratios of members of κ_ι. The elementary properties of representatives are dealt with in the present number.

We denote the representative of P in the family κ by "$\text{rep}_\kappa{}^\backprime P$." In order to insure $E\,!\,\text{rep}_\kappa{}^\backprime P$ under all circumstances, we do not define $\text{rep}_\kappa{}^\backprime P$ as the only member of κ_ι which contains P, but as the logical sum of the class of members of κ_ι which contain P, *i.e.* we put

***332·01.** $\text{rep}_\kappa{}^\backprime P = \dot{s}{}^\backprime(\kappa_\iota \cap \overleftarrow{\mathfrak{C}}{}^\backprime P)$ Df

In a connected family, if P is not null, $\kappa_\iota \cap \overleftarrow{\mathfrak{C}}{}^\backprime P$ cannot have more than one member (*332·21), and therefore the representative of P, if it is not null, must be a member of κ_ι (*332·22). If P is a member of κ_ι, it is its own representative (*332·241).

We prove in this number that, if $P, Q, R, \ldots$ have existent representatives, the representative of their relative product (unless this product is null) is the representative of the relative product of their representatives (*332·37). Among other important propositions in this number are the following:

***332·32.** $\vdash : \kappa \in FM\,\text{conx} \,.\, L, M \in \kappa_\iota \,.\, \supset \,.\, \text{rep}_\kappa{}^\backprime(L \mid M) = \text{rep}_\kappa{}^\backprime(M \mid L)$

***332·51.** $\vdash : \kappa \in FM\,\text{conx} \,.\, P, Q \in \kappa \,.\, \supset \,.\, \text{rep}_\kappa{}^\backprime(P \mid \breve{Q}) = \breve{Q} \mid P$

***332·53.** $\vdash : \kappa \in FM\,\text{conx} \,.\, P, Q \in \kappa \,.\, \rho \in \text{NC induct} \,.\, \supset \,.\, \text{rep}_\kappa{}^\backprime(\breve{P} \mid Q)^\rho = \breve{P}^\rho \mid Q^\rho$

***332·61.** $\vdash : \kappa \in FM\,\text{conx} \,.\, L \in \kappa_\iota \,.\, \supset \,.\, \text{rep}_\kappa{}^{\backprime\backprime}\text{Potid}{}^\backprime L \subset \kappa_\iota$

***332·8.** $\vdash : \kappa \epsilon FM \text{ conx} . L, M \epsilon \kappa_\iota . \xi \epsilon \text{NC ind} . \supset .$
$$\text{rep}_\kappa\text{‘}(L \mid M)^\xi = \text{rep}_\kappa\text{‘}(L^\xi \mid M^\xi)$$

***332·81.** $\vdash : \kappa \epsilon FM \text{ conx} . \nu, \sigma \epsilon \text{NC ind} - \iota\text{‘}0 . L \epsilon \kappa_\iota . \supset .$
$$\text{rep}_\kappa\text{‘}L^{\nu \times_c \sigma} = \text{rep}_\kappa\text{‘}(\text{rep}_\kappa\text{‘}L^\nu)^\sigma$$

***332·01.** $\text{rep}_\kappa\text{‘}P = \dot{s}\text{‘}(\kappa_\iota \cap \overleftarrow{G}\text{‘}P)$ Df

***332·1.** $\vdash . \text{rep}_\kappa\text{‘}P = \dot{s}\text{‘}(\kappa_\iota \cap \overleftarrow{G}\text{‘}P) = \hat{x}\hat{y}\{(\exists L) . L \epsilon \kappa_\iota . P \mathrel{G} L . xLy\}$
[(*332·01)]

***332·11.** $\vdash : \dot{\exists} ! \text{rep}_\kappa\text{‘}P . \supset . P \mathrel{G} \text{rep}_\kappa\text{‘}P$ [*332·1]

***332·12.** $\vdash : \dot{\exists} ! \text{rep}_\kappa\text{‘}P . \supset . \exists ! (\kappa_\iota \cap \overleftarrow{G}\text{‘}P)$ [*332·1]

***332·13.** $\vdash . \text{rep}_\kappa\text{‘}\dot{\Lambda} = \dot{s}\text{‘}\kappa_\iota$ [*332·1]

***332·14.** $\vdash : P \mathrel{G} Q . \supset . \text{rep}_\kappa\text{‘}Q \mathrel{G} \text{rep}_\kappa\text{‘}P$ [*332·1]

***332·15.** $\vdash . \text{rep}_\kappa\text{‘}\breve{P} = \text{Cnv‘rep}_\kappa\text{‘}P$

Dem.

$\vdash . *330·41 . \supset \vdash . \kappa_\iota \cap \overleftarrow{G}\text{‘}\breve{P} = \text{Cnv“}(\kappa_\iota \cap \overleftarrow{G}\text{‘}P)$ (1)
$\vdash . (1) . *332·1 . \supset \vdash . \text{Prop}$

***332·16.** $\vdash : \kappa = \iota\text{‘}\dot{\Lambda} . \supset . \text{rep}_\kappa\text{‘}P = \dot{\Lambda}$ [*332·1]

***332·2.** $\vdash :. \kappa \epsilon FM - \iota\text{‘}\iota\text{‘}\dot{\Lambda} . \supset : \exists ! (\kappa_\iota \cap \overleftarrow{G}\text{‘}P) . \equiv . \dot{\exists} ! \text{rep}_\kappa\text{‘}P$

Dem.

$\vdash . *330·6 . \supset \vdash : \text{Hp} . \exists ! (\kappa_\iota \cap \overleftarrow{G}\text{‘}P) . \supset . \exists ! (\kappa_\iota \cap \overleftarrow{G}\text{‘}P) - \iota\text{‘}\dot{\Lambda} .$
[*332·1] $\supset . \dot{\exists} ! \text{rep}_\kappa\text{‘}P$ (1)
$\vdash . (1) . *332·12 . \supset \vdash . \text{Prop}$

***332·21.** $\vdash : \kappa \epsilon FM \text{ conx} . \dot{\exists} ! P . \supset . (\kappa_\iota \cap \overleftarrow{G}\text{‘}P) \epsilon 0 \cup 1$

Dem.

$\vdash . *331·42 . \supset \vdash : \text{Hp} . L, M \epsilon \kappa_\iota . P \mathrel{G} L . P \mathrel{G} M . \supset . L = M : \supset \vdash . \text{Prop}$

***332·22.** $\vdash :. \kappa \epsilon FM \text{ conx} . \dot{\exists} ! P . \supset : \text{rep}_\kappa\text{‘}P \epsilon \kappa_\iota . \vee . \text{rep}_\kappa\text{‘}P = \dot{\Lambda}$

Dem.

$\vdash . *332·21·12 . \supset \vdash : \text{Hp} . \dot{\exists} ! \text{rep}_\kappa\text{‘}P . \supset . (\kappa_\iota \cap \overleftarrow{G}\text{‘}P) \epsilon 1 .$
[*332·1] $\supset . \text{rep}_\kappa\text{‘}P \epsilon \kappa_\iota : \supset \vdash . \text{Prop}$

***332·23.** $\vdash :. \kappa \epsilon FM \text{ conx} . \dot{\exists} ! P . \supset : \text{rep}_\kappa\text{‘}P \epsilon \kappa_\iota . \equiv . \exists ! (\kappa_\iota \cap \overleftarrow{G}\text{‘}P)$

Dem.

$\vdash . *332·22·2 . \supset \vdash : \text{Hp} . \text{rep}_\kappa\text{‘}P \sim \epsilon \kappa_\iota . \supset . (\kappa_\iota \cap \overleftarrow{G}\text{‘}P) = \Lambda$ (1)
$\vdash . *330·6 . \supset \vdash : \text{Hp} . \text{rep}_\kappa\text{‘}P \epsilon \kappa_\iota . \supset . \dot{\exists} ! \text{rep}_\kappa\text{‘}P .$
[*332·2] $\supset . \exists ! (\kappa_\iota \cap \overleftarrow{G}\text{‘}P)$ (2)
$\vdash . (1) . (2) . \supset \vdash . \text{Prop}$

∗332·231. $\vdash :. \kappa \in FM \,\text{conx} - 1 . \supset : \text{rep}_\kappa\text{‘}P \in \kappa_\iota . \equiv . \dot{\exists} ! P . \exists ! (\kappa_\iota \cap \overleftarrow{C}\text{‘}P)$

Dem.

$\vdash . *331\cdot26 . \supset \vdash :. \text{Hp} . \supset : \text{rep}_\kappa\text{‘}P \in \kappa_\iota . \supset . \text{rep}_\kappa\text{‘}P \neq \dot{s}\text{‘}\kappa_\iota .$

$[*332\cdot13] \qquad \supset . P \neq \dot{\Lambda} \qquad (1)$

$\vdash . (1) . *332\cdot23 . \supset \vdash . \text{Prop}$

∗332·232. $\vdash :. \kappa \in FM \,\text{conx} - 1 . \supset : \text{rep}_\kappa\text{‘}P \in \kappa_\iota . \equiv . \dot{\exists} ! P . \dot{\exists} ! \text{rep}_\kappa\text{‘}P$

$[*332\cdot231\cdot2]$

∗332·24. $\vdash :. \kappa \in FM \,\text{conx} . \dot{\exists} ! P . \supset : L \in (\kappa_\iota \cap \overleftarrow{C}\text{‘}P) . \equiv . \dot{\exists} ! \text{rep}_\kappa\text{‘}P . \text{rep}_\kappa\text{‘}P = L$

Dem.

$\vdash . *332\cdot21\cdot1 . \quad \supset \vdash :. \text{Hp} . \supset : L \in \kappa_\iota \cap \overleftarrow{C}\text{‘}P . \supset . \text{rep}_\kappa\text{‘}P = L \qquad (1)$

$\vdash . *332\cdot2 . \quad \supset \vdash :. \text{Hp} . \supset : L \in \kappa_\iota \cap \overleftarrow{C}\text{‘}P . \supset . \dot{\exists} ! \text{rep}_\kappa\text{‘}P \qquad (2)$

$\vdash . *332\cdot22 . \quad \supset \vdash :. \text{Hp} . \supset : \dot{\exists} ! \text{rep}_\kappa\text{‘}P . \supset . \text{rep}_\kappa\text{‘}P \in \kappa_\iota :$

$[*13\cdot12] \qquad \supset : \dot{\exists} ! \text{rep}_\kappa\text{‘}P . \text{rep}_\kappa\text{‘}P = L . \supset . L \in \kappa_\iota \qquad (3)$

$\vdash . (3) . *332\cdot11 . \supset \vdash :. \text{Hp} . \supset : \dot{\exists} ! \text{rep}_\kappa\text{‘}P . \text{rep}_\kappa\text{‘}P = L . \supset . L \in (\kappa_\iota \cap \overleftarrow{C}\text{‘}P) \qquad (4)$

$\vdash . (1) . (2) . (4) . \supset \vdash . \text{Prop}$

∗332·241. $\vdash : \kappa \in FM \,\text{conx} . P \in \kappa_\iota . \supset . P = \text{rep}_\kappa\text{‘}P$

Dem.

$\vdash . *332\cdot24 . \supset \vdash :. \text{Hp} . \dot{\exists} ! P . \supset : P \in \kappa_\iota \cap \overleftarrow{C}\text{‘}P . \equiv . \dot{\exists} ! \text{rep}_\kappa\text{‘}P . \text{rep}_\kappa\text{‘}P = P :$

$[\text{Hp}] \qquad \supset : \text{rep}_\kappa\text{‘}P = P \qquad (1)$

$\vdash . *330\cdot6 . \supset \vdash : \text{Hp} . \sim \dot{\exists} ! P . \supset . \kappa = \iota\text{‘}\dot{\Lambda} .$

$[*332\cdot13] \qquad \supset . \text{rep}_\kappa\text{‘}P = \dot{\Lambda} \qquad (2)$

$\vdash . (1) . (2) . \supset \vdash . \text{Prop}$

∗332·242. $\vdash : \kappa \in FM \,\text{conx} . \dot{\exists} ! P . \dot{\exists} ! \text{rep}_\kappa\text{‘}P . \supset . \text{rep}_\kappa\text{‘}P = \text{rep}_\kappa\text{‘}\text{rep}_\kappa\text{‘}P$

Dem.

$\vdash . *332\cdot22 \quad \supset \vdash : \text{Hp} . \supset . \text{rep}_\kappa\text{‘}P \in \kappa_\iota \qquad (1)$

$\vdash . (1) . *332\cdot241 . \supset \vdash . \text{Prop}$

∗332·243. $\vdash : \kappa \in FM \,\text{conx} . \dot{\exists} ! P . P \in I \upharpoonright s\text{‘}\text{ᗡ}\text{“}\kappa . \supset . \text{rep}_\kappa\text{‘}P = I \upharpoonright s\text{‘}\text{ᗡ}\text{“}\kappa$

$[*332\cdot24 . *330\cdot43]$

∗332·244. $\vdash :. \kappa \in FM \,\text{conx} - 1 . \supset :$

$\dot{\exists} ! P . P \in I \upharpoonright s\text{‘}\text{ᗡ}\text{“}\kappa . \equiv . \text{rep}_\kappa\text{‘}P = I \upharpoonright s\text{‘}\text{ᗡ}\text{“}\kappa$

Dem.

$\vdash . *331\cdot26 . *330\cdot43 . \supset \vdash :. \text{Hp} . \supset : \dot{s}\text{‘}\kappa_\iota \neq I \upharpoonright s\text{‘}\text{ᗡ}\text{“}\kappa :$

$[*332\cdot13] \qquad \supset : \text{rep}_\kappa\text{‘}P = I \upharpoonright s\text{‘}\text{ᗡ}\text{“}\kappa . \supset . \dot{\exists} ! P \qquad (1)$

$\vdash . *332\cdot11 . \quad \supset \vdash :. \text{Hp} . \supset : \text{rep}_\kappa\text{‘}P = I \upharpoonright s\text{‘}\text{ᗡ}\text{“}\kappa . \supset . P \in I \upharpoonright s\text{‘}\text{ᗡ}\text{“}\kappa \qquad (2)$

$\vdash . (1) . (2) . *332\cdot243 . \supset \vdash . \text{Prop}$

***332·25.** $\vdash : \kappa \in FM\,\text{conx} \,.\, \dot{\exists}\,!\,P \,.\, \dot{\exists}\,!\,\text{rep}_\kappa{}^{\backprime}Q \,.\, P \Subset Q \,.\, \supset .\, \text{rep}_\kappa{}^{\backprime}P = \text{rep}_\kappa{}^{\backprime}Q$

Dem.

$\vdash .\, {*}332{\cdot}11 \,.\, \supset \vdash : \text{Hp} \,.\, \supset .\, P \Subset \text{rep}_\kappa{}^{\backprime}Q$ (1)

$\vdash .\, {*}332{\cdot}22 \,.\, \supset \vdash : \text{Hp} \,.\, \supset .\, \text{rep}_\kappa{}^{\backprime}Q \in \kappa_\iota$ (2)

$\vdash .\, (1) \,.\, (2) \,.\, {*}332{\cdot}24 \,.\, \supset \vdash .\, \text{Prop}$

***332·26.** $\vdash : \kappa \in FM\,\text{conx} \,.\, \dot{\exists}\,!\,P \mathbin{\dot{\cap}} Q \,.\, \dot{\exists}\,!\,\text{rep}_\kappa{}^{\backprime}P \,.\, \dot{\exists}\,!\,\text{rep}_\kappa{}^{\backprime}Q \,.\, \supset .$

$\text{rep}_\kappa{}^{\backprime}P = \text{rep}_\kappa{}^{\backprime}Q = \text{rep}_\kappa{}^{\backprime}(P \mathbin{\dot{\cap}} Q)$ [*332·25]

***332·27.** $\vdash : \kappa \in FM\,\text{conx} \,.\, \dot{\exists}\,!\,P \,.\, \dot{\exists}\,!\,\text{rep}_\kappa{}^{\backprime}Q \,.\, \dot{\exists}\,!\,Q \mathbin{\dot{\cap}} \text{rep}_\kappa{}^{\backprime}P \,.\, \supset .\, \text{rep}_\kappa{}^{\backprime}P = \text{rep}_\kappa{}^{\backprime}Q$

Dem.

$\vdash .\, {*}332{\cdot}11 \,.\, \supset \vdash : \text{Hp} \,.\, \supset .\, Q \Subset \text{rep}_\kappa{}^{\backprime}Q \,.$

[Hp] $\supset .\, \dot{\exists}\,!\,\text{rep}_\kappa{}^{\backprime}P \mathbin{\dot{\cap}} \text{rep}_\kappa{}^{\backprime}Q$ (1)

$\vdash .\, {*}332{\cdot}22 \,.\, \supset \vdash : \text{Hp} \,.\, \supset .\, \text{rep}_\kappa{}^{\backprime}P, \text{rep}_\kappa{}^{\backprime}Q \in \kappa_\iota$ (2)

$\vdash .\, (1) \,.\, (2) \,.\, {*}331{\cdot}42 \,.\, \supset \vdash .\, \text{Prop}$

***332·31.** $\vdash : \kappa \in FM\,\text{conx} \,.\, L, M \in \kappa_\iota \,.\, \supset .\, \text{rep}_\kappa{}^{\backprime}(L \mid M) \in \kappa_\iota$

[*330·611 . *331·47·12 . *332·23]

***332·32.** $\vdash : \kappa \in FM\,\text{conx} \,.\, L, M \in \kappa_\iota \,.\, \supset .\, \text{rep}_\kappa{}^{\backprime}(L \mid M) = \text{rep}_\kappa{}^{\backprime}(M \mid L)$

[*330·611 . *331·47·12 . *332·24]

***332·33.** $\vdash : \kappa \in FM\,\text{conx} \,.\, \text{rep}_\kappa{}^{\backprime}P, \text{rep}_\kappa{}^{\backprime}Q \in \kappa_\iota \,.\, \dot{\exists}\,!\,P \mid Q \,.\, \supset .\, \text{rep}_\kappa{}^{\backprime}(P \mid Q)$

$= \text{rep}_\kappa{}^{\backprime}\{(\text{rep}_\kappa{}^{\backprime}P) \mid (\text{rep}_\kappa{}^{\backprime}Q)\} = \text{rep}_\kappa{}^{\backprime}\{(\text{rep}_\kappa{}^{\backprime}P) \mid Q\} = \text{rep}_\kappa{}^{\backprime}\{P \mid \text{rep}_\kappa{}^{\backprime}Q\}$

Dem.

$\vdash .\, {*}330{\cdot}6 \,.\, {*}331{\cdot}12 \,.\, \supset \vdash : \text{Hp} \,.\, \supset .\, \dot{\exists}\,!\,\text{rep}_\kappa{}^{\backprime}P \,.\, \dot{\exists}\,!\,\text{rep}_\kappa{}^{\backprime}Q \,.$

[*332·11] $\supset .\, P \Subset \text{rep}_\kappa{}^{\backprime}P \,.\, Q \Subset \text{rep}_\kappa{}^{\backprime}Q \,.$ (1)

[Hp] $\supset .\, \dot{\exists}\,!\,P \mid \text{rep}_\kappa{}^{\backprime}Q$ (2)

$\vdash .\, {*}330{\cdot}6 \,.\, {*}332{\cdot}31 \,.\, (1) \,.\, \supset$

$\vdash : \text{Hp} \,.\, \supset .\, P \mid \text{rep}_\kappa{}^{\backprime}Q \Subset \text{rep}_\kappa{}^{\backprime}P \mid \text{rep}_\kappa{}^{\backprime}Q \,.\, \dot{\exists}\,!\,\text{rep}_\kappa{}^{\backprime}\{\text{rep}_\kappa{}^{\backprime}P \mid \text{rep}_\kappa{}^{\backprime}Q\} \,.$

[(2).*332·25]

$\supset .\, \text{rep}_\kappa{}^{\backprime}(P \mid \text{rep}_\kappa{}^{\backprime}Q) = \text{rep}_\kappa{}^{\backprime}\{\text{rep}_\kappa{}^{\backprime}P \mid \text{rep}_\kappa{}^{\backprime}Q\} \,.\, \dot{\exists}\,!\,\text{rep}_\kappa{}^{\backprime}(P \mid \text{rep}_\kappa{}^{\backprime}Q)$ (3)

Similarly $\vdash : \text{Hp} \,.\, \supset .\, \text{rep}_\kappa{}^{\backprime}\{(\text{rep}_\kappa{}^{\backprime}P) \mid Q\} = \text{rep}_\kappa{}^{\backprime}\{(\text{rep}_\kappa{}^{\backprime}P) \mid (\text{rep}_\kappa{}^{\backprime}Q)\}$ (4)

$\vdash .\, (1) \,.\, \supset \vdash : \text{Hp} \,.\, \supset .\, P \mid Q \Subset P \mid \text{rep}_\kappa{}^{\backprime}Q \,.$

[Hp.(3).*332·25] $\supset .\, \text{rep}_\kappa{}^{\backprime}(P \mid Q) = \text{rep}_\kappa{}^{\backprime}(P \mid \text{rep}_\kappa{}^{\backprime}Q)$ (5)

$\vdash .\, (3) \,.\, (4) \,.\, (5) \,.\, \supset \vdash .\, \text{Prop}$

***332·34.** $\vdash : \text{Hp}\,{*}332{\cdot}33 \,.\, \supset .\, \text{rep}_\kappa{}^{\backprime}(P \mid Q) \in \kappa_\iota$ [*332·31·33]

***332·35.** $\vdash : \kappa \in FM\,\text{conx} \,.\, L, M, N \in \kappa_\iota \,.\, \supset .$

$\text{rep}_\kappa{}^{\backprime}(L \mid M \mid N) = \text{rep}_\kappa{}^{\backprime}\{L \mid \text{rep}_\kappa{}^{\backprime}(M \mid N)\} = \text{rep}_\kappa{}^{\backprime}[\{\text{rep}_\kappa{}^{\backprime}(L \mid M)\} \mid N]$

[*330·613 . *332·31·33]

***332·36.** $\vdash : \text{Hp}\,{*}332{\cdot}35 \,.\, \supset .\, \text{rep}_\kappa{}^{\backprime}(L \mid M \mid N) \in \kappa_\iota$ [*332·35·31]

***332·37.** $\vdash : \kappa \in FM \text{ conx} . \text{rep}_\kappa\text{‘}P, \text{rep}_\kappa\text{‘}Q, \text{rep}_\kappa\text{‘}R \in \kappa_\iota . \dot{\exists} ! P \mid Q \mid R . \supset .$

$$\begin{aligned}\text{rep}_\kappa\text{‘}(P \mid Q \mid R) &= \text{rep}_\kappa\text{‘}\{\text{rep}_\kappa\text{‘}P \mid \text{rep}_\kappa\text{‘}Q \mid \text{rep}_\kappa\text{‘}R\} \\ &= \text{rep}_\kappa\text{‘}\{\text{rep}_\kappa\text{‘}P \mid \text{rep}_\kappa\text{‘}R \mid \text{rep}_\kappa\text{‘}Q\} \\ &= \text{rep}_\kappa\text{‘}\{\text{rep}_\kappa\text{‘}Q \mid \text{rep}_\kappa\text{‘}R \mid \text{rep}_\kappa\text{‘}P\}\end{aligned}$$

Dem.

$\vdash . *332·33 . \supset$

$\vdash : \text{Hp} . \supset . \text{rep}_\kappa\text{‘}(P \mid Q \mid R) = \text{rep}_\kappa\text{‘}\{\text{rep}_\kappa\text{‘}P \mid \text{rep}_\kappa\text{‘}(Q \mid R)\}$

[*332·33] $= \text{rep}_\kappa\text{‘}\{\text{rep}_\kappa\text{‘}P \mid \text{rep}_\kappa\text{‘}(\text{rep}_\kappa\text{‘}Q \mid \text{rep}_\kappa\text{‘}R)\}$ (1)

[*332·35] $= \text{rep}_\kappa\text{‘}\{\text{rep}_\kappa\text{‘}P \mid \text{rep}_\kappa\text{‘}Q \mid \text{rep}_\kappa\text{‘}R\}$ (2)

$\vdash . (1) . *332·32 . \supset$

$\vdash : \text{Hp} . \supset . \text{rep}_\kappa\text{‘}(P \mid Q \mid R) = \text{rep}_\kappa\text{‘}\{\text{rep}_\kappa\text{‘}P \mid \text{rep}_\kappa\text{‘}(\text{rep}_\kappa\text{‘}R \mid \text{rep}_\kappa\text{‘}Q)\}$

[*332·35] $= \text{rep}_\kappa\text{‘}\{\text{rep}_\kappa\text{‘}P \mid \text{rep}_\kappa\text{‘}R \mid \text{rep}_\kappa\text{‘}Q\}$ (3)

$\vdash . (1) . *332·33·32 . \supset$

$\vdash : \text{Hp} . \supset . \text{rep}_\kappa\text{‘}(P \mid Q \mid R) = \text{rep}_\kappa\text{‘}[\{\text{rep}_\kappa\text{‘}(\text{rep}_\kappa\text{‘}Q \mid \text{rep}_\kappa\text{‘}R)\} \mid \text{rep}_\kappa\text{‘}P]$

[*332·35] $= \text{rep}_\kappa\text{‘}\{\text{rep}_\kappa\text{‘}Q \mid \text{rep}_\kappa\text{‘}R \mid \text{rep}_\kappa\text{‘}P\}$ (4)

$\vdash . (2) . (3) . (4) . \supset \vdash . \text{Prop}$

***332·41.** $\vdash :. \kappa \in FM \text{ conx} . L, M, N \in \kappa_\iota . \supset :$

$$\text{rep}_\kappa\text{‘}(L \mid M) = \text{rep}_\kappa\text{‘}(L \mid N) . \equiv . M = N$$

Dem.

$\vdash . *34·34 . \supset \vdash : \text{Hp} . \text{rep}_\kappa\text{‘}(L \mid M) = \text{rep}_\kappa\text{‘}(L \mid N) . \supset .$

$\breve{L} \mid \text{rep}_\kappa\text{‘}(L \mid M) = \breve{L} \mid \text{rep}_\kappa\text{‘}(L \mid N) .$

[*332·35] $\supset . \text{rep}_\kappa\text{‘}(\breve{L} \mid L \mid M) = \text{rep}_\kappa\text{‘}(\breve{L} \mid L \mid N) .$

[*330·31] $\supset . \text{rep}_\kappa\text{‘}M = \text{rep}_\kappa\text{‘}N .$

[*332·241] $\supset . M = N : \supset \vdash . \text{Prop}$

***332·411.** $\vdash :. \kappa \in FM \text{ conx} . L, M, N \in \kappa_\iota . \supset : \text{rep}_\kappa\text{‘}(M \mid L) = \text{rep}_\kappa\text{‘}(N \mid L) . \equiv . M = N$
[*332·32·41]

***332·42.** $\vdash : \kappa \in FM \text{ conx} . L, M \in \kappa_\iota . \supset . \text{Cnv‘rep}_\kappa\text{‘}(L \mid M) = \text{rep}_\kappa\text{‘}(\breve{L} \mid \breve{M})$
[*332·32·15]

***332·43.** $\vdash :. \kappa \in FM \text{ conx} . L, M, N \in \kappa_\iota . \supset :$

$$\begin{aligned}N = \text{rep}_\kappa\text{‘}(L \mid M) . \equiv . L = \text{rep}_\kappa\text{‘}(N \mid \breve{M}) . \equiv . L = \text{rep}_\kappa\text{‘}(\breve{M} \mid N) . \\ \equiv . M = \text{rep}_\kappa\text{‘}(N \mid \breve{L}) . \equiv . M = \text{rep}_\kappa\text{‘}(\breve{L} \mid N)\end{aligned}$$

Dem.

$\vdash . *332·35 . *330·41 . \supset$

$\vdash : \text{Hp} . N = \text{rep}_\kappa\text{‘}(L \mid M) . \supset . \text{rep}_\kappa\text{‘}(L \mid M \mid \breve{M}) = \text{rep}_\kappa\text{‘}(N \mid \breve{M}) .$

[*330·31] $\supset . \text{rep}_\kappa\text{‘}L = \text{rep}_\kappa\text{‘}(N \mid \breve{M}) .$

[*332·241] $\supset . L = \text{rep}_\kappa\text{‘}(N \mid \breve{M}) .$ (1)

[*332·32.*330·41] $\supset . L = \text{rep}_\kappa\text{‘}(\breve{M} \mid N)$ (2)

$\vdash . (1) . *330·41 . \supset \vdash : \text{Hp} . L = \text{rep}_\kappa\text{‘}(N \mid \breve{M}) . \supset . N = \text{rep}_\kappa\text{‘}(L \mid M)$ (3)

$\vdash . (1) . (2) . (3) . \supset \vdash . \text{Prop}$

***332·44.** $\vdash :. \kappa \in FM \text{ conx} . L, M, N \in \kappa_\iota . \supset : \text{rep}_\kappa`(L | M) = N . \equiv . L | M \in N$
[*330·6 . *332·24·31]

***332·45.** $\vdash :. \text{Hp} *332\cdot44 . \supset : \text{rep}_\kappa`(L | M) = N . \equiv . \text{rep}_\kappa`(L | M | \breve{N}) = I \upharpoonright s`\text{G}``\kappa$

Dem.

$\vdash . *332\cdot35 . \supset \vdash :. \text{Hp} . \supset : \text{rep}_\kappa`(L | M) = N . \supset . \text{rep}_\kappa`(L | M | \breve{N}) = \text{rep}_\kappa`(N | \breve{N})$
[*332·24.*330·31] $= I \upharpoonright s`\text{G}``\kappa$ (1)

$\vdash . *332\cdot35 . \supset \vdash :. \text{Hp} . \supset : \text{rep}_\kappa`(L | M | \breve{N}) = I \upharpoonright s`\text{G}``\kappa . \supset .$
$\text{rep}_\kappa`[\{\text{rep}_\kappa`(L | M)\} | \breve{N}] = I \upharpoonright s`\text{G}``\kappa .$
[*332·31·43] $\supset . \text{rep}_\kappa`(L | M) = \text{rep}_\kappa`N$
[*332·241] $= N$ (2)

$\vdash . (1) . (2) . \supset \vdash . \text{Prop}$

***332·46.** $\vdash :. \kappa \in FM \text{ conx} . L, M \in \kappa_\iota . \supset : L | M \in I . \equiv . L = \breve{M}$

Dem.

$\vdash . *330\cdot43\cdot611 . *332\cdot243 . \supset$
$\vdash : \text{Hp} . L | M \in I . \supset . \text{rep}_\kappa`(L | M) = I \upharpoonright s`\text{G}``\kappa .$
[*332·43.*330·43] $\supset . L = \text{rep}_\kappa`\breve{M}$
[*332·241.*330·41] $= \breve{M}$ (1)

$\vdash . *71\cdot191 . \supset \vdash : \text{Hp} . L = \breve{M} . \supset . L | M \in I$ (2)

$\vdash . (1) . (2) . \supset \vdash . \text{Prop}$

***332·51.** $\vdash : \kappa \in FM \text{ conx} . P, Q \in \kappa . \supset . \text{rep}_\kappa`(P | \breve{Q}) = \breve{Q} | P$

Dem.

$\vdash . *331\cdot24 . *332\cdot32 . \supset \vdash : \text{Hp} . \supset . \text{rep}_\kappa`(P | \breve{Q}) = \text{rep}_\kappa`(\breve{Q} | P)$
[*332·241] $= \breve{Q} | P : \supset \vdash . \text{Prop}$

***332·52.** $\vdash : \kappa \in FM \text{ conx} . P, Q, R, S \in \kappa . \supset . \text{rep}_\kappa`(P | \breve{Q} | R | \breve{S}) = \breve{Q} | \breve{S} | P | R$

Dem.

$\vdash . *330\cdot613 . *331\cdot12\cdot124 . \supset \vdash : \text{Hp} . \supset . \dot{\exists} ! (P | \breve{Q}) | (R | \breve{S}) .$
[*332·33·51] $\supset . \text{rep}_\kappa`(P | \breve{Q} | R | \breve{S}) = \text{rep}_\kappa`(\breve{Q} | P | \breve{S} | R)$ (1)

$\vdash . *330\cdot561\cdot611 . \supset \vdash : \text{Hp} . \supset . \breve{Q} | P | \breve{S} | R \in \breve{Q} | \breve{S} | P | R . \dot{\exists} ! \breve{Q} | P | \breve{S} | R$ (2)

$\vdash . *331\cdot52 . \quad \supset \vdash : \text{Hp} . \supset . \breve{Q} | \breve{S} | P | R \in \kappa_\iota$ (3)

$\vdash . (1) . (2) . (3) . *332\cdot24 . \supset \vdash . \text{Prop}$

***332·53.** $\vdash : \kappa \in FM \text{ conx} . P, Q \in \kappa . \rho \in \text{NC induct} . \supset . \text{rep}_\kappa `(\breve{P} | Q)^\rho = \breve{P}^\rho | Q^\rho$

Dem.

$\vdash . *330{\cdot}624 . \supset \vdash : \text{Hp} . \supset . \dot{\exists} ! (\breve{P} | Q)^\rho$ (1)

$\vdash . *330{\cdot}73 . \supset \vdash : \text{Hp} . \supset . (\breve{P} | Q)^\rho \in \breve{P}^\rho | Q^\rho$ (2)

$\vdash . *331{\cdot}53 . \supset \vdash : \text{Hp} . \supset . \breve{P}^\rho | Q^\rho \in \kappa_\iota$ (3)

$\vdash . (1) . (2) . (3) . *332{\cdot}24 . \supset \vdash . \text{Prop}$

***332·61.** $\vdash : \kappa \in FM \text{ conx} . L \in \kappa_\iota . \supset . \text{rep}_\kappa `` \text{Potid} `L \subset \kappa_\iota$

Dem.

$\vdash . *332{\cdot}243 . *330{\cdot}43 . \supset \vdash : \text{Hp} . \supset . \text{rep}_\kappa `(I \upharpoonright C`L) \in \kappa_\iota$ (1)

$\vdash . *332{\cdot}31 . \supset \vdash : \text{Hp} . M \in \text{Pot}`L . \text{rep}_\kappa `M \in \kappa_\iota . \supset . \text{rep}_\kappa `\{L | \text{rep}_\kappa `M\} \in \kappa_\iota$ (2)

$\vdash . *330{\cdot}624 . \quad \supset \vdash : \text{Hp} . M \in \text{Pot}`L . \supset . \dot{\exists} ! L | M$ (3)

$\vdash . (2) . (3) . *332{\cdot}33 . \quad \supset \vdash : \text{Hp} (2) . \supset . \text{rep}_\kappa `(L | M) \in \kappa_\iota$ (4)

$\vdash . (1) . (4) . \text{Induct} . \supset \vdash . \text{Prop}$

***332·62.** $\vdash : \kappa \in FM \text{ conx} . \dot{\Lambda} \sim \in \text{Pot}`P . \dot{\exists} ! \text{rep}_\kappa `P . \supset .$

$\text{rep}_\kappa `` \text{Pot}`P \subset \text{rep}_\kappa `` \text{Pot}`\text{rep}_\kappa `P$

Dem.

$\vdash . *332{\cdot}242 . \supset \vdash : \text{Hp} . \supset . \text{rep}_\kappa `P = \text{rep}_\kappa `\text{rep}_\kappa `P$ (1)

$\vdash . *332{\cdot}22 . \quad \supset \vdash : \text{Hp} . \supset . \text{rep}_\kappa `P \in \kappa_\iota$ (2)

$\vdash . (2) . *332{\cdot}61 . \supset$

$\vdash : \text{Hp} . Q \in \text{Pot}`P . \text{rep}_\kappa `Q \in \text{rep}_\kappa `` \text{Pot}`\text{rep}_\kappa `P . \supset . \text{rep}_\kappa `Q \in \kappa_\iota$ (3)

$\vdash . *91{\cdot}36 . \quad \supset \vdash : \text{Hp} . Q \in \text{Pot}`P . \supset . \dot{\exists} ! P | Q$ (4)

$\vdash . (2) . (3) . (4) . *332{\cdot}33 . \supset \vdash : \text{Hp} (3) . \supset . \text{rep}_\kappa `(P | Q) = \text{rep}_\kappa `\{\text{rep}_\kappa `P | \text{rep}_\kappa `Q\} .$

[Hp.*91·36] $\supset . \text{rep}_\kappa `(P | Q) \in \text{rep}_\kappa `` \text{Pot}`\text{rep}_\kappa `P$ (5)

$\vdash . (1) . (5) . \text{Induct} . \supset \vdash . \text{Prop}$

***332·63.** $\vdash : \text{Hp } *332{\cdot}62 . \supset . \text{rep}_\kappa `` \text{Pot}`P \subset \kappa_\iota$

Dem.

$\vdash . *332{\cdot}22 . \supset \vdash : \text{Hp} . \supset . \text{rep}_\kappa `P \in \kappa_\iota$ (1)

$\vdash . (1) . *332{\cdot}62{\cdot}61 . \supset \vdash . \text{Prop}$

***332·64.** $\vdash : \kappa \in FM \text{ conx} . \text{rep}_\kappa `` \text{Pot}`P \subset \kappa_\iota . \supset . \text{rep}_\kappa `` \text{Pot}`P \subset \text{rep}_\kappa `` \text{Pot}`\text{rep}_\kappa `P$

Dem.

$\vdash . *331{\cdot}26 . *332{\cdot}13 . \supset \vdash : \text{Hp} . \kappa \sim \in 1 . \supset . \dot{\Lambda} \sim \in \text{Pot}`P$ (1)

$\vdash . *330{\cdot}6 . *331{\cdot}12 . \quad \supset \vdash : \text{Hp} . \supset . \dot{\Lambda} \sim \in \text{rep}_\kappa `` \text{Pot}`P$ (2)

$\vdash . (1) . (2) . *332{\cdot}62 . \supset \vdash : \text{Hp} . \kappa \sim \in 1 . \supset . \text{rep}_\kappa `` \text{Pot}`P \subset \text{rep}_\kappa `` \text{Pot}`\text{rep}_\kappa `P$ (3)

$\vdash . *330{\cdot}43 . *331{\cdot}22 . \supset \vdash : \text{Hp} . \kappa \in 1 . \supset . \kappa_\iota = \iota `(I \upharpoonright s`\text{Ɑ}``\kappa) = \kappa$ (4)

$\vdash . (2) . (4) . *332\cdot12 . \supset \vdash : \text{Hp}\,(4) . \supset . P \Subset I \upharpoonright s`\text{Ɑ}``\kappa .$ (5)

$[*332\cdot243\cdot13.(4)] \qquad \supset . \text{rep}_\kappa`P = I \upharpoonright s`\text{Ɑ}``\kappa$ (6)

$\vdash . (5) . *301\cdot3 . \quad \supset \vdash : \text{Hp}\,(4) . \supset . \text{Pot}`P = \iota`P .$

$[(6).*332\cdot241] \qquad \supset . \text{rep}_\kappa``\text{Pot}`P = \iota`\text{rep}_\kappa`\text{rep}_\kappa`P$ (7)

$\vdash . (3) . (7) . \supset \vdash . \text{Prop}$

$*332\cdot65$. $\vdash : \dot{\Lambda} \sim \epsilon \, \text{Pot}`P . \dot{\exists} ! \, \text{rep}_\kappa`P . \supset . \text{Pot}`P \subset s`\text{Rl}``\text{Pot}`\text{rep}_\kappa`P$

Dem.

$\vdash . *332\cdot11 . \supset \vdash : \text{Hp} . \supset . P \Subset \text{rep}_\kappa`P$ (1)

$\vdash . (1) . \supset \vdash : \text{Hp} . Q \epsilon \, \text{Pot}`P . R \epsilon \, \text{Pot}`\text{rep}_\kappa`P . Q \Subset R . \supset . Q \,|\, P \Subset R \,|\, \text{rep}_\kappa`P$ (2)

$\vdash . (1) . (2) . \text{Induct} . \supset \vdash . \text{Prop}$

$*332\cdot66$. $\vdash : \dot{\exists} ! \, \text{rep}_\kappa`P . R \epsilon \, \text{Pot}`\text{rep}_\kappa`P . \supset . (\exists Q) . Q \epsilon \, \text{Pot}`P . Q \Subset R$

[Proof as in $*332\cdot65$]

$*332\cdot67$. $\vdash : \kappa \epsilon \, FM \, \text{conx} . \dot{\Lambda} \sim \epsilon \, \text{Pot}`P . \dot{\exists} ! \, \text{rep}_\kappa`P . \supset .$

$\text{rep}_\kappa``\text{Pot}`\text{rep}_\kappa`P = \text{rep}_\kappa``\text{Pot}`P$

Dem.

$\vdash . *332\cdot242 . \quad \supset \vdash : \text{Hp} . \supset . \text{rep}_\kappa`\text{rep}_\kappa`P = \text{rep}_\kappa`P$ (1)

$\vdash . *332\cdot66 . \quad \supset \vdash :. \text{Hp} . \supset : R \epsilon \, \text{Pot}`\text{rep}_\kappa`P . \supset . \dot{\exists} ! \, R \,|\, P$ (2)

$\vdash . *332\cdot22 . \quad \supset \vdash : \text{Hp} . \supset . \text{rep}_\kappa`P \epsilon \kappa_\iota$ (3)

$\vdash . (3) . *332\cdot61 . \supset \vdash :. \text{Hp} . \supset : R \epsilon \, \text{Pot}`\text{rep}_\kappa`P . \supset . \text{rep}_\kappa`R \epsilon \kappa_\iota$ (4)

$\vdash . (2) . (3) . (4) . *332\cdot33 . \supset$

$\vdash :. \text{Hp} . \supset : R \epsilon \, \text{Pot}`\text{rep}_\kappa`P . \supset . \text{rep}_\kappa`(\text{rep}_\kappa`R \,|\, \text{rep}_\kappa`P) = \text{rep}_\kappa`(R \,|\, \text{rep}_\kappa`P)$ (5)

$\vdash . *332\cdot33 . \supset \vdash : \text{Hp} . R \epsilon \, \text{Pot}`\text{rep}_\kappa`P . Q \epsilon \, \text{Pot}`P . \text{rep}_\kappa`R = \text{rep}_\kappa`Q . \supset .$

$\text{rep}_\kappa`(Q \,|\, P) = \text{rep}_\kappa`(\text{rep}_\kappa`R \,|\, \text{rep}_\kappa`P)$

$[(5)] \qquad = \text{rep}_\kappa`(R \,|\, \text{rep}_\kappa`P)$ (6)

$\vdash . (6) . \supset \vdash : \text{Hp} . R \epsilon \, \text{Pot}`\text{rep}_\kappa`P . \text{rep}_\kappa`R \epsilon \, \text{rep}_\kappa``\text{Pot}`P . \supset .$

$\text{rep}_\kappa`(R \,|\, \text{rep}_\kappa`P) \epsilon \, \text{rep}_\kappa``\text{Pot}`P$ (7)

$\vdash . (1) . (7) . \text{Induct} . \supset \vdash : \text{Hp} . \supset . \text{rep}_\kappa``\text{Pot}`\text{rep}_\kappa`P \subset \text{rep}_\kappa``\text{Pot}`P$ (8)

$\vdash . (8) . *332\cdot62 . \supset \vdash . \text{Prop}$

$*332\cdot71$. $\vdash : \kappa \epsilon \, FM \, \text{conx} . L, M \epsilon \kappa_\iota . \supset .$

$\text{rep}_\kappa``\text{Pot}`(L \,|\, M) = \text{rep}_\kappa``\text{Pot}`\text{rep}_\kappa`(L \,|\, M)$

Dem.

$\vdash . *330\cdot626 . \quad \supset \vdash : \text{Hp} . \supset . \dot{\Lambda} \sim \epsilon \, \text{Pot}`(L \,|\, M)$ (1)

$\vdash . *332\cdot31 . *330\cdot6 . \supset \vdash : \text{Hp} . \supset . \dot{\exists} ! \, \text{rep}_\kappa`(L \,|\, M)$ (2)

$\vdash . (1) . (2) . *332\cdot67 . \supset \vdash . \text{Prop}$

***332·72.** $\vdash : \text{Hp} * 332 \cdot 71 . \supset . \text{rep}_\kappa \text{``Pot`}(L \mid M) \subset \kappa_\iota$ [*332·31·61·71]

***332·73.** $\vdash : \kappa \in FM \text{ conx} . L, M \in \kappa_\iota . \supset . \text{Pot`}(L \mid M) \subset s\text{`Rl``Pot`rep}_\kappa\text{`}(L \mid M)$
[*332·65·31 . *330·626]

***332·74.** $\vdash : \kappa \in FM \text{ conx} . L, M \in \kappa_\iota . P \in \text{Pot`}M . \supset .$

$$\text{rep}_\kappa\text{`}(L \mid P) = \text{rep}_\kappa\text{`}(P \mid L) = \text{rep}_\kappa\text{`}(L \mid \text{rep}_\kappa\text{`}P)$$

Dem.

$\vdash . *330 \cdot 627 . *332 \cdot 61 \cdot 33 . \supset$

$\vdash : \text{Hp} . \supset . \text{rep}_\kappa\text{`}(L \mid P) = \text{rep}_\kappa\text{`}\{L \mid \text{rep}_\kappa\text{`}P\}$ (1)

[*332·61·32] $= \text{rep}_\kappa\text{`}\{\text{rep}_\kappa\text{`}P \mid L\}$

[*330·627.*332·61·33] $= \text{rep}_\kappa\text{`}(P \mid L)$ (2)

$\vdash . (1) . (2) . \supset \vdash . \text{Prop}$

***332·75.** $\vdash : \text{Hp} * 332 \cdot 74 . \supset . \dot{\exists} ! \, \text{rep}_\kappa\text{`}(L \mid P)$ [*332·74·61·31 . *330·6]

***332·8.** $\vdash : \kappa \in FM \text{ conx} . L, M \in \kappa_\iota . \xi \in \text{NC ind} . \supset .$

$$\text{rep}_\kappa\text{`}(L \mid M)^\xi = \text{rep}_\kappa\text{`}(L^\xi \mid M^\xi)$$

Dem.

$\vdash . *332 \cdot 243 . \supset$

$\vdash : \text{Hp} . \xi = 0 . \supset . \text{rep}_\kappa\text{`}(L \mid M)^\xi = I \upharpoonright s\text{`}\mathrm{C}\text{``}\kappa = \text{rep}_\kappa\text{`}(L^\xi \mid M^\xi)$ (1)

$\vdash . *301 \cdot 21 . *332 \cdot 33 . *330 \cdot 626 . \supset$

$\vdash : \text{Hp} . \text{rep}_\kappa\text{`}(L \mid M)^\xi = \text{rep}_\kappa\text{`}(L^\xi \mid M^\xi) . \supset .$

$\text{rep}_\kappa\text{`}(L \mid M)^{\xi +_c 1} = \text{rep}_\kappa\text{`}\{L^\xi \mid M^\xi \mid L \mid M\}$

[*332·37] $= \text{rep}_\kappa\text{`}\{L^\xi \mid \text{rep}_\kappa\text{`}(M^\xi \mid L) \mid M\}$

[*332·32·33] $= \text{rep}_\kappa\text{`}\{L^\xi \mid \text{rep}_\kappa\text{`}(L \mid M^\xi) \mid M\}$

[*332·37] $= \text{rep}_\kappa\text{`}\{L^{\xi +_c 1} \mid M^{\xi +_c 1}\}$ (2)

$\vdash . (1) . (2) . \text{Induct} . \supset \vdash . \text{Prop}$

***332·81.** $\vdash : \kappa \in FM \text{ conx} . \nu, \sigma \in \text{NC ind} - \iota\text{`}0 . L \in \kappa_\iota . \supset .$

$$\text{rep}_\kappa\text{`}L^{\nu \times_c \sigma} = \text{rep}_\kappa\text{`}(\text{rep}_\kappa\text{`}L^\nu)^\sigma$$

Dem.

$\vdash . *301 \cdot 23 . \supset \vdash : \text{Hp} . \text{rep}_\kappa\text{`}L^{\nu \times_c \sigma} = \text{rep}_\kappa\text{`}(\text{rep}_\kappa\text{`}L^\nu)^\sigma . \supset .$

$\text{rep}_\kappa\text{`}L^{\nu \times_c (\sigma +_c 1)} = \text{rep}_\kappa\text{`}(L^{\nu \times_c \sigma} \mid L^\nu)$

[*332·33] $= \text{rep}_\kappa\text{`}\{(\text{rep}_\kappa\text{`}L^\nu)^\sigma \mid \text{rep}_\kappa\text{`}L^\nu\}$

[*301·23] $= \text{rep}_\kappa\text{`}(\text{rep}_\kappa\text{`}L^\nu)^{\sigma +_c 1}$ (1)

$\vdash . (1) . \text{Induct} . \supset \vdash . \text{Prop}$

***332·82.** $\vdash : \kappa \in FM \text{ conx} . \nu \in \text{NC ind} - \iota\text{`}0 . L, M \in \kappa_\iota . \supset .$

$$\text{rep}_\kappa\text{`}(L \mid M)^\nu = \text{rep}_\kappa\text{`}\{\text{rep}_\kappa\text{`}(L \mid M)\}^\nu$$

Dem.

$\vdash . *332 \cdot 33 . \supset \vdash : \text{Hp} . \text{rep}_\kappa\text{`}(L \mid M)^\nu = \{\text{rep}_\kappa\text{`}(L \mid M)\}^\nu . \supset .$

$\text{rep}_\kappa\text{`}(L \mid M)^{\nu +_c 1} = \text{rep}_\kappa\text{`}[\{\text{rep}_\kappa\text{`}(L \mid M)\}^\nu \mid \text{rep}_\kappa\text{`}(L \mid M)]$

[*301·23] $= \text{rep}_\kappa\text{`}\{\text{rep}_\kappa\text{`}(L \mid M)\}^{\nu +_c 1}$ (1)

$\vdash . (1) . *113 \cdot 621 . *301 \cdot 2 . \text{Induct} . \supset \vdash . \text{Prop}$

*333. OPEN FAMILIES.

Summary of *333.

An "open" family is defined as one such that, if L is any member of κ_ι which is not contained in identity, then every power of L is contained in diversity, *i.e.* $L_{\mathrm{po}} \subseteq J$. We shall often have occasion, both in this number and later, to consider the class $\kappa_\iota - \mathrm{Rl}'I$, and in later numbers we shall often have occasion to consider the class $\kappa - \mathrm{Rl}'I$. We therefore put

***333·01.** $\kappa_\partial = \kappa - \mathrm{Rl}'I$ Df

***333·011.** $\kappa_{\iota\partial} = (\kappa_\iota)_\partial$ Df

Thus $\kappa_{\iota\partial}$ consists of all members of κ_ι which are not contained in identity, *i.e.* (if κ is a connected family) all members of κ_ι except $I \upharpoonright s'C''\kappa$. The definition of an "open" family is

***333·02.** $FM\,\mathrm{ap} = FM \cap \hat{\kappa}\,\{s'\mathrm{Pot}''\kappa_{\iota\partial} \subset \mathrm{Rl}'J\}$ Df

From the point of view of the application of ratio, the hypothesis that a family is open is very important. To begin with, it insures (*333·18) that $\kappa_{\iota\partial}$ consists of "numerical" relations (cf. *300), so that if $L \in \kappa_{\iota\partial}$, we have $\mathrm{Pot}'L = \mathrm{fin}'L$ (*333·15), and in virtue of *300·491, the existence of open families implies the axiom of infinity (*333·19).

Again, in an open connected family, if L, M are two different members of κ_ι, all the powers of $L \,|\, \breve{M}$ are contained in diversity, and therefore the representatives of these powers are members of $\kappa_{\iota\partial}$; that is, we have

***333·22.** $\vdash : \kappa \in FM\,\mathrm{ap}\,\mathrm{conx} \,.\, L, M \in \kappa_\iota \,.\, L \neq M \,.\supset .\, \mathrm{rep}_\kappa``\mathrm{Pot}`(L \,|\, \breve{M}) \subset \kappa_{\iota\partial}$

It follows from this proposition that, with the above hypothesis, if σ is any inductive cardinal other than 0, $L^\sigma \,|\, \breve{M}^\sigma$ is not contained in identity, and therefore $L^\sigma \neq M^\sigma$ and $\mathrm{rep}_\kappa`L^\sigma \neq \mathrm{rep}_\kappa`M^\sigma$. Hence by transposition we obtain the two propositions:

***333·41.** $\vdash :. \kappa \in FM\,\mathrm{ap}\,\mathrm{conx} \,.\, L, M \in \kappa_\iota \,.\, \sigma \in \mathrm{NC\,ind} - \iota`0 \,.\supset :$

$$\mathrm{rep}_\kappa`L^\sigma = \mathrm{rep}_\kappa`M^\sigma \,.\equiv .\, L = M$$

$*333{\cdot}42$. $\vdash :. \text{Hp} *333{\cdot}41 . \supset : L^\sigma = M^\sigma . \equiv . L = M$

Hence we obtain

$*333{\cdot}43$. $\vdash :. \text{Hp} *333{\cdot}41 . \supset : \dot{\exists} ! L^\sigma \dot{\cap} M^\sigma . \equiv . L = M$

This proposition shows that in an open connected family, no two members of κ_ι have the ratio 1/1 unless they are identical. Again it follows from $*333{\cdot}41$ that if $L^{\rho \times_c \tau}$ and $M^{\sigma \times_c \tau}$ have the same representative, then L^ρ and M^σ have the same representative, and vice versa, *i.e.*

$*333{\cdot}44$. $\vdash :. \kappa \in FM \text{ ap conx} . L, M \in \kappa_\iota . \rho, \sigma, \tau \in \text{NC ind} - \iota\text{‘}0 . \supset :$

$$\text{rep}_\kappa\text{‘}L^{\rho \times_c \tau} = \text{rep}_\kappa\text{‘}M^{\sigma \times_c \tau} . \equiv . \text{rep}_\kappa\text{‘}L^\rho = \text{rep}_\kappa\text{‘}M^\sigma$$

Hence we obtain two propositions which are vital for the application of ratio, namely:

$*333{\cdot}47$. $\vdash :. \kappa \in FM \text{ ap conx} . L, M \in \kappa_\iota . \rho, \sigma \in \text{NC ind} - \iota\text{‘}0 . \supset :$

$$\text{rep}_\kappa\text{‘}L^\rho = \text{rep}_\kappa\text{‘}M^\sigma . \equiv . \dot{\exists} ! L^\rho \dot{\cap} M^\sigma$$

$*333{\cdot}48$. $\vdash :. \kappa \in FM \text{ ap conx} . L, M \in \kappa_\iota . \rho, \sigma, \tau \in \text{NC ind} - \iota\text{‘}0 . \supset :$

$$\dot{\exists} ! L^\rho \dot{\cap} M^\sigma . \equiv . \dot{\exists} ! L^{\rho \times_c \tau} \dot{\cap} M^{\sigma \times_c \tau}$$

On comparing this last proposition with the definition of ratio ($*303{\cdot}01$), it will be seen that, whether ρ is prime to σ or not, L has to M the ratio σ/ρ when, and only when, $\dot{\exists} ! L^\rho \dot{\cap} M^\sigma$, *i.e.* (by $*333{\cdot}47$) when, and only when, $\text{rep}_\kappa\text{‘}L^\rho = \text{rep}_\kappa\text{‘}M^\sigma$.

From $*333{\cdot}47$ it follows also that, if $M \in \kappa_{\iota\partial}$, M^ρ and M^σ will not have the same representative unless $\rho = \sigma$ ($*333{\cdot}51$), *i.e.*

$*333{\cdot}51$. $\vdash :. \kappa \in FM \text{ ap conx} . M \in \kappa_{\iota\partial} . \rho, \sigma \in \text{NC ind} . \supset :$

$$\text{rep}_\kappa\text{‘}M^\rho = \text{rep}_\kappa\text{‘}M^\sigma . \equiv . \rho = \sigma$$

From this it follows that no member of $\kappa_{\iota\partial}$ has any other ratio to itself than 1/1. Again, by $*333{\cdot}47{\cdot}48{\cdot}51$, we have

$*333{\cdot}53$. $\vdash : \kappa \in FM \text{ ap conx} . L, M \in \kappa_{\iota\partial} . \dot{\exists} ! L^\sigma \dot{\cap} M^\rho . \dot{\exists} ! L^\nu \dot{\cap} M^\mu . \supset .$

$$\mu \times_0 \sigma = \nu \times_0 \rho$$

Hence if L and M have the two ratios ρ/σ, μ/ν, we have $\rho/\sigma = \mu/\nu$; that is, no two members of $\kappa_{\iota\partial}$ have more than one ratio.

The applications of ratio indicated in this summary will not be made till the following Section; they are here mentioned in order to show the utility of the propositions of the present number.

$*333{\cdot}01$. $\kappa_\partial = \kappa - \text{Rl‘}I$ Df

$*333{\cdot}011$. $\kappa_{\iota\partial} = (\kappa_\iota)_\partial$ Df

$*333{\cdot}02$. $FM \text{ ap} = FM \cap \hat{\kappa} \{s\text{‘Pot“}\kappa_{\iota\partial} \subset \text{Rl‘}J\}$ Df

$*333{\cdot}03$. $FM \text{ ap conx} = FM \text{ ap} \cap FM \text{ conx}$ Df

***333·1.** $\vdash : M \epsilon \kappa_{\iota\partial} . \equiv . (\exists P, Q) . P, Q \epsilon \kappa . M = \breve{P} | Q . \dot{\exists} ! M \dot{\wedge} J .$
$\equiv . M \epsilon \kappa_\iota . \dot{\exists} ! M \dot{\wedge} J$ [(*333·01·011)]

***333·101.** $\vdash :. \kappa \epsilon FM \,\mathrm{ap} . \equiv : \kappa \epsilon FM : M \epsilon \kappa_{\iota\partial} . P \epsilon \mathrm{Pot}`M . \supset_{M,P} . P \mathrel{\dot{\subset}} J :$
$\equiv : \kappa \epsilon FM : M \epsilon \kappa_{\iota\partial} . \supset_M . M_{\mathrm{po}} \mathrel{\dot{\subset}} J$ [(*333·02)]

***333·11.** $\vdash : \kappa \epsilon FM \,\mathrm{ap} . L \epsilon \kappa_{\iota\partial} . \supset . L \mathrel{\dot{\subset}} J . L^2 \mathrel{\dot{\subset}} J . L \dot{\wedge} \breve{L} = \dot{\Lambda} . L \dot{\neq} \breve{L} . \dot{\exists} ! L$
[*333·1·101]

***333·12.** $\vdash : \kappa \epsilon FM \,\mathrm{ap\,conx} . \dot{\exists} ! \mathrm{rep}_\kappa`P . \dot{\exists} ! P \dot{\wedge} J . \supset .$
$\mathrm{rep}_\kappa`P \epsilon \kappa_{\iota\partial} . (\mathrm{rep}_\kappa`P)_{\mathrm{po}} \mathrel{\dot{\subset}} J$

Dem.

$\vdash . *332·11 . \supset \vdash : \mathrm{Hp} . \supset . \dot{\exists} ! \mathrm{rep}_\kappa`P \dot{\wedge} J .$
[*332·22.*333·1] $\supset . \mathrm{rep}_\kappa`P \epsilon \kappa_{\iota\partial}$ (1)
$\vdash . (1) . *333·101 . \supset \vdash . \mathrm{Prop}$

***333·13.** $\vdash : \kappa \epsilon FM \,\mathrm{ap\,conx} . \dot{\exists} ! \mathrm{rep}_\kappa`P . \dot{\exists} ! P \dot{\wedge} J . \supset . P_{\mathrm{po}} \mathrel{\dot{\subset}} J$

Dem.

$\vdash . *332·11 . \quad \supset \vdash : \mathrm{Hp} . \supset . P \mathrel{\dot{\subset}} \mathrm{rep}_\kappa`P$ (1)
$\vdash . (1) . *332·22 . \supset \vdash : \mathrm{Hp} . \supset . \dot{\exists} ! (\mathrm{rep}_\kappa`P) \dot{\wedge} J . P_{\mathrm{po}} \mathrel{\dot{\subset}} (\mathrm{rep}_\kappa`P)_{\mathrm{po}} . \mathrm{rep}_\kappa`P \epsilon \kappa_\iota .$
[*333·1] $\supset . P_{\mathrm{po}} \mathrel{\dot{\subset}} (\mathrm{rep}_\kappa`P)_{\mathrm{po}} . \mathrm{rep}_\kappa`P \epsilon \kappa_{\iota\partial} .$
[*333·101] $\supset . P_{\mathrm{po}} \mathrel{\dot{\subset}} J : \supset \vdash . \mathrm{Prop}$

***333·14.** $\vdash : \kappa \epsilon FM \,\mathrm{ap\,conx} . L, M \epsilon \kappa_\iota . L \dot{\neq} \breve{M} . \supset . (L | M)_{\mathrm{po}} \mathrel{\dot{\subset}} J$

Dem.

$\vdash . *330·626 . \quad \supset \vdash : \mathrm{Hp} . \supset . \dot{\Lambda} \sim \epsilon \mathrm{Pot}`(L | M)$ (1)
$\vdash . *332·31 . *330·6 . \supset \vdash : \mathrm{Hp} . \supset . \dot{\exists} ! \mathrm{rep}_\kappa`(L | M)$ (2)
$\vdash . *332·46 . \mathrm{Transp} . \supset \vdash : \mathrm{Hp} . \supset . \dot{\exists} ! (L | M) \dot{\wedge} J$ (3)
$\vdash . (1) : (2) . (3) . *333·13 . \supset \vdash . \mathrm{Prop}$

***333·15.** $\vdash : \kappa \epsilon FM \,\mathrm{ap} . L \epsilon \kappa_{\iota\partial} . \supset . \mathrm{Pot}`L = \mathrm{fin}`L = \mathrm{finid}`L - \iota`L_0$
[*121·501 . *333·11·101]

***333·16.** $\vdash : \kappa \epsilon FM \,\mathrm{ap\,conx} . L, M \epsilon \kappa_\iota . L \dot{\neq} \breve{M} . \supset .$
$\mathrm{Pot}`(L | M) = \mathrm{fin}`(L | M) = \mathrm{finid}`(L | M) - \iota`(L | M)_0$
[*121·501 . *333·14]

***333·17.** $\vdash : \kappa \epsilon FM \,\mathrm{ap\,conx} . \dot{\exists} ! \mathrm{rep}_\kappa`P . \dot{\exists} ! P \dot{\wedge} J . \supset .$
$\mathrm{Pot}`P = \mathrm{fin}`P = \mathrm{finid}`P - \iota`P_0$ [*121·501 . *333·13]

***333·18.** $\vdash : \kappa \epsilon FM \,\mathrm{ap} . \supset . \kappa_{\iota\partial} \subset \mathrm{Rel\,num}$ [*333·101 . *300·3]

***333·19.** $\vdash : \kappa \epsilon FM \,\mathrm{ap} - \iota`\iota`\dot{\Lambda} . \supset . \mathrm{Infin\,ax}$ [*333·18 . *330·624 . *300·491]

***333·2.** $\vdash : \exists ! FM \,\mathrm{ap\,conx} . \supset . \mathrm{Infin\,ax}$ [*333·19 . *331·12]

$*333\cdot21$. $\vdash : \kappa \in FM \text{ ap conx} . L \in \kappa_{\iota\partial} . \supset . \text{rep}_\kappa``\text{Pot}`L \subset \kappa_{\iota\partial}$

Dem.

$\vdash . *332\cdot61 . \quad \supset \vdash : \dot{\text{H}}\text{p} . \supset . \text{rep}_\kappa``\text{Pot}`L \subset \kappa_\iota$ (1)

$\vdash . *333\cdot101 . *330\cdot624 . \supset \vdash :. \text{Hp} . \supset : \dot{\Lambda} \sim \in \text{Pot}`L . \text{Pot}`L \subset \text{Rl}`J :$

$[*332\cdot11.(1)] \quad \supset : M \in \text{rep}_\kappa``\text{Pot}`L . \supset . \dot{\exists} ! M \mathbin{\dot{\cap}} J$ (2)

$\vdash . (1) . (2) . *333\cdot1 . \supset \vdash . \text{Prop}$

$*333\cdot22$. $\vdash : \kappa \in FM \text{ ap conx} . L, M \in \kappa_\iota . L \neq M . \supset . \text{rep}_\kappa``\text{Pot}`(L \mid \breve{M}) \subset \kappa_{\iota\partial}$

Dem.

$\vdash . *332\cdot71 . \supset \vdash : \text{Hp} . \supset . \text{rep}_\kappa``\text{Pot}`(L \mid \breve{M}) = \text{rep}_\kappa``\text{Pot}`\text{rep}_\kappa`(L \mid \breve{M})$ (1)

$\vdash . *332\cdot46\cdot11\cdot232\cdot31 . \supset \vdash : \text{Hp} . \supset . \text{rep}_\kappa`(L \mid \breve{M}) \in \kappa_{\iota\partial}$ (2)

$\vdash . (1) . (2) . *333\cdot21 . \supset \vdash . \text{Prop}$

$*333\cdot23$. $\vdash : \kappa \in FM \text{ ap conx} . \dot{\Lambda} \sim \in \text{Pot}`P . \dot{\exists} ! \text{rep}_\kappa`P . \dot{\exists} ! P \mathbin{\dot{\cap}} J . \supset .$
$\text{rep}_\kappa``\text{Pot}`P \subset \kappa_{\iota\partial}$

Dem.

$\vdash . *332\cdot62 . \quad \supset \vdash : \text{Hp} . \supset . \text{rep}_\kappa``\text{Pot}`P \subset \text{rep}_\kappa``\text{Pot}`\text{rep}_\kappa`P$ (1)

$\vdash . *332\cdot11\cdot22 . *333\cdot1 . \supset \vdash : \text{Hp} . \supset . \text{rep}_\kappa`P \in \kappa_{\iota\partial}$ (2)

$\vdash . (1) . (2) . *333\cdot21 . \supset \vdash . \text{Prop}$

$*333\cdot24$. $\vdash : \kappa \in FM \text{ conx} . \dot{\Lambda} \sim \in \text{Pot}`P . \dot{\exists} ! \text{rep}_\kappa`P . \nu \in \text{NC ind} . \exists !$
$(\nu +_c 1) \cap t^{2}`P . \supset . \text{rep}_\kappa`P^\nu = \text{rep}_\kappa`(\text{rep}_\kappa`P)^\nu$

Dem.

$\vdash . *301\cdot2 . *332\cdot243 . \supset \vdash : \text{Hp} . \supset . \text{rep}_\kappa`P^0 = I \upharpoonright s`\text{C}``\kappa = \text{rep}_\kappa`(\text{rep}_\kappa`P)^0$ (1)

$\vdash . *332\cdot63 . *330\cdot6 . *301\cdot16\cdot22 . \supset$

$\vdash : \text{Hp} . \supset . \text{rep}_\kappa`P^\nu, \text{rep}_\kappa`P \in \kappa_\iota . \dot{\exists} ! P^{\nu +_c 1} .$ (2)

$[*301\cdot21.*332\cdot33] \supset . \text{rep}_\kappa`P^{\nu+_c 1} = \text{rep}_\kappa`\{(\text{rep}_\kappa`P^\nu) \mid \text{rep}_\kappa`P\}$ (3)

$\vdash . (2) . (3) . \supset \vdash : \text{Hp} . \text{rep}_\kappa`P^\nu = \text{rep}_\kappa`(\text{rep}_\kappa`P)^\nu . \supset .$

$\text{rep}_\kappa`P^{\nu+_c 1} = \text{rep}_\kappa`\{\text{rep}_\kappa`(\text{rep}_\kappa`P)^\nu \mid \text{rep}_\kappa`P\} .$

$\text{rep}_\kappa`(\text{rep}_\kappa`P)^\nu, \text{rep}_\kappa`P \in \kappa_\iota$ (4)

$\vdash . (2) . *330\cdot624 . *301\cdot21 . \supset \vdash : \text{Hp} . \supset . \dot{\exists} ! (\text{rep}_\kappa`P)^\nu \mid \text{rep}_\kappa`P$ (5)

$\vdash . (4) . (5) . *332\cdot33 . \supset \vdash : \text{Hp (4)} . \supset . \text{rep}_\kappa`P^{\nu+_c 1} = \text{rep}_\kappa`\{(\text{rep}_\kappa`P)^\nu \mid \text{rep}_\kappa`P\}$

$[*301\cdot21] \quad = \text{rep}_\kappa`(\text{rep}_\kappa`P)^{\nu+_c 1}$ (6)

$\vdash . (1) . (6) . \text{Induct} . \supset \vdash . \text{Prop}$

A hypothesis equivalent to $\nu \in \text{NC ind} . \exists ! (\nu +_c 1) \cap t^{2}`P$ is $\nu \in \text{C}`U \upharpoonright t^{3}`P$. It is sometimes convenient to substitute this for the other.

$*333\cdot25$. $\vdash : \kappa \in FM \text{ conx} . L, M \in \kappa_\iota . \nu \in \text{NC ind} . \exists ! (\nu +_c 1) \cap t^{2}`L . \supset .$
$\text{rep}_\kappa`(L \mid M)^\nu = \text{rep}_\kappa`\{\text{rep}_\kappa`(L \mid M)\}^\nu$

Dem.

$\vdash . *330\cdot626 . *331\cdot12 . \supset \vdash : \text{Hp} . \supset . \dot{\Lambda} \sim \in \text{Pot}`(L \mid M)$ (1)

$\vdash . *332\cdot31 . *330\cdot6 . \quad \supset \vdash : \text{Hp} . \supset . \dot{\exists} ! \text{rep}_\kappa`(L \mid M)$ (2)

$\vdash . (1) . (2) . *333\cdot24 . \quad \supset \vdash . \text{Prop}$

***333·32.** $\vdash : \kappa \in FM \text{ conx} . L, M \in \kappa_\iota . \rho, \sigma \in \text{Cl}'(U \restriction t^{3\prime}L) . \supset . \dot{\exists} ! L^\rho | M^\sigma$

Dem.

$\vdash . *330{\cdot}61 . *301{\cdot}2 . \supset \vdash : \text{Hp} . \supset . \dot{\exists} ! L^0 | M^0$ (1)

$\vdash . *330{\cdot}623 . \quad \supset \vdash :. \text{Hp} . \supset : S \in \kappa . \supset_S . S | L^\rho | M^\sigma \Subset L^\rho | M^\sigma | S :$ (2)

$[*330{\cdot}622] \quad \supset : \dot{\exists} ! L^\rho | M^\sigma . \supset . \dot{\exists} ! L^{\rho +_c 1} | M^\sigma$ (3)

$\vdash . (2) . *330{\cdot}621 . \quad \supset \vdash :. \text{Hp} . \supset : \dot{\exists} ! L^\rho | M^\sigma . \supset . \dot{\exists} ! L^\rho | M^{\sigma +_c 1}$ (4)

$\vdash . (1) . (3) . (4) . \text{Induct} . \supset \vdash . \text{Prop}$

***333·33.** $\vdash : \kappa \in FM \text{ conx} . L, M \in \kappa_\iota . \sigma \in \text{Cl}'(U \restriction t^{3\prime}L) . \supset .$

$\text{rep}_\kappa{}'(L^\sigma | M^\sigma) = \text{rep}_\kappa{}'(L | M)^\sigma$

Dem.

$\vdash . *333{\cdot}32 . *332{\cdot}243 . \supset$

$\vdash : \text{Hp} . \supset . \text{rep}_\kappa{}'(L^0 | M^0) = I \restriction s'\text{Cl}''\kappa = \text{rep}_\kappa{}'(L | M)^0$ (1)

$\vdash . *332{\cdot}37 . *301{\cdot}21 . \supset$

$\vdash : \text{Hp} . \supset . \text{rep}_\kappa{}'(L^{\sigma +_c 1} | M^{\sigma +_c 1}) = \text{rep}_\kappa{}'\{\text{rep}_\kappa{}'(L^\sigma | M^\sigma) | \text{rep}_\kappa{}'L | \text{rep}_\kappa{}'M\}$ (2)

$\vdash . (2) . \supset \vdash : \text{Hp} . \text{rep}_\kappa{}'(L^\sigma | M^\sigma) = \text{rep}_\kappa{}'(L | M)^\sigma . \supset .$

$\text{rep}_\kappa{}'(L^{\sigma +_c 1} | M^{\sigma +_c 1}) = \text{rep}_\kappa{}'\{\text{rep}_\kappa{}'(L | M)^\sigma | \text{rep}_\kappa{}'L | \text{rep}_\kappa{}'M\}$ (3)

$\vdash . (3) . *333{\cdot}32 . *332{\cdot}37 . \supset$

$\vdash : \text{Hp} (3) . \supset . \text{rep}_\kappa{}'(L^{\sigma +_c 1} | M^{\sigma +_c 1}) = \text{rep}_\kappa{}'\{(L | M)^\sigma | L | M\}$

$[*301{\cdot}21] \quad = \text{rep}_\kappa{}'(L | M)^{\sigma +_c 1}$ (4)

$\vdash . (1) . (4) . \text{Induct} . \supset \vdash . \text{Prop}$

***333·34.** $\vdash : \text{Hp } *333{\cdot}33 . \supset . \text{rep}_\kappa{}'(L^\sigma | M^\sigma) = \text{rep}_\kappa{}'\{\text{rep}_\kappa{}'(L|M)\}^\sigma = \text{rep}_\kappa{}'(L|M)^\sigma$

Dem.

$\vdash . *330{\cdot}626{\cdot}6 . *332{\cdot}31 . \supset$

$\vdash : \text{Hp} . \supset . \dot{\Lambda} \sim\in \text{Pot}'(L | M) . \dot{\exists} ! \text{rep}_\kappa{}'(L | M)$ (1)

$\vdash . (1) . *333{\cdot}24 . \supset \vdash : \text{Hp} . \supset . \text{rep}_\kappa{}'\{\text{rep}_\kappa{}'(L | M)\}^\sigma = \text{rep}_\kappa{}'(L | M)^\sigma$ (2)

$\vdash . (2) . *333{\cdot}33 . \supset \vdash . \text{Prop}$

***333·41.** $\vdash :. \kappa \in FM \text{ ap conx} . L, M \in \kappa_\iota . \sigma \in \text{NC ind} - \iota'0 . \supset :$

$\text{rep}_\kappa{}'L^\sigma = \text{rep}_\kappa{}'M^\sigma . \equiv . L = M$

Dem.

$\vdash . *333{\cdot}34{\cdot}22{\cdot}2 . \supset \vdash : \text{Hp} . L \neq M . \supset . \text{rep}_\kappa{}'(L^\sigma | \breve{M}^\sigma) \in \kappa_{\iota\partial} .$

$[*333{\cdot}21{\cdot}32 . *332{\cdot}33] \quad \supset . \text{rep}_\kappa{}'\{\text{rep}_\kappa{}'L^\sigma | \text{rep}_\kappa{}'\breve{M}^\sigma\} \in \kappa_{\iota\partial} .$

$[*332{\cdot}44 . \text{Transp}] \quad \supset . \sim \{\text{rep}_\kappa{}'L^\sigma | \text{rep}_\kappa{}'\breve{M}^\sigma \Subset I \restriction s'\text{Cl}''\kappa\} .$

$[*332{\cdot}15{\cdot}46 . \text{Transp}] \quad \supset . \text{rep}_\kappa{}'L^\sigma \neq \text{rep}_\kappa{}'M^\sigma$ (1)

$\vdash . (1) . \text{Transp} . \supset \vdash . \text{Prop}$

***333·42.** $\vdash :. \text{Hp } *333{\cdot}41 . \supset : L^\sigma = M^\sigma . \equiv . L = M \quad [*333{\cdot}41]$

***333·43.** $\vdash :. \text{Hp} * 333\cdot 41 . \supset : \dot{\exists} ! L^\sigma \dot{\frown} M^\sigma . \equiv . L = M$

Dem.

$\vdash . * 333\cdot 21 . * 332\cdot 26 . \supset \vdash : \text{Hp} . \dot{\exists} ! L^\sigma \dot{\frown} M^\sigma . \supset . \text{rep}_\kappa \text{‘} L^\sigma = \text{rep}_\kappa \text{‘} M^\sigma .$

[*333·41] $\supset . L = M$ (1)

$\vdash . (1) . * 330\cdot 624 . \supset \vdash . \text{Prop}$

***333·44.** $\vdash :. \kappa \in FM \text{ ap conx} . L, M \in \kappa_\iota . \rho, \sigma, \tau \in \text{NC ind} - \iota\text{‘}0 . \supset :$
$\text{rep}_\kappa \text{‘} L^{\rho \times_c \tau} = \text{rep}_\kappa \text{‘} M^{\sigma \times_c \tau} . \equiv . \text{rep}_\kappa \text{‘} L^\rho = \text{rep}_\kappa \text{‘} M^\sigma$

Dem.

$\vdash . * 301\cdot 5 . * 333\cdot 24 . \supset$

$\vdash :. \text{Hp} . \supset : \text{rep}_\kappa \text{‘} L^{\rho \times_c \tau} = \text{rep}_\kappa \text{‘} M^{\sigma \times_c \tau} . \equiv . \text{rep}_\kappa \text{‘} (\text{rep}_\kappa \text{‘} L^\rho)^\tau = \text{rep}_\kappa \text{‘} (\text{rep}_\kappa \text{‘} M^\sigma)^\tau .$

[*333·41·21] $\equiv . \text{rep}_\kappa \text{‘} L^\rho = \text{rep}_\kappa \text{‘} M^\sigma :. \supset \vdash . \text{Prop}$

***333·45.** $\vdash :. \text{Hp} * 333\cdot 44 . \supset : L^{\rho \times_c \tau} = M^{\sigma \times_c \tau} . \supset . \text{rep}_\kappa \text{‘} L^\rho = \text{rep}_\kappa \text{‘} M^\sigma$ [*333·44]

***333·46.** $\vdash :. \text{Hp} * 333\cdot 44 . \supset : \dot{\exists} ! L^{\rho \times_c \tau} \dot{\frown} M^{\sigma \times_c \tau} . \supset . \text{rep}_\kappa \text{‘} L^\rho = \text{rep}_\kappa \text{‘} M^\sigma$

Dem.

$\vdash . * 332\cdot 26 . * 333\cdot 21 . \supset$

$\vdash : \text{Hp} . \dot{\exists} ! L^{\rho \times_c \tau} \dot{\frown} M^{\sigma \times_c \tau} . \supset . \text{rep}_\kappa \text{‘} L^{\rho \times_c \tau} = \text{rep}_\kappa \text{‘} M^{\sigma \times_c \tau}$ (1)

$\vdash . (1) . * 333\cdot 44 . \supset \vdash . \text{Prop}$

***333·47.** $\vdash :. \kappa \in FM \text{ ap conx} . L, M \in \kappa_\iota . \rho, \sigma \in \text{NC ind} - \iota\text{‘}0 . \supset :$
$\text{rep}_\kappa \text{‘} L^\rho = \text{rep}_\kappa \text{‘} M^\sigma . \equiv . \dot{\exists} ! L^\rho \dot{\frown} M^\sigma$

Dem.

$\vdash . * 333\cdot 46 . \supset \vdash : \text{Hp} . \dot{\exists} ! L^\rho \dot{\frown} M^\sigma . \supset . \text{rep}_\kappa \text{‘} L^\rho = \text{rep}_\kappa \text{‘} M^\sigma$ (1)

$\vdash . * 332\cdot 53 . * 72\cdot 92 . \supset$

$\vdash : \text{Hp} . P, Q, R, S \in \kappa . L = \breve{P} | Q . M = \breve{R} | S . \supset . L^\rho = (\breve{P}^\rho | Q^\rho) \upharpoonright \text{C}\text{‘} L^\rho .$
$M^\sigma = (\breve{R}^\sigma | S^\sigma) \upharpoonright \text{C}\text{‘} M^\sigma . \text{rep}_\kappa \text{‘} L^\rho = \breve{P}^\rho | Q^\rho . \text{rep}_\kappa \text{‘} M^\sigma = \breve{R}^\sigma | S^\sigma$ (2)

$\vdash . (2) . * 35\cdot 14 . \supset$

$\vdash : \text{Hp} (2) . \text{rep}_\kappa \text{‘} L^\rho = \text{rep}_\kappa \text{‘} M^\sigma . \supset . L^\rho \dot{\frown} M^\sigma = (\breve{P}^\rho | Q^\rho) \upharpoonright (\text{C}\text{‘} L^\rho \cap \text{C}\text{‘} M^\sigma) .$

[*330·72] $\supset . \dot{\exists} ! L^\rho \dot{\frown} M^\sigma$ (3)

$\vdash . (1) . (3) . \supset \vdash . \text{Prop}$

***333·48.** $\vdash :. \kappa \in FM \text{ ap conx} . L, M \in \kappa_\iota . \rho, \sigma, \tau \in \text{NC ind} - \iota\text{‘}0 . \supset :$
$\dot{\exists} ! L^\rho \dot{\frown} M^\sigma . \equiv . \dot{\exists} ! L^{\rho \times_c \tau} \dot{\frown} M^{\sigma \times_c \tau}$

Dem.

$\vdash . * 333\cdot 46 . \supset \vdash : \text{Hp} . \dot{\exists} ! L^\rho \dot{\frown} M^\sigma . \supset . \text{rep}_\kappa \text{‘} L^\rho = \text{rep}_\kappa \text{‘} M^\sigma$ (1)

$\vdash . * 330\cdot 624 . * 332\cdot 61 . \supset \vdash : \text{Hp} . \supset . \dot{\Lambda} \sim \in \text{Pot}\text{‘} L^\rho . \dot{\exists} ! \text{rep}_\kappa \text{‘} L^\rho .$

[*333·24] $\supset . \text{rep}_\kappa \text{‘} L^{\rho \times_c \tau} = \text{rep}_\kappa \text{‘} (\text{rep}_\kappa \text{‘} L^\rho)^\tau$ (2)

Similarly $\vdash : \text{Hp} . \supset . \text{rep}_\kappa \text{‘} M^{\sigma \times_c \tau} = \text{rep}_\kappa \text{‘} (\text{rep}_\kappa \text{‘} M^\sigma)^\tau$ (3)

$\vdash . (1) . (2) . (3) . \supset \vdash : \text{Hp} . \dot{\exists} ! L^\rho \dot{\frown} M^\sigma . \supset . \text{rep}_\kappa \text{‘} L^{\rho \times_c \tau} = \text{rep}_\kappa \text{‘} M^{\sigma \times_c \tau} .$

[*333·47] $\supset . \dot{\exists} ! L^{\rho \times_c \tau} \dot{\frown} M^{\sigma \times_c \tau}$ (4)

$\vdash . * 333\cdot 46\cdot 47 . \supset \vdash : \text{Hp} . \dot{\exists} ! L^{\rho \times_c \tau} \dot{\frown} M^{\sigma \times_c \tau} . \supset . \dot{\exists} ! L^\rho \dot{\frown} M^\sigma$ (5)

$\vdash . (4) . (5) . \supset \vdash . \text{Prop}$

***333·49.** $\vdash : \kappa \in FM \text{ ap conx} . L, M \in \kappa_\iota . \rho, \sigma \in \text{NC ind} - \iota`0 . \text{rep}_\kappa`L^\rho = \text{rep}_\kappa`M^\sigma .$
$\supset . L^\rho \upharpoonright \text{Ɑ}`M^\sigma = M^\sigma \upharpoonright \text{Ɑ}`L^\rho . (\text{D}`M^\sigma) \upharpoonleft L^\rho = (\text{D}`L^\rho) \upharpoonleft M^\sigma$

Dem.

$\vdash . *333·21 . *330·6 . \supset \vdash : \text{Hp} . \supset . \dot{\exists} ! \text{rep}_\kappa`L^\rho .$
[*332·11] $\supset . L^\rho \,\text{G}\, \text{rep}_\kappa`L^\rho .$
[*72·92] $\supset . L^\rho = (\text{rep}_\kappa`L^\rho) \upharpoonright \text{Ɑ}`L^\rho$ (1)
Similarly $\vdash : \text{Hp} . \supset . M^\sigma = (\text{rep}_\kappa`M^\sigma) \upharpoonright \text{Ɑ}`M^\sigma .$
[Hp] $\supset . M^\sigma = (\text{rep}_\kappa`L^\rho) \upharpoonright \text{Ɑ}`M^\sigma$ (2)
$\vdash . (1) . (2) . \supset \vdash : \text{Hp} . \supset . L^\rho \upharpoonright \text{Ɑ}`M^\sigma = (\text{rep}_\kappa`L^\rho) \upharpoonright (\text{Ɑ}`L^\rho \cap \text{Ɑ}`M^\sigma) = M^\sigma \upharpoonright \text{Ɑ}`L^\rho$ (3)
Similarly $\vdash : \text{Hp} . \supset . (\text{D}`M^\sigma) \upharpoonleft L^\rho = (\text{D}`L^\rho) \upharpoonleft M^\sigma$ (4)
$\vdash . (3) . (4) . \supset \vdash . \text{Prop}$

***333·5.** $\vdash :. \kappa \in FM \text{ ap conx} . P, Q \in \kappa . \sigma \in \text{NC ind} - \iota`0 . \supset :$
$P^\sigma = Q^\sigma . \equiv . \dot{\exists} ! P^\sigma \dot{\cap} Q^\sigma . \equiv . P = Q$ [*333·42·43 . *331·24]

***333·51.** $\vdash :. \kappa \in FM \text{ ap conx} . M \in \kappa_{\iota\partial} . \rho, \sigma \in \text{NC ind} . \supset :$
$\text{rep}_\kappa`M^\rho = \text{rep}_\kappa`M^\sigma . \equiv . \rho = \sigma$

Dem.

$\vdash . *333·47 . \supset \vdash :. \text{Hp} . \text{rep}_\kappa`M^\rho = \text{rep}_\kappa`M^\sigma . \supset : \dot{\exists} ! M^\rho \dot{\cap} M^\sigma :$
[*301·23 . *120·412·416] $\supset : \rho \geqslant \sigma . \supset . \dot{\exists} ! M^{\rho -_c \sigma} \dot{\cap} I .$
[*333·101] $\supset . \rho = \sigma$ (1)
Similarly $\vdash :. \text{Hp} (1) . \supset : \sigma \geqslant \rho . \supset . \rho = \sigma$ (2)
$\vdash . (1) . (2) . \supset \vdash . \text{Prop}$

***333·52.** $\vdash :. \text{Hp } *333·51 . \supset : M^\rho = M^\sigma . \equiv . \rho = \sigma$ [*333·51]

***333·53.** $\vdash : \kappa \in FM \text{ ap conx} . L, M \in \kappa_{\iota\partial} . \dot{\exists} ! L^\sigma \dot{\cap} M^\rho . \dot{\exists} ! L^\nu \dot{\cap} M^\mu . \supset .$
$\mu \times_c \sigma = \nu \times_c \rho$

Dem.

$\vdash . *333·48 . *301·16 . \supset \vdash : \text{Hp} . \supset . \dot{\exists} ! L^{\mu \times_c \sigma} \dot{\cap} M^{\mu \times_c \rho} . \dot{\exists} ! L^{\nu \times_c \rho} \dot{\cap} M^{\mu \times_c \rho} .$
[*333·47] $\supset . \text{rep}_\kappa`L^{\mu \times_c \sigma} = \text{rep}_\kappa`M^{\mu \times_c \rho} = \text{rep}_\kappa`L^{\nu \times_c \rho} .$
[*333·51] $\supset . \mu \times_c \sigma = \nu \times_c \rho : \supset \vdash . \text{Prop}$

$*334$. SERIAL FAMILIES.

Summary of $*334$.

The purpose of the present number is to consider what properties of a family κ will insure that $\dot{s}'\kappa_\partial$ is serial, or has one or more of the properties characteristic of serial relations. Suppose, for example, that κ consists of distances on a line. Then κ_∂ consists of those distances which are members of κ and are not zero. Any selection of distances on the line may constitute κ; thus *e.g.* κ may consist of all distances which are integral multiples of a given distance, or of all which are rational multiples of a given distance, or of all distances from left to right, or of all distances on the line in either direction. It is plain to begin with that if $\dot{s}'\kappa_\partial$ is to be serial, κ must not contain equal distances in opposite directions, since if it does, $(\dot{s}'\kappa_\partial)^2$ will not be contained in diversity, *i.e.* $\dot{s}'\kappa_\partial$ will not be asymmetrical. We call a family κ asymmetrical when no member of κ_∂ has a converse which is also a member of κ_∂. The definition is

$$*334\cdot05.\quad FM\,\mathrm{asym} = FM \cap \hat{\kappa}\,(\kappa \cap \mathrm{Cnv}``\kappa \subset \mathrm{Rl}'I) \quad \mathrm{Df}$$

It will be observed that $\dot{s}'\kappa_\partial \Subset J$ in any connected family, by $*331\cdot23$. If $\kappa \in FM\,\mathrm{asym}$, we have also $(\dot{s}'\kappa_\partial)^2 \Subset J$.

In order to secure that $\dot{s}'\kappa_\partial$ shall be *transitive*, we require that the field of κ should contain at least one "transitive point," where a "transitive point" means a point a such that any point which can be reached from a by two successive non-zero steps can also be reached by one non-zero step, *i.e.* such that

$$(\dot{s}'\kappa_\partial)``\overrightarrow{\dot{s}'\kappa_\partial}'a \subset \overrightarrow{\dot{s}'\kappa_\partial}'a.$$

The definition of transitive points is

$$*334\cdot01.\quad \mathrm{trs}'\kappa = s'C``\kappa \cap \hat{a}\,\{(\dot{s}'\kappa_\partial)``\overrightarrow{\dot{s}'\kappa_\partial}'a \subset \overrightarrow{\dot{s}'\kappa_\partial}'a\} \quad \mathrm{Df}$$

Thus if a is a transitive point, and $R, S \in \kappa_\partial$, there is always a member of κ_∂, say T, such that $R'S'a = T'a$. It will be seen that if κ is a connected family, the existence of a transitive point implies that the family is asymmetrical. Again, if there is a transitive point in a connected family, then $R, S \in \kappa_\partial \,.\supset.\, R \,|\, S \in \kappa_\partial$, by $*331\cdot32$, hence κ_∂ is a group. The converse also holds, *i.e.* if κ_∂ is a group, any member $s`\text{C}``\kappa$ is a transitive point (*334·11). Hence if there is any transitive point, every point of $s`\text{C}``\kappa$ is a transitive point.

The definition of a transitive family is

*334·02. $FM\,\text{trs} = FM \cap \hat{\kappa}(\exists\,!\,\text{trs}`\kappa)$ Df

By what has just been said, a connected transitive family is one in which κ_∂ is a group, *i.e.*

*334·13. $\vdash :. \kappa \in FM\,\text{conx} . \supset : \kappa \in FM\,\text{trs} . \equiv . s`\kappa_\partial \,|\, ``\kappa_\partial \subset \kappa_\partial$

A connected family is transitive when, and only when, $\dot{s}`\kappa_\partial$ is a transitive relation, *i.e.*

*334·14. $\vdash :. \kappa \in FM\,\text{conx} . \supset : \kappa \in FM\,\text{trs} . \equiv . \dot{s}`\kappa_\partial \in \text{trans}$

In order to secure that $\dot{s}`\kappa_\partial$ shall be a *connected* relation, it is not enough that $\kappa$ should be an $FM$ conx, *i.e.* that $s`\text{C}``\kappa$ should have at least one connected point. We require that *every* point of $s`\text{C}``\kappa$ should be a connected point. This will be secured if there is a connected point which belongs to the field of every member of κ_ι, *i.e.* if

$$\exists\,!\,\text{conx}`\kappa \cap p`C``\kappa_\iota .$$

For suppose $a \in \text{conx}`\kappa \cap p`C``\kappa_\iota$. Then if $L \in \kappa_\iota$, either $L`a$ or $\breve{L}`a$ exists, and is of the form $R`a$ or $\breve{R}`a$, where $R \in \kappa$. Hence, by *331·32, $L$ is identical with $R$ or with $\breve{R}$; hence $\kappa_\iota = \kappa \cup \text{Cnv}``\kappa$. Hence by *331·4, $\dot{s}`\kappa_\partial \in \text{connex}$. Conversely, if $\kappa \in FM\,\text{conx}$ and $\dot{s}`\kappa_\partial \in \text{connex}$, it follows from *331·32 that $\kappa_\iota = \kappa \cup \text{Cnv}``\kappa$; hence $p`C``\kappa_\iota = s`\text{C}``\kappa$, and therefore we have $\exists\,!\,\text{conx}`\kappa \cap p`C``\kappa_\iota$. Hence putting

*334·03. $FM\,\text{connex} = FM \cap \hat{\kappa}(\exists\,!\,\text{conx}`\kappa \cap p`C``\kappa_\iota)$ Df

where "FM connex" means "families having connexity," we have

*334·26. $\vdash :. \kappa \in FM\,\text{conx} . \supset : \kappa \in FM\,\text{connex} . \equiv . \dot{s}`\kappa_\partial \in \text{connex} .$
$\equiv . \kappa_\iota = \kappa \cup \text{Cnv}``\kappa . \equiv . C``\kappa_\iota = \text{C}``\kappa$

and

*334·27. $\vdash . FM\,\text{connex} = FM \cap \hat{\kappa}(s`\text{C}``\kappa = \text{conx}`\kappa . \kappa \neq \iota`\dot{\Lambda})$

I.e. a family having connexity is one whose field consists wholly of connected points and is not null.

We thus secure (1) $\dot{s}`\kappa_\partial \in J$ by the hypothesis $\kappa \in FM\,\text{conx}$, (2) $\dot{s}`\kappa_\partial \in \text{trans}$ by the hypothesis $\kappa \in FM\,\text{conx} \cap FM\,\text{trs}$, (3) $\dot{s}`\kappa_\partial \in \text{connex}$ by the hypothesis $\kappa \in FM\,\text{connex}$ (which implies $\kappa \in FM\,\text{conx}$). Hence we secure $\dot{s}`\kappa_\partial \in \text{Ser}$ by the hypothesis $\kappa \in FM\,\text{trs} \cap FM\,\text{connex}$. When this hypothesis is fulfilled, we call κ a "serial" family; thus we put

***334·04.** $FM\,\text{sr} = FM\,\text{trs} \cap FM\,\text{connex}$ Df

and we have

***334·3.** $\vdash : \kappa \epsilon FM\,\text{sr} . \supset . \dot{s}`\kappa_\partial \epsilon \text{Ser}$

***334·31.** $\vdash :. \kappa \epsilon FM . I \upharpoonright s`\text{G}``\kappa \epsilon \kappa . \supset : \kappa \epsilon FM\,\text{sr} . \equiv . \dot{s}`\kappa_\partial \epsilon \text{Ser} - \iota`\dot{\Lambda}$

An important special case, which is briefly considered in this number, is the case when the domains of members of κ are the same as their converse domains, *i.e.* when

$$\text{D}``\kappa = \text{G}``\kappa.$$

This case is illustrated, *e.g.* by the family whose members are all relations of the form $(+_g X) \upharpoonright C`H_g$, where $X \epsilon C`H'$. It is also illustrated by cyclic families, which are considered in the next Section but one. When $\text{D}``\kappa = \text{G}``\kappa$, if κ is a family, so is $\kappa \cup \text{Cnv}``\kappa$ (*334·4), and if $\kappa$ is a connected family, so is $\kappa \cup \text{Cnv}``\kappa$ (*334·41). In the case of the above family, whose members are $(+_g X) \upharpoonright C`H_g$ where $X \epsilon C`H'$, $\kappa \cup \text{Cnv}``\kappa$ will consist of all relations $(+_g X) \upharpoonright C`H_g$ where $X \epsilon C`H_g$, *i.e.* it will consist of all additions of positive or negative ratios to positive or negative ratios.

A connected family in which $\text{D}``\kappa = \text{G}``\kappa$ is a family having connexity, *i.e.*

***334·42.** $\vdash : \kappa \epsilon FM\,\text{conx} . \text{D}``\kappa = \text{G}``\kappa . \supset . \kappa \epsilon FM\,\text{connex}$

The definitions and propositions of this number are much used throughout the remainder of Part VI.

***334·01.** $\text{trs}`\kappa = s`\text{G}``\kappa \cap \hat{a}\,\{(\dot{s}`\kappa_\partial)``\overrightarrow{\dot{s}`\kappa_\partial}`a \subset \overrightarrow{\dot{s}`\kappa_\partial}`a\}$ Df

***334·02.** $FM\,\text{trs} = FM \cap \hat{\kappa}\,(\exists ! \text{trs}`\kappa)$ Df

***334·03.** $FM\,\text{connex} = FM \cap \hat{\kappa}\,(\exists ! \text{conx}`\kappa \cap p`C``\kappa_\iota)$ Df

***334·04.** $FM\,\text{sr} = FM\,\text{trs} \cap FM\,\text{connex}$ Df

***334·05.** $FM\,\text{asym} = FM \cap \hat{\kappa}\,(\kappa \cap \text{Cnv}``\kappa \subset \text{Rl}`I)$ Df

***334·09.** $\vdash : \kappa \epsilon FM\,\text{conx} . \supset . \dot{s}`\kappa_\partial \Subset J$ [*331·23]

***334·1.** $\vdash :: \kappa \epsilon FM . \supset :. a \epsilon \text{trs}`\kappa . \equiv :$

$$a \epsilon s`\text{G}``\kappa : R, S \epsilon \kappa_\partial . \supset_{R,S} . (\exists T) . T \epsilon \kappa_\partial . R`S`a = T`a \quad [(*334\cdot01)]$$

***334·11.** $\vdash :. \kappa \epsilon FM\,\text{conx} . \supset : a \epsilon \text{trs}`\kappa . \equiv . a \epsilon s`\text{G}``\kappa . s`\kappa_\partial \,|\, ``\kappa_\partial \subset \kappa_\partial$
 ,,

Dem.

$\vdash . *331\cdot33\cdot24 . \supset \vdash : \text{Hp} . R, S \epsilon \kappa_\partial . \supset . R \,|\, S \epsilon \kappa_\iota$ (1)

$\vdash . (1) . *331\cdot32 . \supset \vdash : \text{Hp} . T \epsilon \kappa_\partial . R`S`a = T`a . \supset . R \,|\, S = T$ (2)

$\vdash . (2) . *334\cdot1 . \supset \vdash :: \text{Hp} . \supset :.$

$$a \epsilon \text{trs}`\kappa . \equiv : a \epsilon s`\text{G}``\kappa : R, S \epsilon \kappa_\partial . \supset_{R,S} . (\exists T) . T \epsilon \kappa_\partial . R \,|\, S = T :$$

[*13·195] $\equiv : a \epsilon s`\text{G}``\kappa : R, S \epsilon \kappa_\partial . \supset_{R,S} . R \,|\, S \epsilon \kappa_\partial :: \supset \vdash . \text{Prop}$

***334·12.** $\vdash :. \kappa \in FM \text{ conx} . a, x \in s\text{‘}\text{Ɑ}\text{“}\kappa . \supset :$
$a \in \text{trs}\text{‘}\kappa . \equiv . x \in \text{trs}\text{‘}\kappa . \equiv . s\text{‘}\kappa_\partial \mid_{,,}\text{“}\kappa_\partial \subset \kappa_\partial$ [*334·11]

***334·13.** $\vdash :. \kappa \in FM \text{ conx} . \supset : \kappa \in FM \text{ trs} . \equiv . s\text{‘}\kappa_\partial \mid_{,,}\text{“}\kappa_\partial \subset \kappa_\partial$
[*334·12 . *331·12 . (*334·02)]

***334·131.** $\vdash : \kappa \in FM \text{ conx} \cap FM \text{ trs} . R \in \kappa_\partial . \supset . \text{Pot}\text{‘}R \subset \kappa_\partial$ [*334·13 . Induct]

***334·132.** $\vdash : \kappa \in FM \text{ conx} \cap FM \text{ trs} . \supset . s\text{‘}\text{Pot}\text{“}\kappa \subset \kappa$ [*334·131]

***334·14.** $\vdash :. \kappa \in FM \text{ conx} . \supset : \kappa \in FM \text{ trs} . \equiv . \dot{s}\text{‘}\kappa_\partial \in \text{trans}$

Dem.

$\vdash . *41{\cdot}51 . *334{\cdot}13 . \supset \vdash :. \text{Hp} . \supset : \kappa \in FM \text{ trs} . \supset . (\dot{s}\text{‘}\kappa_\partial)^2 \in \dot{s}\text{‘}\kappa_\partial$ (1)

$\vdash . *330{\cdot}52 . \quad \supset \vdash :: \text{Hp} . \supset :. \dot{s}\text{‘}\kappa_\partial \in \text{trans} . \supset :$
$R, S \in \kappa_\partial . x \in s\text{‘}\text{Ɑ}\text{“}\kappa . \supset_{R,S,x} . (\exists T) . T \in \kappa_\partial . R\text{‘}S\text{‘}x = T\text{‘}x .$

[*331·31·33·24] $\supset_{R,S,x} . (\exists T) . T \in \kappa_\partial . R \mid S = T .$

[*13·195] $\supset_{R,S,x} . R \mid S \in \kappa_\partial$ (2)

$\vdash . (2) . *331{\cdot}12 . \quad \supset \vdash :: \text{Hp} . \supset :. \dot{s}\text{‘}\kappa_\partial \in \text{trans} . \supset : R, S \in \kappa_\partial . \supset_{R,S} . R \mid S \in \kappa_\partial :$

[*334·13] $\supset : \kappa \in FM \text{ trs}$ (3)

$\vdash . (1) . (3) . \supset \vdash . \text{Prop}$

***334·15.** $\vdash : \kappa \in FM \text{ conx} \cap FM \text{ trs} . \supset . s\text{‘}\kappa \mid_{,,}\text{“}\kappa = \kappa$

Dem.

$\vdash . *331{\cdot}321{\cdot}22 . \quad \supset \vdash :. \text{Hp} . R \in \kappa - \kappa_\partial . \supset : R = I \upharpoonright s\text{‘}\text{Ɑ}\text{“}\kappa :$

[*50·62·63] $\supset : S \in \kappa . \supset . R \mid S, S \mid R \in \kappa$ (1)

$\vdash . (1) . *334{\cdot}13 . \quad \supset \vdash : \text{Hp} . \supset . s\text{‘}\kappa \mid_{,,}\text{“}\kappa \subset \kappa$ (2)

$\vdash . *331{\cdot}22 . *50{\cdot}62{\cdot}63 . \supset \vdash : \text{Hp} . \supset . \kappa \subset s\text{‘}\kappa \mid_{,,}\text{“}\kappa$ (3)

$\vdash . (2) . (3) . \supset \vdash . \text{Prop}$

***334·16.** $\vdash : \kappa \in FM \text{ conx} \cap FM \text{ trs} . R \in \kappa_\partial . \supset . R_{\text{po}} \in J$ [*334·131·09]

***334·161.** $\vdash : \kappa \in FM \text{ conx} \cap FM \text{ trs} . R \in \kappa_\partial . a \in s\text{‘}\text{Ɑ}\text{“}\kappa . \supset . \overrightarrow{R_*}\text{‘}a \in \aleph_0$
[*334·16 . *123·191]

***334·162.** $\vdash : \exists ! FM \text{ conx} \cap FM \text{ trs} - 1 . \supset . \text{Infin ax}$ [*334·161]

***334·17.** $\vdash : \kappa \in FM \text{ conx} \cap 1 . \supset . \kappa_\partial = \Lambda$ [*331·22]

***334·18.** $\vdash : \kappa \in FM \text{ conx} - 1 . \supset . C\text{‘}\dot{s}\text{‘}\kappa_\partial = s\text{‘}\text{Ɑ}\text{“}\kappa = s\text{‘}\text{Ɑ}\text{“}\kappa_\partial . \dot{\exists} ! \dot{s}\text{‘}\kappa_\partial . \exists ! \kappa_\partial$

Dem.

$\vdash . *331{\cdot}22{\cdot}321 . \supset \vdash :. \text{Hp} . \supset : \exists ! \kappa_\partial :$

[*330·52] $\supset : a \in s\text{‘}\text{Ɑ}\text{“}\kappa . \supset . (\exists R) . R \in \kappa_\partial . a \in \text{Ɑ}\text{‘}R .$

[*40·4] $\supset . a \in s\text{‘}\text{Ɑ}\text{“}\kappa_\partial .$ (1)

[*41·45] $\supset . a \in C\text{‘}\dot{s}\text{‘}\kappa_\partial$ (2)

$\vdash . (1) . (2) . *331{\cdot}12 . \supset \vdash . \text{Prop}$

***334·19.** $\vdash : \kappa \epsilon FM . \supset . C`\dot{s}`\kappa_\partial \subset s`\text{Ɑ}``\kappa$ [*41·45 . *330·52]

***334·2.** $\vdash :: . \kappa \epsilon FM . \supset :: a \epsilon p`C``\kappa_\iota . \equiv : . L \epsilon \kappa_\iota . \supset_L : E ! L`a . \vee . E ! \breve{L}`a$
[*330·52]

***334·21.** $\vdash : \kappa \epsilon FM \text{ connex} . \supset . \kappa_\iota = \kappa \cup \text{Cnv}``\kappa$

Dem.

$\vdash . *334\cdot2 . *331\cdot11 . \supset \vdash : . \text{Hp} . a \epsilon \text{conx}`\kappa \cap p`C``\kappa_\iota . L \epsilon \kappa_\iota . \supset :$
$(\exists R) : R \epsilon \kappa \cup \text{Cnv}``\kappa : L`a = R`a . \vee . \breve{L}`a = R`a :$
[*331·42·24] $\supset : (\exists R) : R \epsilon \kappa \cup \text{Cnv}``\kappa : L = R . \vee . \breve{L} = R$ (1)
$\vdash . (1) . *331\cdot24 . \supset \vdash . \text{Prop}$

***334·22.** $\vdash : \kappa \epsilon FM \text{ connex} . \supset . p`C``\kappa_\iota = s`\text{Ɑ}``\kappa$ [*334·21 . *330·52]

***334·23.** $\vdash : \kappa \epsilon FM \text{ connex} . \supset . \text{conx}`\kappa = s`\text{Ɑ}``\kappa$ [*334·21 . *331·4]

***334·24.** $\vdash : \kappa \epsilon FM \text{ connex} . \supset . \dot{s}`\kappa_\partial \epsilon \text{connex}$

Dem.

$\vdash . *334\cdot21 . *331\cdot4 . \supset$
$\vdash : . \text{Hp} . x, y \epsilon s`\text{Ɑ}``\kappa . x \neq y . \supset : (\exists R) : R \epsilon \kappa_\partial : xRy . \vee . yRx : . \supset \vdash . \text{Prop}$

***334·25.** $\vdash : \kappa \epsilon FM \text{ connex} . \supset . C``\kappa_\iota = \text{Ɑ}``\kappa$ [*334·21 . *330·52]

***334·251.** $\vdash : \kappa \epsilon FM . \kappa_\iota = \kappa \cup \text{Cnv}``\kappa . \supset . p`C``\kappa_\iota = s`\text{Ɑ}``\kappa$

Dem.

$\vdash . *40\cdot18 . *33\cdot22 . \supset \vdash : \text{Hp} . \supset . p`C``\kappa_\iota = p`C``\kappa$ (1)
$\vdash . (1) . *330\cdot52 . \supset \vdash . \text{Prop}$

***334·252.** $\vdash : \kappa \epsilon FM \text{ conx} . \dot{s}`\kappa_\partial \epsilon \text{connex} . \supset . \kappa_\iota = \kappa \cup \text{Cnv}``\kappa$

Dem.

$\vdash . *41\cdot11 . \supset \vdash : \text{Hp} . L \epsilon \kappa_\iota . x = L`y . \supset . (\exists R) . R \epsilon \kappa \cup \text{Cnv}``\kappa . xRy .$
[*331·42·24] $\supset . L \epsilon \kappa \cup \text{Cnv}``\kappa$ (1)
$\vdash . (1) . *330\cdot6 . *331\cdot12 . \supset \vdash . \text{Prop}$

***334·253.** $\vdash : \kappa \epsilon FM \text{ conx} . C``\kappa_\iota = \text{Ɑ}``\kappa . \supset . \kappa \epsilon FM \text{ connex}$

Dem.

$\vdash . *330\cdot52 . \supset \vdash : \text{Hp} . \supset . p`C``\kappa = s`\text{Ɑ}``\kappa .$
[*331·1] $\supset . \exists ! p`C``\kappa_\iota \cap \text{conx}`\kappa : \supset \vdash . \text{Prop}$

***334·26.** $\vdash : . \kappa \epsilon FM \text{ conx} . \supset : \kappa \epsilon FM \text{ connex} . \equiv . \dot{s}`\kappa_\partial \epsilon \text{connex} .$
$\equiv . \kappa_\iota = \kappa \cup \text{Cnv}``\kappa . \equiv . C``\kappa_\iota = \text{Ɑ}``\kappa$ [*334·21·24·25·251·252·253]

***334·27.** $\vdash . FM \text{ connex} = FM \cap \hat{\kappa} (s`\text{Ɑ}``\kappa = \text{conx}`\kappa . \kappa \neq \iota`\Lambda)$

Dem.

$\vdash . *331\cdot1 . \supset \vdash : \kappa \epsilon FM . \kappa \neq \iota`\dot{\Lambda} . s`\text{Ɑ}``\kappa = \text{conx}`\kappa . \supset . \dot{s}`\kappa_\partial \epsilon \text{connex} .$
[*334·26.(*331·02)] $\supset . \kappa \epsilon FM \text{ connex}$ (1)
$\vdash . *334\cdot23 . (*334\cdot03) . \supset \vdash : \kappa \epsilon FM \text{ connex} . \supset . s`\text{Ɑ}``\kappa = \text{conx}`\kappa . \kappa \neq \iota`\dot{\Lambda}$ (2)
$\vdash . (1) . (2) . \supset \vdash . \text{Prop}$

***334·3.** $\vdash : \kappa \in FM\,\mathrm{sr} \,.\supset .\, \dot{s}`\kappa_\partial \in \mathrm{Ser}$

Dem.

$\vdash .\, *334\cdot09 \,.\supset \vdash : \mathrm{Hp} \,.\supset .\, \dot{s}`\kappa_\partial \subseteq J$ (1)

$\vdash .\, *334\cdot14 \,.\supset \vdash : \mathrm{Hp} \,.\supset .\, \dot{s}`\kappa_\partial \in \mathrm{trans}$ (2)

$\vdash .\, *334\cdot24 \,.\supset \vdash : \mathrm{Hp} \,.\supset .\, \dot{s}`\kappa_\partial \in \mathrm{connex}$ (3)

$\vdash .\, (1) . (2) . (3) \,.\supset \vdash .\, \mathrm{Prop}$

***334·31.** $\vdash :.\, \kappa \in FM \,.\, I \upharpoonright s`\text{Ɑ}``\kappa \in \kappa \,.\supset : \kappa \in FM\,\mathrm{sr} \,.\equiv .\, \dot{s}`\kappa_\partial \in \mathrm{Ser} - \iota`\dot{\Lambda}$

Dem.

$\vdash .\, *41\cdot11 \,.\supset \vdash :.\, \mathrm{Hp} \,.\, \dot{s}`\kappa_\partial \in \mathrm{Ser} - \iota`\dot{\Lambda} \,.\supset :$

$x, y \in s`\text{Ɑ}``\kappa \,.\supset_{x,y} .\, (\exists R) \,.\, R \in \kappa \,.\, x\,(R \,\dot{\cup}\, \breve{R})\,y :$

[*331·11] $\supset : s`\text{Ɑ}``\kappa = \mathrm{conx}`\kappa$ (1)

$\vdash .\, (1) \,.\, *334\cdot14\cdot26 \,.\supset \vdash : \mathrm{Hp}\,(1) \,.\supset .\, \kappa \in FM\,\mathrm{trs} \,.\, \kappa \in FM\,\mathrm{connex}$ (2)

$\vdash .\, (2) \,.\, *334\cdot3 \,.\, *331\cdot12 \,.\supset \vdash .\, \mathrm{Prop}$

***334·32.** $\vdash .\, FM\,\mathrm{sr} \subset FM\,\mathrm{ap}$ [*334·16·21 . *333·101]

***334·4.** $\vdash : \kappa \in FM \,.\, \mathrm{D}``\kappa = \text{Ɑ}``\kappa \,.\supset .\, \kappa \cup \mathrm{Cnv}``\kappa \in FM$

Dem.

$\vdash .\, *33\cdot2\cdot21 \,.\supset \vdash : \mathrm{Hp} \,.\supset .\, \mathrm{D}``(\kappa \cup \mathrm{Cnv}``\kappa) = \text{Ɑ}``(\kappa \cup \mathrm{Cnv}``\kappa) = \text{Ɑ}``\kappa$ (1)

$\vdash .\, *330\cdot561 \,.\supset \vdash :.\, \mathrm{Hp} \,.\supset : R, S \in \kappa \,.\supset .\, \breve{R} \,|\, S = S \,|\, \breve{R}$ (2)

$\vdash .\, (1) . (2) \,.\, *330\cdot52 \,.\supset \vdash .\, \mathrm{Prop}$

***334·41.** $\vdash : \kappa \in FM\,\mathrm{conx} \,.\, \mathrm{D}``\kappa = \text{Ɑ}``\kappa \,.\supset .\, \kappa \cup \mathrm{Cnv}``\kappa \in FM\,\mathrm{conx}$
[*334·4 . *331·11]

***334·42.** $\vdash : \kappa \in FM\,\mathrm{conx} \,.\, \mathrm{D}``\kappa = \text{Ɑ}``\kappa \,.\supset .\, \kappa \in FM\,\mathrm{connex}$

Dem.

$\vdash .\, *37\cdot323 \,.\supset \vdash :.\, \mathrm{Hp} \,.\supset : R, S \in \kappa \,.\supset .\, \text{Ɑ}`(\breve{R} \,|\, S) = \text{Ɑ}`S :$

[*330·4] $\supset : C``\kappa_\iota = \text{Ɑ}``\kappa$ (1)

$\vdash .\, (1) \,.\, *334\cdot26 \,.\supset \vdash .\, \mathrm{Prop}$

***334·43.** $\vdash : \kappa \in FM\,\mathrm{conx} \cap FM\,\mathrm{trs} \,.\, \mathrm{D}``\kappa = \text{Ɑ}``\kappa \,.\supset .\, \kappa \in FM\,\mathrm{sr}$
[*334·42 . (*334·04)]

***334·44.** $\vdash : \kappa \in FM\,\mathrm{conx} \,.\, \mathrm{D}``\kappa = \text{Ɑ}``\kappa \,.\, L \in \kappa_\iota \,.\supset .\, \mathrm{D}`L = \text{Ɑ}`L = C`L = s`\text{Ɑ}``\kappa$

Dem.

$\vdash .\, *37\cdot323 \,.\supset \vdash : \mathrm{Hp} \,.\, R, S \in \kappa \,.\supset .\, \text{Ɑ}`(\breve{R} \,|\, S) = \text{Ɑ}`S : \supset \vdash .\, \mathrm{Prop}$

***334·45.** $\vdash : \kappa \epsilon FM \text{ conx} . \text{D}``\kappa = \text{G}``\kappa . L, M \epsilon \kappa_\iota . \supset . \text{G}`(L | M) = s`\text{G}``\kappa$
[*334·44]

***334·451.** $\vdash : \text{Hp} *334·44 . S \epsilon \text{Pot}`L . \supset . \text{D}`S = \text{G}`S = C`S = s`\text{G}``\kappa$ [*334·44]

***334·46.** $\vdash :. \text{Hp} *334·44 . M, N \epsilon \kappa_\iota . \supset : \dot{\exists} ! L | M \dot{\wedge} N . \equiv . L | M = N$
[*334·45 . *331·45]

***334·5.** $\vdash : \kappa \epsilon FM \text{ conx} \cap FM \text{ asym} . \supset . (\dot{s}`\kappa_\partial)^2 \in J$

Dem.

$\vdash . *332·46 . \supset \vdash : \text{Hp} . R, S \epsilon \kappa . R | S \in I . \supset . R = \breve{S} .$

[(*334·05)] $\supset . R = I \upharpoonright s`\text{G}``\kappa$ (1)

$\vdash . (1) . \text{Transp} . \supset \vdash :. \text{Hp} . \supset : R, S \epsilon \kappa_\partial . \supset . \sim(R | S \in I) .$

[*331·33·23] $\supset . R | S \in J :. \supset \vdash . \text{Prop}$

$*335$. INITIAL FAMILIES.

Summary of $*335$.

A family of vectors may or may not have a point in its field which is a starting-point but not an end-point of non-zero vectors. For example, the family of which a member is $(+_s X) \upharpoonright C'H'$, where $X \epsilon C'H'$, has such a point in its field, namely 0_q; but the family of which a member is $(+_s X) \upharpoonright C'H$, where $X \epsilon C'H'$, has no such point in its field, and no more has the family of which a member is $(+_g X) \upharpoonright C'H_g$, where $X \epsilon C'H'$. If such a point exists, it is a member of $s'\text{Ɑ}''\kappa$ but not of $s'\mathrm{D}''\kappa_\partial$. Such a point, if it is also a connected point, must be unique, *i.e.* we have

$*335{\cdot}12.\ \vdash :.\ \kappa \epsilon FM\ .\ \supset .\ \text{conx}'\kappa - s'\mathrm{D}''\kappa_\partial \,\epsilon\, 0 \cup 1$

When $\text{conx}'\kappa - s'\mathrm{D}''\kappa_\partial$ exists, we call its only member "the initial point of κ," putting

$*335{\cdot}01.\ \text{init}'\kappa = \breve{\iota}'(\text{conx}'\kappa - s'\mathrm{D}''\kappa_\partial)$ Df

If the initial point of κ exists, we call κ an "initial" family; thus we put

$*335{\cdot}02.\ FM\,\text{init} = FM \cap \text{Ɑ}'\text{init}$ Df

An initial family is asymmetrical ($*335{\cdot}16$) and transitive ($*335{\cdot}18$), and forms a group ($*335{\cdot}17$); and if its initial point is a member of $p'C''\kappa_\iota$, it is a serial family ($*335{\cdot}3$).

$*335{\cdot}01.\ \text{init}'\kappa = \breve{\iota}'(\text{conx}'\kappa - s'\mathrm{D}''\kappa_\partial)$ Df

$*335{\cdot}02.\ FM\,\text{init} = FM \cap \text{Ɑ}'\text{init}$ Df

$*335{\cdot}11.\ \vdash : \kappa \epsilon FM\ .\ a \epsilon \text{conx}'\kappa - s'\mathrm{D}''\kappa_\partial\ .\ \supset .\ s'\text{Ɑ}''\kappa = \overrightarrow{\dot{s}}'\kappa'a\ .\ \iota'a = \overleftarrow{\dot{s}}'\kappa'a$

Dem.

$\vdash .\ *41{\cdot}43\ .\ *33{\cdot}4\ .\ \supset \vdash : \text{Hp}\ .\ \supset .\ \overleftarrow{\dot{s}}'\kappa_\partial'a = \Lambda$ (1)

$\vdash .\ *331{\cdot}23{\cdot}22\ .\ \supset \vdash : \text{Hp}\ .\ \supset .\ \overleftarrow{\dot{s}}'\kappa'a = \overleftarrow{\dot{s}}'\kappa_\partial'a \cup \iota'a$ (2)

$\vdash .\ *331{\cdot}1{\cdot}23{\cdot}22\ .\ \supset \vdash : \text{Hp}\ .\ \supset .\ s'\text{Ɑ}''\kappa = \overrightarrow{\dot{s}}'\kappa'a \cup \overleftarrow{\dot{s}}'\kappa\partial'a$ (3)

$\vdash .\ (1)\ .\ (2)\ .\ (3)\ .\ \supset \vdash .$ Prop

***335·12.** $\vdash : \kappa \in FM . \supset . \text{conx}`\kappa - s`\text{D}``\kappa_\partial \in 0 \cup 1$

Dem.

$\vdash . *335{\cdot}11 . \supset \vdash : \text{Hp} . a, b \in \text{conx}`\kappa - s`\text{D}``\kappa_\partial . \supset . b \in \overrightarrow{\dot{s}`\kappa`}a .$

$[*32{\cdot}182] \qquad \supset . a \in \overleftarrow{\dot{s}`\kappa`}b .$

$[*335{\cdot}11] \qquad \supset . a = b : \supset \vdash . \text{Prop}$

***335·13.** $\vdash :. \kappa \in FM . \supset : \text{E} ! \, \text{init}`\kappa . \equiv . \exists ! \, \text{conx}`\kappa - s`\text{D}``\kappa_\partial$
$[*335{\cdot}12 . (*335{\cdot}01)]$

***335·14.** $\vdash : \kappa \in FM \, \text{init} . \equiv . \kappa \in FM . \exists ! \, \text{conx}`\kappa - s`\text{D}``\kappa_\partial$ $[*335{\cdot}13 . (*335{\cdot}02)]$

***335·15.** $\vdash : \kappa \in FM \, \text{init} . \supset . s`\text{Ɑ}``\kappa = \overrightarrow{\dot{s}`\kappa`}\text{init}`\kappa$ $[*335{\cdot}11 . (*335{\cdot}01)]$

***335·16.** $\vdash . FM \, \text{init} \subset FM \, \text{asym}$

Dem.

$\vdash . *335{\cdot}14 . \supset \vdash :. \kappa \in FM \, \text{init} . \supset :$

$(\exists a) : a \in s`\text{Ɑ}``\kappa : R \in \kappa . a \in \text{D}`R . \supset_R . R \in \text{Rl}`I \quad (1)$

$\vdash . *330{\cdot}52 . \supset \vdash : \kappa \in FM . a \in s`\text{Ɑ}``\kappa . R \in \kappa \cap \text{Cnv}``\kappa . \supset . a \in \text{D}`R \quad (2)$

$\vdash . (1) . (2) . \supset \vdash :. \kappa \in FM \, \text{init} . \supset : R \in \kappa \cap \text{Cnv}``\kappa . \supset_R . R \in \text{Rl}`I :$

$[(*334{\cdot}05)] \qquad \supset : \kappa \in FM \, \text{asym} :. \supset \vdash . \text{Prop}$

***335·17.** $\vdash : \kappa \in FM \, \text{init} . \supset . s`\kappa |_{,,}``\kappa = \kappa$

Dem.

$\vdash . *335{\cdot}15 . \supset \vdash :. \text{Hp} . \supset : R, S \in \kappa . \supset . (\exists T) . T \in \kappa . R`S`\text{init}`\kappa = T`\text{init}`\kappa .$

$[*331{\cdot}24{\cdot}33{\cdot}32] \qquad \supset . (\exists T) . T \in \kappa . R | S = T .$

$[*13{\cdot}195] \qquad \supset . R | S \in \kappa \quad (1)$

$\vdash . *331{\cdot}22 . \supset \vdash : \text{Hp} . \supset . \kappa \subset s`\kappa |_{,,}``\kappa \quad (2)$

$\vdash . (1) . (2) . \supset \vdash . \text{Prop}$

***335·18.** $\vdash . FM \, \text{init} \subset FM \, \text{trs}$

Dem.

$\vdash . *335{\cdot}17 . \qquad \supset \vdash :. \kappa \in FM \, \text{init} . \supset : R, S \in \kappa_\partial . \supset . R | S \in \kappa \quad (1)$

$\vdash . *334{\cdot}5 . *335{\cdot}16 . \supset \vdash :. \kappa \in FM \, \text{init} . \supset : R, S \in \kappa_\partial . \supset . R | S \mathrel{\text{G}} J \quad (2)$

$\vdash . (1) . (2) . *330{\cdot}551 . \supset \vdash :. \kappa \in FM \, \text{init} . \supset : R, S \in \kappa_\partial . \supset . R | S \in \kappa_\partial \quad (3)$

$\vdash . (3) . *334{\cdot}13 . \supset \vdash . \text{Prop}$

***335·19.** $\vdash :. \kappa \in FM \, \text{init} . \supset : \kappa \in FM \, \text{connex} . \equiv . \text{init}`\kappa \in p`C``\kappa_\iota$
$[*334{\cdot}23 . (*334{\cdot}03 . *335{\cdot}02{\cdot}01)]$

***335·21.** $\vdash : \kappa \in FM \, \text{init} . \supset . \dot{s}`\kappa_\partial \in \text{trans} . (\dot{s}`\kappa_\partial)^2 \mathrel{\text{G}} J$ $[*335{\cdot}18{\cdot}16 . *334{\cdot}14{\cdot}5]$

***335·22.** $\vdash :. \kappa \in FM \, \text{init} . \supset : \dot{s}`\kappa_\partial \in \text{connex} . \equiv . C``\kappa_\iota = \text{Ɑ}``\kappa . \equiv . \text{init}`\kappa \in p`C``\kappa_\iota$
$[*334{\cdot}26 . *335{\cdot}19]$

***335·23.** $\vdash :. \kappa \epsilon FM \text{ init} \cap FM \text{ connex} . L \epsilon \kappa_{\iota\partial} . \supset :$

$\text{init}`\kappa \epsilon \text{D}`L . \equiv . \text{init}`\kappa \sim\epsilon \text{Ɑ}`L$

Dem.

$\vdash . *335·19 . \supset \vdash :. \text{Hp} . \supset : \text{init}`\kappa \epsilon \text{D}`L . \vee . \text{init}`\kappa \epsilon \text{Ɑ}`L$ (1)

$\vdash . *334·21 . \supset \vdash : \text{Hp} . \supset . L \epsilon \kappa_\partial \cup \text{Cnv}``\kappa_\partial$ (2)

$\vdash . *335·11 . \supset \vdash :. \text{Hp} . \supset : L \epsilon \kappa_\partial . \supset . \text{init}`\kappa \sim\epsilon \text{D}`L :$

$L \epsilon \text{Cnv}``\kappa_\partial . \supset . \text{init}`\kappa \sim\epsilon \text{Ɑ}`L$ (3)

$\vdash . (2) . (3) . \supset \vdash :. \text{Hp} . \supset : \text{init}`\kappa \sim\epsilon \text{D}`L . \vee . \text{init}`\kappa \sim\epsilon \text{Ɑ}`L$ (4)

$\vdash . (1) . (4) . *5·17 . \supset \vdash . \text{Prop}$

***335·24.** $\vdash :. \kappa \epsilon FM \text{ init} \cap FM \text{ connex} . R, S \epsilon \kappa . R \neq S . \supset :$

$R`\text{init}`\kappa \epsilon \text{D}`S . \equiv . S`\text{init}`\kappa \sim\epsilon \text{D}`R$

Dem.

$\vdash . *71·162 . \supset \vdash :. \text{Hp} . \supset : R`\text{init}`\kappa \epsilon \text{D}`S . \equiv . \text{init}`\kappa \epsilon \text{Ɑ}`(\breve{S} | R) .$

[*333·1.*335·23] $\equiv . \text{init}`\kappa \sim\epsilon \text{D}`(\breve{S} | R) .$

[*71·162] $\equiv . S`\text{init}`\kappa \sim\epsilon \text{D}`R :. \supset \vdash . \text{Prop}$

***335·25.** $\vdash ::. \kappa \epsilon FM \text{ init} . \supset :: \dot{s}`\kappa_\partial \epsilon \text{connex} . \equiv :.$

$R, S \epsilon \kappa . \supset_{R,S} : \text{D}`R \subset \text{D}`S . \vee . \text{D}`S \subset \text{D}`R :.$

$\equiv :. \alpha, \beta \epsilon \text{D}``\kappa . \supset_{\alpha,\beta} : \alpha \subset \beta . \vee . \beta \subset \alpha$

Dem.

$\vdash . *202·135 . \supset \vdash :: \text{Hp} . \dot{s}`\kappa_\partial \epsilon \text{connex} . \supset :. \dot{s}`\kappa \epsilon \text{connex} :.$

[*211·6.*330·542] $\supset :. R, S \epsilon \kappa . \supset : \text{D}`R \subset \text{D}`S . \vee . \text{D}`S \subset \text{D}`R$ (1)

$\vdash . *71·162 . \supset \vdash : \text{Hp} . R`\text{init}`\kappa \epsilon \text{D}`S . \supset . \text{init}`\kappa \epsilon \text{Ɑ}`(\breve{R} | S)$ (2)

$\vdash . *71·162 . \supset \vdash : \text{Hp} . S`\text{init}`\kappa \epsilon \text{D}`R . \supset . \text{init}`\kappa \epsilon \text{D}`(\breve{R} | S)$ (3)

$\vdash . (2) . (3) . \supset \vdash :. \text{Hp} . R, S \epsilon \kappa : \text{D}`R \subset \text{D}`S . \vee . \text{D}`S \subset \text{D}`R : \supset .$

$\text{init}`\kappa \epsilon C`(\breve{R} | S)$ (4)

$\vdash . (4) . *330·4 . \supset \vdash :: \text{Hp} :. R, S \epsilon \kappa . \supset_{R,S} : \text{D}`R \subset \text{D}`S . \vee . \text{D}`S \subset \text{D}`R :. \supset .$

$\text{init}`\kappa \epsilon p`C``\kappa_\iota .$

[*335·22] $\supset . \dot{s}`\kappa_\partial \epsilon \text{connex}$ (5)

$\vdash . (1) . (5) . *37·63 . \supset \vdash . \text{Prop}$

***335·26.** $\vdash : \kappa \epsilon FM \text{ init} \cap FM \text{ connex} . \supset . \text{D} \upharpoonright \kappa \epsilon 1 \rightarrow 1$

Dem.

$\vdash . *33·43 . \supset \vdash : \text{Hp} . R, S \epsilon \kappa . R`\text{init}`\kappa \sim\epsilon \text{D}`S . \supset . \text{D}`R \neq \text{D}`S$ (1)

$\vdash . *335·24 . \supset \vdash : \text{Hp} . R, S \epsilon \kappa . R \neq S . R`\text{init}`\kappa \epsilon \text{D}`S . \supset . S`\text{init}`\kappa \sim\epsilon \text{D}`R .$

[*33·43] $\supset . \text{D}`R \neq \text{D}`S$ (2)

$\vdash . (1) . (2) . \supset \vdash : \text{Hp} . R, S \epsilon \kappa . R \neq S . \supset . \text{D}`R \neq \text{D}`S : \supset \vdash . \text{Prop}$

***335·3.** $\vdash : \kappa \epsilon FM . \text{init}`\kappa \epsilon p`C``\kappa_\iota . \supset . \dot{s}`\kappa_\partial \epsilon \text{Ser}$ [*335·21·22]

$*336$. THE SERIES OF VECTORS.

Summary of $*336$.

In this number we consider a relation between members of κ or of κ_ι which, with suitable limitations as to the nature of the family, may be identified with the relation of greater and less. If there is a member of κ which takes us from a point z to a point y, *i.e.* if $y\,(\dot{s}‘\kappa_\partial)\,z$, we say that z is an earlier point than y; thus we regard $\dot{s}‘\kappa_\partial$ as the relation of later to earlier. If now M and N are two members of κ_ι, and if, for some x, $M‘x$ is later than $N‘x$, we shall say that M is "greater" than N with respect to κ. This relation we denote by V_κ, where "V" is intended to suggest that the relation holds between *vectors*. The definition is:

$*336\cdot01$. $V_\kappa = \hat{M}\hat{N}\{M, N \in \kappa_\iota : (\exists x) . (M‘x)\,(\dot{s}‘\kappa_\partial)\,(N‘x)\}$ Df

For the same relation when confined to members of κ, we use the notation U_κ; thus we put

$*336\cdot011$. $U_\kappa = V_\kappa \upharpoonleft \kappa$ Df

In dealing with V_κ and U_κ it is desirable to be able to express $M‘x$ as a function of M. We wish to consider (say) a fixed origin a, and the various points $R‘a$, $S‘a$, $T‘a$, ... to which the various vectors which are members of κ carry us from a. For this purpose we put

$$R‘a = A_a‘R,$$

where "A" stands for "argument," and "$A_a‘R$" may be read "the value, for the argument a, of R." The definition is

$$A_a = \hat{x}\hat{R}\,(xRa) \quad \text{Df},$$

whence we obtain

$*336\cdot101$. $\vdash : \text{E}\,!\,R‘a\,.\supset.\,R‘a = A_a‘R$

Then the points $R‘a$, $S‘a$, $T‘a$, ..., where $R, S, T, \ldots$ are the various members of κ, form the class $A_a``\kappa$, which is thus the same class as $\overrightarrow{\dot{s}‘\kappa}‘a$. The relation $A_a \upharpoonright \kappa$ correlates the point $R‘a$ with the vector R. The vector R is analogous to the coordinate of $R‘a$ when a is the origin; thus $A_a \upharpoonright \kappa$ is analogous to the relation of a point to its coordinate. A relation which is more exactly that of a point to its coordinate will be explained in Section C, where, in addition to the above correlator $A_a \upharpoonright \kappa$, we shall also correlate a vector with its numerical measure in terms of an assigned unit.

If κ is a connected family, and a is any point of its field, $A_a \upharpoonright \kappa_\iota$ is a one-one relation (*336·2). If κ is an initial family, and a is its initial point, $A_a \upharpoonright \kappa$ is a correlator of s'Ɑ"κ and κ (*336·21), so that in an initial family the class of vectors is similar to the field (*336·22). If κ is a connected family, and a is any point of the field, and λ is those members L of κ_ι for which L'a exists, then $A_a \upharpoonright \lambda$ correlates the field with λ, so that λ is similar to the field (*336·24).

By the definition of A_a, if $M \epsilon \kappa_\iota$ and M'a exists, we have

$$M\text{‘}a = A_a\text{‘}M = A_a \upharpoonright \kappa_\iota\text{‘}M.$$

Hence by the definition of V_κ,

$$\vdash : MV_\kappa N . \equiv . (\exists a) . (A_a \upharpoonright \kappa_\iota\text{‘}M)(\dot{s}\text{‘}\kappa_\partial)(A_a \upharpoonright \kappa_\iota\text{‘}N) .$$
$$\equiv . (\exists a) . M(\kappa_\iota \upharpoonright \breve{A}_a ; \dot{s}\text{‘}\kappa_\partial) N, \text{ by } *150\cdot41.$$

Similarly $\vdash : PU_\kappa Q . \equiv . (\exists a) . P(\kappa \upharpoonright \breve{A}_a ; \dot{s}\text{‘}\kappa_\partial) Q.$

Now in a connected family, if a and b are any two members of the field, and $P, Q \epsilon \kappa$,

$$(P\text{‘}a)(\dot{s}\text{‘}\kappa_\partial)(Q\text{‘}a) . \equiv . (P\text{‘}b)(\dot{s}\text{‘}\kappa_\partial)(Q\text{‘}b) \quad (*336\cdot38);$$

hence $$\kappa \upharpoonright \breve{A}_a ; \dot{s}\text{‘}\kappa_\partial = \kappa \upharpoonright \breve{A}_b ; \dot{s}\text{‘}\kappa_\partial,$$

and hence $$U_\kappa = \kappa \upharpoonright \breve{A}_a ; \dot{s}\text{‘}\kappa_\partial \quad (*336\cdot43).$$

Since $\kappa \upharpoonright \breve{A}_a$ is one-one (by *336·2), the above gives an ordinal correlation of U_κ with $(\dot{s}\text{‘}\kappa_\partial) \upharpoonright A_a\text{“}\kappa$ (*336·461), *i.e.* U_κ is ordinally similar to $\dot{s}\text{‘}\kappa_\partial$ with its field confined to those points which can be reached from a by vectors which are members of κ. If κ is an initial family, it follows that U_κ is similar to $\dot{s}\text{‘}\kappa_\partial$ (*336·44); if not, U_κ is in general only similar to a segment of $\dot{s}\text{‘}\kappa_\partial$ (in the sense of *213).

It should be observed that $\kappa_\iota \upharpoonright \breve{A}_a\text{‘}x$ is the member of κ_ι which takes us from a to x, and $\kappa \upharpoonright \breve{A}_a\text{‘}x$ (if it exists) is the member of κ which takes us from a to x. Thus $\kappa \upharpoonright \breve{A}_a ; \dot{s}\text{‘}\kappa_\partial$ is the series of vectors which take us from a to all the various points which can be reached from a by members of κ, the order of the series being that of the points to which the various vectors take us from a.

If κ is a connected family, U_κ is the relation which holds between two members of κ when one of them is the relative product of the other and a third (other than the zero vector), *i.e.*

***336·41.** $\vdash : \kappa \epsilon FM \text{ conx} . \supset . U_\kappa = \hat{P}\hat{Q}\{P, Q \epsilon \kappa : (\exists T) . T \epsilon \kappa_\partial . P = T \mid Q\}$

This is for many purposes the most convenient formula for U_κ. If, in addition, we have $D``\kappa = \text{Ɑ}``\kappa$, a similar formula holds for V_κ, *i.e.*

***336·54.** $\vdash : \kappa \in FM \text{ conx} . D``\kappa = \text{Ɑ}``\kappa . \supset .$

$$V_\kappa = \hat{M}\hat{N}\{M, N \in \kappa_\iota : (\exists T) . T \in \kappa_{\partial} . M = T \mid N\}$$

If $\kappa \in FM$ conx, V_κ is contained in diversity (*336·6); if κ is also transitive, V_κ is transitive (336·61); and if κ has connexity, so has V_κ (*336·62). Hence if κ is a serial family, V_κ and U_κ are serial (*336·63·64).

In addition to the above-mentioned propositions, the following propositions in this number are important:

***336·411.** $\vdash :. \kappa \in FM \text{ conx} . s`\kappa \mid`` \kappa \subset \kappa . \supset : PU_\kappa Q . R \in \kappa . \supset . (P \mid R) U_\kappa (Q \mid R)$

***336·511.** $\vdash :. \kappa \in FM \text{ sr} . \nu \in \text{NC ind} - \iota`0 . \supset : RU_\kappa S . \equiv . R^\nu U_\kappa S^\nu$

***336·53.** $\vdash :. \kappa \in FM \text{ conx} . M, N \in \kappa_\iota . \supset : MV_\kappa N . \equiv . \breve{N} V_\kappa \breve{M}$

The present number is important, since V_κ and U_κ are the general relations from which greater and less among magnitudes are derived, and the subject of magnitude is therefore intimately dependent upon them.

***336·01.** $V_\kappa = \hat{M}\hat{N}\{M, N \in \kappa_\iota : (\exists x) . (M`x)(\dot{s}`\kappa_{\partial})(N`x)\}$ Df

***336·011.** $U_\kappa = V_\kappa \upharpoonright \kappa$ Df

***336·02.** $A_a = \hat{x}\hat{R}(xRa)$ Df

***336·1.** $\vdash : xA_aR . \equiv . xRa$ [(*336·02)]

***336·101.** $\vdash : E ! R`a . \supset . R`a = A_a`R$ [*336·1]

***336·11.** $\vdash : x(A_a \upharpoonright \kappa) R . \equiv . R \in \kappa . xRa$ [*336·1]

***336·12.** $\vdash . \overrightarrow{\dot{s}`\kappa}`a = A_a``\kappa = D`(A_a \upharpoonright \kappa)$

Dem.

$\vdash . *41·11 . \supset \vdash . \overrightarrow{\dot{s}`\kappa}`a = \hat{x}\{(\exists R) . R \in \kappa . xRa\}$

[*336·1] $= \hat{x}\{(\exists R) . R \in \kappa . xA_aR\} . \supset \vdash . \text{Prop}$

***336·13.** $\vdash . D`A_a \upharpoonright \kappa \subset s`D``\kappa$

Dem.

$\vdash . *336·12 . *33·15 . \supset \vdash . D`A_a \upharpoonright \kappa \subset D`\dot{s}`\kappa . \supset \vdash . \text{Prop}$

***336·14.** $\vdash : \kappa \subset 1 \to \text{Cls} . \supset . A_a \upharpoonright \kappa \in 1 \to \text{Cls}$

Dem.

$\vdash . *336·11 . \supset \vdash : x(A_a \upharpoonright \kappa) R . y(A_a \upharpoonright \kappa) R . \supset . R \in \kappa . xRa . yRa$ (1)

$\vdash . (1) . *71·17 . \supset \vdash : \text{Hp} . \text{Hp}(1) . \supset . x = y$ (2)

$\vdash . (2) . *71·17 . \supset \vdash . \text{Prop}$

***336·15.** $\vdash : \kappa \subset \mathrm{cr}`\alpha \,.\, a \epsilon \alpha \,.\, \supset \,.\, \text{Ɑ}`(A_a \restriction \kappa) = \kappa$

Dem.

$\vdash \,.\, *336{\cdot}11 \,.\, \supset \vdash : R \epsilon \text{Ɑ}`(A_a \restriction \kappa) \,.\, \equiv \,.\, (\exists x) \,.\, R \epsilon \kappa \,.\, xRa$ (1)

$\vdash \,.\, (1) \,.\, (*330{\cdot}01) \,.\, \supset \vdash \,.\, \mathrm{Prop}$

***336·16.** $\vdash : a \epsilon \mathrm{conx}`\kappa \,.\, \equiv \,.\, a \epsilon s`\text{Ɑ}``\kappa \,.\, A_a``(\kappa \cup \mathrm{Cnv}``\kappa) = s`\text{Ɑ}``\kappa$

Dem.

$\vdash \,.\, *331{\cdot}1 \,.\, *336{\cdot}12 \,.\, \supset$

$\vdash : a \epsilon \mathrm{conx}`\kappa \,.\, \equiv \,.\, a \epsilon s`\text{Ɑ}``\kappa \,.\, A_a``\kappa \cup A_a``\mathrm{Cnv}``\kappa = s`\text{Ɑ}``\kappa$ (1)

$\vdash \,.\, (1) \,.\, *37{\cdot}22 \,.\, \supset \vdash \,.\, \mathrm{Prop}$

***336·17.** $\vdash : \kappa \epsilon FM\,\mathrm{conx} \cap FM\,\mathrm{trs} - 1 \,.\, \breve{P} = \dot{s}`\kappa_\partial \,.\, \supset \,.\, A_a``\kappa = \overleftarrow{P_*}`a$

Dem.

$\vdash \,.\, *334{\cdot}14{\cdot}18 \,.\, \supset \vdash : \mathrm{Hp} \,.\, \supset \,.\, \overleftarrow{P_*}`a = \overleftarrow{P}`a \cup \overrightarrow{I \restriction s`\text{Ɑ}``\kappa}`a$

$[*331{\cdot}22{\cdot}23] \quad = \overrightarrow{\dot{s}`\kappa}`a$

$[*336{\cdot}12] \quad = A_a``\kappa : \supset \vdash \,.\, \mathrm{Prop}$

***336·2.** $\vdash : \kappa \epsilon FM\,\mathrm{conx} \,.\, a \epsilon s`\text{Ɑ}``\kappa \,.\, \supset \,.\, A_a \restriction \kappa_\iota \epsilon 1 \to 1$

Dem.

$\vdash \,.\, *336{\cdot}14 \,.\, \supset \vdash : \mathrm{Hp} \,.\, \supset \,.\, A_a \restriction \kappa_\iota \epsilon 1 \to \mathrm{Cls}$ (1)

$\vdash \,.\, *336{\cdot}11 \,.\, \supset \vdash : \mathrm{Hp} \,.\, x(A_a \restriction \kappa_\iota) L \,.\, x(A_a \restriction \kappa_\iota) M \,.\, \supset \,.\, L, M \epsilon \kappa_\iota \,.\, xLa \,.\, xMa \,.$

$[*331{\cdot}42] \quad \supset \,.\, L = M$ (2)

$\vdash \,.\, (1) \,.\, (2) \,.\, \supset \vdash \,.\, \mathrm{Prop}$

***336·21.** $\vdash : \kappa \epsilon FM \,.\, a = \mathrm{init}`\kappa \,.\, \supset \,.\, A_a \restriction \kappa \epsilon (s`\text{Ɑ}``\kappa) \,\overline{\mathrm{sm}}\, \kappa$

Dem.

$\vdash \,.\, *336{\cdot}2 \,. \quad \supset \vdash : \mathrm{Hp} \,.\, \supset \,.\, A_a \restriction \kappa \epsilon 1 \to 1$ (1)

$\vdash \,.\, *335{\cdot}15 \,.\, *336{\cdot}12 \,.\, \supset \vdash : \mathrm{Hp} \,.\, \supset \,.\, \mathrm{D}`A_a \restriction \kappa = s`\text{Ɑ}``\kappa$ (2)

$\vdash \,.\, *336{\cdot}15 \,. \quad \supset \vdash : \mathrm{Hp} \,.\, \supset \,.\, \text{Ɑ}`A_a \restriction \kappa = \kappa$ (3)

$\vdash \,.\, (1) \,.\, (2) \,.\, (3) \,.\, \supset \vdash \,.\, \mathrm{Prop}$

***336·22.** $\vdash : \kappa \epsilon FM\,\mathrm{init} \,.\, \supset \,.\, (s`\text{Ɑ}``\kappa)\,\mathrm{sm}\,\kappa \quad [*336{\cdot}21]$

***336·23.** $\vdash : \kappa \epsilon FM\,\mathrm{conx} \,.\, a \epsilon s`\text{Ɑ}``\kappa \,.\, \lambda = \kappa_\iota \cap \hat{L}(a \epsilon \text{Ɑ}`L) \,.\, \supset \,.$

$A_a \restriction \lambda \epsilon (s`\text{Ɑ}``\kappa) \,\overline{\mathrm{sm}}\, \lambda$

Dem.

$\vdash \,.\, *336{\cdot}2 \,. \quad \supset \vdash : \mathrm{Hp} \,.\, \supset \,.\, A_a \restriction \lambda \epsilon 1 \to 1$ (1)

$\vdash \,.\, *336{\cdot}11 \,.\, \supset \vdash : \mathrm{Hp} \,.\, \supset \,.\, \mathrm{D}`(A_a \restriction \lambda) = \hat{x}\{(\exists L) \,.\, L \epsilon \lambda \,.\, xLa\}$

$[\mathrm{Hp}] \quad = \hat{x}\{(\exists L) \,.\, L \epsilon \kappa_\iota \,.\, xLa\}$

$[*331{\cdot}4] \quad = s`\text{Ɑ}``\kappa$ (2)

$\vdash \,.\, *336{\cdot}11 \,.\, \supset \vdash : \mathrm{Hp} \,.\, \supset \,.\, \text{Ɑ}`(A_a \restriction \lambda) = \hat{L}\{(\exists x) \,.\, L \epsilon \lambda \,.\, xLa\}$

$[\mathrm{Hp}] \quad = \lambda$ (3)

$\vdash \,.\, (1) \,.\, (2) \,.\, (3) \,.\, \supset \vdash \,.\, \mathrm{Prop}$

***336·24.** $\vdash : \mathrm{Hp} * 336{\cdot}23 . \supset . (s`\text{Ɑ}``\kappa) \,\mathrm{sm}\, \lambda \quad [*336{\cdot}23]$

***336·25.** $\vdash : \kappa \epsilon FM \,\mathrm{conx} . a, b \epsilon s`\text{Ɑ}``\kappa . \lambda = \kappa_\iota \cap \hat{L}(a \epsilon \text{Ɑ}`L) .$
$$\mu = \kappa_\iota \cap \hat{M}(b \epsilon \text{Ɑ}`M) . \supset . \lambda \,\mathrm{sm}\, \mu \quad [*336{\cdot}24]$$

***336·26.** $\vdash : \kappa \epsilon FM . a \epsilon \mathrm{conx}`\kappa . \lambda = \kappa \cup \mathrm{Cnv}``\hat{R}(R \epsilon \kappa . a \epsilon \mathrm{D}`R) . \supset .$
$$A_a \upharpoonright \lambda \epsilon (s`\text{Ɑ}``\kappa) \,\overline{\mathrm{sm}}\, \lambda \quad [*336{\cdot}23 . *331{\cdot}48]$$

***336·3.** $\vdash :. \kappa \subset 1 \to \mathrm{Cls} . \supset : R(\kappa \rceil \breve{A}_a ; P) S . \equiv . R, S \epsilon \kappa . (R`a) P (S`a)$

Dem.

$\vdash . *150{\cdot}11 . \supset \vdash : R(\kappa \rceil \breve{A}_a ; P) S . \equiv . (\exists x, y) . R, S \epsilon \kappa . x A_a R . y A_a S . x P y .$

$[*336{\cdot}1] \qquad \equiv . (\exists x, y) . R, S \epsilon \kappa . x R a . y S a . x P y \qquad (1)$

$\vdash . (1) . *71{\cdot}36 . \supset \vdash . \mathrm{Prop}$

***336·31.** $\vdash : \kappa \epsilon FM \,\mathrm{conx} . a \epsilon s`\text{Ɑ}``\kappa . \supset . \kappa_\partial \subset \mathrm{D}`(\kappa \rceil \breve{A}_a ; \dot{s}`\kappa_\partial)$

Dem.

$\vdash . *336{\cdot}3 . \supset$

$\vdash :. \mathrm{Hp} . \supset : R \epsilon \dot{\mathrm{D}}`(\kappa \rceil \breve{A}_a ; \dot{s}`\kappa_\partial) . \equiv . (\exists S, T) . R, S \epsilon \kappa . T \epsilon \kappa_\partial . R`a = T`S`a \quad (1)$

$\vdash . *331{\cdot}22 . \supset \vdash : \mathrm{Hp} . R \epsilon \kappa_\partial . \supset . R \epsilon \kappa_\partial . I \upharpoonright s`\text{Ɑ}``\kappa \epsilon \kappa . R`a = R`(I \upharpoonright s`\text{Ɑ}``\kappa)`a .$

$[(1)] \qquad \supset . R \epsilon \mathrm{D}`(\kappa \rceil \breve{A}_a ; \dot{s}`\kappa_\partial) : \supset \vdash . \mathrm{Prop}$

***336·311.** $\vdash : \kappa \epsilon FM \,\mathrm{conx} - 1 . a \epsilon s`\text{Ɑ}``\kappa . \supset . I \upharpoonright s`\text{Ɑ}``\kappa \epsilon \text{Ɑ}`(\kappa \rceil \breve{A}_a ; \dot{s}`\kappa_\partial)$

Dem.

$\vdash . *336{\cdot}3 . \supset$

$\vdash :. \mathrm{Hp} . \supset : S \epsilon \text{Ɑ}`(\kappa \rceil \breve{A}_a ; \dot{s}`\kappa_\partial) . \equiv . (\exists R, T) . R, S \epsilon \kappa . T \epsilon \kappa_\partial . R`a = T`S`a :$

$[*331{\cdot}22] \supset : I \upharpoonright s`\text{Ɑ}``\kappa \epsilon \text{Ɑ}`(\kappa \rceil \breve{A}_a ; \dot{s}`\kappa_\partial) . \equiv . (\exists R, T) . R \epsilon \kappa . T \epsilon \kappa_\partial . R`a = T`a .$

$[*330{\cdot}52] \qquad \equiv . \exists ! \kappa_\partial \qquad (1)$

$\vdash . (1) . *334{\cdot}18 . \supset \vdash . \mathrm{Prop}$

***336·312.** $\vdash : \kappa \epsilon FM \,\mathrm{conx} - 1 . \supset . C`(\kappa \rceil \breve{A}_a ; \dot{s}`\kappa_\partial) = \kappa \quad [*336{\cdot}31{\cdot}311]$

***336·313.** $\vdash : \kappa \epsilon FM \,\mathrm{conx} \cap FM \,\mathrm{asym} . a \epsilon s`\text{Ɑ}``\kappa . \supset . \mathrm{D}`(\kappa \rceil \breve{A}_a ; \dot{s}`\kappa_\partial) = \kappa_\partial$

Dem.

$\vdash . *336{\cdot}3 . \supset$

$\vdash :. \mathrm{Hp} . \supset : I \upharpoonright s`\text{Ɑ}``\kappa \epsilon \mathrm{D}`(\kappa \rceil \breve{A}_a ; \dot{s}`\kappa_\partial) . \equiv . (\exists S, T) . S \epsilon \kappa . T \epsilon \kappa_\partial . a = T`S`a \quad (1)$

$\vdash . (1) . *334{\cdot}5 . \supset \vdash : \mathrm{Hp} . \supset . I \upharpoonright s`\text{Ɑ}``\kappa \sim\epsilon \mathrm{D}`(\kappa \rceil \breve{A}_a ; \dot{s}`\kappa_\partial) \qquad (2)$

$\vdash . (2) . *336{\cdot}31 . \supset \vdash . \mathrm{Prop}$

***336·32.** $\vdash : \kappa \epsilon FM . a \epsilon \text{conx}`\kappa . \lambda = \kappa \cap \hat{R}(a \epsilon D`R) . \supset .$
$C`\{(\kappa \cup \text{Cnv}``\kappa) \upharpoonright \breve{A}_a ; \dot{s}`\kappa_\partial\} = \kappa \cup \text{Cnv}``\lambda$

Dem.

$\vdash . *336·16 . *334·18 . \supset \vdash : \text{Hp} . \supset . C`\dot{s}`\kappa_\partial = \text{G}`(\kappa \cup \text{Cnv}``\kappa) \upharpoonright \breve{A}_a .$

[*150·23] $\supset . C`\{(\kappa \cup \text{Cnv}``\kappa) \upharpoonright \breve{A}_a ; \dot{s}`\kappa_\partial\} = D`(\kappa \cup \text{Cnv}``\kappa) \upharpoonright \breve{A}_a$

[*336·15·11] $= \kappa \cup \hat{R}\{(\exists x) . R \epsilon \text{Cnv}``\kappa . xRa\}$

[Hp] $= \kappa \cup \text{Cnv}``\lambda : \supset \vdash . \text{Prop}$

***336·34.** $\vdash : \kappa \epsilon FM . a = \text{init}`\kappa . \supset . (\kappa \upharpoonright \breve{A}_a ; \dot{s}`\kappa_\partial) \text{ smor } (\dot{s}`\kappa_\partial)$

Dem.

$\vdash . *336·21 . \supset \vdash : \text{Hp} . \supset . \kappa \upharpoonright \breve{A}_a \epsilon 1 \rightarrow 1 . \text{G}`\kappa \upharpoonright \breve{A}_a = C`\dot{s}`\kappa_\partial : \supset \vdash . \text{Prop}$

***336·35.** $\vdash : \kappa \epsilon FM . a \epsilon \text{conx}`\kappa . \supset . \{(\kappa \cup \text{Cnv}``\kappa) \upharpoonright \breve{A}_a ; \dot{s}`\kappa_\partial\} \text{ smor } (\dot{s}`\kappa_\partial)$
[*336·2·16]

***336·351.** $\vdash : \kappa \epsilon FM \text{ conx} . a \epsilon s`\text{G}``\kappa . \supset . (\kappa \upharpoonright \breve{A}_a ; \dot{s}`\kappa_\partial) \text{ smor } (\dot{s}`\kappa_\partial) \upharpoonright A_a``\kappa$

Dem.

$\vdash . *336·2 . \supset \vdash : \text{Hp} . \supset . \kappa \upharpoonright \breve{A}_a \epsilon 1 \rightarrow 1$ (1)

$\vdash . *150·37 . \supset \vdash : \text{Hp} . \supset . \kappa \upharpoonright \breve{A}_a ; \dot{s}`\kappa_\partial = \kappa \upharpoonright \breve{A}_a ; (\dot{s}`\kappa_\partial) \upharpoonright A_a``\kappa$ (2)

$\vdash . (1) . (2) . \supset \vdash . \text{Prop}$

***336·36.** $\vdash :. \kappa \epsilon FM \text{ conx} . L, M \epsilon \kappa_\iota . a, b \epsilon \text{G}`L \cap \text{G}`M . T \epsilon \kappa . \supset :$
$L`a = T`M`a . \equiv . L`b = T`M`b : L`a = \breve{T}`M`a . \equiv . L`b = \breve{T}`M`b$

Dem.

$\vdash . *13·12 . \supset \vdash :. \text{Hp} . N \epsilon \kappa_\iota . a = N`b . \supset : L`a = T`M`a . \equiv . L`N`b = T`M`N`b .$

[*330·63] $\equiv . N`L`b = N`T`M`b .$

[*71·56] $\equiv : L`b = T`M`b$ (1)

$\vdash . (1) . *331·4 . \supset \vdash :. \text{Hp} . \supset : L`a = T`M`a . \equiv . L`b = T`M`b$ (2)

$\vdash . *71·362 . \supset \vdash :. \text{Hp} . \supset : L`a = \breve{T}`M`a . \equiv . M`a = T`L`a .$

$\left[(2)\dfrac{M, L}{L, M}\right]$ $\equiv . M`b = T`L`b .$

[*71·362] $\equiv . L`b = \breve{T}`M`b$ (3)

$\vdash . (2) . (3) . \supset \vdash . \text{Prop}$

***336·37.** $\vdash :. \kappa \epsilon FM \text{ conx} . L, M \epsilon \kappa_\iota . a, b \epsilon \text{G}`L \cap \text{G}`M . \supset :$
$(L`a)(\dot{s}`\kappa_\partial)(M`a) . \equiv . (L`b)(\dot{s}`\kappa_\partial)(M`b)$

Dem.

$\vdash . *336·36 . \supset$

$\vdash :. \text{Hp} . \supset : (\exists T) . T \epsilon \kappa_\partial . L`a = T`M`a . \equiv . (\exists T) . T \epsilon \kappa_\partial . L`b = T`M`b :. \supset \vdash . \text{Prop}$

***336·371.** $\vdash :. \kappa \in FM \text{ conx} . L, M \in \kappa_\iota . a \in \text{Ꮖ}'L \cap \text{Ꮖ}'M . \supset :$
$LV_\kappa M . \equiv . (L'a)(\dot{s}'\kappa_\partial)(M'a)$ [*336·37 . (*336·01)]

***336·38.** $\vdash :. \kappa \in FM \text{ conx} . P, Q \in \kappa . a, b \in s'\text{Ꮖ}''\kappa . \supset :$
$(P'a)(\dot{s}'\kappa_\partial)(Q'a) . \equiv . (P'b)(\dot{s}'\kappa_\partial)(Q'b)$ [*336·37 . *331·24]

***336·4.** $\vdash : \kappa \in FM \text{ conx} . a \in s'\text{Ꮖ}''\kappa . \supset . U_\kappa = \hat{P}\hat{Q} \{P, Q \in \kappa . (P'a)(\dot{s}'\kappa_\partial)(Q'a)\}$

Dem.

$\vdash . *336·38 . \supset$
$\vdash :. \text{Hp} . \supset : b \in s'\text{Ꮖ}''\kappa . (P'b)(\dot{s}'\kappa_\partial)(Q'b) . \equiv . b \in s'\text{Ꮖ}''\kappa . (P'a)(\dot{s}'\kappa_\partial)(Q'a) :$
[*10·11·281.Hp] $\supset : (\exists b) . b \in s'\text{Ꮖ}''\kappa . (P'b)(\dot{s}'\kappa_\partial)(Q'b) . \equiv . (P'a)(\dot{s}'\kappa_\partial)(Q'a)$ (1)
$\vdash . (1) . (*336·011) . \supset \vdash . \text{Prop}$

***336·41.** $\vdash : \kappa \in FM \text{ conx} . \supset . U_\kappa = \hat{P}\hat{Q} \{P, Q \in \kappa : (\exists T) . T \in \kappa_\partial . P = T | Q\}$

Dem.

$\vdash . *41·11 . \supset \vdash : \text{Hp} . a \in s'\text{Ꮖ}''\kappa . P, Q \in \kappa . T \in \kappa_\partial . P = T|Q . \supset . (P'a)(\dot{s}'\kappa_\partial)(Q'a)$ (1)
$\vdash . *41·11 . \supset \vdash : \text{Hp} . a \in s'\text{Ꮖ}''\kappa . (P'a)(\dot{s}'\kappa_\partial)(Q'a) . \supset . (\exists T) . T \in \kappa_\partial . P'a = T'Q'a .$
[*331·32·33·24] $\supset . (\exists T) . T \in \kappa_\partial . P = T | Q$ (2)
$\vdash . (1) . (2) . *336·4 . \supset \vdash . \text{Prop}$

***336·411.** $\vdash :. \kappa \in FM \text{ conx} . s'\kappa \underset{\prime\prime}{|} ''\kappa \subset \kappa . \supset : PU_\kappa Q . R \in \kappa . \supset . (P | R) U_\kappa (Q | R)$
[*336·41]

***336·412.** $\vdash : \text{Hp } *336·411 . P, Q, R \in \kappa . (P | R) U_\kappa (Q | R) . \supset . PU_\kappa Q$

Dem.

$\vdash . *336·41 . \supset \vdash : \text{Hp} . \supset . (\exists T) . T \in \kappa_\partial . P | R = T | Q | R .$
[*330·5] $\supset . (\exists T) . T \in \kappa_\partial . \breve{R} | R | P = \breve{R} | R | T | Q$
[*330·31] $\supset . (\exists T) . T \in \kappa_\partial . P = T | Q .$
[*336·41] $\supset . PU_\kappa Q : \supset \vdash . \text{Prop}$

***336·413.** $\vdash :. \text{Hp } *336·411 . P, Q, R \in \kappa . \supset : PU_\kappa Q . \equiv . (P | R) U_\kappa (Q | R)$
[*336·411·412]

***336·42.** $\vdash : \kappa \in FM \text{ conx} . a \in p'\text{D}''\kappa . \supset . V_\kappa = \hat{L}\hat{M} \{L, M \in \kappa_\iota . (L'a)(\dot{s}'\kappa_\partial)(M'a)\}$

Dem.

$\vdash . *330·54 . \supset \vdash :. \text{Hp} . L, M \in \kappa_\iota . \supset : a \in \text{Ꮖ}'L \cap \text{Ꮖ}'M :$
[*336·37] $\supset : (L'b)(\dot{s}'\kappa_\partial)(M'b) . \supset . (L'a)(\dot{s}'\kappa_\partial)(M'a) :$
[(*336·01)] $\supset : LV_\kappa M . \supset . (L'a)(\dot{s}'\kappa_\partial)(M'a)$ (1)
$\vdash . (1) . (*336·01) . \supset \vdash . \text{Prop}$

***336·43.** $\vdash : \kappa \in FM \text{ conx} . a \in s'\text{Ꮖ}''\kappa . \supset . U_\kappa = \kappa \upharpoonleft \breve{A}_a \dot{;} \dot{s}'\kappa_\partial$

Dem.

$\vdash . *336·4·101 . \supset \vdash : \text{Hp} . \supset . U_\kappa = \hat{P}\hat{Q} \{P, Q \in \kappa . (A_a'P)(\dot{s}'\kappa_\partial)(A_a'Q)\}$
[*35·7] $= \hat{P}\hat{Q} \{(A_a \upharpoonright \kappa'P)(\dot{s}'\kappa_\partial)(A_a \upharpoonright \kappa'Q)\}$
[*150·41.*336·2] $= \kappa \upharpoonleft \breve{A}_a \dot{;} \dot{s}'\kappa_\partial : \supset \vdash . \text{Prop}$

***336·44.** $\vdash : \kappa \in FM\,\text{init} \,.\supset .\, U_\kappa \,\text{smor}\, (\dot{s}`\kappa_\partial)$

Dem.

$\vdash . *336·41 . \supset \vdash : \text{Hp} . a = \text{init}`\kappa . \supset . U_\kappa = \kappa \upharpoonright \breve{A}_a ; \dot{s}`\kappa_\partial$ (1)

$\vdash . *336·21 . \supset \vdash : \text{Hp} . a = \text{init}`\kappa . \supset . \kappa \upharpoonright \breve{A}_a \in 1 \rightarrow 1 . \text{Ɑ}`(\kappa \upharpoonright \breve{A}_a) = s`\text{Ɑ}``\kappa$ (2)

$\vdash . (1) . (2) . *334·19 . \supset \vdash . \text{Prop}$

***336·45.** $\vdash : \kappa \in FM . a \in \text{conx}`\kappa . \lambda = \kappa \cap \hat{R}(a \in \text{D}`R) . \supset .$

$V_\kappa \sqsubset (\kappa \cup \text{Cnv}``\lambda) = (\kappa \cup \text{Cnv}``\kappa) \upharpoonright \breve{A}_a ; \dot{s}`\kappa_\partial$

Dem.

$\vdash . *41·11 . (*336·01) . \supset$

$\vdash :. P \{V_\kappa \sqsubset (\kappa \cup \text{Cnv}``\lambda)\} Q . \equiv : P, Q \in \kappa \cup \text{Cnv}``\lambda : (\exists x, T) . T \in \kappa_\partial . P`x = T`Q`x$ (1)

$\vdash . (1) . *336·36 . \supset \vdash :: \text{Hp} . \supset :.$

$P \{V_\kappa \sqsubset (\kappa \cup \text{Cnv}``\lambda)\} Q . \equiv : P, Q \in \kappa \cup \text{Cnv}``\lambda : (\exists T) . T \in \kappa_\partial . P`a = T`Q`a :$

[*14·21.Hp] $\equiv : P, Q \in \kappa \cup \text{Cnv}``\kappa : (\exists T) . T \in \kappa_\partial . P`a = T`Q`a :$

[*41·11] $\equiv : P, Q \in \kappa \cup \text{Cnv}``\kappa . (P`a)(\dot{s}`\kappa_\partial)(Q`a) :$

[*336·3] $\equiv : P \{(\kappa \cup \text{Cnv}``\kappa) \upharpoonright \breve{A}_a ; \dot{s}`\kappa_\partial\} Q :: \supset \vdash . \text{Prop}$

***336·46.** $\vdash : \text{Hp}\, *336·45 . \supset . V_\kappa \sqsubset (\kappa \cup \text{Cnv}``\lambda) \,\text{smor}\, (\dot{s}`\kappa_\partial)$ [*336·45·2·16]

***336·461.** $\vdash : \kappa \in FM\,\text{conx} . a \in s`\text{Ɑ}``\kappa . \supset . U_\kappa \,\text{smor}\, (\dot{s}`\kappa_\partial) \sqsubset (A_a``\kappa)$
[*336·351·43]

***336·462.** $\vdash : \kappa \in FM\,\text{conx} \cap FM\,\text{trs} . a \in s`\text{Ɑ}``\kappa . \breve{P} = \dot{s}`\kappa_\partial . \supset . \breve{U}_\kappa \,\text{smor}\, (P \sqsubset \overleftarrow{P_*}`a)$
[*336·461·17 . *334·17]

***336·47.** $\vdash : \kappa \in FM\,\text{conx} . \supset . \kappa_\partial \subset \text{D}`U_\kappa$ [*336·31·43]

***336·471.** $\vdash : \kappa \in FM\,\text{conx} - 1 . \supset . \kappa = C`U_\kappa$ [*336·312·43]

***336·472.** $\vdash : \kappa \in FM\,\text{conx} \cap FM\,\text{asym} . \supset . \kappa_\partial = \text{D}`U_\kappa$ [*336·313·43]

***336·51.** $\vdash :. \kappa \in FM\,\text{sr} . R, S \in \kappa . \nu \in \text{NC ind} - \iota`0 . \supset :$

$(R`a)(\dot{s}`\kappa_\partial)(S`a) . \equiv . (R^\nu`a)(\dot{s}`\kappa_\partial)(S^\nu`a)$

Dem.

$\vdash . *333·42 . *334·32 . *330·57 . *331·42 . \supset$

$\vdash :. \text{Hp} . \supset : T \in \kappa_\partial . R`a = T`S`a . \supset . R^\nu`a = T^\nu`S^\nu`a .$

[*334·131] $\supset . (R^\nu`a)(\dot{s}`\kappa_\partial)(S^\nu`a)$ (1)

$\vdash . (1) . *41·11 . \supset \vdash :. \text{Hp} . \supset : (R`a)(\dot{s}`\kappa_\partial)(S`a) . \supset . (R^\nu`a)(\dot{s}`\kappa_\partial)(S^\nu`a)$ (2)

$\vdash . (2) \dfrac{S, R}{R, S} . \quad \supset \vdash :. \text{Hp} . \supset : (S`a)(\dot{s}`\kappa_\partial)(R`a) . \supset . (S^\nu`a)(\dot{s}`\kappa_\partial)(R^\nu`a)$ (3)

$\vdash . *331·42 . \quad \supset \vdash :. \text{Hp} . \supset : R`a = S`a . \supset . R^\nu`a = S^\nu`a$ (4)

$\vdash . (3) . (4) . *334·3 . \supset$

$\vdash :. \text{Hp} . \supset : \sim \{(R`a)(\dot{s}`\kappa_\partial)(S`a)\} . \supset . \sim \{(R^\nu`a)(\dot{s}`\kappa_\partial)(S^\nu`a)\}$ (5)

$\vdash . (2) . (5) . \supset \vdash . \text{Prop}$

***336·511.** $\vdash :. \kappa \epsilon FM \,\mathrm{sr} \,.\, \nu \epsilon \mathrm{NC\,ind} - \iota'0 \,.\supset: RU_\kappa S \,.\equiv.\, R^\nu U_\kappa S^\nu$ [*336·51·4]

***336·52.** $\vdash :. \kappa \epsilon FM \,\mathrm{conx} \,.\, Q, R, S, T \epsilon \kappa \,.\, x \epsilon \mathrm{C}'(\breve{Q} | R) \cap \mathrm{C}'(\breve{S} | T) \,.\supset:$

$$(\breve{Q} | R) V_\kappa (\breve{S} | T) \,.\equiv.\, (S'R'x)(\dot{s}'\kappa_\partial)(Q'T'x)$$

Dem.

$\vdash . *336·371 . \supset$

$\vdash :. \mathrm{Hp} \,.\supset: (\breve{Q} | R) V_\kappa (\breve{S} | T) \,.\equiv.\, (\exists P) \,.\, P \epsilon \kappa_\partial \,.\, \breve{Q}'R'x = P'\breve{S}'T'x$ (1)

$\vdash . *330·56 . \supset \vdash :. \mathrm{Hp} \,.\, P \epsilon \kappa_\partial \,.\supset: \breve{Q}'R'x = P'\breve{S}'T'x \,.\equiv.\, \breve{Q}'R'x = \breve{S}'P'T'x.$

[*71·362] $\equiv .\, R'x = Q'\breve{S}'P'T'x.$

[*330·54·56] $\equiv .\, R'x = \breve{S}'Q'P'T'x.$

[*71·362.*330·5] $\equiv .\, S'R'x = P'Q'T'x$ (2)

$\vdash . (1) . (2) . \supset \vdash :. \mathrm{Hp} \,.\supset: (\breve{Q} | R) V_\kappa (\breve{S} | T) \,.\equiv.\, (\exists P) \,.\, P \epsilon \kappa_\partial \,.\, S'R'x = P'Q'T'x \,.$

[*41·11] $\equiv .\, (S'R'x)(\dot{s}'\kappa_\partial)(Q'T'x) :. \supset \vdash .$ Prop

***336·53.** $\vdash :. \kappa \epsilon FM \,\mathrm{conx} \,.\, M, N \epsilon \kappa_\iota \,.\supset: M V_\kappa N \,.\equiv.\, \breve{N} V_\kappa \breve{M}$

Dem.

$\vdash . *330·5·54 . \supset$

$\vdash : \mathrm{Hp} \,.\, Q, R, S, T \epsilon \kappa \,.\, M = \breve{Q} | R \,.\, N = \breve{S} | T \,.\, a \epsilon s'\mathrm{C}''\kappa \,.\, x = Q'R'S'T'a \,.\supset.$

$$\mathrm{E} ! M'x \,.\, \mathrm{E} ! N'x \,.\, \mathrm{E} ! \breve{M}'x \,.\, \mathrm{E} ! \breve{N}'x \quad (1)$$

$\vdash . (1) . *336·52 . \supset \vdash :. \mathrm{Hp}(1) \,.\supset: M V_\kappa N \,.\equiv.\, (S'R'x)(\dot{s}'\kappa_\partial)(Q'T'x) \,.$

[*330·5] $\equiv .\, (R'S'x)(\dot{s}'\kappa_\partial)(T'Q'x) \,.$

[*336·52] $\equiv .\, (\breve{T} | S) V_\kappa (\breve{R} | Q) \,.$

[Hp] $\equiv .\, \breve{N} V_\kappa \breve{M}$ (2)

$\vdash . (2) . *331·12 . \supset \vdash .$ Prop

***336·54.** $\vdash : \kappa \epsilon FM \,\mathrm{conx} \,.\, \mathrm{D}''\kappa = \mathrm{C}''\kappa \,.\supset.$

$$V_\kappa = \hat{M}\hat{N} \{ M, N \epsilon \kappa_\iota : (\exists T) \,.\, T \epsilon \kappa_\partial \,.\, M = T | N \}$$

Dem.

$\vdash . *334·46 . \supset \vdash :. \mathrm{Hp} \,.\, M, N \epsilon \kappa_\iota \,.\supset:$

$$(\exists T, x) \,.\, T \epsilon \kappa_\partial \,.\, M'x = T'N'x \,.\equiv.\, (\exists T) \,.\, T \epsilon \kappa_\partial \,.\, M = T | N \quad (1)$$

$\vdash . (1) . (*336·01) . \supset \vdash .$ Prop

***336·6.** $\vdash : \kappa \epsilon FM \,\mathrm{conx} \,.\supset.\, V_\kappa \subset J$

Dem.

$\vdash . *331·23 . \supset \vdash :. \mathrm{Hp} \,.\supset: M V_\kappa N \,.\supset.\, (\exists x) \,.\, M'x \neq N'x :. \supset \vdash .$ Prop

Observe that, by the conventions explained in *14, "$M'x \neq N'x$" implies $\mathrm{E} ! M'x \,.\, \mathrm{E} ! N'x$. From "$(\exists x) \,.\, \sim (M'x = N'x)$" we cannot infer $M \neq N$.

∗336·61. $\vdash : \kappa \in FM \text{ conx trs} . \supset . V_\kappa \in \text{trs}$

Dem.

$\vdash . ∗330·612 . \supset \vdash : \text{Hp} . L, M, N \in \kappa_\iota . \supset . \exists ! \text{Ɑ}'\text{D}'L \cap \text{Ɑ}'\text{D}'M \cap \text{Ɑ}'\text{D}'N$ (1)

$\vdash . ∗336·371 . \supset \vdash : \text{Hp} . L V_\kappa M . M V_\kappa N . a \in \text{Ɑ}'\text{D}'L \cap \text{Ɑ}'\text{D}'M \cap \text{Ɑ}'\text{D}'N . \supset .$

$(L'a)(\dot{s}'\kappa_\partial)(M'a) . (M'a)(\dot{s}'\kappa_\partial)(N'a) .$

[∗334·14] $\supset . (L'a)(\dot{s}'\kappa_\partial)(N'a) .$

[(∗336·01)] $\supset . L V_\kappa N$ (2)

$\vdash . (1 . (2) . \supset \vdash . \text{Prop}$

∗336·62. $\vdash : \kappa \in FM \text{ connex} . \supset . V_\kappa \in \text{connex}$

Dem.

$\vdash . ∗330·61 . \supset \vdash : \text{Hp} . L, M \in \kappa_\iota . \supset . \exists ! \text{Ɑ}'\text{D}'L \cap \text{Ɑ}'\text{D}'M$ (1)

$\vdash . ∗334·24 . \supset \vdash :. \text{Hp} . L, M \in \kappa_\iota . a \in \text{Ɑ}'\text{D}'L \cap \text{Ɑ}'\text{D}'M . \supset :$

$L'a = M'a . \lor . (L'a)(\dot{s}'\kappa_\partial)(M'a) . \lor . (M'a)(\dot{s}'\kappa_\partial)(L'a) :$

[∗331·42.(∗336·01)] $\supset : L = M . \lor . L V_\kappa M . \lor . M V_\kappa L$ (2)

$\vdash . (1) . (2) . \supset \vdash . \text{Prop}$

∗336·63. $\vdash : \kappa \in FM \text{ sr} . \supset . V_\kappa \in \text{Ser}$ [∗336·6·61·62]

∗336·64. $\vdash : \kappa \in FM \text{ sr} . \supset . U_\kappa \in \text{Ser}$ [∗336·63]

*337. MULTIPLES AND SUB-MULTIPLES OF VECTORS.

Summary of *337.

In this number, we are concerned with the axiom of Archimedes and the axiom of divisibility. If κ is a family of vectors, κ obeys the axiom of Archimedes if, given any two points x, a in the field of κ, and any vector R which is a member of κ, there is some power R^ν of R such that $R^\nu{}^\backprime a$ is later than x. That is, κ obeys the axiom of Archimedes if, starting from any given point in the field, a sufficient finite number of repetitions of any given vector will take us beyond any other assigned point. A sufficient hypothesis for this is that κ should be serial and $\text{Cnv}^\backprime \dot{s}^\backprime \kappa_\partial$ should be semi-Dedekindian (cf. *214), *i.e.* we have

$$*337\cdot13.\quad \vdash :. \kappa \in FM\,\text{sr} . \breve{P} = \dot{s}^\backprime \kappa_\partial . P \in \text{semi Ded} . R \in \kappa_\partial . a \in C^\backprime P . \supset : x \in C^\backprime P . \supset . (\exists \nu) . \nu \in \text{NC ind} - \iota^\backprime 0 . xP(R^\nu{}^\backprime a)$$

The hypothesis $\breve{P} = \dot{s}^\backprime \kappa_\partial$, which appears in the above proposition, is often notationally convenient. It will be observed that $\dot{s}^\backprime \kappa_\partial$ gives us the series in the opposite order to that in which it is usually wanted; hence the introduction of the above relation P tends to avoid confusions.

A family κ is said to obey the axiom of divisibility when, given any member R of κ, and any inductive cardinal ν other than 0, there is a member L of κ such that $L^\nu = R$. When this axiom holds, every vector can be divided into any assigned finite number of equal parts. We shall in the next Section (*351) define a family for which this holds as a "sub-multipliable family," denoted by "FM subm." For the present we are concerned to find a hypothesis as to $\dot{s}^\backprime \kappa_\partial$ from which this property can be deduced. The hypothesis in question is that $\text{Cnv}^\backprime \dot{s}^\backprime \kappa_\partial$ is serial, compact, and semi-Dedekindian; *i.e.* we have

$$*337\cdot27.\quad \vdash :. \kappa \in FM\,\text{sr} . \text{Cnv}^\backprime \dot{s}^\backprime \kappa_\partial \in \text{comp} \cap \text{semi Ded} . \supset : S \in \kappa . \nu \in \text{NC ind} - \iota^\backprime 0 . \supset . (\exists L) . L \in \kappa . S = L^\nu$$

The proof proceeds by taking two points a, x in the field of κ, of which a is earlier than x, and considering the class

$$\lambda = \kappa_\partial \cap \breve{R}\{(R^\nu{}^\backprime a)\, Px\},$$

i.e. the class of vectors such that ν repetitions of them, starting from a, do not take us as far as x. It is easy to show that, when P is compact, this class has no maximum (*337·23), and therefore, when P is also semi-Dedekindian, has a limit, whose νth power is the vector which takes us from a to x (*337·26). Hence our result follows.

***337·1.** $\vdash : \kappa \in FM . \breve{P} = \dot{s}\text{‘}\kappa_\partial . R \in \kappa_\partial . a \in C\text{‘}P . \supset . \overrightarrow{R_*}\text{‘}a \subset P\text{“}\overrightarrow{R_*}\text{‘}a$

Dem.

$\vdash . *90\cdot16 . *41\cdot141 . \supset \vdash : \mathrm{Hp} . xR_*a . y = R\text{‘}x . \supset . y \in \overrightarrow{R_*}\text{‘}a . xPy .$

$[*37\cdot1] \qquad \supset . x \in P\text{“}\overrightarrow{R_*}\text{‘}a : \supset \vdash . \mathrm{Prop}$

***337·11.** $\vdash : \kappa \in FM\ \mathrm{connex\ asym} . \breve{P} = \dot{s}\text{‘}\kappa_\partial . R \in \kappa_\partial . a \in C\text{‘}P . \supset . \mathrm{seq}_P\text{‘}\overrightarrow{\overrightarrow{R_*}}\text{‘}a = \Lambda$

Dem.

$\vdash . *206\cdot15 . \qquad \supset \vdash : \mathrm{Hp} . \supset . \mathrm{seq}_P\text{‘}\overrightarrow{\overrightarrow{R_*}}\text{‘}a = p\text{‘}\overleftarrow{P}\text{“}\overrightarrow{R_*}\text{‘}a - \breve{P}\text{“}p\text{‘}\overleftarrow{P}\text{“}\overrightarrow{R_*}\text{‘}a$ (1)

$\vdash . *330\cdot542 . *40\cdot61 . \supset \vdash : \mathrm{Hp} . x \in p\text{‘}\overleftarrow{P}\text{“}\overrightarrow{R_*}\text{‘}a . \supset . x \in \mathrm{D}\text{‘}R .$

$[\mathrm{Hp}] \qquad \supset . (\exists c) . x = R\text{‘}c . cPx$ (2)

$\vdash . *90\cdot172 . \qquad \supset \vdash : c \in \overrightarrow{R_*}\text{‘}a . \supset . R\text{‘}c \in \overrightarrow{R_*}\text{‘}a$ (3)

$\vdash . (3) . \mathrm{Transp} . *200\cdot5 . *334\cdot5 . \supset \vdash : \mathrm{Hp}\,(2) . x = R\text{‘}c . \supset . c \sim\in \overrightarrow{R_*}\text{‘}a$ (4)

$\vdash . *37\cdot1 . \qquad \supset \vdash : c \in P\text{“}\overrightarrow{R_*}\text{‘}a . \supset . (\exists b) . b \in \overrightarrow{R_*}\text{‘}a . cPb$ (5)

$\vdash . (5) . *208\cdot2 . \supset \vdash : \mathrm{Hp} . c \in P\text{“}\overrightarrow{R_*}\text{‘}a . x = R\text{‘}c . \supset . (\exists b) . b \in \overrightarrow{R_*}\text{‘}a . xP(R\text{‘}b) .$

$[*90\cdot172] \qquad \supset . x \in P\text{“}\overrightarrow{R_*}\text{‘}a$ (6)

$\vdash . (6) . \mathrm{Transp} . *200\cdot53 . \qquad \supset \vdash : \mathrm{Hp}\,(2) . x = R\text{‘}c . \supset . c \sim\in P\text{“}\overrightarrow{R_*}\text{‘}a$ (7)

$\vdash . (4) . (7) . *202\cdot502 . *334\cdot24 . \supset \vdash : \mathrm{Hp}\,(2) . x = R\text{‘}c . \supset . c \in p\text{‘}\overleftarrow{P}\text{“}\overrightarrow{R_*}\text{‘}a$ (8)

$\vdash . (2) . (8) . \qquad \supset \vdash : \mathrm{Hp}\,(2) . \supset . x \in \breve{P}\text{“}p\text{‘}\overleftarrow{P}\text{“}\overrightarrow{R_*}\text{‘}a$ (9)

$\vdash . (1) . (9) . \supset \vdash . \mathrm{Prop}$

***337·12.** $\vdash : \kappa \in FM\ \mathrm{sr} . \breve{P} = \dot{s}\text{‘}\kappa_\partial . P \in \mathrm{semi\ Ded} . R \in \kappa_\partial . a \in C\text{‘}P . \supset . P\text{“}\overrightarrow{R_*}\text{‘}a = C\text{‘}P$

Dem.

$\vdash . *337\cdot1 . \qquad \supset \vdash : \mathrm{Hp} . \supset . \sim \exists ! \max_P\text{‘}\overrightarrow{R_*}\text{‘}a .$

$[*205\cdot7] \qquad \supset . \sim \exists ! \max_P\text{‘}P\text{“}\overrightarrow{R_*}\text{‘}a$ (1)

$\vdash . (1) . *206\cdot33 . *337\cdot11 . \supset \vdash : \mathrm{Hp} . \supset . \sim \exists ! \mathrm{seq}_P\text{‘}P\text{“}\overrightarrow{R_*}\text{‘}a$ (2)

$\vdash . (1) . (2) . *214\cdot7 . \supset \vdash . \mathrm{Prop}$

***337·13.** $\vdash :. \kappa \in FM\ \mathrm{sr} . \breve{P} = \dot{s}\text{‘}\kappa_\partial . P \in \mathrm{semi\ Ded} . R \in \kappa_\partial . a \in C\text{‘}P . \supset :$
$x \in C\text{‘}P . \supset . (\exists \nu) . \nu \in \mathrm{NC\ ind} - \iota\text{‘}0 . xP(R^\nu\text{‘}a)$ [*337·12 . *301·26]

***337·14.** $\vdash : \kappa \in FM \operatorname{sr} . \breve{P} = \dot{s}`\kappa_\partial . P \in \text{semi Ded} . \supset . \breve{U}_\kappa \in \text{semi Ded}$
[*336·462 . *214·74·75]

***337·2.** $\vdash : \kappa \in FM \operatorname{conx} . LU_\kappa R . R \neq I \upharpoonright s`\text{C}``\kappa . \supset . LU_\kappa(\breve{R} | L)$

Dem.

$\vdash . *336·41 . \supset \vdash : \text{Hp} . \supset . (\exists T) . L, R \in \kappa . T \in \kappa_\partial . L = T | R .$

[*330·31] $\supset . (\exists T) . T \in \kappa_\partial . \breve{R} | L = T . L = T | R .$

[*13·195] $\supset . \breve{R} | L \in \kappa_\partial . L = (\breve{R} | L) | R .$

[*330·5.*336·41] $\supset . LU_\kappa (\breve{R} | L) : \supset \vdash . \text{Prop}$

***337·21.** $\vdash : \kappa \in FM \operatorname{conx} \cap FM \operatorname{trs} . R \in \kappa_\partial . \nu \in \text{NC ind} - \iota`0 - \iota`1 . \supset . R^\nu U_\kappa R$

Dem.

$\vdash . *334·162 . *301·23 . \supset \vdash : \text{Hp} . \supset . R^\nu = R^{\nu -_c 1} | R$ (1)

$\vdash . *334·131 . \supset \vdash : \text{Hp} . \supset . R, R^\nu, R^{\nu -_c 1} \in \kappa_\partial$ (2)

$\vdash . (1) . (2) . *336·41 . \supset \vdash . \text{Prop}$

***337·22.** $\vdash : \kappa \in FM \operatorname{sr} . \breve{P} = \dot{s}`\kappa_\partial . P \in \text{comp} . aPx . \nu \in \text{NC ind} - \iota`0 . \supset .$
$(\exists R) . R \epsilon \kappa \ . (R^\nu`a) Px$

Dem.

$\vdash . *270·11 . \supset \vdash : \text{Hp} . \supset . (\exists y) . aPy . yPx .$

[*41·11] $\supset . (\exists R, y) . R \in \kappa_\partial . y = R`a . (R`a) Px$ (1)

$\vdash . (1) \dfrac{R^\nu`a}{a} . \supset \vdash : \text{Hp} . R \in \kappa_\partial . (R^\nu`a) Px . \supset . (\exists S) . S \in \kappa_\partial . (S`R^\nu`a) Px$ (2)

$\vdash . *336·64 . \supset \vdash :. \text{Hp}(2) . S \in \kappa_\partial . (S`R^\nu`a) Px . \supset : R = S . \lor . RU_\kappa S . \lor . SU_\kappa R :$

[*336·511·4] $\supset : R = S . \lor . (R^{\nu +_c 1}`a) P (S`R^\nu`a) . \lor . (S^{\nu +_c 1}`a) P (S`R^\nu`a)$ (3)

$\vdash . (2) . (3) . *334·3 . \supset \vdash : \text{Hp}(2) . \supset . (\exists S) . S \in \kappa_\partial . (S^{\nu +_c 1}`a) Px$ (4)

$\vdash . (1) . (4) . \text{Induct} . \supset \vdash . \text{Prop}$

***337·23.** $\vdash : \text{Hp } *337·22 . \lambda = \kappa_\partial \cap \hat{R} \{(R^\nu`a) Px\} . \supset . \lambda = \breve{U}_\kappa``\lambda$

Dem.

$\vdash . *336·511 . \supset \vdash : \text{Hp} . R \in \lambda . S\breve{U}_\kappa R . \supset . (S^\nu`a) P (R^\nu`a) . (R^\nu`a) Px .$

[*334·3.Hp] $\supset . S \in \lambda$ (1)

$\vdash . *337·22 . \supset \vdash : \text{Hp} . R \in \lambda . \supset . (\exists S) . S \in \kappa_\partial . (S^\nu`R^\nu`a) Px .$

[*330·57·5.*334·13] $\supset . (\exists S) . R | S \in \kappa_\partial . \{(R | S)^\nu`a\} Px .$

[*336·41] $\supset . (\exists S) . R | S \in \kappa_\partial . \{(R | S)^\nu`a\} Px . R\breve{U}_\kappa(R | S) .$

[*37·1] $\supset . R \in \breve{U}_\kappa``\lambda$ (2)

$\vdash . (1) . (2) . \supset \vdash . \text{Prop}$

***337·24.** $\vdash : \text{Hp} *337\cdot23 \,.\, L = \text{tl}\,(U_\kappa)`\lambda \,.\, \supset .\, \sim \{(L_\nu`a)\, P x\}$

Dem.

$\vdash . *206\cdot2 . \supset \vdash : \text{Hp} . \supset . L \sim \epsilon\, \lambda .$

$[\text{Hp}] \qquad \supset . \sim \{(L_\nu`a)\, Px\} : \supset \vdash . \text{Prop}$

***337·241.** $\vdash : \text{Hp} *337\cdot24 . \supset . \sim \{xP\,(L_\nu`a)\}$

Dem.

$\vdash . *337\cdot2\cdot23 . \supset \vdash : \text{Hp} . R \epsilon \lambda . \supset . \breve{R} \,|\, L \epsilon \lambda .$

$[*332\cdot53\cdot241 . *334\cdot131] \qquad \supset . \breve{R} \,|\, L \epsilon \lambda . (\breve{R} \,|\, L)_\nu = \breve{R}_\nu \,|\, L_\nu .$

$[\text{Hp}] \qquad \supset . (\breve{R}_\nu`L_\nu`a)\, Px .$

$[*71\cdot362 . *41\cdot11] \qquad \supset . (L_\nu`a)\, P\, (R_\nu`x) \qquad (1)$

$\vdash . *337\cdot23 . \supset \vdash : \text{Hp} . R \epsilon \kappa_\partial - \lambda . \supset . \sim \{L U_\kappa R\} .$

$[*336\cdot511] \qquad \supset . \sim \{(R_\nu`a)\, P\, (L_\nu`a)\} .$

$[*330\cdot5 . \text{Hp} . *334\cdot14] \qquad \supset . \sim \{(R_\nu`x)\, P\, (L_\nu`a)\} \qquad (2)$

$\vdash . (1) . (2) . \supset \vdash : \text{Hp} . \supset . \sim (\exists R) . R \epsilon \kappa_\partial . (R_\nu`x)\, P\, (L_\nu`a) .$

$[*337\cdot22 . \text{Transp}] \qquad \supset . \sim \{xP\,(L_\nu`a)\} : \supset \vdash . \text{Prop}$

***337·25.** $\vdash : \text{Hp} *337\cdot24 . \supset . L_\nu = \kappa \,\rceil\, \breve{A}_a`x$

Dem.

$\vdash . *337\cdot24\cdot241 . \supset \vdash : \text{Hp} . \supset . L_\nu`a = x : \supset \vdash . \text{Prop}$

***337·26.** $\vdash : \text{Hp} *337\cdot23 . P \epsilon \text{semi Ded} . \supset . \{\text{tl}\,(U_\kappa)`\lambda\}_\nu = \kappa \,\rceil\, \breve{A}_a`x$

Dem.

$\vdash . *337\cdot21 . \qquad \supset \vdash :. \text{Hp} . \supset : R \epsilon \lambda . \supset_R . (R`a)\, Px :$

$[*336\cdot4] \qquad \supset : \kappa \,\rceil\, \breve{A}_a`x \,\epsilon\, p`\overrightarrow{U_\kappa}``\lambda \qquad (1)$

$\vdash . (1) . *337\cdot23\cdot14 . \supset \vdash : \text{Hp} . \supset . E!\, \text{tl}\,(U_\kappa)`\lambda \qquad (2)$

$\vdash . (2) . *337\cdot25 . \supset \vdash . \text{Prop}$

***337·27.** $\vdash :. \kappa \epsilon FM\, \text{sr} . \text{Cnv}`\dot{s}`\kappa_\partial \epsilon\, \text{comp} \cap \text{semi Ded} . \supset :$

$S \epsilon \kappa . \nu \epsilon \text{NC ind} - \iota`0 . \supset . (\exists L) . L \epsilon \kappa . S = L_\nu \qquad [*337\cdot26]$

SECTION C.

MEASUREMENT.

Summary of Section C.

In this Section, the "pure" theory of ratios and real numbers developed in Section A is applied to vector-families. A vector-family, if it has suitable properties, may be regarded as a kind of magnitude. In order to derive from the "pure" theory of ratio a theory of measurement having the properties which we should expect, it is necessary to confine ourselves to some one vector-family; that is, instead of considering the general relation X, where X is a ratio, we consider the relation $X \upharpoonright \kappa$, where κ is the vector-family in question; or sometimes we consider $X \upharpoonright \kappa_\iota$, or sometimes $X \upharpoonright (\kappa \cup \text{Cnv}``\kappa)$.

Concerning ratios with their fields thus limited, which are what we may call "applied" ratios, we have to prove various propositions.

(1) No two members of a family must have two different ratios. This is proved, for an open and connected family, in ∗350·44.

(2) All ratios except 0_q and ∞_q must be one-one relations when limited to a single family. This is proved, for an open and connected family, in ∗350·5; with the same hypothesis, 0_q is one-many (∗350·51).

(3) The relative product of two applied ratios ought to be equal to the arithmetical product of the corresponding pure ratios with its field limited, *i.e.* if X, Y are ratios, we ought to have

$$X \upharpoonright \kappa \mid Y \upharpoonright \kappa = (X \times_s Y) \upharpoonright \kappa$$

or

$$X \upharpoonright \kappa_\iota \mid Y \upharpoonright \kappa_\iota = (X \times_s Y) \upharpoonright \kappa_\iota .$$

That is to say, two-thirds of half a pound of cheese ought to be $(2/3 \times_s 1/2)$ of a pound of cheese; and similarly in any other case. For any open connected family, we have (∗350·6)

$$X \upharpoonright \kappa_\iota \mid Y \upharpoonright \kappa_\iota \subset (X \times_s Y) \upharpoonright \kappa_\iota ,$$

but in order to obtain an equation instead of an inclusion, it is necessary (∗351·31) that κ should be "submultipliable," *i.e.* that if R is any member of κ, and ν any inductive cardinal other than zero, there should be a member of κ whose νth power is R. The class of such families is denoted by "FM subm," and considered in ∗351.

(4) If X, Y are ratios, and T is a member of the family κ, we ought to have

$$(X \upharpoonright \kappa`T) | (Y \upharpoonright \kappa`T) = (X +_s Y) \upharpoonright \kappa`T,$$

that is, two-thirds of a pound of cheese together with half a pound of cheese ought to be $(2/3 +_s 1/2)$ of a pound of cheese, and similarly in any other instance. This property is shown, in *351·43, to hold for any open connected submultipliable family in which all powers of members are members. In any open connected family, if $R, S, T \in \kappa$, we have

$$RXT \,.\, SYT \,.\supset .\, (R | S)(X +_s Y) T \quad (*350{\cdot}62).$$

The remainder of the hypothesis of *351·43 is required in order to prove (a) that $X \upharpoonright \kappa`T$, $Y \upharpoonright \kappa`T$ and $(X +_s Y) \upharpoonright \kappa`T$ exist, ($b$) that $(X \upharpoonright \kappa`T) | (Y \upharpoonright \kappa`T)$, which is the $R | S$ of *350·62, is a member of κ. As applied to κ_ι, we have to take the representative (cf. *332) of the relative product; if $L \in \kappa_\iota$, we have (*351·42)

$$\text{rep}_\kappa`\{(X \upharpoonright \kappa_\iota`L) | (Y \upharpoonright \kappa_\iota`L)\} = (X +_s Y) \upharpoonright \kappa_\iota`L,$$

provided κ is open and connected and submultipliable.

The fact that the above propositions can be proved for suitable vector-families constitutes the reason for studying such families, as we did in Section B. The proof of the above propositions, together with other elementary properties of applied ratios, occupies the first two numbers of this Section.

We proceed next (*352) to consider all the rational multiples of a given vector in a given family, *i.e.* all the members of a given family κ which have, to a given vector T, a ratio which is a member of $C`H'$, or, alternatively, all the members of $\kappa_\iota$ which have to $T$ a ratio which is a member of $C`H_g$. It will be observed that, in virtue of *307, if R and S have a ratio X which is a member of $C`H'$, $R$ and $\breve{S}$ have the corresponding negative ratio $X | \text{Cnv}$. The members of $\kappa$ which have to $T$ a ratio which is a member of $C`H'$ are those vectors R for which we have

$$(\exists X) \,.\, X \in C`H' \,.\, RXT,$$

i.e. using the notation of *336, those for which we have

$$(\exists X) \,.\, X \in C`H' \,.\, RA_T X.$$

Thus they constitute the class

$$\kappa \cap A_T``C`H'.$$

Assuming that $T \in \kappa$, the vector which has the ratio X to T is $\kappa \rceil A_T`X$. This is the vector whose measure is $X$ when $T$ is the unit. Thus $\kappa \rceil A_T \upharpoonright C`H'$ is the correlator of a vector with its measure. It is easy to prove (*352·12) that $\kappa \rceil A_T \upharpoonright C`H'$ is one-one.

We can arrange the vectors which are rational multiples of T in a series by correlation with their measures, putting vectors with smaller measures before those with larger measures. The ordering relation is T_κ, where

$$T_\kappa = \kappa \upharpoonright A_T \,;\, H' \quad \text{Df.}$$

Similarly the members of κ_ι which are positive or negative rational multiples of T may be ordered by the relation $T_{\kappa\iota}$, where

$$T_{\kappa\iota} = \kappa_\iota \upharpoonright A_T \,;\, H_g \quad \text{Df.}$$

We prove that change of units makes no difference to T_κ, *i.e.* if S is any member of κ which is a rational multiple of T, then $S_\kappa = T_\kappa$ (∗352·45). The corresponding proposition holds for $T_{\kappa\iota}$ if S has a positive ratio to T, but if S has a negative ratio, $S_{\kappa\iota} = \breve{T}_{\kappa\iota}$ (∗352·56·57).

If κ is a serial family, T_κ is the converse of U_κ (cf. ∗336) with its field limited to rational multiples of T (∗352·72). This proposition connects the generalized form of greater and less represented by U_κ with the form of greater and less derived from greater and less among the measures of vectors, since it shows that, in a serial family, the vectors which have greater measures come later in the series $\breve{U}_\kappa$, and those with smaller measures come earlier.

We next proceed (∗353) to consider "rational" families. These are families in which every member is a rational multiple of some one unit T, *i.e.* in which

$$(\exists T) \,.\, T \in \kappa_\partial \,.\, \kappa \subset A_T``C`H'.$$

It is obvious that, given any family, the rational multiples of one of its members constitute a rational sub-family. In a rational family, rationals are sufficient for measurement, and irrationals are not required. If the family has connexity, it will be serial; in fact, if T is one of its vectors and a is a member of its field, we have (cf. ∗353·32·33)

$$U_\kappa = \kappa \upharpoonright A_T \,;\, \breve{H}' \,.\, \dot{s}`\kappa_\partial = A_a \,;\, \kappa \upharpoonright A_T \,;\, \breve{H}'.$$

Thus both U_κ and $\dot{s}`\kappa_\partial$ are ordinally similar to $\breve{H}' \upharpoonright \breve{A}_T``\kappa$. If κ is submultipliable, U_κ is ordinally similar to $\breve{H}'$ (∗353·44).

We proceed next (∗354) to consider "rational nets," which are important in connection with the introduction of coordinates in geometry. A rational net is obtained from a given family, roughly speaking, by selecting those vectors which are rational multiples of a given vector, and then limiting their fields to the points which can be reached by means of them from a given point. In order to make this more precise, we proceed as follows: Let us define as the "connection" of a with respect to κ the class $A_a``\kappa_\iota$, *i.e.* all the points which can be reached from a by a member of κ_ι. We will now define as the "a-connected derivative of κ" the class of relations obtained by limiting the field of every member of κ to the connection of a with respect to κ. This class of relations we denote by $\text{cx}_a{}^{\backprime}\kappa$, putting

$$\text{cx}_a{}^{\backprime}\kappa = \complement\,(A_a{}^{\backprime\backprime}\kappa_\iota)^{\backprime\backprime}\kappa \quad \text{Df.}$$

Instead of κ, we take, in order to obtain a rational net, all the rational multiples (in κ) of a given member T of κ, *i.e.* $C^{\backprime}T_\kappa$. Then $\text{cx}_a{}^{\backprime}C^{\backprime}T_\kappa$ is a rational net, namely the rational net associated with the origin a and the unit vector T.

In proving propositions concerning the rational net $\text{cx}_a{}^{\backprime}C^{\backprime}T_\kappa$, we often require the hypothesis that κ is a group. In order to avoid having to make this hypothesis concerning our original family, we construct a closely allied family, which is always a group when κ is connected. This family, which we call κ_g, is obtained from κ by including the converses of those members of κ, if any, whose domains are equal to their converse domains, *i.e.* we put

$$\kappa_g = \kappa \cup \text{Cnv}^{\backprime\backprime}(\kappa \cap \overleftarrow{\text{D}}{}^{\backprime}s^{\backprime}\text{C}^{\backprime\backprime}\kappa) \quad \text{Df.}$$

Then if κ is a connected family, κ_g is a connected family which is a group (*354·14·16), and $(\kappa_g)_\iota = \kappa_\iota$ (*354·15). Then putting $\lambda = \kappa_g$, we take $\text{cx}_a{}^{\backprime}C^{\backprime}T_\lambda$ rather than $\text{cx}_a{}^{\backprime}C^{\backprime}T_\kappa$ as the rational net to be considered. If κ is an open and connected family, this rational net is a family which is open, connected, rational, transitive and asymmetrical (*354·41).

We proceed next (*356) to the application of real numbers to vector-families. For the application of real numbers, it is essential that our family should be serial. Given a serial family in which a given vector S is the limit (in the series U_κ) of a set of vectors which are rational multiples of another vector R, it is natural to take as the measure of S, with the unit R, the limit of the measures of the vectors whose limit is S. It is convenient to take our real numbers in the relational form given in *314, *i.e.* if ξ is a segment of H, we take $\dot{s}^{\backprime}\xi$ as the corresponding real number. Thus positive real numbers are the class $\dot{s}^{\backprime\backprime}C^{\backprime}\Theta$, while positive and negative real numbers together with zero are the class $\dot{s}^{\backprime\backprime}C^{\backprime}\Theta_g$. If $\xi \in C^{\backprime}\Theta$, a vector which has to R a ratio which is a member of ξ has a measure which is less than $\dot{s}^{\backprime}\xi$. The class of all such vectors is $\overrightarrow{\dot{s}^{\backprime}\xi}{}^{\backprime}R$, *i.e.* if $X = \dot{s}^{\backprime}\xi$, it is $\overrightarrow{X}{}^{\backprime}R$. The limit of such vectors in the series U_κ, if it exists, will naturally be taken as the vector whose measure is X. Remembering that U_κ proceeds from greater to smaller vectors, we see that the first vector which is greater than every member of $\overrightarrow{X}{}^{\backprime}R$ will be the *lower* limit of $\overrightarrow{X}{}^{\backprime}R$ with respect to U_κ. Hence, if we write $X_\kappa{}^{\backprime}R$ for the vector whose measure with the unit R is X, we have

$$X_\kappa{}^{\backprime}R = \text{prec}\,(U_\kappa)^{\backprime}\overrightarrow{X}{}^{\backprime}R.$$

Hence we may take as our definition of X_κ

$$X_\kappa = \text{prec}\,(U_\kappa) \,|\, \overrightarrow{X} \upharpoonright \kappa \quad \text{Df.}$$

Then X_κ is an "applied" real number.

The properties to be proved concerning applied real numbers almost all require that the family to which they are applied should be serial and submultipliable, and most of them also require that Cnv$`\dot{s}`\kappa_\partial$ should be semi-Dedekindian. Assuming this, we can prove that, if $X, Y \epsilon \dot{s}``C`\Theta$, $X_\kappa \upharpoonright \kappa$ is one-one, and, with various hypotheses,

$$(X \upharpoonright \kappa) | (Y \upharpoonright \kappa) = (X \times_r Y) \upharpoonright \kappa \quad (*356\cdot31),$$

$$X_\kappa | Y_\kappa = (X \times_r Y)_\kappa \quad (*356\cdot33),$$

$$(X_\kappa`R) | (Y_\kappa`R) = (X +_r Y)_\kappa`R \quad (*356\cdot54).$$

These are the essential properties required of measurement, as in the analogous case of ratios.

We might proceed to consider "real" multiples of a given vector, and "real" nets. But these subjects have less importance than in the analogous case of rationals, and are therefore not discussed.

The Section ends (*359) with a number on existence-theorems for vector-families. The most important of these are derived from rationals and real numbers. The family whose members are of the form $(+_s X) \upharpoonright C`H'$, where $X \epsilon C`H'$, is initial, serial, and submultipliable (*359·21). The family whose members are of the form $(+_p \mu) \upharpoonright C`\Theta'$, where $\mu \epsilon C`\Theta'$, is initial, serial, and submultipliable, and has Cnv$`\dot{s}`\kappa_\partial = \Theta'$, so that Cnv$`\dot{s}`\kappa_\partial \epsilon$ semi Ded (*359·31). Finally we prove that the properties of families are unaffected by the application of correlators, whence it follows that, given any series P whose relation-number is $\dot{1} \dot{+} \eta$, or is θ' where $\theta' \dot{+} \dot{1} = \theta$, there is an initial serial submultipliable family κ such that Cnv$`\dot{s}`\kappa_\partial = P$. Such a family may be used for the measurement of distances in P.

It is of some interest to observe that, given a suitable family κ, ratios with their field limited to κ_∂ form a family whose field is κ_∂. In this family, the zero vector is $(1/1) \upharpoonright \kappa_\partial$, and the family is connected if κ is a rational family. If we wish to obtain a serial family, we must limit ourselves to ratios not less than 1/1, *i.e.* to

$$\upharpoonright \kappa_\partial `` \overleftarrow{H}_* `(1/1).$$

This family is serial, and if we call it λ, we have (with a suitable hypothesis)

$$\dot{s}`\lambda_\partial = U_\kappa \upharpoonright \kappa_\partial.$$

It is necessary, however, if we are to obtain a family, that our original family should be submultipliable, since otherwise we do not necessarily have $\text{G}`X \upharpoonright \kappa_\partial = \kappa_\partial$. For this reason, we cannot use the family of ratios without a frequent loss of generality in the resulting theorems.

The theory of measurement developed in this Section is only applicable to open families. The application of ratio to cyclic families is more complicated and is considered separately in Section D.

$*350$. RATIOS OF MEMBERS OF A FAMILY.

Summary of $*350$.

In this number we introduce no new definitions, but merely bring together the propositions of $*303$ on the pure theory of ratio, and the propositions of $*333$ on powers of vectors in open connected families, especially $*333\cdot47\cdot48$. We thus find that, if κ is an open connected family, and μ, ν are inductive cardinals which are not both zero,

$$M\{(\mu/\nu) \upharpoonright \kappa_\iota\} N . \equiv . M, N \epsilon \kappa_\iota . \dot{\exists} ! M^\nu \dot{\cap} N^\mu . \qquad (*350\cdot4)$$

$$\equiv . M, N \epsilon \kappa_\iota . \text{rep}_\kappa{}^\backprime M^\nu = \text{rep}_\kappa{}^\backprime N^\mu \qquad (*350\cdot41),$$

while if R, T are members of κ,

$$R(\mu/\nu) T . \equiv . R^\nu = T^\mu \qquad (*350\cdot43).$$

We prove also, by means of $*333\cdot53$, that if L and M are members of κ_ι other than $I \upharpoonright s{}^\backprime \text{Cl}{}^{\backprime\backprime}\kappa$, they cannot have more than one ratio, *i.e.*

$*350\cdot44$. $\vdash : \kappa \epsilon FM \text{ ap conx} . X, Y \epsilon C{}^\backprime H' . \dot{\exists} ! X \upharpoonright \kappa_{\iota\partial} \dot{\cap} Y \upharpoonright \kappa_{\iota\partial} . \supset . X = Y$

We next prove that any ratio other than 0_q and ∞_q becomes one-one when its field is limited to κ_ι ($*350\cdot5$), while 0_q becomes one-many ($*350\cdot51$) and ∞_q becomes many-one ($*350\cdot511$), 0_q being in fact the ratio of the zero vector $I \upharpoonright s{}^\backprime \text{Cl}{}^{\backprime\backprime}\kappa$ to any member of κ_ι, and ∞_q being the converse of 0_q.

We consider next the multiplication and addition of ratios, but in this subject we cannot obtain some of the main theorems without the hypothesis that our family is submultipliable (introduced in $*351$). In the present number, we prove that, if κ is an open connected family, and μ, ν are inductive cardinals other than 0,

$$(\mu/1) \upharpoonright \kappa_\iota \,|\, (1/\nu) \upharpoonright \kappa_\iota \subseteq (\mu/\nu) \upharpoonright \kappa_\iota \qquad (*350\cdot53),$$

$$(1/\nu) \upharpoonright \kappa_\iota \,|\, (\mu/1) \upharpoonright \kappa_\iota = (\mu/\nu) \upharpoonright \kappa_\iota \qquad (*350\cdot54),$$

$$(\mu/1) \upharpoonright \kappa_\iota \,|\, (\nu/1) \upharpoonright \kappa_\iota = \{(\mu \times_c \nu)/1\} \upharpoonright \kappa_\iota \qquad (*350\cdot55),$$

and

$$(1/\mu) \upharpoonright \kappa_\iota \,|\, (1/\nu) \upharpoonright \kappa_\iota = \{1/(\mu \times_c \nu)\} \upharpoonright \kappa_\iota \qquad (*350\cdot56).$$

Hence we find that, if X, Y are ratios other than 0_q and ∞_q,

$$X \upharpoonright \kappa_\iota \,|\, Y \upharpoonright \kappa_\iota \subseteq (X \times_s Y) \upharpoonright \kappa_\iota \qquad (*350\cdot6),$$

while if R, S, T are members of κ,

$$RXT . SYT . \supset . (R|S)(X +_s Y) T \qquad (*350\cdot62),$$

and if L, M, N are members of κ_ι,

$$LXN . MYN . \supset . \{\text{rep}_\kappa{}^\backprime(L|M)\}(X +_s Y) N \qquad (*350\cdot63).$$

We then prove similar results for subtraction, and thus arrive at the following proposition concerning generalized addition of positive or negative ratios:

***350·66.** $\vdash : \kappa \in FM \text{ ap conx} . L, M, N \in \kappa_\iota . X, Y \in C\text{`}H_g . LXN . MYN . \supset .$
$\text{rep}_\kappa\text{`}(L \mid M) = (X +_g Y) \upharpoonright \kappa_\iota\text{`}N$

***350·1.** $\vdash : \kappa \in FM \text{ ap} . \supset . \kappa_\iota \subset \text{Rel num id} . \kappa_{\iota\partial} \subset \text{Rel num}$

Dem.

$\vdash . *333\cdot101 . \quad \supset \vdash : \text{Hp} . L \in \kappa_{\iota\partial} . \supset . L \in 1 \rightarrow 1 . L_{po} \Subset J$ (1)
$\vdash . (1) . *300\cdot3 . \supset \vdash : \text{Hp} . \supset . \kappa_{\iota\partial} \subset \text{Rel num}$ (2)
$\vdash . *333\cdot1\cdot101 . \supset \vdash : \text{Hp} . L \in \kappa_\iota - \kappa_{\iota\partial} . \supset . L \Subset I .$
[*300·325] $\supset . L \in \text{Rel num id}$ (3)
$\vdash . (2) . (3) . \supset \vdash . \text{Prop}$

***350·2.** $\vdash : \kappa \in FM \text{ ap conx} . \exists ! \kappa_{\iota\partial} . \supset . \text{Infin ax}$

Dem.

$\vdash . *330\cdot624 . *333\cdot15 . \supset \vdash :. \text{Hp} . L \in \kappa_{\iota\partial} . \supset : \dot{\Lambda} \sim\in \text{finid`}L :$
[*121·11·12] $\supset : \nu \in \text{NC induct} . \supset_\nu . (\exists x, y) . L(x \mapsto y) \in \nu +_c 1 :$
[*120·3] $\supset : \text{Infin ax} :. \supset \vdash . \text{Prop}$

***350·21.** $\vdash : \exists ! FM \text{ ap conx} - 1 . \supset . \text{Infin ax}$ [*334·18 . *350·2]

***350·31.** $\vdash :. \kappa \in FM \text{ ap conx} . \mu, \nu \in \text{NC ind} - \iota\text{`}0 . M, N \in \kappa_{\iota\partial} . \supset :$
$M(\mu/\nu)N . \equiv . \dot{\exists} ! M^\nu \dot{\wedge} N^\mu$

Dem.

$\vdash . *303\cdot1 . (*302\cdot02\cdot03) . *113\cdot602 . \supset$
$\vdash :: \text{Hp} . \supset :. M(\mu/\nu)N . \equiv : (\exists \rho, \sigma, \tau) . \rho \text{ Prm } \sigma . \tau \in \text{NC ind} - \iota\text{`}0 .$
$\mu = \rho \times_c \tau . \nu = \sigma \times_c \tau . \dot{\exists} ! M^\sigma \dot{\wedge} N^\rho . \rho \neq 0 . \sigma \neq 0 :$
[*333·48] $\equiv : (\exists \rho, \sigma, \tau) . \rho \text{ Prm } \sigma . \tau \in \text{NC ind} - \iota\text{`}0 . \rho \neq 0 . \sigma \neq 0 .$
$\mu = \rho \times_c \tau . \nu = \sigma \times_c \tau : \dot{\exists} ! M^\nu \dot{\wedge} N^\mu :$
[*113·602.(*302·02·03)] $\equiv : (\exists \rho, \sigma) . (\rho, \sigma) \text{ Prm } (\mu, \nu) : \dot{\exists} ! M^\nu \dot{\wedge} N^\mu :$
[*302·36] $\equiv : \dot{\exists} ! M^\nu \dot{\wedge} N^\mu :: \supset \vdash . \text{Prop}$

***350·32.** $\vdash :. \text{Hp } *350\cdot31 . \supset : M(\mu/\nu)N . \equiv . \text{rep}_\kappa\text{`}M^\nu = \text{rep}_\kappa\text{`}N^\mu$
[*350·31 . *333·47]

***350·33.** $\vdash :. \kappa \in FM \text{ ap conx} . \mu, \nu \in \text{NC ind} - \iota\text{`}0 . M = I \upharpoonright s\text{`}\text{G}\text{``}\kappa . N \in \kappa_\iota . \supset :$
$M(\mu/\nu)N . \equiv . M = N . \equiv . \dot{\exists} ! M^\nu \dot{\wedge} N^\mu$

Dem.

$\vdash . *301\cdot3 . *333\cdot2 . \supset \vdash :. \text{Hp} . \supset : \sigma \in \text{NC ind} - \iota\text{`}0 . \supset . M^\sigma = M$ (1)
$\vdash . (1) . *303\cdot1 . \supset$
$\vdash :. \text{Hp} . \supset : M(\mu/\nu)N . \equiv . (\exists \rho, \sigma) . (\rho, \sigma) \text{ Prm } (\mu, \nu) . \dot{\exists} ! M \dot{\wedge} N^\rho .$
[*333·101] $\equiv . (\exists \rho, \sigma) . (\rho, \sigma) \text{ Prm } (\mu, \nu) . M = N .$
[*302·36] $\equiv . M = N .$ (2)
[(1).*331·42] $\equiv . \dot{\exists} ! M^\nu \dot{\wedge} N^\mu$ (3)
$\vdash . (2) . (3) . \supset \vdash . \text{Prop}$

***350·331.** $\vdash :. \kappa \in FM \text{ ap conx} . \mu, \nu \in \text{NC ind} - \iota`0 . M \in \kappa_\iota . N = I \upharpoonright s`\text{ᗡ}``\kappa . \supset :$

$$M(\mu/\nu) N . \equiv . M = N . \equiv . \dot{\exists} ! M^\nu \dot{\cap} N^\mu \quad [*350\cdot33 . *303\cdot13]$$

***350·34.** $\vdash :. \kappa \in FM \text{ ap conx} . \nu \in \text{NC ind} - \iota`0 . M, N \in \kappa_\iota . \supset :$

$$M(0/\nu) N . \equiv . M = I \upharpoonright s`\text{ᗡ}``\kappa$$

Dem.

$\vdash . *303\cdot151 . \supset \vdash :. \text{Hp} . \supset : M(0/\nu) N . \equiv . M \mathrel{\dot{\subset}} I . \dot{\exists} ! C`M \cap C`N .$

$[*330\cdot43\cdot61] \quad \equiv . M = I \upharpoonright s`\text{ᗡ}``\kappa :. \supset \vdash . \text{Prop}$

***350·35.** $\vdash :. \kappa \in FM \text{ ap conx} . \nu \in \text{NC ind} - \iota`0 . M, N \in \kappa_\iota . \supset :$

$$M(0/\nu) N . \equiv . \dot{\exists} ! M^\nu \dot{\cap} N^0$$

Dem.

$\vdash . *301\cdot2 . \supset \vdash :. \text{Hp} . \supset : \dot{\exists} ! M^\nu \dot{\cap} N^0 . \equiv . \dot{\exists} ! M^\nu \dot{\cap} I \upharpoonright s`\text{ᗡ}``\kappa .$

$[*333\cdot101 . *331\cdot12] \quad \equiv . M = I \upharpoonright s`\text{ᗡ}``\kappa \quad (1)$

$\vdash . (1) . *350\cdot34 . \supset \vdash . \text{Prop}$

***350·351.** $\vdash :. \kappa \in FM \text{ ap conx} . \mu \in \text{NC ind} - \iota`0 . \supset :$

$$M(\mu/0) N . \equiv . N = I \upharpoonright s`\text{ᗡ}``\kappa \quad [*350\cdot35 . *303\cdot13]$$

***350·4.** $\vdash :. \kappa \in FM \text{ ap conx} . \mu, \nu \in \text{NC ind} . \sim(\mu = \nu = 0) . \supset :$

$$M \{(\mu/\nu) \lceil \kappa_\iota\} N . \equiv . M, N \in \kappa_\iota . \dot{\exists} ! M^\nu \dot{\cap} N^\mu \quad [*350\cdot31\cdot33\cdot331\cdot35\cdot351]$$

***350·41.** $\vdash :. \text{Hp } *350\cdot4 . \supset : M \{(\mu/\nu) \lceil \kappa_\iota\} N . \equiv . M, N \in \kappa_\iota . \text{rep}_\kappa`M^\nu = \text{rep}_\kappa`N^\mu$

Dem.

$\vdash . *332\cdot243 . *301\cdot3 . \supset \vdash : \text{Hp} . M = I \upharpoonright s`\text{ᗡ}``\kappa . \supset . \text{rep}_\kappa`M^\nu = M \quad (1)$

$\vdash . (1) . *350\cdot33\cdot331\cdot32 . \supset \vdash . \text{Prop}$

***350·42.** $\vdash :. \text{Hp } *350\cdot4 . Q, R, S, T \in \kappa . \supset :$

$$(\breve{Q} \mid R)(\mu/\nu)(\breve{S} \mid T) . \equiv . \breve{Q}^\nu \mid R^\nu = \breve{S}^\mu \mid T^\mu \quad [*350\cdot41 . *332\cdot53]$$

***350·43.** $\vdash :. \text{Hp } *350\cdot4 . R, T \in \kappa . \supset : R(\mu/\nu) T . \equiv . R^\nu = T^\mu$

$$\left[*350\cdot42 \frac{I \upharpoonright s`\text{ᗡ}``\kappa, \; I \upharpoonright s`\text{ᗡ}``\kappa}{Q, \qquad S} \right]$$

***350·44.** $\vdash : \kappa \in FM \text{ ap conx} . X, Y \in C`H' . \dot{\exists} ! X \lceil \kappa_{\iota\partial} \dot{\cap} Y \lceil \kappa_{\iota\partial} . \supset . X = Y$

Dem.

$\vdash . *350\cdot4 . \supset \vdash : \text{Hp} . \supset . (\exists L, M, \mu, \nu, \rho, \sigma) . L, M \in \kappa_{\iota\partial} .$

$\dot{\exists} ! L^\sigma \dot{\cap} M^\rho . \dot{\exists} ! L^\nu \dot{\cap} M^\mu . X = \mu/\nu . Y = \rho/\sigma .$

$[*333\cdot53] \quad \supset . \mu \times_c \sigma = \nu \times_c \rho . X = \mu/\nu . Y = \rho/\sigma .$

$[*303\cdot39] \quad \supset . X = Y : \supset \vdash . \text{Prop}$

***350·5.** $\vdash : \kappa \in FM \text{ ap conx} . \mu, \nu \in \text{NC ind} - \iota`0 . \supset . (\mu/\nu) \upharpoonright \kappa_\iota \in 1 \to 1$

Dem.

$\vdash . *350·41 . \supset \vdash :. \text{Hp} . \supset :$

$$L, M, N \in \kappa_\iota . L (\mu/\nu) N . M (\mu/\nu) N . \supset . \text{rep}_\kappa`L^\nu = \text{rep}_\kappa`N^\mu = \text{rep}_\kappa`M^\nu .$$

[*333·41] $\supset . L = M$ (1)

$\vdash . (1) . \quad \supset \vdash : \text{Hp} . \supset . (\mu/\nu) \upharpoonright \kappa_\iota \in 1 \to \text{Cls}$ (2)

Similarly $\vdash : \text{Hp} . \supset . (\mu/\nu) \upharpoonright \kappa_\iota \in \text{Cls} \to 1$ (3)

$\vdash . (2) . (3) . \supset \vdash . \text{Prop}$

***350·51.** $\vdash : \kappa \in FM \text{ ap conx} . \nu \in \text{NC ind} - \iota`0 . \supset .$

$(0/\nu) \upharpoonright \kappa_\iota \in 1 \to \text{Cls} . \text{Ɑ}`(0/\nu) \upharpoonright \kappa_\iota = \kappa_\iota . \text{D}`(0/\nu) \upharpoonright \kappa_\iota = \iota`I \upharpoonright s`\text{Ɑ}``\kappa$ [*350·34]

***350·511.** $\vdash : \text{Hp} *350·51 . \supset .$

$(\nu/0) \upharpoonright \kappa_\iota \in \text{Cls} \to 1 . \text{D}`(\nu/0) \upharpoonright \kappa_\iota = \kappa_\iota . \text{Ɑ}`(\nu/0) \upharpoonright \kappa_\iota = \iota`I \upharpoonright s`\text{Ɑ}``\kappa$

[*350·51 . *303·13]

***350·52.** $\vdash : \kappa \in FM \text{ ap conx} . X \in C`H . \supset . X \upharpoonright \kappa_\iota \in 1 \to 1$

[*350·5 . *304·34 . *333·2]

***350·521.** $\vdash : \kappa \in FM \text{ ap conx} . X \in C`H' . \supset . X \upharpoonright \kappa_\iota \in 1 \to \text{Cls}$

[*350·52·51 . *303·1]

***350·53.** $\vdash : \text{Hp} *350·5 . \supset . \{(\mu/1) \upharpoonright \kappa_\iota\} | \{(1/\nu) \upharpoonright \kappa_\iota\} \subset (\mu/\nu) \upharpoonright \kappa_\iota$

Dem.

$\vdash . *350·4 . \supset \vdash : \text{Hp} . L \{(\mu/1) \upharpoonright \kappa_\iota\} M . M \{(1/\nu) \upharpoonright \kappa_\iota\} N . \supset .$

$$L, M, N \in \kappa_\iota . \dot{\exists} ! L \dot{\frown} M^\mu . \dot{\exists} ! N \dot{\frown} M^\nu .$$

[*333·48] $\supset . L, M, N \in \kappa_\iota . \dot{\exists} ! L^\nu \dot{\frown} M^{\mu \times_c \nu} . \dot{\exists} ! N^\mu \dot{\frown} M^{\mu \times_c \nu} .$

[*333·47] $\supset . L, M, N \in \kappa_\iota . \text{rep}_\kappa`L^\nu = \text{rep}_\kappa`M^{\mu \times_c \nu} = \text{rep}_\kappa`N^\mu .$

[*350·41] $\supset . L \{(\mu/\nu) \upharpoonright \kappa_\iota\} N : \supset \vdash . \text{Prop}$

***350·54.** $\vdash : \text{Hp} *350·5 . \supset . \{(1/\nu) \upharpoonright \kappa_\iota\} | \{(\mu/1) \upharpoonright \kappa_\iota\} = (\mu/\nu) \upharpoonright \kappa_\iota$

Dem.

$\vdash . *350·41 . *332·241 . \supset$

$\vdash :. \text{Hp} . \supset : L [\{(1/\nu) \upharpoonright \kappa_\iota\} | \{(\mu/1) \upharpoonright \kappa_\iota\}] N . \equiv .$

$$(\exists M) . L, M, N \in \kappa_\iota . \text{rep}_\kappa`L^\nu = M = \text{rep}_\kappa`N^\mu .$$

[*332·22] $\equiv . L, N \in \kappa_\iota . \text{rep}_\kappa`L^\nu = \text{rep}_\kappa`N^\mu .$

[*350·41] $\equiv . L (\mu/\nu) N :. \supset \vdash . \text{Prop}$

***350·55.** $\vdash : \mathrm{Hp} * 350\cdot5 . \supset . \{(\mu/1) \upharpoonright \kappa_\iota\} \,|\, \{(\nu/1) \upharpoonright \kappa_\iota\} = \{(\mu \times_c \nu)/1\} \upharpoonright \kappa_\iota$

$= \{(\nu/1) \upharpoonright \kappa_\iota\} \,|\, \{(\mu/1) \upharpoonright \kappa_\iota\}$

Dem.

$\vdash . *350\cdot4 . \supset \vdash :. \mathrm{Hp} . \supset : L[\{(\mu/1) \upharpoonright \kappa_\iota\} \,|\, \{(\nu/1) \upharpoonright \kappa_\iota\}] N . \equiv .$

$(\exists M) . L, M, N \in \kappa_\iota . \dot{\exists} ! L \dot{\cap} M^\mu . \dot{\exists} ! M \dot{\cap} N^\nu .$

[*333·47] $\equiv . (\exists M) . L, M, N \in \kappa_\iota . \dot{\exists} ! L \cap M^\mu . M = \mathrm{rep}_\kappa{}^{\backprime} N^\nu .$

[*333·21] $\equiv . L, N \in \kappa_\iota . \dot{\exists} ! L \cap (\mathrm{rep}_\kappa{}^{\backprime} N^\nu)^\mu .$

[*333·47] $\equiv . L, N \in \kappa_\iota . L = \mathrm{rep}_\kappa{}^{\backprime}\{(\mathrm{rep}_\kappa{}^{\backprime} N^\nu)^\mu\} .$

[*333·24] $\equiv . L, N \in \kappa_\iota . L = \mathrm{rep}_\kappa{}^{\backprime}(N^\nu)^\mu .$

[*350·41.*301·5] $\equiv . L[\{(\nu \times_c \mu)/1\} \upharpoonright \kappa_\iota] N$ (1)

$\vdash . (1) . *113\cdot27 . \supset \vdash . \mathrm{Prop}$

***350·56.** $\vdash : \mathrm{Hp} * 350\cdot5 . \supset . \{(1/\mu) \upharpoonright \kappa_\iota\} \,|\, \{(1/\nu) \upharpoonright \kappa_\iota\} = \{1/(\mu \times_c \nu)\} \upharpoonright \kappa_\iota$

$= \{(1/\nu) \upharpoonright \kappa_\iota\} \,|\, \{(1/\mu) \upharpoonright \kappa_\iota\}$ [*350·55 . *303·13]

***350·6.** $\vdash : \kappa \in FM \text{ ap conx} . X, Y \in C{}^{\backprime}H . \supset . (X \upharpoonright \kappa_\iota) \,|\, (Y \upharpoonright \kappa_\iota) \mathrel{\Subset} (X \times_s Y) \upharpoonright \kappa_\iota$

Dem.

$\vdash . *304\cdot34 . \supset$

$\vdash : \mathrm{Hp} . \supset . (\exists \mu, \nu, \rho, \sigma) . \mu, \nu, \rho, \sigma \in \mathrm{NC\ induct} - \iota{}^{\backprime}0 . X = \mu/\nu . Y = \rho/\sigma$ (1)

$\vdash . *350\cdot54 . \supset \vdash : \kappa \in FM \text{ ap conx} . \mu, \nu, \rho, \sigma \in \mathrm{NC\ induct} - \iota{}^{\backprime}0 . \supset .$

$\{(\mu/\nu) \upharpoonright \kappa_\iota\} \,|\, \{(\rho/\sigma) \upharpoonright \kappa_\iota\} = \{(1/\nu) \upharpoonright \kappa_\iota\} \,|\, \{(\mu/1) \upharpoonright \kappa_\iota\} \,|\, \{(1/\sigma) \upharpoonright \kappa_\iota\} \,|\, \{(\rho/1) \upharpoonright \kappa_\iota\}$

[*350·53·54] $\Subset \{(1/\nu) \upharpoonright \kappa_\iota\} \,|\, \{(1/\sigma) \upharpoonright \kappa_\iota\} \,|\, \{(\mu/1) \upharpoonright \kappa_\iota\} \,|\, \{(\rho/1) \upharpoonright \kappa_\iota\}$

[*350·56·55] $\Subset \{1/(\nu \times_c \sigma)\} \upharpoonright \kappa_\iota \,|\, \{(\mu \times_c \rho)/1\} \upharpoonright \kappa_\iota$

[*350·54] $\Subset \{(\mu \times_c \rho)/(\nu \times_c \sigma)\} \upharpoonright \kappa_\iota$

[*305·14] $\Subset \{\mu/\nu \times_s \rho/\sigma\} \upharpoonright \kappa_\iota$ (2)

$\vdash . (1) . (2) . \supset \vdash . \mathrm{Prop}$

***350·61.** $\vdash :. \kappa \in FM \text{ ap conx} . X \in C{}^{\backprime}H . \supset : M = (X \upharpoonright \kappa_\iota){}^{\backprime}N . \equiv . N = (\breve{X} \upharpoonright \kappa_\iota){}^{\backprime}M$

[*350·52]

***350·62.** $\vdash : \kappa \in FM \text{ ap conx} . X, Y \in C{}^{\backprime}H' . R, S, T \in \kappa . RXT . SYT . \supset .$

$(R \,|\, S)(X +_s Y) T$

Dem.

$\vdash . *350\cdot43 . \supset \vdash : \mathrm{Hp} . X = \mu/\nu . Y = \rho/\sigma . \supset .$

$R^\nu = T^\mu . S^\sigma = T^\rho$

[*301·5] $\supset . R^{\nu \times_c \sigma} = T^{\mu \times_c \sigma} . S^{\nu \times_c \sigma} = T^{\nu \times_c \rho} .$

[*330·57] $\supset . (R \,|\, S)^{\nu \times_c \sigma} = T^{(\mu \times_c \sigma) +_c (\nu \times_c \rho)} .$

[*350·41.*306·14] $\supset . (R \,|\, S)(X +_s Y) T : \supset \vdash . \mathrm{Prop}$

*350·63. $\vdash : \kappa \epsilon FM$ ap conx $. X, Y \epsilon C^\iota H . L, M, N \epsilon \kappa_\iota . LXN . MYN . \supset .$

$$\{\operatorname{rep}_\kappa{}^\iota(L \mid M)\} (X +_s Y) N$$

Dem.

$\vdash . \ast 350·41 . \supset$

$\vdash : \operatorname{Hp} . X = \mu/\nu . Y = \rho/\sigma . \supset . \operatorname{rep}_\kappa{}^\iota L^\nu = \operatorname{rep}_\kappa{}^\iota N^\mu . \operatorname{rep}_\kappa{}^\iota M^\sigma = \operatorname{rep}_\kappa{}^\iota N^\rho .$

$[\ast 332·81] \supset . \operatorname{rep}_\kappa{}^\iota L^{\nu \times_c \sigma} = \operatorname{rep}_\kappa{}^\iota N^{\mu \times_c \sigma} . \operatorname{rep}_\kappa{}^\iota M^{\nu \times_c \sigma} = \operatorname{rep}_\kappa{}^\iota N^{\nu \times_c \rho} .$

$[\ast 332·33] \supset . \operatorname{rep}_\kappa{}^\iota (L^{\nu \times_c \sigma} \mid M^{\nu \times_c \sigma}) = \operatorname{rep}_\kappa{}^\iota N^{(\mu \times_c \sigma) +_c (\nu \times_c \rho)} .$

$[\ast 332·8] \supset . \operatorname{rep}_\kappa{}^\iota (L \mid M)^{\nu \times_c \sigma} = \operatorname{rep}_\kappa{}^\iota N^{(\mu \times_c \sigma) +_c (\nu \times_c \rho)} .$

$[\ast 332·82] \supset . \operatorname{rep}_\kappa{}^\iota \{\operatorname{rep}_\kappa{}^\iota (L \mid M)\}^{\nu \times_c \sigma} = \operatorname{rep}_\kappa{}^\iota N^{(\mu \times_c \sigma) +_c (\nu \times_c \rho)} .$

$[\ast 350·41] \supset . \{\operatorname{rep}_\kappa{}^\iota (L \mid M)\} [\{(\mu \times_c \sigma) +_c (\nu \times_c \rho)\}/(\nu \times_c \sigma)] N .$

$[\ast 306·14] \supset . \{\operatorname{rep}_\kappa{}^\iota (L \mid M)\} (X +_s Y) N : \supset \vdash . \operatorname{Prop}$

*350·64. $\vdash : \operatorname{Hp} \ast 350·63 . XHY . \supset . \{\operatorname{rep}_\kappa{}^\iota (\breve{L} \mid M)\} (Y -_s X) N$

Dem.

$\vdash . \ast 332·15·81 . \supset \vdash : \operatorname{Hp} . \supset . \operatorname{rep}_\kappa{}^\iota \breve{L}^{\nu \times_c \sigma} = \operatorname{Cnv}{}^\iota (\operatorname{rep}_\kappa{}^\iota L)^{\nu \times_c \sigma}$ (1)

Thence the proof proceeds as in *350·63.

*350·65. $\vdash : \operatorname{Hp} \ast 350·62 . \supset . (\breve{R} \mid S)(Y -_s X) T$ [*350·64 . *308·21]

*350·66. $\vdash : \kappa \epsilon FM$ ap conx $. L, M, N \epsilon \kappa_\iota . X, Y \epsilon C^\iota H_g . LXN . MYN . \supset .$

$$\operatorname{rep}_\kappa{}^\iota (L \mid M) = (X +_g Y) \upharpoonright \kappa_\iota{}^\iota N$$

Dem.

$\vdash . \ast 350·63 . \supset$

$\vdash :. \operatorname{Hp} . W = \operatorname{rep}_\kappa{}^\iota (L \mid M) . \supset : X, Y \epsilon C^\iota H . \supset . W = (X +_g Y) \upharpoonright \kappa_\iota{}^\iota N$ (1)

$\vdash . \ast 350·64 . \supset \vdash : \operatorname{Hp}(1) . X \epsilon C^\iota H_n . Y \epsilon C^\iota H . \supset . W = (X +_g Y) \upharpoonright \kappa_\iota{}^\iota N$ (2)

$\vdash . \ast 350·63 . \ast 307·1 . \supset \vdash : \operatorname{Hp}(1) . X, Y \epsilon C^\iota H_n . \supset . W = (X +_g Y) \upharpoonright \kappa_\iota{}^\iota N$ (3)

$\vdash . \ast 350·34 . \supset \vdash : \operatorname{Hp} . X = 0_q . \supset . \operatorname{rep}_\kappa{}^\iota (L \mid M) = M$

$[\ast 308·51]$ $\qquad\qquad\qquad\qquad = (X +_g Y) \upharpoonright \kappa_\iota{}^\iota N$ (4)

Similarly $\qquad \vdash : \operatorname{Hp} . Y = 0_q . \supset . \operatorname{rep}_\kappa{}^\iota (L \mid M) = (X +_g Y) \upharpoonright \kappa_\iota{}^\iota N$ (5)

$\vdash . (1) . (2) . (3) . (4) . (5) . \supset \vdash . \operatorname{Prop}$

$*351$. SUBMULTIPLIABLE FAMILIES.

Summary of $*351$.

A "submultipliable" family is one in which any vector can be divided into ν equal parts (where ν is any inductive cardinal other than 0), *i.e.* in which, if $R \in \kappa$, there is a vector S which is a member of κ and is such that $S^\nu = R$. The definition is

$*351 \cdot 01$. FM subm =

$$FM \cap \hat{\kappa}\{R \in \kappa \,.\, \nu \in \text{NC ind} - \iota\text{‘}0 \,.\, \supset_{R,\nu} \,.\, (\exists S) \,.\, S \in \kappa \,.\, R = S^\nu\} \quad \text{Df}$$

In open families, such as we are considering in this Section, S will be unique when R and ν are given. But in cyclic families, as we shall show in Section D, there will be ν values of S. For example, let κ be a family of angles. Then the vector-angle $2\mu\pi/\nu$ has its νth power equal to 2π for any integral value of μ, since $2\mu\pi$ is the same vector as 2π; and $2\mu\pi/\nu$ has ν different values, since, considered as a vector, any angle θ is identical with $\theta + 2\pi$. In the present Section, however, these complications are excluded, owing to the fact that we confine our attention to open families.

In virtue of $*337 \cdot 27$, a family is submultipliable if it is serial and $\text{Cnv‘}\dot{s}\text{‘}\kappa_\partial$ is compact and semi-Dedekindian ($*351 \cdot 11$).

When κ is a family which is open, connected, and submultipliable, if $L \in \kappa_\iota$ and $\mu \in \text{NC ind} - \iota\text{‘}0$, we have

$$(\exists M) \,.\, M \in \kappa_\iota \,.\, \text{rep}_\kappa\text{‘}M^\mu = L \quad (*351 \cdot 2).$$

Hence if X is any ratio (excluding ∞_q, now and always henceforth), we have

$$\text{E}\,!\, X \,\lceil\, \kappa_\iota\text{‘}L \quad (*351 \cdot 21).$$

In order to obtain the same result for κ, we have to assume that all powers of members of κ are members of κ ($*351 \cdot 22$), but we can obtain the same result for $\kappa \cup \text{Cnv“}\kappa$ without this assumption ($*351 \cdot 221$), because of $*331 \cdot 54$, which shows that in any connected family all powers of members of $\kappa \cup \text{Cnv“}\kappa$ are members of $\kappa \cup \text{Cnv“}\kappa$.

In virtue of the above propositions, the propositions on products and sums of ratios, which in $*350$ only stated inclusions, now state identities. Thus if $X, Y \in C\text{‘}H'$, we have

$$(X \lceil \kappa_\iota) \,|\, (Y \lceil \kappa_\iota) = (X \times_s Y) \lceil \kappa_\iota \qquad (*351 \cdot 31),$$

$$\text{rep}_\kappa\text{‘}\{(X \lceil \kappa_\iota\text{‘}L) \,|\, (Y \lceil \kappa_\iota\text{‘}L)\} = (X +_s Y) \lceil \kappa_\iota\text{‘}L \quad (*351 \cdot 42),$$

where $L \epsilon \kappa_\iota$; also

$$\text{rep}_\kappa\text{‘}\{(X \upharpoonright \kappa_\iota\text{‘}L) \,|\, (Y \upharpoonright \kappa_\iota\text{‘}\breve{L})\} = (X -_s Y) \upharpoonright \kappa_\iota\text{‘}L \quad (*351\cdot45).$$

The corresponding propositions for ratios confined to κ instead of to κ_ι require the additional hypothesis $s\text{‘Pot“}\kappa \subset \kappa$, because this hypothesis is required in $*351\cdot22$; on the other hand, in the analogue of $*351\cdot42$ "rep_κ" does not appear, and we have (with the above hypothesis)

$$(X \upharpoonright \kappa\text{‘}R) \,|\, (Y \upharpoonright \kappa\text{‘}R) = (X +_s Y) \upharpoonright \kappa\text{‘}R \quad (*351\cdot43),$$

where $R \epsilon \kappa$. For ratios confined to $\kappa \cup \text{Cnv“}\kappa$ instead of to κ, the corresponding result can be proved without the hypothesis $s\text{‘Pot“}\kappa \subset \kappa$ ($*351\cdot431$). It will be observed that the hypothesis $s\text{‘Pot“}\kappa \subset \kappa$ is satisfied if κ is a group, though it may also be satisfied when κ is not a group. Since a transitive connected family is a group, a transitive connected family always satisfies $s\text{‘Pot“}\kappa \subset \kappa$, as has been proved already ($*334\cdot132$).

$*351\cdot01$. $FM \text{ subm} =$
$$FM \cap \hat{\kappa}\{R \epsilon \kappa \,.\, \nu \epsilon \text{NC ind} - \iota\text{‘}0 \,.\, \supset_{R,\nu} .\, (\exists S) \,.\, S \epsilon \kappa \,.\, R = S^\nu\} \quad \text{Df}$$

$*351\cdot1$. $\vdash :.\, \kappa \epsilon FM \text{ subm} \,.\, \equiv :\, \kappa \epsilon FM : R \epsilon \kappa \,.\, \nu \epsilon \text{NC ind} - \iota\text{‘}0 \,.\, \supset_{R,\nu} .$
$$(\exists S) \,.\, S \epsilon \kappa \,.\, R = S^\nu \quad [(*351\cdot01)]$$

$*351\cdot101$. $\vdash : \exists ! FM \text{ subm} \,.\, \supset .\, \text{Infin ax} \quad [*351\cdot1 \,.\, *301\cdot16 \,.\, *300\cdot14]$

$*351\cdot11$. $\vdash : \kappa \epsilon FM \text{ sr} \,.\, \text{Cnv‘}\dot{s}\text{‘}\kappa_\partial \epsilon \text{comp} \cap \text{semi Ded} \,.\, \supset .\, \kappa \epsilon FM \text{ subm}$
$[*337\cdot27]$

$*351\cdot2$. $\vdash :.\, \kappa \epsilon FM \text{ ap subm conx} \,.\, \supset : \mu \epsilon \text{NC ind} - \iota\text{‘}0 \,.\, L \epsilon \kappa_\iota \,.\, \supset .$
$$(\exists M) \,.\, M \epsilon \kappa_\iota \,.\, \text{rep}_\kappa\text{‘}M^\mu = L$$

Dem.

$\vdash .\, *351\cdot1 \,.\, \supset \vdash : \text{Hp} \,.\, \mu \epsilon \text{NC ind} - \iota\text{‘}0 \,.\, Q, R \epsilon \kappa \,.\, L = \breve{Q} \,|\, R \,.\, \supset .$
$(\exists S, T) \,.\, S, T \epsilon \kappa \,.\, Q = S^\mu \,.\, R = T^\mu \,.$
$[*332\cdot53] \quad \supset .\, (\exists S, T) \,.\, S, T \epsilon \kappa \,.\, L = \text{rep}_\kappa\text{‘}(\breve{S} \,|\, T)^\mu : \supset \vdash .\, \text{Prop}$

$*351\cdot21$. $\vdash : \text{Hp}\, *351\cdot2 \,.\, X \epsilon C\text{‘}H' \,.\, L \epsilon \kappa_\iota \,.\, \supset .\, \text{E} ! X \upharpoonright \kappa_\iota\text{‘}L$

Dem.

$\vdash .\, *351\cdot2 \,.\, *332\cdot61 \,.\, \supset$
$\vdash : \text{Hp} \,.\, \mu, \nu \epsilon \text{NC ind} - \iota\text{‘}0 \,.\, X = \mu/\nu \,.\, \supset .\, (\exists M) \,.\, M \epsilon \kappa_\iota \,.\, \text{rep}_\kappa\text{‘}M^\mu = \text{rep}_\kappa\text{‘}L^\nu \,.$
$[*350\cdot41\cdot5] \quad \supset .\, \text{E} ! X \upharpoonright \kappa_\iota\text{‘}L \quad (1)$
$\vdash .\, *350\cdot34 \,.\, \supset$
$\vdash : \text{Hp} \,.\, \mu = 0 \,.\, \nu \epsilon \text{NC ind} - \iota\text{‘}0 \,.\, X = \mu/\nu \,.\, \supset .\, X \upharpoonright \kappa_\iota\text{‘}L = I \upharpoonright s\text{‘}\text{Cl“}\kappa \quad (2)$
$\vdash .\, (1) \,.\, (2) \,.\, \supset \vdash .\, \text{Prop}$

***351·22.** $\vdash : \text{Hp} * 351\cdot 2 \,.\, s`\text{Pot}``\kappa \subset \kappa \,.\, X \in C`H' \,.\, R \in \kappa \,.\, \supset \,.\, E\,!\, X \upharpoonright \kappa`R$

Dem.

$\vdash . *301\cdot 22 . \supset \vdash : \text{Hp} . \mu, \nu \in \text{NC ind} . \nu \neq 0 . \supset . R^\mu \in \kappa .$

$[*351\cdot 1] \quad \supset . (\exists S) . S \in \kappa . R^\mu = S^\nu .$

$[*350\cdot 4 . *331\cdot 12] \quad \supset . (\exists S) . S \in \kappa . S (\mu/\nu) R$ (1)

$\vdash . (1) . *350\cdot 521 . \supset \vdash . \text{Prop}$

***351·221.** $\vdash : \text{Hp} * 351\cdot 2 \,.\, X \in C`H' \,.\, \lambda = \kappa \cup \text{Cnv}``\kappa \,.\, R \in \lambda \,.\, \supset \,.\, E\,!\, X \upharpoonright \lambda`R$

[Proof as in *351·22, using *331·54]

***351·3.** $\vdash : \text{Hp} * 351\cdot 2 \,.\, \mu, \nu \in \text{NC ind} \,.\, \nu \neq 0 \,.\, \supset .$

$$\{(\mu/1) \upharpoonright \kappa_\iota\} \,|\, \{(1/\nu) \upharpoonright \kappa_\iota\} = (\mu/\nu) \upharpoonright \kappa_\iota$$

Dem.

$\vdash . *350\cdot 41 . \supset \vdash :. \text{Hp} . \mu \neq 0 . \supset :$

$$L \{(\mu/\nu) \upharpoonright \kappa_\iota\} N . \equiv . L, N \in \kappa_\iota . \text{rep}_\kappa`L^\nu = \text{rep}_\kappa`N^\mu .$$

$[*351\cdot 2] \equiv . (\exists M) . L, M, N \in \kappa_\iota . L = \text{rep}_\kappa`M^\mu . \text{rep}_\kappa`L^\nu = \text{rep}_\kappa`N^\mu .$

$[*333\cdot 24] \equiv . (\exists M) . L, M, N \in \kappa_\iota . L = \text{rep}_\kappa`M^\mu . \text{rep}_\kappa`M^{\mu \times_c \nu} = \text{rep}_\kappa`N^\mu .$

$[*333\cdot 44] \equiv . (\exists M) . L, M, N \in \kappa_\iota . L = \text{rep}_\kappa`M^\mu . \text{rep}_\kappa`M^\nu = \text{rep}_\kappa`N .$

$[*350\cdot 41] \equiv . (\exists M) . L \{(\mu/1) \upharpoonright \kappa_\iota\} M . M \{(1/\nu) \upharpoonright \kappa_\iota\} N$ (1)

$\vdash . *350\cdot 34 . \supset \vdash :. \text{Hp} . \mu = 0 . \supset :$

$$L \{(\mu/\nu) \upharpoonright \kappa_\iota\} N . \equiv . L = I \upharpoonright s`\text{Ɑ}``\kappa . N \in \kappa_\iota \quad (2)$$

$\vdash . *350\cdot 34 . *351\cdot 21 . \supset \vdash :. \text{Hp} . \mu = 0 . \supset :$

$$L \{(\mu/1) \upharpoonright \kappa_\iota\} \,|\, \{(1/\nu) \upharpoonright \kappa_\iota\} N . \equiv . L = I \upharpoonright s`\text{Ɑ}``\kappa . N \in \kappa_\iota \quad (3)$$

$\vdash . (1) . (2) . (3) . \supset \vdash . \text{Prop}$

***351·31.** $\vdash : \text{Hp} * 351\cdot 2 \,.\, X, Y \in C`H' \,.\, \supset . (X \upharpoonright \kappa_\iota) \,|\, (Y \upharpoonright \kappa_\iota) = (X \times_s Y) \upharpoonright \kappa_\iota$

[Proof as in *350·6, using *351·3 instead of *350·53]

***351·4.** $\vdash : \kappa \in FM \text{ ap subm conx} \,.\, \mu, \nu, \rho, \sigma \in \text{NC ind} \,.\, \nu \neq 0 \,.\, \sigma \neq 0 \,.\, L \in \kappa_\iota \,.\, \supset .$

$$\text{rep}_\kappa`[\{(\mu/\nu) \upharpoonright \kappa_\iota`L\} \,|\, \{(\rho/\sigma) \upharpoonright \kappa_\iota`L\}] = (\mu/\nu +_s \rho/\sigma) \upharpoonright \kappa_\iota`L$$

Dem.

$\vdash . *350\cdot 41 . \supset \vdash : \text{Hp} . \mu \neq 0 . \rho \neq 0 . M = (\mu/\nu) \upharpoonright \kappa_\iota`L . \supset . \text{rep}_\kappa`M^\nu = \text{rep}_\kappa`L^\mu .$

$[*333\cdot 44] \quad \supset . \text{rep}_\kappa`M^{\nu \times_c \sigma} = \text{rep}_\kappa`L^{\mu \times_c \sigma}$ (1)

Similarly

$\vdash : \text{Hp} . \mu \neq 0 . \rho \neq 0 . N = (\rho/\sigma) \upharpoonright \kappa_\iota`L . \supset . \text{rep}_\kappa`N^{\nu \times_c \sigma} = \text{rep}_\kappa`L^{\nu \times_c \rho}$ (2)

$\vdash . (1) . (2) . *333\cdot 34 . *332\cdot 33 . \supset$

$\vdash : \text{Hp}(1) . \text{Hp}(2) . \supset . \text{rep}_\kappa`(M \,|\, N)^{\nu \times_c \sigma} = \text{rep}_\kappa`\{L^{(\mu \times_c \sigma)} \,|\, L^{(\nu \times_c \rho)}\} .$

$[*301\cdot 23 . *333\cdot 24] \quad \supset . \{\text{rep}_\kappa`(M \,|\, N)\}^{\nu \times_c \sigma} = \text{rep}_\kappa`L^{(\mu \times_c \sigma) +_c (\nu \times_c \rho)} .$

$[*306\cdot 14 . *350\cdot 41] \quad \supset . \text{rep}_\kappa`(M \,|\, N) = (\mu/\nu +_s \rho/\sigma) \upharpoonright \kappa_\iota`L$ (3)

$\vdash . (3) . *351\cdot 21 . *350\cdot 34 . \supset \vdash . \text{Prop}$

$*351{\cdot}41$. $\vdash : \kappa \epsilon FM \text{ ap subm conx} . s`\text{Pot}``\kappa \subset \kappa .$

$$\mu, \nu, \rho, \sigma \epsilon \text{NC ind} . \nu \neq 0 . \sigma \neq 0 . R \epsilon \kappa . \supset .$$
$$\{(\mu/\nu) \upharpoonright \kappa`R\} \mid \{(\rho/\sigma) \upharpoonright \kappa`R\} = (\mu/\nu +_s \rho/\sigma) \upharpoonright \kappa`R$$

Dem.

$\vdash . *351{\cdot}21{\cdot}22 . \supset$

$\vdash : \text{Hp} . \supset . (\mu/\nu) \upharpoonright \kappa`R = (\mu/\nu) \upharpoonright \kappa_\iota`R . (\rho/\sigma) \upharpoonright \kappa`R = (\rho/\sigma) \upharpoonright \kappa_\iota`R$ (1)

$\vdash . (1) . *332{\cdot}241 . *331{\cdot}24{\cdot}33 . \supset$

$\vdash : \text{Hp} . \supset . \{(\mu/\nu) \upharpoonright \kappa`R\} \mid \{(\rho/\sigma) \upharpoonright \kappa`R\} = \text{rep}_\kappa`[\{(\mu/\nu) \upharpoonright \kappa_\iota`R\} \mid \{(\rho/\sigma) \upharpoonright \kappa_\iota`R\}]$

[$*351{\cdot}4.(1)$] $= (\mu/\nu +_s \rho/\sigma) \upharpoonright \kappa`R : \supset \vdash . \text{Prop}$

$*351{\cdot}411$. $\vdash : \text{Hp} *351{\cdot}4 . \lambda = \kappa \cup \text{Cnv}``\kappa . S \epsilon \lambda . \supset .$

$$\{(\mu/\nu) \upharpoonright \lambda`S\} \mid \{(\rho/\sigma) \upharpoonright \lambda`S\} = (\mu/\nu +_s \rho/\sigma) \upharpoonright \lambda`S$$

[Proof as in $*351{\cdot}41$, using $*331{\cdot}54$]

$*351{\cdot}42$. $\vdash : \kappa \epsilon FM \text{ ap subm conx} . X, Y \epsilon C`H' . L \epsilon \kappa_\iota . \supset .$

$$\text{rep}_\kappa`\{(X \upharpoonright \kappa_\iota`L) \mid (Y \upharpoonright \kappa_\iota`L)\} = (X +_s Y) \upharpoonright \kappa_\iota`L \quad [*351{\cdot}4]$$

$*351{\cdot}43$. $\vdash : \kappa \epsilon FM \text{ ap subm conx} . s`\text{Pot}``\kappa \subset \kappa . X, Y \epsilon C`H' . R \epsilon \kappa . \supset .$

$$(X \upharpoonright \kappa`R) \mid (Y \upharpoonright \kappa`R) = (X +_s Y) \upharpoonright \kappa`R \quad [*351{\cdot}41]$$

$*351{\cdot}431$. $\vdash : \text{Hp} *351{\cdot}42 . \lambda = \kappa \cup \text{Cnv}``\kappa . S \epsilon \lambda . \supset .$

$$(X \upharpoonright \lambda`S) \mid (Y \upharpoonright \lambda`S) = (X +_s Y) \upharpoonright \lambda`S \quad [*351{\cdot}411]$$

$*351{\cdot}44$. $\vdash : \kappa \epsilon FM \text{ ap subm conx} .$

$$\mu, \nu, \rho, \sigma \epsilon \text{NC ind} . \nu \neq 0 . \sigma \neq 0 . (\rho/\sigma) H' (\mu/\nu) . L \epsilon \kappa_\iota . \supset .$$
$$\text{rep}_\kappa`[\{(\mu/\nu) \upharpoonright \kappa_\iota`L\} \mid \{(\rho/\sigma) \upharpoonright \kappa_\iota`\breve{L}\}] = (\mu/\nu -_s \rho/\sigma) \upharpoonright \kappa_\iota`L$$

Dem.

As in $*351{\cdot}4$,

$\vdash : \text{Hp} . M = (\mu/\nu) \upharpoonright \kappa_\iota`L . N = (\rho/\sigma) \upharpoonright \kappa_\iota`\breve{L} . \supset .$

$$\{\text{rep}_\kappa`(M \mid N)\}^{\nu \times_c \sigma} = \text{rep}_\kappa`\{L^{\mu \times_c \sigma} \mid \breve{L}^{\nu \times_c \rho}\} \quad (1)$$

$\vdash . *301{\cdot}23 . *308{\cdot}13 . \supset \vdash : \text{Hp} . \tau = (\mu \times_c \sigma) -_c (\nu \times_c \rho) . \supset .$

$$\text{rep}_\kappa`\{L^{\mu \times_c \sigma} \mid \breve{L}^{\nu \times_c \rho}\} = \text{rep}_\kappa`\{L^\tau \mid L^{\nu \times_c \rho} \mid \breve{L}^{\nu \times_c \rho}\}$$

[$*72{\cdot}59 . *332{\cdot}25$] $= \text{rep}_\kappa`L^\tau$ (2)

$\vdash . (1) . (2) . *350{\cdot}41 . \supset$

$\vdash : \text{Hp} (1) . \text{Hp} (2) . \supset . \text{rep}_\kappa`(M \mid N) = \{\tau/(\nu \times_c \sigma)\} \upharpoonright \kappa_\iota`L$ (3)

$\vdash . (3) . *308{\cdot}24 . \supset \vdash . \text{Prop}$

***351·441**. $\vdash : \kappa \in FM \text{ ap subm conx} .$
$\mu, \nu, \rho, \sigma \in \text{NC ind} . \nu \neq 0 . \sigma \neq 0 . (\mu/\nu) H' (\rho/\sigma) . L \in \kappa_\iota . \supset .$
$\text{rep}_\kappa{}'[\{(\mu/\nu) \upharpoonright \kappa_\iota{}'L\} \mid \{(\rho/\sigma) \upharpoonright \kappa_\iota{}'\breve{L}\}] = (\mu/\nu -_s \rho/\sigma) \upharpoonright \kappa_\iota{}'L$

Dem.

$\vdash . *332{\cdot}15 . *303{\cdot}19 . \supset$

$\vdash : \text{Hp} . \supset . \text{rep}_\kappa{}'[\{(\mu/\nu) \upharpoonright \kappa_\iota{}'L\} \mid \{(\rho/\sigma) \upharpoonright \kappa_\iota{}'\breve{L}\}] =$
$\text{Cnv}'\text{rep}_\kappa{}'[\{(\rho/\sigma) \upharpoonright \kappa_\iota{}'L\} \mid \{(\mu/\nu) \upharpoonright \kappa_\iota{}'\breve{L}\}]$

$[*351{\cdot}44] = \text{Cnv}'(\rho/\sigma -_s \mu/\nu) \upharpoonright \kappa_\iota{}'L$

$[*303{\cdot}19] = (\rho/\sigma -_s \mu/\nu) \upharpoonright \kappa_\iota{}'\breve{L}$

$[*308{\cdot}21] = (\mu/\nu -_s \rho/\sigma) \upharpoonright \kappa_\iota{}'L : \supset \vdash . \text{Prop}$

***351·45**. $\vdash : \kappa \in FM \text{ ap subm conx} . X, Y \in C'H' . L \in \kappa_\iota . \supset .$
$\text{rep}_\kappa{}'\{(X \upharpoonright \kappa_\iota{}'L) \mid (Y \upharpoonright \kappa_\iota{}'\breve{L})\} = (X -_s Y) \upharpoonright \kappa_\iota{}'L$

Dem.

$\vdash . *351{\cdot}21 . *350{\cdot}34 . *308{\cdot}12 . \supset \vdash : \text{Hp} . X = Y . \supset .$

$\text{rep}_\kappa{}'\{(X \upharpoonright \kappa_\iota{}'L) \mid (Y \upharpoonright \kappa_\iota{}'\breve{L})\} = I \upharpoonright s'\text{Ɑ}''\kappa = (X -_s Y) \upharpoonright \kappa_\iota{}'L$ (1)

$\vdash . (1) . *351{\cdot}44{\cdot}441 . \supset \vdash . \text{Prop}$

***351·46**. $\vdash : \kappa \in FM \text{ ap subm conx} . s'\text{Pot}''\kappa \subset \kappa . X, Y \in C'H' . R \in \kappa . \supset .$
$(\text{Cnv}'Y \upharpoonright \kappa'R) \mid (X \upharpoonright \kappa'R) \in \kappa_\iota$

Dem.

$\vdash . *351{\cdot}22 . \supset \vdash : \text{Hp} . \supset . X \upharpoonright \kappa'R \in \kappa . Y \upharpoonright \kappa'R \in \kappa .$

$[*37{\cdot}62]$ $\supset . X \upharpoonright \kappa'R \in \kappa . \text{Cnv}'Y \upharpoonright \kappa'R \in \text{Cnv}''\kappa : \supset \vdash . \text{Prop}$

***351·47**. $\vdash : \text{Hp} *351{\cdot}46 . \supset . (\text{Cnv}'Y \upharpoonright \kappa'R) \mid (X \upharpoonright \kappa'R) = (X -_s Y) \upharpoonright \kappa_\iota{}'R$
$[*351{\cdot}45{\cdot}46]$

*352. RATIONAL MULTIPLES OF A GIVEN VECTOR.

Summary of *352.

By a "rational multiple" of a given vector in a family κ we mean, if we are dealing with κ, any vector in the family which has to the given vector a relation which is a member of $C\text{‘}H'$, and if we are dealing with κ_ι, we mean any member of κ_ι which has to the given member of κ_ι a relation which is a member of $C\text{‘}H_g$. We will call the former "rational κ-multiples" and the latter "*generalized* rational multiples." It will be observed that if κ contains pairs of members which are each other's converses, only one member of such a pair can be contained among the rational κ-multiples of a given member of κ, provided κ is an open family. Hence the rational κ-multiples of a given vector all have one "sense," even if this was not the case with the original family.

Rational multiples of a given vector T can be arranged in a series by correlation with their measures with T as unit. These measures are ordered, in the case of rational κ-multiples, by the relation H', and in the case of generalized rational multiples, by the relation H_g. Moreover if X is the measure of a given member of κ with T as unit, the given member of κ is $\kappa \rceil A_T\text{‘}X$; while if X is the measure of a given member of κ_ι, the given member of κ_ι is $\kappa_\iota \rceil A_T\text{‘}X$. Hence the rational κ-multiples of T are ordered by the relation $\kappa \rceil A_T \dot{;} H'$, and the generalized rational multiples are ordered by the relation $\kappa_\iota \rceil A_T \dot{;} H_g$. These two relations, therefore, are the relations we shall consider in this number. We put

***352·01.** $T_\kappa = \kappa \rceil A_T \dot{;} H'$ Df

***352·02.** $T_{\kappa\iota} = \kappa_\iota \rceil A_T \dot{;} H_g$ Df

We assume throughout this number that κ is open and connected. In dealing with T_κ, we assume $T \epsilon \kappa_\partial$, and in dealing with $T_{\kappa\iota}$, we assume $T \epsilon \kappa_{\iota\partial}$. We then prove the following propositions among others:

$$\kappa \rceil A_T \upharpoonright C\text{‘}H' \epsilon 1 \rightarrow 1 \quad (*352{\cdot}12),$$

$$\kappa_\iota \rceil A_T \upharpoonright C\text{‘}H_g \epsilon 1 \rightarrow 1 \quad (*352{\cdot}15),$$

i.e. the relation of a rational multiple of T to its measure is one-one.

$$T_\kappa, T_{\kappa\iota} \in \text{Ser} \quad (*352{\cdot}16{\cdot}17).$$

Observe that this requires only that κ should be open and connected. The serial property results from the correlation with H' or H_g.

$$C`T_\kappa = \kappa \cap A_T``C`H' . C`T_{\kappa\iota} = \kappa_\iota \cap A_T``C`H_g \quad (*352{\cdot}3{\cdot}31).$$

If S is any non-zero member of $C`T_\kappa$, $C`S_\kappa = C`T_\kappa$ (*352·41), *i.e.* the rational $\kappa$-multiples of $T$ are the same as those of any rational $\kappa$-multiple of $T$; with a similar proposition for $C`T_{\kappa\iota}$ (*352·42).

$$RT_\kappa S . \equiv : R, S \in \kappa \cap A_T``C`H' : (\exists \mu, \nu) . \mu, \nu \in \text{NC ind} . \mu < \nu . R^\nu = S^\mu \quad (*352{\cdot}43).$$

This is a convenient formula for T_κ, and leads immediately to

$$T_\kappa = \{\dot{s}`\overrightarrow{H'}`(1/1)\} \upharpoonright (\kappa \cap A_T``C`H') \quad (*352{\cdot}44).$$

Observe that $\overrightarrow{H'}`(1/1)$ is the class of rational proper fractions, including $0_q$. By *352·44 and *352·41·3, we see that, if $S \neq I \upharpoonright s`\text{G}``\kappa$,

$$S \in C`T_\kappa . \supset . S_\kappa = T_\kappa \quad (*352{\cdot}45),$$

i.e. the order of magnitude of a set of vectors which are rational κ-multiples of a given unit is independent of the choice of the unit.

In order to establish the analogous property for $T_{\kappa\iota}$, we first prove a formula analogous to *352·44, namely

$$T_{\kappa\iota} = \text{Cnv} ; \{\dot{s}`\overleftarrow{H}`(1/1)\} \upharpoonright (\kappa_\iota \cap A_T``C`H) \dagger \{\dot{s}`\overrightarrow{H'}`(1/1)\} \upharpoonright (\kappa_\iota \cap A_T``C`H') \quad (*352{\cdot}54).$$

Here the first term gives the series of negative multiples of T, while the second gives the series of positive multiples of T (including $I \upharpoonright s`\text{G}``\kappa$).

From the above formula it follows, as in the case of T_κ, that if S is a positive multiple of T (not including $I \upharpoonright s`\text{G}``\kappa$), $S_{\kappa\iota} = T_{\kappa\iota}$, while if S is a negative multiple of T, $S_{\kappa\iota} = \breve{T}_{\kappa\iota}$ (*352·56·57).

Finally we deal with the relation of U_κ to T_κ. Here we have to assume that κ is a *serial* family. We then find that U_κ with its field confined to rational κ-multiples of T is the converse of T_κ, *i.e.* we have

***352·72.** $\vdash : \kappa \in FM\,\text{sr} . T \in \kappa_\partial . \supset . U_\kappa \upharpoonright C`T_\kappa = \kappa \rceil A_T ; \breve{H}' = \breve{T}_\kappa$

***352·01.** $T_\kappa = \kappa \rceil A_T ; H'$ Df

***352·02.** $T_{\kappa\iota} = \kappa_\iota \rceil A_T ; H_g$ Df

***352·1.** $\vdash :. RT_\kappa S . \equiv : R, S \in \kappa : (\exists X, Y) . XH'Y . RXT . SYT$ [(*352·01)]

***352·11.** $\vdash :. RT_{\kappa\iota} S . \equiv : R, S \in \kappa_\iota : (\exists X, Y) . XH_g Y . RXT . SYT$ [(*352·02)]

***352·12.** $\vdash : \kappa \epsilon FM \text{ ap conx} . T \epsilon \kappa_\partial . \supset . \kappa \upharpoonleft A_T \upharpoonright C\text{‘}H' \epsilon 1 \rightarrow 1$

Dem.

$\vdash . *336·1 . \quad \supset \vdash : R (\kappa \upharpoonleft A_T \upharpoonright C\text{‘}H') X . \equiv . R \epsilon \kappa . X \epsilon C\text{‘}H' . RXT$ (1)

$\vdash . *350·521 . \supset \vdash : \text{Hp} . R, S \epsilon \kappa . X \epsilon C\text{‘}H' . RXT . SXT . \supset . R = S$ (2)

$\vdash . *350·44 . \quad \supset \vdash : \text{Hp} . R \epsilon \kappa_\partial . X, Y \epsilon C\text{‘}H' . RXT . RYT . \supset . X = Y$ (3)

$\vdash . *350·34·4 . \supset$

$\vdash : \text{Hp} . R = I \upharpoonright s\text{‘}\text{Ǝ}\text{“}\kappa . X, Y \epsilon C\text{‘}H' . RXT . SYT . \supset . X = 0_q . Y = 0_q$ (4)

$\vdash . (3) . (4) . \supset \vdash : \text{Hp} . R \epsilon \kappa . X, Y \epsilon C\text{‘}H' . RXT . SYT . \supset . X = Y$ (5)

$\vdash . (1) . (2) . (5) . \supset \vdash . \text{Prop}$

***352·13.** $\vdash : \kappa \epsilon FM \text{ ap conx} . T \epsilon \kappa_{\iota\partial} . \supset . \kappa_\iota \cap A_T\text{“}C\text{‘}H \subset \kappa_{\iota\partial}$

Dem.

$\vdash . *350·4 . \supset \vdash : \text{Hp} . R \epsilon \kappa_\iota \cap A_T\text{“}C\text{‘}H . \supset .$

$(\exists \mu, \nu) . \mu, \nu \epsilon \text{NC ind} - \iota\text{‘}0 . \dot{\exists} ! R^\nu \dot{\cap} T^\mu .$

$[*333·101] \quad \supset . R \epsilon \kappa_{\iota\partial} : \supset \vdash . \text{Prop}$

***352·131.** $\vdash : \text{Hp} *352·13 . \supset . \kappa_\iota \cap A_T\text{“}C\text{‘}H_n = \text{Cnv}\text{“}(\kappa_\iota \cap A_T\text{“}C\text{‘}H)$ [*307·1]

***352·132.** $\vdash : \text{Hp} *352·13 . \supset . \kappa_\iota \cap A_T\text{“}C\text{‘}H_n \subset \kappa_{\iota\partial}$ [*352·13·131]

***352·14.** $\vdash : \kappa \epsilon FM \text{ ap conx} . T \epsilon \kappa_{\iota\partial} . \supset . \kappa_\iota \cap A_T\text{“}C\text{‘}H' \cap A_T\text{“}C\text{‘}H_n = \Lambda$

Dem.

$\vdash . *307·1 . *350·4 . *352·132 . \supset \vdash : \text{Hp} . R, S \epsilon \kappa_\iota . R \epsilon A_T\text{“}C\text{‘}H_n . S \epsilon A_T\text{“}C\text{‘}H' . \supset .$

$(\exists \mu, \nu, \rho, \sigma) . \mu, \nu, \rho, \sigma \epsilon \text{NC ind} . \nu \neq 0 . \rho \neq 0 . \sigma \neq 0 . R \epsilon \kappa_{\iota\partial} .$

$\text{rep}_\kappa\text{‘}\breve{R}^\nu = \text{rep}_\kappa\text{‘}T^\mu . \text{rep}_\kappa\text{‘}S^\sigma = \text{rep}_\kappa\text{‘}T^\rho .$

$[*333·44] \quad \supset . (\exists \mu, \nu, \rho, \sigma) . \mu, \nu, \rho, \sigma \epsilon \text{NC ind} . \nu \neq 0 . \rho \neq 0 . \sigma \neq 0 . R \epsilon \kappa_{\iota\partial} .$

$\text{rep}_\kappa\text{‘}\breve{R}^{\nu \times_c \rho} = \text{rep}_\kappa\text{‘}T^{\mu \times_c \rho} = \text{rep}_\kappa\text{‘}S^{\sigma \times_c \mu} .$

$[*333·47] \quad \supset . (\exists \xi, \eta) . \xi, \eta \epsilon \text{NC ind} . \xi \neq 0 . \dot{\exists} ! \breve{R}^\xi \dot{\cap} S^\eta . R \epsilon \kappa_{\iota\partial} .$

$[*71·192] \quad \supset . (\exists \xi, \eta) . \xi, \eta \epsilon \text{NC ind} . \xi \neq 0 . \dot{\exists} ! I \dot{\cap} R^\xi | S^\eta . R \epsilon \kappa_{\iota\partial} .$

$[*333·101 . \text{Transp}] \supset . R \neq S : \supset \vdash . \text{Prop}$

***352·15.** $\vdash : \kappa \epsilon FM \text{ ap conx} . T \epsilon \kappa_{\iota\partial} . \supset . \kappa_\iota \upharpoonleft A_T \upharpoonright C\text{‘}H_g \epsilon 1 \rightarrow 1$

Dem.

$\vdash . *336·1 . \supset \vdash : \text{Hp} . R (\kappa_\iota \upharpoonleft A_T \upharpoonright C\text{‘}H_g) X . R (\kappa_\iota \upharpoonleft A_T \upharpoonright C\text{‘}H_g) Y . \supset .$

$R \epsilon \kappa_\iota . X, Y \epsilon C\text{‘}H_g . RXT . RYT$ (1)

$\vdash . (1) . *352·14 . \supset \vdash :. \text{Hp} (1) . \supset :$

$R \epsilon \kappa_\iota . X, Y \epsilon C\text{‘}H' . RXT . RYT . \vee . R \epsilon \kappa_\iota . X, Y \epsilon C\text{‘}H_n . RXT . RYT :$

$[*307·1 . *350·44 . *352·13·132] \supset : X = Y$ (2)

$\vdash . *336·1 . \supset \vdash : \text{Hp} . R (\kappa_\iota \upharpoonleft A_T \upharpoonright C\text{‘}H_g) X . S (\kappa_\iota \upharpoonleft A_T \upharpoonright C\text{‘}H_g) X . \supset .$

$R, S \epsilon \kappa_\iota . X \epsilon C\text{‘}H_g . RXT . SXT .$

$[*350·521 . *307·1] \supset . R = S$ (3)

$\vdash . (2) . (3) . \supset \vdash . \text{Prop}$

∗352·16. $\vdash : \kappa \in FM \text{ ap conx} . T \in \kappa_\partial . \supset . T_\kappa \in \text{Ser}$ [∗352·12 . ∗304·48]

∗352·17. $\vdash : \kappa \in FM \text{ ap conx} . T \in \kappa_{\iota\partial} . \supset . T_{\kappa\iota} \in \text{Ser}$ [∗352·15 . ∗307·45 . ∗304·23]

∗352·18. $\vdash : \kappa \in FM \text{ ap conx} . s\text{‘Pot“}\kappa_\partial \subset \kappa_\partial . \kappa_\partial \cap \text{Cnv“}\kappa_\partial = \Lambda . T \in \kappa_\partial . \supset .$
$\kappa \cap A_T\text{“}C\text{‘}H_n = \Lambda$

Dem.

$\vdash . ∗350·43 . \supset$

$\vdash :. \text{Hp} . \mu, \nu \in \text{NC ind} - \iota\text{‘}0 . X = (\mu/\nu) \,|\, \text{Cnv} . S \in \kappa . \supset : SXT . \equiv . S^\nu = \breve{T}^\mu .$

[Hp] $\supset . S^\nu \in \kappa_\partial \cap \text{Cnv“}\kappa_\partial$ (1)

$\vdash . (1) . \text{Transp} . \supset \vdash : \text{Hp} . \supset . \sim (\exists X, S) . X \in C\text{‘}H_n . S \in \kappa . SXT : \supset \vdash . \text{Prop}$

∗352·181. $\vdash : \kappa \in FM \text{ init} . T \in \kappa_\partial . \supset . \kappa \cap A_T\text{“}C\text{‘}H_n = \Lambda$ [∗352·18 . ∗335·21]

∗352·2. $\vdash : \kappa \in FM \text{ ap conx} . T \in \kappa_\partial . \supset . (I \restriction s\text{‘}\text{Ⅎ“}\kappa)\, T_\kappa T$

Dem.

$\vdash . ∗350·34 . ∗331·22 . \supset \vdash : \text{Hp} . \supset . (I \restriction s\text{‘}\text{Ⅎ“}\kappa)\, 0_q\, T$ (1)

$\vdash . ∗350·31 .$ $\supset \vdash : \text{Hp} . \supset . T (1/1) T$ (2)

$\vdash . ∗304·45·48 .$ $\supset \vdash : \text{Hp} . \supset . 0_q\, H' (1/1)$ (3)

$\vdash . (1) . (2) . (3) . ∗352·1 . \supset \vdash . \text{Prop}$

∗352·21. $\vdash : \kappa \in FM \text{ ap conx} . T \in \kappa_{\iota\partial} . \supset . (I \restriction s\text{‘}\text{Ⅎ“}\kappa)\, T_{\kappa\iota} T$ [Proof as in ∗352·2]

∗352·22. $\vdash : \kappa \in FM \text{ ap conx} . T \in \kappa_\partial . \supset . \dot{\exists} \,!\, T_\kappa$ [∗352·2]

∗352·23. $\vdash : \kappa \in FM \text{ ap conx} . T \in \kappa_{\iota\partial} . \supset . \dot{\exists} \,!\, T_{\kappa\iota}$ [∗352·21]

∗352·3. $\vdash : \kappa \in FM \text{ ap conx} . T \in \kappa_\partial . \supset . C\text{‘}T_\kappa = \kappa \cap A_T\text{“}C\text{‘}H'$

Dem.

$\vdash . ∗350·31 . ∗304·48 . \supset$

$\vdash : \text{Hp} . X \in C\text{‘}H' . X \neq 1/1 . \supset . X (H' \cup \breve{H}') (1/1) . T (1/1) T .$

[∗306·1] $\supset . X \in (H' \cup \breve{H}')\text{“}A_T\text{“}\kappa$ (1)

$\vdash . ∗350·34 . ∗331·22 . ∗304·45·48 . \supset$

$\vdash : \text{Hp} . X = 1/1 . \supset . X \breve{H}'\, 0_q . (I \restriction s\text{‘}\text{Ⅎ“}\kappa)\, 0_q\, T . I \restriction s\text{‘}\text{Ⅎ“}\kappa \in \kappa .$

[∗306·1] $\supset . X \in \breve{H}'\text{“}\breve{A}_T\text{“}\kappa$ (2)

$\vdash . (1) . (2) .$ $\supset \vdash : \text{Hp} . \supset . C\text{‘}H' \subset (H' \cup \breve{H}')\text{“}\breve{A}_T\text{“}\kappa$ (3)

$\vdash . ∗150·201 . \supset \vdash : \text{Hp} . \supset . C\text{‘}T_\kappa = \kappa \,\rceil\, A_T\text{“}(H' \cup \breve{H}')\text{“}\breve{A}_T\text{“}\kappa .$

[(3)] $\supset . \kappa \,\rceil\, A_T\text{“}C\text{‘}H' \subset C\text{‘}T_\kappa$ (4)

$\vdash . (4) . ∗150·202 . \supset \vdash . \text{Prop}$

***352·31.** $\vdash : \kappa \in FM \text{ ap conx} . T \in \kappa_{\iota\partial} . \supset . C`T_{\kappa\iota} = \kappa_\iota \cap A_T``C`H_g$

Dem.

As in *352·3, $\vdash : \text{Hp} . \supset . C`H' \subset (H_g \cup \breve{H}_g)``\breve{A}_T``\kappa$ (1)

$\vdash . *350·31 . (*307·05) . \supset \vdash : \text{Hp} . X \in C`H_n . \supset . XH_g(1/1) . T(1/1)T .$

[*336·1] $\supset . X \in H_g``\breve{A}_T``\kappa$ (2)

$\vdash . (1) . (2) . \supset \vdash : \text{Hp} . \supset . C`H_g \subset (H_g \cup \breve{H}_g)``\breve{A}_T``\kappa$ (3)

$\vdash . (3) . *150·201·202 . \supset \vdash . \text{Prop}$

***352·32.** $\vdash :. \text{Hp} *352·3 . X, Y \in C`H' . R = X \upharpoonright \kappa`T . S = Y \upharpoonright \kappa`T . \supset :$
$RT_\kappa S . \equiv . XH'Y$ [*352·1 . *350·521]

***352·33.** $\vdash :. \text{Hp} *352·31 . X, Y \in C`H_g . R = X \upharpoonright \kappa_\iota`T . S = Y \upharpoonright \kappa_\iota`T . \supset :$
$RT_{\kappa\iota}S . \equiv . XH_gY$ [*352·11·15]

***352·34.** $\vdash :. \text{Hp} *352·3 . \supset : RT_\kappa T . \equiv . (\exists X) . XH'(1/1) . R = X \upharpoonright \kappa`T$
[*352·1 . *350·521·31]

***352·341.** $\vdash :. \text{Hp} *352·3 . \supset : TT_\kappa R . \equiv . (\exists X) . (1/1)H'X . R = X \upharpoonright \kappa`T$

***352·35.** $\vdash :. \text{Hp} *352·31 . \supset : RT_{\kappa\iota}T . \equiv . (\exists X) . XH_g(1/1) . R = X \upharpoonright \kappa_\iota`T$
[*352·11·15]

***352·351.** $\vdash :. \text{Hp} *352·31 . \supset : TT_{\kappa\iota}R . \equiv . (\exists X) . (1/1)H_gX . R = X \upharpoonright \kappa_\iota`T$

***352·36.** $\vdash : \text{Hp} *352·3 . s`\text{Pot}``\kappa \subset \kappa . \supset . \text{Pot}`T - \iota`T \subset \overleftarrow{T_\kappa}`T$

Dem.

$\vdash . *350·43 . \supset \vdash : \text{Hp} . \nu \in \text{NC ind} - \iota`0 - \iota`1 . \supset . T^\nu(\nu/1)T .$

[*304·4.*352·341] $\supset . TT_\kappa T^\nu : \supset \vdash . \text{Prop}$

***352·37.** $\vdash : \text{Hp} *352·31 . T \in \kappa \cup \text{Cnv}``\kappa . \supset . \text{Pot}`T - \iota`T \subset \overleftarrow{T_{\kappa\iota}}`T$

Dem.

$\vdash . *331·24·54 . \supset \vdash : \text{Hp} . \supset . \text{Pot}`T \subset \kappa_\iota$

Hence as in *352·36.

***352·38.** $\vdash : \text{Hp} *352·31 . \supset . \text{rep}_\kappa``(\text{Pot}`T - \iota`T) \subset \overleftarrow{T_{\kappa\iota}}`T$

Dem.

$\vdash . *332·61 . \supset \vdash : \text{Hp} . \supset . \text{rep}_\kappa``(\text{Pot}`T - \iota`T) \subset \kappa_\iota$

Hence as in *352·36.

***352·41.** $\vdash : \kappa \in FM \text{ ap conx} . S, T \in \kappa_\partial . S \in C`T_\kappa . \supset .$
$C`S_\kappa = C`T_\kappa = \kappa \cap A_T``C`H' = \kappa \cap A_S``C`H$

Dem.

$\vdash . *352·3 . *350·43 . \supset \vdash : \text{Hp} . \supset . (\exists \mu, \nu) . \mu, \nu \in \text{NC ind} - \iota`0 . S^\mu = T^\nu .$ (1)

[*352·3] $\supset . T \in C`S_\kappa$ (2)

$\vdash . (1) . *352\cdot3 . *350\cdot43 . \supset \vdash : \text{Hp} . R \epsilon C\text{‘}S_\kappa . \supset .$

$(\exists \mu, \nu, \rho, \sigma) . \mu, \nu, \sigma \epsilon \text{NC ind} - \iota\text{‘}0 . \rho \epsilon \text{NC ind} . S^\mu = T^\nu . R^\sigma = S^\rho .$

$[*301\cdot504] \supset . (\exists \mu, \nu, \rho, \sigma) . \mu, \nu, \sigma \epsilon \text{NC ind} - \iota\text{‘}0 . \rho \epsilon \text{NC ind} . R^{\sigma \times_c \mu} = T^{\nu \times_c \rho} .$

$[*352\cdot3 . *350\cdot43] \supset . R \epsilon C\text{‘}T_\kappa$ (3)

$\vdash . (2) . (3) \frac{T, S}{S, T} . \supset \vdash : \text{Hp} . R \epsilon C\text{‘}T_\kappa . \supset . R \epsilon C\text{‘}S_\kappa$ (4)

$\vdash . (3) . (4) . *352\cdot3 . \supset \vdash . \text{Prop}$

***352·42.** $\vdash : \kappa \epsilon FM \text{ ap conx} . S, T \epsilon \kappa_{\iota\partial} . S \epsilon C\text{‘}T_{\kappa\iota} . \supset . C\text{‘}S_{\kappa\iota} = C\text{‘}T_{\kappa\iota}$

Dem.

$\vdash . *352\cdot3 . *350\cdot4 . *307\cdot1 . \supset$

$\vdash :. \text{Hp} . \supset : (\exists \mu, \nu) : \mu, \nu \epsilon \text{NC ind} - \iota\text{‘}0 : \dot{\exists} ! S^\nu \dot{\wedge} T^\mu . \vee . \dot{\exists} ! \breve{S}^\nu \dot{\wedge} T^\mu :$ (1)

$[*352\cdot31] \supset : T \epsilon C\text{‘}S_{\kappa\iota}$ (2)

$\vdash . (1) . *352\cdot3 . *350\cdot4 . *307\cdot1 . \supset$

$\vdash :. \text{Hp} . R \epsilon C\text{‘}S_{\kappa\iota} . \supset : (\exists \mu, \nu, \rho, \sigma) : \mu, \nu, \sigma \epsilon \text{NC ind} - \iota\text{‘}0 . \rho \epsilon \text{NC ind} :$

$\dot{\exists} ! S^\nu \dot{\wedge} T^\mu . \vee . \dot{\exists} ! \breve{S}^\nu \dot{\wedge} T^\mu : \dot{\exists} ! R^\sigma \dot{\wedge} S^\rho . \vee . \dot{\exists} ! \breve{R}^\sigma \dot{\wedge} S^\rho :$

$[*333\cdot48] \supset : (\exists \mu, \nu, \rho, \sigma) : \mu, \nu, \sigma \epsilon \text{NC ind} - \iota\text{‘}0 . \rho \epsilon \text{NC ind} :$

$\dot{\exists} ! R^{\sigma \times_c \mu} \dot{\wedge} T^{\nu \times_c \rho} . \vee . \dot{\exists} ! \breve{R}^{\sigma \times_c \mu} \dot{\wedge} T^{\nu \times_c \rho} :$

$[*352\cdot31] \supset : R \epsilon C\text{‘}T_{\kappa\iota}$ (3)

$\vdash . (2) . (3) \frac{T, S}{S, T} . \supset \vdash : \text{Hp} . R \epsilon C\text{‘}T_{\kappa\iota} . \supset . R \epsilon C\text{‘}S_{\kappa\iota}$ (4)

$\vdash . (3) . (4) . \supset \vdash . \text{Prop}$

***352·43.** $\vdash :: \kappa \epsilon FM \text{ ap conx} . T \epsilon \kappa_\partial . \supset :.$

$RT_\kappa S . \equiv : R, S \epsilon \kappa \cap A_T\text{‘‘}C\text{‘}H' : (\exists \mu, \nu) . \mu, \nu \epsilon \text{NC ind} . \mu < \nu . R^\nu = S^\mu$

Dem.

$\vdash . *33\cdot17 . \supset \vdash : RT_\kappa S . \equiv . R, S \epsilon C\text{‘}T_\kappa . RT_\kappa S$ (1)

$\vdash . (1) . *352\cdot31 . *350\cdot43 . \supset \vdash :: \text{Hp} . \supset :.$

$RT_\kappa S . \equiv : R, S \epsilon \kappa \cap A_T\text{‘‘}C\text{‘}H' : (\exists \rho, \sigma, \xi, \eta) . \sigma, \xi, \eta \epsilon \text{NC ind} - \iota\text{‘}0 . \rho \epsilon \text{NC ind} .$

$\rho \times_c \eta < \sigma \times_c \xi . R^\sigma = T^\rho . S^\eta = T^\xi :$

$[*333\cdot5] \equiv : R, S \epsilon \kappa \cap A_T\text{‘‘}C\text{‘}H' : (\exists \rho, \sigma, \xi, \eta) . \sigma, \xi, \eta \epsilon \text{NC ind} - \iota\text{‘}0 . \rho \epsilon \text{NC ind} .$

$\rho \times_c \eta < \sigma \times_c \xi . R^{\sigma \times_c \xi} = T^{\rho \times_c \xi} = S^{\rho \times_c \eta} :$

$[*126\cdot14] \supset : R, S \epsilon \kappa \cap A_T\text{‘‘}C\text{‘}H' : (\exists \mu, \nu) . \mu, \nu \epsilon \text{NC ind} . \mu < \nu . R^\nu = S^\mu$ (2)

$\vdash . *350\cdot43 . *304\cdot4 . \supset$

$\vdash :. R, S \epsilon \kappa \cap A_T\text{‘‘}C\text{‘}H' : (\exists \mu, \nu) . \mu, \nu \epsilon \text{NC ind} . \mu < \nu . R^\nu = S^\mu : \supset :$

$R, S \epsilon \kappa \cap A_T\text{‘‘}C\text{‘}H' : (\exists X) . XH' (1/1) . RXS :$

$[*336\cdot1] \supset : R, S \epsilon \kappa : (\exists X, Y, Z) . XH' (1/1) . Y, Z \epsilon C\text{‘}H' . RXS . RYT . SZT :$

$[*350\cdot6 . *305\cdot71\cdot51] \supset : R, S \epsilon \kappa : (\exists X, Z) . (X \times_s Z) H'Z . R (X \times_s Z) T . SZT :$

$[*352\cdot1] \supset : RT_\kappa S$ (3)

$\vdash . (2) . (3) . \supset \vdash . \text{Prop}$

***352·44.** $\vdash : \kappa \epsilon FM \text{ ap conx} . T \epsilon \kappa_\partial . \supset . T_\kappa = \{\dot{s}`\overrightarrow{H'}`(1/1)\} \upharpoonright (\kappa \cap A_T``C`H')$

Dem.

$\vdash . *352\cdot43 . *304\cdot4 . \supset \vdash :: \text{Hp} . \supset :.$

$RT_\kappa S . \equiv : R, S \epsilon \kappa \cap A_T``C`H' : (\exists X) . XH'(1/1) . RXS :: \supset \vdash . \text{Prop}$

***352·45.** $\vdash : \kappa \epsilon FM \text{ ap conx} . S, T \epsilon \kappa_\partial . S \epsilon C`T_\kappa . \supset . S_\kappa = T_\kappa$ [*352·44·41]

***352·5.** $\vdash : \kappa \epsilon FM \text{ ap conx} . T \epsilon \kappa_{\iota\partial} . \supset . C`\kappa_\iota \rceil A_T ; H' = \kappa_\iota \cap A_T``C`H'$

[Proof as in *352·3]

***352·51.** $\vdash : \kappa \epsilon FM \text{ ap conx} . T \epsilon \kappa_{\iota\partial} . \supset . C`\kappa_\iota \rceil A_T ; H_n = \kappa_\iota \cap A_T``C`H_n$

Dem.

$\vdash . *150\cdot202 . \supset \vdash : \text{Hp} . \supset . C`\kappa_\iota \rceil A_T ; H_n \subset \kappa_\iota \cap A_T``C`H_n$ (1)

$\vdash . *352\cdot131 . \supset \vdash : \text{Hp} . R \epsilon \kappa_\iota \cap A_T``C`H_n . \supset . (\exists X) . X \epsilon C`H . \breve{R} \epsilon \kappa_\iota . \breve{R}XT$ (2)

$\vdash . *304\cdot23 . \supset \vdash : \text{Hp} . X \epsilon C`H - \iota`(1/1) . \breve{R} \epsilon \kappa_\iota . \breve{R}XT . \supset .$

$X (H \cup \breve{H})(1/1) . \breve{R} \epsilon \kappa_\iota . \breve{R}XT . T(1/1)T .$

[*307·1.*336·1] $\supset . R \epsilon C`\kappa_\iota \rceil A_T ; H_n$ (3)

$\vdash . *352\cdot38 . \supset \vdash : \text{Hp} . X = 1/1 . \breve{R} \epsilon \kappa_\iota . \breve{R}XT . \supset . \breve{R} (\kappa_\iota \rceil A_T ; H) (\text{rep}_\kappa`T^2) .$

[*307·1] $\supset . R \epsilon C`\kappa_\iota \rceil A_T ; H_n$ (4)

$\vdash . (3) . (4) . \supset \vdash : \text{Hp} . X \epsilon C`H . \breve{R} \epsilon \kappa_\iota . \breve{R}XT . \supset . R \epsilon C`\kappa_\iota \rceil A_T ; H_n$ (5)

$\vdash . (2) . (5) . \supset \vdash : \text{Hp} . \supset . \kappa_\iota \cap A_T``C`H_n \subset C`\kappa_\iota \rceil A_T ; H_n$ (6)

$\vdash . (1) . (6) . \supset \vdash . \text{Prop}$

***352·52.** $\vdash : \kappa \epsilon FM \text{ ap conx} . T \epsilon \kappa_{\iota\partial} . \supset . T_{\kappa\iota} = \kappa_\iota \rceil A_T ; \breve{H}_n \Uparrow \kappa_\iota \rceil A_T ; H'$

$= \text{Cnv} ; \kappa_\iota \rceil A_T ; \breve{H} \Uparrow \kappa_\iota \rceil A_T ; H'$

Dem.

$\vdash . *160\cdot43 . (*307\cdot05) . \supset$

$\vdash . T_{\kappa\iota} = \kappa_\iota \rceil A_T ; \breve{H}_n \dot{\cup} \kappa_\iota \rceil A_T ; H' \dot{\cup} (\kappa_\iota \rceil A_T``C`H_n) \uparrow (\kappa_\iota \rceil A_T``C`H')$ (1)

$\vdash . (1) . *352\cdot5\cdot51 . *307\cdot1 . \supset \vdash . \text{Prop}$

***352·53.** $\vdash : \kappa \epsilon FM \text{ ap conx} . T \epsilon \kappa_{\iota\partial} . \supset .$

$\kappa_\iota \rceil A_T ; H' = \{\dot{s}`\overrightarrow{H'}`(1/1)\} \upharpoonright (\kappa_\iota \cap A_T``C`H')$ [Proof as in *352·44]

***352·531.** $\vdash : \text{Hp } *352\cdot53 . \supset . \kappa_\iota \rceil A_T ; \breve{H} = \{\dot{s}`\overleftarrow{H}`(1/1)\} \upharpoonright (\kappa_\iota \cap A_T``C`H)$

[Proof as in *352·44]

***352·54.** $\vdash : \text{Hp } *352\cdot53 . \supset . T_{\kappa\iota} = \text{Cnv} ; \{\dot{s}`\overleftarrow{H}`(1/1)\} \upharpoonright (\kappa_\iota \cap A_T``C`H) \Uparrow$

$\{\dot{s}`\overrightarrow{H'}`(1/1)\} \upharpoonright (\kappa_\iota \cap A_T``C`H')$ [*352·52·53·531]

***352·55.** $\vdash : \kappa \epsilon FM \text{ ap conx} . S, T \epsilon \kappa_{\iota\partial} . S \epsilon \kappa_\iota \cap A_T``C`H . \supset .$

$\kappa_\iota \cap A_S``C`H' = \kappa_\iota \cap A_T``C`H' . \kappa_\iota \cap A_S``C`H = \kappa_\iota \cap A_T``C`H$

[Proof as in *352·41]

***352·56.** $\vdash : \kappa \epsilon FM \text{ ap conx} . S, T \epsilon \kappa_{\iota\partial} . S \epsilon \kappa_\iota \cap A_T``C`H . \supset . S_{\kappa\iota} = T_{\kappa\iota}$
[*352·54·55]

***352·57.** $\vdash : \kappa \epsilon FM \text{ ap conx} . S, T \epsilon \kappa_{\iota\partial} . S \epsilon \kappa_\iota \cap A_T``C`H_n . \supset . S_{\kappa\iota} = \breve{T}_{\kappa\iota}$
[*352·54·55 . *307·1]

***352·7.** $\vdash :. \kappa \epsilon FM \text{ sr} . X, Y \epsilon C`H' . T \epsilon \kappa_\partial . P, Q \epsilon \kappa . PXT . QYT . \supset :$
$PU_\kappa Q . \equiv . X\breve{H}'Y$

Dem.

$\vdash . *352·18 . \supset \vdash : \text{Hp} . \breve{Q} | P \epsilon \kappa_\partial . \supset . \breve{Q} | P \sim \epsilon A_T``C`H_n .$
[*350·65] $\supset . X -_s Y \epsilon C`H'$ (1)
$\vdash . *350·52 . \supset \vdash : \text{Hp}(1) . \supset . X \neq Y$ (2)
$\vdash . (1) . (2) . *336·41 . \supset \vdash : \text{Hp} . PU_\kappa Q . \supset . X -_s Y \epsilon C`H .$
[*308·12·19.Transp] $\supset . X\breve{H}'Y$ (3)
$\vdash . *336·64 . \supset \vdash :. \text{Hp} . \sim(PU_\kappa Q) . \supset : P = Q . \vee . QU_\kappa P :$
[*350·44.(3)] $\supset : X = Y . \vee . Y\breve{H}'X :$
[*304·48] $\supset : \sim(X\breve{H}'Y)$ (4)
$\vdash . (3) . (4) . \supset \vdash . \text{Prop}$

***352·71.** $\vdash :. \kappa \epsilon FM \text{ sr} . T \epsilon \kappa_\partial . P, Q \epsilon C`T_\kappa . \supset : PU_\kappa Q . \equiv . P(A_T \overset{\circ}{,} \breve{H}')Q$
[*352·7·3]

***352·72.** $\vdash : \kappa \epsilon FM \text{ sr} . T \epsilon \kappa_\partial . \supset . U_\kappa \upharpoonright C`T_\kappa = \kappa \upharpoonleft A_T \overset{\circ}{,} \breve{H}' = \breve{T}_\kappa$ [*352·71]

***352·73.** $\vdash :. \kappa \epsilon FM \text{ sr subm} . X, Y \epsilon C`H' . T \epsilon \kappa_\partial . \supset :$
$(X \upharpoonright \kappa`T) U_\kappa (Y \upharpoonright \kappa`T) . \equiv . X\breve{H}'Y$ [*352·7 . *351·22]

*353. RATIONAL FAMILIES.

Summary of *353.

A "rational family" is one which consists entirely of positive rational multiples of one of its members. We denote rational families by "*FM* rt"; the definition is

*353·01. $FM \text{ rt} = FM \cap \hat{\kappa} \{(\exists T) . T \in \kappa_\partial . \kappa \subset A_T``C`H'\}$ Df

It is obvious that, if κ is any family, $\kappa \cap A_T``C`H'$, which we considered in the last number, is a rational family. If $\kappa$ is a connected family, it does not follow that $\kappa \cap A_T``C`H'$ is a connected family, but the proofs of its properties, as we saw in *352, make use of the fact that it is contained in a connected family. Many of the most important properties of connected families hold equally of sub-classes of connected families, notably the property that two members of κ or κ_ι whose logical product exists are identical (*331·42·24). In dealing with rational families, a good many propositions can be proved by merely assuming that they are contained in connected families. We put

*353·02. $FM \text{ cx} = FM \cap \hat{\lambda} \{(\exists \kappa) . \kappa \in FM \text{ conx} . \lambda \subset \kappa\}$ Df

*353·03. $FM \text{ rt cx} = FM \text{ rt} \cap FM \text{ cx}$ Df

We will call a family "sub-connected" when it is contained in a connected family. When a family κ is open, rational, and sub-connected, any member of κ_∂ may be taken as the T of the definition *353·01 (this is proved in *353·13); and if S, T are any two members of κ_∂, some power of S will be identical with some power of T (*353·12). An open rational sub-connected family is asymmetrical (*353·2); no power of a member, and no product of two members, is the converse of a non-zero member (*353·22·23). Hence by *331·54·33, if the family is connected, and not merely sub-connected, it is a group and transitive (*353·25·27).

If λ is a family which, besides being open and rational, has connexity, then if a is a member of the field and $T \in \kappa_\partial$ we shall have

$$\dot{s}`\lambda_\partial = A_a{}^{\dot{}}\lambda \upharpoonright A_T{}^{\dot{}}\breve{H}' . U_\lambda = \lambda \upharpoonright A_T{}^{\dot{}}\breve{H}' \quad (*353·32·33).$$

That is, the series of points in the field and the series of vectors are both ordinally similar to part or the whole of the series of ratios; they will be similar to the whole if λ is submultipliable (*353·44). But when λ is submultipliable, a smaller hypothesis suffices, for in that case we can prove that if λ is connected, then $\lambda_\iota = \lambda \cup \text{Cnv}``\lambda$ (*353·41), so that λ has connexity, and is serial (*353·42). Thus we have

***353·44.** $\vdash : \lambda \epsilon FM \text{ ap conx rt subm} . \supset . \dot{s}`\lambda_\partial \text{ smor } \breve{H}'$

***353·45.** $\vdash . FM \text{ ap conx rt subm} \subset FM \text{ sr}$

***353·01.** $FM \text{ rt} = FM \cap \hat{\kappa}\{(\exists T) . T \epsilon \kappa_\partial . \kappa \subset A_T``C`H'\}$ Df

***353·02.** $FM \text{ cx} = FM \cap \hat{\lambda}\{(\exists \kappa) . \kappa \epsilon FM \text{ conx} . \lambda \subset \kappa\}$ Df

***353·03.** $FM \text{ rt cx} = FM \text{ rt} \cap FM \text{ cx}$ Df

***353·1.** $\vdash :. \kappa \epsilon FM \text{ rt} . \equiv : \kappa \epsilon FM : (\exists T) . T \epsilon \kappa_\partial . \kappa \subset A_T``C`H'$ [(*353·01)]

***353·12.** $\vdash : \lambda \epsilon FM \text{ ap rt cx} . S, T \epsilon \lambda_\partial . \lambda \subset A_T``C`H' . \supset .$
$(\exists \mu, \nu) . \mu, \nu \epsilon \text{NC ind} . \nu \neq 0 . S^\nu = T^\mu$ [*350·43]

***353·13.** $\vdash : \lambda \epsilon FM \text{ ap rt cx} . T \epsilon \lambda_\partial . \supset . \lambda \subset A_T``C`H'$

Dem.

$\vdash . *353·12 . \supset \vdash : \text{Hp} . S \epsilon \lambda_\partial . \lambda \subset A_S``C`H' . R \epsilon \lambda . \supset .$
$(\exists \mu, \nu, \rho, \sigma) . \mu, \nu, \rho, \sigma \epsilon \text{NC ind} . \rho \neq 0 . \nu \neq 0 . \sigma \neq 0 . R^\nu = S^\mu . T^\sigma = S^\rho .$

[*333·5]
$\supset . (\exists \mu, \nu, \rho, \sigma) . \mu, \nu, \rho, \sigma \epsilon \text{NC ind} . \rho \neq 0 . \nu \neq 0 . \sigma \neq 0 . R^{\nu \times_c \rho} = S^{\mu \times_c \rho} = T^{\mu \times_c \sigma} .$

[*350·43] $\supset . R \epsilon A_T``C`H' : \supset \vdash . \text{Prop}$

***353·14.** $\vdash : \text{Hp } *353·13 . \supset . \lambda_\iota \subset A_T``C`H_g$

Dem.

$\vdash . *353·13 . \supset \vdash : \text{Hp} . R, S \epsilon \lambda . \supset . (\exists X, Y) . X, Y \epsilon C`H' . RXT . SYT .$

[*350·65] $\supset . (\breve{R} | S)(Y -_s X) T .$

[*308·2] $\supset . \breve{R} | S \epsilon A_T``C`H_g : \supset \vdash . \text{Prop}$

***353·15.** $\vdash : \kappa \epsilon FM \text{ conx} . T \epsilon \kappa_\partial . \supset . \kappa \cap A_T``C`H' \epsilon FM \text{ rt cx}$
[*353·1 . (*353·02)]

***353·2.** $\vdash : \lambda \epsilon FM \text{ ap rt cx} . \supset . \lambda_\partial \cap \text{Cnv}``\lambda_\partial = \Lambda . \lambda \epsilon FM \text{ asym}$

Dem.

$\vdash . *353·12·13 . \supset$

$\vdash : \text{Hp} . R, \breve{R} \epsilon \lambda_\partial . \supset . (\exists \mu, \nu) . \mu, \nu \epsilon \text{NC ind} - \iota`0 . R^\mu = \breve{R}^\nu$ (1)

$\vdash . (1) . *301·23 . \supset \vdash : \text{Hp}(1) . \supset . (\exists \mu, \nu) . \mu, \nu \epsilon \text{NC ind} - \iota`0 . R^{\mu +_c \nu} \in I$ (2)

$\vdash . *333·101 . \supset \vdash : \text{Hp}(1) . \supset . \text{Pot}`R \subset \text{Rl}`J$ (3)

$\vdash . (3) . (2) . \text{Transp} . (*334·05) . \supset \vdash . \text{Prop}$

∗353·22.   ⊢ : Hp ∗353·2 . ⊃ . $s‘\text{Pot}“λ_∂ ⌢ \text{Cnv}“λ_∂ = Λ$

Dem.

⊢ . ∗353·12·13 . ∗301·5 . ⊃ ⊢ : Hp . $σ ∈ \text{NC ind} − ι‘0 . R, \breve{R}^σ ∈ λ_∂$. ⊃ .

$\qquad\qquad (\exists μ, ν) . μ, ν ∈ \text{NC ind} − ι‘0 . \breve{R}^{σ×_c ν} = R^μ$.

[∗301·23]   ⊃ . $(\exists μ, ν) . μ, ν ∈ \text{NC ind} − ι‘0 . R^{μ+_c(σ×_c ν)} ⊂̧ I$ (1)

⊢ . ∗333·101 . ∗330·23 . ⊃ ⊢ : Hp . $R ∈ λ_∂$. ⊃ . $\text{Pot‘}R ⊂̧ J . \dot{Λ} \sim ∈ \text{Pot‘}R$ (2)

⊢ . (2) . (1) . Transp.   ⊃ ⊢ : Hp . $R ∈ λ_∂$. ⊃ . $\sim \exists ! \text{Pot‘}R ⌢ \text{Cnv}“λ$: ⊃ ⊢ . Prop

∗353·23.   ⊢ : Hp ∗353·2 . ⊃ . $(s‘λ \underset{,,}{|} “λ) ⌢ \text{Cnv}“λ_∂ = Λ$ [Proof as in ∗353·22]

∗353·24.   ⊢ : Hp ∗353·2 . $λ ∈ FM$ conx . ⊃ . $s‘\text{Pot}“λ ⊂ λ$ [∗353·22 . ∗331·54]

∗353·25.   ⊢ : Hp ∗353·24 . ⊃ . $s‘λ \underset{,,}{|} “λ ⊂ λ$ [∗353·23 . ∗331·33]

∗353·26.   ⊢ : Hp ∗353·24 . ⊃ . $s‘λ_∂ \underset{,,}{|} “λ_∂ ⊂ λ_∂$

Dem.

⊢ . ∗353·12·13 . ⊃ ⊢ : Hp . $R, S ∈ λ_∂$. ⊃ . $(\exists μ, ν) . μ, ν ∈ \text{NC ind} − ι‘0 . R^ν = S^μ$.

[∗330·57]   ⊃ . $(\exists μ, ν) . μ, ν ∈ \text{NC ind} − ι‘0 . (R|S)^ν = S^{μ+_c ν}$.

[∗333·101]   ⊃ . $\exists ! \text{Pot‘}(R|S)^ν ⌢ \text{Rl‘}J$.

[∗301·3.Transp.∗331·23]   ⊃ . $R|S ∈ \text{Rl‘}J$ (1)

⊢ . (1) . ∗353·25 . ⊃ ⊢ . Prop

∗353·27.   ⊢ : Hp ∗353·24 . ⊃ . $λ ∈ FM$ trs asym   [∗353·26·2 . ∗334·13]

∗353·3.   ⊢ :. Hp ∗353·2 . $ν ∈ \text{NC ind} − ι‘0 . s‘\text{Pot}“λ ⊂ λ$. ⊃ : $RU_λ S$. ⊃ . $R^ν U_λ S^ν$
Dem.

⊢ . ∗336·41 . ⊃ ⊢ : Hp . ⊃ . $(\exists T) . T ∈ λ_∂ . R = T|S$.

[∗330·57]   ⊃ . $(\exists T) . T ∈ λ_∂ . R^ν = T^ν | S^ν$.

[∗336·41.Hp]   ⊃ . $R^ν U_λ S^ν$: ⊃ ⊢ . Prop

∗353·31.   ⊢ :. $λ ∈ FM$ ap rt connex . $R, S ∈ λ . ν ∈ \text{NC ind} − ι‘0$. ⊃ :

$\qquad\qquad\qquad\qquad\qquad RU_λ S . ≡ . R^ν U_λ S^ν$

Dem.

⊢ . ∗336·62 . ⊃ ⊢ : Hp . $R \neq S . \sim (RU_λ S)$. ⊃ . $SU_λ R$.

[∗353·3·24]   ⊃ . $S^ν U_λ R^ν$.

[∗336·6·61 . ∗353·27]   ⊃ . $\sim (R^ν U_λ S^ν)$ (1)

⊢ . ∗336·6 . ⊃ ⊢ : Hp . $R = S . ⊃ . \sim (R^ν U_λ S^ν)$ (2)

⊢ . (1) . (2) . ⊃ ⊢ : Hp . $\sim (RU_λ S) . ⊃ . \sim (R^ν U_λ S^ν)$ (3)

⊢ . (3) . ∗353·3 . ⊃ ⊢ . Prop

***353·32.** $\vdash : \lambda \in FM \text{ ap rt connex} . T \in \lambda_\partial . \supset . U_\lambda = \lambda \upharpoonright A_T ; \breve{H}'$

Dem.

$\vdash . *353{\cdot}12{\cdot}13 . *350{\cdot}5 . \supset \vdash : \text{Hp} . R, S \in \lambda . R \neq S . \supset .$

$(\exists \mu, \nu, \rho, \sigma) . \mu, \nu, \rho, \sigma \in \text{NC ind} . \nu \neq 0 . \sigma \neq 0 . R^\nu = T^\mu . S^\sigma = T^\rho . \mu/\nu \neq \rho/\sigma$ (1)

$\vdash . (1) . *350{\cdot}43 . \supset \vdash :. \text{Hp}(1) . \supset : R (\lambda \upharpoonright A_T ; H') S . \vee . S (\lambda \upharpoonright A_T ; H') R$ (2)

$\vdash . *301{\cdot}5 . \supset$

$\vdash : \text{Hp}(1) . \mu, \nu, \rho, \sigma \in \text{NC ind} . \nu \neq 0 . \sigma \neq 0 . R^\nu = T^\mu . S^\sigma = T^\rho . \mu \times_c \sigma < \nu \times_c \rho . \supset .$

$\breve{R}^{\nu \times_c \sigma} \mid S^{\nu \times_c \sigma} = T^{(\nu \times_c \rho) -_c (\mu \times_c \sigma)}$ (3)

$\vdash . *334{\cdot}21 . \supset \vdash : \text{Hp}(3) . \supset . \breve{R} \mid S \in \lambda \cup \text{Cnv}``\lambda .$

[*331·54.*332·241] $\supset . (\breve{R} \mid S)^{\nu \times_c \sigma} = \text{rep}_\kappa`(\breve{R} \mid S)^{\nu \times_c \sigma}$

[*332·53.(3)] $= T^{(\nu \times_c \rho) -_c (\mu \times_c \sigma)}$ (4)

$\vdash . (4) . *353{\cdot}24{\cdot}2 . \supset \vdash : \text{Hp}(3) . \supset . \breve{R} \mid S \in \lambda .$

[*336·41] $\supset . S U_\kappa R$ (5)

$\vdash . (1) . (5) . *304{\cdot}4 . \supset \vdash : \text{Hp} . R (\lambda \upharpoonright A_T ; H') S . \supset . S U_\kappa R$ (6)

$\vdash . (2) . *304{\cdot}4 . \supset \vdash : \text{Hp}(1) . \sim \{R (\lambda \upharpoonright A_T ; H') S\} . \supset . S (\lambda \upharpoonright A_T ; H') R .$

[(6)] $\supset . R U_\kappa S .$

[*336·6·61.*353·27] $\supset . \sim (S U_\kappa R)$ (7)

$\vdash . *336{\cdot}6 . \supset \vdash : \text{Hp} . R = S . \supset . \sim (S U_\kappa R)$ (8)

$\vdash . (6) . (7) . (8) . \supset \vdash . \text{Prop}$

***353·33.** $\vdash : \text{Hp } *353{\cdot}32 . a \in s`\text{C}``\lambda . \supset . \dot{s}`\lambda_\partial = A_a ; \lambda \upharpoonright A_T ; \breve{H}'$

Dem.

$\vdash . *336{\cdot}43 . \quad \supset \vdash : \text{Hp} . \supset . U_\lambda = \lambda \upharpoonright \breve{A}_a ; \dot{s}`\lambda_\partial$ (1)

$\vdash . (1) . *336{\cdot}2 . \quad \supset \vdash : \text{Hp} . \supset . \dot{s}`\lambda_\partial = A_a ; U_\lambda$ (2)

$\vdash . (2) . *353{\cdot}32 . \supset \vdash . \text{Prop}$

***353·34.** $\vdash . FM \text{ ap rt connex} \subset FM \text{ sr}$ [*353·27]

***353·4.** $\vdash : \lambda \in FM \text{ ap rt cx} . s`\text{Pot}``\lambda \subset \lambda . L \in \lambda_{\iota\partial} . \supset .$

$(\exists \sigma) . \sigma \in \text{NC ind} - \iota`0 . \text{rep}_\lambda`L^\sigma \in \lambda \cup \text{Cnv}``\lambda$

Dem.

$\vdash . *353{\cdot}12{\cdot}13 . \supset$

$\vdash : \text{Hp} . \supset . (\exists \mu, \nu, R, S) . \mu, \nu \in \text{NC ind} . R, S \in \lambda . L = \breve{R} \mid S . \mu \neq \nu . R^\nu = S^\mu$ (1)

$\vdash . *301{\cdot}23 . \supset$

$\vdash :. \text{Hp} . \mu, \nu \in \text{NC ind} . R, S \in \lambda . R^\nu = S^\mu . \supset : \mu < \nu . \supset . \breve{R}^\nu \mid S^\nu = S^{\nu -_c \mu} .$

[*332·53] $\supset . \text{rep}_\kappa`(\breve{R} \mid S)^\nu \in \lambda$ (2)

Similarly $\vdash :. \text{Hp}(2) . \supset : \mu > \nu . \supset . \text{rep}_\kappa`(\breve{R} \mid S)^\mu \in \text{Cnv}``\kappa$ (3)

$\vdash . (1) . (2) . (3) . \supset \vdash . \text{Prop}$

***353·41.** $\vdash : \lambda \in FM$ ap conx rt subm $. \supset . \lambda_\iota = \lambda \cup \text{Cnv}``\lambda$

Dem.

$\vdash . *353·4 . \supset$

$\vdash : \text{Hp} . L \in \lambda_{\iota\partial} . \supset . (\exists R, \sigma) . R \in \lambda \cup \text{Cnv}``\lambda . \sigma \in \text{NC ind} - \iota`0 . \text{rep}_\kappa`L^\sigma = R^\sigma .$

[*333·41] $\supset . L \in \lambda \cup \text{Cnv}``\lambda : \supset \vdash . \text{Prop}$

***353·42.** $\vdash : \text{Hp} *353·41 . \supset . \lambda \in FM$ sr [*353·41 . *334·26 . *353·27]

***353·43.** $\vdash : \lambda \in FM$ ap cx rt subm $. T \in \lambda_\partial . \text{Potid}`T \subset \lambda . \supset . C`H' \subset \breve{A}_T``\lambda$

Dem.

$\vdash . *351·1 . \supset \vdash : \text{Hp} . \mu, \nu \in \text{NC ind} . \nu \neq 0 . \supset . (\exists S) . S \in \lambda . S^\nu = T^\mu .$

[*350·43] $\supset . (\exists S) . S \in \lambda . S (\mu/\nu) T$ (1)

$\vdash . (1) . *336·1 . \supset \vdash : \text{Hp} . X \in C`H' . \supset . (\exists S) . S \in \lambda . SA_T X : \supset \vdash . \text{Prop}$

***353·44.** $\vdash : \lambda \in FM$ ap conx rt subm $. \supset . \dot{s}`\lambda_\partial$ smor $\breve{H}'$

Dem.

$\vdash . *353·42·33 . \supset \vdash : \text{Hp} . \alpha \in s`\text{G}``\lambda . \supset . \dot{s}`\lambda_\partial = A_\alpha ; \lambda \upharpoonleft A_T ; \breve{H}'$ (1)

$\vdash . *353·43 . \supset \vdash : \text{Hp} (1) . \supset . C`H' \subset \text{G}`(A_\alpha | \lambda \upharpoonleft A_T)$ (2)

$\vdash . *336·2 . *352·15 . \supset \vdash : \text{Hp} (1) . \supset . A_\alpha | \lambda \upharpoonleft A_T \upharpoonright C`H' \in 1 \to 1$ (3)

$\vdash . (1) . (2) . (3) . \supset \vdash . \text{Prop}$

***353·45.** $\vdash . FM$ ap conx rt subm $\subset FM$ sr [*353·42]

*354. RATIONAL NETS.

Summary of *354.

The subject of "rational nets," which is to be considered in this number, is of importance for the introduction of coordinates in geometry. We have three stages in the construction of a rational net. First, taking any vector T in a family κ, we construct $C\text{‘}T_\kappa$, *i.e.* the positive rational multiples of T, as in *352. The result is, as a rule, a family which is not connected, even when the family κ is connected. For if there are in κ any vectors other than $C\text{‘}T_\kappa$, any point of the field which is reached from a given point a by one of these "irrational" vectors cannot be reached from a by a member of $C\text{‘}T_\kappa$, though it will be in the field of $C\text{‘}T_\kappa$. Thus in order to obtain from $C\text{‘}T_\kappa$ a connected family, we shall have to limit the fields of its members to the points which can be reached from a given point a by one or more rational steps backwards or forwards, *i.e.* to the points $A_a\text{“}(C\text{‘}T_\kappa)_\iota$. It will be observed that whereas, in the construction of $C\text{‘}T_\kappa$, only positive vectors are used, negative vectors, *i.e.* the converses of positive vectors, are also admitted in constructing what we may call the "rational points" with respect to a and T. Having constructed these points, *i.e.* the class $A_a\text{“}(C\text{‘}T_\kappa)_\iota$, we then proceed to the third and last stage in constructing a rational net, by limiting the field of every member of $C\text{‘}T_\kappa$ to $A_a\text{“}(C\text{‘}T_\kappa)_\iota$.

Many of the propositions concerning rational nets require the hypothesis that the family concerned is a group. If this is not the case with the family κ from which we start, we replace κ by κ_g, where κ_g is formed by adding to κ the converses of those members of κ (if any) whose domains are identical with the common converse domain of members of κ. The definition is

***354·01.** $\kappa_g = \kappa \cup \text{Cnv}\text{“}(\kappa \cap \overleftarrow{\text{D}}\text{‘}s\text{‘}\text{Ɑ}\text{“}\kappa)$ Df

We put also

***354·03.** $FM\,\text{grp} = FM \cap \hat{\kappa}\,(s\text{‘}\kappa \,|_{{}_{,,}}\, \text{“}\kappa \subset \kappa)$ Df

We then easily prove that if κ is connected, κ_g is a group (*354·14), and if κ is open and connected, κ_g is open and connected and a group (*354·17). If κ is connected, $(\kappa_g)_\iota = \kappa_\iota$ (*354·15), so that properties only dependent on κ_ι, like that of openness, always hold for κ_g when they hold for κ.

Next, we prove that if κ is open, connected, and a group, $C\text{‘}T_\kappa$ is open, rational, sub-connected and a group (∗354·22). Hence if κ is open and connected, and $\lambda = \kappa_g$, $C\text{‘}T_\lambda$ is open, rational, sub-connected and a group (∗354·24).

The "rational points" with respect to a and T are $A_a\text{“}(C\text{‘}T_\kappa)_\iota$. In order to study them, we consider $A_a\text{“}\lambda_\iota$, where λ is a family concerning which we make hypotheses which will be fulfilled in the case of $C\text{‘}T_\kappa$. We prove that if λ is a family which is a group, and $S \in \lambda \,.\, a \in s\text{‘}\text{Ɑ}\text{“}\lambda$, then

$$A_a\text{“}\lambda_\iota \subset \breve{S}\text{“}A_a\text{“}\lambda_\iota \quad (∗354·31),$$

whence $\quad S \upharpoonleft (A_a\text{“}\lambda_\iota) = (A_a\text{“}\lambda_\iota) \restriction S = S \upharpoonright (A_a\text{“}\lambda_\iota) \quad$ (∗354·312).

Next we prove that, with the same hypothesis, if b is any other member of $A_a\text{“}\lambda_\iota$, then

$$A_a\text{“}\lambda_\iota = A_b\text{“}\lambda_\iota \quad (∗354·33).$$

Thus the rational points with respect to a and T are the same as the rational points with respect to b and T, if b is one of these rational points.

The "rational net" is the family $\upharpoonleft \{A_a\text{“}(C\text{‘}T_\kappa)_\iota\}\text{“}C\text{‘}T_\kappa$. Writing λ for $C\text{‘}T_\kappa$, this becomes $\upharpoonleft (A_a\text{“}\lambda_\iota)\text{“}\lambda$. In order to obtain the properties of the rational net, we therefore continue to consider a family λ, concerning which we make hypotheses which are verified in the case of $C\text{‘}T_\kappa$, and we put

∗354·02. $\text{cx}_a\text{‘}\lambda = \upharpoonleft (A_a\text{“}\lambda_\iota)\text{“}\lambda$ Df

Thus $\text{cx}_a\text{‘}C\text{‘}T_\kappa$ is the rational net defined by κ, T, and a. We prove (∗354·4) that if λ is a group, $\text{cx}_a\text{‘}\lambda$ is a family whose field is $A_a\text{“}\lambda_\iota$. We prove that if λ is a family, and a a member of its field such that any member L of λ_ι for which $L\text{‘}a$ exists is a member of $\lambda \cup \text{Cnv}\text{“}\lambda$, then a is a connected point of $\text{cx}_a\text{‘}\lambda$, *i.e.*

∗354·32 $\vdash : \lambda \in FM \,.\, a \in s\text{‘}\text{Ɑ}\text{“}\lambda \,.\, \lambda_\iota \cap \text{Ɑ}\text{‘}A_a \subset \lambda \cup \text{Cnv}\text{“}\lambda \,.\, \supset .\, a \in \text{conx}\text{‘}\text{cx}_a\text{‘}\lambda$

The hypothesis $\lambda_\iota \cap \text{Ɑ}\text{‘}A_a \subset \lambda \cup \text{Cnv}\text{“}\lambda$ would be verified if λ were a connected family and a were a connected point of λ. But we want to be able to replace λ by $C\text{‘}T_\kappa$, which is in general not connected. The above hypothesis, unlike $\lambda \in FM\,\text{conx}$, is satisfied by $C\text{‘}T_\kappa$, provided κ is open and a group and a is a connected point of κ (∗354·34). Hence it follows that if κ is a family which is open, connected, and a group, and a is a connected point of κ, $\text{cx}_a\text{‘}C\text{‘}T_\kappa$ is open and connected, and a is a connected point of $\text{cx}_a\text{‘}C\text{‘}T_\kappa$ (∗354·401). Again, in virtue of ∗354·312, if λ is a family which is a group, and a is any member of its field, $\text{cx}_a\text{‘}\lambda$ is a group (∗354·313); hence when κ is a family which is open, connected, and a group, $\text{cx}_a\text{‘}C\text{‘}T_\kappa$ is a group (∗354·402); and it is easy to prove that it is also a rational family (∗354·403). Hence, by ∗353·27, $\text{cx}_a\text{‘}C\text{‘}T_\kappa$ is a family which is open, connected, rational, a group, transitive, and asymmetrical (∗354·404). If our original family is open and connected but not a group, we only have to substitute κ_g for κ, *i.e.* putting $\lambda = \kappa_g$, we only have to take $\mathrm{cx}_a`C`T_\lambda$, in order to obtain a rational net with all the above properties. This is stated in the proposition

***354·41.** $\vdash : \kappa \in FM \,\mathrm{ap\,conx} \,.\, T \in \kappa_\partial \,.\, a \in \mathrm{conx}`\kappa \,.\, \lambda = \kappa_g \,.\supset .$
$\mathrm{cx}_a`C`T_\lambda \in FM \,\mathrm{ap\,conx\,rt\,trs\,asym}$

***354·01.** $\kappa_g = \kappa \cup \mathrm{Cnv}``(\kappa \cap \overleftarrow{\mathrm{D}}`s`\text{ᗡ}``\kappa)$ Df

***354·02.** $\mathrm{cx}_a`\lambda = \lceil\,(A_a``\lambda_\iota)``\lambda$ Df

***354·03.** $FM \,\mathrm{grp} = FM \cap \hat{\kappa}\,(s`\kappa \,|_{\prime\prime}\, ``\kappa \subset \kappa)$ Df

***354·1.** $\vdash :. R \in \kappa_g \,.\equiv :\, R \in \kappa \,.\vee.\, \breve{R} \in \kappa \,.\, \text{ᗡ}`R = s`\text{ᗡ}``\kappa$ [(*354·01)]

***354·11.** $\vdash : \kappa \in FM \,\mathrm{conx} \,.\, R, S \in \kappa \,.\supset .\, R \,|\, S \in \kappa_g$ [*331·33 . *354·1]

***354·12.** $\vdash : \mathrm{Hp} \ast 354{\cdot}11 \,.\, \mathrm{D}`R = s`\text{ᗡ}``\kappa \,.\supset .\, \breve{R} \,|\, S = S \,|\, \breve{R} \,.\, \breve{R} \,|\, S \in \kappa_g$

Dem.

$\vdash . \ast 330{\cdot}52 \,.\supset \vdash : \mathrm{Hp} \,.\, a \in \mathrm{conx}`\kappa \,.\supset .\, \mathrm{E}\,!\, \breve{R}`S`a \,.\, \text{ᗡ}`(\breve{R} \,|\, S) = s`\text{ᗡ}``\kappa \,.$

[*331·11·42] $\supset .\, \breve{R} \,|\, S \,\sim\!\in \kappa \cup \mathrm{Cnv}``\kappa \,.\, \text{ᗡ}`(\breve{R} \,|\, S) = s`\text{ᗡ}``\kappa \,.$

[*354·1.*330·561] $\supset .\, \breve{R} \,|\, S \in \kappa_g \,.\, S \,|\, \breve{R} = \breve{R} \,|\, S : \supset \vdash . \mathrm{Prop}$

***354·13.** $\vdash : \mathrm{Hp} \ast 354{\cdot}11 \,.\, \mathrm{D}`R = \mathrm{D}`S = s`\text{ᗡ}``\kappa \,.\supset .\, \breve{R} \,|\, \breve{S} \in \kappa_g$

Dem.

$\vdash . \ast 331{\cdot}33 \,.\supset \vdash : \mathrm{Hp} \,.\supset .\, \breve{R} \,|\, \breve{S} \in \kappa \cup \mathrm{Cnv}``\kappa$ (1)

$\vdash . \ast 37{\cdot}323 \,.\supset \vdash : \mathrm{Hp} \,.\supset .\, \text{ᗡ}`(\breve{R} \,|\, \breve{S}) = s`\text{ᗡ}``\kappa$ (2)

$\vdash . (1) . (2) . \ast 354{\cdot}1 \,.\supset \vdash . \mathrm{Prop}$

***354·14.** $\vdash : \kappa \in FM \,\mathrm{conx} \,.\supset .\, s`\kappa_g \,|_{\prime\prime}\, ``\kappa_g \subset \kappa_g$ [*354·11·12·13·1]

***354·15.** $\vdash : \kappa \in FM \,\mathrm{conx} \,.\supset .\, (\kappa_g)_\iota = \kappa_\iota$

Dem.

$\vdash . \ast 354{\cdot}1 \,.\supset \vdash :. \mathrm{Hp} \,.\, R, S \in \kappa_g \,.\supset :$

$R, S \in \kappa \,.\vee.\, \breve{R}, S \in \kappa \,.\vee.\, R, \breve{S} \in \kappa \,.\vee.\, \breve{R}, \breve{S} \in \kappa \,.\, \text{ᗡ}`R = \text{ᗡ}`S = s`\text{ᗡ}``\kappa$ (1)

$\vdash . \ast 330{\cdot}4 \,. \quad \supset \vdash : \mathrm{Hp} \,.\, R, S \in \kappa \,.\supset .\, \breve{R} \,|\, S \in \kappa_\iota$ (2)

$\vdash . \ast 331{\cdot}33{\cdot}24 \,.\supset \vdash :. \mathrm{Hp} : \breve{R}, S \in \kappa \,.\vee.\, R, \breve{S} \in \kappa : \supset .\, \breve{R} \,|\, S \in \kappa_\iota$ (3)

$\vdash . \ast 354{\cdot}12 \,. \quad \supset \vdash : \mathrm{Hp} \,.\, \breve{R}, \breve{S} \in \kappa \,.\, \text{ᗡ}`R = \text{ᗡ}`S = s`\text{ᗡ}``\kappa \,.\supset .\, \breve{R} \,|\, S \in \kappa_\iota$ (4)

$\vdash . (1) . (2) . (3) . (4) \,.\supset \vdash . \mathrm{Prop}$

***354·16.** $\vdash : \kappa \in FM \,\mathrm{conx} \,.\supset .\, \kappa_g \in FM \,\mathrm{conx}$ [*354·1·12]

***354·17.** $\vdash : \kappa \in FM \,\mathrm{ap\,conx} \,.\supset .\, \kappa_g \in FM \,\mathrm{ap\,conx\,grp}$
[*354·16·15·14 . *333·101]

*354·18. $\vdash :. \kappa \in FM\,\mathrm{grp} . \equiv : \kappa \in FM : R, S \in \kappa . \supset_{R,S} . R|S \in \kappa$ [(*354·03)]

*354·19. $\vdash : \kappa \in FM\,\mathrm{grp} . \supset . s‘\mathrm{Pot}“\kappa \subset \kappa$ [*354·18 . Induct]

*354·2. $\vdash : \kappa \in FM\,\mathrm{ap\ conx} . T \in \kappa_\partial . \supset . C‘T_\kappa \in FM\,\mathrm{ap\ rt\ cx}$
[*353·15 . *352·3]

*354·22. $\vdash : \kappa \in FM\,\mathrm{ap\ conx\ grp} . T \in \kappa_\partial . \supset . C‘T_\kappa \in FM\,\mathrm{ap\ rt\ cx\ grp}$

Dem.

$\vdash . *350·62 . *354·18 . \supset \vdash : \mathrm{Hp} . R, S, T \in \kappa . X, Y \in C‘H' . RXT . SYT . \supset .$
$(R|S)(X +_s Y)\,T . R|S \in \kappa .$

[*306·67.*352·3] $\supset . R|S \in C‘T_\kappa$ (1)

$\vdash . (1) . *352·3 . \supset \vdash : \mathrm{Hp} . R, S \in C‘T_\kappa . \supset . R|S \in C‘T_\kappa$ (2)

$\vdash . (2) . *354·2 . \supset \vdash . \mathrm{Prop}$

*354·23 $\vdash : \kappa \in FM\,\mathrm{rt\ conx} . T \in \kappa_\partial . \supset . C‘T_\kappa = \kappa$ [*353·13 . *352·3]

*354·24. $\vdash : \kappa \in FM\,\mathrm{ap\ conx} . T \in \kappa_\partial . \lambda = \kappa_g . \supset . C‘T_\lambda \in FM\,\mathrm{ap\ rt\ cx\ grp}$
[*354·22·17]

*354·31. $\vdash : \lambda \in FM\,\mathrm{grp} . a \in s‘\text{Ɑ}“\lambda . S \in \lambda . \supset . A_a“\lambda_\iota \subset \breve{S}“A_a“\lambda_\iota$

Dem.

$\vdash . *336·1 . \supset \vdash :. \mathrm{Hp} . \supset : x \in A_a“\lambda_\iota . \supset . (\exists P, Q) . P, Q \in \kappa . x = \breve{P}‘Q‘a .$

[*330·56] $\supset . (\exists P, Q) . P, Q \in \kappa . S‘x = \breve{P}‘S‘Q‘a .$

[*354·18] $\supset . (\exists P, R) . P, R \in \kappa . S‘x = \breve{P}‘R‘a .$

[*336·1] $\supset . S‘x \in A_a“\lambda_\iota .$

[*37·106] $\supset . x \in \breve{S}“A_a“\lambda_\iota :. \supset \vdash . \mathrm{Prop}$

*354·311. $\vdash : \mathrm{Hp}\ *354·31 . \supset . S“A_a“\lambda_\iota \subset A_a“\lambda_\iota$ [*354·31]

*354·312. $\vdash : \mathrm{Hp}\ *354·31 . \supset . S \sqsubset (A_a“\lambda_\iota) = (A_a“\lambda_\iota) \upharpoonleft S = S \upharpoonright (A_a“\lambda_\iota)$
[*354·31·311]

*354·313. $\vdash : \lambda \in FM\,\mathrm{grp} . a \in s‘\text{Ɑ}“\lambda . \mu = \mathrm{cx}_a‘\lambda . \supset . s‘\mu\,|_{,,}“\mu \subset \mu$

Dem.

$\vdash . *354·312 . \supset$

$\vdash : \mathrm{Hp} . R, S \in \lambda . \supset . \{R \sqsubset (A_a“\lambda_\iota)\} | \{S \sqsubset (A_a“\lambda_\iota)\} = (R|S) \sqsubset (A_a“\lambda_\iota)$ (1)

$\vdash . (1) . *354·18 . \supset$

$\vdash : \mathrm{Hp} . R, S \in \lambda . \supset . \{R \sqsubset (A_a“\lambda_\iota)\} | \{S \sqsubset (A_a“\lambda_\iota)\} \in \mathrm{cx}_a‘\lambda : \supset \vdash . \mathrm{Prop}$

*354·32. $\vdash : \lambda \in FM . a \in s‘\text{Ɑ}“\lambda . \lambda_\iota \cap \text{Ɑ}‘A_a \subset \lambda \cup \mathrm{Cnv}“\lambda . \supset . a \in \mathrm{conx}‘\mathrm{cx}_a‘\lambda$

Dem.

$\vdash . *336·1 . \supset \vdash :. \mathrm{Hp} . \supset : x \in A_a“\lambda_\iota . \supset . (\exists L) . L \in \lambda_\iota . x = L‘a . L \in \text{Ɑ}‘A_a .$

[Hp] $\supset . (\exists L) . L \in \lambda \cup \mathrm{Cnv}“\lambda . x = L‘a .$

[*330·43] $\supset . (\exists M) . M \in \mathrm{cx}_a‘\lambda \cup \mathrm{Cnv}“\mathrm{cx}_a‘\lambda . x = M‘a :$

[*331·11] $\supset : a \in \mathrm{conx}‘\mathrm{cx}_a‘\lambda :. \supset \vdash . \mathrm{Prop}$

***354·33.** $\vdash : \lambda \,\epsilon\, FM \,\mathrm{grp} \,.\, a \,\epsilon\, s\text{‘}\text{Ɑ}\text{“}\lambda \,.\, b \,\epsilon\, A_a\text{“}\lambda_\iota \,.\, \supset .\, A_a\text{“}\lambda_\iota = A_b\text{“}\lambda_\iota$

Dem.

$\vdash .\, *336\cdot1 \,.\, \supset$

$\vdash : \mathrm{Hp} \,.\, c \,\epsilon\, A_b\text{“}\lambda_\iota \,.\, \supset .\, (\exists P, Q, R, S) \,.\, P, Q, R, S \,\epsilon\, \kappa \,.\, c = \breve{R}\text{‘}\breve{S}\text{‘}P\text{‘}Q\text{‘}a \,.$

$[*330\cdot56] \qquad \supset .\, (\exists P, Q, R, S) \,.\, P, Q, R, S \,\epsilon\, \kappa \,.\, c = \breve{R}\text{‘}P\text{‘}\breve{S}\text{‘}Q\text{‘}a \,.$

$[*354\cdot18] \qquad \supset .\, (\exists M, N) \,.\, M, N \,\epsilon\, \kappa \,.\, c = \breve{M}\text{‘}N\text{‘}a \,.$

$[*336\cdot1] \qquad \supset .\, c \,\epsilon\, A_a\text{“}\lambda_\iota$ (1)

Similarly $\vdash : \mathrm{Hp} \,.\, c \,\epsilon\, A_a\text{“}\lambda_\iota \,.\, \supset .\, c \,\epsilon\, A_b\text{“}\lambda_\iota$ (2)

$\vdash .\, (1) \,.\, (2) \,.\, \supset \vdash .\, \mathrm{Prop}$

***354·34.** $\vdash : \kappa \,\epsilon\, FM \,\mathrm{ap\ conx\ grp} \,.\, T \,\epsilon\, \kappa_\partial \,.\, \lambda = C\text{‘}T_\kappa \,.\, a \,\epsilon\, \mathrm{conx}\text{‘}\kappa \,.\, \supset .$
$\lambda_\iota \cap \text{Ɑ}\text{‘}A_a \subset \lambda \cup \mathrm{Cnv}\text{“}\lambda$

Dem.

$\vdash .\, *354\cdot22 \,.\quad \supset \vdash : \mathrm{Hp} \,.\, \supset .\, \lambda \,\epsilon\, FM \,\mathrm{ap\ rt\ cx} \,.$

$[*353\cdot14] \qquad \supset .\, \lambda_\iota \cap (\kappa \cup \mathrm{Cnv}\text{“}\kappa) \subset \lambda \cup \mathrm{Cnv}\text{“}\lambda$ (1)

$\vdash .\, *331\cdot11\cdot32 \,.\, \supset \vdash : \mathrm{Hp} \,.\, L \,\epsilon\, \lambda_\iota \cap \text{Ɑ}\text{‘}A_a \,.\, \supset .\, L \,\epsilon\, \kappa \cup \mathrm{Cnv}\text{“}\kappa \,.$

$[(1)] \qquad \supset .\, L \,\epsilon\, \lambda \cup \mathrm{Cnv}\text{“}\lambda : \supset \vdash .\, \mathrm{Prop}$

***354·35.** $\vdash : \kappa \,\epsilon\, FM \,\mathrm{ap\ conx} \,.\, T \,\epsilon\, \kappa_\partial \,.\, \mu = \kappa_g \,.\, \lambda = C\text{‘}T_\mu \,.\, a \,\epsilon\, \mathrm{conx}\text{‘}\kappa \,.\, \supset .$
$\lambda_\iota \cap \text{Ɑ}\text{‘}A_a \subset \lambda \cup \mathrm{Cnv}\text{“}\lambda$ [*354·34·17]

***354·4.** $\vdash : \lambda \,\epsilon\, FM \,\mathrm{grp} \,.\, a \,\epsilon\, s\text{‘}\text{Ɑ}\text{“}\lambda \,.\, \supset .\, \mathrm{cx}_a\text{‘}\lambda \,\epsilon\, FM \,.\, s\text{‘}\text{Ɑ}\text{“}\mathrm{cx}_a\text{‘}\lambda = A_a\text{“}\lambda_\iota$

Dem.

$\vdash .\, *330\cdot52 \,.\quad \supset \vdash : \mathrm{Hp} \,.\, \supset .\, \mathrm{cx}_a\text{‘}\lambda \subset 1 \to 1$ (1)

$\vdash .\, *354\cdot311 \,.\, \supset \vdash :.\, \mathrm{Hp} \,.\, \supset : R \,\epsilon\, \lambda \,.\, \supset .\, \text{Ɑ}\text{‘}R = A_a\text{“}\lambda_\iota \,.\, \mathrm{D}\text{‘}R \subset \text{Ɑ}\text{‘}R$ (2)

$\vdash .\, *354\cdot312 \,.\, \supset \vdash : \mathrm{Hp} \,.\, R, S \,\epsilon\, \lambda \,.\, \supset .\, \{R \upharpoonright (A_a\text{“}\lambda_\iota)\} \,|\, \{S \upharpoonright (A_a\text{“}\lambda_\iota)\} = (R \,|\, S) \upharpoonright (A_a\text{“}\lambda_\iota)$

$[*330\cdot5\cdot52] \qquad = (S \,|\, R) \upharpoonright (A_a\text{“}\lambda_\iota)$

$[*354\cdot312] \qquad = \{S \upharpoonright (A_a\text{“}\lambda_\iota)\} \,|\, \{R \upharpoonright (A_a\text{“}\lambda_\iota)\}$ (3)

$\vdash .\, (3) \,.\, *330\cdot5 \,.\, \supset \vdash : \mathrm{Hp} \,.\, \supset .\, \mathrm{cx}_a\text{‘}\lambda \,\epsilon\, \mathrm{Abel}$ (4)

$\vdash .\, (1) \,.\, (2) \,.\, (4) \,.\, *330\cdot52 \,.\, \supset \vdash .\, \mathrm{Prop}$

***354·401.** $\vdash : \kappa \,\epsilon\, FM \,\mathrm{ap\ conx\ grp} \,.\, a \,\epsilon\, \mathrm{conx}\text{‘}\kappa \,.\, T \,\epsilon\, \kappa_\partial \,.\, \supset .$
$\mathrm{cx}_a\text{‘}C\text{‘}T_\kappa \,\epsilon\, FM \,\mathrm{ap\ conx} \,.\, a \,\epsilon\, \mathrm{conx}\text{‘}\mathrm{cx}_a\text{‘}C\text{‘}T_\kappa$

Dem.

$\vdash .\, *354\cdot4\cdot22 \,.\quad \supset \vdash : \mathrm{Hp} \,.\, \supset .\, \mathrm{cx}_a\text{‘}C\text{‘}T_\kappa \,\epsilon\, FM$ (1)

$\vdash .\, *354\cdot34\cdot32\cdot2 \,.\, \supset \vdash : \mathrm{Hp} \,.\, \supset .\, a \,\epsilon\, \mathrm{conx}\text{‘}\mathrm{cx}_a\text{‘}C\text{‘}T_\kappa$ (2)

$\vdash .\, (1) \,.\, (2) \,.\, *333\cdot101 \,.\, \supset \vdash .\, \mathrm{Prop}$

***354·402.** $\vdash : \mathrm{Hp}\, *354\cdot401 \,.\, \supset .\, \mathrm{cx}_a\text{‘}C\text{‘}T_\kappa \,\epsilon\, FM \,\mathrm{grp}$ [*354·313·22·401]

***354·403.** $\vdash : \mathrm{Hp} *354\cdot401 . \supset . \mathrm{cx}_a`C`T_\kappa \in FM \text{ rt}$

Dem.

$\vdash . *353\cdot12 . *354\cdot2 . \supset$

$\vdash : \mathrm{Hp} . S \in C`T_\kappa . \lambda = C`T_\kappa . \supset . (\exists\mu, \nu) . \mu, \nu \in \mathrm{NC\,ind} . \nu \neq 0 . S^\nu = T^\mu .$

[*354·312.Induct] $\supset . (\exists\mu, \nu) . \mu, \nu \in \mathrm{NC\,ind} . \nu \neq 0 .$

$\{S \upharpoonright (A_a``\lambda_\iota)\}^\nu = S^\nu \upharpoonright (A_a``\lambda_\iota) = T^\mu \upharpoonright (A_a``\lambda_\iota) = \{T \upharpoonright (A_a``\lambda_\iota)\}^\mu .$

[*350·43.*354·401]

$\supset . (\exists\mu, \nu) . \mu, \nu \in \mathrm{NC\,ind} . \nu \neq 0 . \{S \upharpoonright (A_a``\lambda_\iota)\} (\mu/\nu) \{T \upharpoonright (A_a``\lambda_\iota)\}$ (1)

$\vdash . (1) . *353\cdot1 . \supset \vdash . \mathrm{Prop}$

***354·404.** $\vdash : \kappa \in FM \text{ ap conx grp} . a \in \mathrm{conx}`\kappa . T \in \kappa_\partial . \supset .$

$\mathrm{cx}_a`C`T_\kappa \in FM \text{ ap conx rt grp trs asym}$ [*354·401·402·403 . *353·27]

***354·41.** $\vdash : \kappa \in FM \text{ ap conx} . T \in \kappa_\partial . a \in \mathrm{conx}`\kappa . \lambda = \kappa_g . \supset .$

$\mathrm{cx}_a`C`T_\lambda \in FM \text{ ap conx rt trs asym}$ [*354·17·404]

*356. MEASUREMENT BY REAL NUMBERS.

Summary of *356.

In this number we consider the application of real numbers to the measurement of vectors in a family. The principle of this application is as follows: If a given set of vectors, all of which are rational multiples of a given vector R, have a limit with respect to U_κ, and if their measures determine a segment of H, then we take the real number represented by this segment as the measure of the limit of the given set of vectors. For the sake of homogeneity with rational measures, it is well to take our real numbers in the relational form given in *314; *i.e.* if $\xi \epsilon C\text{'}\Theta$, we take $\dot{s}\text{'}\xi$ as the corresponding real number. With a suitable hypothesis, the result of the above principle for applying real numbers is, where rational multiples of the unit R are concerned, to replace the ratio X by the rational real number $\dot{s}\text{'}\overrightarrow{H}\text{'}X$, as the measure of the vector $X \upharpoonright \kappa\text{'}R$ (cf. *356·63). Then the measure of the limit of a set of rational vectors will be, by our principle, the limit of their measures. Thus our principle is conformable to what is required for an application of real numbers.

It should be observed that, if any application of irrationals is to be possible, it is necessary that the vectors of the family concerned should have a serial or quasi-serial order, independently of the order generated by their measures. The order generated, among rational multiples of T, by the ratios which are measures of these multiples, is T_κ (cf. *352). A vector which is not a member of $C\text{'}T_\kappa$ cannot be the limit of any set of vectors with respect to T_κ. But we saw (*352·72) that if κ is a serial family,

$$T_\kappa = \breve{U}_\kappa \upharpoonright C\text{'}T_\kappa.$$

Hence when κ is a serial family, a vector which is not a member of $C\text{'}T_\kappa$ may be the limit of a set of members of $C\text{'}T_\kappa$ with respect to U_κ. It is the existence of an independent series U_κ, not generated by measurement, which makes the application of irrationals as measures possible.

The following phraseology may be found convenient. Taking a unit T in a family κ, and an origin a in its field, if $X \epsilon C\text{'}H'$ and $S = X \upharpoonright \kappa\text{'}T$ and $x = S\text{'}a = (X \upharpoonright \kappa\text{'}T)\text{'}a$, we call X the "rational measure" of S and the "rational coordinate" of x. We have, in the same circumstances,

$$S = \kappa \upharpoonright A_T\text{'}X \,.\, x = A_a\text{'}S = A_a\text{'}\kappa \upharpoonright A_T\text{'}X.$$

We will call S the vector of X, and x the point of X; and the same phraseology will be employed for the vectors and points obtained by measures which are real numbers. We may now state the principle according to which we apply real numbers as measures as follows. Given a segment ξ of H, take all the vectors of ξ's: these form the class $\kappa \cap A_T``\xi$. Then the real number $\dot{s}`\xi$ is to be the measure of the limit (with respect to $U_\kappa$) of the class $\kappa \cap A_T``\xi$. Since U_κ has the opposite sense to that of T_κ, *i.e.* U_κ proceeds from the vectors with bigger measures to those with smaller ones, the limit we shall have to take will be the *lower* limit with respect to U_κ. Thus the vector whose measure is $\dot{s}`\xi$ will be

$$\text{prec}(U_\kappa)`(\kappa \cap A_T``\xi).$$

Now if we put $X = \dot{s}`\xi$, $A_T``\xi = \overrightarrow{X}`T$, and $X$ is a relational real number. Hence using *206·131, the vector whose measure is $X$ is $\text{prec}(U_\kappa)`\overrightarrow{X}`T$. Hence if "$X_\kappa`T$" represents the vector whose measure is X (unit T), we put

***356·01.** $X_\kappa = \text{prec}(U_\kappa) \,|\, \overrightarrow{X} \upharpoonright \kappa$ Df

Assuming now that κ is a serial submultipliable family, in which we take R as the unit and a as the origin, and putting, for notational convenience,

$$\breve{P} = U_\kappa \,.\, \breve{Q} = \dot{s}`\kappa_\partial,$$

we have first a set of preliminary propositions (*356·1—·191), of which the most important are

$$H' = (C`H') \rceil \breve{A}_R ; P = (C`H') \rceil \breve{A}_R ; \breve{A}_a ; Q \quad (*356·13),$$

$$P \upharpoonright C`R_\kappa = \kappa \rceil A_R ; H' \quad (*356·14),$$

giving the relations between the series of ratios, the series of their vectors, and the series of their points.

We proceed next (*356·2—·26) to the proof that $X_\kappa \upharpoonright \kappa \in 1 \to 1$. This requires, in addition to our previous hypothesis, that Q should be semi-Dedekindian. With this hypothesis, we first prove that if X, Y are relational real numbers,

$$\text{ᗡ}`X_\kappa = \text{ᗡ}`Y_\kappa = \kappa_\partial : X_\kappa = Y_\kappa \,.\equiv.\, X = Y \quad (*356·21).$$

We then prove, by the help of some arithmetical lemmas, that the lower limit of the submultiples of a given vector is the zero vector, *i.e.*

$$\text{tl}_P`\hat{S}\{S \in \kappa : (\exists \nu) \,.\, R = S^\nu\} = I \upharpoonright C`Q \quad (*356·22).$$

Hence we easily prove that, if R is any non-zero vector, and λ is a class of vectors having a lower limit L, the lower limit of the relative products of R and members of λ is the relative product of R and L, *i.e.*

$$\lambda \subset \kappa \,.\, L = \text{tl}_P`\lambda \,.\, R \in \kappa_\partial \,.\supset.\, R \,|\, L = \text{tl}_P`R \,|``\lambda \quad (*356·221).$$

Remembering that the relative product is represented arithmetically by the sum, we may express the above proposition by saying that the limit of the sums of a given vector and a set of vectors is the sum of the given vector and the limit of the set. From this proposition we easily deduce that if RPS, $X_\kappa{}^\backprime R \neq X_\kappa{}^\backprime S$, whence it follows that

$$X_\kappa \upharpoonright \kappa \in 1 \rightarrow 1 \quad (*356\cdot26).$$

Our next set of propositions ($*356\cdot3$—$\cdot33$) is concerned in connecting the relative product of X_κ and Y_κ with the arithmetical product $X \times_r Y$, where "$\times_r$" has the meaning defined in $*314$. Here we only require that κ should be serial and submultipliable, and we obtain

$$X_\kappa \mid Y_\kappa = (X \times_r Y)_\kappa \quad (*356\cdot33).$$

This proposition is the analogue of $*351\cdot31$ (except that κ_ι is replaced by κ); it has a similar importance, and calls for similar remarks.

Our next set of propositions ($*356\cdot4$—$\cdot43$) is concerned in proving that the limit of the points of a segment of ratios is the point of their limit, in other words, that the limit of a set of points whose coordinates are a segment of rationals is the point whose coordinate is the limit of the segment. Here we again require that our family should be semi-Dedekindian; then if ξ is a segment of ratios, and $X = \dot{s}{}^\backprime \xi$, the above proposition is

$$(X_\kappa{}^\backprime R)^\backprime a = \mathrm{seq}_Q{}^\backprime A_a{}^{\backprime\backprime} A_R{}^{\backprime\backprime} \xi = \mathrm{seq}_Q{}^\backprime A_a{}^{\backprime\backprime} \overrightarrow{X}{}^\backprime R \quad (*356\cdot43).$$

Here $X_\kappa{}^\backprime R$ is the vector of X, $(X_\kappa{}^\backprime R)^\backprime a$ is the point of X; $A_R{}^{\backprime\backprime}\xi = \overrightarrow{X}{}^\backprime R$, and each is the class of vectors of members of ξ; and $A_a{}^{\backprime\backprime} A_R{}^{\backprime\backprime}\xi$ or $A_a{}^{\backprime\backprime}\overrightarrow{X}{}^\backprime R$ is the class of points of members of ξ. Moreover X is a relational real number. Thus the above proposition states that the point of X is the segment (*i.e.* the limit) of the points of the ratios contained in X; *i.e.* of the ratios which may be considered less than X.

We next proceed ($*356\cdot5$—$\cdot54$) to connect the relative multiplication of vectors with the addition of their measures. Here we require that κ should be semi-Dedekindian as well as serial and submultipliable. We then find that if X, Y are relational real numbers, and R is a non-zero vector,

$$(X_\kappa{}^\backprime R) \mid (Y_\kappa{}^\backprime R) = (X +_r Y)_\kappa{}^\backprime R \quad (*356\cdot54).$$

This proposition is the analogue of $*351\cdot43$, and calls for similar remarks. The proof proceeds without much difficulty by means of $*356\cdot43$.

Finally we have a set of propositions ($*356\cdot6$—$\cdot63$) to prove that the real number which measures a rational vector is the real number corresponding to the ratio which is its measure; *i.e.* if X is a ratio, the vector which has the ratio X to the unit has the real number $\dot{s}{}^\backprime \overrightarrow{H}{}^\backprime X$ for its measure. It is to be remembered that rational real numbers must not be identified with ratios, any more than integral ratios (*i.e.* ratios of the form $\nu/1$) must be identified with cardinals. The real number corresponding to a ratio X is $\dot{s}`\overrightarrow{H}`X$; this is what we call a "rational real number." In measurement, when we are measuring by ratios, if R is our unit, X will be the measure of $X \upharpoonright \kappa`R$; but when we are measuring by real numbers, the measure of $X \upharpoonright \kappa`R$ must be a real number. The real number which is the measure of $X \upharpoonright \kappa`R$ will, by our definition, be a real number Z such that

$$X \upharpoonright \kappa`R = \text{prec}\,(U_\kappa)`\overrightarrow{Z}`R.$$

Thus we have to prove that, if X is a ratio, the above equation is satisfied if we put $Z = \dot{s}`\overrightarrow{H}`X$. This requires that κ should be serial, submultipliable and semi-Dedekindian; we then have

$$X \in C`H \,.\supset .\, (\dot{s}`\overrightarrow{H}`X)_\kappa = X \upharpoonright \kappa \quad (*356\cdot63).$$

Thus although the "pure" real number $\dot{s}`\overrightarrow{H}`X$ is not identical with the "pure" ratio X, yet the "applied" real number $(\dot{s}`\overrightarrow{H}`X)_\kappa$ *is* identical with the "applied" ratio $X \upharpoonright \kappa$. This fact explains why the results of the habitual confusion between a ratio and a rational real number have not been even more disastrous.

***356·01.** $X_\kappa = \text{prec}\,(U_\kappa) \,|\, \overrightarrow{X} \upharpoonright \kappa$ Df

***356·1.** $\vdash :. R \in \kappa \,.\supset : S = X_\kappa`R \,.\equiv .\, S = \text{prec}\,(U_\kappa)`\overrightarrow{X}`R$ [(*356·01)]

***356·11.** $\vdash :. R \in \kappa \,.\supset : S = (\dot{s}`\xi)_\kappa`R \,.\equiv .\, S = \text{prec}\,(U_\kappa)`A_R``\xi$
[*356·1 . *336·12]

***356·12.** $\vdash :. \kappa \in FM\,\text{sr subm}\,.$
$X, Y \in C`H' \,.\, R \in \kappa_\partial \,.\, a \in s`\text{Cl}``\kappa \,.\, \breve{Q} = \dot{s}`\kappa_\partial \,.\, \breve{P} = U_\kappa \,.\supset :$
$XH'Y \,.\equiv .\, (X \upharpoonright \kappa`R)\, P\, (Y \upharpoonright \kappa`R) \,.\equiv .\, \{(X \upharpoonright \kappa`R)`a\}\, Q\, \{(Y \upharpoonright \kappa`R)`a\}$
[*352·73 . *336·4]

***356·13.** $\vdash : \kappa \in FM\,\text{sr subm}\,.\, R \in \kappa_\partial \,.\, a \in s`\text{Cl}``\kappa \,.\, \breve{Q} = \dot{s}`\kappa_\partial \,.\, \breve{P} = U_\kappa \,.\supset .$
$H' = (C`H') \upharpoonright \breve{A}_R ; P = (C`H') \upharpoonright \breve{A}_R ; \breve{A}_a ; Q$ [*356·12]

***356·14.** $\vdash : \text{Hp}\,*356\cdot13 \,.\supset .\, P \upharpoonright C`R_\kappa = \kappa \upharpoonright A_R ; H'$ [*352·72]

***356·15.** $\vdash : \text{Hp}\,*356\cdot13 \,.\, \lambda \subset C`H \,.\, X = \dot{s}`\lambda \,.\supset .\, \text{max}_P`\overrightarrow{X}`R = \kappa \upharpoonright A_R``\text{max}_H`\lambda$

Dem.

$\vdash .\, *352\cdot41 \,.\quad \supset \vdash : \text{Hp} \,.\supset .\, \kappa \cap \overrightarrow{X}`R \subset C`R_\kappa \,.\, \overrightarrow{X}`R = A_R``\lambda$ (1)

$\vdash .\, (1) \,.\, *356\cdot14 \,.\supset \vdash : \text{Hp} \,.\supset .\, \text{max}_P`\overrightarrow{X}`R = \text{max}\,(P \upharpoonright C`R_\kappa)`\overrightarrow{X}`R$

[*356·14] $= \kappa \upharpoonright A_R``\text{max}_H`\lambda : \supset \vdash .\, \text{Prop}$

***356·16.** $\vdash : \text{Hp} *356\cdot13 . \lambda \in C`\Theta . X = \dot{s}`\lambda . \supset . \max_P`\overrightarrow{X}`R = \Lambda$ [*356·15]

***356·17.** $\vdash : \text{Hp} *356\cdot16 . \supset . X_\kappa = \text{lt}_P \mid \overrightarrow{X} \upharpoonright C`P$ [*356·16]

***356·18.** $\vdash : \kappa \in FM \text{ connex} . \supset . X_\kappa \in 1 \rightarrow \text{Cls}$
[*206·161 . *336·62 . (*353·01)]

***356·19.** $\vdash :. \kappa \in FM \text{ sr} . P = \breve{U}_\kappa . \supset : Z \in C`H . \supset . Z \upharpoonright \kappa ; P \subseteq P$

Dem.

$\vdash . *336\cdot511 . \supset \vdash :. \text{Hp} . R, S \in \kappa . \mu, \nu \in \text{NC ind} - \iota`0 . Z = \mu/\nu . \supset :$
$RPS . \equiv . R^\mu P S^\mu .$
[*350·43] $\supset : RPS . M = (\mu/\nu) \upharpoonright \kappa`R . N = (\mu/\nu) \upharpoonright \kappa`S . \supset . M^\nu P N^\nu .$
[*336·511] $\supset . MPN :. \supset \vdash . \text{Prop}$

***356·191.** $\vdash : \text{Hp} *356\cdot19 . X \in \dot{s}``C`\Theta . \supset . X \upharpoonright \kappa \mid P \subseteq P \mid X \upharpoonright \kappa$

Dem.

$\vdash . *356\cdot19 . \supset$
$\vdash :. \text{Hp} . \supset : \lambda \in C`\Theta . X = \dot{s}`\lambda . Z \in \lambda . \supset . Z \upharpoonright \kappa \mid P \subseteq P \mid Z \upharpoonright \kappa :. \supset \vdash . \text{Prop}$

***356·2.** $\vdash : \text{Hp} *356\cdot16 . \mu \in C`\Theta . L \in \lambda - \mu . \supset . \kappa \urcorner A_R`L \in p`\overleftarrow{P}``A_R``\mu$

Dem.

$\vdash . *310\cdot11 . \supset \vdash : \text{Hp} . \supset . L \in p`\overleftarrow{H}``\mu .$
[*206·6.*352·12] $\supset . \kappa \urcorner A_R`L \in p`\overleftarrow{\kappa \urcorner A_R ; H}``A_R``\mu .$
[*356·14] $\supset . \kappa \urcorner A_R`L \in p`\overleftarrow{P}``A_R``\mu : \supset \vdash . \text{Prop}$

***356·21.** $\vdash :. \kappa \in FM \text{ sr subm} . \text{Cnv}`\dot{s}`\kappa_\partial \in \text{semi Ded} . X, Y \in \dot{s}``C`\Theta . \supset :$
$\text{D}`X_\kappa = \text{D}`Y_\kappa = \kappa_\partial : X_\kappa = Y_\kappa . \equiv . X = Y$

Dem.

$\vdash . *356\cdot16 . *214\cdot7 . \supset$
$\vdash : \text{Hp} . \lambda, \mu \in C`\Theta . X = \dot{s}`\lambda . Y = \dot{s}`\mu . R \in \kappa_\partial . \supset . \text{E}! X_\kappa`R . \text{E}! Y_\kappa`R$ (1)
$\vdash . (1) . *356\cdot2 . \supset \vdash : \text{Hp}(1) . P = \breve{U}_\kappa . \exists ! \lambda - \mu . \supset . (Y_\kappa`R) P (X_\kappa`R)$ (2)
Similarly $\vdash : \text{Hp}(1) . P = \breve{U}_\kappa . \exists ! \mu - \lambda . \supset . (X_\kappa`R) P (Y_\kappa`R)$ (3)
$\vdash . (1) . (2) . (3) . \supset \vdash : \text{Hp}(1) . X_\kappa`R = Y_\kappa`R . \supset . \lambda = \mu .$
[Hp] $\supset . X = Y$ (4)
$\vdash . (1) . (4) . \supset \vdash . \text{Prop}$

***356·211.** $\vdash : \sigma, \tau \in \text{NC ind} - \iota`0 . \nu \in \text{NC ind} - \iota`0 - \iota`1 . \supset .$
$(\sigma +_c \tau)^\nu > \sigma^\nu +_c (\nu \times_c \sigma^{\nu -_c 1} \times_c \tau)$

Dem.

$\vdash . *113\cdot43\cdot66 . *116\cdot34 . \supset \vdash . (\sigma \times_c \tau)^2 = \sigma^2 +_c (2 \times_c \sigma \times_c \tau) +_c \tau^2$ (1)
$\vdash . *126\cdot5 . \supset \vdash :. \text{Hp} . \supset : (\sigma +_c \tau)^\nu > \sigma^\nu +_c (\nu \times_c \sigma^{\nu -_c 1} \times_c \tau) . \supset .$
$(\sigma +_c \tau)^{\nu +_c 1} > \sigma^{\nu +_c 1} +_c (\nu \times_c \sigma^\nu \times_c \tau) +_c (\sigma^\nu \times_c \tau)$ (2)
$\vdash . (1) . (2) . \text{Induct} . \supset \vdash . \text{Prop}$

***356·212.** $\vdash : \rho > \sigma . \rho, \sigma, \zeta \in \text{NC ind} . \supset . (\exists \nu) . \nu \in \text{NC ind} . \rho^\nu > \sigma^\nu \times_c \zeta$

Dem.

$\vdash . *356{\cdot}211 . \supset$

$\vdash : \text{Hp} . \nu \in \text{NC ind} . \rho = \sigma +_c \tau . \supset . \rho^\nu > \sigma^{\nu -_c 1} \times_c \{\sigma +_c (\nu \times_c \tau)\}$ (1)

$\vdash . (1) . *126{\cdot}51 . \supset \vdash : \text{Hp}(1) . \sigma +_c (\nu \times_c \tau) > \sigma \times_c \zeta . \supset . \rho^\nu > \sigma^\nu \times_c \zeta$ (2)

$\vdash . (2) . *113{\cdot}43 . *120{\cdot}416 . *126{\cdot}5 . \supset$

$\vdash : \text{Hp}(1) . \nu \times_c \tau > \sigma \times_c (\zeta -_c 1) . \supset . \rho^\nu > \sigma^\nu \times_c \zeta : \supset \vdash . \text{Prop}$

***356·213.** $\vdash : \rho > \sigma . \rho, \sigma, \xi, \eta \in \text{NC ind} . \eta \neq 0 . \supset .$

$(\exists \nu) . \nu \in \text{NC ind} . \rho^\nu \times_c \eta > \sigma^\nu \times_c \xi$

Dem.

$\vdash . *356{\cdot}212 . \supset \vdash : \text{Hp} . \supset . (\exists \nu) . \nu \in \text{NC ind} . \rho^\nu > \sigma^\nu \times_c \xi : \supset \vdash . \text{Prop}$

***356·214.** $\vdash : \rho, \sigma \in \text{NC ind} - \iota`0 . \rho > \sigma . X \in C`H . \supset .$

$(\exists \nu) . \nu \in \text{NC ind} . (\rho/\sigma)^\nu \breve{H} X$ [*356·213]

***356·215.** $\vdash : \lambda \in C`\Theta . \rho, \sigma \in \text{NC ind} - \iota`0 . \rho > \sigma . \supset .$

$(\exists X) . X \in \lambda . X \times_s \rho/\sigma \sim\in \lambda$

Dem.

$\vdash . *305{\cdot}142 . \text{Induct} . \supset \vdash :. \lambda \subset C`H . \exists ! \lambda . \nu \in \text{NC ind} - \iota`0 :$

$X \in \lambda . \supset_X . X \times_s \rho/\sigma \in \lambda : \supset : X \in \lambda . \supset_X . X \times_s \rho^\nu/\sigma^\nu \in \lambda :$

[*356·214] $\supset : H``\lambda = C`H$ (1)

$\vdash . (1) . \text{Transp} . \supset \vdash . \text{Prop}$

***356·22.** $\vdash : \text{Hp } *356{\cdot}13 . Q \in \text{semi Ded} . \supset .$

$\text{tl}_P`\hat{S} \{S \in \kappa : (\exists \nu) . R = S^\nu\} = I \upharpoonright C`Q$

Dem.

$\vdash . *336{\cdot}511 . \supset \vdash :. \text{Hp} . L = \text{tl}_P`\hat{S} \{(\exists \nu) . R = S^\nu\} . \mu, \nu \in \text{NC ind} - \iota`0 . \supset :$

$S \in \kappa . S^{\mu \times_c \nu} = R . \supset . L^\nu P S^\nu :$

[*301·5] $\supset : T \in \kappa . T^\mu = R . \supset . L^\nu P T :$

[Hp] $\supset : L^\nu P_* L$ (1)

$\vdash . *337{\cdot}21 . \supset \vdash : \text{Hp} . \nu \in \text{NC ind} - \iota`0 - \iota`1 . L \in \kappa_\partial . \supset . L P L^\nu$ (2)

$\vdash . (1) . (2) . \supset \vdash : \text{Hp} . \supset . L \sim\in \kappa_\partial : \supset \vdash . \text{Prop}$

***356·221.** $\vdash : \text{Hp } *356{\cdot}19 . \breve{Q} = \dot{s}`\kappa_\partial . \lambda \subset \kappa . L = \text{tl}_P`\lambda . R \in \kappa_\partial . \supset .$

$R | L = \text{tl}_P`R | ``\lambda$

Dem.

$\vdash . *334{\cdot}15 . *336{\cdot}411 . \supset \vdash :. \text{Hp} . \supset : LPM . \supset . (R | L) P (R | M) :$

[Hp] $\supset : M \in \lambda . \supset . (R | L) P (R | M) :$

[*37·61] $\supset : R | ``\lambda \subset \overleftarrow{P}`(R | L)$ (1)

$\vdash . *336 \cdot 41 . \supset \vdash : \text{Hp} . (R \mid L) PM . \supset . (\exists N) . N \in \kappa_\partial . M = R \mid L \mid N .$

[*330·31] $\supset . (\exists N) . N \in \kappa_\partial . \breve{R} \mid M = L \mid N .$

[*336·41.*334·13] $\supset . LP(\breve{R} \mid M) . \breve{R} \mid \dot{M} \in \kappa_\partial .$ (2)

[Hp] $\supset . (\exists N) . N \in \lambda . NP(\breve{R} \mid M) .$

[*336·411.(2)] $\supset . (\exists N) . N \in \lambda . (R \mid N) PM .$

[*37·1] $\supset . M \in \breve{P}``R \mid ``\lambda$ (3)

$\vdash . (1) . (3) . *207 \cdot 21 . \supset \vdash .$ Prop

***356·23.** $\vdash : \text{Hp} *356 \cdot 22 . RPS . \supset . (\exists \nu) . \nu \in \text{NC ind} - \iota`0 . [\{(\nu +_c 1)/\nu\} \upharpoonright \kappa`R] PS$

Dem.

$\vdash . *356 \cdot 22 \cdot 221 . \supset \vdash : \text{Hp} . \lambda = \hat{T} \{T \in \kappa : (\exists \nu) . R = T^\nu\} . \supset . \text{tl}_P`R \mid ``\lambda = R .$

[Hp] $\supset . (\exists T) . T \in \lambda . (R \mid T) PS .$

[Hp] $\supset . (\exists \nu) . \nu \in \text{NC ind} - \iota`0 . \{R \mid (1/\nu) \upharpoonright \kappa`R\} PS .$

[*350·62.*334·32] $\supset . (\exists \nu) . \nu \in \text{NC ind} - \iota`0 . [\{(\nu +_c 1)/\nu\} \upharpoonright \kappa`R] PS : \supset \vdash .$ Prop

***356·231.** $\vdash : \text{Hp} *356 \cdot 23 . \supset . (\exists \nu) . \nu \in \text{NC ind} - \iota`0 . SP[\{(\nu -_c 1)/\nu\} \upharpoonright \kappa`R]$

[Proof as in *356·23]

***356·24.** $\vdash : \text{Hp} *356 \cdot 23 . X \in \dot{s}``C`\Theta . \supset . X_\kappa`R \neq X_\kappa`S$

Dem.

$\vdash . *356 \cdot 23 . \supset \vdash : \text{Hp} . \lambda \in C`\Theta . X = \dot{s}`\lambda . \supset .$

$(\exists \rho, \sigma) . \rho, \sigma \in \text{NC ind} - \iota`0 . \rho > \sigma . \{(\rho/\sigma) \upharpoonright \kappa`R\} PS .$

[*356·215] $\supset . (\exists \rho, \sigma, Y) . \rho, \sigma \in \text{NC induct} - \iota`0 . \rho > \sigma . Y \in \lambda . Y \times_s \rho/\sigma \sim \in \lambda .$

$\{(\rho/\sigma) \upharpoonright \kappa`R\} PS .$

[*336·511] $\supset . (\exists \rho, \sigma, Y) . \rho, \sigma \in \text{NC ind} - \iota`0 . \rho > \sigma . Y \in \lambda . Y \times_s \rho/\sigma \in p`\overleftarrow{H}``\lambda .$

$\{Y \upharpoonright \kappa`(\rho/\sigma) \upharpoonright \kappa`R\} P \{Y \upharpoonright \kappa`S\} .$

[*351·31.*356·13] $\supset . (\exists \rho, \sigma, Y) . Y \upharpoonright \kappa`(\rho/\sigma) \upharpoonright \kappa`R . \in p`\overleftarrow{P}``\overrightarrow{X}`R \cap P``\overrightarrow{X}`S .$

[*356·1] $\supset . X_\kappa`R \neq Y_\kappa`R : \supset \vdash .$ Prop

***356·25.** $\vdash : \text{Hp} *356 \cdot 22 . X \in \dot{s}``C`\Theta . \supset . X_\kappa`R \in \breve{Q}$

Dem.

$\vdash . *356 \cdot 1 \cdot 21 . \supset \vdash : \text{Hp} . \supset . X_\kappa`R \in \kappa_\partial$ (1)

$\vdash . (1) . *41 \cdot 13 . \supset \vdash .$ Prop

***356·26.** $\vdash : \text{Hp} *356 \cdot 25 . \supset . X_\kappa \upharpoonright \kappa \in 1 \to 1$

Dem.

$\vdash . *356 \cdot 24 . \text{Transp} . \supset \vdash : \text{Hp} . R, S \in \kappa_\partial . X_\kappa`R = X_\kappa`S . \supset . R = S$ (1)

$\vdash . (1) . *356 \cdot 18 \cdot 21 . \supset \vdash .$ Prop

***356·3.** $\vdash :. \kappa \epsilon FM \text{ ap conx subm} . s'\text{Pot}``\kappa \subset \kappa . \mu, \nu \epsilon C'\Theta . R, S \epsilon \kappa . \supset :$

$$R (\dot{s}'\mu \times_r \dot{s}'\nu) S . \equiv . R \{(\dot{s}'\mu) \upharpoonright \kappa \mid (\dot{s}'\nu)\} S$$

Dem.

$\vdash . *314\cdot14 . *313\cdot21 . \supset \vdash : \text{Hp} . \supset . \dot{s}'\mu \times_r \dot{s}'\nu = \dot{s}'\dot{s}'\mu \underset{,,}{\times_s} ``\nu$ (1)

$\vdash . (1) . \supset \vdash :. \text{Hp} . \supset : R (\dot{s}'\mu \times_r \dot{s}'\nu) S . \equiv . (\exists M, N) . M \epsilon \mu . N \epsilon \nu . R (M \times_s N) S .$

$[*351\cdot31\cdot22] \equiv . (\exists M, N) . M \epsilon \mu . N \epsilon \nu . R (M \upharpoonright \kappa \mid N) S :. \supset \vdash . \text{Prop}$

***356·31.** $\vdash : \kappa \epsilon FM \text{ ap conx subm} . s'\text{Pot}``\kappa \subset \kappa . X, Y \epsilon \dot{s}``C'\Theta . \supset .$

$$(X \times_r Y) \lceil \kappa = (X \lceil \kappa) \mid (Y \lceil \kappa) \quad [*356\cdot3]$$

***356·32.** $\vdash : \kappa \epsilon FM \text{ sr subm} . X, Y \epsilon \dot{s}``C'\Theta . R \epsilon \kappa_\partial . \supset . X_\kappa{}'Y_\kappa{}'R = (X \mid Y)_\kappa{}'R$

Dem.

$\vdash . *356\cdot191 . \supset \vdash :. \text{Hp} . \supset : S \epsilon \kappa \cap \overrightarrow{Y}'R . \supset . \kappa \cap \overrightarrow{X}'S \subset P``\overrightarrow{X}'Y_\kappa{}'R :$

$[*37\cdot63] \quad \supset : X``(\kappa \cap \overrightarrow{Y}'R) \subset P``\overrightarrow{X}'Y_\kappa{}'R$ (1)

$\vdash . *305\cdot6 . \quad \supset \vdash : \text{Hp} . \lambda \epsilon C'\Theta . X = \dot{s}'\lambda . Z, Z' \epsilon \lambda . ZHZ' . \supset .$

$$Z \lceil \kappa' Y_\kappa{}'R = Z' \lceil \kappa'(Z \mid \breve{Z}') \lceil \kappa' Y_\kappa{}'R .$$

$[*356\cdot12] \quad \supset . Z \lceil \kappa' Y_\kappa{}'R \epsilon Z' \lceil \kappa``\overrightarrow{P}'Y_\kappa{}'R .$

$[*356\cdot17] \quad \supset . Z \lceil \kappa' Y_\kappa{}'R \epsilon Z' \lceil \kappa``P``\overrightarrow{Y}'R .$

$[*356\cdot19] \quad \supset . Z \lceil \kappa' Y_\kappa{}'R \epsilon P``Z' \lceil \kappa``\overrightarrow{Y}'R .$

$[\text{Hp}] \quad \supset . Z \lceil \kappa' Y_\kappa{}'R \epsilon P``X``\overrightarrow{Y}'R$ (2)

$\vdash . (1) . (2) . \quad \supset \vdash : \text{Hp} . \supset . P``X``\overrightarrow{Y}'R = P``\overrightarrow{X}'Y_\kappa{}'R .$

$[*356\cdot1] \quad \supset . (X \mid Y)_\kappa{}'R = X_\kappa{}'Y_\kappa{}'R : \supset \vdash . \text{Prop}$

***356·33.** $\vdash : \text{Hp} *356\cdot32 . \supset . X_\kappa \mid Y_\kappa = (X \times_r Y)_\kappa \quad [*356\cdot31\cdot32]$

***356·4.** $\vdash : \kappa \epsilon FM \text{ conx} . Q = \text{Cnv}'\dot{s}'\kappa_\partial . S \epsilon \kappa . \alpha \subset C'Q . \exists ! \alpha . \text{E} ! \text{seq}_Q{}'\alpha . \supset .$

$$S'\text{seq}_Q{}'\alpha = \text{seq}_Q{}'S``\alpha$$

Dem.

$\vdash . *330\cdot563 . \supset \vdash : \text{Hp} . \supset . S'\text{seq}_Q{}'\alpha \epsilon p'\overleftarrow{Q}``S``\alpha$ (1)

$\vdash . *37\cdot1 . \quad \supset \vdash :: \text{Hp} . \supset :. S'z \epsilon \breve{Q}``p'\overleftarrow{Q}``S``\alpha . \equiv :$

$$(\exists y) : x \epsilon \alpha . \supset_x . S'xQy : yQS'z :$$

$[*330\cdot542] \quad \equiv : (\exists w) : x \epsilon \alpha . \supset_x . S'x \, Q \, S'w : S'w \, Q \, S'z :$

$[*208\cdot2] \quad \equiv : (\exists w) : x \epsilon \alpha . \supset_x . xQw : wQz :$

$[*37\cdot1] \quad \equiv : z \epsilon \breve{Q}``p'\overleftarrow{Q}``\alpha$ (2)

$\vdash . (2) . \text{Transp} . \supset \vdash :. \text{Hp} . \supset : z \sim \epsilon \breve{Q}``p'\overleftarrow{Q}``\alpha . \equiv . S'z \sim \epsilon \breve{Q}``p'\overleftarrow{Q}``S``\alpha$ (3)

$\vdash . (1) . (3) . *330\cdot542 . \supset \vdash . \text{Prop}$

∗356·41. $\vdash :. \kappa \epsilon FM \text{ conx trs} . \breve{P} = U_\kappa . \breve{Q} = \dot{s}`\kappa_{\partial} . a \epsilon C`Q . \lambda \subset \kappa . \exists ! \lambda . \supset :$

$N = \text{seq}_P`\lambda . \equiv . N \epsilon \kappa . \text{seq}_Q`A_a``\lambda = N`a$

Dem.

$\vdash . ∗336·43·2 . ∗206·61 . \supset$

$\vdash :. \text{Hp} . \supset : N = \text{seq}_P`\lambda . \equiv . N \epsilon \kappa . A_a`N = \text{seq}\,(Q \upharpoonright A_a``\kappa)`A_a``\lambda$ (1)

$\vdash . ∗206·211 . \supset \vdash : \text{Hp} . b = \text{seq}_Q`A_a``\lambda . \supset . (\exists R) . R \epsilon \lambda . R`aQb .$

[Hp] $\supset . (\exists S) . S \epsilon \kappa . bSa .$

[∗336·11] $\supset . b \epsilon A_a``\kappa$ (2)

$\vdash . (1) . (2) . \supset \vdash :. \text{Hp} . \supset : N = \text{seq}_P`\lambda . \equiv . N \epsilon \kappa . A_a`N = \text{seq}_Q`A_a``\lambda$ (3)

$\vdash . (3) . ∗336·11 . \supset \vdash . \text{Prop}$

∗356·42. $\vdash : \text{Hp} ∗356·41 . E ! \text{seq}_P`\lambda . \supset . (\text{seq}_P`\lambda)`a = \text{seq}_Q`A_a``\lambda$ [∗356·41]

∗356·43. $\vdash : \text{Hp} ∗356·22 . \xi \epsilon C`\Theta . X = \dot{s}`\xi . a \epsilon C`Q . \supset .$

$(X_\kappa`R)`a = \text{seq}_Q`A_a``A_R``\xi = \text{seq}_Q`A_a``\overrightarrow{X}`R$

[∗356·42·11·21 . ∗336·12]

∗356·5. $\vdash : \text{Hp} ∗356·22 .$

$X, Y \epsilon \dot{s}``C`\Theta . a \epsilon C`Q . R \epsilon \kappa . \lambda = \kappa \cap \overrightarrow{X}`R . \mu = \kappa \cap \overrightarrow{Y}`R . \supset .$

$(X_\kappa`R)`(Y_\kappa`R)`a = \text{seq}_Q`\overrightarrow{\dot{s}`\lambda}`\text{seq}_Q`\overrightarrow{\dot{s}`\mu}`a$

Dem.

$\vdash . ∗356·43 . ∗336·12 . \supset \vdash : \text{Hp} . \supset . (X_\kappa`R)`(Y_\kappa`R)`a = \text{seq}_Q`\overrightarrow{\dot{s}`\lambda}`(Y_\kappa`R)`a$

[∗356·43.∗336·12] $= \text{seq}_Q`\overrightarrow{\dot{s}`\lambda}`\text{seq}_Q`\overrightarrow{\dot{s}`\mu}`a : \supset \vdash . \text{Prop}$

∗356·51. $\vdash : \text{Hp} ∗356·5 . \supset . (X +_r Y)_\kappa`R = \text{seq}_P`s`\lambda \,|_{,,}\, ``\mu$

Dem.

$\vdash . ∗356·11 . ∗314·13 . \supset \vdash : \text{Hp} . \xi, \eta \epsilon C`\Theta . X = \dot{s}`\xi . Y = \dot{s}`\eta . \supset .$

$(X +_r Y)_\kappa`R = \text{seq}_P`A_R``(\xi +_a \eta)$

[∗312·32.∗311·11.∗308·32] $= \text{seq}_P`A_R``s`\xi \,+_{s,,}\, ``\eta$

[∗336·11] $= \text{seq}_P`\hat{N}\{(\exists L, M) . L \epsilon \xi . M \epsilon \eta . N = (L +_s M) \upharpoonright \kappa`R\}$

[∗351·43] $= \text{seq}_P`\hat{N}\{(\exists L, M) . L \epsilon \xi . M \epsilon \eta . N = (L \upharpoonright \kappa`R) \,|\, (M \upharpoonright \kappa`R)\}$

[Hp] $= \text{seq}_P`\hat{N}\{(\exists U, W) . U \epsilon \lambda . W \epsilon \mu . N = U \,|\, W\} : \supset \vdash . \text{Prop}$

∗356·52. $\vdash : \text{Hp} ∗356·5 . \supset . \{(X +_r Y)_\kappa`R\}`a = \text{seq}_Q`(\dot{s}`\lambda)``\overrightarrow{\dot{s}`\mu}`a$

Dem.

$\vdash . ∗356·51 . \supset \vdash : \text{Hp} . \supset . \{(X +_r Y)_\kappa`R\}`a = (\text{seq}_P`s`\lambda \,|_{,,}\, ``\mu)`a$

[∗356·42] $= \text{seq}_Q`A_a``s`\lambda \,|_{,,}\, ``\mu$

[∗336·11] $= \text{seq}_Q`\hat{x}\{(\exists X, Y) . X \epsilon \lambda . Y \epsilon \mu . x = (X \,|\, Y)`a\}$

[∗41·11] $= \text{seq}_Q`\hat{x}\{(\exists X) . X \epsilon \lambda . x \epsilon X``\overrightarrow{\dot{s}`\mu}`a\}$

[∗41·11] $= \text{seq}_Q`(\dot{s}`\lambda)``\overrightarrow{\dot{s}`\mu}`a : \supset \vdash . \text{Prop}$

$*356\cdot53$. $\vdash : \text{Hp} *356\cdot5 . \supset . \text{seq}_Q{}^{\backprime}\overrightarrow{\dot{s}{}^{\backprime}\lambda}{}^{\backprime}\text{seq}_Q{}^{\backprime}\overrightarrow{\dot{s}{}^{\backprime}\mu}{}^{\backprime}a = \text{seq}_Q{}^{\backprime}(\dot{s}{}^{\backprime}\lambda){}^{\backprime\backprime}\overrightarrow{\dot{s}{}^{\backprime}\mu}{}^{\backprime}a$

Dem.

$$\begin{aligned}
&\vdash . *356\cdot16 . \supset \vdash : \text{Hp} . \supset . \text{seq}_Q{}^{\backprime}\overrightarrow{\dot{s}{}^{\backprime}\lambda}{}^{\backprime}\text{seq}_Q{}^{\backprime}\overrightarrow{\dot{s}{}^{\backprime}\mu}{}^{\backprime}a = \text{lt}_Q{}^{\backprime}\overrightarrow{\dot{s}{}^{\backprime}\lambda}{}^{\backprime}\text{seq}_Q{}^{\backprime}\overrightarrow{\dot{s}{}^{\backprime}\mu}{}^{\backprime}a \\
&[*41\cdot11] \quad = \text{lt}_Q{}^{\backprime}\hat{x}\{(\exists L) . L \in \lambda . x = L{}^{\backprime}\text{seq}_Q{}^{\backprime}\overrightarrow{\dot{s}{}^{\backprime}\mu}{}^{\backprime}a\} \\
&[*356\cdot4] \quad = \text{lt}_Q{}^{\backprime}\hat{x}\{(\exists L) . L \in \lambda . x = \text{seq}_Q{}^{\backprime}L{}^{\backprime\backprime}\overrightarrow{\dot{s}{}^{\backprime}\mu}{}^{\backprime}a\} \\
&[*356\cdot16.\text{Hp}] = \text{lt}_Q{}^{\backprime}\hat{x}\{(\exists L) . L \in \lambda . x = \text{lt}_Q{}^{\backprime}L{}^{\backprime\backprime}\overrightarrow{\dot{s}{}^{\backprime}\mu}{}^{\backprime}a\} \\
&[*207\cdot55] \quad = \text{lt}_Q{}^{\backprime}s{}^{\backprime}\hat{\alpha}\{(\exists L) . L \in \lambda . \alpha = L{}^{\backprime\backprime}\overrightarrow{\dot{s}{}^{\backprime}\mu}{}^{\backprime}a\} \\
&[*41\cdot11] \quad = \text{lt}_Q{}^{\backprime}(\dot{s}{}^{\backprime}\lambda){}^{\backprime\backprime}\overrightarrow{\dot{s}{}^{\backprime}\mu}{}^{\backprime}a \\
&[*356\cdot16] \quad = \text{seq}_Q{}^{\backprime}(\dot{s}{}^{\backprime}\lambda){}^{\backprime\backprime}\overrightarrow{\dot{s}{}^{\backprime}\mu}{}^{\backprime}a : \supset \vdash . \text{Prop}
\end{aligned}$$

$*356\cdot54$. $\vdash : \kappa \in FM \text{ sr subm} . \text{Cnv}{}^{\backprime}\dot{s}{}^{\backprime}\kappa_\partial \in \text{semi Ded} . X, Y \in \dot{s}{}^{\backprime\backprime}C{}^{\backprime}\Theta . R \in \kappa_\partial . \supset .$

$$(X_\kappa{}^{\backprime}R) | (Y_\kappa{}^{\backprime}R) = (X +_r Y)_\kappa{}^{\backprime}R \quad [*356\cdot5\cdot53\cdot52]$$

$*356\cdot6$. $\vdash : \kappa \in FM \text{ sr} . R \in \kappa_\partial . \breve{P} = U_\kappa . \breve{Q} = \dot{s}{}^{\backprime}\kappa_\partial . X \in C{}^{\backprime}H . \supset .$

$$\kappa \cap A_R{}^{\backprime\backprime}\overrightarrow{H}{}^{\backprime}X \subset \overrightarrow{P}{}^{\backprime}X \upharpoonright \kappa{}^{\backprime}R$$

Dem.

$$\begin{aligned}
&\vdash . *37\cdot6 . \supset \vdash :. \text{Hp} . \supset : M \in A_R{}^{\backprime\backprime}\overrightarrow{H}{}^{\backprime}X . \equiv . (\exists Y) . YHX . MYR . \\
&[*352\cdot7] \qquad \supset . MP(X \upharpoonright \kappa{}^{\backprime}R) :. \supset \vdash . \text{Prop}
\end{aligned}$$

$*356\cdot61$. $\vdash : \text{Hp} *356\cdot6 . \kappa \in FM \text{ subm} . Q \in \text{semi Ded} . SP(X \upharpoonright \kappa{}^{\backprime}R) . \supset .$

$$(\exists Y) . YHX . SP(Y \upharpoonright \kappa{}^{\backprime}R)$$

Dem.

$$\begin{aligned}
&\vdash . *356\cdot231 . \supset \vdash : \text{Hp} . \supset . (\exists \nu) . \nu \in \text{NC ind} - \iota{}^{\backprime}0 . SP[\{(\nu -_c 1)/\nu\} \upharpoonright \kappa{}^{\backprime}X \upharpoonright \kappa{}^{\backprime}R] \\
&[*351\cdot31] \qquad \supset . (\exists \nu) . \nu \in \text{NC ind} - \iota{}^{\backprime}0 . SP[\{(\nu -_c 1)/\nu \times_s X\} \upharpoonright \kappa{}^{\backprime}R] \\
&[*305\cdot71\cdot51] \qquad \supset . (\exists Y) . YHX . SP(Y \upharpoonright \kappa{}^{\backprime}R) : \supset \vdash . \text{Prop}
\end{aligned}$$

$*356\cdot62$. $\vdash : \text{Hp} *356\cdot6 . \kappa \in FM \text{ subm} . Q \in \text{semi Ded} . \supset .$

$$\overrightarrow{P}{}^{\backprime}X \upharpoonright \kappa{}^{\backprime}R \subset P{}^{\backprime\backprime}A_R{}^{\backprime\backprime}\overrightarrow{H}{}^{\backprime}X \quad [*356\cdot61]$$

$*356\cdot63$. $\vdash : \text{Hp} *356\cdot62 . \supset . (\dot{s}{}^{\backprime}\overrightarrow{H}{}^{\backprime}X)_\kappa = X \upharpoonright \kappa$

Dem.

$$\begin{aligned}
&\vdash . *356\cdot6\cdot62 . \supset \vdash : \text{Hp} . \supset . X \upharpoonright \kappa{}^{\backprime}R = \text{lt}_P{}^{\backprime}A_R{}^{\backprime\backprime}\overrightarrow{H}{}^{\backprime}X . \\
&[*356\cdot11] \qquad \supset . X \upharpoonright \kappa{}^{\backprime}R = (\dot{s}{}^{\backprime}\overrightarrow{H}{}^{\backprime}X)_\kappa{}^{\backprime}R \qquad (1) \\
&\vdash . (1) . *356\cdot21 . \supset \vdash . \text{Prop}
\end{aligned}$$

$*359$. EXISTENCE-THEOREMS FOR VECTOR-FAMILIES.

Summary of $*359$.

In this number we prove that, assuming the axiom of infinity, there are vector-families of the various kinds considered in previous numbers.

If P is any well-ordered series having no last term, the converses of the interval-relations, *i.e.* the class $\text{finid}`\breve{P}$, form an open family of $C`P$ ($*359\cdot11$). If P is a progression, this family is serial and initial ($*359\cdot12$).

The family consisting of additions of positive ratios to positive ratios (including 0_q), *i.e.* consisting of all terms of the form $(+_s X) \upharpoonright C`H'$, where $X \in C`H'$, is initial, serial, open, and submultipliable ($*359\cdot21$), assuming the axiom of infinity. The family consisting of generalized additions of positive ratios to generalized ratios is serial, open, and submultipliable, but not initial ($*359\cdot25$).

The family consisting of multiplications of positive ratios not 0_q by positive ratios not 0_q is open and connected, but not serial or submultipliable ($*359\cdot22$); if we confine the multipliers to ratios not less than $1/1$, the family becomes serial ($*359\cdot25$).

The family consisting of additions of positive real numbers to positive real numbers (including $\iota`0_q$) is serial, initial, and submultipliable ($*359\cdot31$); the family consisting of generalized additions of positive real numbers (including $\iota`0_q$) to generalized real numbers is serial and submultipliable, but not initial ($*359\cdot32$). Similar propositions hold for multiplication, provided $\iota`0_q$ is omitted; but the resulting families will not be serial. In the case where the field is confined to positive real numbers, however, the family becomes serial if the multipliers are confined to such as are not less than $\overrightarrow{H}`(1/1)$, which is the real number 1.

The last set of propositions in this number ($*359\cdot4$—$\cdot44$) are concerned in proving that, given a family κ whose field is β, if S is a correlator of α and β, $S\dagger``\kappa$ is a family whose field is α, and which has the same properties of being connected, open, etc. as the original family κ. Hence if κ is a family whose field is the real numbers, and we are given any class α similar to the real numbers (in other words the field of any continuous series), if S is the correlator of this class with the real numbers, $S\dagger\text{“}\kappa$ gives a family whose field is α. Hence from our previous existence-theorems we derive the existence, for α, of an initial serial family, giving us a system of measurement for α. Similarly if α is similar to the rationals.

***359·1.** $\vdash : P \epsilon \Omega \,.\, \sim E\,!\, B\text{‘}\breve{P} \,.\supset.\, \text{finid}\text{‘}\breve{P} \epsilon \text{Cl ex‘cr‘}C\text{‘}P$

Dem.

$\vdash .\, *260{\cdot}23{\cdot}28 \,.\supset \vdash : \text{Hp} \,.\supset.\, \text{finid}\text{‘}\breve{P} \subset 1 \rightarrow 1$ (1)

$\vdash .\, *121{\cdot}302 \,.\quad \supset \vdash : \text{Hp} \,.\supset.\, \text{D}\text{‘}P_0 = C\text{‘}P$ (2)

$\vdash .\, (2) \,.\, *121{\cdot}302{\cdot}35 \,.\, *260{\cdot}28 \,.\supset$

$\vdash : \text{Hp} \,.\, \nu \epsilon \text{NC ind} \,.\, \text{D}\text{‘}P_\nu = C\text{‘}P \,.\supset.\, \text{D}\text{‘}P_{\nu +_c 1} = C\text{‘}P$ (3)

$\vdash .\, (2) \,.\, (3) \,.\, \text{Induct} \,.\supset \vdash : \text{Hp} \,.\, R \epsilon \text{finid}\text{‘}P \,.\supset.\, \text{D}\text{‘}R = C\text{‘}P$ (4)

$\vdash .\, *121{\cdot}322 \,.\qquad \supset \vdash : R \epsilon \text{finid}\text{‘}P \,.\supset.\, \text{G}\text{‘}R \subset C\text{‘}P$ (5)

$\vdash .\, (1) \,.\, (4) \,.\, (5) \,.\, *330{\cdot}1 \,.\supset \vdash .\, \text{Prop}$

***359·11.** $\vdash : P \epsilon \Omega \,.\, \sim E\,!\, B\text{‘}\breve{P} \,.\supset.\, \text{finid}\text{‘}\breve{P} \epsilon \text{fm ap‘}C\text{‘}P$

Dem.

$\vdash .\, *260{\cdot}28 \,.\, *121{\cdot}352 \,.\supset \vdash : \text{Hp} \,.\supset.\, \text{finid}\text{‘}\breve{P} \epsilon \text{Abel}$ (1)

$\vdash .\, *71{\cdot}19 \,.\qquad \supset \vdash : \text{Hp} \,.\, \mu, \nu \epsilon \text{NC ind} \,.\, \dot{\exists}\,!\, P_\mu \,|\, \breve{P}_\nu \dot{\wedge} J \,.\supset.\, \mu \neq \nu$ (2)

$\vdash .\, *121{\cdot}35 \,.\qquad \supset \vdash : \text{Hp}(2) \,.\, \mu > \nu \,.\supset.\, P_\mu \,|\, \breve{P}_\nu \mathrel{\dot\subset} P_{\mu -_c \nu} \,.$

$[*91{\cdot}6 . *121{\cdot}36] \qquad \supset.\, (P_\mu \,|\, \breve{P}_\nu)_{\text{po}} \mathrel{\dot\subset} J$ (3)

Similarly $\qquad \vdash : \text{Hp}(2) \,.\, \nu > \mu \,.\supset.\, (P_\mu \,|\, \breve{P}_\nu)_{\text{po}} \mathrel{\dot\subset} J$ (4)

$\vdash .\, (2) \,.\, (3) \,.\, (4) \,.\supset \vdash : \text{Hp} \,.\, L \epsilon (\text{finid}\text{‘}\breve{P})_{\iota\partial} \,.\supset.\, L_{\text{po}} \mathrel{\dot\subset} J$ (5)

$\vdash .\, (1) \,.\, (5) \,.\, *359{\cdot}1 \,.\supset \vdash .\, \text{Prop}$

***359·12.** $\vdash : P \epsilon \omega \,.\, \kappa = \text{finid}\text{‘}\breve{P} \,.\supset.\, \kappa \epsilon \text{fm sr init‘}C\text{‘}P \,.\, \dot{s}\text{‘}\kappa_\partial = \breve{P}$

Dem

$\vdash .\, *263{\cdot}14{\cdot}141 \,.\, *122{\cdot}1 \,.\supset \vdash : \text{Hp} \,.\supset.\, \dot{s}\text{‘}\overrightarrow{\kappa\text{‘}B\text{‘}P} = C\text{‘}P$ (1)

$\vdash .\, *263{\cdot}14{\cdot}141 \,.\qquad \supset \vdash : \text{Hp} \,.\supset.\, \dot{s}\text{‘}\kappa_\partial = \breve{P} \,.$ (2)

$[*334{\cdot}31 . *359{\cdot}11] \qquad \supset.\, \kappa \epsilon FM \text{ sr}$ (3)

$\vdash .\, (1) \,.\, (2) \,.\, (3) \,.\, *335{\cdot}14 \,.\supset \vdash .\, \text{Prop}$

***359·2.** $\vdash : \text{Infin ax} \,.\, \kappa = \hat{R}\{(\exists X) \,.\, X \epsilon C\text{‘}H' \,.\, R = (+_s X) \upharpoonright C\text{‘}H'\} \,.\supset.$
$\kappa \epsilon FM \,.\, \dot{s}\text{‘}\kappa_\partial = \breve{H}'$

Dem.

$\vdash .\, *306{\cdot}54{\cdot}25 \,.\, *304{\cdot}49 \,.\supset \vdash : \text{Hp} \,.\supset.\, \kappa \subset 1 \rightarrow 1$ (1)

$\vdash .\, *306{\cdot}25 \,.\, *304{\cdot}49 \,.\qquad \supset \vdash : \text{Hp} \,.\, R \epsilon \kappa \,.\supset.\, \text{G}\text{‘}R = C\text{‘}H' \,.\, \text{D}\text{‘}R \subset C\text{‘}H'$ (2)

$\vdash .\, *306{\cdot}11{\cdot}31 \,.\qquad \supset \vdash : \text{Hp} \,.\, R, S \epsilon \kappa \,.\supset.\, R \,|\, S = S \,|\, R$ (3)

$\vdash .\, *306{\cdot}52 \,.\qquad \supset \vdash : \text{Hp} \,.\supset.\, \dot{s}\text{‘}\kappa_\partial = \breve{H}'$ (4)

$\vdash .\, (1) \,.\, (2) \,.\, (3) \,.\, (4) \,.\supset \vdash .\, \text{Prop}$

***359·21.** $\vdash :$ Hp *359·2 . $\supset . \kappa \epsilon FM$ init sr subm . $\dot{s}`\kappa_\partial = \breve{H}'$

Dem.

$\vdash$. *306·24 . $\supset \vdash :$ Hp . $\supset . \dot{s}`\overrightarrow{\kappa}`0_q = C`H'$ (1)

$\vdash$. *306·41 . $\supset$

$\vdash :.$ Hp . $X \epsilon C`H' . \mu, \nu \epsilon$ NC ind $- \iota`0 . S = \{+_s (X \times_s 1/\nu)\} \upharpoonright C`H' . \supset :$

$S^\mu = \{+_s (X \times_s \mu/\nu)\} \upharpoonright C`H' . \supset . S^{\mu +_c 1} = \{+_s (X \times_s \overline{\mu +_c 1}/\nu)\} \upharpoonright C`H' :$

[Induct] $\supset : S^\mu = \{+_s (X \times_s \mu/\nu)\} \upharpoonright C`H' :$

[*305·51] $\supset : S^\nu = (+_s X) \upharpoonright C`H'$ (2)

$\vdash$. (2) . *351·1 . *359·2 . $\supset \vdash :$ Hp . $\supset . \kappa \epsilon FM$ subm (3)

$\vdash$. (1) . (3) . *359·2 . *334·31 . $\supset \vdash$. Prop

***359·22.** $\vdash :$ Infin ax . $\kappa = \hat{R} \{(\exists X) . X \epsilon C`H' . R = (+_g X) \upharpoonright C`H_g\} . \supset .$

$\kappa \epsilon FM$ sr subm . $\dot{s}`\kappa_\partial = \breve{H}_g$

The proof proceeds as in *359·21, but in this case there is no origin. Every member of κ is a connected point, *i.e.* a member of conx‘κ. This results from *308·54. If, in *359·21, we substitute H for H', the proposition holds except that κ has no origin.

***359·23.** $\vdash :$ Infin ax . $\kappa = \hat{R} \{(\exists X) . X \epsilon C`H . R = (\times_s X) \upharpoonright C`H\} . \supset .$

$\kappa \epsilon FM$ ap conx

The proof proceeds as in *359·21. We have to take H instead of H', because $(\times_s 0_q) \upharpoonright C`H'$ is not $1 \rightarrow 1$. We do not get $\kappa \epsilon FM$ subm, because not every rational has a rational νth root.

***359·24.** $\vdash :$ Infin ax .

$\kappa = \hat{R} \{(\exists X) . X \epsilon C`H_g - \iota`0_q . R = (\times_g X) \upharpoonright (C`H_g - \iota`0_q)\} . \supset .$

$\kappa \epsilon FM$ ap conx

The proof proceeds as in *359·23.

***359·25.** $\vdash :$ Infin ax . $\kappa = \hat{R} \{(\exists X) . (1/1) H_* X . R = (\times_s X) \upharpoonright C`H\} . \supset .$

$\kappa \epsilon FM$ sr . $\dot{s}`\kappa_\partial = \breve{H}$

The proof proceeds as in *359·21.

***359·31.** $\vdash :$ Infin ax . $\kappa = \hat{R} \{(\exists \mu) . \mu \epsilon C`\Theta' . R = (+_p \mu) \upharpoonright C`\Theta'\} . \supset .$

$\kappa \epsilon FM$ sr init subm . $\dot{s}`\kappa_\partial = \breve{\Theta}'$

Dem.

$\vdash$. *311·74 . $\supset \vdash :$ Hp . $\supset . \kappa \subset 1 \rightarrow 1$ (1)

$\vdash$. *311·27 . $\supset \vdash :$ Hp . $R \epsilon \kappa . \supset .$ Ꮖ‘$R = C`\Theta'$ . D‘$R \subset C`\Theta'$ (2)

$\vdash$. *311·43 . $\supset \vdash :$ Hp . $\supset . \iota`0_q \upharpoonright C`\Theta' =$ init‘κ (3)

$\vdash$. *311·12·121 . $\supset \vdash :$ Hp . $\supset . \kappa \epsilon$ Abel (4)

$\vdash$. *311·65 . $\supset \vdash :$ Hp . $\supset . \dot{s}`\kappa_\partial = \breve{\Theta}'$ (5)

$\vdash . (1) . (2) . (3) . (4) . (5) . \quad \supset \vdash : \text{Hp} . \supset . \kappa \epsilon FM \text{ sr init} . \dot{s}`\kappa_\partial = \breve{\Theta}'$ (6)

$\vdash . (6) . *310{\cdot}151 . *351{\cdot}11 . \supset \vdash : \text{Hp} . \supset . \kappa \epsilon FM \text{ subm}$ (7)

$\vdash . (6) . (7) . \supset \vdash . \text{Prop}$

***359·32.** $\vdash : \text{Infin ax} . \kappa = \hat{R} \{(\exists \mu) . \mu \epsilon C`\Theta' . R = (+_a \mu) \upharpoonright C`\Theta_g\} . \supset .$

$\kappa \epsilon FM \text{ sr subm} . \dot{s}`\kappa_\partial = \breve{\Theta}_g$

The proof proceeds as in *359·22. Similarly the analogues of *359·23·24·25 can be proved for real numbers; the resulting families, in these cases, will be submultipliable, but it will be necessary to omit $\iota`0_q$ from their fields.

***359·4.** $\vdash : \kappa \epsilon \text{Cl ex}`\text{cr}`\beta . S \epsilon \alpha \overline{\text{sm}} \beta . \supset . S\dagger``\kappa \epsilon \text{Cl ex}`\text{cr}`\alpha$

Dem.

$\vdash . *330{\cdot}1 . *71{\cdot}252 . \quad \supset \vdash : \text{Hp} . \supset . S\dagger``\kappa \subset 1 \rightarrow 1$ (1)

$\vdash . *150{\cdot}21{\cdot}211 . *330{\cdot}1 . \supset \vdash : \text{Hp} . R \epsilon S\dagger``\kappa . \supset . \text{Ɑ}`R = S``\beta . \text{D}`R \subset \text{Ɑ}`R .$

[*73·03] $\supset . \text{Ɑ}`R = \alpha . \text{D}`R \subset \alpha$ (2)

$\vdash . (1) . (2) . *330{\cdot}1 . \supset \vdash . \text{Prop}$

***359·401.** $\vdash : \kappa \epsilon \text{Abel} . S \epsilon \text{Cls} \rightarrow 1 . s`\text{Ɑ}``\kappa \subset \text{Ɑ}`S . \supset . S\dagger``\kappa \epsilon \text{Abel}$

Dem.

$\vdash . *72{\cdot}601 . \supset \vdash :. \text{Hp} . \supset : P, Q \epsilon \kappa . \supset . P | \breve{S} | S = P . Q | \breve{S} | S = Q .$ (1)

[*150·1] $\supset . (S\dagger P) | (S\dagger Q) = S | P | Q | \breve{S}$

[*330·5] $= S | Q | P | \breve{S}$

[(1).*150·1] $= (S\dagger Q) | (S\dagger P)$ (2)

$\vdash . (2) . *330{\cdot}5 . \supset \vdash . \text{Prop}$

***359·41.** $\vdash : \kappa \epsilon \text{fm}`\beta . S \epsilon \alpha \overline{\text{sm}} \beta . \supset . S\dagger``\kappa \epsilon \text{fm}`\alpha$ [*359·4·401 . *330·51]

***359·411.** $\vdash : \kappa \epsilon FM . a \epsilon \text{conx}`\kappa . S \epsilon 1 \rightarrow 1 . s`\text{Ɑ}``\kappa = \text{Ɑ}`S . \supset . S`a \epsilon \text{conx}`S\dagger``\kappa$

Dem.

$\vdash . *151{\cdot}11 . \supset \vdash : \text{Hp} . P = S \,\dot{;}\, \dot{s}`\kappa . \supset . S \epsilon P \,\overline{\text{smor}}\, (\dot{s}`\kappa) .$

[*151·33] $\supset . \overrightarrow{P}`S`a \cup \overleftarrow{P}`S`a = S``\overrightarrow{\dot{s}`\kappa}`a \cup S``\overleftarrow{\dot{s}`\kappa}`a$

[*331·1] $= S``s`\text{Ɑ}``\kappa$

[*330·13.*150·211] $= \text{Ɑ}`S \,\dot{;}\, \dot{s}`\kappa$

[Hp] $= \text{Ɑ}`P$ (1)

$\vdash . *150{\cdot}16 . \supset \vdash : \text{Hp}(1) . \supset . P = \dot{s}`S\dagger``\kappa$ (2)

$\vdash . (1) . (2) . *331{\cdot}1 . \supset \vdash . \text{Prop}$

***359·412.** $\vdash : \kappa \epsilon \text{fm conx}`\beta . S \epsilon \alpha \overline{\text{sm}} \beta . \supset . S\dagger``\kappa \epsilon \text{fm conx}`\alpha$ [*359·41·411]

∗359·413. $\vdash : \kappa \in FM \text{ ap} . S \in 1 \rightarrow 1 . s`\text{G}``\kappa = \text{G}`S . \supset . S\dagger``\kappa \in FM \text{ ap}$

Dem.

$\vdash . *72\cdot601 . \supset \vdash : \text{Hp} . P, Q \in \kappa . \supset . (S ; \breve{P}) | (S ; Q) = S ; (\breve{P} | Q)$ (1)

$\vdash . (1) . *150\cdot4 . \supset \vdash : \text{Hp}(1) . \dot{\exists} ! (S ; \breve{P}) | (S ; Q) \dot{\cap} J . \supset . \dot{\exists} ! \breve{P} | Q \dot{\cap} J .$

$[*333\cdot101] \qquad \supset . (\breve{P} | Q)_{po} \in J .$

$[*200\cdot21] \qquad \supset . S ; (\breve{P} | Q)_{po} \in J .$

$[*150\cdot83] \qquad \supset . \{S ; (\breve{P} | Q)\}_{po} \in J$ (2)

$\vdash . (1) . (2) . \supset \vdash :. \text{Hp} . \supset : X, Y \in S\dagger``\kappa . \dot{\exists} ! \breve{X} \, Y \dot{\cap} J . \supset . (\breve{X} | Y)_{po} \in J$ (3)

$\vdash . *359\cdot4 . \supset \vdash : \text{Hp} . \supset . S\dagger``\kappa \in FM$ (4)

$\vdash . (3) . (4) . *333\cdot101 . \supset \vdash . \text{Prop}$

∗359·414. $\vdash : \kappa \in FM . S \in 1 \rightarrow 1 . s`\text{G}``\kappa = \text{G}`S . a = \text{init}`\kappa . \supset . S`a = \text{init}`S\dagger``\kappa$

[Proof as in ∗359·411]

∗359·415. $\vdash : \kappa \in FM \text{ subm} . S \in 1 \rightarrow 1 . \text{G}`S = s`\text{G}``\kappa . \supset . S\dagger``\kappa \in FM \text{ subm}$

Dem.

$\vdash . *301\cdot21 . \supset \vdash : \text{Hp} . Y \in \kappa . \nu \in \text{NC ind} . \supset . Y^{\nu +_c 1} = Y^{\nu} | Y$ (1)

$\vdash . (1) . *72\cdot601 . \supset \vdash : \text{Hp} . S ; Y^{\nu} = (S ; Y)^{\nu} . \supset . S ; Y^{\nu +_c 1} = (S ; Y)^{\nu +_c 1}$ (2)

$\vdash . (2) . \text{Induct} . \supset \vdash : \text{Hp}(1) . \supset . S ; Y^{\nu} = (S ; Y)^{\nu}$ (3)

$\vdash . *351\cdot1 . \supset \vdash : \text{Hp} . \nu \in \text{NC ind} - \iota`0 . X \in \kappa . \supset . (\exists Y) . X = Y^{\nu} . Y \in \kappa .$

$[(3)] \qquad \supset . (\exists Y) . Y \in \kappa . S ; X = (S ; Y)^{\nu}$ (4)

$\vdash . (4) . *351\cdot1 . *359\cdot41 . \supset \vdash . \text{Prop}$

∗359·42. $\vdash : \exists ! \text{fm conx ap subm}`\beta . \alpha \text{ sm } \beta . \supset . \exists ! \text{fm conx ap subm}`\alpha$

[∗359·41·412·413·415]

∗359·43. $\vdash : P \in \dot{1} \dotplus \eta . \supset . \exists ! FM \text{ init sr subm} \cap \hat{\kappa} (\dot{s}`\kappa_\partial = \breve{P})$

[∗359·42·21·414 . ∗274·44 . ∗123·18 . ∗304·47 . ∗273·4]

∗359·44. $\vdash : \text{Nr}`P \dotplus \dot{1} = \theta . \supset . \exists ! FM \text{ init sr subm} \cap \hat{\kappa} (\dot{s}`\kappa_\partial = \breve{P})$

[∗359·42·31·414 . ∗275·3 . ∗310·15 . ∗204·47]

SECTION D.

CYCLIC FAMILIES.

Summary of Section D.

The theory of measurement hitherto developed has been only applicable to *open* families. But in order to be able to deal with such cases as the angles at a point, or the elliptic straight line, we require a theory of measurement applicable to families which are not open. This theory is given briefly in the present Section.

When a family is not open, two vectors which have one ratio will usually also have many others, *i.e.* we shall not have $\dot{\exists} ! X \upharpoonright \kappa \mathbin{\dot{\frown}} Y \upharpoonright \kappa . \supset . X = Y$, where X, Y are ratios. Also a ratio confined to the family will not usually be one-one. Under these circumstances, it is necessary, if measurement is to be possible, that there should be some way of distinguishing one among the ratios of two vectors as their "principal" ratio, and of then showing that, by confining ourselves to principal ratios, the requisite properties of ratios reappear.

The case of angles will serve to illustrate our procedure. Considered geometrically, not kinematically, a vector which is a multiple of 2π is identical with the null-vector, and if θ is any angle, $\theta = 2\nu\pi + \theta$, where ν is any integer positive or negative. We are here considering an angle as a vector whose field is all the rays in a given plane through a given point. Thus there will be two angles which are half of the null-vector, namely π and 2π, and four angles which are a quarter of the null-vector, namely $\pi/2$, π, $3\pi/2$ and 2π; and so on. The ratio of $\pi/2$ to π is any number of the form $(2\mu + 1)/(4\nu + 2)$; thus two terms may have many different ratios.

In order to evade this difficulty, we first arrange angles in a series ending with 2π, and having no first term, but proceeding from smaller to greater angles. Then the angles which have a given ratio μ/ν to a given angle will be finite in number, and therefore one of them will be the smallest. We take this as the "principal" angle having the ratio μ/ν to the given angle, and define "$(\mu/\nu)_\kappa$" to mean the relation between two angles consisting in the fact that the first is the "principal" angle having the ratio μ/ν to the second. Then of all the ratios between the two angles, the ratio μ/ν may be regarded as the "principal" ratio. It will be found that, with suitable hypotheses, $(\mu/\nu)_\kappa$ has the properties required in order to make measurement possible.

In order to make the above method feasible, certain properties must be assumed to hold concerning the family κ. (These properties are all verified in the cases that arise in practice.) We shall therefore only speak of a family as cyclic when it fulfils the following conditions:

(1) It must be connected.

(2) It must contain a non-zero member which is identical with its converse. This is the property which makes the family cyclic. In the case of angles, the member in question is π.

(3) It must be such that $\kappa_\partial \rceil U_\kappa$ is transitive. This is the property which enables us to arrange the field in a series. It will be observed that U_κ cannot be transitive, since, if K_κ is the member which is its own converse, we have

$$(I \upharpoonright s\text{‘}\mathrm{C}\text{“}\kappa)\, U_\kappa K_\kappa \,.\, K_\kappa U_\kappa (I \upharpoonright s\text{‘}\mathrm{C}\text{“}\kappa),$$

but we do not have $(I \upharpoonright s\text{‘}\mathrm{C}\text{“}\kappa)\, U_\kappa (I \upharpoonright s\text{‘}\mathrm{C}\text{“}\kappa)$, because U_κ is contained in diversity (by $*336\cdot6$). It is, however, possible that U_κ should be transitive so long as we do not start from $I \upharpoonright s\text{‘}\mathrm{C}\text{“}\kappa$, and this we assume as part of the definition of cyclic families.

(4) In order to avoid trivial exceptions, we assume that κ does not have only two members, since otherwise it might consist only of $I \upharpoonright s\text{‘}\mathrm{C}\text{“}\kappa$ and K_κ.

We are thus led to the following definition:

$$FM\,\mathrm{cycl} = (FM\,\mathrm{conx} - 2) \cap \hat{\kappa}\,\{\kappa_\partial \rceil U_\kappa \in \mathrm{trans} : (\exists K) \,.\, K \in \kappa_\partial \,.\, K = \breve{K}\} \quad \mathrm{Df.}$$

We prove that there is only one such relation as K, and therefore put

$$K_\kappa = (\imath K)(K \in \kappa_\partial \,.\, K = \breve{K}) \quad \mathrm{Df.}$$

Also for the sake of brevity we put

$$I_\kappa = I \upharpoonright s\text{‘}\mathrm{C}\text{“}\kappa \qquad \mathrm{Df.}$$

We then prove that κ is a family having connexity, and satisfying the condition

$$\mathrm{D}\text{“}\kappa = \mathrm{C}\text{“}\kappa,$$

i.e. having the domain of a member always identical with the common converse domain. Thus by $*334\cdot21$, $\kappa_\iota = \kappa \cup \mathrm{Cnv}\text{“}\kappa$.

In a cyclic family, $\kappa \cup \mathrm{Cnv}\text{“}\kappa$ consists of two mutually exclusive parts, namely κ_∂ and $K_\kappa |\text{“}\kappa_\partial$. (In the case of angles, $K_\kappa | R$ would be $\pi + R$. Thus κ_∂ would be the angles from 0 (exclusive) to π (inclusive), and $K_\kappa |\text{“}\kappa_\partial$ would be the angles from π (exclusive) to 2π (inclusive).) Also $K_\kappa |\text{“}\kappa_\partial$ consists of the converses of $\kappa - \iota\text{‘}K_\kappa$.

We take up next ($*371$) the question of arranging $\kappa \cup \mathrm{Cnv}\text{“}\kappa$ in a series. For this purpose, in order to avoid circularity, we have to erect a barrier at some point; we choose I_κ as this point. By the definition of cyclic families,

$\kappa_\partial \upharpoonleft U_\kappa$ is transitive; hence, since the family has connexity, $U_\kappa \upharpoonright \kappa_\partial$ is serial. This relation therefore arranges all the members of κ_∂ in a series, beginning with K_κ and proceeding towards I_κ. In order to extend our series to $K_\kappa|``\kappa_\partial$, we only have to make $K_\kappa|R$ precede $K_\kappa|S$ if $R$ precedes $S$, where $R$ and $S$ are members of $\kappa_\partial$. That is, we arrange $K_\kappa|``\kappa_\partial$ in the order $K_\kappa |; U_\kappa \upharpoonright \kappa_\partial$. This gives a series which begins with I_κ and proceeds towards K_κ without reaching it. Thus taking the sum of the above two series (in the sense of ∗160), we get a series whose field is $\kappa \cup \mathrm{Cnv}``\kappa$, which begins with $I_\kappa$, travels through $K_\kappa|``\kappa_\partial$ to K_κ, and on through κ_∂ towards I_κ, without quite reaching I_κ again. This relation we call W_κ; the definition is

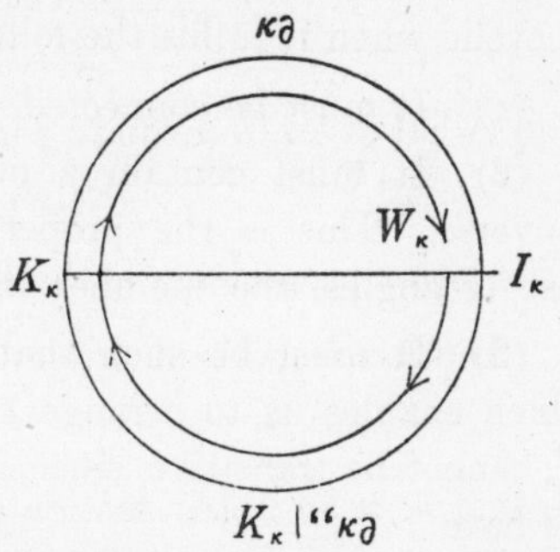

$$W_\kappa = K_\kappa |; U_\kappa \upharpoonright \kappa_\partial \Uparrow U_\kappa \upharpoonright \kappa_\partial \quad \text{Df.}$$

Taking an arbitrary origin, a vector may be indicated by the point to which it carries the origin. Thus in the figure, I_κ is at the origin, K_κ is opposite the origin; the upper semi-circle, including both ends, is κ; not including the right-hand end, it is κ_∂; the lower semi-circle, including both ends, is $\mathrm{Cnv}``\kappa$; including $K_\kappa$ but not $I_\kappa$, it is $\mathrm{Cnv}``\kappa_\partial$; including I_κ but not K_κ, it is $K_\kappa|``\kappa_\partial$. Then W_κ starts from I_κ, and proceeds through the lower semi-circle first, and afterwards through the upper semi-circle, stopping just short of I_κ.

If κ is cyclic, W_κ is a series. Under most circumstances, if $R \in \kappa$, we shall have

$$P W_\kappa Q . \supset . (P|R) W_\kappa (Q|R).$$

The investigation of the various cases in which this holds occupies a large part of ∗371.

In the remainder of this Section, our work becomes more full of ordinary arithmetic than it has been hitherto. We shall therefore, where cardinals are concerned, abandon the explicit notation we have hitherto employed, and substitute the ordinary notation. Thus we shall write $\mu + \nu$ in place of $\mu +_c \nu$, and $\mu\nu$ in place of $\mu \times_c \nu$. We shall, however, retain $\mu -_c \nu$ for subtraction, in order to avoid confusion with the sign of negation of a class.

We proceed next (∗372) to consider what is in effect the class of vectors not greater than the νth part of a complete revolution (*e.g.* in the case of angles, not greater than $2\pi/\nu$). We define this by means of the relation W_κ. It will be seen from the figure that if R is a non-zero vector, we shall have $R^{\sigma+1} W_\kappa R^\sigma$, unless R^σ belongs to the lower semi-circle and $R^{\sigma+1}$ to the upper, in which case $R^\sigma W_\kappa R^{\sigma+1}$. The first time this happens is the first time that $R^{\sigma+1}$ becomes greater than one complete revolution. Hence if, for every number σ less than ν and not zero, $R^{\sigma+1} W_\kappa R^\sigma$, it follows that R^ν is not greater than one complete revolution, and therefore R is not greater than the νth part of a complete revolution. The class of such relations we call ν_κ; thus we put

$$\nu_\kappa = (\kappa \cup \mathrm{Cnv}``\kappa) \cap \hat{R}(\sigma < \nu \,.\, \sigma \neq 0 \,.\, \supset_\sigma .\, R^{\sigma+1} W_\kappa R^\sigma) \quad \text{Df.}$$

The main propositions to be proved in this subject are

$$P \in \nu_\kappa \,.\, P W_\kappa Q \,.\, \supset .\, P^\nu W_\kappa Q^\nu$$

and (what is an immediate consequence)

$$P, Q \in \nu_\kappa \,.\, \supset : P^\nu = Q^\nu \,.\, \equiv .\, P = Q.$$

This latter proposition is the foundation of the theory of principal ratios.

Another important property of ν_κ is

$$\breve{W}_\kappa``\nu_\kappa \subset \nu_\kappa,$$

so that ν_κ is an upper section of W_κ.

We proceed next (*373) to consider submultiples of identity, *i.e.* vectors R such that $R^\nu = I_\kappa$, where ν is a cardinal. We assume here, and almost always henceforth, that κ is a submultipliable family. We first consider vectors which can be reached from I_κ by successive bisections. We know that $K_\kappa{}^2 = I_\kappa$; if $R^2 = K_\kappa$, then $R \neq K_\kappa$, because $K_\kappa{}^2 \neq K_\kappa$. Hence by continuing the same process we arrive at the existence of a vector Q such that

$$Q^{2^\nu} = I_\kappa : \rho < 2^\nu \,.\, \rho \neq 0 \,.\, \supset_\rho .\, Q^\rho \neq I_\kappa.$$

Hence we easily arrive at the result that, if ν is any inductive cardinal, there is a non-zero vector whose νth power is I_κ. (This does not follow from $\kappa \in FM$ subm alone, because $I_\kappa{}^\nu = I_\kappa$, so that from the definition of FM subm we cannot know that there is any vector except I_κ whose νth power is I_κ.) Thence we prove that there are non-zero vectors whose νth power is I_κ, and which are such that no earlier power is I_κ, *i.e.* we prove

$$(\exists R) : R \in \kappa_\partial \,.\, R^\nu = I_\kappa : \sigma < \nu \,.\, \sigma \neq 0 \,.\, \supset_\sigma .\, R^\sigma \neq I_\kappa.$$

The class of such vectors we call (I_κ, ν). If R is such a vector, the number of different vectors which are powers of R is ν. Hence the powers of R have a maximum in the order W_κ; since W_κ proceeds from greater to smaller vectors, this will be the smallest vector, other than I_κ, which is a power of R. Concerning this vector, we show that it is a member of ν_κ, *i.e.* it is such that, if $\sigma < \nu \,.\, \sigma \neq 0$, $R^{\sigma+1} W_\kappa R^\sigma$. Finally we prove that there is only one member of ν_κ whose νth power is I_κ. This will be what we may call the "principal" νth submultiple of I_κ; in the case of angles, it will be the angle $2\pi/\nu$. It will be observed that $2\pi\mu/\nu$ always has identity for its νth power, and has no lower power equal to identity if μ is prime to ν. Thus the uniqueness of the "principal" νth submultiple depends upon the fact that it is a member of ν_κ, so that, by what has been proved in the previous number, no other member of ν_κ has the same νth power.

We next, in a short number (∗374), extend the last of the above results to any vector, proving that, if R is any member of $\kappa \cup \text{Cnv}``\kappa$, there is a unique member of ν_κ whose νth power is R. We may call this the "principal" νth submultiple of R. We prove also in this number that, if S is the principal νth submultiple of I_κ, ν_κ consists of all vectors not earlier than S in the order W_κ, *i.e.* of all vectors not greater than S.

Finally (∗375) we define "principal ratios" and show that they are one-one and mutually exclusive. We denote the "principal ratio" corresponding to μ/ν by "$(\mu/\nu)_\kappa$." This is defined as the relation holding between R and S when the principal μth submultiple of R is identical with the principal νth submultiple of S; that is, we put

$$(\mu/\nu)_\kappa = \hat{R}\hat{S}\{(\exists T) . T \in \mu_\kappa \cap \nu_\kappa . R = T^\mu . S = T^\nu\} \quad \text{Df.}$$

It is obvious that $(\mu/\nu)_\kappa \subset (\mu/\nu) \upharpoonright \kappa_\iota$; and there is no difficulty in showing that principal ratios are one-one and mutually exclusive.

We have not thought it necessary to carry the development of this subject any farther, since, from this point onwards, everything proceeds as in the case of open families. We have given proofs rather shortly in this Section, particularly in the case of purely arithmetical lemmas, of which the proofs are perfectly straightforward, but tedious if written out at length.

$*370$. ELEMENTARY PROPERTIES OF CYCLIC FAMILIES.

Summary of $*370$.

In this number, after the definition of cyclic families already cited, we proceed first to prove that only one non-zero vector is equal to its converse ($*370\cdot23$). This one we define as K_κ. Next we prove that, if R is a non-zero vector other than K_κ, $R | K_\kappa$ is the converse of a non-zero vector, and $\breve{R} | K_\kappa$ is a non-zero vector ($*370\cdot31\cdot311$), whence it follows that

$$\text{D}`R = \text{Q}`R = s`\text{Q}``\kappa \quad (*370\cdot32),$$

whence further we obtain

$$\text{D}``\kappa = \text{Q}``\kappa \,.\, \kappa \in FM \text{ connex} \quad (*370\cdot33).$$

Hence further, since by definition $\kappa_\partial \upharpoonright U_\kappa$ is transitive, it follows that $\kappa_\partial \upharpoonright U_\kappa$ is a series ($*370\cdot37$). The remaining propositions ($*370\cdot4$—$\cdot44$) are concerned with the relations of the two semi-circles κ_∂ and $K_\kappa | ``\kappa_\partial$ (cf. figure, p. 459). We have

$$\text{Cnv}``\kappa = K_\kappa | ``\kappa \quad (*370\cdot4),$$

$$\kappa \cap \text{Cnv}``\kappa = \iota`I_\kappa \cup \iota`K_\kappa \quad (*370\cdot42),$$

$$K_\kappa | ``\kappa_{\bar\partial} = \text{Cnv}``\kappa - \iota`K_\kappa \quad (*370\cdot43),$$

and

$$\kappa_\partial \cap K_\kappa | ``\kappa_\partial = \Lambda \quad (*370\cdot44).$$

$*370\cdot01$. $FM \text{ cycl} =$

$$(FM \text{ conx} - 2) \cap \hat{\kappa}\{\kappa_\partial \upharpoonright U_\kappa \in \text{trans} : (\exists K) \,.\, K \in \kappa_\partial \,.\, K = \breve{K}\} \quad \text{Df}$$

$*370\cdot02$. $K_\kappa = (\imath K)(K \in \kappa_\partial \,.\, K = \breve{K}) \quad \text{Df}$

$*370\cdot03$. $I_\kappa = I \upharpoonright s`\text{Q}``\kappa \quad \text{Df}$

$*370\cdot1$. $\vdash :. \kappa \in FM \text{ cycl} \,.\equiv :$

$$\kappa \in FM \text{ conx} - 2 \,.\, \kappa_\partial \upharpoonright U_\kappa \in \text{trans} : (\exists K) \,.\, K \in \kappa_\partial \,.\, K = \breve{K} \quad [(*370\cdot01)]$$

$*370\cdot11$. $\vdash : \kappa \in FM \text{ conx} \,.\supset .\, \kappa_\partial \upharpoonright U_\kappa \subseteq J \quad [*336\cdot6 \,.\, (*336\cdot011)]$

$*370\cdot12$. $\vdash : \kappa \in FM \text{ conx} \,.\, \kappa_\partial \upharpoonright U_\kappa \in \text{trans} \,.\, R, S \in \kappa_\partial \,.\, RU_\kappa S \,.\, SU_\kappa T \,.\supset .\, R \neq T$ $[*370\cdot11]$

$*370\cdot13$. $\vdash : \kappa \in FM \,.\, K \in \kappa \,.\, K = \breve{K} \,.\supset .\, K^2 = I_\kappa \quad [*330\cdot31]$

***370·2.** $\vdash :. \kappa \in FM\,\text{conx} \,.\, \kappa_\partial \upharpoonright U_\kappa \in \text{trans} \,.\, K \in \kappa_\partial \,.\, K = \breve{K} \,.\, \supset :$
$R \in \kappa_\partial \,.\, R \mid K \in \kappa \,.\, \supset .\, R U_\kappa (R \mid K) \,.\, (R \mid K) U_\kappa R$

Dem.

$\vdash .\, *370{\cdot}13 \,.\quad \supset \vdash : \text{Hp} \,.\, \supset .\, R \mid K^2 = R$ (1)

$\vdash .\, *336{\cdot}41 \,.\, (1) \,.\, \supset \vdash : \text{Hp} \,.\, \supset .\, R U_\kappa (R \mid K) \,.\, (R \mid K) U_\kappa R : \supset \vdash .\, \text{Prop}$

***370·21.** $\vdash : \text{Hp}\, *370{\cdot}2 \,.\, R \in \kappa_\partial \,.\, R \mid K \in \kappa \,.\, \supset .\, R \mid K = I_\kappa$

Dem.

$\vdash .\, *370{\cdot}12 \,.\, \text{Transp} \,.\, \supset \vdash : \text{Hp} \,.\, R U_\kappa (R \mid K) \,.\, (R \mid K) U_\kappa R \,.\, \supset .\, R \mid K \sim\in \kappa_\partial$ (1)

$\vdash .\, (1) \,.\, *370{\cdot}2 \,.\, \supset \vdash .\, \text{Prop}$

***370·22.** $\vdash : \text{Hp}\, *370{\cdot}2 \,.\, R \in \kappa_\partial - \iota`K \,.\, \supset .\, R \mid K \sim\in \kappa$

Dem.

$\vdash .\, *370{\cdot}21 \,.\, *330{\cdot}32{\cdot}5 \,.\, \supset \vdash : \text{Hp}\, *370{\cdot}21 \,.\, \supset .\, R = K$ (1)

$\vdash .\, (1) \,.\, \text{Transp} \,.\, \supset \vdash .\, \text{Prop}$

***370·23.** $\vdash : \text{Hp}\, *370{\cdot}2 \,.\, R \in \kappa_\partial \,.\, R = \breve{R} \,.\, \supset .\, R = K$

Dem.

$\vdash .\, *331{\cdot}33 \,.\qquad \supset \vdash : \text{Hp} \,.\, \supset .\, R \mid K \in \kappa \cup \text{Cnv}``\kappa$ (1)

$\vdash .\, *330{\cdot}5{\cdot}52 \,.\, *34{\cdot}2 \,.\, \supset \vdash : \text{Hp} \,.\, \supset .\, R \mid K = \text{Cnv}`(R \mid K)$ (2)

$\vdash .\, (1) \,.\, (2) \,.\qquad \supset \vdash : \text{Hp} \,.\, \supset .\, R \mid K \in \kappa \,.$

[*370·22.Transp] $\qquad \supset .\, R = K : \supset \vdash .\, \text{Prop}$

***370·24.** $\vdash : \kappa \in FM\,\text{cycl} \,.\, \supset .\, E\,!\, K_\kappa$ [*370·1·23.(*370·02)]

***370·25.** $\vdash :. \kappa \in FM\,\text{cycl} \,.\, \supset : R \in \kappa_\partial \,.\, R = \breve{R} \,.\equiv .\, R = K_\kappa$ [*370·24.(*370·02)]

***370·26.** $\vdash : \kappa \in FM\,\text{cycl} \,.\, \supset .\, K_\kappa \in \kappa_\partial \,.\, K_\kappa = \breve{K}_\kappa \,.\, K_\kappa{}^2 = I_\kappa$ [*370·24·25·13]

***370·3.** $\vdash : \kappa \in FM\,\text{cycl} \,.\, R U_\kappa K_\kappa \,.\, \supset .\, R = I_\kappa$

Dem.

$\vdash .\, *336{\cdot}41 \,.\, \supset \vdash :.\, \text{Hp} \,.\, \supset : R \in \kappa : (\exists S) \,.\, S \in \kappa_\partial \,.\, R = K_\kappa \mid S$ (1)

$\vdash .\, (1) \,.\, *370{\cdot}21{\cdot}24 \,.\, \supset \vdash .\, \text{Prop}$

***370·31.** $\vdash : \kappa \in FM\,\text{cycl} \,.\, R \in \kappa_\partial - \iota`K_\kappa \,.\, \supset .\, R \mid K_\kappa \in \text{Cnv}``\kappa_\partial$
[*331·33 . *370·22]

***370·311.** $\vdash : \text{Hp}\, *370{\cdot}31 \,.\, \supset .\, \breve{R}\ \ K_\kappa \in \kappa_\partial$

Dem.

$\vdash .\, *370{\cdot}31 \,.\, \supset \vdash : \text{Hp} \,.\, \supset .\, \breve{K}_\kappa \mid \breve{R} \in \kappa_\partial \,.$

[*330·5.*370·26] $\qquad \supset .\, \breve{R} \mid K_\kappa \in \kappa_\partial : \supset \vdash .\, \text{Prop}$

***370·32.** $\vdash : \kappa \in FM\,\text{cycl} \,.\, R \in \kappa \,.\, \supset \,.\, \text{D}'R = \text{Ɑ}'R = s'\text{Ɑ}``\kappa$

Dem.

$\vdash \,.\, *50\cdot5\cdot52 \,. \qquad \supset \vdash \,.\, \text{D}'I_\kappa = \text{Ɑ}'I_\kappa = s'\text{Ɑ}``\kappa$ (1)

$\vdash \,.\, *370\cdot26 \,.\, *330\cdot52 \,.\, \supset \vdash : \text{Hp} \,.\, \supset \,.\, \text{D}'K_\kappa = \text{Ɑ}'K_\kappa = s'\text{Ɑ}``\kappa$ (2)

$\vdash \,.\, *370\cdot31 \,.\, *330\cdot52 \,.\, \supset \vdash : \text{Hp} \,.\, R \in \kappa_\partial - \iota'K_\kappa \,.\, \supset \,.\, \text{D}'(R \,|\, K_\kappa) = s'\text{Ɑ}``\kappa \,.$

[*330·52.*34·36] $\supset \,.\, \text{D}'R = s'\text{Ɑ}``\kappa$ (3)

$\vdash \,.\, (1) \,.\, (2) \,.\, (3) \,.\, \supset \vdash \,.\, \text{Prop}$

***370·33.** $\vdash : \kappa \in FM\,\text{cycl} \,.\, \supset \,.\, \text{D}``\kappa = \text{Ɑ}``\kappa \,.\, \kappa \in FM\,\text{connex}$

[*370·32 . *334·42]

***370·34.** $\vdash : \kappa \in FM\,\text{cycl} \,.\, \supset \,.\, U_\kappa \in \text{connex}$ [*370·33 . *336·62 . (*336·011)]

***370·35.** $\vdash : \text{Hp}\, *370\cdot31 \,.\, \supset \,.\, K_\kappa U_\kappa R \,.\, \sim (R U_\kappa K_\kappa)$

[*370·3 . Transp . *370·34]

***370·36.** $\vdash : \kappa \in FM\,\text{cycl} \,.\, \supset \,.\, \kappa_\partial \upharpoonright U_\kappa \in \text{connex} \,.\, C``\kappa_\partial \upharpoonright U_\kappa = \kappa$

Dem.

$\vdash \,.\, *336\cdot41 \,. \qquad \supset \vdash : \text{Hp} \,.\, \supset \,.\, C``\kappa_\partial \upharpoonright U_\kappa \subset \kappa$ (1)

$\vdash \,.\, *370\cdot34 \,. \qquad \supset \vdash :. \text{Hp} \,.\, R, S \in \kappa_\partial \,.\, R \neq S \,.\, \supset :$

$R\,(\kappa_\partial \upharpoonright U_\kappa)\,S \,.\, \mathbf{v} \,.\, S\,(\kappa_\partial \upharpoonright U_\kappa)\,R$ (2)

$\vdash \,.\, *336\cdot41 \,. \qquad \supset \vdash : \text{Hp} \,.\, R \in \kappa_\partial \,.\, S = I_\kappa \,.\, \supset \,.\, R\,(\kappa_\partial \upharpoonright U_\kappa)\,S$ (3)

$\vdash \,.\, *336\cdot41 \,. \qquad \supset \vdash : \text{Hp} \,.\, S \in \kappa_\partial \,.\, R = I_\kappa \,.\, \supset \,.\, S\,(\kappa_\partial \upharpoonright U_\kappa)\,R$ (4)

$\vdash \,.\, (2) \,.\, (3) \,.\, (4) \,.\, \supset \vdash :. \text{Hp} \,.\, R, S \in \kappa \,.\, R \neq S \,.\, \supset :$

$R\,(\kappa_\partial \upharpoonright U_\kappa)\,S \,.\, \mathbf{v} \,.\, S\,(\kappa_\partial \upharpoonright U_\kappa)\,R$ (5)

$\vdash \,.\, (1) \,.\, (5) \,.\, \supset \vdash \,.\, \text{Prop}$

***370·37.** $\vdash : \kappa \in FM\,\text{cycl} \,.\, \supset \,.\, \kappa_\partial \upharpoonright U_\kappa \in \text{Ser}$ [*370·11·1·36]

***370·38.** $\vdash : \kappa \in FM\,\text{cycl} \,.\, R, S \in \kappa \,.\, \supset \,.\, \breve{R} \,|\, S = S \,|\, \breve{R}$ [*330·561 . *370·32]

***370·4.** $\vdash : \kappa \in FM\,\text{cycl} \,.\, \supset \,.\, \text{Cnv}``\kappa = K_\kappa \,|\, ``\kappa$

Dem.

$\vdash \,.\, *370\cdot31 \,.\, *330\cdot5 \,.\, \supset \vdash : \text{Hp} \,.\, \supset \,.\, K_\kappa \,|\, ``(\kappa_\partial - \iota'K_\kappa) \subset \text{Cnv}``\kappa$ (1)

$\vdash \,.\, (1) \,.\, *370\cdot26 \,. \qquad \supset \vdash : \text{Hp} \,.\, \supset \,.\, K_\kappa \,|\, ``\kappa \subset \text{Cnv}``\kappa$ (2)

$\vdash \,.\, *370\cdot311\cdot26 \,. \qquad \supset \vdash : \text{Hp} \,.\, R \in \kappa \,.\, \supset \,.\, \breve{R} \,|\, K_\kappa \in \kappa \,.$

[*370·26] $\supset \,.\, (\exists S) \,.\, S \in \kappa \,.\, \breve{R} = S \,|\, K_\kappa \,.$

[*330·5.*37·6] $\supset \,.\, \breve{R} \in K_\kappa \,|\, ``\kappa$ (3)

$\vdash \,.\, (2) \,.\, (3) \,.\, \supset \vdash \,.\, \text{Prop}$

***370·41.** $\vdash :. \kappa \in FM\,\text{cycl} \,.\, R, S \in \kappa \,.\, \supset : (K_\kappa \,|\, R)\, V_\kappa\, (K_\kappa \,|\, S) \,.\, \equiv \,.\, R U_\kappa S$

Dem.

$\vdash \,.\, *336\cdot54 \,.\, *370\cdot33 \,.\, \supset$

$\vdash :. \text{Hp} \,.\, \supset : (K_\kappa \,|\, R)\, V_\kappa\, (K_\kappa \,|\, S) \,.\, \equiv \,.\, (\exists T) \,.\, T \in \kappa_\partial \,.\, K_\kappa \,|\, R = T \,|\, K_\kappa \,|\, S \,.$

[*330·5.*370·26] $\equiv \,.\, (\exists T) \,.\, T \in \kappa_\partial \,.\, R = T \,|\, S \,.$

[*336·41] $\equiv \,.\, R U_\kappa S :. \supset \vdash \,.\, \text{Prop}$

***370·42.** $\vdash : \kappa \epsilon FM \text{ cycl} . \supset . \kappa \cap \text{Cnv}``\kappa = \iota`I_\kappa \cup \iota`K_\kappa$

Dem.

$\vdash . *370·22 . \supset \vdash : \text{Hp} . \breve{R} \epsilon \kappa_\partial - \iota`K_\kappa . \supset . \breve{R} | K \sim\epsilon \kappa .$

[*370·311.Transp] $\supset . R \sim\epsilon \kappa_\partial - \iota`K_\kappa$ (1)

$\vdash . (1) . \supset \vdash :. \text{Hp} . \supset : R, \breve{R} \epsilon \kappa . \supset . R \epsilon \iota`I_\kappa \cup \iota`K_\kappa$ (2)

$\vdash . (2) . *370·26 . \supset \vdash . \text{Prop}$

***370·43.** $\vdash : \kappa \epsilon FM \text{ cycl} . \supset . K_\kappa | ``\kappa_\partial = \text{Cnv}``\kappa - \iota`K_\kappa$ [*370·4]

***370·44.** $\vdash : \kappa \epsilon FM \text{ cycl} . \supset . \kappa_\partial \cap K_\kappa | ``\kappa_\partial = \Lambda$ [*370·42·43]

*371. THE SERIES OF VECTORS.

Summary of *371.

In this number, we begin by defining the relation W_κ, which takes the place, for cyclic families, of the relation V_κ defined in *336. The definition is

***371·01.** $W_\kappa = K_\kappa \,|\,; U_\kappa \upharpoonleft \kappa_\partial \ddagger U_\kappa \upharpoonleft \kappa_\partial$ Df

Then if κ is a cyclic family, W_κ is a series (*371·12), and its field is $\kappa \cup \text{Cnv}\text{``}\kappa$ (*371·14), which $= \kappa_\iota$ since κ has connexity. It will be observed that V_κ is not a series if κ is a cyclic family; we have *e.g.* $I_\kappa V_\kappa K_\kappa \,.\, K_\kappa V_\kappa I_\kappa$. The above relation W_κ is constructed so as to make a barrier at I_κ, thereby preventing the relation W_κ from being cyclic.

If P, Q are both members of κ_∂ or both members of $K_\kappa \,|\, \text{``}\kappa_\partial$,

$$PW_\kappa Q \,.\equiv.\, (\exists T) \,.\, T \in \kappa_\partial \,.\, P = Q \,|\, T \quad (*371·15·151).$$

Most of the properties of W_κ depend upon the fact that $\kappa_\partial \rceil U_\kappa$ is transitive, in virtue of the definition of cyclic families. If κ is any connected family, we have

$$\kappa_\partial \rceil U_\kappa \in \text{trans} \,.\equiv:\, P, Q, Q \,|\, R, P \,|\, Q \,|\, R \in \kappa_\partial \,.\, R \in \kappa \,.\supset_{P,Q,R} .\, P \,|\, Q \in \kappa_\partial \quad (*371·2).$$

This proposition is required for most of the subsequent proofs in this number. It leads at once to

***371·21.** $\vdash : \kappa \in FM\,\text{cycl} \,.\, P, Q, Q \,|\, R, P \,|\, Q \,|\, R \in \kappa_\partial \,.\, R \in \kappa \,.\supset.\, P \,|\, Q \in \kappa_\partial$

Most of the propositions of this number are concerned with the circumstances under which we can infer $(P \,|\, R) W_\kappa (Q \,|\, R)$ from $PW_\kappa Q$. We have

***371·31.** $\vdash :. \kappa \in FM\,\text{cycl} \,.\, R \in \kappa_\partial : P \in \kappa_\partial \,.\vee.\, P \,|\, R \sim\in \kappa_\partial :\supset:$
$$PW_\kappa Q \,.\supset.\, (P \,|\, R) W_\kappa (Q \,|\, R)$$

Another useful proposition is

***371·27.** $\vdash :. \kappa \in FM\,\text{cycl} \,.\, P, Q \in \kappa_\partial \,.\supset: PW_\kappa Q \,.\equiv.\, \breve{Q} W_\kappa \breve{P}$

***371·01.** $W_\kappa = K_\kappa \,|\,; U_\kappa \upharpoonleft \kappa_\partial \ddagger U_\kappa \upharpoonleft \kappa_\partial$ Df

***371·1.** $\vdash ::. \kappa \in FM\,\text{cycl} \,.\supset:: PW_\kappa Q \,.\equiv:.\, P, Q \in K_\kappa \,|\, \text{``}\kappa_\partial :$
$$(\exists R, S) \,.\, R, S \in \kappa_\partial \,.\, RU_\kappa S \,.\, P = K_\kappa \,|\, R \,.\, Q = K_\kappa \,|\, S :\vee:$$
$$P, Q \in \kappa_\partial \,.\, PU_\kappa Q :\vee: P \in K_\kappa \,|\, \text{``}\kappa_\partial \,.\, Q \in \kappa_\partial$$

[*202·55 . *370·34 . (*371·01)]

***371·11.** $\vdash : \kappa \in FM . K \in \kappa . \supset . (K|) \upharpoonright \kappa \in 1 \rightarrow 1$

Dem.

$\vdash . *330·31 . \supset \vdash : \text{Hp} . R, S \in \kappa . K|R = K|S . \supset . R = S : \supset \vdash . \text{Prop}$

***371·12.** $\vdash : \kappa \in FM\,\text{cycl} . \supset . W_\kappa \in \text{Ser}$ [*370·37·44 . *371·11 . *204·21·5]

***371·13.** $\vdash : \kappa \in FM\,\text{cycl} . \supset . W_\kappa = V_\kappa \,\text{£}\, (\text{Cnv}``\kappa - \iota`K_\kappa) ⇞ U_\kappa \,\text{£}\, \kappa_\partial$ [*370·41·43]

***371·14.** $\vdash : \kappa \in FM\,\text{cycl} . \supset . C`W_\kappa = \kappa \cup \text{Cnv}``\kappa = \kappa_\partial \cup K_\kappa|``\kappa_\partial$

Dem.

$\vdash . *202·55 . *370·34 . *160·14 . \supset \vdash : \text{Hp} . \supset . C`W_\kappa = K_\kappa|``\kappa_\partial \cup \kappa_\partial$

[*370·43] $\qquad = \kappa \cup \text{Cnv}``\kappa : \supset \vdash . \text{Prop}$

***371·15.** $\vdash :. \kappa \in FM\,\text{cycl} . P, Q \in \kappa_\partial . \supset : P W_\kappa Q . \equiv . (\exists T) . T \in \kappa_\partial . P = Q|T$
[*370·44 . *336·41 . (*371·01)]

***371·151.** $\vdash :. \kappa \in FM\,\text{cycl} . P, Q \in K_\kappa|``\kappa_\partial . \supset : P W_\kappa Q . \equiv . (\exists T) . T \in \kappa_\partial . P = Q|T$

Dem.

$\vdash . *370·44 . *336·41 . \supset \vdash :. \text{Hp} . \supset :$

$P W_\kappa Q . \equiv . (\exists R, S, T) . R, S, T \in \kappa_\partial . R = S|T . P = K_\kappa|R . Q = K_\kappa|S .$

[*370·26] $\qquad \equiv . (\exists T) . T \in \kappa_\partial . P = Q|T :. \supset \vdash . \text{Prop}$

***371·152.** $\vdash : \kappa \in FM\,\text{cycl} . P \in K_\kappa|``\kappa_\partial . Q \in \kappa_\partial . \supset . P W_\kappa Q$ [*371·1]

***371·16.** $\vdash : \kappa \in FM\,\text{cycl} . P \in \kappa_\partial . P W_\kappa Q . \supset . Q \in \kappa_\partial$ [*370·44 . *371·1]

***371·161** $\vdash : \kappa \in FM\,\text{cycl} . Q \in K_\kappa|``\kappa_\partial . P W_\kappa Q . \supset . P \in K_\kappa|``\kappa_\partial$
[*370·44 . *371·1]

***371·17.** $\vdash : \kappa \in FM\,\text{cycl} . Q, T \in \kappa_\partial . \supset . (Q|T) W_\kappa Q . (Q|T) W_\kappa T$
[*371·15·152]

***371·18.** $\vdash : \kappa \in FM\,\text{cycl} . \supset . \overrightarrow{W_\kappa}`K_\kappa = K_\kappa|``\kappa_\partial . \overleftarrow{W_\kappa}`K_\kappa = \kappa_\partial - \iota`K_\kappa$
[*371·15·152 . *370·311·22]

***371·19.** $\vdash :. \kappa \in FM\,\text{cycl} . P \neq I_\kappa . \supset : P W_\kappa K_\kappa . \equiv . K_\kappa W_\kappa \breve{P}$
[*371·18 . *370·43]

***371·2.** $\vdash :: \kappa \in FM\,\text{conx} . \supset :. \kappa_\partial \upharpoonleft U_\kappa \in \text{trans} . \equiv :$

$P, Q, Q|R, P|Q|R \in \kappa_\partial . R \in \kappa . \supset_{P,Q,R} . P|Q \in \kappa_\partial$

Dem.

$\vdash . *336·41 . \quad \supset \vdash :. \text{Hp} . \supset : T(\kappa_\partial \upharpoonleft U_\kappa) S . S(\kappa_\partial \upharpoonleft U_\kappa) R . \equiv .$

$(\exists P, Q) . P, Q, S, T \in \kappa_\partial . R \in \kappa . T = P|S . S = Q|R \qquad (1)$

$\vdash . (1) . *13·21 . \supset \vdash :: \text{Hp} . \supset :. \kappa_\partial \upharpoonleft U_\kappa \in \text{trans} . \equiv :$

$P, Q, Q|R, P|Q|R \in \kappa_\partial . R \in \kappa . \supset_{P,Q,R} . (P|Q|R) U_\kappa R \qquad (2)$

$\vdash . *330·31·5 . \supset$

$\vdash :. \text{Hp} . P, Q, R \in \kappa . M \in \kappa_\partial . P|Q|R = M|R . \supset . P|Q = M \qquad (3)$

$\vdash . (3) . *336·41 . \supset \vdash :. \text{Hp} . P, Q, R, P|Q|R \in \kappa . \supset :$

$(P|Q|R) U_\kappa R . \equiv . P|Q \in \kappa_\partial \qquad (4)$

$\vdash . (2) . (4) . \supset \vdash . \text{Prop}$

***371·21.** $\vdash : \kappa \in FM\,\text{cycl} \,.\, P, Q, Q \,|\, R, P \,|\, Q \,|\, R \in \kappa_\partial \,.\, R \in \kappa \,.\, \supset \,.\, P \,|\, Q \in \kappa_\partial$
[*371·2 . *370·1]

***371·22.** $\vdash : \kappa \in FM\,\text{cycl} \,.\, P, R, P \,|\, R \in \kappa_\partial \,.\, P W_\kappa Q \,.\, \supset \,.\, Q \,|\, R \in \kappa_\partial$

Dem.

$\vdash \,.\, *371{\cdot}15{\cdot}16 \,.\, \supset \vdash : \text{Hp} \,.\, \supset \,.\, (\exists T) \,.\, Q, T \in \kappa_\partial \,.\, P = Q \,|\, T$ (1)

$\vdash \,.\, (1) \,.\, \supset \vdash : \text{Hp} \,.\, \supset \,.\, (\exists T) \,.\, Q, R, T, Q \,|\, T, Q \,|\, T \,|\, R \in \kappa_\partial \,.$

[*371·21] $\supset \,.\, Q \,|\, R \in \kappa_\partial : \supset \vdash \,.\, \text{Prop}$

***371·23.** $\vdash : \kappa \in FM\,\text{cycl} \,.\, T W_\kappa S \,.\, \supset \,.\, T W_\kappa (\breve{S} \,|\, T)$

Dem.

$\vdash \,.\, *330{\cdot}31 \,.\, *370{\cdot}38 \,.\, \supset \vdash : \text{Hp} \,.\, \supset \,.\, T = S \,|\, (\breve{S} \,|\, T)$ (1)

$\vdash \,.\, (1) \,.\, *371{\cdot}15{\cdot}16 \,.\, \supset \vdash : \text{Hp} \,.\, T, \breve{S} \,|\, T \in \kappa_\partial \,.\, \supset \,.\, T W_\kappa (\breve{S} \,|\, T)$ (2)

$\vdash \,.\, *371{\cdot}15{\cdot}16 \,.\, \supset \vdash : \text{Hp} \,.\, T \in \kappa_\partial \,.\, \supset \,.\, \breve{S} \,|\, T \in \kappa_\partial$ (3)

$\vdash \,.\, (2) \,.\, (3) \,.\, \supset \vdash : \text{Hp} \,.\, T \in \kappa_\partial \,.\, \supset \,.\, T W_\kappa (\breve{S} \,|\, T)$ (4)

$\vdash \,.\, *371{\cdot}152 \,.\, \supset \vdash : \text{Hp} \,.\, T \sim\in \kappa_\partial \,.\, \breve{S} \,|\, T \in \kappa_\partial \,.\, \supset \,.\, T W_\kappa (\breve{S} \,|\, T)$ (5)

$\vdash \,.\, *371{\cdot}151{\cdot}161 \,.\, \supset \vdash : \text{Hp} \,.\, S \sim\in \kappa_\partial \,.\, \supset \,.\, T \sim\in \kappa_\partial \,.\, \breve{S} \,|\, T \in \kappa_\partial$ (6)

$\vdash \,.\, (5) \,.\, (6) \,.\, \supset \vdash : \text{Hp} \,.\, S \sim\in \kappa_\partial \,.\, \supset \,.\, T W_\kappa (\breve{S} \,|\, T)$ (7)

$\vdash \,.\, (1) \,.\, *371{\cdot}151 \,.\, \supset \vdash : \text{Hp} \,.\, T, \breve{S} \,|\, T \sim\in \kappa_\partial \,.\, S \in \kappa_\partial \,.\, \supset \,.\, T W_\kappa (\breve{S} \,|\, T)$ (8)

$\vdash \,.\, (5) \,.\, (8) \,.\, \supset \vdash : \text{Hp} \,.\, T \sim\in \kappa_\partial \,.\, S \in \kappa_\partial \,.\, \supset \,.\, T W_\kappa (\breve{S} \,|\, T)$ (9)

$\vdash \,.\, (4) \,.\, (7) \,.\, (9) \,.\, \supset \vdash \,.\, \text{Prop}$

***371·24.** $\vdash : \kappa \in FM\,\text{cycl} \,.\, P, R, P \,|\, R \in \kappa_\partial \,.\, P W_\kappa Q \,.\, \supset \,.\, (P \,|\, R) W_\kappa (Q \,|\, R)$

Dem.

$\vdash \,.\, *371{\cdot}15{\cdot}16 \,.\, \supset \vdash : \text{Hp} \,.\, \supset \,.\, (\exists T) \,.\, P, Q, R, P \,|\, R, T \in \kappa_\partial \,.\, P = Q \,|\, T \,.$

[*371·21.*330·5] $\supset \,.\, (\exists T) \,.\, P \,|\, R, Q \,|\, R, T \in \kappa_\partial \,.\, P \,|\, R = Q \,|\, R \,|\, T \,.$

[*371·15] $\supset \,.\, (P \,|\, R) W_\kappa (Q \,|\, R) : \supset \vdash \,.\, \text{Prop}$

***371·241.** $\vdash : \kappa \in FM\,\text{cycl} \,.\, P, R \in \kappa_\partial \,.\, P \,|\, R \sim\in \kappa_\partial \,.\, P W_\kappa Q \,.\, \supset \,.\, (P \,|\, R) W_\kappa (Q \,|\, R)$

Dem.

$\vdash \,.\, *371{\cdot}152 \,.\, \supset \vdash : \text{Hp} \,.\, Q \,|\, R \in \kappa_\partial \,.\, \supset \,.\, (P \,|\, R) W_\kappa (Q \,|\, R)$ (1)

$\vdash \,.\, *371{\cdot}15 \,.\, \supset$

$\vdash : \text{Hp} \,.\, Q \,|\, R \sim\in \kappa_\partial \,.\, \supset \,.\, (\exists T) \,.\, T \in \kappa_\partial \,.\, P \,|\, R, Q \,|\, R \sim\in \kappa_\partial \,.\, P \,|\, R = Q \,|\, R \,|\, T \,.$

[*371·151] $\supset \,.\, (P \,|\, R) W_\kappa (Q \,|\, R)$ (2)

$\vdash \,.\, (1) \,.\, (2) \,.\, \supset \vdash \,.\, \text{Prop}$

***371·25.** $\vdash : \kappa \in FM\,\text{cycl} \,.\, P, R \in \kappa_\partial \,.\, P W_\kappa Q \,.\, \supset \,.\, (P \,|\, R) W_\kappa (Q \,|\, R)$
[*371·24·241]

***371·251.** $\vdash : \kappa \in FM \text{ cycl} . R, \breve{R} | Q \in \kappa_\partial . P W_\kappa Q . \supset . (\breve{R} | P) W_\kappa (\breve{R} | Q)$

Dem.

$\vdash . *371·25 . \text{Transp} . *371·12 . \supset$

$\vdash : \kappa \in FM \text{ cycl} . P, R \in \kappa_\partial . (Q | R) W_\kappa (P | R) . \supset . Q W_\kappa P$ (1)

$\vdash . (1) \dfrac{\breve{R} | Q, \breve{R} | P}{P, \quad Q} . \supset \vdash . \text{Prop}$

***371·26.** $\vdash :. \kappa \in FM \text{ cycl} : P, Q \in \kappa_\partial . \vee . P, Q \sim \in \kappa_\partial : \supset :$

$P W_\kappa Q . \equiv . (K_\kappa | P) W_\kappa (K_\kappa | Q)$

Dem.

$\vdash . *371·25 . *370·26 . \supset \vdash : \text{Hp} . P \in \kappa_\partial . P W_\kappa Q . \supset . (K_\kappa | P) W_\kappa (K_\kappa | Q)$ (1)

$\vdash . *371·251 . *370·26 . \supset \vdash : \text{Hp} . Q \in \kappa_\partial . (K_\kappa | P) W_\kappa (K_\kappa | Q) . \supset . P W_\kappa Q$ (2)

$\vdash . (1) . (2) . \supset \vdash :. \text{Hp} . P, Q \in \kappa_\partial . \supset : P W_\kappa Q . \equiv . (K_\kappa | P) W_\kappa (K_\kappa | Q)$ (3)

$\vdash . (3) \dfrac{K_\kappa | P, K_\kappa | Q}{P, \quad Q} . *371·14 . \supset$

$\vdash :. \text{Hp} . P, Q \sim \in \kappa_\partial . \supset : P W_\kappa Q . \equiv . (K_\kappa | P) W_\kappa (K_\kappa | Q)$ (4)

$\vdash . (3) . (4) . \supset \vdash . \text{Prop}$

***371·27.** $\vdash :. \kappa \in FM \text{ cycl} . P, Q \in \kappa_\partial . \supset : P W_\kappa Q . \equiv . \breve{Q} W_\kappa \breve{P}$

Dem.

$\vdash . *371·15 . \supset \vdash :. \text{Hp} . \supset : P W_\kappa Q . \equiv . (\exists T) . T \in \kappa_\partial . P = Q | T .$

[*370·33] $\equiv . (\exists T) . T \in \kappa_\partial . \breve{Q} = \breve{P} | T .$

[*371·151·19.*370·43] $\equiv . \breve{Q} W_\kappa \breve{P} :. \supset \vdash . \text{Prop}$

***371·3.** $\vdash : \kappa \in FM \text{ cycl} . R \in \kappa_\partial . P | R \sim \in \kappa_\partial . P W_\kappa Q . \supset . (P | R) W_\kappa (Q | R)$

Dem.

$\vdash . *371·27 . \supset \vdash : \text{Hp} . \supset . \breve{Q} W_\kappa \breve{P} .$

[*371·251] $\supset . (\breve{R} | \breve{Q}) W_\kappa (\breve{R} | \breve{P}) .$

[*371·27] $\supset . (P | R) W_\kappa (Q | R) : \supset \vdash . \text{Prop}$

***371·31.** $\vdash :. \kappa \in FM \text{ cycl} . R \in \kappa_\partial : P \in \kappa_\partial . \vee . P | R \sim \in \kappa_\partial : \supset :$

$P W_\kappa Q . \supset . (P | \dot{R}) W_\kappa (Q | R)$ [*371·25·3]

*372. INTEGRAL SECTIONS OF THE SERIES OF VECTORS.

Summary of *372.

The subject of this number is that section of $\breve{W}_\kappa$ which consists of vectors not greater than the νth part of the whole circumference of the cycle. This is defined by means of W_κ, as consisting of those vectors which (taking W_κ as "greater than") are such that $R^{\sigma+1}$ is greater than R^σ so long as $\sigma < \nu$. It will be seen that so long as R^ν and all earlier powers of R do not exceed I_κ, R satisfies this condition; but if $R^\sigma \epsilon K_\kappa | ``\kappa_\partial$, while $R^{\sigma+1} \epsilon \kappa_\partial$, we shall have $R^\sigma W_\kappa R^{\sigma+1}$. Thus our definition selects those vectors which, starting from any origin, do not, by ν repetitions, take us farther than once round the cycle. The definition is

*372·01. $\nu_\kappa = (\kappa \cup \text{Cnv}``\kappa) \cap \hat{R}(\sigma < \nu . \sigma \neq 0 . \supset_\sigma . R^{\sigma+1} W_\kappa R^\sigma)$ Df

We then have $1_\kappa = \kappa \cup \text{Cnv}``\kappa$ (*372·11), $2_\kappa = \kappa_\partial$ (*372·13), $\mu \leqslant \nu . \supset . \nu_\kappa \subset \mu_\kappa$, *i.e.* ν_κ diminishes as ν increases (*372·15); $\nu > 1 . \supset . \nu_\kappa \subset \kappa_\partial$ (*372·16).

An alternative formula for ν_κ, sometimes more convenient than the one given in the definition, is (assuming $\nu > 1$)

$$\nu_\kappa = \kappa_\partial \cap \hat{P}(\mu < \nu . \mu \neq 0 . P^{\mu+1} \epsilon \kappa_\partial . \supset_\mu . P^\mu \epsilon \kappa_\partial) \quad (*372·17);$$

i.e. so long as $\mu < \nu$, either P^μ comes in the upper semi-circle, or $P^{\mu+1}$ comes in the lower semi-circle; that is to say, the step from P^μ to $P^{\mu+1}$ does not cross I_κ. For an even number (not zero), this leads to a simpler formula, namely

$$(2\nu)_\kappa = \kappa_\partial \cap \hat{P}(\mu \leqslant \nu . \mu \neq 0 . \supset_\mu . P^\mu \epsilon \kappa_\partial) \quad (*372·18).$$

We have next a set of propositions leading up to

*372·27. $\vdash :. \kappa \epsilon FM \text{cycl} . \nu \epsilon \text{NC ind} - \iota`0 . P \epsilon \nu_\kappa . PW_\kappa Q . \supset :$
$\mu \leqslant \nu . \mu \neq 0 . \supset . P^\mu W_\kappa Q^\mu$

whence, since W_κ is a series, we obtain

*372·28. $\vdash :. \kappa \epsilon FM \text{cycl} . \nu \epsilon \text{NC ind} - \iota`0 . P, Q \epsilon \nu_\kappa . \supset : P^\nu = Q^\nu . \equiv . P = Q$

It is largely owing to this proposition that ν_κ is important. In virtue of this proposition, there is in ν_κ at most one vector which is the νth submultiple of a given vector. We shall show later that, if κ is a submultipliable cyclic family, there is at least one such vector; hence there is a unique vector in ν_κ which is the νth submultiple of a given vector. This does not hold in general for larger classes than ν_κ.

A specially useful case of the above proposition is obtained by putting $\nu = 2$, which gives, in virtue of *372·13,

***372·29.** $\vdash :. \kappa \epsilon FM \text{ cycl} . P, Q \epsilon \kappa_\partial . \supset : P^2 = Q^2 . \equiv . P = Q$

The remaining propositions of this number are concerned in proving that ν_κ is an upper section of W_κ, *i.e.*

***372·33.** $\vdash : \kappa \epsilon FM \text{ cycl} . \nu \epsilon \text{NC ind} . \supset . \breve{W}_\kappa``\nu_\kappa \subset \nu_\kappa$

***372·01.** $\nu_\kappa = (\kappa \cup \text{Cnv}``\kappa) \cap \hat{R}(\sigma < \nu . \sigma \neq 0 . \supset_\sigma . R^{\sigma+1} W_\kappa R^\sigma)$ Df

***372·1.** $\vdash :. R \epsilon \nu_\kappa . \equiv : R \epsilon \kappa \cup \text{Cnv}``\kappa : \sigma < \nu . \sigma \neq 0 . \supset_\sigma . R^{\sigma+1} W_\kappa R^\sigma$ [(*372·01)]

***372·11.** $\vdash . 1_\kappa = \kappa \cup \text{Cnv}``\kappa$ [*372·1 . *117·53]

***372·12.** $\vdash : \kappa \epsilon FM \text{ cycl} . R \epsilon K | ``\kappa_\partial . \supset . R W_\kappa R^2$

Dem.

$\vdash . *371·152 . \supset \vdash : \text{Hp} . R^2 \epsilon \kappa_\partial . \supset . R W_\kappa R^2$ (1)

$\vdash . *370·44 . \supset \vdash : \text{Hp} . R^2 \sim \epsilon \kappa_\partial . \supset . R, R^2 \sim \epsilon \kappa_\partial . \breve{R} \epsilon \kappa_\partial . R = \breve{R} | R^2 .$

[*371·151] $\supset . R W_\kappa R^2$ (2)

$\vdash . (1) . (2) . \supset \vdash . \text{Prop}$

***372·121.** $\vdash : \kappa \epsilon FM \text{ cycl} . R \epsilon \kappa_\partial . \supset . R^2 W_\kappa R$ [*371·17]

***372·122.** $\vdash :. \kappa \epsilon FM \text{ cycl} . \supset : R \epsilon \kappa_\partial . \equiv . R^2 W_\kappa R$ [*372·12·121 . *371·12]

***372·13.** $\vdash : \kappa \epsilon FM \text{ cycl} . \supset . 2_\kappa = \kappa_\partial$ [*372·122]

***372·14.** $\vdash : \kappa \epsilon FM \text{ cycl} . \supset . K_\kappa \sim \epsilon 3_\kappa$

Dem. $\vdash . *371·152 . \supset \vdash : \text{Hp} . \supset . K_\kappa{}^2 W_\kappa K_\kappa{}^3 : \supset \vdash . \text{Prop}$

***372·15.** $\vdash : \mu \leqslant \nu . \supset . \nu_\kappa \subset \mu_\kappa$ [*372·1]

***372·16.** $\vdash : \kappa \epsilon FM \text{ cycl} . \nu > 1 . \supset . \nu_\kappa \subset \kappa_\partial$ [*372·15·13]

***372·17.** $\vdash : \kappa \epsilon FM \text{ cycl} . \nu > 1 . \supset .$

$$\nu_\kappa = \kappa_\partial \cap \hat{P}(\mu < \nu . \mu \neq 0 . P^{\mu+1} \epsilon \kappa_\partial . \supset_\mu . P^\mu \epsilon \kappa_\partial)$$

Dem.

$\vdash . *372·1·16 . *371·16 . \supset$

$\vdash : \text{Hp} . \supset . \nu_\kappa \subset \kappa_\partial \cap \hat{P}(\mu < \nu . \mu \neq 0 . P^{\mu+1} \epsilon \kappa_\partial . \supset_\mu . P^\mu \epsilon \kappa_\partial)$ (1)

$\vdash . *371·15 . \supset \vdash : \text{Hp} . P, P^\mu, P^{\mu+1} \epsilon \kappa_\partial . \supset . P^{\mu+1} W_\kappa P^\mu$ (2)

$\vdash . *371·152 . \supset \vdash : \text{Hp} . P, P^\mu \epsilon \kappa_\partial . P^{\mu+1} \sim \epsilon \kappa_\partial . \supset . P^{\mu+1} W_\kappa P^\mu$ (3)

$\vdash . *371·151 . \supset \vdash : \text{Hp} . P \epsilon \kappa_\partial . P^\mu, P^{\mu+1} \sim \epsilon \kappa_\partial . \supset . P^{\mu+1} W_\kappa P^\mu$ (4)

$\vdash . (2) . (3) . (4) . \supset \vdash :. \text{Hp} . P \epsilon \kappa_\partial : P^\mu \epsilon \kappa_\partial . \vee . P^{\mu+1} \sim \epsilon \kappa_\partial : \supset . P^{\mu+1} W_\kappa P^\mu$ (5)

$\vdash . (5) . *372·1 . \supset \vdash : \text{Hp} . \supset . \kappa_\partial \cap \hat{P}(\mu < \nu . \mu \neq 0 . P^{\mu+1} \epsilon \kappa_\partial . \supset_\mu . P^\mu \epsilon \kappa_\partial) \subset \nu_\kappa$ (6)

$\vdash . (1) . (6) . \supset \vdash . \text{Prop}$

***372·18.** $\vdash : \kappa \in FM \text{ cycl} . \nu > 0 . \supset . (2\nu)_\kappa = \kappa_\partial \cap \hat{P} (\mu \leqslant \nu . \mu \neq 0 . \supset_\mu . P^\mu \in \kappa_\partial)$

Dem.

$\vdash . *372·1 . *371·12 . \supset \vdash : \text{Hp} . P \in (2\nu)_\kappa . \supset . P^{2\nu} W_\kappa P^\nu .$

[*372·122] $\supset . P^\nu \in \kappa_\partial$ (1)

$\vdash . (1) . *372·17 . \supset \vdash : \text{Hp} . \supset . (2\nu)_\kappa \subset \kappa_\partial \cap \hat{P} (\mu \leqslant \nu . \mu \neq 0 . \supset_\mu . P^\mu \in \kappa_\partial)$ (2)

$\vdash . *371·15·152 . \supset \vdash : \text{Hp} . P, P^\mu \in \kappa_\partial . \supset . P^{\mu+1} W_\kappa P^\mu$ (3)

$\vdash . (3) . *371·25 . \supset \vdash : \text{Hp} . P, P^{\mu+1} \; P^\rho \in \kappa_\partial . \supset . P^{\mu+\rho+1} W_\kappa P^{\mu+\rho}$ (4)

$\vdash . (4) . \supset \vdash :. P \in \kappa_\partial : \mu \leqslant \nu . \mu \neq 0 . \supset_\mu . P^\mu \in \kappa_\partial : \supset :$

$\mu + 1 \leqslant \nu . \rho \leqslant \nu . \supset_{\mu, \rho} . P^{\mu+\rho+1} W_\kappa P^{\mu+\rho} :$

[*117·561] $\supset : \sigma < 2\nu . \supset_\sigma . P^{\sigma+1} W_\kappa P^\sigma$

[*372·1] $\supset : P \in (2\nu)_\kappa$ (5)

$\vdash . (2) . (5) . \supset \vdash . \text{Prop}$

***372·19.** $\vdash : \kappa \in FM \text{ cycl} . \mu, \nu \in \text{NC ind} - \iota`0 . P \in (\mu\nu)_\kappa . \supset . P^\mu \in \nu_\kappa$
[*372·1 . *371·12]

***372·2.** $\vdash : \kappa \in FM \text{ cycl} . \nu \in \text{NC ind} . P \in \nu_\kappa . \mu \leqslant \nu . \sigma < \mu . \sigma \neq 0 . \supset . P^\mu W_\kappa P^\sigma$
[*372·1 . *371·12]

***372·21.** $\vdash : \kappa \in FM \text{ cycl} . \nu \in \text{NC ind} . P \in \nu_\kappa . 2\mu \leqslant \nu . \mu \neq 0 . \supset .$
$P^{2\mu} W_\kappa P^\mu . P^\mu \in \kappa_\partial$

Dem.

$\vdash . *372·2 . \supset \vdash : \text{Hp} . \supset . P^{2\mu} W_\kappa P^\mu .$ (1)

[*372·122] $\supset . P^\mu \in \kappa_\partial$ (2)

$\vdash . (1) . (2) . \supset \vdash . \text{Prop}$

***372·22.** $\vdash : \kappa \in FM \text{ cycl} . P W_\kappa Q . P, P^\mu \in \kappa_\partial . P^\mu W_\kappa Q^\mu . \supset . P^{\mu+1} W_\kappa Q^{\mu+1}$

Dem.

$\vdash . *371·25 . \supset \vdash : \text{Hp} . \supset . P^{\mu+1} W_\kappa P \,|\, Q^\mu$ (1)

$\vdash . *371·16 . \supset \vdash : \text{Hp} . \supset . Q^\mu \in \kappa_\partial .$

[*371·25] $\supset . P \,|\, Q^\mu W_\kappa Q^{\mu+1}$ (2)

$\vdash . (1) . (2) . *371·12 . \supset \vdash . \text{Prop}$

***372·23.** $\vdash : \kappa \in FM \text{ cycl} . \nu \in \text{NC ind} . P \in \nu_\kappa . 2\mu \leqslant \nu . \mu \neq 0 . P W_\kappa Q . \supset .$
$P^{\mu+1} W_\kappa Q^{\mu+1}$ [*372·21·22 . Induct]

***372·24.** $\vdash :. \kappa \in FM \text{ cycl} . \sigma \in \text{NC ind} - \iota`0 . P \in (2\sigma)_\kappa . P W_\kappa Q . \supset :$
$\mu \leqslant 2\sigma . \mu \neq 0 . \supset . P^\mu W_\kappa Q^\mu$

Dem.

$\vdash . *372·21·23 . \supset \vdash : \text{Hp} . \xi \leqslant \sigma . \eta \leqslant \sigma . \supset . P^\eta, Q^\xi \in \kappa_\partial . P^\xi W_\kappa Q^\xi . P^\eta W_\kappa Q^\eta .$

[*371·25] $\supset . P^{\xi+\eta} W_\kappa P^\eta \,|\, Q^\xi . P^\eta \,|\, Q^\xi W_\kappa Q^{\xi+\eta} .$

[*371·12] $\supset . P^{\xi+\eta} W_\kappa Q^{\xi+\eta} : \supset \vdash . \text{Prop}$

***372·25.** $\vdash :. \kappa \in FM \text{ cycl} . \sigma \in \text{NC ind} - \iota`0 . P \in (2\sigma+1)_\kappa . P W_\kappa Q . \supset :$
$\mu \leqslant 2\sigma . \mu \neq 0 . \supset . P^\mu W_\kappa Q^\mu$ [*372·24·15]

***372·26.** $\vdash : \kappa \in FM \text{ cycl} . \sigma \in \text{NC ind} . P \in (2\sigma+1)_\kappa . P W_\kappa Q . \supset . P^{2\sigma+1} W_\kappa Q^{2\sigma+1}$

Dem.

$\vdash . *372·25 . \quad \supset \vdash :. \text{Hp} . \supset : P^{\sigma+1} W_\kappa Q^{\sigma+1} :$ (1)

[*371·3] $\quad \supset : P^{2\sigma+1} \sim \in \kappa_\partial . \supset . P^{2\sigma+1} W_\kappa P^\sigma | Q^{\sigma+1}$ (2)

$\vdash . *371·31 . (1) . \quad \supset \vdash :. \text{Hp} : P^\sigma | Q^{\sigma+1} \sim \in \kappa_\partial . \vee . Q^{\sigma+1} \in \kappa_\partial : \supset .$
$P^\sigma | Q^{\sigma+1} W_\kappa Q^{2\sigma+1}$ (3)

$\vdash . *372·21 . *371·15·151·152 . \supset \vdash :. \text{Hp} . \supset : P^\sigma | Q^{\sigma+1} W_\kappa P^\sigma :$

[*371·16] $\quad \supset : P^\sigma | Q^{\sigma+1} \in \kappa_\partial . \supset . Q^{\sigma+1} \in \kappa_\partial$ (4)

$\vdash . (3) . (4) . \quad \supset \vdash : \text{Hp} . \supset . P^\sigma | Q^{\sigma+1} W_\kappa Q^{2\sigma+1}$ (5)

$\vdash . (2) . (5) . *371·12 . \supset \vdash : \text{Hp} . P^{2\sigma+1} \sim \in \kappa_\partial . \supset . P^{2\sigma+1} W_\kappa Q^{2\sigma+1}$ (6)

$\vdash . *372·22 . \quad \supset \vdash : \text{Hp} . P^{2\sigma} \in \kappa_\partial . \supset . P^{2\sigma+1} W_\kappa Q^{2\sigma+1}$ (7)

$\vdash . *371·16 . *372·1 . \quad \supset \vdash : \text{Hp} . P^{2\sigma+1} \in \kappa_\partial . \supset . P^{2\sigma} \in \kappa_\partial$ (8)

$\vdash . (6) . (7) . (8) . \supset \vdash . \text{Prop}$

***372·27.** $\vdash :. \kappa \in FM \text{ cycl} . \nu \in \text{NC ind} - \iota`0 . P \in \nu_\kappa . P W_\kappa Q . \supset :$
$\mu \leqslant \nu . \mu \neq 0 . \supset . P^\mu W_\kappa Q^\mu$ [*372·24·25·26]

***372·28.** $\vdash :. \kappa \in FM \text{ cycl} . \nu \in \text{NC ind} - \iota`0 . P, Q \in \nu_\kappa . \supset : P^\nu = Q^\nu . \equiv . P = Q$

Dem.

$\vdash . *371·12 . \supset \vdash :. \text{Hp} . P \neq Q . \supset : P W_\kappa Q . \vee . Q W_\kappa P :$

[*372·27] $\quad \supset : P^\nu W_\kappa Q^\nu . \vee . Q^\nu W_\kappa P^\nu :$

[*371·12] $\quad \supset : P^\nu \neq Q^\nu$ (1)

$\vdash . (1) . \text{Transp} . \supset \vdash . \text{Prop}$

***372·29.** $\vdash :. \kappa \in FM \text{ cycl} . P, Q \in \kappa_\partial . \supset : P^2 = Q^2 . \equiv . P = Q$ [*372·28·13]

***372·3.** $\vdash : \kappa \in FM \text{ cycl} . \sigma \in \text{NC ind} - \iota`0 . P \in (2\sigma)_\kappa . P W_\kappa Q . \supset . Q \in (2\sigma)_\kappa$

Dem.

$\vdash . *372·18·27 . \supset \vdash :. \text{Hp} . \supset : \mu \leqslant \sigma . \mu \neq 0 . \supset_\mu . P^\mu \in \kappa_\partial . P^\mu W_\kappa Q^\mu .$

[*371·16] $\quad \supset_\mu . Q^\mu \in \kappa_\partial :$

[*372·18] $\quad \supset : Q \in \nu_\kappa :. \supset \vdash . \text{Prop}$

***372·31.** $\vdash :. \kappa \in FM \text{ cycl} . \sigma \in \text{NC ind} - \iota`0 . P \in \kappa_\partial . \supset : P W_\kappa \breve{P}^{2\sigma} . \supset . P^{2\sigma+1} \in \kappa_\partial$

Dem.

$\vdash . *371·16 . \quad \supset \vdash : \text{Hp} . P W_\kappa \breve{P}^{2\sigma} . \supset . \breve{P}^{2\sigma} \in \kappa_\partial$ (1)

$\vdash . *301·23 . \quad \supset \vdash : \text{Hp} . \supset . P = \breve{P}^{2\sigma} | P^{2\sigma+1}$ (2)

$\vdash . (1) . (2) . *371·15 . \supset \vdash : \text{Hp} . P W_\kappa \breve{P}^{2\sigma} . \supset . P^{2\sigma+1} \in \kappa_\partial : \supset \vdash . \text{Prop}$

***372·32.** $\vdash : \kappa \in FM \text{ cycl} . \sigma \in \text{NC ind} . P \in (2\sigma+1)_\kappa . P W_\kappa Q . \supset . Q \in (2\sigma+1)_\kappa$

Dem.

$\vdash . *372·3·15·17 . \quad \supset \vdash :. \text{Hp} . \supset : \mu \leqslant 2\sigma . Q^\mu \in \kappa_\partial . \supset . Q^{\mu-1} \in \kappa_\partial$ (1)

$\vdash . *371·16 . *372·27·1 . \supset \vdash : \text{Hp} . Q^{2\sigma} \sim \in \kappa_\partial . \supset . P^{2\sigma+1} \sim \in \kappa_\partial .$

[*372·31.Transp] $\supset . \breve{P}^{2\sigma} W_\kappa P .$

[*371·27] $\supset . \breve{Q}^{2\sigma} W_\kappa P .$

[Hp] $\supset . \breve{Q}^{2\sigma} W_\kappa Q .$

[*372·31.Transp] $\supset . Q^{2\sigma+1} \sim \in \kappa_\partial$ (2)

$\vdash . (1) . (2) . \text{Transp} . \quad \supset \vdash :. \text{Hp} . \supset : \mu \leqslant 2\sigma+1 . Q^\mu \in \kappa_\partial . \supset_\mu . Q^{\mu-1} \in \kappa_\partial :$

[*372·17] $\supset : Q \in (2\sigma+1)_\kappa :. \supset \vdash . \text{Prop}$

***372·33.** $\vdash : \kappa \in FM \text{ cycl} . \nu \in \text{NC ind} . \supset . \breve{W}_\kappa \text{“} \nu_\kappa \subset \nu_\kappa$ [*372·3·32]

*373. SUBMULTIPLES OF IDENTITY.

Summary of *373.

The purpose of this number is to prove that, in a cyclic submultipliable family, there exists a unique vector which is a member of ν_κ and satisfies $R^\nu = I_\kappa$. This we call the "principal" νth submultiple of I_κ. It is the smallest vector (other than I_κ) which satisfies $R^\nu = I_\kappa$. The proof of its existence proceeds by several stages; the problem is analogous to that of the construction of a regular polygon. Suppose the cycle divided into ν equal parts. Then a vector which takes us from any one point of division to any other is a νth submultiple of identity. If ν is prime, every such vector will have every power less than the νth different from I_κ; but if ν has factors, say ρ and σ, if $R^\nu = I_\kappa$, $(R^\rho)^\sigma = I_\kappa$; thus R^ρ, which is one of the νth submultiples of identity, has a power less than the νth which is equal to I_κ. We define (I_κ, ν) as the class of those νth submultiples of I_κ which have no power less than the νth equal to I_κ; more generally, we put

***373·03.** $(S, \nu) = \hat{P}(P^\nu = S : \sigma < \nu . \sigma \neq 0 . \supset_\sigma . P^\sigma \neq S)$ Dft

We then have first to prove the existence of $\kappa_\partial \cap (I_\kappa, \nu)$ when κ is cyclic and submultipliable. For this purpose, we put

***373·01.** $M_{\nu\kappa} = \hat{Q}\hat{P}(Q \epsilon \kappa_\partial . Q^\nu = P)$ Dft

I.e. $M_{\nu\kappa}$ is the relation of a νth submultiple of P to P, when the submultiple of P is a member of κ_∂. It is to be observed that although κ is submultipliable, we do not know to begin with that I_κ has submultiples which are members of κ_∂, except in the case of K_κ, which is half of I_κ. Owing to this, we proceed first by bisection, *i.e.* by means of the relation $M_{2\kappa}$. We prove that the process of bisection can be applied endlessly to any member of κ_∂, and always gives new terms (*373·14·13), hence it gives a progression starting from any member of κ_∂ (*373·141), and therefore the existence of a cyclic submultipliable family implies the axiom of infinity (*373·142); also we prove that ν bisections starting from a member of κ_∂ give a member of $(2^{\nu+1})_\kappa$ (*373·15). Hence, taking K_κ as the member of κ_∂ to be bisected, we arrive at

$$\mu = 2^{\nu+1} . \supset . \exists ! \kappa_\partial \cap (I_\kappa, \mu) \quad (*373{\cdot}17).$$

In order to extend this result to numbers not of the form $2^{\nu+1}$, we have first to prove that there are μth submultiples of identity. This we prove first for numbers of the form $2^\nu + 1$, then for $(2\sigma+1)2^\nu+1$, and then for 2σ (*373·21·22·23); hence it holds generally, *i.e.* we have

***373·25.** $\vdash : \kappa \epsilon FM \text{ cycl subm} . \mu \epsilon \text{NC ind} - \iota`0 - \iota`1 . \supset . (\exists Q) . Q \epsilon \kappa_\partial . Q^\mu = I_\kappa$

Next, we prove that, if $R \epsilon \kappa_\partial$ and $R^\mu = R^\nu = I_\kappa$, then μ, ν have some common factor ρ such that $R \epsilon (I_\kappa, \rho)$, *i.e.* such that R^ρ is the earliest power of R which is I_κ (*373·3). Hence if μ is prime, and $R^\mu = I_\kappa$, it follows that no earlier power of R is I_κ, *i.e.* $R \epsilon (I_\kappa, \mu)$ (*373·32), and that, if $R \epsilon (I_\kappa, \rho)$ and $R^\mu = I_\kappa$, then μ is a multiple of ρ (*373·33).

We now make a fresh start with the general relation $M_{\nu\kappa}$. Owing to *373·25, we know that $I_\kappa \epsilon \text{ᗡ}`M_{\nu\kappa}$. Also since $\kappa$ is submultipliable, $\kappa_\partial \subset \text{ᗡ}`M_{\nu\kappa}$. Hence if α is any inductive cardinal, $I_\kappa \epsilon \text{ᗡ}`M_{\nu\kappa}{}^\alpha$ (*373·404). Also it is easy to show that if ν is a prime, and $QM_{\nu\kappa}{}^\alpha I_\kappa$, Q^{ν^α} is the first power of Q which is I_κ. Hence when ν is prime, $\kappa_\partial \cap (I_\kappa, \nu^\alpha)$ exists (*373·43). In order to extend this result to numbers which are not powers of primes, we prove

***373·45.** $\vdash : \kappa \epsilon FM \text{ cycl} . \rho \text{ Prm } \sigma . R \epsilon (I_\kappa, \rho) . S \epsilon (I_\kappa, \sigma) . \supset . \breve{R} | S \epsilon (I_\kappa, \rho\sigma)$

Hence by the help of a little elementary arithmetic we arrive at

***373·46.** $\vdash : \kappa \epsilon FM \text{ cycl subm} . \rho \epsilon \text{NC ind} - \iota`0 - \iota`1 . \supset . \exists ! \kappa_\partial \cap (I_\kappa, \rho)$

Having now proved that there are νth submultiples of I_κ which have no power short of the νth equal to I_κ, we have still to show that there is one among them which is a member of ν_κ. For this purpose, we take any one of them and consider its powers. It is obvious that it has only ν different powers (*373·5), since after reaching I_κ the previous values repeat themselves. It is this fact which makes it easier to deal with submultiples of I_κ than with submultiples of other vectors.

Now let R be any νth submultiple of identity, and assume that S, T are powers of R, but T is not a power of S, and $TW_\kappa S$. Then $\breve{S} | T$ is a power of R but not of S, and $TW_\kappa(\breve{S} | T)$ (*373·53). Hence T is not the maximum, in the series W_κ, of the class $\text{Pot}`R - \text{Pot}`S$. Hence by transposition, if T is the maximum of $\text{Pot}`R - \text{Pot}`S$, we must have $SW_\kappa T$. Now since $\text{Pot}`R$ is a finite class, $\text{Pot}`R - \text{Pot}`S$ must have a maximum if it exists; but since $S$ has the relation $W_\kappa$ to this maximum, $S$ is not the maximum of $\text{Pot}`R$. Hence by transposition, if S is the maximum of $\text{Pot}`R$, $\text{Pot}`R - \text{Pot}`S$ is null, and therefore $\text{Pot}`R = \text{Pot}`S$ (*373·54). Hence it follows easily that, if $R \epsilon \kappa_\partial \cap (I_\kappa, \nu)$, the maximum of the powers of R is a member of $\kappa_\partial \cap (I_\kappa, \nu)$ (*373·55), and further that it is a member of ν_κ (*373·56). Since we have already proved (*373·46) the existence of $\kappa_\partial \cap (I_\kappa, \nu)$, we thus have

***373·6.** $\vdash : \kappa \epsilon FM \text{ cycl subm} . \nu \epsilon \text{NC ind} - \iota`0 . \supset . \exists ! \nu_\kappa \cap \hat{S}(S^\nu = I_\kappa)$

The uniqueness of $\nu_\kappa \cap \hat{S}(S^\nu = I_\kappa)$ follows from *372·28, and thus the principal νth submultiple of I_κ exists. Hence also it immediately follows that the other νth submultiples of I_κ are powers of the principal νth submultiple, and that the total number of νth submultiples is ν (*373·63·64).

***373·01.** $M_{\nu\kappa} = \hat{Q}\hat{P}(Q \,\epsilon\, \kappa_\partial \,.\, Q^\nu = P)$ Dft [*373—5]

***373·02.** Prime = NC ind $\cap\, \hat{\mu}(\mu = \sigma \times_c \tau \,.\, \supset_{\sigma,\tau} : \sigma = 1 \,.\, \vee \,.\, \sigma = \mu)$ Df

***373·03.** $(S, \nu) = \hat{P}(P^\nu = S : \sigma < \nu \,.\, \sigma \neq 0 \,.\, \supset_\sigma \,.\, P^\sigma \neq S)$ Dft [*373—5]

***373·1.** $\vdash : Q M_{2\kappa} P \,.\, \equiv \,.\, Q \,\epsilon\, \kappa_\partial \,.\, Q^2 = P$ [(*373·01)]

***373·11.** $\vdash : \kappa \,\epsilon\, FM$ cycl $. \supset .\, M_{2\kappa} \,\epsilon\, 1 \to 1$ [*372·29]

***373·12.** $\vdash : \kappa \,\epsilon\, FM$ cycl $. \supset .\, M_{2\kappa} \Subset \breve{W}_\kappa$ [*372·121]

***373·13.** $\vdash : \kappa \,\epsilon\, FM$ cycl $. \supset .\, (M_{2\kappa})_{po} \Subset \breve{W}_\kappa \,.\, (M_{2\kappa})_{po} \Subset J$ [*373·12 . *371·12]

***373·14.** $\vdash : \kappa \,\epsilon\, FM$ cycl subm $.\, P \,\epsilon\, \kappa_\partial \,.\, \nu \,\epsilon$ NC ind $- \iota\text{‘}0 \,.\supset .\, E\,!\, M_{2\kappa}{}^{\nu}\text{‘}P$

Dem.

$\vdash$. *372·29 . *351·1 . $\supset \vdash$:. Hp . $\supset : Q \,\epsilon\, \kappa_\partial \,.\supset .\, E\,!\, M_{2\kappa}\text{‘}P$ (1)

$\vdash$. (1) . Induct . $\supset \vdash$. Prop

***373·141.** $\vdash : \kappa \,\epsilon\, FM$ cycl subm $.\, P \,\epsilon\, \kappa_\partial \,.\supset .\, \breve{M}_{2\kappa} \upharpoonright (\overrightarrow{M_{2\kappa}})_*\text{‘}P \,\epsilon$ Prog
[*373·11·13·14]

***373·142.** $\vdash : \exists\,!\, FM$ cycl subm . $\supset$. Infin ax [*373·141]

***373·15.** $\vdash : \kappa \,\epsilon\, FM$ cycl subm $.\, P \,\epsilon\, \kappa_\partial \,.\, \nu \,\epsilon$ NC ind $. \supset .\, M_{2\kappa}{}^{\nu}\text{‘}P \,\epsilon\, (2^{\nu+1})_\kappa$.

Dem.

$\vdash$. *373·1·14 . $\supset \vdash : \text{Hp} \,.\, Q = M_{2\kappa}{}^{\nu-1}\text{‘}P \,.\, R = M_{2\kappa}{}^{\nu}\text{‘}P \,.\supset .\, Q^\sigma = R^{2\sigma}$ (1)

$\vdash$. (1) . *372·18 . $\supset \vdash$:. Hp (1) $.\, Q \,\epsilon\, (2^\nu)_\kappa \,.\supset : 2\sigma \leqslant 2^\nu \,.\supset .\, R^{2\sigma} \,\epsilon\, \kappa_\partial$ (2)

$\vdash$. (2) . *373·1 . $\supset \vdash$:. Hp (2) $. \supset : 2\sigma < 2^\nu \,.\supset .\, R^{2\sigma}, R^{2\sigma+2}, R^2, R \,\epsilon\, \kappa_\partial$.

[*371·2] $\supset .\, R^{2\sigma+1} \,\epsilon\, \kappa_\partial$ (3)

$\vdash$. (2) . (3) . $\supset \vdash$:. Hp (2) $. \supset : \mu \leqslant 2^\nu \,.\supset .\, R^\mu \,\epsilon\, \kappa_\partial$:

[*372·18] $\supset : R \,\epsilon\, (2^{\nu+1})_\kappa$ (4)

$\vdash$. *372·13 . $\supset \vdash : \text{Hp} \,.\, \nu = 0 \,.\supset .\, M_{2\kappa}{}^{\nu}\text{‘}P \,\epsilon\, 2_\kappa$ (5)

$\vdash$. (4) . (5) . Induct . $\supset \vdash$. Prop

***373·16.** $\vdash :. \kappa \,\epsilon\, FM$ cycl subm $.\, \nu \,\epsilon$ NC ind $.\, Q = M_{2\kappa}{}^{\nu}\text{‘}K_\kappa \,.\supset :$

$Q^{2^{\nu+1}} = I_\kappa : \rho < 2^{\nu+1} \,.\, \rho \neq 0 \,.\supset_\rho .\, Q^\rho \neq I_\kappa$

Dem.

$\vdash$. *373·1 . $\supset \vdash : \text{Hp} \,.\supset .\, Q^{2^\nu} = K_\kappa$.

[*371·26] $\supset .\, Q^{2^{\nu+1}} = I_\kappa$ (1)

$\vdash$. *373·15 . *372·2 . (1) . $\supset \vdash$:. Hp $. \supset : \rho < 2^{\nu+1} \,.\, \rho \neq 0 \,.\supset .\, Q^\rho W_\kappa I_\kappa$ (2)

$\vdash$. (1) . (2) . $\supset \vdash$. Prop

***373·17.** $\vdash : \kappa \in FM \text{ cycl subm} . \nu \in \text{NC ind} . \mu = 2^{\nu+1} . \supset . \exists ! \kappa_\partial \cap (I_\kappa, \mu)$
[*373·16·14 . (*373·03)]

***373·18.** $\vdash : Q \in \text{Cnv}``\kappa_\partial . Q^\nu = I_\kappa . \supset . \breve{Q} \in \kappa_\partial . \breve{Q}^\nu = I_\kappa$ [*50·5·51]

***373·19.** $\vdash : (\exists Q) . Q \in \kappa_\partial \cup \text{Cnv}``\kappa_\partial . Q^\nu = I_\kappa . \equiv . (\exists Q) . Q \in \kappa_\partial . Q^\nu = I_\kappa$
[*373·18]

***373·2.** $\vdash :. \kappa \in FM \text{ cycl subm} . \nu \in \text{NC ind} . P = M_{2\kappa}{}^{\nu}{}^{\backprime}K_\kappa .$
$S \in \kappa_\partial . S^{2^\nu+1} = P . S^{2^{\nu+1}} = Q . \supset . Q^{2^\nu+1} = I_\kappa . Q \neq I_\kappa$

Dem.

$\vdash . *301{\cdot}5 . \quad \supset \vdash : \text{Hp} . \supset . Q^{2^\nu+1} = P^{2^\nu+1} = I_\kappa$ (1)
$\vdash . *373{\cdot}1 . \quad \supset \vdash : \text{Hp} . \supset . P^{2^\nu+1} = K_\kappa | P .$
[*370·22] $\supset . P^{2^\nu+1} \neq P .$
[Hp] $\supset . P^{2^\nu+1} \neq S^{2^\nu+1} .$
[*30·37] $\supset . P \neq S$ (2)
$\vdash . *301{\cdot}5{\cdot}23 . \supset \vdash : \text{Hp} . \supset . Q = (S^{2^\nu+1})^2 | \breve{S}^2$
[Hp] $= P^2 | \breve{S}^2$
[(2).*372·29] $\neq I_\kappa$ (3)
$\vdash . (1) . (3) . \supset \vdash . \text{Prop}$

***373·21.** $\vdash : \kappa \in FM \text{ cycl subm} . \nu \in \text{NC ind} . \mu = 2^\nu + 1 . \supset .$
$(\exists Q) . Q \in \kappa_\partial . Q^\mu = I_\kappa$ [*373·2·19]

***373·22.** $\vdash : \kappa \in FM \text{ cycl subm} . \nu, \sigma \in \text{NC ind} . \mu = (2\sigma + 1) 2^\nu + 1 . \supset .$
$(\exists Q) . Q \in \kappa_\partial . Q^\mu = I_\kappa$

[The proof proceeds as in *373·2·21]

***373·23.** $\vdash : \kappa \in FM \text{ cycl subm} . \sigma \in \text{NC ind} . \mu = 2\sigma . \supset . (\exists Q) . Q \in \kappa_\partial . Q^\mu = I_\kappa$

Dem.

$\vdash . *370{\cdot}26 . \supset \vdash : \text{Hp} . \supset . K \in \kappa_\partial . K^\mu = I_\kappa : \supset \vdash . \text{Prop}$

***373·231.** $\vdash :. \tau \in \text{NC ind} . \supset : (\exists \sigma) : \sigma \in \text{NC ind} : \tau = 2\sigma . \vee . \tau = 2\sigma + 1$ [Induct]

***373·24.** $\vdash : \rho \in \text{NC ind} . \rho \neq 0 . \supset .$
$(\exists \nu, \sigma) . \nu, \sigma \in \text{NC ind} . 2\rho + 1 = (2\sigma + 1) 2^\nu + 1$

Dem.

$\vdash . *117{\cdot}661 . \supset$
$\vdash :. \text{Hp} . \lambda = \hat{\nu} \{(\exists \tau) . \tau \in \text{NC ind} - \iota{}^{\backprime}0 . \rho = \tau 2^\nu\} . \supset : \nu \in \lambda . \supset . \rho > \nu$ (1)
$\vdash . *116{\cdot}301 . \supset \vdash : \text{Hp} (1) . \supset . \rho = \rho 2^0 .$
[*10·24] $\supset . 0 \in \lambda$ (2)
$\vdash . (1) . (2) . *261{\cdot}26 . *263{\cdot}47 . \supset \vdash :. \text{Hp} (1) . \supset :$
$(\exists \nu) : \nu \in \lambda : \mu > \nu . \supset_\mu . \mu \sim\in \lambda$ (3)
$\vdash . *116{\cdot}52{\cdot}321 . \supset \vdash : \rho = \tau 2^\nu . \tau = 2\sigma . \supset . \rho = \sigma 2^{\nu+1}$ (4)

$\vdash . (3) . (4) . \supset \vdash :. \text{Hp} . \supset : (\exists \nu, \tau) : \nu, \tau \in \text{NC ind} . \rho = \tau 2^\nu : \mu > \nu . \supset_\mu .$

$\sim (\exists \tau) . \rho = \tau 2^\mu : \sim (\exists \sigma) . \tau = 2\sigma :$

[∗373·231] $\supset : (\exists \nu, \sigma) . \nu, \sigma \in \text{NC ind} . \rho = (2\sigma + 1) 2^\nu :$

[∗116·52·321] $\supset : (\exists \nu, \sigma) . \nu, \sigma \in \text{NC ind} . 2\rho + 1 = (2\sigma + 1) 2^{\nu+1} + 1 :. \supset \vdash . \text{Prop}$

∗373·25. $\vdash : \kappa \in FM \text{ cycl subm} . \mu \in \text{NC ind} - \iota`0 - \iota`1 . \supset .$

$(\exists Q) . Q \in \kappa_\partial . Q^\mu = I_\kappa$ [∗373·22·24·23·14]

∗373·3. $\vdash : \kappa \in FM \text{ cycl} . \mu \neq 0 . \nu \neq 0 . R \in \kappa_\partial . R^\mu = R^\nu = I_\kappa . \supset .$

$(\exists \rho, \alpha, \beta) . \rho \neq 0 . \rho \neq 1 . \mu = \alpha\rho . \nu = \beta\rho . R \in (I_\kappa, \rho)$

Dem.

$\vdash . ∗300·23 . \supset \vdash :. \text{Hp} . \supset : (\exists \rho) . \rho \neq 0 . R^\rho = I_\kappa : \sigma < \rho . \sigma \neq 0 . \supset_\sigma . R^\sigma \neq I_\kappa$ (1)

$\vdash . ∗301·2 . \supset \vdash : \text{Hp} . R^\rho = I_\kappa . \supset . \rho \neq 1$ (2)

$\vdash . ∗302·25 . \supset \vdash : \text{Hp} . \rho \in \text{NC ind} - \iota`0 . \supset .$

$(\exists \alpha, \beta, \gamma, \delta) . \mu = \alpha\rho + \beta . \nu = \gamma\rho + \delta . \beta < \rho . \delta < \rho$ (3)

$\vdash . ∗301·23·504 . \supset$

$\vdash : \text{Hp}(3) . R^\rho = I_\kappa . \mu = \alpha\rho + \beta . \nu = \gamma\rho + \delta . R^\mu = R^\nu = I_\kappa . \supset . R^\beta = R^\delta = I_\kappa$ (4)

$\vdash . (4) . \supset \vdash :. \text{Hp}(4) : \sigma < \rho . \sigma \neq 0 . \supset_\sigma . R^\sigma \neq I_\kappa :$

$\mu = \alpha\rho + \beta . \nu = \gamma\rho + \delta : \supset . \beta = 0 . \delta = 0$ (5)

$\vdash . (3) . (5) . \supset \vdash :. \text{Hp} : \rho \neq 0 . R^\rho = I_\kappa : \sigma < \rho . \sigma \neq 0 . \supset_\sigma . R^\sigma \neq I_\kappa : \supset .$

$(\exists \alpha, \gamma) . \mu = \alpha\rho . \nu = \gamma\rho$ (6)

$\vdash . (1) . (2) . (6) . (∗373·03) . \supset \vdash . \text{Prop}$

∗373·31. $\vdash : \kappa \in FM \text{ cycl} . R \in \kappa_\partial . \mu \neq 0 . \nu \neq 0 . R^\mu = R^\nu = I_\kappa . \supset . \sim (\mu \text{ Prm } \nu)$
[∗373·3]

∗373·32. $\vdash : \kappa \in FM \text{ cycl} . R \in \kappa_\partial . \mu \in \text{Prime} . R^\mu = I_\kappa . \supset . R \in (I_\kappa, \mu)$
[∗373·31 . Transp . (∗373·03)]

We assume here that a prime number is prime to all numbers less than itself except 1. This follows at once from the definition.

∗373·33. $\vdash : \kappa \in FM \text{ cycl} . R \in \kappa_\partial \cap (I_\kappa, \rho) . R^\mu = I_\kappa . \supset . (\exists \tau) . \mu = \rho\tau$ [∗373·3]

∗373·4. $\vdash : Q M_{\nu\kappa} P . \equiv . Q \in \kappa_\partial . P = Q^\nu$ [(∗373·01)]

∗373·401. $\vdash : \kappa \in FM \text{ cycl subm} . \nu \in \text{NC ind} - \iota`0 . \supset . I_\kappa \in \text{Q}`M_{\nu\kappa}$ [∗373·25]

∗373·402. $\vdash : \kappa \in FM \text{ subm} . \nu \in \text{NC ind} - \iota`0 . \supset . \kappa_\partial \subset \text{Q}`M_{\nu\kappa}$ [∗373·4]

∗373·403. $\vdash : \nu \in \text{NC ind} - \iota`0 . \supset . \text{D}`M_{\nu\kappa} \subset \kappa_\partial$ [∗373·4]

∗373·404. $\vdash : \kappa \in FM \text{ cycl subm} . \nu, \alpha \in \text{NC ind} - \iota`0 . \supset . I_\kappa \in \text{Q}`M_{\nu\kappa}{}^\alpha$
[∗373·401·402·403 . Induct]

∗373·405. $\vdash : \nu, \alpha \in \text{NC ind} - \iota`0 . Q M_{\nu\kappa}{}^\alpha I_\kappa . \supset . Q^{\nu^\alpha} = I_\kappa$ [∗373·4 . Induct]

***373·406.** $\vdash : \nu, \alpha \in \text{NC ind} - \iota`0 \,.\, R \in \text{D}`M_{\nu\kappa}{}^{\alpha} \,.\, \supset \,.\, \breve{M}_{\nu\kappa}{}^{\alpha}`R = R^{\nu^{\alpha}}$
[*373·4 . Induct]

***373·407.** $\vdash : \nu, \alpha, \gamma \in \text{NC ind} - \iota`0 \,.\, RM_{\nu\kappa}{}^{\alpha+\gamma}I_{\kappa} \,.\, \supset \,.\, R^{\nu^{\alpha}}M_{\nu\kappa}{}^{\gamma}I_{\kappa}$ [*373·406]

***373·41.** $\vdash : \nu, \alpha, \beta \in \text{NC ind} - \iota`0 \,.\, QM_{\nu\kappa}{}^{\alpha}I_{\kappa} \,.\, RM_{\nu\kappa}{}^{\beta}I_{\kappa} \,.\, \alpha < \beta \,.\, \supset \,.\, Q \neq R$

Dem.

$\vdash \,.\, *373·405·407·403 \,.\, \supset \vdash : \text{Hp} \,.\, \supset \,.\, Q^{\nu^{\alpha}} = I_{\kappa} \,.\, R^{\nu^{\alpha}} \in \kappa_{\partial} : \supset \vdash \,.\, \text{Prop}$

***373·42.** $\vdash : \kappa \in FM \text{ cycl} \,.\, \nu \in \text{Prime} - \iota`1 \,.\, \alpha \in \text{NC ind} \,.$
$QM_{\nu\kappa}{}^{\alpha}I_{\kappa} \,.\, \sigma < \nu^{\alpha} \,.\, \sigma \neq 0 \,.\, \supset \,.\, Q^{\sigma} \neq I_{\kappa}$

Dem.

$\vdash \,.\, *373·405 \,.\, *300·23 \,.\, \supset$

$\vdash :. \text{Hp} \,.\, \supset : (\exists \rho) : \rho \neq 0 \,.\, Q^{\rho} = I_{\kappa} : \sigma < \rho \,.\, \sigma \neq 0 \,.\, \supset_{\sigma} \,.\, Q^{\sigma} \neq I_{\kappa}$ (1)

$\vdash \,.\, *373·33·405 \,.\, \supset$

$\vdash :. \text{Hp} : \rho \neq 0 \,.\, Q^{\rho} = I_{\kappa} : \sigma < \rho \,.\, \sigma \neq 0 \,.\, \supset_{\sigma} \,.\, Q^{\sigma} \neq I_{\kappa} : \supset \,.\, (\exists \tau) \,.\, \nu^{\alpha} = \rho\tau \,.$

[Hp] $\supset \,.\, (\exists \beta) \,.\, \rho = \nu^{\beta}$ (2)

$\vdash \,.\, *373·407 \,.\, \supset \vdash : \text{Hp} \,.\, \beta < \alpha \,.\, \supset \,.\, Q^{\nu^{\beta}} \neq I_{\kappa}$ (3)

$\vdash \,.\, (2) \,.\, (3) \,.\, \supset \vdash : \text{Hp}(2) \,.\, \supset \,.\, \rho = \nu^{\alpha}$ (4)

$\vdash \,.\, (1) \,.\, (4) \,.\, \supset \vdash \,.\, \text{Prop}$

In obtaining (2) of the above proof, we assume that if ν is a prime, and $\rho\tau$ is a power of ν, then ρ is a power of ν. This is easily proved.

***373·43.** $\vdash : \kappa \in FM \text{ cycl subm} \,.\, \nu \in \text{Prime} - \iota`1 \,.\, \alpha \in \text{NC ind} - \iota`1 \,.\, \supset \,.$
$\exists ! \, \kappa_{\partial} \cap (I_{\kappa}, \nu^{\alpha})$ [*373·404·405·42]

***373·44.** $\vdash : \gamma \text{ Prm } \rho \,.\, \gamma \text{ Prm } \sigma \,.\, \supset \,.\, \gamma \text{ Prm } \rho\sigma$

Dem.

$\vdash \,.\, *302·1 \,.\, \supset \vdash :. \gamma \text{ Prm } \rho \,.\, \sim(\gamma \text{ Prm } \rho\sigma) \,.\, \sigma \in \text{NC ind} \,.\, \supset \,.$
$(\exists \tau, \alpha, \beta) \,.\, \tau \in \text{NC ind} - \iota`0 - \iota`1 \,.\, \gamma = \alpha\tau \,.\, \rho\sigma = \beta\tau$ (1)

$\vdash \,.\, *303·39 \,.\, \supset \vdash : \text{Hp}(1) \,.\, \tau \in \text{NC ind} - \iota`0 - \iota`1 \,.\, \gamma = \alpha\tau \,.\, \rho\sigma = \beta\tau \,.\, \supset \,.$
$\gamma/\rho = \alpha\sigma/\beta$ (2)

$\vdash \,.\, (2) \,.\, *303·341 \,.\, \supset \vdash : \text{Hp}(2) \,.\, \alpha\sigma \text{ Prm } \beta \,.\, \supset \,.\, \gamma = \alpha\sigma$ (3)

$\vdash \,.\, (3) \,.\, *302·1 \,.\, \supset \vdash : \text{Hp}(3) \,.\, \sigma \neq 1 \,.\, \supset \,.\, \sim(\gamma \text{ Prm } \sigma)$ (4)

$\vdash \,.\, *113·621 \,.\, \supset \vdash : \rho \in \text{NC} \,.\, \sigma = 1 \,.\, \sim(\gamma \text{ Prm } \rho\sigma) \,.\, \supset \,.\, \sim(\gamma \text{ Prm } \rho)$ (5)

$\vdash \,.\, (5) \,.\, \text{Transp} \,.\, \supset \vdash : \text{Hp}(1) \,.\, \supset \,.\, \sigma \neq 1 :$

[(4)] $\supset \vdash : \text{Hp}(3) \,.\, \supset \,.\, \sim(\gamma \text{ Prm } \sigma)$ (6)

$\vdash \,.\, *302·36 \,.\, \supset \vdash : \text{Hp}(2) \,.\, \sim(\alpha\sigma \text{ Prm } \beta) \,.\, \supset \,.$
$(\exists \xi, \eta, \zeta) \,.\, \xi \text{ Prm } \eta \,.\, \zeta \neq 1 \,.\, \alpha\sigma = \xi\zeta \,.\, \beta = \eta\zeta$ (7)

$\vdash \,.\, *303·39 \,.\, \supset \vdash : \text{Hp}(7) \,.\, \xi \text{ Prm } \eta \,.\, \zeta \neq 1 \,.\, \alpha\sigma = \xi\zeta \,.\, \beta = \eta\zeta \,.\, \supset \,.\, \alpha\sigma/\beta = \xi/\eta \,.$

[(2).*303·341] $\supset \,.\, \gamma = \xi \,.\, \rho = \eta \,.$

[Hp] $\supset \,.\, \alpha\rho\sigma = \beta\gamma = \alpha\rho\zeta\tau \,.$

[*126·41] $\supset \,.\, \sigma = \zeta\tau$ (8)

$\vdash . (7) . (8) . \quad \supset \vdash : \text{Hp}(7) . \supset . (\exists \zeta) . \gamma = \alpha\tau . \sigma = \zeta\tau .$

[$*302\cdot1$.Hp] $\quad \supset . \sim (\gamma \text{ Prm } \sigma)$ (9)

$\vdash . (6) . (9) . \quad \supset \vdash : \text{Hp}(2) . \supset . \sim (\gamma \text{ Prm } \sigma)$ (10)

$\vdash . (1) . (10) . \supset \vdash : \gamma \text{ Prm } \rho . \sim (\gamma \text{ Prm } \rho\sigma) . \sigma \in \text{NC ind} . \supset . \sim (\gamma \text{ Prm } \sigma)$ (11)

$\vdash . (11) . \text{Transp} . \supset \vdash . \text{Prop}$

$*373\cdot441$. $\vdash :. \rho \text{ Prm } \sigma : (\exists \delta) . \rho\beta = \delta\sigma : \supset . (\exists \zeta) . \beta = \zeta\sigma$

Dem.

$\vdash . *126\cdot41 . \supset$

$\vdash : \text{Hp} . \rho\beta = \delta\sigma . \rho = \xi\varpi . \delta = \eta\varpi . \xi \text{ Prm } \eta . \supset . \xi\beta = \eta\sigma . \xi \text{ Prm } \eta . \xi \text{ Prm } \sigma .$

[$*373\cdot44$] $\quad \supset . \xi\beta = \eta\sigma . \xi \text{ Prm } \eta\sigma$ (1)

$\vdash . (1) . \quad \supset \vdash : \text{Hp}(1) . \xi \neq 1 . \supset . \xi \neq 1 . \xi = \xi \times_c 1 . \eta\sigma = \xi \times_c \beta .$

[$*302\cdot1$] $\quad \supset . \sim (\xi \text{ Prm } \eta\sigma)$ (2)

$\vdash . (2) . \text{Transp} . (1) . \supset \vdash : \text{Hp}(1) . \supset . \xi = 1$ (3)

$\vdash . (1) . (3) . \supset \vdash . \text{Prop}$

$*373\cdot45$. $\vdash : \kappa \in FM \text{ cycl} . \rho \text{ Prm } \sigma . R \in (I_\kappa, \rho) . S \in (I_\kappa, \sigma) . \supset . \breve{R} \mid S \in (I_\kappa, \rho\sigma)$

Dem.

$\vdash . *370\cdot33 . \quad \supset \vdash : \text{Hp} . \supset . (\breve{R} \mid S)^{\rho\sigma} = I_\kappa$ (1)

$\vdash . (1) . *373\cdot31 . \supset \vdash :. \text{Hp} . (\breve{R} \mid S)^\gamma = I_\kappa . \gamma \neq 0 . \supset : \sim (\gamma \text{ Prm } \rho\sigma) :$

[$*373\cdot44$] $\quad \supset : \sim (\gamma \text{ Prm } \rho) . \vee . \sim (\gamma \text{ Prm } \sigma)$ (2)

$\vdash . *370\cdot33 . *301\cdot504 . \supset$

$\vdash : \text{Hp}(2) . \rho = \alpha\tau . \gamma = \beta\tau . \supset . I_\kappa = (\breve{R} \mid S)^{\alpha\beta\tau} = S^{\alpha\beta\tau} = S^{\rho\beta} .$

[$*373\cdot33$] $\quad \supset . (\exists \delta) . \rho\beta = \delta\sigma .$

[$*373\cdot441$] $\quad \supset . (\exists \zeta) . \beta = \zeta\sigma$ (3)

$\vdash . (3) . \quad \supset \vdash : \text{Hp}(3) . \supset . (\breve{R} \mid S)^{\beta\tau} = I_\kappa . S^{\beta\tau} = I_\kappa .$

[$*370\cdot33$] $\quad \supset . R^{\beta\tau} = I_\kappa .$

[$*373\cdot33$] $\quad \supset . (\exists \mu) . \beta\tau = \mu\alpha\tau .$

[Hp] $\quad \supset . (\exists \mu) . \gamma = \mu\rho . \mu \neq 0$ (4)

$\vdash . (3) . (4) . \supset \vdash : \text{Hp}(3) . \supset . (\exists \nu) . \gamma = \nu\rho\sigma . \nu \neq 0$ (5)

Similarly $\quad \vdash : \text{Hp} . \sim (\gamma \text{ Prm } \sigma) . \supset . (\exists \nu) . \gamma = \nu\rho\sigma . \nu \neq 0$ (6)

$\vdash . (2) . (5) . (6) . \supset \vdash : \text{Hp}(2) . \supset . (\exists \nu) . \nu \neq 0 . \gamma = \nu\rho\sigma$ (7)

$\vdash . (1) . (7) . *117\cdot62 . \supset \vdash . \text{Prop}$

$*373\cdot451$. $\vdash :. \rho \in \text{NC ind} - \iota\text{‘}0 : \sim (\exists \nu, \alpha) . \nu \in \text{Prime} . \rho = \nu^\alpha : \supset .$

$(\exists \mu, \nu) . \mu \text{ Prm } \nu . \mu < \rho . \nu < \rho . \rho = \mu\nu$

Dem.

$\vdash . *261\cdot26 . *263\cdot47 . \supset$

$\vdash : \text{Hp} . \supset . (\exists \gamma, \alpha) . \gamma \in \text{Prime} . \rho \in \text{D‘}\times_c \gamma^\alpha . \rho \sim\in \text{D‘}\times_c \gamma^{\alpha+1} . \rho \neq \gamma^\alpha .$

[$*373\cdot44$.Induct] $\supset . (\exists \gamma, \alpha, \beta) . \gamma \in \text{Prime} . \rho = \gamma^\alpha\beta . \beta \text{ Prm } \gamma^\alpha . \beta \neq 1 : \supset \vdash . \text{Prop}$

***373·452.** $\vdash :. \nu \epsilon \text{Prime} . \alpha \epsilon \text{NC ind} . \supset_{\nu, \alpha} . \phi(\nu^{\alpha}) : \mu \text{ Prm } \nu . \phi\mu . \phi\nu . \supset_{\mu,\nu} .$
$\phi(\mu\nu) : \supset : \rho \epsilon \text{NC ind} - \iota\text{‘}0 . \supset_{\rho} . \phi(\rho)$ [*373·451]

***373·46.** $\vdash : \kappa \epsilon FM \text{ cycl subm} . \rho \epsilon \text{NC ind} - \iota\text{‘}0 - \iota\text{‘}1 . \supset . \exists ! \kappa_{\partial} \cap (I_{\kappa}, \rho)$
[*373·43·45·18·452]

***373·5.** $\vdash : \kappa \epsilon FM \text{ cycl} . \nu \epsilon \text{NC ind} . R \epsilon \kappa_{\partial} \cap (I_{\kappa}, \nu) . \supset . \text{Pot‘}R \epsilon \nu$

Dem.

$\vdash . *302·25 . *301·504 . \supset$
$\vdash : \text{Hp} . \alpha \epsilon \text{NC ind} . \supset . (\exists \xi, \eta) . \alpha = \xi\nu + \eta . \eta < \nu . R^{\alpha} = R^{\eta} .$
[*120·57] $\supset . \text{Nc‘Pot‘}R \leqslant \nu$ (1)
$\vdash . *301·23 . \quad \supset \vdash : \text{Hp} . \rho < \nu . \sigma < \rho . \supset . \breve{R}^{\sigma} | R^{\rho} = R^{\rho \dot{-} \sigma} .$
[Hp] $\supset . \breve{R}^{\sigma} | R^{\rho} \neq I_{\kappa} .$
[*330·32] $\supset . R^{\rho} \neq R^{\sigma}$ (2)
$\vdash . (2) . \text{Transp} . \supset \vdash : \text{Hp} . \rho < \nu . \sigma < \nu . R^{\rho} = R^{\sigma} . \supset . \rho = \nu$ (3)
$\vdash . (3) . *120·57 . \supset \vdash : \text{Hp} . \supset . \text{Nc‘Pot‘}R \geqslant \nu$ (4)
$\vdash . (1) . (4) . \supset \vdash . \text{Prop}$

***373·51.** $\vdash : \kappa \epsilon FM \text{ cycl} . R \epsilon \kappa_{\partial} \cap (I_{\kappa}, \mu\nu) . \supset . R^{\mu} \epsilon (I_{\kappa}, \nu) . \text{Pot‘}R^{\mu} \epsilon \nu$

Dem.

$\vdash . *301·504 . \supset$
$\vdash :. \text{Hp} . \supset : (R^{\mu})^{\nu} = I_{\kappa} : \sigma < \nu . \sigma \neq 0 . \supset_{\sigma} . (R^{\mu})^{\sigma} \neq I_{\kappa} :. \supset \vdash . \text{Prop}$

***373·52.** $\vdash : \kappa \epsilon FM \text{ cycl} . R \epsilon \kappa_{\partial} \cap (I_{\kappa}, \nu) . \mu \text{ Prm } \nu . \supset .$
$R^{\mu} \epsilon (I_{\kappa}, \nu) . \text{Pot‘}R^{\mu} = \text{Pot‘}R$

Dem.

$\vdash . *373·33 . \quad \supset \vdash : \text{Hp} . R^{\mu} \epsilon (I_{\kappa}, \rho) . \supset . (\exists \tau) . \mu\rho = \nu\tau .$
[*373·441] $\supset . (\exists \zeta) . \rho = \nu\zeta$ (1)
$\vdash . *301·504 . \quad \supset \vdash : \text{Hp}(1) . \supset . (R^{\mu})^{\nu} = I_{\kappa} .$
[Hp] $\supset . \rho \leqslant \nu$ (2)
$\vdash . (1) . (2) . \quad \supset \vdash : \text{Hp} . \supset . R^{\mu} \epsilon (I_{\kappa}, \nu)$ (3)
$\vdash . (3) . *373·51 . \supset \vdash : \text{Hp} . \supset . \text{Nc‘Pot‘}R^{\mu} = \text{Nc‘Pot‘}R = \nu$ (4)
$\vdash . *91·6 . \quad \supset \vdash : \text{Hp} . \supset . \text{Pot‘}R^{\mu} \subset \text{Pot‘}R$ (5)
$\vdash . (4) . (5) . *120·426 . \text{Transp} . \supset \vdash : \text{Hp} . \supset . \text{Pot‘}R^{\mu} = \text{Pot‘}R$ (6)
$\vdash . (3) . (6) . \supset \vdash . \text{Prop}$

***373·521.** $\vdash : \kappa \epsilon FM \text{ cycl} . R \epsilon (\kappa_{\partial} \cup \text{Cnv‘‘}\kappa_{\partial}) . \nu \epsilon \text{NC ind} . R^{\nu} = I_{\kappa} . \supset . \breve{R} \epsilon \text{Pot‘}R$

Dem.

$\vdash . *301·2 . *13·14 . \supset \vdash : \text{Hp} . \supset . \nu \neq 0$ (1)
$\vdash . (1) . *301·21 . \quad \supset \vdash : \text{Hp} . \supset . \breve{R} = R^{\nu \dot{-} 1} : \supset \vdash . \text{Prop}$

∗373·522. $\vdash :$ Hp ∗373·521 . $S, T \epsilon$ Pot‘R . ⊃ . $\breve{S} | T \epsilon$ Pot‘R

Dem.

$\vdash$. ∗373·521 . ⊃ $\vdash$: Hp . ⊃ . $\breve{S} \epsilon$ Pot‘S .

[∗91·6] ⊃ . $\breve{S} \epsilon$ Pot‘R .

[∗91·343] ⊃ . $\breve{S} | T \epsilon$ Pot‘R : ⊃ $\vdash$. Prop

∗373·53. $\vdash :$ Hp ∗373·521 . $S, T \epsilon$ Pot‘R . $T \sim\epsilon$ Pot‘S . $TW_\kappa S$. ⊃ .
$TW_\kappa (\breve{S} | T)$. $\breve{S} | T \epsilon$ Pot‘R − Pot‘S

Dem.

$\vdash$. ∗371·23 . ⊃ $\vdash$: Hp . ⊃ . $TW_\kappa (\breve{S} | T)$ (1)

$\vdash$. ∗373·522 . ⊃ $\vdash$: Hp . ⊃ . $\breve{S} | T \epsilon$ Pot‘R (2)

$\vdash$. ∗91·36 . Transp . ⊃ $\vdash$: Hp . ⊃ . $\breve{S} | T \sim\epsilon$ Pot‘S (3)

$\vdash$. (1) . (2) . (3) . ⊃ $\vdash$. Prop

∗373·531. $\vdash :$ Hp ∗373·53 . ⊃ . $\sim \{T = \max (W_\kappa)$‘(Pot‘$R$ − Pot‘S)} [∗373·53]

∗373·532. $\vdash :$ Hp ∗373·521 . $S \epsilon$ Pot‘R . $T = \max (W_\kappa)$‘(Pot‘R − Pot‘S) . ⊃ .
$SW_\kappa T$ [∗373·531 . Transp . ∗371·12]

∗373·533. $\vdash :$ Hp ∗373·521 . $S \epsilon$ Pot‘R . E ! max (W_κ)‘(Pot‘R − Pot‘S) . ⊃ .
$\sim \{S = \max (W_\kappa)$‘Pot‘$R\}$ [∗373·532]

∗373·54. $\vdash :$ Hp ∗373·521 . $S = \max (W_\kappa)$‘Pot‘R . ⊃ . Pot‘R = Pot‘S

Dem.

$\vdash$. ∗373·533 . Transp . ⊃ $\vdash$: Hp . ⊃ . $\sim$ E ! max (W_κ)‘(Pot‘R − Pot‘S) (1)

$\vdash$. (1) . ∗373·3·5 . ∗261·26 . Transp . ⊃ $\vdash$: Hp . ⊃ . Pot‘R − Pot‘$S = \Lambda$ (2)

$\vdash$. (2) . ∗91·6 . ⊃ $\vdash$. Prop

∗373·55. $\vdash : \kappa \epsilon FM$ cycl . $\nu \epsilon$ NC ind − ι‘0 . $R \epsilon \kappa_\partial \cap (I_\kappa, \nu)$.
$S = \max (W_\kappa)$‘Pot‘R . ⊃ . $S \epsilon (I_\kappa, \nu)$

Dem.

$\vdash$. ∗373·3·5 . ⊃ $\vdash$: Hp . ⊃ . $(\exists \rho)$. $\rho \epsilon$ NC ind − ι‘0 . $S \epsilon (I_\kappa, \rho)$. Pot‘$S \epsilon \rho$ (1)

$\vdash$. ∗373·54·5 . ⊃ $\vdash$:. Hp . ⊃ : Pot‘$S \epsilon \nu$:

[∗100·34] ⊃ : $\rho \epsilon$ NC . Pot‘$S \epsilon \rho$. ⊃ . $\rho = \nu$ (2)

$\vdash$. (1) . (2) . ⊃ $\vdash$. Prop

∗373·56. $\vdash :$ Hp ∗373·55 . ⊃ . $S \epsilon \nu_\kappa$

Dem.

$\vdash$. ∗205·21 . ⊃ $\vdash$: Hp . $Q \epsilon$ Pot‘R − ι‘S . ⊃ . $QW_\kappa S$ (1)

$\vdash$. (1) . ∗301·21 . ⊃ $\vdash$:. Hp . $\alpha \epsilon$ NC ind . $S^{\alpha+1} \neq S$. ⊃ : $S^{\alpha+1} W_\kappa S$. $S^{\alpha+1} = S^\alpha | S$:

[∗371·15] ⊃ : $S^{\alpha+1} \epsilon \kappa_\partial$. ⊃ . $S^\alpha \epsilon \kappa_\partial$ (2)

$\vdash$. (2) . ∗373·55 . ⊃ $\vdash$:. Hp . ⊃ : $\alpha \neq 0$. $\alpha < \nu$. $S^{\alpha+1} \epsilon \kappa_\partial$. ⊃ . $S^\alpha \epsilon \kappa_\partial$ (3)

$\vdash$. ∗371·16 . ⊃ $\vdash$: Hp . ⊃ . $S \epsilon \kappa_\partial$ (4)

$\vdash$. ∗301·2 . ∗13·14 . ⊃ $\vdash$: Hp . ⊃ . $\nu > 1$ (5)

$\vdash$. (3) . (4) . (5) . ∗372·17 . ⊃ $\vdash$. Prop

***373·6.** $\vdash : \kappa \in FM \text{ cycl subm} . \nu \in \text{NC ind} - \iota`0 . \supset . \exists ! \nu_\kappa \cap \hat{S}(S^\nu = I_\kappa)$
[*373·46·56·5 . *261·26 . *372·11]

***373·61.** $\vdash : \text{Hp} *373\cdot6 . \supset . \nu_\kappa \cap \hat{S}(S^\nu = I_\kappa) \in 1$ [*372·28 . *373·6]

***373·62.** $\vdash : \text{Hp} *373\cdot6 . S \in \nu_\kappa . S^\nu = I_\kappa . \supset .$

$$S \in (I_\kappa, \nu) . \text{Pot}`S = \hat{P}(P^\nu = I_\kappa) \cap (\kappa \cup \text{Cnv}``\kappa)$$

Dem.

$\vdash . *373\cdot55\cdot56\cdot61 . \supset \vdash : \text{Hp} . \supset . S \in (I_\kappa, \nu)$ (1)

$\vdash . *373\cdot56\cdot54 . \quad \supset \vdash : \text{Hp} . R \in (I_\kappa, \nu) \cap \kappa_\partial . T = \max(W_\kappa)`\text{Pot}`R . \supset .$

$\qquad S, T \in \nu_\kappa . S^\nu = T^\nu . R \in \text{Pot}`T .$

[*372·28] $\supset . S = T . R \in \text{Pot}`T .$

[*13·12] $\supset . R \in \text{Pot}`S$ (2)

$\vdash . *373\cdot33 . \quad \supset \vdash : \text{Hp} . R \in (I_\kappa, \mu) \cap \kappa_\partial . R^\nu = I_\kappa . \supset . (\exists \tau) . \nu = \mu\tau$ (3)

$\vdash . *372\cdot19 . \quad \supset \vdash :. \text{Hp} . \supset : \nu = \mu\tau . \supset . S^\tau \in \mu_\kappa .$

[(2)] $\supset . R \in \text{Pot}`S^\tau$ (4)

$\vdash . (3) . (4) . \quad \supset \vdash : \text{Hp}(3) . \supset . R \in \text{Pot}`S$ (5)

$\vdash . (1) . (2) . (5) . \supset \vdash . \text{Prop}$

***373·63.** $\vdash : \kappa \in FM \text{ cycl subm} . \nu \in \text{NC ind} - \iota`0 . \supset .$
$\hat{P}(P^\nu = I_\kappa) \cap (\kappa \cup \text{Cnv}``\kappa) = \text{Pot}`(\imath S)(S \in \nu_\kappa . S^\nu = I_\kappa)$ [*373·61·62]

***373·64.** $\vdash : \kappa \in FM \text{ cycl subm} . \nu \in \text{NC ind} - \iota`0 . \supset .$

$$\text{Nc}`\{\hat{P}(P^\nu = I_\kappa) \cap (\kappa \cup \text{Cnv}``\kappa)\} = \nu$$ [*373·63·5]

*374. PRINCIPAL SUBMULTIPLES.

Summary of *374.

In this number we prove for any vector what was proved for I_κ in *373, namely that, if ν is any inductive cardinal not zero, and R is any vector, there is just one member of ν_κ whose νth power is R. This one we call the "principal" νth submultiple of R. The proof of its existence is as follows.

Assume R is a non-zero vector, and Q is a νth submultiple of R. (Q exists provided we assume that κ is submultipliable.) Let T be the principal νth submultiple of I_κ, whose existence has been proved at the end of *373. We wish to prove that there is a νth submultiple of R which is a member of ν_κ. By *372·33, Q is a member of ν_κ if $TW_\kappa Q$. But if $QW_\kappa T$, then T must have a last power T^σ such that $QW_\kappa T^\sigma$, and for this value of σ we shall therefore have $T^{\sigma+1} W_\kappa Q$. (We cannot have $T^{\sigma+1} = Q$, because if Q were a power of T, we should have $Q^\nu = I_\kappa$, whereas by hypothesis $Q^\nu = R$.) Now if $T^{\sigma+1} W_\kappa Q \,.\, QW_\kappa T^\sigma$, the vector $\breve{T}^\sigma | Q$ must be less than T, *i.e.* we shall have $TW_\kappa(\breve{T}^\sigma | Q)$, and therefore $\breve{T}^\sigma | Q$ will be a member of ν_κ, by *372·33. Moreover since $T^\nu = I_\kappa$, we have $(\breve{T}^\sigma | Q)^\nu = Q^\nu = R$ by hypothesis. Hence $\breve{T}^\sigma | Q$ is a νth submultiple of R and a member of ν_κ. In virtue of *372·28, it is the only νth submultiple of R which is a member of ν_κ. Thus the existence of the principal νth submultiple of any vector is proved, assuming the family concerned to be cyclic and submultipliable.

We prove also in this number that ν_κ consists of all non-zero vectors not greater than the principal νth submultiple of I_κ, which is therefore the greatest member of ν_κ; that is, we have

***374·21.** $\vdash : \kappa \in FM \,\text{cycl subm} \,.\, \supset .\, \nu_\kappa = \overleftarrow{(W_\kappa)_*}\text{‘}(\imath R)(R \in \nu_\kappa \,.\, R^\nu = I_\kappa)$

***374·1.** $\vdash :.\, \kappa \in FM \,\text{cycl} \,.\, R, Q \in \kappa_\partial \,.\, Q^\nu = R \,.\, T \in \nu_\kappa \,.\, T^\nu = I_\kappa \,.\, \supset :$

$TW_\kappa Q \,.\, \supset .\, Q \in \nu_\kappa$ [*372·33]

The above hypothesis is not all necessary for the conclusion, but is adopted because it gives the construction with which we shall be concerned.

***374·11.** $\vdash : \text{Hp} *374\cdot 1 \,.\, QW_\kappa T \,.\, \supset .\, (\exists\sigma) \,.\, T^{\sigma+1} W_\kappa Q \,.\, QW_\kappa T^\sigma$

Dem.

$\vdash . *301\cdot 504\cdot 3 \,.\, \supset \vdash : \text{Hp} \,.\, \sigma \in \text{NC ind} \,.\, \supset .\, Q \neq T^\sigma$ (1)

$\vdash . *373\cdot 62\cdot 5 \,.\, \supset \vdash : \text{Hp} \,.\, \supset .\, \text{Pot}`T \in \nu \,.$

$[*261\cdot 26] \qquad \supset .\, E!\, \min(W_\kappa)`(\text{Pot}`T \cap \overleftarrow{W_\kappa}`Q)$ (2)

$\vdash . (1) . (2) . *372\cdot 1 \,.\, \supset \vdash .\, \text{Prop}$

***374·12.** $\vdash : \text{Hp} *374\cdot 11 \,.\, T^{\sigma+1} W_\kappa Q \,.\, QW_\kappa T^\sigma \,.\, P = \breve{T}^\sigma | Q \,.\, \supset .\, P \in \nu_\kappa$

Dem.

$\vdash . *371\cdot 23\cdot 16 \,.\, \supset \vdash :. \text{Hp} \,.\, \supset : P \in \kappa_\partial \,.\, T^\sigma \in \kappa_\partial :$

$[*371\cdot 25] \qquad \supset : PW_\kappa T \,.\, \supset .\, P | T^\sigma W_\kappa T^{\sigma+1} \,.$

$[\text{Hp}] \qquad \supset .\, QW_\kappa T^{\sigma+1} :$

$[\text{Transp.Hp}] \qquad \supset : TW_\kappa P :$

$[*372\cdot 33] \qquad \supset : P \in \nu_\kappa :. \supset \vdash .\, \text{Prop}$

***374·13.** $\vdash : \kappa \in FM \text{ cycl subm} \,.\, R \in \kappa_\partial \,.\, \supset .\, (\exists P) \,.\, P \in \nu_\kappa \,.\, P^\nu = R$

Dem.

$\vdash . *374\cdot 1 \,.\qquad \supset \vdash : \text{Hp} *374\cdot 1 \,.\, TW_\kappa Q \,.\, \supset .\, Q \in \nu_\kappa \,.\, Q^\nu = R$ (1)

$\vdash . *374\cdot 12 \,.\qquad \supset \vdash : \text{Hp} *374\cdot 12 \,.\, \supset .\, P \in \nu_\kappa \,.\, P^\nu = R$ (2)

$\vdash . (1) . (2) . *374\cdot 11 \,.\, \supset \vdash : \text{Hp} *374\cdot 1 \,.\, \supset .\, (\exists P) \,.\, P \in \nu_\kappa \,.\, P^\nu = R$ (3)

$\vdash . *373\cdot 6 \,.\qquad \supset \vdash : \text{Hp} \,.\, \supset .\, (\exists T) \,.\, T \in \nu_\kappa \,.\, T^\nu = I_\kappa$ (4)

$\vdash . (3) . (4) \,.\, \supset \vdash .\, \text{Prop}$

***374·14.** $\vdash : \kappa \in FM \text{ cycl subm} \,.\, R \in \kappa \cup \text{Cnv}``\kappa \,.\, \supset .\, (\exists P) \,.\, P \in \nu_\kappa \,.\, P^\nu = R$

Dem.

$\vdash . *374\cdot 13 \,.\, *373\cdot 6 \,.\, \supset \vdash : \text{Hp} \,.\, S \in \kappa_\partial \,.\, R = \breve{S} \,.\, \supset .$

$\qquad (\exists T, Q) \,.\, T, Q \in \nu_\kappa \,.\, T^\nu = I_\kappa \,.\, Q^\nu = S \,.\, R = \breve{S} \,.$

$[*372\cdot 27] \qquad \supset .\, (\exists T, Q) \,.\, T, Q \in \nu_\kappa \,.\, TW_\kappa Q \,.\, (\breve{Q} | T)^\nu = \breve{S} = R \,.$

$[*371\cdot 16 . *372\cdot 33] \supset .\, (\exists T, Q) \,.\, T, Q \in \nu_\kappa \,.\, \breve{Q} | T \in \nu_\kappa \,.\, (\breve{Q} | T)^\nu = R$ (1)

$\vdash . (1) . *374\cdot 13 \,.\, *373\cdot 6 \,.\, \supset \vdash .\, \text{Prop}$

***374·2.** $\vdash : \kappa \in FM \text{ cycl subm} \,.\, R \in \kappa \cup \text{Cnv}``\kappa \,.\, \supset .\, \nu_\kappa \cap \hat{P}(P^\nu = R) \in 1$
$[*374\cdot 14 \,.\, *372\cdot 28]$

***374·21.** $\vdash : \kappa \in FM \text{ cycl subm} \,.\, \supset .\, \nu_\kappa = \overleftarrow{(W_\kappa)_*}`(\imath R)(R \in \nu_\kappa \,.\, R^\nu = I_\kappa)$

Dem.

$\vdash . *374\cdot 2 \,.\qquad \supset \vdash : \text{Hp} \,.\, \supset .\, E!(\imath R)(R \in \nu_\kappa \,.\, R^\nu = I_\kappa)$ (1)

$\vdash . *372\cdot 33 \,.\, \supset \vdash : \text{Hp} \,.\, R \in \nu_\kappa \,.\, R^\nu = I_\kappa \,.\, \supset .\, \overleftarrow{(W_\kappa)_*}`R \subset \nu_\kappa$ (2)

$\vdash . *372\cdot 152 \,.\, \supset \vdash : \text{Hp} \,.\, R \in \nu_\kappa \,.\, R^\nu = I_\kappa \,.\, P \in \nu_\kappa \,.\, \supset .\, R^\nu (W_\kappa)_* P^\nu \,.$

$[*372\cdot 27] \qquad \supset .\, R (W_\kappa)_* P$ (3)

$\vdash . (1) . (2) . (3) \,.\, \supset \vdash .\, \text{Prop}$

*375. PRINCIPAL RATIOS

Summary of *375.

In this number we define a relation $(\mu/\nu)_\kappa$, which is contained in $(\mu/\nu) \upharpoonright \kappa_\iota$*, but has the advantage of being one-one, and of excluding $(\rho/\sigma)_\kappa$ unless $\mu/\nu = \rho/\sigma$. The relation $(\mu/\nu)_\kappa$ is defined as holding between R and S when the principal μth submultiple of R is identical with the principal νth submultiple of S, *i.e.* we put

*375·01. $(\mu/\nu)_\kappa = \hat{R}\hat{S}\{(\exists T) . T \epsilon \mu_\kappa \cap \nu_\kappa . R = T^\mu . S = T^\nu\}$ Df

(Here $\mu_\kappa \cap \nu_\kappa = \mu_\kappa$ if $\mu \geqslant \nu$, and $= \nu_\kappa$ if $\nu \geqslant \mu$, by *372·15.)

The properties of $(\mu/\nu)_\kappa$ result from *374·2. We find that, except when $\mu = \nu = 0$ or $\xi = \eta = 0$,

$$\mu/\nu = \xi/\eta . \equiv . (\mu/\nu)_\kappa = (\xi/\eta)_\kappa \quad (*375·27).$$

If $\mu \leqslant \nu$, $\quad \text{Cl}`(\mu/\nu)_\kappa = \kappa \cup \text{Cnv}``\kappa \quad$ (*375·141),

and $\quad \text{D}`(\mu/\nu)_\kappa = (\overleftarrow{W_\kappa})_*`(\mu/\nu)_\kappa`I_\kappa \quad$ (*375·22).

The principal νth submultiple of S is $(1/\nu)_\kappa`S$, and its $\mu$th power is $(\mu/\nu)_\kappa`S$. Also we have

$$(1/\rho)_\kappa`(1/\nu)_\kappa`S = (1/\rho\nu)_\kappa`S \quad (*375·15),$$

$$N \epsilon \nu_\kappa . \supset . (1/\rho)_\kappa`N \epsilon (\rho\nu)_\kappa \quad (*375·16),$$

$$(\mu/\nu)_\kappa = (\mu/1)_\kappa \,|\, (1/\nu)_\kappa \quad (*375·2).$$

The propositions

$$(\mu/\nu)_\kappa \,|\, (\rho/\sigma)_\kappa = (\mu/\nu \times_s \rho/\sigma)_\kappa$$

and $\quad \{(\mu/\nu)_\kappa`R\} \,|\, \{(\rho/\sigma)_\kappa`R\} = (\mu/\nu +_s \rho/\sigma)_\kappa`R$

do not hold without limitation. The former requires either

$$\mu \geqslant \nu . \vee . \sigma \geqslant \rho,$$

or that the converse domain should be limited to

$$(\overleftarrow{W_\kappa})_*`(\sigma/\rho)_\kappa`I_\kappa,$$

i.e. to $\quad \text{D}`(\sigma/\rho)_\kappa$.

The latter requires either

$$\mu/\nu +_s \rho/\sigma <_r 1/1,$$

or $\quad R \epsilon \text{Cl}`(\mu/\nu +_s \rho/\sigma)_\kappa$.

---

* Except in the trivial case when $\mu = 0 . \nu = 0$. In this case, $(\mu/\nu) \upharpoonright \kappa_\iota = \dot{\Lambda}$ but $(\mu/\nu)_\kappa = I_\kappa \dot{\downarrow} I_\kappa$.

***375·01.** $(\mu/\nu)_\kappa = \hat{R}\hat{S}\{(\exists T) . T \in \mu_\kappa \cap \nu_\kappa . R = T^\mu . S = T^\nu\}$ Df

***375·1.** $\vdash : R (\mu/\nu)_\kappa S . \equiv . (\exists T) . T \in \mu_\kappa \cap \nu_\kappa . R = T^\mu . S = T^\nu$ [(*375·01)]

***375·11.** $\vdash : \kappa \in FM \text{ cycl} . \mu, \nu \in \text{NC ind} - \iota\text{‘}0 . \supset . (\mu/\nu)_\kappa \in 1 \rightarrow 1$

Dem.

$\vdash . *372{\cdot}28 . \supset$

$\vdash : \text{Hp} . R \in \kappa \cup \text{Cnv}\text{‘‘}\kappa . T, W \in \mu_\kappa \cap \nu_\kappa . R = T^\mu = W^\mu . \supset . T = W$ (1)

$\vdash . (1) . *375{\cdot}1 . \supset \vdash : \text{Hp} . R (\mu/\nu)_\kappa S . R (\mu/\nu)_\kappa S' . \supset . S = S'$ (2)

Similarly $\vdash : \text{Hp} . R (\mu/\nu)_\kappa S . R' (\mu/\nu)_\kappa S . \supset . R = R'$ (3)

$\vdash . (2) . (3) . \supset \vdash . \text{Prop}$

***375·12.** $\vdash : \kappa \in FM \text{ cycl} . \sim(\mu = \nu = 0) . \supset . (\mu/\nu)_\kappa \Subset (\mu/\nu) \upharpoonright \kappa_\iota$ [*370·33]

***375·13.** $\vdash . (\nu/\mu)_\kappa = \text{Cnv}\text{‘}(\mu/\nu)_\kappa$ [*375·1]

***375·14.** $\vdash : \mu \geqslant \nu . \kappa \in FM \text{ cycl subm} . \supset . \text{D}\text{‘}(\mu/\nu)_\kappa = \kappa \cup \text{Cnv}\text{‘‘}\kappa$
[*374·2 . *372·15]

***375·141.** $\vdash : \mu \leqslant \nu . \kappa \in FM \text{ cycl subm} . \supset . \text{Cl}\text{‘}(\mu/\nu)_\kappa = \kappa \cup \text{Cnv}\text{‘‘}\kappa$ [*375·13·14]

***375·15.** $\vdash : \kappa \in FM \text{ cycl subm} . S \in \kappa \cup \text{Cnv}\text{‘‘}\kappa . \rho, \nu \in \text{NC ind} - \iota\text{‘}0 . \supset .$
$(1/\rho)_\kappa\text{‘}(1/\nu)_\kappa\text{‘}S = (1/\rho\nu)_\kappa\text{‘}S$

Dem.

$\vdash . *375{\cdot}14 . \quad \supset \vdash : \text{Hp} . \supset . \text{E} ! (1/\rho)_\kappa\text{‘}(1/\nu)_\kappa\text{‘}S . \text{E} ! (1/\rho\nu)_\kappa\text{‘}S$ (1)

$\vdash . (1) . *375{\cdot}1 . \supset \vdash :. \text{Hp} . \supset : M = (1/\rho)_\kappa\text{‘}(1/\nu)_\kappa\text{‘}S . \equiv .$
$(\exists N) . N \in \nu_\kappa . M \in \rho_\kappa . N^\nu = S . M^\rho = N$ (2)

$\vdash . (1) . *375{\cdot}1 . \supset \vdash :. \text{Hp} . \supset : M = (1/\rho\nu)_\kappa\text{‘}S . \equiv . M \in (\rho\nu)_\kappa . M^{\rho\nu} = S .$

[*372·19] $\supset . M \in \rho_\kappa . M^\rho \in \nu_\kappa . (M^\rho)^\nu = S .$

[(2)] $\supset . M = (1/\rho)_\kappa\text{‘}(1/\nu)_\kappa\text{‘}S$ (3)

$\vdash . (1) . (3) . \supset \vdash . \text{Prop}$

***375·151.** $\vdash : \kappa \in FM \text{ cycl} . N \in \nu_\kappa . \supset . N = (1/\nu)_\kappa\text{‘}N^\nu$ [*375·1]

***375·16.** $\vdash : \kappa \in FM \text{ cycl subm} . N \in \nu_\kappa . \rho \in \text{NC ind} - \iota\text{‘}0 . \supset . (1/\rho)_\kappa\text{‘}N \in (\rho\nu)_\kappa$

Dem.

$\vdash . *375{\cdot}15{\cdot}151 . \supset \vdash : \text{Hp} . \supset . (1/\rho)_\kappa\text{‘}N = (1/\rho\nu)_\kappa\text{‘}N^\nu .$

[*375·1] $\supset . (1/\rho)_\kappa\text{‘}N \in (\rho\nu)_\kappa : \supset \vdash . \text{Prop}$

***375·2.** $\vdash : \kappa \in FM \text{ cycl} . \mu, \nu \in \text{NC ind} - \iota\text{‘}0 . \supset . (\mu/\nu)_\kappa = (\mu/1)_\kappa \mid (1/\nu)_\kappa$

Dem.

$\vdash . *375{\cdot}1 . \supset \vdash :. \text{Hp} . \supset : R \{(\mu/1)_\kappa \mid (1/\nu)_\kappa\} S . \equiv .$
$(\exists T) . T \in \mu_\kappa \cap \nu_\kappa . R = T^\mu . S = T^\nu :. \supset \vdash . \text{Prop}$

***375·21.** $\vdash : \kappa \epsilon FM \text{ cycl subm} . \dot{\exists} ! (\mu/\nu)_\kappa \dot{\cap} (\rho/\sigma)_\kappa . \supset . \mu/\nu = \rho/\sigma$

Dem.

$\vdash . *375\cdot1 . \supset \vdash : \text{Hp} . P (\mu/\nu)_\kappa Q . P (\rho/\sigma)_\kappa Q . \supset .$

$(\exists S, T) . S \epsilon \mu_\kappa \cap \nu_\kappa . T \epsilon \rho_\kappa \cap \sigma_\kappa . P = S^\mu = T^\rho . Q = S^\nu = T^\sigma \quad (1)$

$\vdash . (1) . *374\cdot2 . *375\cdot16 . \supset \vdash : \text{Hp} (1) . \supset . (\exists R, S, T) . S \epsilon \mu_\kappa \cap \nu_\kappa .$

$T \epsilon \rho_\kappa \cap \sigma_\kappa . P = S^\mu = T^\rho . Q = S^\nu = T^\sigma . S = R^\sigma . R \epsilon (\mu\sigma)_\kappa \cap (\nu\sigma)_\kappa .$

$[*301\cdot504] \supset . (\exists R, S, T) . S \epsilon \mu_\kappa \cap \nu_\kappa .$

$T \epsilon \rho_\kappa \cap \sigma_\kappa . R \epsilon (\mu\sigma)_\kappa \cap (\nu\sigma)_\kappa . P = S^\mu = T^\rho = R^{\mu\sigma} . Q = S^\nu = T^\sigma = R^{\nu\sigma} .$

$[*372\cdot28] \supset . (\exists R, S, T) . S \epsilon \mu_\kappa \cap \nu_\kappa .$

$T \epsilon \rho_\kappa \cap \sigma_\kappa . R \epsilon (\mu\sigma)_\kappa \cap (\nu\sigma)_\kappa . P = S^\mu = T^\rho = R^{\mu\sigma} . T = R^\nu .$

$[*301\cdot504] \supset . (\exists R) . R \epsilon (\mu\sigma)_\kappa \cap (\nu\rho)_\kappa . R^{\nu\rho} = R^{\mu\sigma} \quad (2)$

$\vdash . *372\cdot2 . (2) . \supset \vdash : \text{Hp} (1) . \mu\sigma \geqslant \nu\rho . \supset . \mu\sigma = \nu\rho \quad (3)$

Similarly $\vdash : \text{Hp} (1) . \nu\rho \geqslant \mu\sigma . \supset . \mu\sigma = \nu\rho \quad (4)$

$\vdash . (3) . (4) . \supset \vdash : \text{Hp} . \supset . \mu\sigma = \nu\rho : \supset \vdash . \text{Prop}$

***375·22.** $\vdash : \kappa \epsilon FM \text{ cycl subm} . \mu \leqslant \nu . \supset . \text{D}'(\mu/\nu)_\kappa = \overleftarrow{(W_\kappa)_*}'(\mu/\nu)_\kappa{}'I_\kappa$

Dem.

$\vdash . *375\cdot1 . \supset$

$\vdash :. \text{Hp} . \supset : R \epsilon \text{D}'(\mu/\nu)_\kappa . \equiv . (\exists S, T) . T \epsilon \mu_\kappa \cap \nu_\kappa . R = T^\mu . S = T^\nu .$

$[*372\cdot15 . *21\cdot2] \quad \equiv . (\exists T) . T \epsilon \nu_\kappa . R = T^\mu .$

$[*374\cdot21] \quad \equiv . (\exists S, T) . S \epsilon \nu_\kappa . S^\nu = I_\kappa . S (W_\kappa)_* T . R = T^\mu .$

$[*372\cdot27] \quad \equiv . (\exists S, T) . S \epsilon \nu_\kappa . S^\nu = I_\kappa . S^\mu (W_\kappa)_* T^\mu . R = T^\mu .$

$[\text{Hp}] \quad \equiv . (\exists S) . S \epsilon \nu_\kappa . S^\nu = I_\kappa . S^\mu (W_\kappa)_* R .$

$[*375\cdot1\cdot11] \quad \equiv . \{(\mu/\nu)_\kappa{}'I_\kappa\} (W_\kappa)_* R :. \supset \vdash . \text{Prop}$

***375·221.** $\vdash : \kappa \epsilon FM \text{ cycl subm} . \mu \geqslant \nu . \supset . \text{Cl}'(\mu/\nu)_\kappa = \overleftarrow{(W_\kappa)_*}'(\nu/\mu)_\kappa{}'I_\kappa$

$\left[*375\cdot22 \dfrac{\nu, \mu}{\mu, \nu} . *375\cdot13 \right]$

***375·23.** $\vdash : \kappa \epsilon FM \text{ cycl subm} . \mu, \nu \epsilon \text{NC ind} . \sim (\mu = \nu = 0) . \supset . \dot{\exists} ! (\mu/\nu)_\kappa$

$[*375\cdot14\cdot141]$

***375·24.** $\vdash : \kappa \epsilon FM \text{ cycl subm} . (\mu/\nu)_\kappa = (\rho/\sigma)_\kappa . \supset . \mu/\nu = \rho/\sigma \quad [*375\cdot21\cdot23]$

The cases when we do not have $\mu, \nu, \rho, \sigma \epsilon \text{NC ind} - \iota'0$ require separate treatment in obtaining *375·24, but they offer no difficulty.

***375·25.** $\vdash : \kappa \in FM \text{ cycl subm} . \rho \text{ Prm } \sigma . \mu/\nu = \rho/\sigma . \supset . (\mu/\nu)_\kappa = (\rho/\sigma)_\kappa$

Dem.

$\vdash . *303\cdot39 . *302\cdot35 . \supset \vdash : \text{Hp} . \supset . (\exists\tau) . \mu = \rho\tau . \nu = \sigma\tau$ (1)

$\vdash . *372\cdot19 . \supset \vdash : \text{Hp} . \mu = \rho\tau . \nu = \sigma\tau . T \in \mu_\kappa \cap \nu_\kappa . R = T^\mu . S = T^\nu . P = T^\tau . \supset .$

$P \in \rho_\kappa \cap \sigma_\kappa . R = P^\rho . S = P^\sigma$ (2)

$\vdash . (1) . (2) . *375\cdot1 . \supset \vdash : \text{Hp} . \supset . (\mu/\nu)_\kappa \subset (\rho/\sigma)_\kappa$ (3)

$\vdash . *375\cdot15 . \supset$

$\vdash : \text{Hp}(1) . \mu = \rho\tau . \nu = \sigma\tau . P \in \rho_\kappa \cap \sigma_\kappa . R = P^\rho . S = P^\sigma . T = (1/\tau)_\kappa \text{‘} P . \supset .$

$T \in \mu_\kappa \cap \nu_\kappa . R = T^\mu . S = T^\nu$ (4)

$\vdash . (1) . (4) . *375\cdot1 . \supset \vdash : \text{Hp} . \supset . (\rho/\sigma)_\kappa \subset (\mu/\nu)_\kappa$ (5)

$\vdash . (3) . (5) . \supset \vdash . \text{Prop}$

***375·26.** $\vdash : \kappa \in FM \text{ cycl subm} . \sim(\mu = \nu = 0) . \sim(\xi = \eta = 0) . \mu/\nu = \xi/\eta . \supset .$

$(\mu/\nu)_\kappa = (\xi/\eta)_\kappa$

Dem.

$\vdash . *303\cdot39 . *302\cdot34 . \supset$

$\vdash : \text{Hp} . \mu, \nu, \xi, \eta \in \text{NC ind} . \supset . (\exists\rho, \sigma) . (\rho, \sigma) \text{ Prm } (\mu, \nu) . (\rho, \sigma) \text{ Prm } (\xi, \eta) .$

[*375·25.*303·211] $\supset . (\exists\rho, \sigma) . (\rho/\sigma)_\kappa = (\mu/\nu)_\kappa . (\rho/\sigma)_\kappa = (\xi/\eta)_\kappa .$

[*13·171] $\supset . (\mu/\nu)_\kappa = (\rho/\sigma)_\kappa$ (1)

$\vdash . *375\cdot1 . *303\cdot11\cdot14\cdot182 . \supset$

$\vdash : \text{Hp} . \sim(\mu, \nu, \xi, \eta) \in \text{NC ind} . \supset . (\mu/\nu)_\kappa = \dot\Lambda . (\rho/\sigma)_\kappa = \dot\Lambda$ (2)

$\vdash . (1) . (2) . \supset \vdash . \text{Prop}$

***375·27.** $\vdash :. \kappa \in FM \text{ cycl subm} . \sim(\mu = \nu = 0) . \sim(\xi = \eta = 0) . \supset :$

$\mu/\nu = \xi/\eta . \equiv . (\mu/\nu)_\kappa = (\xi/\eta)_\kappa$ [*375·24·26]

***375·3.** $\vdash : \kappa \in FM \text{ cycl subm} . \mu, \nu, \rho, \sigma \in \text{NC ind} - \iota\text{‘}0 . \supset .$

$(\mu/\nu)_\kappa \,|\, (\rho/\sigma)_\kappa \subset (\mu\rho/\nu\sigma)_\kappa$

Dem.

$\vdash . *375\cdot1 . \supset \vdash : \text{Hp} . P(\mu/\nu)_\kappa Q . Q(\rho/\sigma)_\kappa R . \supset .$

$(\exists S, T) . S \in \mu_\kappa \cap \nu_\kappa . P = S^\mu . Q = S^\nu . T \in \rho_\kappa \cap \sigma_\kappa . Q = T^\rho . R = T^\sigma$ (1)

$\vdash . *375\cdot141\cdot15 . \supset$

$\vdash : \text{Hp} . S \in \mu_\kappa \cap \nu_\kappa . P = S^\mu . Q = S^\nu . T \in \rho_\kappa \cap \sigma_\kappa . Q = T^\rho . R = T^\sigma . \supset .$

$(\exists M) . M = (1/\rho)_\kappa \text{‘} S . P = M^{\mu\rho} . Q = M^{\nu\rho} = T^\rho . R = T^\sigma . M \in (\mu\rho)_\kappa .$

[*372·28] $\supset . (\exists M) . M \in (\mu\rho)_\kappa . P = M^{\mu\rho} . T = M^\nu . R = T^\sigma$ (2)

$\vdash . (2) . *375\cdot1 . \supset \vdash : \text{Hp}(2) . \mu\rho \geqslant \nu\sigma . \supset . P(\mu\rho/\nu\sigma)_\kappa R$ (3)

$\vdash . (1) . (3) . \quad \supset \vdash : \text{Hp}(1) . \mu\rho \geqslant \nu\sigma . \supset . P(\mu\rho/\nu\sigma)_\kappa R$ (4)

Similarly $\vdash : \text{Hp}(1) . \nu\sigma \geqslant \mu\rho . \supset . P(\mu\rho/\nu\sigma)_\kappa R$ (5)

$\vdash . (4) . (5) . \supset \vdash . \text{Prop}$

***375·31.** $\vdash :. \kappa \in FM \text{ cycl subm} . \mu, \nu, \rho, \sigma \in \text{NC ind} - \iota`0 : \mu \geqslant \nu . \vee . \sigma \geqslant \rho : \supset .$

$$(\mu\rho/\nu\sigma)_\kappa = (\mu/\nu)_\kappa \,|\, (\rho/\sigma)_\kappa$$

Dem.

If $P\,(\mu\rho/\nu\sigma)_\kappa\, R$, we have

$$(\exists M) . M \in (\mu\rho)_\kappa \cap (\nu\sigma)_\kappa . P = M^{\mu\rho} . R = M^{\nu\sigma}.$$

The result follows by putting $Q = M^{\nu\rho}$.

Without the hypothesis $\mu \geqslant \nu . \vee . \sigma \geqslant \rho$, we have

$$(\mu\rho/\nu\sigma)_\kappa`R = (\mu/\nu)_\kappa`(\rho/\sigma)_\kappa`R,$$

if R is sufficiently small to ensure $(1/\nu\sigma)_\kappa`R \in (\nu\rho)_\kappa$, *i.e.* if

$$(\sigma/\rho)_\kappa`I_\kappa\,(W_\kappa)_* \, R,$$

i.e. if

$$R \in \text{Cl}`(\rho/\sigma)_\kappa .$$

***375·32.** $\vdash : \kappa \in FM \text{ cycl subm} . \mu/\nu +_s \rho/\sigma <_r 1/1 . R \in \kappa \cup \text{Cnv}``\kappa . \supset .$

$$\{(\mu/\nu)_\kappa`R\} \,|\, \{(\rho/\sigma)_\kappa`R\} = \{(\mu/\nu +_s \rho/\sigma)_\kappa`R\}$$

The proof follows immediately from the definitions.

The same result follows without the hypothesis $\mu/\nu +_s \rho/\sigma <_r 1/1$ provided R is sufficiently small to ensure

$$(1/\nu\sigma)_\kappa`R \in (\mu\rho + \nu\sigma)_\kappa,$$

i.e.

$$R \in \text{Cl}`(\mu/\nu +_s \rho/\sigma)_\kappa .$$